ENCYCLOPEDIA OF
BIOETHICS

3RD EDITION

EDITORIAL BOARD

ENCYCLOPEDIA OF
BIOETHICS

3 RD EDITION

EDITED BY

STEPHEN G. POST

VOLUME

I - M

**MACMILLAN
REFERENCE
USA™**

New York • Detroit • San Diego • San Francisco • Cleveland • New Haven, Conn. • Waterville, Maine • London • Munich

Encyclopedia of Bioethics, 3rd edition

Stephen G. Post

Editor in Chief

©2004 by Macmillan Reference USA. Macmillan Reference USA is an imprint of The Gale Group, Inc., a division of Thomson Learning, Inc.

Macmillan Reference USA™ and Thomson Learning™ are trademarks used herein under license.

For more information, contact
Macmillan Reference USA
300 Park Avenue South, 9th Floor
New York, NY 10010
Or you can visit our Internet site at
http://www.gale.com

While every effort has been made to ensure the reliability of the information presented in this publication, The Gale Group, Inc. does not guarantee the accuracy of the data contained herein. The Gale Group, Inc. accepts no payment for listing; and inclusion in the publication of any organization, agency, institution, publication, service, or individual does not imply endorsement of the editors or publisher. Errors brought to the attention of the publisher and verified to the satisfaction of the publisher will be corrected in future editions.

Library of Congress Cataloging-in-Publication Data

Encyclopedia of bioethics / Stephen G. Post, editor in chief.— 3rd ed.
p. cm.
Includes bibliographical references and index.
ISBN 0-02-865774-8 (set : hardcover : alk. paper) — ISBN
0-02-865775-6 (vol. 1) — ISBN 0-02-865776-4 (vol. 2) — ISBN
0-02-865777-2 (vol. 3) — ISBN 0-02-865778-0 (vol. 4) — ISBN
0-02-865779-9 (vol. 5)
    1. Bioethics—Encyclopedias. 2. Medical ethics—Encyclopedias. I.
Post, Stephen Garrard, 1951-
QH332.E52 2003
174'.957'03—dc22

2003015694

This title is also available as an e-book.
ISBN 0-02-865916-3 (set)
Contact your Gale sales representative for ordering information.

Printed in the United States of America
10 9 8 7 6 5 4 3 2

Front cover photos (from left to right): Custom Medical Stock; Photo Researchers; Photodisc; Photodisc; AP/Worldwide Photos.

IMMIGRATION, ETHICAL AND HEALTH ISSUES OF

• • •

As of March 2000 it was estimated that approximately 10.4 percent of the United States population, or 28.4 million individuals, were immigrants. Prior to 1965 the majority of immigrants came from European countries, such as the United Kingdom, Greece, Poland, Portugal, Germany, and Ireland. Since then, however, an increasing number of immigrants has come from Latin American, Asian, and Caribbean countries, including El Salvador, Colombia, Vietnam, China, Haiti, and the Dominican Republic.

Individuals may seek to enter the United States for any number of reasons, including a desire to reunite with family members, the acceptance of a new employment opportunity, or a need to leave one's country of origin due to persecution. The majority of individuals entering the United States from other countries do so legally, through established immigration procedures. Others enter illegally, oftentimes in search of a safe haven from persecutors.

Findings relating to the health of immigrants have been inconsistent, in part due to reliance on different definitions of *immigrant*. For instance, some studies consider the health or illness of all foreign-born individuals, regardless of the legality or duration of their residence in the United States, while others may examine either the health of those who are here legally or of those who are here illegally (Loue and Bunce). Some studies have utilized the term *newcomers* to encompass those who are here permanently and temporarily, as well as those who are here legally and illegally (Smith). Refugees who are seeking safety from persecution within their own countries may be considered separately, or they may be included in broader discussions relating to immigrants.

Morbidity and Mortality

The risk of morbidity and mortality varies by immigrant group and by disease. In general, the health problems of immigrant populations mirror those that are prominent in the countries from which they have come. For instance, between 14 percent and 20 percent of Indo-Chinese refugees carry hepatitis B, and up to 15 percent of Southeast Asian refugees may be chronic carriers of the infection. This is not surprising in view of the fact that hepatitis B virus is endemic in many Asian countries (Tong and Hwang). During the period from 1986 through 1994, the rate of mycobacterium tuberculosis was four times higher among foreign-born individuals than among those born in the United States. Because more than half of the cases among the foreign-born were diagnosed less than five years after their arrival in the United States, it appears that imported tuberculosis is responsible for the majority of tuberculosis cases among immigrants in the United States (Zuber, McKenna, Binkin, et al.).

However, a number of studies have found that immigrants to the United States may experience lower rates of mortality than persons who remain in the sending countries. In addition, immigrants' risks of smoking, substance use, obesity, hypertension, and some forms of cancer are lower than the risks experienced by United States-born individuals of equivalent demographic and socioeconomic backgrounds. It has been hypothesized that this health advantage may result from a self-selection for immigration by healthier individuals (Swallen). However, for a number of immigrant groups, the risk of these illnesses appears to increase with increasing length of residence in the United States (Frisbie, Cho, and Hummer).

Immigrants may be at particularly high risk for a variety of occupationally related illnesses. Many may be able to find employment only in sweatshop-like conditions or in agricultural work where they may face continuous exposure to pesticides and herbicides, generally without adequate protection (Stephenson).

Women who immigrate to the United States may experience a number of gender-related health problems. Women may suffer significant trauma during their transit to the United States, including sexual assaults and forced labor (sometimes in the form of sexual slavery). Once they arrive in the United States, they may confront additional gender-related problems. For instance, many immigrant women are more willing than their male partners to accept low-paying jobs in order to support themselves and their families. Once they become wage earners, they may be introduced to North American conceptualizations of gender roles. Their male partners may, as a result of their own unemployment, feel threatened by what appears to be a shift in the power structure within the family due to their inability to earn a living and their partners' newfound independence. For some women, these changes in family structure have been associated with an increase in domestic violence. Still other immigrant women may become subject to abuse by spouses or boyfriends who are United States citizens or legal permanent residents. These men may have promised to file immigration papers on the women's behalf, but failed to do so. The women may be afraid to leave their abusive partners or to report their abusers to law enforcement authorities because of their own illegal status and the consequent fear of deportation. Often, the women may be financially, as well as legally, dependent on their abusers, so that it becomes difficult for them to leave these situations. Specific provisions in U.S. immigration law now permit abused immigrant women in such situations to file petitions on their own behalf so that they will not have to remain captives in abusive relationships.

Barriers to Care

Immigrants may be reluctant to rely on Western-style medicine due to differing traditions of symptom identification, diagnosis, and healing. Additional barriers are presented by language differences and the relative unavailability of competent interpreters, by transportation difficulties, and by providers' lack of familiarity with the healing beliefs and practices of their immigrant patients. For example, a study of the utilization of mental health services by a sample of Mexican Americans in Fresno County, California, found

that those who were born outside of the United States had a utilization rate that was only two-fifths that of the Mexican Americans born in the United States (Vega, Kolody, Aguilar-Gaxiola et al.). This differential utilization rate may have been attributable to the nonexistence of Spanish-speaking mental health professionals, a lack of insurance, the lack of a regular doctor or course of care, or to physical isolation in rural areas.

Southeast Asian immigrants have been found to have the lowest levels of Pap testing of any racial or ethnic group in the United States. A recent study of Cambodian immigrants found that barriers to the use of the Pap test included a traditional orientation to the prevention, causation, and treatment of disease; a lack of familiarity with Western concepts of early disease detection; low levels of knowledge about cervical cancer; concerns about the Pap test procedure; and difficulties with transportation and language interpretation (Jackson, Taylor, Chitnarong et al.).

Immigrants, both those who are in the United States legally and those who are not, must often confront a patchwork of federal programs that, despite their number and complexity, often do not assure access to necessary care. The Centers for Disease Control and Prevention (CDC) oversee specific programs for infectious diseases. The CDC is also responsible for the review of applications for waivers from those immigrants seeking legal entry who may be excludable from the United States pursuant to legal provisions prohibiting the entry of those with specified diseases, such as active tuberculosis, various sexually transmitted diseases, and various forms of mental illness. The Office of Refugee Resettlement of the U.S. Department of Health and Human Services provides funds to the CDC to oversee the infectious disease programs. The Migrant Health Program also provides some funding for preventive services and immunizations.

Numerous federal and state laws place restrictions on immigrants' ability to access care that is publicly funded. In 1994, for instance, California's Proposition 187 severely curtailed the ability of individuals who were in the United States illegally to obtain publicly funded care and required that specified agencies and healthcare professionals report these individuals' presence to the Immigration and Naturalization Service. Although numerous portions of the law were ultimately found by the courts to be unconstitutional, researchers noted a 5 percent decrease in the number of clients appearing at clinics for the diagnosis and treatment of sexually transmitted disease immediately following the law's passage (the law was not implemented because it was immediately enjoined by the court). Approximately 25 percent of these individuals indicated that they were in the country illegally (Hu, Donovan, Ford, et al.). A similar decrease was noted in the number of individuals presenting for other medical services (Marx, Thach, Grayson, et al.). The possibility that physicians and other healthcare professionals would report their patients' illegal presence to government authorities raised significant ethical concerns about the imposition of conflicting loyalties, the breach of physician–patient confidentiality that would attend such reporting, and the potential threat to public health as a result of delays in seeking care due to fear of disclosure (Ziv and Lo).

Despite several amendments since their original passage, the provisions of the 1996 Personal Responsibility and Work Opportunity Reconciliation Act (commonly known as the Welfare Reform Act) and the Illegal Immigration Reform and Immigrant Responsibility Act (IIRAIRA) continue to severely restrict the ability of even legal immigrants to rely on publicly funded medical services, apart from emergency medical needs and the diagnosis and treatment of specified infectious diseases. The legislation has engendered significant controversy because many of the immigrants who are denied publicly funded care, such as Medicaid, actually pay into the system through their taxes. In addition, many states have not adopted state legislation that would permit immigrants to rely on publicly funded care when they do not have privately funded health insurance. This is particularly problematic for women of childbearing age, who may not have the funds or the private insurance to cover the costs of prenatal care, labor and delivery services, or care for their newborns.

Within those states that have implemented legislation permitting immigrants to receive publicly funded care, many may still be denied access to recommended treatments. In New York, which has been one of the most forward-thinking states in the provision of publicly funded health services to immigrants, a panel consisting of physicians, medical ethicists, and AIDS advocates charged that physicians are withholding certain HIV-related treatment regimens from immigrant patients in the belief that they will not adhere to the recommended regimen (Newsline People AIDS Coalition New York).

Both the Welfare Reform Act and IIRAIRA limit the ability of immigrants, whether legal or not, to utilize other types of publicly funded services, such as food stamps. The impact of welfare reform has thus disproportionately affected immigrant groups. For instance, although noncitizens represented only 9 percent of the households receiving welfare, they accounted for 23 percent of the total decline in welfare caseloads following the enactment of these laws (Fix and Passel).

Healthcare providers also face difficulties due to the limitations imposed on access to public funds by federal laws. Hospitals are required by the federal Emergency Medical Treatment and Active Labor Act (1986) to provide emergency medical care to those presenting for such care, regardless of their legal status in the United States (Galloro). There may be an ethical, as well as a legal, responsibility to care for those presenting at emergency departments with life-threatening situations. The hospitals are not reimbursed by the federal government for the full cost of these services, although the federal government is responsible for the enforcement of the immigration laws, and many of the injuries that are treated result directly from dangerous attempts to cross the border. As a result, many hospitals in border areas are experiencing critical losses in revenue due to uncompensated care (Galloro). Of the five states that are most impacted by illegal immigration (California, New York, Texas, Florida, and Illinois), two have unsuccessfully sued the federal government in an effort to obtain reimbursement for the costs incurred in providing uncompensated care to illegal entrants.

Negotiating the Provider-Patient Relationship

Numerous issues may arise in the context of the provider–patient relationship due to differing beliefs regarding, and experiences with, such relationships, concepts of autonomy, and understandings about disease and illness. Some patients may have come from countries in which medical practitioners functioned as agents of the government, reporting to law enforcement officers the names of patients whose illnesses may have been related to illegal activities (e.g. sexually transmitted diseases that may have resulted from extramarital sexual relations or commercial sex activities, or pelvic infections resulting from illegal abortions). Others may have experienced torture at the hands of government-employed medical professionals. Not surprisingly, such experiences may hinder the patient's willingness and ability to divulge sensitive information to a healthcare provider. A lack of provider sensitivity to this possibility may inadvertently exacerbate the difficulty of communication. Even patients who have not experienced such trauma may feel reticent to discuss deeply sensitive issues due to perceived disparities in power between the healthcare provider and the patient.

Western medicine emphasizes the importance of self-determination and autonomous decision making in the context of medical care. However, some immigrant patients, and particularly those from non-Western cultures, may conceive of the individual not as an autonomous and disconnected entity, but rather as a function of the roles that one maintains in relation to those around one, such as extended family members and community members. In such instances, the patient may want the healthcare provider to discuss the details of his or her situation in as much, or even more, detail with the family or community members as with the patient. For instance, the patient may believe that the entire family should be involved in a decision to undergo chemotherapeutic treatment for cancer. Other patients may not want to know their own diagnosis, but may want family members to be fully informed.

The use of interpreters may also present challenges. At the most basic level, English phrases or terms may not be easily translatable into the language used by the patient. Other aspects of the interpreting function, however, may be more subtle and, consequently, more difficult to remedy. Differences in social status between the interpreter and the patient may influence the quality of the communication in ways that are not obvious to the healthcare provider. Interpreters may also incorporate their own beliefs and agendas into the communication. For instance, family members who serve as interpreters may inadvertently or intentionally minimize or exaggerate aspects of the information to be communicated.

Providers cannot realistically be expected to understand and be familiar with every possible culture and language. Providers may find it helpful, however, to consult with professionals in community-based organizations and agencies who have experience working with particular cultures. Family members of patients may be willing and able to provide additional background, particularly when it is clear that the provider is making a sincere effort to understand his or her patient.

Issues in Health Research

Immigrants may also face significant difficulties in the context of health research. For instance, many clinical trials do not provide care to trial participants. In such cases, examinations are provided only for the purpose of the trial and individuals are advised that they must consult with their own physicians for any necessary medical attention. In some cases, individuals are excluded if they do not have health insurance of some sort or if they do not have a regular provider of care. As a result, many immigrants may be ineligible for participation in a research study because they do not have employment-based health coverage, because they do not earn a salary that is sufficient to cover the costs of health insurance, or because they do not have a regular provider of care. In addition, many studies may limit participation to speakers of English, and those immigrants who have not yet mastered the language may be excluded from participation. Individuals may also be excluded due to the instability of their legal status and residence, in part because of the possibility that follow-up with them during the course of the study will be difficult and costly.

As in the clinical context, the development of a satisfactory informed-consent process for use with immigrant participants may require significant attention to ensure that the information provided to participants is understandable, both in terms of the language used and the sophistication of that language. An appropriate process may require, depending upon the culture of the participants, that the participant's family members or community members be engaged at some level. For example, information may be provided to the male head of the household, in addition to the prospective participant, so that the prospective participant can discuss the study with him. This does not, however, obviate the need for the individual consent of the participant.

As noted above, many immigrants may face extraordinary obstacles in attempting to obtain medical care. As a result, the offer of financial compensation or medical care in conjunction with participation in research may inadvertently place undue pressure on immigrants to agree to participate.

In the United States, immigrants have not traditionally been conceived of as constituting an especially vulnerable class of persons in need of special protections in the context of research. However, many of the characteristics of at least some members of this population may render them especially vulnerable. Poverty, lack of access to care, illiteracy, traumatic experiences, language, and illegal status can all have an effect in this regard. It is significant that Uganda has taken official note of these circumstances and has designated refugees as a class as being especially vulnerable and in need of special protections in the context of research. To address this situation, Ugandan institutional review committees reviewing proposed research that will involve refugees must include in its membership at least one individual from an agency whose primary responsibility is attention to refugee concerns, as well as a representative from a human rights organization.

SANA LOUE

SEE ALSO: *Human Rights; Justice; Medicaid; Organ and Tissue Procurement; Population Ethics: History of Theories; Public Health Law; Race and Racism; Warfare*

BIBLIOGRAPHY

Fix, Michael, and Passel, Jeffrey S. 1999. *Trends in Noncitizens' and Citizens' Use of Public Benefits Following Welfare Reform 1994–97.* Washington, D.C.: Urban Institute.

Frisbie, William Parker; Cho, Youngtae; and Hummer, Robert A. 2001. "Immigration and the Health of Asian and Pacific Islander Adults in the United States." *American Journal of Epidemiology* 153(4): 372–380.

Galloro, Vince. 2001. "Disproportionate Burden: Providers Near U.S.–Mexico Border Face a Flood of Problems in Caring for Immigrants." *Modern Healthcare* November 5: 24–25.

Hu, Yanyin; Donovan, Suzanne; Ford, Wesley L; et al. 1995. "The Impact of Proposition 187 on the Use of Public Health Services by Undocumented Immigrants in Los Angeles County." 123rd Annual Meeting of the American Public Health Association (abstract 1008).

Jackson, J. Carey; Taylor, Victoria M.; Chitnarong, Kamolthip; et al. 2000. "Development of a Cervical Cancer Control Intervention Program for Cambodian American Women." *Journal of Community Health* 25: 359–375.

Loue, Sana, ed. 1998. *Handbook of Immigrant Health*. New York: Plenum.

Loue, Sana, and Bunce, Arwen. 1999. *The Assessment of Immigration Status in Health Research*. (DHHS Publication No. PHS 99–1327). Hyattsville, MD: U.S. Department of Health and Human Services.

Marx, Jeffrey L.; Thach, Allen B.; Grayson, Galen; et al. 1996. "The Effects of California Proposition 187 on Ophthalmology Clinic Utilization at an Inner-City Urban Hospital." *Ophthalmology* 103: 847–851.

Newsline People AIDS Coalition New York. 1999. *Ethics Panel: HIV Treatment Options Not Available To All*. New York: Author.

Smith, Linda S. 2001. "Health of America's Newcomers." *Journal of Community Health Nursing* 18: 53–68.

Stephenson, Joan. 1995. "Good Workers May Get Bad Breaks on Health." *Journal of the American Medical Association* 273: 1643–1646.

Swallen, Karen C. 1997. "Do Health Selection Effects Last? A Comparison of Morbidity Rates for Elderly Adult Immigrants and U.S.-Born Elderly Persons." *Journal of Cross-Cultural Gerontology* 12: 317–339.

Tong, Myron J., and Hwang, Shinn Jang. 1994. "Hepatitis B Virus Infection in Asian Americans." *Gastroenterology Clinics of North America* 2: 523–526.

Vega, William A.; Kolody, Bohdan; Aguilar-Gaxiola, Sergio; et al. 1999. "Gaps in Service Utilization by Mexican Americans with Mental Health Problems." *American Journal of Psychiatry* 156: 928–934.

Ziv, Tal Ann, and Lo, Bernard. 1995. "Denial of Care to Illegal Immigrants: Proposition 187 in California." *New England Journal of Medicine* 332: 1095–1098.

Zuber, Patrick L. F.; McKenna, Matthew T.; Binkin, Nancy J.; et al. 1997. "Long-Term Risk of Tuberculosis among Foreign-Born Persons in the United States." *Journal of the American Medical Association* 278: 304–307.

IMPAIRED PROFESSIONALS

• • •

Impairment is a widespread problem of professional life. An impaired member of any profession creates legal and ethical difficulties for himself or herself, and can cause harm to others as well. For these reasons, the impaired professional merits serious attention (Boisaubin and Levine; Allan).

Defining the Problem

In common usage, the word *impair* connotes worsening or deterioration. An impairment diminishes the value or excellence of an individual or item. An impaired person has deteriorated significantly enough to endanger his or her capacity to function adequately.

When impairment refers to a professional, its meaning becomes more technical and restrictive. Because professions are self-regulating and resist external oversight, professionals largely determine for themselves what impairment means. Things that might impair an individual in the eyes of the lay community might not be defined as impairments within the professional community.

Typically, the impaired professional is one whose ability to function in his or her professional capacity has deteriorated because of a physical or mental difficulty. Impairing conditions traditionally have included drug dependency, alcohol dependency, illness, and disability (physical as well as mental). The American Medical Association (AMA), for example, defines the impaired physician as one "unable to practice medicine with reasonable skill and safety to patients because of physical or mental illness, including deteriorations through the aging process or loss of motor skill, or excessive use or abuse of drugs including alcohol" (La Puma and Schiedermayer, p. 91). A professional also may be regarded as impaired if abilities are significantly compromised as the result of stress or other factors (Nelson and Jennings).

While impairment raises concerns about an individual's professional competence, being impaired is not necessarily the same as being incompetent. An incompetent professional lacks the minimally acceptable levels of knowledge and skill needed to practice within a field. Such a person once may have been competent, then fails to maintain adequate knowledge and skill. One can be incompetent without being impaired.

Impairment's Social and Professional Implications

The impaired professional poses a serious problem to self and others. An impairment may adversely affect the professional's relationships with colleagues, patients and families, and the professional's institution or workplace. It can affect a professional's relationship with friends and family. An impaired professional may engage in self-destructive behavior.

Impairment is a grave problem to those who put trust in professionals and expect them to be competent and to protect the public against impaired practitioners. Members of the public seldom possess the expertise needed to evaluate the quality of services being provided to them. Their potential vulnerability becomes even more significant when other factors (e.g., being sick or injured, being in an unfamiliar setting, or being a member of a different socioeconomic class) make it difficult for a layperson to question a professional's assistance. People have a right to expect competent help from an unimpaired professional.

If severe, unrecognized and unaddressed professional impairment can spell disaster. The impaired professional can cause severe harm, even death, to others. This can give rise to legal liability for the professional, colleagues, coworkers, and the institution in which the impaired professional works.

The Persistence of Impairment

For many reasons, impairment is an enduring, ubiquitous phenomenon of professional life. First, instead of responsibly discharging the responsibility of self-regulation, professionals sometimes abuse their power or office. Second, professionals may protect inept colleagues. Third, professional impairment does not receive much attention in the education and training of those who are entering a profession. While medical students may be quick to identify and chastise a patient who has a serious emotional or drinking problem, they are less likely to learn how to recognize or respond constructively to self-impairment or impairment in a colleague. Fourth, some professions foster impairment. The idealized image of the competitive, self-reliant practitioner drives professionals to succeed and to work in isolation, patterns of behavior that are conducive to impairment.

Even a medical professional who knows about professional impairment may not recognize it (Boisaubin and Levine). Medical professionals still are relatively autonomous practitioners, which means that they tend to be self-supervising. When contact is occasional, they may neither have the opportunity to discern that a colleague is impaired nor feel responsible for doing something if they suspect it.

When contact is frequent, they may cover for an impaired colleague. To the extent that medical professionals practice as independent contractors without supervision or sustained periods of collaboration and regular contact, the ability to recognize that a professional is impaired is impeded. To the extent that medical professionals work together, collegiality may supplant professional concern.

Initial signs of impairment are frequently subtle, not obvious. Moreover, just as few individuals are looking for impairment, few wish to discover that someone is impaired. The ability to recognize impairment is affected by the willingness to see it. Missed appointments, tardiness, or sloppiness in one's work might be attributed to a passing stress and not taken as signs of something seriously wrong. A friendly inquiry met with a plausible response may be enough to assuage concern about a colleague.

Professionals may sympathize or identify with a troubled colleague. Given how much time, money, and effort professionals invest to establish their careers, the potential consequences of finding impairment can be enough to cause a professional to accommodate rather than report a colleague who is in trouble. The tendency of professionals to protect an inept colleague limits society's ability to respond to the impaired professional.

Fear of possible recrimination from the individual and one's peers also affects the professional's response to the suspicion or recognition that a colleague is impaired. The professional may worry that reporting or taking action on another's impairment may cause exposure to civil liability. Even if reporting a colleague poses no genuine threat of legal action, peers may de facto punish an individual for initiating the process of exposing a colleague to shame and institutional or legal action. These and other anxieties may make even conscientious professionals reluctant to report an apparently impaired colleague.

The professional and institutional response to professional impairment may be significant. A reported impaired professional is likely to encounter problems at the place of employment and difficulties regarding licensure (see below) and obtaining liability insurance. Depending on the nature and severity of the impairment, rehabilitation and recovery may not resolve these difficulties.

Confronting or reporting an impaired professional may be more difficult when that person is unable or unwilling to recognize the impairment. Admitting an impairment may damage one's image and reputation in the community and be fatal to a career.

The risk an impaired professional poses does not disappear or diminish if the impairment is ignored or unaddressed. On the contrary, it is likely to worsen. To ignore or dismiss the signs of impairment creates and sustains a potentially tragic situation. When the professional's impairment manifests itself, it is likely to be severe. At that point, those around the impaired professional are likely to be asked why no one intervened sooner, when the harm done could have been avoided or minimized.

Legal Implications

In every state, professional practice Acts specify as a grounds for professional discipline (including suspension or revocation of the license to practice) the inability to practice one's profession according to acceptable and prevailing standards of care by reason of mental or physical illness or habitual or excessive use or abuse of drugs, alcohol, or other substances that impair the ability to practice (Sanbar). In many states, professional boards operate treatment programs for impaired professionals (Ameringer; Talbott). Generally, successful participation in an approved treatment program is a prerequisite to licensure reinstatement for a rehabilitated, previously impaired professional (Spoon).

In many states, professionals are required by law to report impaired colleagues to relevant state professional boards and pertinent healthcare facility/agency administrators. Professionals are granted immunity from liability when they make such reports. When the reporting of impairment is mandatory under state law, failure to report is grounds for disciplinary action, although the actual enforcement of such statutes remains lax. Because the purpose of the law is prophylactic and arises out of the state's interest in protecting the public against harm, actual harm to a patient need not occur in order for a physician to be considered impaired. Because professional regulation is a matter of state law and is in constant flux, specific requirements, immunities, and programs vary considerably over place and time (Walzer).

Legal and ethical issues regarding informed consent arise in the case of impaired professionals who care for patients or clients. It has been suggested, for example, that the professional has an affirmative obligation to notify a patient/client about any impairment of that professional that might influence the decision to receive care from that professional, and that failure to share such information is a violation of the professional's fiduciary obligations (Furrow). Other commentators argue that information about specific professionals' impairments should be listed on publicly available data bases, raising a tension between the public's right to know and the professional's personal interest in privacy (Pape).

The Americans with Disabilities Act, 42 U.S.C. §§ 12101–12213, and §504 of the Rehabilitation Act, 29 U.S.C. § 794, prohibit discrimination against persons with physical and mental disabilities in such areas as employment and public accommodations These statutes affect, among other things, the licensing, discipline, institutional privileges, and insurability of impaired professionals (Rothstein, Piltch et al.).

GILES R. SCOFIELD (1995)
REVISED BY MARSHALL B. KAPP

SEE ALSO: *Alcohol and Other Drugs in a Public Health Context; Alcoholism; Competence; Conflict of Interest; Conscience, Rights of; Disability; Emotions; Harm; Healing; Medicine, Profession of; Mistakes, Medical; Nursing, Profession of; Race and Racism; Responsibility; Sexism; Trust; Virtue and Character*

BIBLIOGRAPHY

Allan, Rick B. 1997. "Alcoholism, Drug Abuse and Lawyers: Are We Ready to Address the Denial?" *Creighton Law Review* 31: 265–277.

Americans with Disabilities Act. 42 U.S.C. § 12101 et seq.

Ameringer, Carl F. 1999. *State Medical Boards and the Politics of Public Protection.* Baltimore: Johns Hopkins University Press.

Boisaubin, Eugene V. and Levine, Ruth E. 2001. "Identifying and Assisting the Impaired Physician." *American Journal of the Medical Sciences* 322: 31–36.

Furrow, Barry R. 1998. "Doctors' Dirty Little Secrets: The Dark Side of Medical Privacy." *Washburn Law Journal* 37: 283–316.

La Puma, John, and Schiedermayer, David. 1994. *Ethics Consultation: A Practical Guide.* Boston: Jones and Bartlett.

Nelson, James Lindemann, and Jennings, Bruce. 1992. "Properly Diagnosing Impairment." *QRB: Quality Review Bulletin* 18: 24–25.

Pape, Julie B. 1997. "Physician Data Banks: The Public's Right to Know Versus the Physician's Right to Privacy." *Fordham Law Review* 66: 975–1028.

Piltch, Deborah L.; Katz, Jamie W.; and Valles, Janine. 1993. "The Americans with Disabilities Act and Professional Licensing." *Mental and Physical Disability Law Reporter* 17: 556–562.

Rehabilitation Act. 29 U.S.C. § 791 et seq.

Rothstein, Laura F. 1997. "Health Care Professionals With Mental and Physical Impairments: Developments in Disability Discrimination Law." *Saint Louis University Law Journal* 41: 973–1003.

Sanbar, S. Sandy. 2001. "Education and Licensure." In *Legal Medicine,* 5th edition, ed. Textbook Committee of American College of Legal Medicine. St. Louis, MO: Mosby.

Spoon, Barry D. 2002. "The Impaired Physician: The Role of the State Board of Healing Arts." *Missouri Medicine* 99: 169–170.

Talbott, G. Douglas. 1997. "Elements of the Impaired Physician Program." In *Employee Assistance Programs: A Basic Text,* 2nd edition, eds. William S. Hutchison, Jr. and William G. Eminer. Springfield, IL: Charles C. Thomas Publisher.

Walzer, Robert S. 1990. "Impaired Physicians: An Overview and Update of the Legal Issues." *Journal of Legal Medicine* 11: 131–198.

INFANTICIDE

• • •

Infanticide is the practice of intentionally killing human newborns. Because the term *infant* descends from a Latin word that means *not speaking,* infanticide should be distinguished from feticide, or abortion, intentionally killing fetuses, on the one hand, and felicide, intentionally killing children who are mature enough to speak, particularly one's own, on the other.

Infanticide has been practiced all over the world throughout the whole of human history. Newborns who have not yet learned to talk have been intentionally killed because they were thought to be:

1. terminally ill;
2. experiencing unbearable pain or suffering;
3. born with unacceptable anomalies;
4. of the wrong gender, race, class, maternity, or paternity;
5. political threats;
6. economic threats;
7. fitting sacrifices in religious rituals; and
8. embarrassing, frustrating, or inconvenient.

The single most common reason for the practice of infanticide in the past and present has been the desire to be rid of female newborns. The histories of infanticide and gender bias are interwoven. Not to study them together is to overlook their interdependence.

Human newborns, particularly females, have been intentionally killed in many ways. They have been incinerated, decapitated, and suffocated. They have also been sundered, stabbed, stoned, shot, hung, drowned, struck, shaken, stomped, crushed, raped, poisoned, buried, starved, fed to animals, and exposed to the elements. They have been denied air, food, water, warmth, and protection from diseases. Their blood vessels have been injected with toxic substances and bubbles of air. It is impossible to understand the history of infanticide without taking into account its diverse and often cruel methods.

In many societies infanticide was not only tolerated but also sometimes promoted as a solution to the problem of unwanted infants, whether deformed or healthy. This entry provides a historical account of infanticide in Western societies, beginning with its practice in Graeco-Roman antiquity and concluding with modern evidence.

Infanticide in Antiquity

In Greek society, an infant's worth was measured by its potential to fulfill a useful function in society. Thus Plato, in his *Republic,* maintained that society was better served if deformed newborns were "hidden away, in some appropriate manner that must be kept secret," a practice that likely included infanticide (460). Similarly Aristotle wrote in *Politics*: "As to the exposure and rearing of children, let there be a law that no deformed child shall live." Aristotle also condoned abandonment as a method of population control, although he recommended early abortion in regions where the "regular customs hinder any of those born being exposed" (1335b). In Sparta, where military strength was highly valued, infanticide may have reached its zenith. In *Life of Lycurgus,* Plutarch gives an account of the Spartan custom: "But if it was ill born and deformed they sent it to … a chasm-like place at the foot of Mount Taygetus, in the conviction that the life of that which nature had not well-equipped at the very beginning for health and strength, was of no advantage, either to itself or to the state" (16).

It is difficult to distinguish between infanticide, with the intent to kill the infant, and abandonment, which may or may not have involved this intention. Failure to distinguish between the two has made accurate assessment of each difficult (Boswell). Historians have generally interpreted the Greek word for abandonment, translated as "exposure, putting out, or hiding away," as equivalent to infanticide. However, the Greek terms for abandonment do not convey the sense of injury or harm associated with infanticide. Historical evidence is not clear as to whether abandoned infants usually died or if those who abandoned them intended their death. Often abandonment was viewed as an alternative to infanticide. Nevertheless it is reasonable to infer that some deformed and healthy infants, particularly females, were exposed with the intent that they would not survive. Further it is likely that direct infanticide was practiced for both eugenic purposes and population control. Laws neither prohibited the killing of defective infants nor protected healthy infants from death by exposure.

Evidence from classical sources suggests that infanticide was practiced widely and with impunity in Roman society. While Romans continued the practice of disposing of defective infants for eugenic and economic reasons, an additional motivation stemmed from the Roman belief in the phenomenon of unnatural events, or *prodigia* (Amundsen). The Greeks saw deformities in newborns as natural occurrences. In contrast the Romans viewed *portentosi,* meaning *unnatural* or *monstrous* births, as ominous or numinous signs that needed to be destroyed in order to rid the community of guilt and fear. The historian Livy of the first century B.C.E. wrote, in *Histories,* about the birth of an infant who was both unusually large and of indeterminate gender:

> [M]en were troubled again by the report that at Frusino there had been born a child as large as a four year old, and not so much a wonder for size as because … it was uncertain whether male or female. In fact the soothsayers summoned from Etruria said it was a terrible and loathsome portent; it must be removed from Roman territory, far away from contact with earth, and drowned in the sea. They put it alive into a chest, carried it out to sea and threw it overboard. (37.27)

Roman literature is rife with testimony to such killings. According to the Laws of the Twelve Tables (fifth century B.C.E., considered to be the basis of Roman law), deformed children, *puer ad deformitatem,* were to be killed quickly. Historians disagree whether the law required that these infants be killed or whether it merely allowed infanticide. In any case Roman society appears to have accepted infanticide as a reasonable solution to the problem of deformed infants both for eugenic and superstitious motives. In a gynecological treatise entitled "How to Recognize a Newborn Worth Rearing," the Graeco-Roman physician Soranus (first–second century C.E.) specifies that such an infant "immediately cries with proper vigor, is perfect in all its parts, members and senses [and] has been born at the due time, best at the end of nine months. And by conditions contrary to those mentioned, the infant not worth rearing is recognized" (*Gynecology,* p. 79–80).

In his *Moral Essays,* Seneca argued that the practice of infanticide is rationally motivated: "Mad dogs we knock on the head; the fierce and savage ox we slay; sickly sheep we put to the knife to keep them from infecting the flock; unnatural progeny we destroy; we drown even children who at birth are weakly and abnormal. Yet it is not anger, but reason that separates the harmful from the sound" (1.15). Even if it were not legally mandated, it is unlikely infanticide was penalized in Roman society given the tradition of *patria potestas,* which granted fathers absolute authority over other members of the family. Roman fathers had power of life and death over their children and were allowed to execute even a grown son (Boswell). The most likely victims, however, were infants, especially deformed ones *and* female children who—even when healthy—were considered of little social value.

Some Roman philosophers objected to abandonment and infanticide. Musonius Rufus, writing in the first century C.E., opposed infanticide because it reduced the population. Epictetus, a Stoic philosopher and a contemporary of Musonius, condemned abandonment as a violation of the natural affection that parents should have for their offspring. Such apparent concern for the infant was not based on a belief in the child's intrinsic right to life, but was motivated by the desires to follow natural law and to increase the population. Thus, although evidence for the practice of infanticide under the Roman empire is somewhat inconclusive, Roman law and custom apparently did not prohibit parents from killing their children.

Early Jewish and Christian Traditions

The people of ancient Israel were acquainted with infanticide, particularly as it was practiced in the religious rituals of their neighbors. As evidenced by the frequency and vigor with which infanticide was denounced by their leaders, it appears that some Israelites were attracted to it. The ancient story of Abraham's apparent willingness to sacrifice his son Isaac, who was not an infant but a young man, only to be instructed by a heavenly messenger to kill a ram instead, was told and retold over the centuries (Genesis 22). Among other things, the recitation of this story reiterated a preference for animal sacrifices in Israel's religious rituals, at least until the some of Israel's prophets condemned that practice too.

Jewish scholars were thus among the first to clearly condemn the killing of infants. Jews believed that humans were created in the image of their creator, Yahweh. Hence all human life was sacred from the moment of birth. The Torah speaks of defective individuals as Yahweh's creations and it mandates protection to the blind, the deaf, the weak, and others who are needy (Leviticus 19:14). Human life had intrinsic value by virtue of divine endowment, not merely instrumental value by virtue of social utility, as in classical Greek and Roman society.

The first-century Jewish philosopher Philo denounced infanticide and emphasized adults's duties toward children. His account equated abandonment with infanticide:

> Some [parents] do the deed with their own hands; with monstrous cruelty and barbarity they stifle and throttle the first breath which the infants draw or throw them into a river or into the depths of the sea, after attaching some heavy substance to make them sink more quickly under its weight. Others take them to be exposed in some desert place, hoping, they themselves say, that they may be

saved, but leaving them in actual truth to suffer the most distressing fate. For all the beasts that feed in human flesh visit the spot and feast unhindered on the infants, a fine banquet provided by their sole guardians, those who above all others should keep them safe, their fathers and mothers.

Philo further condemned the practice, in *Works,* by claiming, "Infanticide undoubtedly is murder, since the displeasure of the law is not concerned with ages but with a breach to the human race" (Vol. 7).

However, it was the advent of Christianity, rooted in Judaism, that significantly altered public attitudes toward the practice of infanticide. Christians inherited the Jewish doctrine that humans were divinely created, including the emphasis on the sanctity of all human life. They also recalled with horror the New Testament report that King Herod had slaughtered many infants in his attempts to exterminate the infant Jesus (Matthew 2). Believers were urged to emulate Christ's self-sacrificing love through benevolence and charity, providing a new rationale for philanthropy (Ferngren, 1987a). The consequences of this philanthropy were seen in Christian charities and endeavors for the poor, the sick, and the needy. Rescue and care of exposed infants was viewed as a special Christian duty. During the medieval period through the nineteenth century, Christians established foundling hospitals, and institutions for abandoned and unwanted children.

Two other Christian concepts important for their effect on the practice of infanticide were original sin and its correlative ritual of infant baptism, thought to have become common during the third century. Christians believed that infants who died without baptism were condemned to eternal hell. Because baptisms were performed only on holy days, not necessarily soon after birth, many parents already were committed to raising the child by the time of the ritual. Thus baptism served as an important deterrent to both abandonment and infanticide.

Although Jews and Christians vigorously opposed infanticide, their opposition had little impact until Christianity became widespread and officially recognized in the fourth century. A church council in Spain issued the first canon against infanticide in 305 C.E., and soon after, both local and ecumenical councils throughout Europe took similar actions. The penalty prescribed by the church for infanticide was either penance or excommunication.

The first secular law concerning the killing of children was issued in 318 C.E. by Constantine, the first Christian emperor. However, the law mentions children killing parents as well as parents killing children and thus was not directed specifically against infanticide. In 374 C.E. Valentinian enacted legislation declaring infanticide to be murder and punishable by law. Soon after a statute was issued that appears to have prohibited exposure of infants. Although Christian emperors promulgated many laws reflecting Christian morality, fear of losing salvation made the penitential system of the churches far more effective in influencing moral behavior than did state legislation. Church leaders continued to put pressure on the state, bringing about a series of legal codes aimed at protecting newborn children.

Although the laws did not distinguish between healthy and defective infants, one may assume that Christian condemnation of infanticide extended to all infants. Early Christian apologists reflect this position. In *City of God,* Saint Augustine (354–430) argued that differences between healthy and deformed people should be seen in the same light as racial and ethnic diversity:

> If whole peoples have been monsters, we must explain the phenomenon as we explain the individual monsters who are born among us. God is the Creator of all; He knows best where and when and what is, or was, best for Him to create, since He deliberately fashioned the beauty of the whole out of both the similarity and dis-similarity of its parts.... It would be impossible to list all the human offspring who have been very different from the parents from whom they were certainly born. Still all these monsters undeniably owe their origin to Adam. (16.8)

Augustine's writings show a concern for children unusual in his time, placing the infant and the child under the protection of the Lord.

Despite decisive changes in attitudes and laws, infanticide persisted even after the official triumph of Christianity as the imperial religion. While the practice may have diminished, episodic killing of infants continued throughout Western history. What changed in subsequent periods were the motivations, methods, and penalties associated with infanticide as well as the options available to parents of unwanted children.

Medieval Period

Christianity's beliefs mixed with pagan myth, superstition, and folklore during Europe's medieval period. This commingling had significant implications for deformed infants and the practice of infanticide. Some thought, for example, that parental sexual behavior or *ill-timed passions* generated abnormal births or that sexual relations during menstruation, pregnancy, or lactation resulted in dire consequences for the unborn. In addition the birth of an anomalous infant was sometimes attributed to demonic intervention: Such births were seen as the product of either a sexual liaison between the mother/witch and the devil or a changeling left by the devil as punishment for parental sins. Parents, particularly mothers, were held morally responsible for their infants's abnormalities.

The changeling myth, derived from pagan sources, maintained that fairies, motivated by jealousy, substituted an elf child for the real child (Haffter). This version did not impute guilt to the parents; instead, blame was placed on demon fairies of the underworld and their envy of humans. Once the myth was Christianized, however, it became the devil who stole the real child and left a demon-child in its place. Thus God allowed parents to be punished for impiety or for bearing children outside matrimony. This change transformed the rationalization for the birth of defective infants from external forces to parental responsibility. Brutal and frequently lethal methods were employed either to exorcise the devil from the child or to compel the devil to return the normal child. Few infants survived the ordeal. However violent infanticide of this sort was probably the exception rather than the rule, even during the Middle Ages.

There was some secular legislation against infanticide, particularly in the later medieval period, and the crime was usually considered to be homicide. But overlaying (suffocation in the parental bed), the most frequent cause of infanticide, was easy to conceal and intent was nearly impossible to establish, thus making prosecution extremely difficult. When cases of infanticide did reach secular courts, the accused were readily acquitted on pleas of insanity or poverty. Secular authorities displayed remarkable ambivalence toward the killing of infants. By law it was considered a serious crime, yet in practice it was generally excused (Damme).

Throughout most of the medieval period, infanticide was regulated largely by church courts rather than civil courts. Ecclesiastical penalties for married women convicted of infanticide were also remarkably light, considering the Church's position. Punishment involved penance and was comparable to that imposed for sexual offenses such as adultery and fornication. Once the penance had been performed, the guilty person was not prosecuted in civil courts. The relatively light penance and the failure of secular authorities to prosecute cases of infanticide suggests that the crime was considered something less than homicide (Helmholz). Cases involving unwed mothers, however, were treated differently. Unmarried mothers who killed their infants were often accused of being witches. In fact, infanticide was the most common charge brought against *witches*

during the Middle Ages. Unlike their married counterparts, alleged witches were punished severely, usually by drowning, burial alive, or impalement.

The only reference to the status of infants under medieval secular laws was a civil law definition of a freeman (in the law "Of Different Kinds of Children"), which appears to have excluded both illegitimate and seriously deformed infants from what little protection the law offered: "Among freemen there may not be reckoned those who are born of unlawful intercourse … nor those who are created pervertedly, against the way of human kind, as for example, if a woman bring forth a monster or a prodigy" (Fleta 1.5). As legal historian Catherine Damme comments, "Clearly, these pitiful non-persons were vulnerable to the murderous attacks of their progenitors" (p. 7).

Although direct infanticide was practiced to some extent, the more common and insidious cause of infant death during the Middle Ages was abandonment. The distinction between infanticide and abandonment became increasingly important because abandonment was generally regarded as a venial offense, punishable only if the child died. In the early-Middle Ages, abandonment was widespread, motivated primarily by poverty and illegitimacy. Although a few churchmen believed it was equivalent to infanticide, two forms of abandonment were virtually institutionalized: oblation (or donating infants to the Church) and leaving infants at foundling hospitals. From a Christian point of view, both were improvements over the morally objectionable practices of exposure and infanticide. A canonical decree of the tenth century urged women to leave their illegitimate infants at the church rather than kill them (Boswell). Although oblates were tied irrevocably to the Church for life, the Church provided food, clothing, and a secure monastic life.

Foundling homes were established to diminish the practice of exposure and to provide a humane solution to infanticide. In reality, however, the foundling home often was equivalent to consigning the child to death through neglect, disease, and sometimes more direct action. Once infants arrived at a foundling home, they frequently were sent to the country with a wet nurse who was likely to be negligent and more interested in a steady flow of babies than in nurturing. Death rates were high, especially for female infants (Trexler). Markedly high demographic ratios of males to females throughout Europe during this period suggest that selective female infanticide may have been widely practiced. The disparity between male and female deaths was probably due to greater social value for males and a greater likelihood that, when put into foundling homes, they would be reclaimed by their parents. Thus such institutions did little to secure the lives of unwanted infants. They were successful only in transferring the problem of unwanted infants from a public arena to an institutional one, shielding society from the realities of abandoned children and possibly encouraging the very practice they were intended to alleviate.

Renaissance and Reformation

During the sixteenth and seventeenth centuries there was a concerted effort to stem the practice of infanticide throughout Europe. Despite a dramatic surge in reported cases, it is not clear whether or not the increase meant more frequent practice; urbanization undoubtedly made it more difficult to destroy infants secretly. Authorities were more successful at promulgating harsh legislation aimed at ending the practice and were also increasingly vigilant in prosecuting murdering mothers. An intense focus on the problems of poverty and sexual promiscuity and their purported ties to infanticide led to laws that were strongly moral in tone and selective against unmarried mothers.

The first attempt to strengthen and unify infanticide laws under the Holy Roman Empire was a statute known as the Carolina, issued in 1532 by Emperor Charles V. The law decreed that those found guilty were to be buried alive, or impaled, or drowned. The law also made concealment of pregnancy a crime, as it was presumed that such secrecy indicated infanticidal intentions. Many judges, under the pretext of the Carolina, "engaged in a policy of terror," the most notorious being the Saxon jurist Benedict Carpozof, who claimed that he assisted in the executions of 20,000 women (Piers, p. 69). The Carolina was only the first in a series of laws over the next few centuries that dealt severely with alleged infanticidal mothers.

In England Henry VIII's split from the Roman Catholic church resulted in increased secular control. Growing concern about sexual immorality and criminality among the swelling numbers of urban poor led to the enactment of several social control laws. The Poor Law of 1576 (18 Eliz. I, c.3) made bearing bastard children a crime. The fact that punishment was severe and involved substantial social disgrace for the mother increased the incentive for these women to commit infanticide. It is not surprising, therefore, that English criminal court records show that the number of indictments and guilty verdicts for infanticide rose dramatically after 1576. Most cases involved bastard children, and concealment of pregnancy was mentioned frequently (Hoffer and Hull).

The reasons for the increased zeal in punishing illegitimacy are somewhat obscure, but Puritan interests seem to have played a role. The 1623 Jacobean infanticide statute

(21 Jac. I, c.27), influenced by the Puritan element in parliament, allowed courts to convict on the basis of circumstantial evidence of concealment and prior sexual misconduct. The law presumed that the child was born alive and then killed unless the mother could prove otherwise. Prosecutions of infanticide showed a fourfold increase immediately following its enactment (Hoffer and Hull).

Ideas about the role of witches in the death of infants, even the deaths of children in foundling hospitals, persisted. Infanticide and witchcraft were so strongly interrelated during this period that their rates of indictments rose and fell in parallel. Witchcraft continued to play a major part in the drama of infanticide until the early 1800s.

Foundling hospitals continued to remove unwanted and abandoned children from public view throughout the sixteenth and seventeenth centuries. As in earlier centuries, the fate of these children was precarious. Overcrowded conditions, disease, lack of enough wet nurses, and general neglect continued to claim the lives of many of the institutions's charges.

The overwhelming majority of the victims of infanticide during this period were children born out of wedlock. Demographic information does not show the strong gender bias seen in the medieval years, nor is there evidence that defective newborns were consistently selected out. Apparently the shame associated with immoral sexual behavior was the primary selective force associated with the killing of infants.

Eighteenth and Nineteenth Centuries

In the eighteenth century, a steep decline occurred in indictments for infanticide; the courts showed greater leniency toward those accused of killing their children. In addition illegitimacy was more common; as a result the stigma associated with it lessened and its strong correlation to infanticide began to diminish. Attitudes toward parenting changed as well, with a new emphasis on the emotional nurturing of children. Wet-nursing lost popularity, and it became more common for children to spend their early months with their mothers. The greater value placed on children resulted in increased beneficence in child rearing, and so parents were probably less likely to kill their offspring. In any case juries were less willing to convict parents of infanticide solely on the basis of concealment.

New defenses for the suspected infanticidal mother were developed and more readily accepted by juries. One of the first of these defenses, known as *benefit of linen,* was based on evidence that the mother had made linen for the baby before its birth and therefore had no intention to kill it. This line of argument became very popular after 1700 and virtually guaranteed acquittal. Another major defense commonly used was the *want of help* plea. Various accidents and calamities, such as failure to tie the umbilical cord, falls of either the mother or baby, illness of the mother, and unheeded cries for help, all effectively helped to sway jurors.

Efforts to reform the English infanticide statute of 1624 began in 1773 but were not successful until 1803. In the ambivalence of eighteenth-century English society, infanticide was considered homicide yet somehow not quite the equivalent of killing an adult. Despite the failure of reform resolutions until the nineteenth century, juries tended to ignore the severe infanticide law aimed selectively at unwed mothers.

A similar trend occurred in Prussia during the reign of Frederick the Great. In his *Dissertation sur les raisons d'établir ou d'abroger les lois* (1756), Frederick argued that the prevalence of infanticide was due to the harsh penalties for illegitimacy. He therefore abolished laws penalizing pregnancies out of wedlock and eventually provided legal protection for unwed mothers. Scholars throughout Europe, including Cesare Beccaria, Voltaire, Johann Heinrich Pestalozzi, and Johann Wolfgang von Goethe, also called for legal reform and urged authorities to prevent the circumstances leading to infanticide.

Despite moderately successful reform efforts, however, infanticide did not disappear. During the nineteenth century high rates of illegitimate births continued; so, consequently, did infant killing. Corpses of infants found in privies, parks, rivers, and other public places fueled the perception that infanticide was reaching intolerable proportions. This perception may or may not have represented an actual increase in the incidence of the crime, but it did serve to stimulate an unprecedented public outcry. By the mid-nineteenth century, the concern over the *slaughter of innocents* appeared in the press (Behlmer). The British newspaper *Morning Star* (June 23, 1863) declared, "This crime is positively becoming a national institution"; and the *Pall Mall Gazette* (April 30, 1866) protested, "It is exceedingly unpleasant to find ourselves stigmatized in foreign newspapers … as a nation of infanticides.… 13,000 children are yearly murdered by their mothers in heretical England." *The Saturday Review* (1865, p. 161–162) asserted that infanticide "is the characteristic at once of the rudest barbarism and of that more terrible epoch of national life when the wheel has gone its full circle, and society falls to pieces by the vices of civilization."

Physicians were among those who led reform efforts. In his essay on infanticide in 1862, William Burke Ryan wrote

passionately against the horrors of infant murder; he and several colleagues formed the Infant Life Protection Society. By 1870 the group had achieved many of its goals, including mandatory registration of all births. In 1872 Parliament passed the first Infant Life Protection Act requiring registration of all *baby farms,* houses with more than one child under the age of one.

Legal prosecution of infanticide also underwent significant changes. Ellenborough's Act of 1803, which replaced the Infanticide Act of 1623, reinstated the common-law presumption of stillbirth, shifting the burden of proof from the defendant (mother) back to the prosecutor. In 1828 the law was expanded to include legitimate as well as illegitimate births, removing the obvious selection against unwed mothers. The fact that courts consistently acquitted the accused or mitigated penalties on the basis of insanity is testimony to the court's continued hesitancy to consider infanticide the moral equivalent of murder. There was a "visceral feeling that such a crime simply could not be a rational act.… [t]he minds of the jury and jurist could not accept that such a heinous act could be committed by a rational person—the accused's mind had to be deranged, if only temporarily" (Damme, p. 14).

Twentieth Century

The most notorious instances of infanticide in the twentieth century were committed secretly in Nazi Germany, under the auspices of the Committee for the Scientific Treatment of Severe, Genetically Determined Illness. Doctors, nurses, and teachers were required to register all children with congenital abnormalities or mental retardation. Failure to comply meant civil penalties or imprisonment. Defective children were removed from their homes and routinely euthanized at hospitals by morphine injection, gas, lethal poisons, or sometimes starvation. To ensure secrecy, the bodies were cremated immediately. Parents who protected their children were sent to labor camps and their children were taken from them. Documents reveal substantial public support for the euthanasia of defective children, even from parents with abnormal children (Proctor).

Calls for legalized euthanasia also arose from the United States, where it was justified primarily as a way of limiting the social costs associated with defective infants. W. A. Gould, writing in the *Journal of the American Institute of Homeopathy,* cited the "elimination of the unfit" in ancient Sparta as a defense of the economic arguments for euthanasia in the twentieth century (Gould). In 1938 W. G. Lennox advocated the "privilege of death for the congenitally mindless and for the incurable sick who wish to die" because saving these lives "adds a load to the back of society" (Lennox, p. 454). But as the realities of the Nazi extermination programs began to surface in the United States in the 1940s, promotion of euthanasia in general began to decline.

Yet in 1942, Foster Kennedy, professor of neurology at Cornell Medical College, wrote an article entitled "The Problem of Social Control of the Congenital Defective" advocating "euthanasia for those hopeless ones who should never have been born—Nature's mistakes." Kennedy believed "we have too many feebleminded people among us," and it was most humane to relieve defective individuals of their tortured and useless existence (Foster). Furthermore, he maintained that in diagnosis and prognosis there could be no mistakes in this *category* of children. A Gallup poll conducted twelve years earlier indicated that Kennedy's position probably was not without support within the American community. According to the poll, 45 percent of Americans in 1930 favored euthanasia of anomalous infants (Proctor, p. 180).

Toward the end of the twentieth century, the possibility of killing newborns with anencephaly in the course of acquiring transplantable organs from them was debated in professional circles. Babies with this condition are born without cerebral hemispheres, with an open skull that is empty except for the top of the spinal cord. They are wholly and permanently unconscious. Some viewed the possibility of acquiring rare transplantable organs from such infants as a way to squeeze something of value out of a tragic set of circumstances. This option was restricted by the convergence of two widely accepted norms, however. The first was that vital organs must be acquired only from dead donors. The second was that death must mean either the irreversible loss of spontaneous circulation and respiration or the irreversible loss of the functioning of the whole brain, including the brain stem. Several attempts at Loma Linda University in Southern California to acquire transplantable organs from babies born with anencephaly within the constraints of these two norms established that either the dead donor rule or the usual definition of death must first be changed. Several years later, The Council on Judicial and Ethical Opinions of the American Medical Association (AMA) proposed that in cases of anencephaly the requirement that donors of vital organs must be dead be relaxed. Shortly thereafter it withdrew this proposal in deference to intensely negative reactions. Some believed that the Council had put the wrong foot forward while attempting to move in a helpful direction. They thought that when babies are born with anencephaly it would have been less controversial to allow parents to opt for a *higher brain* rather than a *whole-brain* definition of death. If this change had been made, babies born with accurately confirmed cases of the anomaly would have been declared legally dead before transplantable organs were acquired from them. Some held that this would have honored the important ethical conviction that no one of any age or condition should be killed merely to provide transplantable organs for someone else.

The practice of infanticide was debated in the popular culture of the United States and elsewhere when Peter Singer of Australia joined the faculty of Princeton University one year before the end of the twentieth century. An accomplished utilitarian moral philosopher who was well known beyond academic circles for his advocacy of animal liberation, Singer troubled many. He contended that in general it is ethically permissible to treat human newborns in ways that parallel the ways we are morally permitted to treat other animals with approximately the same traits and abilities. He held that it is ethically acceptable to kill infants born with some serious anomalies. He also suggested that there is a sense in which parents are free to kill a handicapped infant and rear a healthier one instead. His point was that in infancy the value or interests of one newborn can often be interchanged with those of another with little or no overall loss of value, and sometimes with a gain.

These issues proved difficult to resolve in academic and popular settings in the last part of the twentieth century. This was partly because, even in many of the most widely used English dictionaries, the ability to distinguish between the basic meanings of *possible* and *potential* had all but vanished. The claim that a human infant is a potential embodiment of value, interests, or rights weighty enough to protect him or her from death at the sheer discretion of others was typically understood to mean that for a newborn this eventual state is merely possible. Common although it was, this understanding of potential failed to capture and convey the senses of inner *power, capacity,* and *endowment* in its root meaning, as was still sensed in related terms like *potent, potentiate,* and *potentate.* Wider recognition of the differences in basic meaning between potential and possible would not have settled the debates about infanticide in the last part of the twentieth century; however, it would have enabled these exchanges to proceed with greater precision and plausibility.

Conclusion

Authors who have explored the ethical dimensions of infanticide have frequently prefaced their discussions with surveys of its practice throughout history. The ostensible purpose of these discussions generally has been to provide a broader, less culturally bound perspective. However, Stephen Post argues that many writers selectively present "a one-sided and reductionist view of the history of infanticide to support their position ... that active killing of neonates is morally acceptable" (Post, p. 14). He contends that the extent of infanticide has been misrepresented and overstated. The argument is that commentators on the history of infanticide have drawn, at least to some extent, from historical surveys plagued by interpretations that tend to view history in a positivist or linear fashion. The French historian Phillipe Ariès maintains that the idea of a separate childhood was unknown until the later Middle Ages (Ariès). Similarly Lloyd DeMause contends: "The further back in history one goes, the lower the level of child care, and the more likely children are to be killed, abandoned, beaten, terrorized, and sexually abused" (DeMause, p. 1).

Revisionist historians, focusing on social, economic, and cultural forces, offer a significantly altered perspective on infanticide. While infanticide has been practiced continuously throughout Western history, it is not obvious that filicidal tendencies are widespread among parents. On the contrary, parents have usually resorted to infanticide only in exceptional circumstances. Although accurate estimates of the frequency of infanticide are almost nonexistent (largely due to inadequate and inconsistent record keeping), the prevalence of infanticide throughout Western history seems to have been episodic. Rates of infant killing have shown a tendency to rise and fall depending on prevailing economic and social forces. There have been striking discrepancies between the official position of the law, the frequency of the crime, the rate of prosecutions, the severity of punishment, and public sentiment concerning infanticide. Although the law has been relatively consistent in prohibiting its practice, the law has not always been an accurate gauge of societal values. Finally the availability of alternatives to infanticide—including abandonment, foundling hospitals, oblation, contraception, and abortion—appears to have had more impact on its practice than have official prohibitions.

CINDY BOUILLON-JENSEN (1995)
REVISED BY DAVID R. LARSON

SEE ALSO: *Abortion: Contemporary Ethical and Legal Aspects; Abuse, Interpersonal: Child Abuse; Children; Family and Family Medicine; Harm; Holocaust; Homicide; Human Rights; Infants; Insanity and the Insanity Defense; Maternal-Fetal Relationship; Mentally Disabled and Mentally Ill Persons; Moral Status; Natural Law; Sexism*

BIBLIOGRAPHY

Amundsen, Darrel W. 1987. "Medicine and the Birth of Defective Children: Approaches of the Ancient World." In *Euthanasia and the Newborn: Conflicts Regarding Saving Lives,* ed. Richard C. McMillan; H. Tristram Engelhardt, Jr.; and Stuart F. Spicker. Boston: D. Reidel.

Ariès, Phillipe. 1962. *Centuries of Childhood: A Social History of Family Life,* tr. Robert Baldick. New York: Vintage Books.

Behlmer, George K. 1979. "Deadly Motherhood: Infanticide and Medical Opinion in Mid-Victorian England." *Journal of the History of Medicine and Allied Sciences* 34(4): 403–427.

Boswell, John. 1988. *The Kindness of Strangers: The Abandonment of Children in Western Europe from Late Antiquity to the Renaissance.* New York: Pantheon.

Damme, Catherine. 1978. "Infanticide: The Worth of an Infant Under Law." *Medical History* 22(1): 1–24.

DeMause, Lloyd, ed. 1974. *The History of Childhood: The Untold Story of Child Abuse.* New York: Psychohistory Press.

Ferngren, Gary B. 1987a. "The Imago Dei and the Sanctity of Life: The Origins of an Idea." In *Euthanasia and the Newborn: Conflicts Regarding Saving Lives,* ed. Richard C. McMillan; H. Tristram Engelhardt, Jr.; and Stuart F. Spicker. Boston: D. Reidel.

Ferngren, Gary B. 1987b. "The Status of Defective Newborns from Late Antiquity to the Reformation." In *Euthanasia and the Newborn: Conflicts Regarding Saving Lives,* ed. Richard C. McMillan; H. Tristram Engelhardt, Jr.; and Stuart F. Spicker. Boston: D. Reidel.

Gould, W. A. 1993. "Euthanasia." *Journal of the Institute of Homeopathy* 27: 82.

Haffter, Carl. 1968. "The Changeling: History and Psychodynamics of Attitudes to Handicapped Children in European Folklore." *Journal of the History of the Behavioral Sciences* 4(1): 55–61.

Hanawalt, Barbara. 1977. "Childrearing Among Lower Classes of Late Medieval England." *Journal of Interdisciplinary History* 8(1): 1–22.

Helmholz, R. H. 1974. "Infanticide in the Province of Canterbury During the Fifteenth Century." *History of Childhood Quarterly* 2(3): 379–390.

Hoffer, Peter C., and Hull, N. E. H. 1981. *Murdering Mothers: Infanticide in England and New England.*. New York: New York University Press.

Jackson, Mark, ed. 2002. *Infanticide: Historical Perspectives on Child Murder and Concealment.* Burlington, Vermont: Ashgate Publishing Company.

Kellum, Barbara A. 1974. "Infanticide in England in the Later Middle Ages." *History of Childhood Quarterly* 1(3): 367–388.

Langer, William L. 1974. "Infanticide: A Historical Survey." *History of Childhood Quarterly* 1(3): 353–365.

Lennox, W. G. 1938. "Should They Live? Certain Economic Aspects of Medicine." *American Scholar* 7: 454–466.

Piers, Maria W. 1978. *Infanticide.* New York: W. W. Norton.

Post, Stephen. 1988. "History, Infanticide, and Imperiled Newborns." *Hastings Center Report* 18: 14–17.

Proctor, Richard. 1988. *Racial Hygiene: Medicine Under the Nazis.* Cambridge, MA: Harvard University Press.

Schulte, Regina. 1994. *Village in Court: Arson, Infanticide and Poaching in the Court Records of Upper Bavaria, 1848–1900.* Cambridge, Eng.: Cambridge University Press.

Sen, Mala. 2002. *Death by Fire: Sati, Dowry Death, and Female Infanticide in Modern India.* Piscataway, NJ: Rutgers University Press.

Singer, Peter. 1993. *Practical Ethics,* 2nd edition. Cambridge, Eng.: Cambridge University Press.

Symonds, Deborah A. 1997. *Weep Not for Me: Women, Ballads and Infanticide in Early Modern Scotland.* University Park: Pennsylvania State University Press.

Trexler, Richard C. 1973. "Infanticide in Florence: New Sources and First Results." *History of Childhood Quarterly* 1(1): 98–116.

Van Shaik, Carl P., and Janson, Charles H., eds. 2000. *Infanticide By Males and Its Implications.* Cambridge, Eng.: Cambridge University Press.

Wrightson, Keith. 1975. "Infanticide in Earlier Seventeenth-Century England." *Local Population Studies* 15(Autumn): 10–22.

INFANTS, ETHICAL ISSUES WITH

• • •

The birth of a baby can be one of the most satisfying, fulfilling experiences of a parent's life or a couple's marriage. After months of *infanticipating,* the experiences connected with the first few hours and days of the baby's life can be intensely rewarding for the parents, providing them with joy, gratitude, and perhaps humility as they contemplate the new life that is now entrusted to them for care and support. If they are religious believers, they may be inclined to think of the baby's life as a divine gift and to regard their parental role as involving responsible stewardship over that gift. At the very least, they will probably be thankful that the baby has a normal brain, the correct number of fingers and toes, and the rest of a physical endowment that would suggest normal human development.

Unfortunately, in a small minority of cases the months of parental dreams and plans for a normal baby turn out to be false hope. In some instances, even when prenatal diagnosis has already indicated that the baby will not be normal, there may still be parental surprise and disappointment at the range of medical problems and the degree of neurologic impairment the child has. In other instances, when prenatal diagnosis was not done and the potential parents had no

opportunity for anticipatory grief over the loss of a normal baby, the birth of a premature and/or congenitally disabled infant can have an enormous emotional impact on the parents that severely tests their most deeply held beliefs, values, and hopes for the future.

The birth of such a baby can also reflect the diversity of ethical perspectives that exist among parents, physicians, and other persons regarding the value of infants with life–threatening medical conditions, especially when the projected future lives of these children are filled with a mixture of neurologic impairments, mental and physical disabilities, and, sometimes, considerable medical uncertainty regarding the degree of those disabilities. For many persons, such cases raise important substantive questions: What is the moral status of infants with mental and physical disabilities? Should all of these infants receive life-sustaining medical interventions regardless of the severity of their medical conditions? What should be the ethical standard according to which a few infants would not receive life-sustaining efforts? Is there any moral difference between withholding and withdrawing life-sustaining treatments? Are there important moral differences between decisions about life-sustaining treatment in cases of severely disabled infants compared with cases of adults who have never been autonomous because of severe mental retardation? Would it be justifiable, in rare cases, intentionally to kill any of these infants?

Cases of premature and disabled infants also raise important procedural questions: Who should have the authority to make these life-and-death decisions? Should physicians, and in particular neonatologists, make these decisions because of their greater technical knowledge and experience with similar cases? Should the infant's parents decide because of their roles in conceiving and caring for the child, and because of their greater emotional and financial stake in the child's death or disabled life? Should a collective body (e.g., a pediatric ethics committee) make the borderline decisions?

In addition, important questions are sometimes raised about contextual and methodological matters related to decisions about the care of infants: What lessons can we learn about caring and nurturing from parents who have learned to cope with and transcend one of life's personal tragedies? Is a philosophical approach that focuses on principles, rights, interests, and obligations the correct model for ethical analysis? Do theological claims about the sanctity of life, the meaning of suffering, and the importance of stewardship over life have a significant place in decisions about the appropriate level of care for infants, whether normal or abnormal in some way? To what extent should the realities of medical economics influence the decision about whether a premature and severely disabled infant lives or dies? How much should decision makers in individual cases consider the implications of their decisions in terms of public policy?

This article has five parts: (1) a brief historical overview; (2) international perspectives among pediatricians; (3) alternative perspectives on the moral status of infants; (4) perspectives on abating life-sustaining treatment; and (5) the emerging mainstream ethical perspective. Additional information on some of these points is found in the other articles in this entry.

Historical Overview

Throughout history, as at the present time, the birth of a baby has often been the occasion for joy, celebration, and thanksgiving. In earlier centuries, the birth of a healthy, normal baby was frequently the occasion for celebration because the baby, especially if the infant was male, offered future promise for the family: another hunter for food supplies, another worker for the field or factory, another opportunity for continuing the family lineage. The birth of a baby was often an occasion for celebration for another reason: the mother had survived the dangers inherent in pregnancy and childbirth, dangers that posed a significant risk to maternal health and life in every pregnancy before the advent of modern medicine.

However, not all births were celebratory occasions. In many societies and in virtually all historical periods, very young infants, female infants, bastards, and infants and older children believed to be *defective* in some way were frequently killed. The intentional destruction of infants and children through starvation, drowning, strangulation, burning, smothering, poisoning, exposure, and a variety of lethal weapons was a tragically common practice. Such practices were widely accepted ways of dealing with unwanted children, with the responses of governments varying from required infanticidal practices (e.g., in Sparta), to acceptance of or at least indifference to the killing of female infants (e.g., in China and India), to considerable uncertainty as to how to punish parents who may have committed an illegal act by killing one of their children under questionable circumstances.

Mothers and fathers have historically had several possible reasons for killing one or more of their children. Some of them have killed for economic reasons: A dead child would mean one less mouth to feed. Others have killed their infants because of social customs and pressures: An illegitimate child, an *extra* child beyond a certain number, or another female child was especially vulnerable. Still other parents have killed their children because the infants were physically or mentally abnormal, with their congenital abnormalities being interpreted as works of the devil, signs of fate, punishment for the sins of the parents, or tricks played by witches (Weir).

Some of these older explanations of congenital disabilities seem strange now, but two features of traditional infanticidal practices remain a part of the modern world. First, infants are still sometimes killed by their parents or, perhaps more commonly, abandoned without food, shelter, or parental protection. No society is exempt from such events, with media reports of dead or abandoned babies coming from China, India, Brazil, the United States, Romania, and other countries. Second, even for parents who cannot imagine killing their own children, the birth of an extremely premature and/or severely disabled infant is a mixed blessing. For that reason, parental decisions about medical efforts to prolong a child's life frequently involve concerns about the future of the family as well as considerations about the welfare of the child.

In many parts of the world, such decisions, whether made by a child's parents or physicians, are strikingly similar to decisions made about sick and disabled children in earlier historical periods because many countries still lack the medicines, the medical and nursing personnel, and the medical technology that are common to the rest of the world. In technologically developed countries, by contrast, the development of neonatal intensive-care units (NICUs), neonatologists and other pediatric subspecialists, sophisticated medical technology, new medicines, and new surgical techniques has brought unprecedented opportunities and challenges to physicians, parents, nurses, and all other persons interested in prolonging the lives and improving the health of critically ill children. Likewise, changes in neonatal medicine since the 1970s have meant that physicians, parents, or some combination of health-care professionals in a hospital can sometimes decide that the appropriate course of moral action in a case is not to initiate or continue life-sustaining treatments, given the child's severe neurologic impairments and likelihood of continued suffering.

Such decisions—not to use medical technology to sustain an extremely premature or severely disabled infant's life—are usually difficult and sometimes controversial. In the United States, public and professional responses to publicized pediatric cases in the 1980s generated two efforts at regulating selective nontreatment decisions. The two attempts at regulation, while not always in conflict, reflected two quite different ethical perspectives regarding how and by whom selective nontreatment decisions should be made.

One effort at regulation took the form of two sets of published federal regulations during the administration of President Ronald Reagan. The *Baby Doe* regulations, first proposed in 1983, and the subsequent childabuse regulations, established in 1985, differed in legal philosophy, implementation, and influence. Yet both agreed on the ethical perspective that should govern life-and-death decisions made in NICUs and pediatric intensive-care units (PICUs): Every infant, unless permanently unconscious, irretrievably dying, or salvageable only with treatment that would be "virtually futile and inhumane," should be given life-sustaining treatment, no matter how small, young, or disabled the infant might be.

The other effort at regulation was made by the U.S. President's Commission for the Study of Ethical Problems in Medicine (1983), the American Academy of Pediatrics, and numerous writers on ethics in pediatric medicine. Given the complexity of some pediatric cases and the life-and-death nature of selective nontreatment decisions, the common recommendation was to have an ethics committee consult on the cases and give advice to the physicians in the cases. The ethical perspective at the heart of this recommendation was straightforward: In truly difficult cases, the most prudent procedure for decision making is the achievement of consensus by a multidisciplinary committee that is knowledgeable, impartial, emotionally stable, and consistent from case to case.

Similar efforts at regulating selective nontreatment decisions in NICUs and PICUs have not occurred in other countries having technological medicine. In Britain and Australia, for example, governments interested in regulating assisted reproduction technologies to protect pre-embryos have not had a similar interest in regulating selective nontreatment decisions to protect young infants, either from premature deaths or from profoundly impaired lives. Likewise, neither the governments nor the medical societies in these countries have chosen to establish pediatric ethics committees, preferring instead to leave decisions to abate life-sustaining treatment for young infants to the discretion of the physicians and parents of the children.

Nevertheless, some themes and problems are common as decision makers in technologically advanced countries confront the difficult choices presented by premature and disabled infants. First, the ongoing technological development of pediatrics (e.g., the use of exogenous surfactants and high-frequency oscillatory ventilation for treating pulmonary problems) has resulted in improved mortality and morbidity rates for numerous infants and young children. Second, unprecedented surgical techniques (e.g., surgery for short-bowel syndrome and for hypoplastic left ventricle) have resulted in the prolongation of life for many infants who would have died without surgery only a few years ago. Third, these technological and surgical achievements have

created a trend in some pediatric subspecialties toward overtreatment of premature and disabled infants, a trend that seems to be contrary to the best interests of some of these children (Caplan et al.). Fourth, even with the technological progress in pediatrics, neonatologists and the parents with whom they work in individual cases are still frequently confronted with an inescapable problem: medical uncertainty regarding the degree and range of disability a neurologically impaired child will have, if the child survives with medical treatment (Hastings Center).

Compared with earlier historical periods, the period of technological medicine has produced unprecedented changes and challenges for parents, physicians, and other persons concerned about the care of infants. The rapidity and extent of the change is noticeable in the types of cases that now present the greatest ethical challenges for parents and physicians in NICUs. In the 1970s and 1980s, considerable debate centered on whether infants with Down's syndrome plus complications and infants with myelomeningocele should receive surgical correction of their physical abnormalities. In the 1990s these types of cases have largely been replaced as ethical challenges by other kinds: (1) cases of extremely premature neonates with birth weights below 600 grams, gestational ages of approximately twenty-four weeks, and severe cardiac, pulmonary, and neurologic impairments; (2) cases of very small and disabled neonates whose low birth weights and disabilities are the result of factors during pregnancy, such as maternal malnutrition, infection (e.g., HIV and AIDS), smoking, consumption of alcohol, or use of cocaine and other drugs; and (3) cases of neonates with anencephaly whose organs could be transplanted into other infants, if the parents of the anencephalic infants were to consent and the law were to permit the transplantation (Walters).

International Perspectives among Pediatricians

The roles of physicians, parents, and nurses in the care of premature and disabled infants vary significantly from country to country. In general, pediatricians in countries that in recent decades have been characterized by authoritarian or totalitarian political regimes tend to take a similar approach to decisions made in NICUs: The decisions to treat or not to treat are made by physicians with only minimal participation by parents, nurses, or other health professionals. By contrast, pediatricians in democratic societies tend to have a more democratic attitude toward decisions made in NICUs: With some variation from physician to physician, the decisions to treat or not to treat are often made in consultation with the parents of the imperiled infants, with some physicians also finding merit in having pediatric ethics committees consult on some of the truly difficult decisions.

For example, one study indicated significant differences between pediatricians in Poland and pediatricians in Australia. The majority of both groups of physicians indicated that they had been confronted with the necessity of making decisions regarding the withholding or withdrawing of life-sustaining treatment from severely disabled infants. However, their views regarding the substantive and procedural features of such decisions were quite different. Whereas virtually all the pediatricians surveyed in Australia (98.2 %) indicated that they did not believe that "every possible effort" should be made to sustain life in every case, half of the pediatricians surveyed in Poland (50 %) stated that they thought that all possible efforts at sustaining life should be made in every case. Regarding specific diagnostic cases, significant numbers of Australian pediatricians thought that life-sustaining treatment could be withheld or withdrawn in cases of anencephaly and microcephaly (29.7 % of the responding physicians), spina bifida and myelomeningocele (25.2 %), extreme prematurity (9.0 %), Down's syndrome with complications (16.2 %), and brain damage with projected mental retardation (26.1 %). By contrast, the pediatricians in Poland, while agreeing with the Australian physicians regarding cases of extreme prematurity and brain damage, were much more reluctant to abate life-sustaining treatment for infants having microcephaly, spina bifida, or Down's syndrome (Szawarski and Tulczynski).

The differences between the Australian and Polish pediatricians were even more significant when they were asked about the procedural aspects of decisions that would probably result in an infant's death. The majority of responding Australian pediatricians indicated that they discussed such decisions with other physicians (90.9 %), the parents of the infant (90.1 %), and nurses (84.7 %). The Polish pediatricians, by contrast, almost always consulted with other physicians (99.0 %) but rarely discussed the decisions with the parents (8.1 %) or nurses (4.3 %).

Another study suggested that there are differences among pediatricians in the United States, Sweden, Britain, and Australia on both substantive and procedural aspects of selective nontreatment decisions. According to this interpretive study, the dominant practice among American pediatricians, especially neonatologists, is to initiate aggressive life-sustaining treatments early, continue those medical interventions while diagnostic tests are being done and various pediatric specialists are consulted, and talk with parents about the alternative of abating treatment only when the parents bring up the subject or when a grim prognosis becomes increasingly clear. This perspective is described as a "wait until certainty" approach, an approach involving a clear ethical choice: Saving an infant who will have severe-to-profound disabilities is preferable to permitting the death of an infant who could have lived a tolerable life. This strategy ensures that all errors are in one direction: the promotion of the infant's life, even a severely disabled life. Treatment that sustains the infant's life can therefore be terminated only when death or profoundly impaired life is inevitable (Rhoden).

This study suggests that pediatricians in Sweden have a different perspective, one that is described as a "statistical prognostic" strategy. This approach seeks to minimize the number of infants whose deaths would come slowly as well as those whose lives would be characterized by profound disabilities. At the risk of sacrificing some potentially normal infants to avoid prolonging the lives of severely impaired infants, this approach uses statistical data, like birth weight, gestational age, and early diagnostic tests, to make selective nontreatment decisions. This strategy also ensures that all errors are in one direction: the promotion of healthy life, even at the cost of allowing some infants to die who could have lived with disabling conditions.

Pediatricians in Britain and Australia are described in the study as having medical and ethical perspectives that frequently differ from those of their American and Swedish counterparts. In contrast to many pediatricians in the United States, pediatricians in Britain and Australia are willing to withhold or withdraw treatment with much less prognostic certainty. Yet in contrast to many pediatricians in Sweden, British and Australian pediatricians are willing to engage in time-limited trials to give various treatments a chance to work, even when the child being treated is likely to have ongoing disabilities. Called an "individualized prognostic" strategy, this approach reflects an ethical perspective that realizes the inherent uncertainty in medicine, permits some role for parental discretion, and affirms the appropriateness of selective nontreatment decisions once a child's prognosis appears poor (Rhoden).

In much of the world, the ethical perspectives among physicians are quite different from the approaches described above because the provision of care to infants takes place outside the confines of technological medicine. In the People's Republic of China, India, the countries of the former Soviet Union, and many of the other countries in the world, the differences in medical management that have just been described have no significance. The shortages of medicine, the obsolescence of medical equipment, the inadequacies of prenatal care, the limited number of pediatricians, and the ongoing problems of malnutrition and infectious disease contribute to a social context in which the lives of infants are frequently short and often characterized by disease and disability.

Alternative Perspectives on the Moral Status of Infants

Ethical perspectives on the care of infants are significantly influenced by views that are held regarding the ontological status and moral standing of infants, whether premature, disabled, or normal. What kind of entity is it whose life, health status, or death is at stake in the decisions made by physicians and/or parents? Is a neonate, in terms of ontological status, the same as an older child and an adult? Does an infant count as a person, in the same way that you and I count as persons? Or are questions about personhood irrelevant in terms of the moral standing that adults choose to grant infants? In terms of moral standing, what kinds of moral rights do infants possess? Do human infants possess full moral standing, making them morally equal to adult persons? Is the moral standing of neonates to be understood as somehow less than that of human adults but more than of human fetuses, or are fetuses, neonates, and adults to be understood as morally the same?

For many philosophers in recent years, questions related to the moral standing of infants have been addressed in the broader context of a discussion about ontological status and, more specifically, the meaning of personhood. One approach is to define *person* as meaning *a living being with full moral standing*. According to this definition, all persons have such standing, leaving open the question of just which characteristics give that standing.

Given this general philosophical perspective on personhood, at least three positions can be identified that link the ontological status of neonates with the moral standard granted to infants. The first position holds that all neonates, whether normal or neurologically impaired, count as actual persons in the same way that you and I count as persons. According to this view, the personhood of neonates is merely an extension of the personhood possessed earlier by fetuses. With this ontological status, neonates, like all other actual persons, have the moral right not to be killed or prematurely allowed to die, since the possession of personhood entails full moral standing, regardless of the age of the person. Personhood, according to this view, is based on genetic code or some other characteristic possessed at conception, not on possession of consciousness, self-awareness, rationality, or any other neurological characteristic.

The second position holds that in order to count as persons, infants (and other beings, whether human or nonhuman) must possess the intrinsic qualities or traits

often defined by philosophers as being the threefold combination of consciousness, self-awareness, and at least minimum rationality (Feinberg). If infants lack these core properties, they have an ontological status that is more similar to the status of human fetuses than to the status of older children or adults. Holders of this view claim that all neonates, including normal babies, fail to pass the neurologic tests for personhood and are thus to be classified as nonpersons. In this view, all neonates lack the cognitive qualities that make a human into a person. In addition, the notion of potential personhood is discarded as flawed, largely because the advocates of this second position argue that personhood cannot be possessed in varying degrees. Holders of this second view also claim that only those who have the neurological characteristics of persons possess the rights of persons, including the right not to be killed or prematurely allowed to die. The result, in terms of the moral standing of neonates, is straightforward: Neonates do not possess the moral rights of persons, leaving them at risk of being killed or prematurely allowed to die unless their parents and physicians are motivated by psychological or legal considerations to sustain their lives (Tooley).

The third position stands between the other positions. It identifies the same neurological characteristics of personhood, but according to this view, most neonates (those lacking severe neurologic impairment) are to be regarded as potential persons, not yet possessing the ontological status of actual persons but on the way to the possession of the core properties of personhood through the normal course of human development. Agreeing with advocates of the first two positions on the linkage between ontological status and moral standing, philosophers holding the third position maintain that when infants develop and subsequently become persons, they will acquire full moral standing. Until that time, including during the neonatal period, they are regarded as having a prima facie claim not to be killed, prematurely allowed to die, or significantly harmed in some other way, precisely because they will subsequently and naturally become actual persons.

The differences in these philosophical views have practical consequences in terms of the ways that adults value the lives of infants, including infants who may be extremely premature or severely disabled. Advocates of the first position tend to call for life-sustaining treatment to be administered to all infants in NICUs regardless of birth weight, gestational age, or neurological status, because all infants are actual persons in possession of the full panoply of moral rights common to persons. By contrast, any parents or physicians in NICUs who regard neonates as nonpersons (and who believe that only persons bear the rights borne by persons) are likely to be ready to withhold or withdraw treatment much more quickly, if the law permits them to do so, because the infant lives that are lost do not yet count for much morally. For advocates of the third position, the concept of potential personhood provides an intellectual framework in which difficult prognostic judgments make some sense. In this view, at least part of the difficulty in making decisions to provide life-sustaining treatment or to abate treatment, especially in cases of severe neurologic impairment, has to do with judgments about whether a particular baby has the potential even to become a person in the normal course of his or her development.

Other perspectives on the moral status of infants, some of which are grounded in theological ethics, suggest that the philosophical debate about the personhood of infants is intellectually restrictive and of little practical significance. For example, one fairly common view is that the moral standing of infants cannot depend on whether they meet a philosophically strict definition of personhood, because all infants fail to meet that standard. Rather, what is important is a social understanding of *person* according to which infants are regarded by their parents, physicians, and others *as if* they were persons. This social sense of personhood involves the imputing of personlike rights to infants because of their special roles in families and in society. The practical consequence of this view is that infants, who are given the imputed status of *person* in a social sense, have the same kind of moral standing as older human beings who are persons in a more formal sense (Engelhardt).

Another widely held view is that the personhood question simply does not apply to infants, either in a strict sense or in a social sense. Rather, what is important is that infants are understood to have moral standing as *fellow human beings*. Advocates of this view may regard fetuses and infants as having equal moral standing as human beings, or they may have a developmental view in which viable fetuses and infants, but not nonviable fetuses, have equal moral standing as human beings. Either way, infants are regarded as having the same kinds of moral rights that older human beings have, including the right not to be killed or allowed to die prematurely unless, in unusual cases, the burdens of continued life are regarded as outweighing the benefits of that life to the child (Fletcher). Holders of this view give the same moral standing to infants and fetuses as do holders of the first position above, but deny that these beings have to be called persons.

The personhood approach to the moral status of infants, according to another theological view, is unrelated to the possession of the neurological characteristics identified

with personhood discussed above for another reason. The limiting of an infant's value to the question of whether that infant possesses the intrinsic properties of personhood entirely omits another approach to the understanding of the value that infants have: namely, a relational view of value that results from interpersonal bonding, affection, and care by parents and other adults. Even when an infant has a future that will, because of neurologic impairments, be characterized by developmental delay and mental retardation, the parents of the child still usually go through a process of bonding with the child. That process of bonding, which involves the replacement of a hoped-for child with a healthy attachment to the child one has been given, results in a valuing of the child by parents that is surely equal to the valuing of normal children by their parents (May).

A related view is that philosophical arguments about the moral status of infants need to be supplemented, if not replaced, by an experiential ethic of care. This view emphasizes the importance of the various perspectives that parents, physicians, nurses, and other persons bring to pediatric cases. Rather than focusing on the ontological and moral status of infants, most commonly with questions related to the possession of personhood and moral rights, this approach concentrates on the various values and virtues present, or possible, in the context of decision making about an infant's impending death or projected life with disabilities. The practical result is that questions in difficult cases are raised not only about what should be done for the patient but also about what kinds of moral agents the parents, physicians, and nurses should be as they provide care for an imperiled infant (Reich).

Ethical Perspectives on Abating Life-Sustaining Treatment

The ethical perspective that became enacted into the *Baby Doe* regulations and child abuse regulations was only one of the ethical perspectives on the medical care of infants that received considerable attention in the United States in the 1970s–1990s. Other ethical perspectives have also been widely held, both before and after the federal regulations became policy.

For example, for some persons the important ethical question is not whether a given infant can be salvaged through medical treatment. Rather, the important question is what quality of life the child will probably have later, especially if the child's future is predicted to be dominated by severe-to-profound neurologic impairments, multiple surgeries, and numerous other medical problems. The question is sometimes posed in terms of the future relational potential possessed by a child with severe neurologic impairments, with the moral judgment being that an infant who lacks relational capacity will never have the quality of life that would justify the continuation of the child's life (McCormick).

A closely related ethical perspective focuses on a child's best interests. For persons holding this position, the important question is whether the life-sustaining treatment that could be given to imperiled newborns will, on balance, provide the infants with more benefits than burdens. Since quality-of-life projections can sometimes extend to include persons other than the patient, this position's strength is in framing the ethical debate primarily in terms of the patient's best interests, not the interests of the family or society (U.S. President's Commission).

Another ethical perspective emphasizes procedural issues. According to this view, the most important aspect of decisions not to sustain some infants' lives is the question of who should make these difficult decisions. Advocates of this position maintain that in most cases, the parents of a premature or disabled infant are the appropriate decision makers.

A very different ethical perspective on selective treatment decisions also has some advocates. As described in the previous section, some philosophers hold that life-sustaining treatment can morally be withheld or withdrawn from any infant, regardless of birth weight or disability, because the only deaths that matter are the deaths of persons, and no infants meet the requirements of personhood.

Three of these ethical perspectives continue to play major roles in selective nontreatment decisions, with the dominant perspective in individual cases varying from hospital to hospital, physician to physician, parent to parent, case to case. The perspective that calls for life-sustaining treatment to be administered to all infants who are conscious, not dying, and for whom treatment is not "virtually futile and inhumane" remains influential, even if the federal regulations that reflect this perspective have been largely unenforced throughout the country. The reasons for its continuing influence are twofold. First, this perspective is consistent with the reasons that motivate neonatologists to do the work they do: to prolong and enhance the lives of the youngest, smallest, most disabled, and most vulnerable human beings among us. Second, this perspective offers the simplest way of dealing with the multiple problems that constitute the *ethics lab* known as the NICU: It minimizes the factor of medical and moral uncertainty in cases, the role of parents as decision makers, and any considerations of the harm that may be done through prolonged, aggressive efforts to salvage imperiled young lives.

The second perspective that remains influential is the position that emphasizes the role of parents as decision makers. Advocates of this view rarely suggest that parents alone should make the selective nontreatment decisions that could result in the deaths of their children, or that parents should be given unlimited discretion in making such decisions. Rather, the claim that is often made is that parents should, in response to appropriate medical information and advice, have reasonable discretion in making a life-and-death decision regarding their child in the NICU, subject to certain ethical and legal constraints. They are the ones, after all, who may be saddled with the enormous financial costs of neonatal intensive care. They are the ones, in addition to the child, who will have to deal with the child's ongoing medical problems, repeated hospitalizations and surgeries, neurologic abnormalities, and developmental delays. They are the ones who will have to struggle to sustain their marriage, their family life, their careers, and their own physical and mental health.

The third perspective that remains influential is the patient's-best-interests position. Advocates of this position acknowledge the medical and moral uncertainty inherent in many cases, affirm an important role for parents as decision makers, and recognize that the same medical and surgical interventions that produce great benefit for some patients can produce undue harm for others. In contrast to the parental perspective, proponents of this view emphasize that the focal point of decision making in neonatal and pediatric cases should be the best interests of the patient, even when the patient's interests conflict with the interests of the parents. In this manner, the patient's-best-interests position emphasizes the linkage between life-sustaining medical treatment and patient-centered considerations regarding the quality of life—without broadening quality-of-life judgments to include the family, the society, or arbitrary standards for normalcy and acceptability, as quality-of-life projections sometimes do.

The Emerging Mainstream Perspective

If any of these positions can be correctly designated as the mainstream ethical position, at least in the United States, it is the patient's-best-interests position. Advocates of this position are concerned about the treatment-related harms that sometimes occur when neonatologists and other pediatric subspecialists persist, perhaps under the influence of the federal regulations, in overtreating infants who have extremely low birth weights and severe disabling conditions but who are neither unconscious nor dying. At the same time, proponents of the best-interests view are reluctant to grant the parents of premature and disabled infants as much discretion in deciding to abate life-sustaining treatment as some parents would like to have.

In clinical cases, the best-interests position relies on eight variables that help to determine whether to initiate, continue, or abate life-sustaining treatment: (1) the severity of the patient's medical condition, as determined by diagnostic evaluation and comparison with (a) all infants and (b) infants having the same medical condition; (2) the achievability of curative or corrective treatment, in an effort to determine what is meant by *beneficial* treatment in a given case; (3) the important medical goals in the case, such as the prolongation of life, the effective relief of pain and other suffering, and the amelioration of disabling conditions; (4) the presence of serious neurologic impairments, such as permanent unconsciousness or severe mental retardation; (5) the extent of the infant's suffering, as determined by the signs of suffering that infants send by means of elevated blood pressure, elevated heart rate, degree of agitation, and crying; (6) the multiplicity of other serious medical problems, with the most serious cases usually involving a combination of neurologic, cardiac, pulmonary, renal, and other medical complications; (7) the life expectancy of the infant, because some of the severe congenital anomalies involve a life expectancy of only a few weeks or months; and (8) the proportionality of treatment-related benefits and burdens to the infant, a medical and ethical "bottom line" for determining whether life-sustaining treatment or the abatement of such treatment is in a particular infant's best interests (Weir and Bale).

Even with these variables, the ethical analysis of cases involving neonates or other young pediatric patients is anything but easy. Although there are numerous cases about which almost everyone agrees, there continue to be many cases that combine unprecedented medical and moral territory, advances in medical management and technology, medical uncertainty, and ethical conflicts between physicians and parents in such a way as to present serious ethical challenges to all the parties involved in the cases. In such instances, the discernment of the infant's best interests can be a challenging and humbling experience.

ROBERT F. WEIR (1995)
BIBLIOGRAPHY REVISED

SEE ALSO: *Abuse, Interpersonal: Child Abuse; Care: Contemporary Ethics of ; Children; Clinical Ethics; Compassionate Love; Embryo and Fetus; Family and Family Medicine; Feminism; Genetic Testing and Screening; Life, Quality of:* *Quality of Life in Clinical Decisions; Maternal-Fetal Relationship; Medicaid; Moral Status; Pediatrics; Research Policy, Risk and Vulnerable Groups; Sexism*

BIBLIOGRAPHY

Bermudez, Jose Luis. 1996. "The Moral Significance of Birth." *Ethics* 106(2): 378–403.

Caplan, Arthur L.; Blank, Robert H.; and Merrick, Janna C., eds. 1992. *Compelled Compassion: Government Intervention in the Treatment of Critically Ill Newborns.* Totowa, NJ: Humana.

Carter, Brian S., and Stahlman, Mildred. 2001. "Reflections on Neonatal Intensive Care in the U.S.: Limited Success or Success with Limits?" *Journal of Clinical Ethics* 12(3): 215–222.

Dickenson, Donna L. 2002. *Ethical Issues in Maternal-Fetal Medicine.* New York: Cambridge University Press.

Engelhardt, H. Tristram, Jr. 1978. "Medicine and the Concept of Person." In *Ethical Issues in Death and Dying,* pp. 271–284, ed. Tom Beauchamp and Seymour Perlin. Englewood Cliffs, NJ: Prentice-Hall.

Feinberg, Joel. 1986. "Abortion." In *Matters of Life and Death: New Introductory Essays in Moral Philosophy,* 2nd edition, pp. 256–293, ed. Tom L. Beauchamp and Tom Regan. New York: Random House.

Fletcher, John C. 1975. "Abortion, Euthanasia, and Care of Defective Newborns." *New England Journal of Medicine* 292(2): 75–78.

Frader, Joel. 1986. "Forgoing Life-Sustaining Food and Water: Newborns." In *By No Extraordinary Means: The Choice to Forgo Life-Sustaining Food and Water,* pp. 180–185, ed. Joanne Lynn. Bloomington: Indiana University Press.

Ford, Norman M. 2002. *The Prenatal Person: Ethics from Conception to Birth.* Williston, VT: Blackwell Publishers.

Franck, Linda, and Lefrak, Linda. 2001. "For Crying Out Loud: The Ethical Treatment of Infants' Pain." *Journal of Clinical Ethics* 12(3): 275–281.

Hastings Center. 1987. "Imperiled Newborns." *Hastings Center Report* 17(6): 5–32.

Headings, Verle. 2000. "Comment: Collaborative Decision Making with HIV-Infected Mothers." *Journal of Clinical Ethics* 11(2): 126–127.

Horan, Dennis J., and Delahoyde, Melinda, eds. 1982. *Infanticide and the Handicapped Newborn.* Provo, Utah: Brigham Young University Press.

Kipnis, Kenneth, and Diamond, Milton. 1998. "Pediatric Ethics and the Surgical Assignment of Sex." *Journal of Clinical Ethics* 9(4): 398–410

Koch, Tom, and Ridgley, Mark. 1998. "Distanced Perspectives: Aids, Anencephaly, and AHP." *Theoretical Medicine* 19(1): 47–58.

Kopelman, Loretta M.; Irons, Thomas G.; and Kopelman, Arthur E. 1988. "Neonatologists Judge the 'Baby Doe' Regulations.'" *New England Journal of Medicine* 318(11): 677–683.

Kuhse, Helga, and Singer, Peter. 1985. *Should the Baby Live?: The Problem of Handicapped Infants.* Oxford: Oxford University Press.

Magnet, Joseph E., and Kluge, Eike-Henner W. 1985. *Withholding Treatment from Defective Newborn Children.* Cowansville, Quebec: Brown Legal Publications.

May, William F. 1984. "Parenting, Bonding, and Valuing the Retarded." In *Ethics and Mental Retardation,* pp. 141–160, ed. Loretta M. Kopelman and John C. Moskop. Dordrecht, Netherlands: D. Reidel.

McCormick, Richard A. 1974. "To Save or Let Die: The Dilemma of Modern Medicine." *Journal of the American Medical Association* 229(2): 172–176.

McMahan, Jeff. 2002. *The Ethics of Killing: Problems at the Margins of Life.* New York: Oxford University Press.

Murray, Thomas H., and Caplan, Arthur L., eds. 1985. *Which Babies Shall Live? Humanistic Dimensions of the Care of Imperiled Newborns.* Clifton, NJ: Humana.

Paris, John J.; Crone, Robert K.; and Reardon, Frank. 1990. "Physicians' Refusal of Requested Treatment: The Case of Baby L." *New England Journal of Medicine* 322(14): 1012–1015.

Reich, Warren Thomas. 1987. "Caring for Life in the First of It: Moral Paradigms for Perinatal and Neonatal Ethics." *Seminars in Perinatology* 11(3): 279–287.

Rhoden, Nancy K. 1986. "Treating Baby Doe: The Ethics of Uncertainty." *Hastings Center Report* 16(4): 34–42.

Rhoden, Nancy K., and Arras, John D. 1985. "Withholding Treatment from Baby Doe: From Discrimination to Child Abuse." *Milbank Memorial Fund Quarterly* 63(1): 18–51.

Shelp, Earl E. 1986. *Born to Die? Deciding the Fate of Critically Ill Newborns.* New York: Free Press.

Shinnar, Shlomo, and Arras, John D. 1989. "Ethical Issues in the Use of Anencephalic Infants as Organ Donors." *Neurologic Clinics* 7(4): 729–743.

Spence, K. 1998. "Ethical Issues for Neonatal Nurses." *Nursing Ethics* 5(3): 206–17.

Strong, Carson. 1984. "The Neonatologist's Duty to Patient and Parents." *Hastings Center Report* 14(4): 10–16.

Szawarski, Zbigniew, and Tulczynski, Aleksander. 1988. "Treatment of Defective Newborns—A Survey of Paediatricians in Poland." *Journal of Medical Ethics* 14(1): 11–17.

Todres, I. David; Guillemin, Jeanne; Grodin, Michael A.; and Batten, Dick. 1988. "Life-Saving Therapy for Newborns: A Questionnaire Survey in the State of Massachusetts." *Pediatrics* 81(5): 643–649.

Tooley, Michael. 1983. *Abortion and Infanticide.* Oxford: Clarendon Press.

U.S. President's Commission for the Study of Ethical Problems in Medicine and Biomedical and Behavioral Research. 1983. "Seriously Ill Newborns." In *Deciding to Forego Life-Sustaining Treatment: A Report on the Ethical, Medical, and Legal Issues in Treatment Decisions,* pp. 197–229. Washington, D.C.: U.S. Government Printing Office.

Walters, James W. 1991. "Report from North America: Anencephalic Infants as Organ Sources." *Bioethics* 5(4): 326–341.

Weir, Robert F. 1984. *Selective Nontreatment of Handicapped Newborns: Moral Dilemmas in Neonatal Medicine.* New York: Oxford University Press.

Weir, Robert F. 1996. *Selective Nontreatment of Handicapped Newborns: Moral Dilemmas in Neonatal Medicine.* New York: Oxford University Press.

Weir, Robert F., and Bale, James F., Jr. 1989. "Selective Nontreatment of Neurologically Impaired Neonates." *Neurologic Clinics* 7(4): 807–822.

INFANTS, MEDICAL ASPECTS AND ISSUES IN THE CARE OF

• • •

Overall, there are three relatively distinct groups of babies who are admitted to neonatal intensive care units (NICUs). These groups are different in ways that are ethically relevant. The first group consists of full-term or near-term babies with acute illnesses such as pneumonia or sepsis, as well as babies with surgically correctable anatomic abnormalities. The second group comprises babies with congenital anomalies, including chromosomal anomalies, which are not correctable at the present time. Many of these babies have problems that can be ameliorated but not corrected with surgical or medical treatment. The final group of babies includes those born prematurely who are otherwise physically normal— that is, they have no acute illness or congenital anomaly except their prematurity. The first two groups raise problems that are essentially similar to those that arise in other patient groups. They are different from other patients only in that they are babies. The third group is entirely unique. There are no other clinical populations in which the primary clinical problem arises from an arrested developmental process, and in which the clinical problem will correct itself if development is allowed to continue. This entry describes, in separate sections, the three groups and the different ethical issues associated with them.

Acute Illnesses

Acute illnesses in full-term babies are usually the least morally controversial of the clinical problems that arise in neonatology. Most acute illnesses can be treated if they are accurately diagnosed. The problems that arise in babies are similar to the problems in other high-risk populations. Diagnosis must be made quickly and treatment initiated expeditiously. The babies generally either get better quickly or they die quickly.

Rarely, treatment is only partially successful, and the babies survive but with severe long-term complications of their acute illness. For example, term babies might develop meningitis. The disease can be diagnosed and treated, but some babies are left with severe neurological impairment. In situations where treatment is only partially successful, the babies become similar to babies with uncorrectable congenital anomalies. The only difference is that, in these cases, the anomaly was acquired after birth rather than before. The process of decision-making, however, will be similar to that outlined below.

In general, the issues that arise in this group of NICU patients are not unique to NICU patients. The primary concerns are accurate diagnosis and appropriate treatment. If there is a treatment that works, it should be provided. There is rarely disagreement between doctors and parents in these cases. The ethical issues are driven almost entirely by the medical indications for treatment. Ethics simply dictates that doctors should be competent and should communicate well with parents.

Congenital Anomalies

Congenital anomalies were the primary focus of legal and moral controversy in the 1970s regarding treatment decisions for newborns (Lantos). The key cases focused on syndromes such as trisomy 21 (Down syndrome), spina bifida, and cases of multiple congenital malformations. Generally, the issue that arose was whether or not to attempt surgical treatment to correct some but not all of the congenital anomalies. Thus, for babies with Down syndrome, the issue was whether to correct an associated intestinal or cardiac malformation. In babies with spina bifida, the issue was whether to treat the hydrocephalus by placing a shunt in the brain, or whether to close an open lesion of the spinal canal.

It is understood that, in these situations, the underlying syndromes themselves cannot be treated. Babies with Down syndrome will still have Down syndrome, even if their intestinal or cardiac anomalies are repaired. Babies with spina bifida will still have the long-term neurological problems associated with the spinal cord injury, even if their hydrocephalus is treated. Thus, the issues that drive these decisions are fundamentally different from those in cases of acute illness. The primary focus in these cases is on long-term quality of life for survivors.

Congenital anomalies focus discussion on anticipated quality of life as opposed to prognosis for survival. The discussions often involve the ethical implications of active intervention as opposed to "letting nature take its course." In many of the discussions, there is a sense of fatalism in the face of what are seen as mistakes of nature. Perhaps, the thought goes, these babies were somehow meant to die, and interventions are both unnatural and inhumane.

Many congenital malformations that were once thought to be incompatible with life can now be treated. Given the capabilities of modern intensive care, there are very few congenital anomalies that are truly incompatible with life. Babies with severe congenital heart disease can have open-heart surgery, babies with no intestines can be given total parenteral nutrition, and babies with minimal brain function can be kept alive on ventilators. Unlike cases of acute illness, decisions in these cases are not driven primarily by the medical indications for treatment. Those are usually straightforward. Instead, the decisions are driven by judgments about whether the results of successful treatment will be acceptable. In other words, will the consequential quality of life be sufficient to make the life worth living? In analyzing such decisions, it is necessary to have a nuanced understanding of the different components of "quality of life."

QUALITY OF LIFE COMPONENTS. Quality of life can be broken down into a number of ethically relevant components, each of which must be considered in these cases. These components include the anticipated cognitive or neurological function, the anticipated physical disabilities, the pain and suffering that is associated with the disease itself, and the burdens of the treatments that will be necessary in the future.

Most people today hold that a certain minimal level of cognitive or neurological function is essential for a life to be considered worth living. This was one of the rare areas of consensus in the 1980s controversy about federal regulation of nontreatment decisions for newborns. The agreement, in principle, that cognitive function is an important consideration begs the question of appropriate thresholds. Babies with no cortical function at all, such as babies with anencephaly or babies with prolonged cortical unresponsiveness as a result of anoxic (oxygen-deficiency) injuries, define one extreme. Babies with syndromes such as Down syndrome that lead to mild mental retardation are at the other end of the spectrum. In between are babies with other chromosomal or genetic anomalies, babies with intraventricular hemorrhages, or babies with neurological damage as an aftereffect of treatment for an acute illness.

The process for decision making in such cases requires recognition of a real but constantly shifting boundary or threshold that has clearly defined extremes and a well-recognized "gray zone" in the middle. Today, as a matter of societal consensus, the quality of life in Down syndrome is considered to be above the threshold, so these babies, and babies like them, must be treated. The quality of life in anencephaly is considered to fall below the threshold, so babies with this syndrome generally ought not be treated. There are, occasionally, exceptional cases of anencephaly in which treatment is provided at the parents' insistence, but they are noteworthy because they are exceedingly rare. Exceptions to the rule do not undermine the validity of the rule, they simply highlight the difficulty of imposing universal compliance with the rule. Cases in between these extremes are still difficult and controversial.

The physical disabilities associated with a condition must be addressed separately from the cognitive or neurological disabilities. Often, babies have an intact brain but have other physical disabilities. In severe spina bifida, for example, the spinal cord damage may make it impossible for a person to move about independently. Generally, physical disabilities, by themselves, cannot justify a decision to withhold life-sustaining treatment. It is clear from studies of adults with spinal cord injuries that it is possible for a person with severe physical disabilities to lead a rich and satisfying life. Thus, in such cases, the focus of discussion is usually on developing an adequate support system and insuring access to rehabilitation services so that function can be maximized.

A third part of any assessment of quality of life has to do with the pain and suffering associated with the disease. Some diseases lead to unrelenting pain and suffering. For example, severe epidermolysis bullosa is a disease that causes blistering of the skin over the entire body, including the oral cavity and intestinal tract. Swallowing is impossible. Scarring of the skin leads to contractures (permanent shortenings) of all the joints. Even comfort care is difficult because merely handling babies with this syndrome causes pain and exacerbates the condition. In such a case, an attempt to prolong life inevitably prolongs the suffering. It is appropriate in such cases, or in cases like them (though there are not many other syndromes that are relevantly similar to epidermolysis bullosa), to withhold life-sustaining treatment based solely on the pain and suffering associated with the disease.

Another component of quality of life has to do not with the pain and suffering of the underlying condition but with the pain and other burdens associated with the necessary treatments. Babies with short gut syndrome, for example, can survive, but only with indwelling venous catheters placed into large veins in the chest or neck. These central lines often become infected and must be replaced. When they become infected, patients must be admitted to the hospital for intravenous antibiotics. Parenteral nutrition

often causes secondary problems such as liver failure. In extreme cases, patients are frequently hospitalized to deal with the complications of the treatment, and further treatment predictably exacerbates these complications in ways that cannot be prevented. Another example of excessively burdensome treatment is the provision of mechanical ventilation for babies with progressive and degenerative motor neuron disease. Some such babies are unable to eat, breathe, or talk, but their cerebral cortex is intact, so that they can think. Prolonged mechanical ventilation can prolong life for such babies, but the burdens of the treatment are thought to be high enough that a decision not to initiate mechanical ventilation, or to discontinue it once started, is usually considered acceptable. In such cases, the burdens of treatment drive the decision.

Any adequate discussion of quality of life must separate the components. Nevertheless, in most cases, a combination of these components exists. Generally, the task of moral reasoning about any unique individual case requires doctors and parents to analogize the case with better known paradigm cases. For doctors and parents, the question may be whether a particular case is more like Down syndrome than it is like anencephaly, or whether a burdensome treatment is more like lifetime mechanical ventilation than it is like lifetime dependence on insulin.

Extreme Prematurity

Babies with extreme prematurity comprise the third group of babies admitted to the NICU. The moral considerations involved with these babies include not only all of the considerations in the other two groups but also an important new one—long-term prognostic uncertainty.

Prematurity is both an acute crisis and a chronic condition. The acute crisis requires an emergency response driven by medical indications, just as in the cases of full-term babies with acute medical problems. At the time treatment is initiated, however, the baby's prognosis is usually uncertain in a different way than in the other two situations. With acute pneumonia, treatment usually either succeeds, in which case the problem is completed resolved, or it fails, in which case the baby dies. There is almost no middle ground. With congenital anomalies and syndromes, treatment cannot cure the underlying disease. So a baby with Down syndrome will still have Down syndrome, even if the congenital heart disease is repaired. The long-term prognosis for survivors is clearly predictable. Again, there is almost no middle ground of uncertainty. With extremely premature babies, by contrast, the prognosis is radically uncertain. It ranges from early death through later death to survival with severe disabilities, moderate disabilities, or no disabilities.

The disabilities can be cognitive, pulmonary, or involve virtually any other organ system. When treatment must be initiated, nearly all babies are in a prognostic gray zone. The outcome for any particular baby simply cannot be known, and it can range across the entire spectrum of possibilities from the very best to the very worst. This raises a whole different set of ethical considerations.

PROGNOSIS FOR SURVIVAL AND THE BIRTHWEIGHT FACTOR. At the time of birth, it is difficult to say whether a particular baby will live or die. It is difficult to predict how long life can be prolonged in cases where death will ultimately ensue. And it is difficult to predict whether survivors will have mild, moderate, or severe chronic problems or no problems. Obviously, an accurate prognosis for a particular baby would be essential to making the best ethical decision for that baby. If survival is impossible, then treatment should not be provided. If intact survival is likely, then treatment is morally obligatory. To a certain extent, clinical research in neonatal intensive care since the early 1980s has helped bring about a greater understanding of these issues and helped to refine, though not perfect, doctors' prognostic abilities.

The goal of this research has been to develop a method to precisely predict the anticipated outcome for each premature baby. The most powerful prognostic measure has always been birthweight. Overall, bigger babies do much better than smaller babies. Almost no babies who weigh less than 500 grams at birth survive, whereas nearly all babies who weigh more than 875 grams at birth survive. The zone of controversy is in between these two birthweights. The weights correspond, roughly, to the time between about twenty-three weeks of gestation and twenty-six weeks of gestation, or between the fifth and sixth months of pregnancy.

One plausible response to these data would be to suggest that only babies over 850 grams should be treated. If this course were taken, however, there would be many babies in the 500- to 850-gram birthweight range who might have survived but who would be allowed to die. Another response might be to treat all babies over 500 grams. With this option, however, treatment is provided to many babies whose death is likely. One way to refine the prognostic estimates is to look a little more closely at the clinical course of these babies.

It turns out that most premature babies who are going to die do so in the first few days of life. The sickest babies are very sick. Because the sickest babies die quickly, the babies who survive for even three days are, by definition, much more likely to survive than other babies of the same birthweight. In fact, by seventy-two hours of age, birthweight virtually disappears as a relevant predictor of survival. The

600-gram babies who survive do just as well as the 1,000-gram babies who survive (Meadow, Reimshisel, and Lantos).

These clinical epidemiological facts have shaped the moral responses of NICU professionals. Prior to the 1980s, discussions about the appropriateness of decisions involving whether or not to treat premature babies presumed that the decision should be made at birth and in the delivery room. It was seen as a one-time, either/or decision. The newly understood clinical realities show why that did not make sense. Among all babies born at less than 750 grams today, half can be saved and half cannot. At the time of birth, however, it is almost impossible to tell which baby will be in which group. The only way to separate the two groups is to initiate treatment on all of them. The sickest babies then *declare themselves* by getting sicker in spite of medical treatment, and the healthier babies *declare themselves* by improving.

NEUROLOGICAL OUTCOMES. Determining the prognosis for neurological outcome is even more difficult than determining the prognosis for survival. Clearly, premature babies have worse neurological outcomes than full-term babies. Numerous studies have shown a higher incidence of cerebral palsy, seizures, chronic lung disease, and educational problems among premature babies than among their full-term peers. Nicholas S. Wood and colleagues summarized outcomes for tiny babies in a 2000 issue of the *New England Journal of Medicine* (see Figure 1).

These statistics, however, are like the statistics showing poor survival for tiny babies. The relevant question for clinicians and parents is not whether, overall, a group of babies has a worse prognosis but whether for any particular baby the likely outcome can be predicted. There are predictors of bad outcomes, but they are imperfect.

As they reported in 2002, Carl T. D'Angio and colleagues studied long-term neurologic, cognitive, and educational outcomes for babies born at less then twenty-nine weeks of gestation. They showed that the only predictors of bad neurologic outcomes were neonatal intraventricular hemorrhage, severe lung disease, and low socioeconomic status. Betty R. Vohr and colleagues found similar results in a 2000 study. Interestingly, the first two factors are physiological while the third is social, but each is independently associated with bad outcomes. At the very least, this suggests a complex interplay between physiological and sociological factors. Importantly, neither birthweight nor gestational age is, by itself, associated with poor neurological outcomes for these babies. This again suggests that, in the clinical setting, a simple criterion for treatment or nontreatment based on birthweight alone is likely to be relatively inaccurate in tailoring treatment decisions in an ethically appropriate way.

FIGURE 1

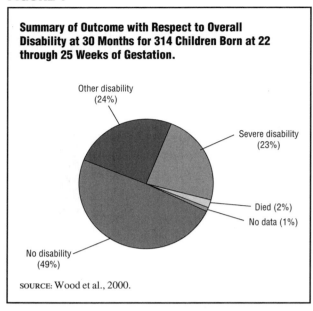

Summary of Outcome with Respect to Overall Disability at 30 Months for 314 Children Born at 22 through 25 Weeks of Gestation.

Other disability (24%)

Severe disability (23%)

Died (2%)

No data (1%)

No disability (49%)

SOURCE: Wood et al., 2000.

Implications of Clinical Knowledge for Ethical Decision Making

These epidemiological facts help define the zone of parental discretion. In order for a decision to withhold life-sustaining treatment to even be considered, doctors must first determine that a baby has an appropriately severe condition. Thus, doctors initiate most discussions of treatment withdrawal. Sometimes, parents will initiate the discussions but when they do, the doctor's task is the same—deciding whether or not the baby fits into one of the categories in which treatment withdrawal is permissible. If not, the doctor must rebuff the parents' request. If so, the doctor should facilitate the process in a way similar to the way she would if she had initiated it herself.

Over the years, different schools of thought have evolved about the proper tone and structure for such discussions. These might be characterized as the *objective information* approach and the *broad shoulders* approach.

In the objective approach, doctors see it as their responsibility to give parents information in the most nondirective way. They simply provide the facts and try to empower parents to understand those facts and to come to a decision that reflects the parents' personal moral or spiritual values. In this approach, the doctor does not make a recommendation about the appropriate course of treatment. If they are asked what they would do, they refuse to answer. The moral psychology of this approach is based upon a fear of being coercive. It views doctors as inappropriately empowered and parents as problematically vulnerable to being overpowered.

Given that sociological background, doctors have a moral obligation to restrain their own implicit dominating impulses. Sociologists, who examine the power structures of human communities, often see this sort of pattern of interaction. Some philosophers, especially those for whom individual autonomy is a paramount moral principle, are the most articulate defenders of this approach.

The broad shoulders approach takes a different tack. By this view, parents' particular vulnerabilities require doctors to take some of the burden of decision making upon themselves. Instead of simply giving parents the facts, doctors are obligated to make a recommendation. Advocates of this approach point out that the circumstances of serious illness are circumstances of personal moral and psychological crisis in which ordinary moral principles may not be applicable. Individuals may not be capable of the same sort of autonomy in such situations as they are in other situations. They may need subtle and often implicit assistance to understand their own wants, needs, and values, and they may have trouble owning the decision that flows from these values.

In spite of these radical differences in understandings of the moral underpinnings of the conversations that lead to decisions, in practice, the structure of conversations between doctors and parents look similar in both. The first discussion is one of facts and possibilities. The clinical facts are explained. The possibilities for treatment or nontreatment or presented. Questions are answered. Usually, this first discussion is then adjourned, and parents are allowed time to think. In most cases, they seek outside support—from extended family, from clergy, or from mental health professionals.

A second discussion, during which a decision is reached, usually follows within a few days. Three sorts of conclusions can be reached. In the first, parents decide that they do not want to stop treatment and do not want to reconsider their decision in the future. They want *everything done* to keep their baby alive. Generally, this leads to a discussion of the ambiguity of the term *everything done* in today's medical environment. The second sort of conclusion that can be reached is for a *time-limited trial* of continued treatment. By this approach, doctors agree to continue treatment for a defined period and to set certain parameters or endpoints that they might then look for to see if the treatment is leading to anticipated goals. For example, doctors might offer to continue mechanical ventilation for another week and if, at that point, the ventilator can be safely discontinued, then it will be. If not, however, it will be discontinued anyway in a manner that will likely lead to the death of the baby. The final sort of conclusion that can be reached is a decision to withdraw life-sustaining treatment immediately.

In these situations, a standard set of rituals, familiar to the staff in most NICUs, ensue. The baby is moved to a separate room, the parents are called in, the ventilator or the intravenous fluid pumps are removed, and the parents are allowed time alone to hold their dying baby.

These approaches reflect the inherent uncertainty of the process. When death is inevitable, there is no moral decision to be made. In those circumstances, heroic efforts are often made to prolong life and those efforts fail. A moral statement has been made, a moral commitment fulfilled. Moral decisions arise only when there is ambiguity or uncertainty about the prognosis and about the efficacy of treatment. As has been shown above, however, there is almost always uncertainty. Uncertainty creates the necessity for moral, as opposed to simply clinical, decision making.

Conclusion

The current state of ethical decision making for infants in neonatal intensive care units involves several tasks. The first task is to correctly categorize the clinical indication for intensive care treatment. The second is to determine, as accurately as possible, the baby's prognosis for survival. Finally, doctors must estimate the prognosis for long-term outcome among survivors in terms of neurologic disability and quality of life. These facts ground discussions of the proper ethical course of action. In most cases, they lead quickly to a consensus about the proper course of action.

JOHN D. LANTOS
KATHRYN L. MOSELEY (1995)
REVISED BY JOHN D. LANTOS
WILLIAM MEADOW

SEE ALSO: *Abuse, Interpersonal: Child Abuse; AIDS; Care: Contemporary Ethics of; Children; Clinical Ethics; Compassionate Love; Embryo and Fetus; Family and Family Medicine; Feminism; Genetic Testing and Screening; Infants, Ethical Issues with; Life, Quality of: Quality of Life in Clinical Decisions; Maternal-Fetal Relationship; Medicaid; Moral Status; Pediatrics; Research Policy: Risk and Vulnerable Groups; Sexism; Trust*

BIBLIOGRAPHY

D'Angio, Carl T.; Sinkin, Robert A.; Stevens, Timothy P., et al. 2002. "Longitudinal, Fifteen-Year Follow-Up of Children Born at Less Than Twenty-Nine Weeks' Gestation after Introduction of Surfactant Therapy into a Region: Neurologic, Cognitive, and Educational Outcomes." *Pediatrics* 110(6): 1094–1102.

Lantos, John D. 1987. "Baby Doe Five Years Later: Implications for Child Health." *New England Journal of Medicine* 317(7): 444–447.

Meadow, William,; Reimshisel, Tom; and Lantos, John. 1996. "Birth Weight–Specific Mortality for Extremely Low Birth Weight Infants Vanishes by Four Days of Life: Epidemiology and Ethics in the Neonatal Intensive Care Unit." *Pediatrics* 97(5): 636–643.

Vohr, Betty R.; Wright, Linda L.; Dusick, Anna M., et al. 2000. "Neurodevelopmental and Functional Outcomes of Extremely Low Birth Weight Infants in the National Institute of Child Health and Human Development Neonatal Research Network, 1993–1994." *Pediatrics* 105(6): 1216–1226.

Wood, Nicholas S.; Marlow, Neil; Costeloe, Kate; et al. 2000. "Neurologic and Developmental Disability after Extremely Preterm Birth." *New England Journal of Medicine* 343(6): 378–384.

INFANTS, PUBLIC POLICY AND LEGAL ISSUES

• • •

Medical decisions regarding infants vary in the seriousness of their consequences for infants, families, health providers, and society. They range from decisions about home birth and male circumcision—debatable but generally agreed to be matters of private choice—to vaccination, genetic screening, female genital mutilation, and high technology interventions for critically ill newborns. In the United States, parents' legal right to select even the most invasive treatment—or to refuse lifesaving measures—was nearly unquestioned until late in the twentieth century. From the early 1980s into the early twenty-first century, this right became a focal point of litigation, extensive scholarly comment, and public concern. Because much of the legal and public policy debate has focused on infants who require life support, decision making will be discussed here in that context.

The Infant's Interests

The increasing complexity of decisions about the treatment and nontreatment of infants has exacerbated the struggle over who may make these decisions. Advances in medical technology, surgical procedures, and pharmaceuticals allow severely compromised infants to survive. These new technologies frequently entail painful procedures for the infant and the possibility of adverse effects that further attenuate the infant's already fragile hold on life. For example, resuscitation techniques allow many more premature infants to survive; but these infants frequently need prolonged ventilatory assistance and invasive diagnostic and treatment procedures. They are also at increased risk both for cerebral hemorrhages, which create severe neurological deficits, and for significant treatment-related adverse effects, such as blindness and deafness.

Decisions on treatment have traditionally rested with parents, healthcare providers, or some combination of the two. Since the 1980s, the decision-making powers of these parties have been challenged. In the United States, the older body of law has been partially eroded by legislative enactments and court decisions that highlight the rights of the infant (Cooper). Indeed, recognition of the infant's individual rights arising from the celebrated 1982 Baby Doe case became the basis for substantial federal intervention in medical practice and family life.

Baby Doe was afflicted with Down syndrome, a chromosomal abnormality resulting in mental retardation and a propensity for cardiac and other congenital malformations. The infant had such a congenital defect, a tracheo-esophageal fistula (an abnormal passage connecting the trachea and esophagus), which if not surgically corrected results in death. The parents, after consultation with and with the concurrence of their attending physician, refused to consent to the surgery, primarily on the grounds that a child with Down syndrome could not attain a "minimally acceptable quality of life." That conclusion was, and continues to be, strongly disputed. A trial court, however, ruled that the parents had the right to refuse surgery for their child (*In re Infant Doe,* 1982).

Immediately after the infant's death, President Ronald Reagan directed the U.S. Department of Health and Human Services (DHHS) to issue regulations protecting infants with disabilities from treatment discrimination by parents, healthcare providers, or both. Through the regulations, issued in March 1983, DHHS claimed authority under the Rehabilitation Act of 1973 to order healthcare facilities receiving federal assistance to provide sustenance and aggressive medical treatment to infants with disabilities. The regulations required posting signs announcing the new federal protection in treatment areas of hospitals; established "Baby Doe Squads" to investigate alleged instances of treatment discrimination; and provided for a toll-free hot line to facilitate the reporting of discrimination (Lawton, Carder, and Weisman). Most healthcare providers, as well as many members of the public and of Congress, reacted negatively. A prestigious national group studying healthcare decisions—the U.S. President's Commission for the Study of Ethical Problems in Medicine and Biomedical and Behavioral Research (hereafter, U.S. President's Commission)—and the American Academy of Pediatrics (AAP) both vehemently criticized the regulations. The U.S. President's Commission argued for a standard that would focus on the "best interests" of the infant. The AAP, along with several other parties, sought help from the federal courts, which invalidated the regulations only a few weeks after they became final (*American Academy of Pediatrics v. Heckler,* 1983).

DHHS next produced the "Baby Doe II" regulations, modifying the requirements for signs and providing for an infant-care review committee in each hospital rather than an outside investigative team. These regulations too were rejected—ultimately by the U.S. Supreme Court—on the grounds that the Rehabilitation Act did not give DHHS any authority to regulate parental decisions about infant treatment (*Bowen v. American Hospital Association,* 1986).

In a final effort to influence the care of newborns, Congress enacted the Child Abuse Amendments of 1984, which directed DHHS to develop regulations governing infant care and guidelines for hospital infant-care review committees. As of 1985, federal funding for state child-abuse prevention and treatment efforts was conditioned on compliance; only a few states chose to decline the funding. Under the amendments, the child protective service agency of a state is the only party that may initiate an action of neglect. Nevertheless, the act broadened the definition of child abuse to include "withholding of medically indicated treatment," thereby affecting physician practice standards. The amendments require that an infant with a disability receive appropriate nutrition, hydration, medication, and the "most effective" treatment according to the reasonable judgment of the treating physician. In only three situations may treatment be withheld: (1) when the child is chronically and irreversibly comatose; (2) when treatment could not save the child's life for any substantial length of time; or (3) when the treatment would be inhumane and "virtually futile" with respect to survival. The distinction between inability to save the life (situation 2) and "virtually futile" (situation 3) lies in the "degree of probability or uncertainty in determining the futility of treatment" (Boyd and Thompson). This distinction has become increasingly difficult to draw, in the context of both withdrawal and continuation of treatment.

In the wake of the Child Abuse Amendments, the U.S. President's Commission continued to advocate that the standard for infant treatment or nontreatment be based on the "best interests" of the infant. This standard draws on the standard of "substituted judgment" that is often applied to incapacitated, but once competent, patients. In such cases, a proxy attempts to make treatment decisions, as she or he believes the patient would, if able. For newborns, the commission recommended that decision makers attempt to assess the best interests of the infant "by reference to more objective, societally shared criteria." In sum, the commission recommended that decision makers "choose a course that will promote the patient's well-being as it would be conceived by a reasonable person in the patient's circumstances" (U.S. President's Commission, pp. 135–136). Numerous courts have since adopted the "best interests" standard in making infant treatment decisions, and it has become the prevalent standard.

Ascertaining the infant's best interests generally falls to the primary caregivers—in most cases, the parents, who, although assisted by numerous directors, nurses, and social workers, must make and bear the brunt of these difficult decisions. Unfortunately, the guidelines available to decision makers from the U.S. President's Commission and subsequent case law are far from concrete. In describing the "best interests" standard, the commission stressed that normal adults must not impose their values or external concerns upon the beleaguered infant. In its guidelines, the commission stated that futile treatment for severely compromised infants with a lifespan of hours or days need not be provided; at the other end of the spectrum, the commission condemned the withholding of treatment for a correctable problem when the infant was afflicted with an unrelated, non-life-threatening disorder, such as Down syndrome (U.S. President's Commission, 1983). For the vast territory in between, however, there is little guidance.

Determining the best interests of a compromised infant using the commission's guidelines presents considerable problems of interpretation (Rhoden, 1985). Some believe that the best interests of the infant require providing maximum treatment in virtually all cases (Smith; Wells; Wells, Alldridge, and Morgan). Under this construction, infants express their interest in surviving by responding positively to treatment (Cooper). Others believe that nontreatment may be justified when the infant's life can be viewed as an injury rather than as a gift to the infant; an *injury* is inferred when there is no prospect of meaningful life, which might occur because: life expectancy is very short, there are severe mental deficits, or no curative or corrective treatments are available (Weir).

Some argue that the rational interests of the infant in treatment or nontreatment should not be limited to avoiding suffering (including the pain of treatment) and to minimizing physical and mental deficits, but should also include factors such as the burden on the family and society (Wells, Alldridge, and Morgan; Smith). Such a view holds that when an infant's condition lacks any "truly human qualities" or "relational potential," the best decision is not to

treat (Smith, p. 56). One can presume that an infant has an interest in his or her "standing and memory within the family" (Mitchell, p. 341). If so, the infant's best interests cannot be determined in isolation from the feelings and concerns of others. Although such "quality of life" considerations are given short shrift under the current federal law and under the U.S. President's Commission's best-interests standard, they are an inevitable subtext to the debate (Rhoden).

Parents' Interests

U.S. jurisprudence still strongly favors parents as decision makers for children's medical care, although it does not accord constitutional status to this preference (*Cruzan v. Director, Missouri Department of Health,* 1990). Though some dispute the basis for a parental preference—asking whether it is for the parents' sake, the children's, or society's (Schneider)—the law is willing to assume that parents, with physicians' help, generally can best judge the child's interest and will best protect it. Moreover, it seems fair to defer to those who will live intimately with the results of the decisions.

Nevertheless, the wisdom of this presumption is challenged on many fronts, both from within and outside the legal establishment. Parental authority is not absolute, but rather conditional. It is settled law that the state may intervene if necessary, superseding parents' authority by proving them unable or unwilling to safeguard the child's welfare. In the late 1990s and early 2000s, there was increasing willingness to resort to child-endangerment provisions to subvert parental decision making with respect to critically ill infants (*Tabatha R. v. Ronda R.,* 1997; *In re K.I.,* 1999; *In the Matter of D.R.,* 2001). Some scholars have posited that paradoxically greater deference is given to parental authority when an adolescent is involved as compared to when an infant is involved, with parents of compromised infants frequently being referred to child protection authorities for questioning or opposing the recommendations of physicians (Rosato). In extreme cases, parents may be criminally prosecuted for failing to fulfill their responsibility to provide ordinary care (*Lundman v. McKown,* 1995).

Many scholars and practitioners question how well parents are able to judge the needs of a critically ill infant. The task is daunting, because the medical specialists on whom parents depend often cannot predict a child's chances of survival or normality with any certainty at the point when decisions must be made, nor adequately warn of the suffering that treatment may eventually entail (Bouregy). In addition, parents come to the task exhausted by childbirth and the child's medical crisis, grief-stricken, and in near shock (Jellinek et al.). Physicians do not always share essential information with parents, and parents often absorb poorly the limited information they receive (Perlman et al.). Even observers who find parents the best possible decision makers speak of their vulnerability during the crisis, especially to manipulation by physicians and others (Rushton and Glover).

On the other hand, parents may wholly reject medical guidance. Parents have sought to prevent necessary medical treatment of their infants despite entreaties of medical professionals (*In the Matter of D.R.,* 2001; *HCA, Inc. v. Miller,* 2000). Conversely, parents have fought to continue extraordinary medical intervention for infants and children, despite physicians considering such treatment virtually futile in terms of ultimate survival (*In the Matter of Baby "K",* 1994; *Rideout v. Hershey Medical Center,* 1995; *In re K.I.,* 1999). Several have protested the removal of a *legally* dead infant from life support, insisting on continued treatment (*In the Matter of Long Island Jewish Medical Center,* 1996). In other cases, parents have commandeered treatment; in one notorious incident, a father, Rudy Linares, disconnected his infant son's respirator and held off nurses at gunpoint until the boy died (Gostin).

A second criticism of giving parents authority is that they may deliberately elect not to satisfy an infant's dire needs. In this view, it is naive to posit an identity of interest between infant and parent. Parents guard their own interests, those of the family as a unit, and those of current and future siblings—all of which may be gravely threatened by the sick newborn. Some observers of such behavior describe it neutrally. To a sociobiologist, "individual infants may attempt to extract greater investment from their parents than the parents have been selected to give," causing parents to reduce their investment in the child (Hrdy, p. 410). A philosopher writing on the subject actively encouraged parents to weigh the child's interests, including life itself, against others' needs: "The neonate is not born into the family circle so much as outside it, awaiting inclusion or exclusion. The moral problem the parents must confront is whether the child should become a part of the family unit" (Blustein, p. 166). But other commentators condemn any deviation on the part of parents from pursuit of the child's interest. Among these were the proponents of the Baby Doe regulations and, later, a majority of the U.S. Supreme Court, which noted that family members "may have a strong feeling—a feeling not at all ignoble or unworthy, but not entirely disinterested either—that they do not wish to witness the continuation of the life of a loved one which they regard as hopeless, meaningless, and even degrading" (*Cruzan v. Director, Missouri Department of Health,* p. 286). Echoing this view, in a case from 2000 (*HCA, Inc. v. Miller*), a couple sued their healthcare providers for having resuscitated their prematurely born infant, against the parents express wishes, when all agreed that the infant would be severely impaired if she survived.

Practitioners—doctors, lawyers, and social workers—observe parents acting from mixed motives in accepting or rejecting medical care. By forgoing treatment, they may hope to spare the infant suffering and lessen their own, avoid financial and other burdens on the family, and/or prevent the child's eventual institutionalization (Newman). They may instinctively fear the damage to parent-child relations created by medicine's lifesaving technology (Boyce; Kratochvil, Robertson, and Kyle).

Not infrequently, the parents' religious beliefs discourage medical intervention. When the infant is in peril and medical attention will ameliorate or cure the illness or disability, there is an increasing tendency to seek a court order to terminate parental rights to further the best interests of the child. In a case from 2001 (*In the Matter of D.R.*), the parents were followers of the Church of Truth, which rejects medical treatment of all illnesses in favor of spiritual healing. Their infant was beset with developmental delays and numerous disabilities, including a severe seizure disorder. Unmedicated, the seizure disorder was likely to cause additional neurological injury to the infant, worsening her already poor prognosis. At the insistence of the paternal grandparents, the child came to the attention of physicians and child protection authorities. The parents steadfastly refused to comply with the infant's medication regimen, and ultimately the court deemed the child deprived and neglected, awarding custody to the paternal grandparents. The court professed respect for the parents' religious preferences and their right to raise their child in concert with those preferences but was bound to take action to preserve the child's health and welfare. The court noted that the statutory requirements for deeming the infant *deprived* had little to do with the parents' religious beliefs, but rather turned on the child's need of special medical care and the parents' willful failure to provide such care.

This increasingly protective posture toward the infant is evident even before birth. In the case of a pregnant Jehovah's Witness with a dangerously low blood count, a court asserted custody over the thirty-four-week-old fetus and mandated blood transfusion against the mother's will to safeguard the fetus. An appeals court subsequently held that the unconsented-to blood transfusion was an invasive medical procedure and a violation of the mother's rights to bodily integrity (*In re Fetus Brown,* 1997). This case demonstrates the willingness of the courts to favor the alleged best interests of the child, or even fetus, over the well-enunciated religious beliefs of the parent.

Parents also may insist on extraordinary measures in an attempt to be faithful to their understanding of their religion's tenets, as well as to assuage perceived guilt; or to please the other parent, friends, and family; or from selfless devotion to the child that the parent cannot reconcile with consenting to death (Nelson and Nelson). In such cases, ultimately, the best interests of the child are likely to be valued above the parents' beliefs and needs. Before a decision is made to cease extraordinary life-support measures in opposition to the parents' wishes, however, the parents must be afforded appropriate due process to argue for continuation of therapy (*Rideout v. Hershey Medical Center,* 1995). Although parental rights are not absolute, they are a formidable factor in medical decision making for infants and children and remain so even if the parents are not *model parents* (*Tabatha R. v. Ronda R.,* 1997).

The law is relatively clear in its expectation of parents, though the mandate may be excruciatingly difficult to follow. Federal and state constitutions, as well as statutory and decisional law, accord equal status to all living human beings. Parents must act in their child's interest, weighing the immediate physical and long-term emotional suffering for the infant to be expected from aggressive treatment against the consequences of no or lesser treatment. Thus, while some object to consideration of the infant's quality of life in these decisions, such factoring is central to the parents' legal duty.

Healthcare Providers' Interests

Historically, treatment decisions rested with the midwife or physician caring for the newborn and its mother. Although parents ostensibly *owned* their children, they routinely ceded control to the healthcare provider. During the twentieth century, the decision-making model shifted to one in which the parent and the provider jointly decided on medical intervention for the infant. In recent decades, the parents' role has markedly increased as a result of a greater number of treatment options, increased parental knowledge and awareness, and greater respect for patient autonomy (Cooper).

Organized medicine has not opposed this development. A 1975 AAP survey indicated broad support among pediatricians for the proposition that infant treatment decisions should be made jointly by the parents and physician, with the parents taking the pivotal role. In a 1990 report, the Society of Critical Care Medicine's Task Force on Ethics recommended that parents set priorities for the treatment of critically ill pediatric patients. The American Medical Association also defers to parents but emphasizes use of the best-interests standard proposed by the U.S. President's Commission.

Physicians readily acknowledge the frequent conflicts between their dual commitment to save lives and to alleviate suffering. In reality, these factors are rarely the only ones that affect the physician treating a critically ill infant. Healthcare providers may have varying philosophies with respect to treatment of infants afflicted with certain disabilities; they may also be influenced by their research agendas, possess insufficient knowledge to assess accurately the infant's disability and prognosis, or be influenced by real or perceived risk of legal liability (Rushton and Glover; Rosato). In addition, physicians focus on the diagnosis rather than on the prognosis and long-term care of their infant patients (Perlman et al.). As a result of all these factors, physicians may not be optimally effective partners for the parents in the decision-making process. For example, an obstetrician may act in a paternalistic fashion toward a patient, a mother, seeking to protect her from the tragedy of dealing with the fate of an impaired infant. Alternatively, a neonatologist may be overly optimistic in judging and discussing with the parents the infant's potential for meaningful life (Cooper).

Frequently, nurses serve as the primary information conduit between doctors and parents, and naturally there are biases inherent in their perspective, too. Because they are the healthcare providers who care for patients most intimately, they may personalize severely disabled infants beyond reality in order to deal with the burden of nursing them on a day-to-day basis. As a result, nurses may be incapable of advocating against treatment when it is futile and thus be unable to serve as effective advocates for either the infant or the family. In addition, they are limited by the practical realities of their role in the employment hierarchy of the hospital (Mitchell).

In some cases, healthcare facilities and providers may overtreat a severely compromised infant to avoid legal liability. The Linares case, while an extreme example, arose from tensions that are often present. The healthcare providers in that case, despite their acknowledged sympathy and agreement with the father's desire for his son's death, insisted for many months on treating the infant. They did so, they said later, because they believed that state law required continued life support. Critics alleged that individual healthcare providers and the facility (through its lawyer) had abandoned the best interests of both the child and the family to protect themselves. Indeed, some see an "overwhelming fear of possible, indeed theoretical, adverse legal repercussions" among healthcare providers (Nelson and Cranford, p. 3210). This fear is not unfounded; as mentioned earlier, in the 2000 *HCA, Inc. v. Miller* case, healthcare providers were sued, albeit unsuccessfully, for wrongful resuscitation of a severely premature infant. On the other side of the treatment coin, the 1994 Baby "K" case, in which healthcare providers were forbidden to refuse to provide treatment they considered futile, also speaks to the risk of legal reprisal. There is no safe harbor that ensures freedom from liability for healthcare providers in these difficult, emotionally charged situations.

Society's Interests

A society such as that of the United States has numerous, sometimes contradictory, interests in the healthcare of infants. These include preservation of the life and health of the next generation; the guarantee of the rights of individuals; the support of families; the conservation and wise expenditure of economic resources; the maintenance of a just and predictable legal system; and the compromise between—or at least the orderly expression of—clashing values of groups within society. Two of these issues, cost and the social effect of litigating treatment decisions, are discussed below.

Concern for the cost of neonatal intensive care—the most expensive element in the care of infants—preceded the currently intense focus on health costs in general. This treatment is the exception to the rule that the United States directs resources disproportionately to adults, especially the elderly. Technological advances in the treatment of newborns halved the neonatal death rate between 1970 and 1980 (U.S. President's Commission, 1983). Since then, the extraordinary cost of the technology has helped to focus attention on how many and which infants should be treated.

Many families cannot cover the cost, and there is debate over whether the resources available for a particular infant should be taken into account by decision makers. Most commentators share the view expressed in a seminal article from 1975 on the subject: "Just as a parent is not obligated to attempt to save a drowning child if the parent cannot swim, neither is he obligated to incur enormous expense in providing treatment with a slight chance of success" (Robertson, p. 236; see also Newman). No judicial decision, however, accepts the proposition that personal resources should dictate life or death. Usually, the issue is avoided in litigation. When it is specifically cited, a typical court reply is that the "cost of care in human or financial terms is irrelevant" (*In re Care and Protection of Beth,* p. 1383).

Whether or not cost should affect decisions on treatment, there is evidence that it does. Although providers may not abandon a patient without incurring liability, a study comparing medical need to the services sick newborns receive indicates that healthcare providers do not allocate services solely according to need, but are instead influenced by the newborn's insurance coverage—private, governmental, or none (Braveman et al.). Governmental insurance is less attractive to providers than private insurance because government does not reimburse the full cost of care. Thus, at times it appears that while society insists on extending the life of premature and seriously ill infants, it simultaneously refuses to absorb the cost of their immediate and long-term care—a result described as "political hypocrisy in its cruelest form" (Holder, p. 113).

A second salient issue for society is whether it has erred by assigning this category of treatment decisions increasingly to the courts. Criticism of the failure to treat Baby Doe was widespread and severe, but the legal processes that ensued were also criticized. Numerous objections are raised to the removal of medical decisions from the private sphere. The judicial system may be too cumbersome and costly and may further traumatize family members and invade their privacy. The publicity surrounding infant-care cases may prevent other parents from exercising their right to forgo treatment. In addition, the practice of medicine is negatively affected. Explicit direction from some courts to extend life whenever possible and the implicit threat of litigation reinforce U.S. medicine's alleged tendency to overtreat (Newman). For example, one in three neonatologists state that the Baby Doe regulations require treatment *not* in an infant's best interest (Fost). Finally, in investigating and deciding these cases, judges and other officials must choose among competing moral and religious philosophies, a problematic choice in a society that values diversity (Newman).

Obviously, the law is disadvantaged in attempting to supervise medical care for particular infants. In most jurisdictions, understanding of the legal requirements for forgoing treatment is imperfect, even among lawyers (Gostin). The scarcity of prosecutions and precedents suggests a high degree of social ambivalence on this subject—leading, according to Carl Schneider, to "a troubling disjunction between the law on the books, which seems to make neonatal euthanasia criminal, and the law in action, which does not punish it" (p. 152). Schneider further contends that there is no social consensus on the central questions: What is human life? When is death preferable to life? What do parents owe their children? What does society owe the suffering? As a result, he and others see a tendency to abandon the search for substantive principles in the law and instead adopt procedures for reviewing individual cases (Schneider).

One such procedure is the assignment of a role in decision making to institutional ethics committees. Virtually unknown before 1983 (fewer than 1 percent of U.S. hospitals had such committees at that time), they came to prominence through two avenues. First, the influential U.S. President's Commission report in 1983 recommended their use; second, the establishment of committees became a major point of compromise in negotiations between the government and healthcare providers over the Baby Doe regulations (Lawton, Carder, and Weisman). By 1986 the AAP, which had strongly endorsed the committees, found them in 60 percent of hospitals.

In some instances, the committees have functioned as it was hoped they would. For example, in the case of Baby "L," a physician applied to the hospital's ethics committee for permission to cease extraordinary treatment of an infant who was capable only of pain perception and to transfer the infant to another facility and provider. The parent opposed this action and sought an opinion from the courts. The court upheld the decision of the hospital and the physician and allowed the transfer of the child to a facility willing to continue treatment (Paris, Crone, and Reardon). In other cases, however, a hospital's ethics committee failed to persuade either the parent or the trial court that treatment was futile (*In the Matter of Baby "K"*, 1994; *Rideout v. Hershey Medical Center*, 1995). Although concerns are expressed about the committees' role, makeup, criteria for decision making, influence, results, and effectiveness, ethics committees appear entrenched as a visible, albeit not dispositive, representative of society in controversies over care for infants.

Long-standing respect for the discretion of parents and healthcare providers in making infant treatment decisions appears to be gradually giving way to greater emphasis on the rights of the infant. Debate is ongoing as to whether this emphasis has been overaccentuated, to the detriment of parents and critically ill infants alike. Parents and healthcare providers continue to look to the courts and society at large for guidance, finding precious little consensus.

ANNE M. DELLINGER
PATRICIA C. KUSZLER (1995)
REVISED BY PATRICIA C. KUSZLER

SEE ALSO: *Abuse, Interpersonal: Child Abuse; AIDS; Children; Clinical Ethics; Family and Family Medicine; Healthcare Resources, Allocation of; Infants, Ethical Issues with; Infants, Medical Aspects and Issues in the Care of; Life, Quality of: Quality of Life in Clinical Decisions; Maternal-Fetal Relationship; Medicaid; Pediatrics; Research Policy: Risk and Vulnerable Groups*

BIBLIOGRAPHY

American Academy of Pediatrics v. Heckler. 561 F.Supp. 395 (D.D.C. 1983).

Baby "K," In the Matter of. 1994. 16 F.3d 590 (4th Cir.).

Beth, In re Care and Protection of. 1992. 587 N.E.2d 1377 (Mass.).

Blustein, Jeffrey. 1989. "The Rights Approach and the Intimacy Approach: Family Suffering and Care of Defective Newborns." *Mount Sinai Journal of Medicine* 56(3): 164–167.

Bouregy, William L. 1988. "Parental Refusal of Consent for Treatment of Handicapped Newborns: Comparing Case Results in England and the United States." *New York Law School Journal of International and Comparative Law* 9: 379–433.

Bowen v. American Hospital Association. 476 U.S. 610; 106 Sup. Ct. 2101 (1986).

Boyce, W. Thomas. 1992. "The Vulnerable Child: New Evidence, New Approaches." *Advances in Pediatrics* 39: 1–33.

Boyd, Diane E., and Thompson, Peter J. 1990. "United States Commission on Civil Rights—Medical Discrimination against Children with Disabilities: An Abstract." *Journal of Contemporary Health Law and Policy* 6: 379–410.

Braveman, Paula A.; Egerter, Susan; Bennett, Trude; and Showstack, Jonathan. 1991. "Differences in Hospital Resource Allocation among Sick Newborns According to Insurance Coverage." *Journal of the American Medical Association* 255(23): 3300–3308.

Cooper, Rebecca. 1992. "Delivery Room Resuscitation of the High Risk Infant: A Conflict of Rights." *Catholic Lawyer* 33(4): 325–360.

Cruzan v. Director, Missouri Department of Health. 497 U.S. 261 (1990).

D.R. v. Rogers, In the Matter of. 20 P.3d 166 (Okla. Civ. App. 2001).

Fetus Brown, In re. 1997. 689 N.E.2d 397 (Ill. App. 3d).

Fost, Norman. 1989. "Do the Right Thing: Samuel Linares and Defensive Law." *Law, Medicine, and Health Care* 17(4): 330–334.

Goldman, Gilbert M.; Stratton, Karen M.; and Brown, Max Douglas. 1989. "What Actually Happened: An Informed Review of the Linares Incident." *Law, Medicine, and Health Care* 17(4): 298–307.

Gostin, Larry O., ed. 1989. "Family Privacy and Persistent Vegetative State: A Symposium on the Linares Case." *Law, Medicine, and Health Care* 17(4): 295–346.

HCA, Inc. v. Miller. 38 S.W.3d 187 (Tex. Ct. App. 2000).

Holder, Angela. 1985. "The Child and Death." In *Legal Issues in Pediatrics and Adolescent Medicine.* New Haven, CT: Yale University Press.

Hrdy, Sarah Blaffer. 1992. "Fitness Tradeoffs in the History and Evolution of Delegated Mothering with Special Reference to Wet-Nursing, Abandonment, and Infanticide." *Ethnology and Sociobiology* 13(5/6): 409–442.

Infant Doe, In re. No. GU 8204–004A (Monroe County, Ind., Cir. Ct. 1982); writ of mandamus dismissed subnom. *State ex. rel. Infant Doe v. Baker.* 1982. No. 482 140 (Sup. Ct. Ind.); cert. denied *Infant Doe v. Bloomington Hospital.* 464 U.S. 961; 104 Sup. Ct. 394 (1983).

Jane Doe, In re. 418 S.E.2d 3 (Ga. 1992).

Jellinek, Michael S.; Catlin, Elizabeth A.; Todres, I. David; and Cassem, Edwin H. 1992. "Facing Tragic Decisions with

Parents in the Neonatal Intensive Care Unit: Clinical Perspectives." *Pediatrics* 89(1): 119–122.

K.I., B.I., and D.M.; In re. 735 A.2d 448 (D.C. Ct. App. 1999).

Kratochvil, Marianne; Robertson, Charlene; and Kyle, Janis. 1991. "Parents' View of Parent–Child Relationship Eight Years After Neonatal Intensive Care." *Social Work in Health Care* 16(1): 95–118.

Lawton, Stephan E.; Carder, Elizabeth B.; and Weisman, Anne W. 1985. "Recent Governmental Action Regarding the Treatment of Seriously Ill Newborns." *Journal of College and University Law* 11(4): 405–416.

Long Island Jewish Medical Center, In the Matter of. 1996. 641 N.Y.S.2d 989 (Queens County, N.Y., Sup. Ct.).

Lundman v. McKown. 530 N.W.2d 807 (Minn. Ct. App. 1995).

Mitchell, Christine. 1989. "On Heroes and Villains in the Linares Drama." *Law, Medicine, and Health Care* 17(4): 339–346.

Nelson, Lawrence J., and Cranford, Robert. 1989. "Legal Advice, Moral Paralysis, and the Death of Samuel Linares." *Law, Medicine, and Health Care* 17(4): 316–324.

Nelson, Lawrence J., and Nelson, Robert M. 1992. "Ethics and the Provision of Futile, Harmful, or Burdensome Treatment to Children." *Critical Care Medicine* 20(3): 427–433.

Newman, Stephan A. 1989. "Baby Doe, Congress, and the States: Challenging the Federal Treatment Standard for Impaired Infants." *American Journal of Law and Medicine* 15(1): 1–60.

Paris, John J.; Crone, Robert K.; and Reardon, Frank. 1990. "Physicians' Refusal of Requested Treatment: The Case of Baby L." *New England Journal of Medicine* 322(14): 1012–1015.

Perlman, Nitza B.; Freedman, Jonathan L.; Abramovitch, Rena; et al. 1991. "Informational Needs of Parents of Sick Neonates." *Pediatrics* 88(3): 512–518.

Rhoden, Nancy K. 1985. "Treatment Dilemmas for Imperiled Newborns: Why Quality of Life Counts." *Southern California Law Review* 58(5): 1283–1347.

Rideout v. Hershey Medical Center. WL 924561 (1995).

Robertson, John A. 1975. "Involuntary Euthanasia of Defective Newborns: A Legal Analysis." *Stanford Law Review* 27: 213–269.

Rosato, Jennifer. 2000a. "The Ethics of Clinical Trials: A Child's View." *Journal of Law, Medicine, and Ethics* 28(4): 362–378.

Rosato, Jennifer. 2000b. "Using Bioethics Discourse to Determine When Parents Should Make Care Decisions for Their Children: Is Deference Justified?" *Temple Law Review* 73(1): 1–68.

Rushton, Cindy Hylton, and Glover, Jacqueline J. 1990. "Involving Parents in Decisions to Forgo Life-Sustaining Treatment for Critically Ill Infants and Children." *Clinical Issues in Critical Care Nursing* 1(1): 206–214.

Schneider, Carl E. 1988. "Rights Discourse and Neonatal Euthanasia." *California Law Review* 76(1): 151–176.

Smith, George. 1992. "Murder, She Wrote or Was It Merely Selective Nontreatment?" *Journal of Contemporary Health Law and Policy* 8: 49–71.

Tabatha R. v. Ronda R., In re the Interest of. 564 N.W.2d 598 (Neb. 1997).

Task Force on Ethics of the Society of Critical Care Medicine. 1990. "Consensus Report on the Ethics of Forgoing Life-Sustaining Treatments in the Critically Ill." *Critical Care Medicine* 18(12): 1435–1439.

U. S. President's Commission for the Study of Ethical Problems in Medicine and Biomedical and Behavioral Research. 1983. *Deciding to Forego Life-Sustaining Treatment: A Report of the Ethical, Medical, and Legal Issues in Treatment Decisions.* Washington, D.C.: U.S. Government Printing Office.

Weir, Robert F. 1994. *Selective Nontreatment of Handicapped Newborns: Moral Dilemmas in Neonatal Care.* Oxford: Oxford University Press.

Wells, Celia. 1988. "Whose Baby Is It?" *Journal of Law and Society* 15(4): 323–341.

Wells, Celia; Alldridge, Peter; and Morgan, Derek. 1990. "An Unsuitable Case for Treatment." *New Law Journal* 140(6478): 1544–1545.

INFORMATION DISCLOSURE, ETHICAL ISSUES OF

• • •

Since 1970, ethically recommended healthcare practice in the United States has increasingly supported a high level of information disclosure to patients. This article reviews the change, notes some reasons for it, and explores several concerns about disclosure and its implications for particular information types.

Philosophical Background of Current Opinion

Generally, philosophical discussion has supported veracity as a moral principle, obligation, or virtue. Veracity draws its strength from the complex support it provides to diverse values—respecting others, avoiding coercion and manipulation, supporting community, maintaining reciprocity in relationships, supporting the value of communication generally, eliminating the costs and complexities of deception, refraining from unduly assuming responsibility, and maintaining trust.

Philosophers have generally treated veracity as an obligation flowing from more fundamental theoretical principles, such as utility, religious duty, respect for persons, or some combination of beneficence, fidelity, and autonomy. John Stuart Mill, for instance, regarded truth-telling as justified by utilitarian considerations, and W. D. Ross included honesty among the duties of fidelity. A few have given it more basic status. Some theologians, such as Dietrich Bonhoeffer, have set truth telling in the context of greater religious truths and treated false doctrines as forms of deception. Aristotle described falsehood as "in itself mean and culpable" (Bok, p. 24); G. J. Warnock listed veracity as a major virtue with the same status as beneficence and justice. Immanuel Kant and Augustine are notable for having defended truth-telling most strongly. In a brief article, Kant argued that it would be wrong to lie even to a murderer seeking the hiding place of an intended victim.

However, not all theorists have defended veracity; Henry Sidgwick denied that it could stand as a "definite moral axiom" because of its variable applications and numerous exceptions (Bok, p. 293). David Nyberg argued that trusting relationships among people normally require "the adroit management of deception" (Nyberg, p. 24). Moreover, most philosophers have defended deception in at least some cases. Plato defended lying to the public for the sake of society as a whole, and many philosophers have warranted deception when truthfulness might result in serious harm (Bok).

Application to Healthcare

Until the late twentieth century, philosophers often regarded a physician's withholding a fatal diagnosis from a patient as a stock exception to general precepts of veracity. Philosophers and physicians regarded the distress expected from such news as sufficiently harmful to outweigh the presumption favoring disclosure. Withholding a fatal diagnosis functioned as a paradigm for sharing other medical information with patients. The ethical tradition concerning the doctor-patient relationship thus tended, with some notable exceptions such as Worthington Hooker and Richard Cabot, to emphasize the obligations of confidentiality and to ignore and even deprecate disclosure (Radovsky). Oaths and codes omitted truth telling, and precepts and discussions of talking with patients tended to recommend caution in revealing information. Ethicists perceived the doctor-patient relationship as oriented to therapy, reassurance, and avoiding harm; physicians were to provide lies and truth instrumentally only insofar as they aided therapy.

Since the 1960s, opinion on the role of disclosure in healthcare has changed rapidly in the United States. The patients' rights movement and the rise of bioethics have created a climate of opinion supporting honest disclosure of medical information. The affirmation in 1972 of "A Patient's Bill of Rights" by the Board of Trustees of the American Hospital Association notably marked this shift in opinion. The bill stated, "The patient has the right to obtain from his physician complete current information concerning his diagnosis, treatment, and prognosis in terms the patient can be reasonably expected to understand" (Lee and Jacobs, p. 41).

These changes in opinion developed in concert with the spread of informed consent as standard practice in research and therapy. Informed consent derived from a view of respect for persons that emphasized an individual's power to make decisions adequately. This view required honest disclosure. Thus, most ethicists in the 1970s and 1980s supported fuller disclosure as a means of respecting patient autonomy (Katz).

The patients' rights movement favored empowering patients and increasing their control over medical care. As Howard Waitzkin argued in his observations of physicians' communications with patients, the traditional pattern of withholding information reflected a habit of dominating patients and keeping the course of therapy firmly under professional control (Waitzkin). Reformers saw a wider patient understanding of care as supporting a less paternalistic and more contractual relationship, as well as empowering particular classes of patients, such as women and people of color. Susan Sherwin, for example, identified one of the main tasks of feminist healthcare ethics as being to increase equity "by distributing the specialized knowledge on health matters in ways that allow persons maximum control over their own health" (Sherwin, p. 93).

The codes of ethics of the health professions began to reflect this important shift in opinion. The American Nurses' Association's Code for Nurses linked disclosure with truth-telling and self-determination: "Clients have the moral right ... to be given accurate information, and all the information necessary for making informed judgments." The code counseled nurses to avoid "claims that are false, fraudulent, misleading, deceptive, or unfair" in their relations with the public (American Nurses' Association, p. 2). The 1980 revision of the American Medical Association's "Principles of Medical Ethics" included the principle, "A physician shall deal honestly with patients and colleagues, and strive to expose those physicians deficient in character or competence, or who engage in fraud or deception" (Council on Ethical and Judicial Affairs, p. ix). The American College of Physicians' (ACP) Ethics Manual recommended that patients be "well informed to make health care decisions and work intelligently in partnership with the physician." The manual advised that communication can "dispel uncertainty and fear and enhance healing and patient satisfaction." In general, the ACP held, "disclosure to patients is a fundamental ethical requirement" (p. 950). Subspecialty ethics codes—such as those of the American Academy of Orthopaedic Surgeons, the World Psychiatric Association, and the American College of Obstetricians and Gynecologists—also began to include recommendations supporting veracity.

Changing Contexts for Veracity in Healthcare

While a high level of disclosure became the recommended practice, cross-currents of thought emerged regarding the motivations for informing patients. First, observers discussed the psychological benefits and risks of giving patients bad news. Second, the increasingly institutional setting of healthcare practice influenced patterns of disclosure. Third, discussion distinguished the obligation to disclose information from the obligation to refrain from lying. Fourth, the uncertainty of medicine modulated the obligation to disclose. Finally, an increasing philosophical emphasis on relational aspects of practitioner-patient ethics broadened the foundations for veracity beyond the single element of respect for autonomy.

HEALTHY DISCLOSURE. Medical works prior to the 1970s tended to assume that revealing a fatal diagnosis would cause patients to experience painful emotions, commit suicide, refuse needed care, or give up hope and die more swiftly. In her important work *Lying: Moral Choice in Public and Private Life,* Sissela Bok argued that traditionalists exaggerated such problems. Patients generally want to be informed, and the benefits to a well-informed and cooperating patient outweigh the risks of disclosure (Bok). Others supplied case histories illustrating the emotional perils of withholding a terminal diagnosis from vulnerable and trusting patients (Dunbar; Sherwin).

Elisabeth Kübler-Ross provided crucial support for the psychological benefits of disclosure by her research on the emotional processes of coming to terms with expected death. In extensive interviews with dying cancer patients, she observed that patients' initial negativity was normally followed by a staged sequence of feelings resolving in acceptance with hope. She regarded disclosure as part of the healthy process of maintaining ongoing communication with dying patients, and her stage theory permitted clinicians to engage in a therapeutic process around disclosure of a fatal diagnosis. The hospice movement accepted this perspective as key to humane care of the dying. Kübler-Ross nevertheless strongly opposed disclosing detailed predictions of life expectancy.

Patients' powerful emotional reactions and personal transformations during grave illnesses involve caregivers in intimate, significant connections with patients. The belief that knowledge of death is healthy has changed the image of the clinician from that of maintaining a cool distance to one of performing emotional work with patients (Hochschild). Ethicists often suggested that health professionals who withheld information from patients reflected several concerns: denial of their own and the patient's fear of dying, unconscious wishes to foster dependency in their clients, concern that discussing death constituted admitting failure, and manipulation of hope to encourage more extensive treatment choices.

Some commentators have challenged the positive emotional benefits of discussing death. Ernest Becker argued that the fear of death is too powerfully terrifying to permit most people to accept it (Becker). Some studies have found at least a few patients showing regret over being informed (Temmerman). Others have criticized the cold delivery of information, the image of the physician "bearing down" on the patient with bad news (Byrne). But in most of the literature, the question has become not whether to tell but how to tell; sharing bad news involves timing and a commitment to continuing empathy, compassion, reassurance, and conversation (Buckman and Kason; Kessel; Kübler-Ross; Radovsky).

THE INSTITUTIONAL CONTEXT. Expanding healthcare delivery organizations and complex technologies have multiplied the number of personnel providing patient care. These changes have magnified the obstacles to easily orchestrated and effective deception; a physician must not only deceive the patient and family but also involve dozens of other staff in the process. Institutional growth has also increased the need for accurate recordkeeping to cope with the expanding quantity of information.

Although information flow to patients has traditionally been the responsibility of physicians, other healthcare team members spend more time with patients, have the knowledge and opportunity to disclose information to patients and their families, and belong to professions assuming responsibility for educating patients. Coordinating communication has become an organizational challenge as hospital staffing has become more efficient, patient acuity greater, and lengths of stay shorter (Zussman). Who should talk with the patient when the physician is absent poses ethical questions for staff members, who may feel reluctant to provide information without explicit delegation even though disclosure may be timely for the patient. Nurses experience ethical conflicts when physicians order them to withhold information to which patients are entitled (Chadwick and

Tadd). Staff members may make promises to patients and their families about disclosure, promises that other staff members cannot keep.

Legally, the information in the hospital record belongs to the patient (Annas), but patients are not employees, and so patients' rights are hard to define procedurally. Patients' responsibility to provide honest disclosure to healthcare staff similarly lacks explicit definition. Thus, although large healthcare institutions have fostered a need for improved communication with patients and made systematic deception difficult, smoothing the flow of appropriate information to patients presents a daunting institutional task.

DISCLOSURE AND DECEPTION. The principle of veracity suffers ambiguity; it may simply prohibit lying and deception, or it may express a broader obligation to disclose information. Ethicists have tended to deploy arguments against lying and deception to support a high level of disclosure in healthcare, because lying and deception have often accompanied withholding information in maintaining illusory hopes. But, one can avoid lies and deception and yet disclose scant information. Since the obligation of full disclosure is role-dependent, supporting it involves considerations beyond criticizing deception. Arguments for full disclosure require normative arguments concerning appropriate relationships of healthcare professionals and institutions to patients in their service.

In healthcare, the principle of full disclosure stands in a reciprocal relationship to the obligation to keep confidentiality. Clinicians often have an obligation to disclose information to the patient, and at the same time, keep the same information from others. Moral judgment requires appreciating the range of application of both principles, that is, knowing which information should be disclosed or withheld in what circumstances (Jonsen and Toulmin). The more formal arguments justifying disclosure parallel the arguments for informed consent by appealing to autonomy, but broader notions of serving patient psychological good and building relationships provide less clear guidance as to the full extent of disclosure. Although favoring disclosure of a fatal diagnosis, as the worst possible news, has tended to encourage wide disclosure of less frightening information, it is still unclear what patients should or should not be told about hospital procedures, student participation in procedures, financial information, names of manufacturers, opinions on the skills of clinicians, personal information about practitioners, mistakes, and so on.

DOUBTS AND UNCERTAINTIES. The phrase "information disclosure" connotes a level of certainty absent from many diagnoses, prognoses, and therapeutic options. Do guesses and projections *belong* to the patient as much as the contents of the case record? Kathryn Taylor observed that physicians diagnosing cancer often exaggerate their uncertainty in order to soften the blow of a diagnosis or suppress it in order to hide feelings of doubt (Taylor). Physicians diagnosing symptoms often consider unlikely possibilities, which would frighten patients if shared unnecessarily with them. Nurses may discover or obtain information about which they are uncertain or lack authority to know and wonder whether or not to share it with patients.

Prevailing uncertainty has motivated some physicians to argue that the truth is so uncertain and variable that veracity is irrelevant to patient care. They argue that prospects and options can be framed in so many ways that clinicians inevitably control patient decisions. Even in the relatively well-studied area of informed consent, what to tell about unlikely dangers remains a contested area. Although some physicians have chosen to limit disclosure on the grounds of uncertainty, David Hilfiker characterized giving false reassurances and concealing uncertainty as forms of dishonest misrepresentation.

BUILDING RELATIONSHIPS. Although bioethics in the 1970s and 1980s rooted disclosure in autonomous decision making, the practice of disclosure has become so widespread in the United States that it has received support on broader grounds. Feminist ethics began to shift the basis of philosophical discussion from the language of autonomy to the language of caring and community. This trend, by diminishing the use of rights language, might have relaxed the new emphasis on disclosure; however, the trend expanded grounds for it, and a conception of the practitioner-patient relationship developed that sees disclosure as a key element in a good professional-patient relationship, apart from its role in decision making.

Lorraine Code, for instance, noted that there is "no stark dichotomy between interdependence and autonomy" (p. 74). Howard Brody recommended that as part of the ongoing "conversation" between physicians and patients, physicians should "think out loud" (Brody, p. 116) in order to share medical reasoning more fully with patients. Charles Lidz and his colleagues found that patients generally wanted procedures explained to them, not to participate in decision making, but as a sign of respect and to assist in therapy. Annette Baier advocated the necessity of going beyond the contract model and of appreciating disclosure in a context in which power relationships are unequal. Baier emphasized trust in relationships as a priority over decision making. Trust thrives most readily in relationships free of deception and where good mutual communication maintains connections between people.

Specific Concerns in Disclosure

Although terminal diagnoses have served as the paradigm for exploring disclosure, they cover only a portion of the possible concerns involving communication with patients. This section briefly describes a few of the other concerns. Many can arise, such as using placebos; therapeutic privilege; giving patients information about the costs of care; disclosing brain death to the family; lying to an insurance company to obtain coverage for a treatment or diagnostic test; falsifying records to help patients escape war service or school busing; reporting an accidentally discovered serious condition to the patient when the doctor-patient relationship is undefined; offering information to patients concerning futile therapeutic options; deceptively introducing medical students to patients as *doctor*; concealing the histocompatibility (mutual tolerance of tissues or organs to be grafted) of an unwilling potential organ donor; revealing to patients that a caregiver has tested positive for the human immunodeficiency virus (HIV); revealing HIV diagnoses to patients; encouraging patients to disclose HIV diagnoses to sexual partners; communicating psychiatric interpretations to patients; expecting disclosure by patients to health professionals; and disclosing genetic information to patients.

DISEASES LACKING EFFECTIVE TREATMENT. When a diagnostic test can predict a dread and incurable disease—such as Huntington or Alzheimer's disease—some physicians consider the possibility of withholding the diagnosis. An instrumental view of communication tends to support the view that the burden to the patient of knowing outweighs the value of disclosure. This concern arose with regard to Huntington disease when a levodopa test became available in the early 1970s; the concern was renewed when genetic marker tests became available in 1983. Although some critics continued to express reservations, genetic counselors tended to find that disclosure helped both patient and family to make long-range plans. Gwen Terrenoire emphasized that a consensus favoring testing and disclosure resulted from counselors working with organized patient groups involved with Huntington disease (Terrenoire). In 1989, the Huntington Disease Society of America published guidelines for testing for the condition. They recommended counseling patients prior to the screening decision and before disclosing results. They also recommended against screening patients who have conditions that diminish judgment, while thoroughly evaluating them for suicide risk (DeGrazia).

DISCLOSING DIAGNOSTIC TESTS. Hospitals and clinics often screen patients upon admission for a wide range of conditions without informing them of the reasons for testing. Services may standardly screen for HIV, sexually transmitted diseases, or pregnancy without informing the patient. They may also wish to make surreptitious tests when they believe a patient is claiming false symptoms. One case study described a patient as suffering from mysterious bruising, which could most probably be explained by drug abuse; she denied taking drugs and refused to permit a blood test. Physicians considered whether to administer the diagnostic test without informing her of its purpose. The discussants of the case argued that a contractual model of the doctor-patient relationship is inadequate because patients frequently lie to physicians and are poor historians. They suggested also that such tests need not be disclosed since they yield such diverse results; they are often based on guesses; and their interpretation depends on patient histories (Vanderpool and Weiss).

REVEALING MISTAKES TO PATIENTS. Surely, practitioners should tell patients of mistakes pertinent to their welfare or requiring changes in treatment plans. However, the possibility of lawsuits, the fear of losing patient confidence, painful feelings of incompetence, and solidarity between healthcare team members often outweigh patient benefits in frankness regarding errors. Charles Bosk observed that discussion of medical errors tends to be highly ritualized, confined to well-defined hospital subgroups, and used to reaffirm a strong collective sense of competence. Hilfiker, however, in a remarkably frank discussion of his own errors, recommended that patients can be accepting of physician limitations, that maintenance of illusions about competence tends ultimately to undermine trust in physicians, and that hiding mistakes tends to alienate caregivers from the healing process of confessing and handling mistakes. The ACP Ethics Manual also recommends disclosing significant "procedural or judgment errors" (American College of Physicians, p. 950).

PATIENT REFUSAL OF INFORMATION. The bioethics literature has debated the proper handling of patient refusals of information (Ost; Strasser). On the one hand, the literature usually has regarded refusing information as an autonomous choice and therefore has supported it: A caregiver may ethically choose to respect a patient's wish to rely more heavily on the caregiver. Raanan Gillon argued that "forcing" information on a patient is both harmful and disrespectful of autonomy. The issue can also be regarded as a feature of relational style; Edmund Pellegrino noted that "some patients need a more authoritative approach than others" (p. 1735).

On the other hand, autonomy is not the only basis for disclosure; caregivers have some role-dependent duties to disclose information to the reluctant; and patients have responsibilities as well as rights to use information on their own behalf. Some information may be so surprising and crucial for patients or so necessary for a working partnership that caregivers have an obligation to disclose despite patient protests. Caregivers may feel that a patient's denial is slowing recovery, or that patients may have a duty to act on information, such as that they are HIV-positive, in order to protect others. It is thus doubtful that the question of refusals can be answered generally.

DISCLOSURE TO FAMILY MEMBERS. Kübler-Ross suggested entrusting some information to family members rather than the patient; this has also been the pattern reported in several countries, such as Hungary, Italy, Japan, and China. This approach may result from seeing the patient as "an extension of the family" (Christakis and Fox, p. 1101), respecting the family as a strongly interdependent unit, or wishing others to carry the burden of knowledge. Yoshitomo Takahashi reported that some Japanese practitioners consider talking about death as threatening family relationships and separating the patient from others (Takahashi), and Eric Feldman noted that many Japanese practitioners perceive disclosing terminal diagnoses as "a callous practice" (p. 21). However, supporters of patient autonomy have expressed concern that leaving the patient uninformed is more likely to isolate the patient psychologically (Quill and Townsend). From both perspectives, the main concern appears to be to include the dying patient in the community, but it is difficult to make reliable cross-cultural generalizations because recommended practices, actual practices, and patient attitudes often vary widely within each culture.

Difficult questions balancing disclosure and confidentiality arise in keeping family members appropriately informed along with the patient. The family may be the recipient of disclosure when an unconscious patient is admitted to the hospital; when the patient recovers competency, the pattern of leaving the family in charge may continue or the family may become excluded from communication. Or family members may give clinicians important information about the patient and ask that the patient not be told; however, the ACP Ethics Manual holds that practitioners are "not obliged" to keep such secrets and should "use sensitivity and judgment" in disclosing such information (American College of Physicians, p. 949).

DISCLOSURE IN THE SOCIAL ARENA. Although bioethical discussion has focused primarily on disclosure and honesty at the bedside, similar issues arise in the larger healthcare arena. For instance, a study of advertising in medical journals showed that a high proportion of pharmaceutical advertisements failed to meet U.S. Food and Drug Administration standards for honesty (Wilkes et al.). Many physicians rely on advertisements and pharmaceutical representatives for their information. Consequently, deceiving physicians leads to misinformed patients.

Occupational and public-health physicians face conflicts affecting disclosure. For instance, some clinicians and medical researchers cooperated for many years in industry suppression of information on the carcinogenicity of asbestos (Lilienfeld); other health professionals have been active in political struggles over posting health warnings on cigarette and alcohol labels. In recent years, the U.S. Occupational Safety and Health Administration has expanded workers' rights to know about their exposure to toxic materials in the workplace, although the complexity of state and federal regulations makes application difficult. Pressures arising from fear of litigation, protection of trade secrets, and concern for individual confidentiality create tensions in pursuing public-health goals of improving public health by keeping workers and the public better informed of their exposure (Ashford and Caldart).

Conclusion

Beneath this sketch of disclosure lie a number of ethical concerns of great subtlety and depth. Brief reflection on honesty links veracity primarily to telling others what one believes. But the complex interactions between clinicians and patients require clinicians to consider carefully how patients interpret their words; skill in listening to patients has often been identified as the key element in effective patient teaching. Moreover, health professionals bear serious duties to service and science that require them to examine honestly the limits of their knowledge, the help they can promise, and their insights into the meanings of illness and death. Thus, accepting honest disclosure calls upon professionals to reflect deeply on the relationship of medical science to health, the consequences of individual service to public health, and the impact of healthcare institutions and practices on the public's understanding of health, illness, and death.

ANDREW JAMETON (1995)
BIBLIOGRAPHY REVISED

SEE ALSO: *Advance Directives and Advance Care Planning; Autonomy; Coercion; Competence; Freedom and Free Will; Genetic Testing and Screening; Human Dignity; Human Rights; Informed Consent: Meaning and Elements; Pastoral Care and Healthcare Chaplaincy; Patients' Rights; Professional-Patient Relationship*

BIBLIOGRAPHY

American College of Physicians (ACP). 1992. "American College of Physicians Ethics Manual: Third Edition." *Annals of Internal Medicine* 117(11): 947–960.

American Nurses' Association. 1985. *Code for Nurses: With Interpretive Statements.* Washington, D.C.: Author.

Anderlik, M. R.; Pentz, R. D.; and Hess, K. R. "Revisiting the Truth-Telling Debate: A Study of Disclosure Practices at a Major Cancer Center." *Journal of Clinical Ethics* 11(3): 251–259.

Annas, George J. 1992. *The Rights of Patients: The Basic ACLU Guide to Patient Rights,* 2nd edition, rev. Totowa, NJ: Humana.

Ashford, Nicholas A., and Caldart, Charles C. 1985. "The 'Right to Know': Toxics Information Transfer in the Workplace." *Annual Review of Public Health* 6: 383–401.

Baier, Annette. 1986. "Trust and Antitrust." *Ethics* 96(2): 231–260.

Baylis, Franciose. 1997. "Errors in Medicine: Nurturing Truthfulness." *Journal of Clinical Ethics* 8(4): 336–40.

Becker, Ernest. 1973. *The Denial of Death.* New York: Free Press.

Bok, Sissela. 1978. *Lying: Moral Choice in Public and Private Life.* New York: Vintage.

Bosk, Charles L. 1980. "Occupational Rituals in Patient Management." *New England Journal of Medicine* 303(2): 71–76.

Brody, Howard. 1992. *The Healer's Power.* New Haven, CT: Yale University Press.

Buckman, Robert, and Kason, Yvonne. 1992. *How to Break Bad News: A Guide for Health Professionals.* Baltimore: Johns Hopkins University Press.

Byrne, Peter. 1990. "Comments on an Obstructed Death—A Case Conference Revisited." *Journal of Medical Ethics* 16(2): 88–89.

Chadwick, Ruth F., and Tadd, Win. 1992. *Ethics & Nursing Practice: A Case Study Approach.* Hampshire, Eng.: Macmillan.

Christakis, Nicholas A., and Fox, Renée C. 1992. "Informed Consent in Africa." *New England Journal of Medicine* 327(15): 1101–1102.

Code, Lorraine. 1991. *What Can She Know? Feminist Theory and the Construction of Knowledge.* Ithaca, NY: Cornell University Press.

Council on Ethical and Judicial Affairs. American Medical Association. 1989. "Principles of Medical Ethics." In *Current Opinions,* p. ix. Chicago: American Medical Association.

DeGrazia, David. 1991. "The Ethical Justification for Minimal Paternalism in the Use of the Predictive Test for Huntington's Disease." *Journal of Clinical Ethics* 2(4): 219–228.

Dunbar, Scott. 1990. "An Obstructed Death and Medical Ethics." *Journal of Medical Ethics* 16(2): 83–87.

Feldman, Eric. 1985. "Medical Ethics the Japanese Way." *Hastings Center Report* 15(5): 21–24.

Gillon, Raanan. 1990. "Deceit, Principles and Philosophical Medical Ethics." *Journal of Medical Ethics* 16(2): 59–60.

Hilfiker, David. 1985. *Healing the Wounds: A Physician Looks at His Work.* New York: Pantheon.

Hochschild, Arlie R. 1983. *The Managed Heart: Commercialization of Human Feeling.* Berkeley: University of California Press.

Jonsen, Albert R., and Toulmin, Stephen E. 1988. *The Abuse of Casuistry: A History of Moral Reasoning.* Berkeley: University of California Press.

Katz, Jay. 1984. *The Silent World of Doctor and Patient.* New York: Free Press.

Katz, Jay. 2002. *The Silent World of Doctor and Patient.* Reprint Edition. Baltimore: Johns Hopkins University Press.

Kessel, Neil. 1979. "Reassurance." *Lancet* 1(8126): 1128–1133.

Kübler-Ross, Elisabeth. 1969. *On Death and Dying.* New York: Macmillan.

Lee, Andre L., and Jacobs, Godfrey. 1973. "Workshop Airs Patients' Rights." *Hospitals* 47(4): 39–43.

Lidz, Charles W.; Meisel, Alan; Osterweis, Marian; Holden, Janice L.; Marx, John H.; and Munetz, Mark R. 1983. "Barriers to Informed Consent." *Annals of Internal Medicine* 99(4): 539–543.

Lilienfeld, David E. 1991. "The Silence: The Asbestos Industry and Early Occupational Cancer Research—A Case Study." *American Journal of Public Health* 81(16): 791–800.

Nyberg, David. 1993. *The Varnished Truth: Truth Telling and Deceiving in Ordinary Life.* Chicago: University of Chicago Press.

Ost, David E. 1984. "The 'Right' Not to Know." *Journal of Medicine and Philosophy* 9(3): 301–312.

Pellegrino, Edmund D. 1992. "Is Truth Telling to the Patient a Cultural Artifact?" *Journal of the American Medical Association* 268(13): 1734–1735.

Pellegrino, Edmund D.; Kissell, Judith Lee; and Thomasma, David C., eds. 2000. *The Health Care Professional As Friend and Healer: Building on the Work of Edmunnd D. Pellegrino.* Washington, D.C.: Georgetown University Press.

Quill, Timothy E., and Townsend, Penelope. 1991. "Bad News: Delivery, Dialogue, and Dilemmas." *Archives of Internal Medicine* 151(3): 463–468.

Radovsky, Saul S. 1985. "Bearing the News." *New England Journal of Medicine* 313(9): 586–588.

Schneider, Carl E. 1998. *The Practice of Autonomy: Patients, Doctors, and Medical Decisions.* New York: Oxford University Press.

Sherwin, Susan. 1992. *No Longer Patient: Feminist Ethics and Health Care.* Philadelphia: Temple University Press.

Strasser, Mark. 1986. "Mill and the Right to Remain Uninformed." *Journal of Medicine and Philosophy* 11(3): 265–278.

Sullivan, R. J., Menapace, L. W.; and White, R. M. 2001. "Truth-telling and Patient Diagnoses." *Journal of Medical Ethics* 27(3): 192–197.

Takahashi, Yoshitomo. 1990. "Informing a Patient of a Malignant Illness: Commentary from a Cross-Cultural Viewpoint." *Death Studies* 14(1): 83–91.

Taylor, Kathryn M. 1988. "Physicians and the Disclosure of Undesirable Information." In *Biomedicine Examined,* pp. 441–463, ed. Margaret M. Lock and Deborah R. Gordon. Dordrecht, Netherlands: Kluwer.

Temmerman, Marleen. 1992. "Informed Consent in Africa." *New England Journal of Medicine* 327(15): 1102–1103.

Terrenoire, Gwen. 1992. "Huntington's Disease and the Ethics of Genetic Prediction." *Journal of Medical Ethics* 18(2): 79–85.

Vanderpool, Harold Y., and Weiss, Gary B. 1984. "Patient Truthfulness: A Test of Models of the Physician-Patient Relationship." *Journal of Medicine and Philosophy* 9(4): 353–372.

Waitzkin, Howard. 1991. *The Politics of Medical Encounters: How Patients and Doctors Deal with Social Problems.* New Haven, CT: Yale University Press.

Wilkes, Michael S.; Doblin, Bruce H.; and Shapiro, Martin F. 1992. "Pharmaceutical Advertisements in Leading Medical Journals: Experts' Assessments." *Annals of Internal Medicine* 116(11): 912–919.

Wilkinson, T. M. 2001. "Research, Informed Consent, and the Limits of Disclosure." *Bioethics* 15(4): 341–363.

Zussman, Robert. 1993. "Life in the Hospital: A Review." *Milbank Quarterly* 71(1): 167–185.

INFORMED CONSENT

• • •

I. HISTORY OF INFORMED CONSENT

Informed consent is not an ancient concept with a rich medical tradition. The term *informed consent* first appeared in 1957, and serious discussion of the concept began only around 1972. As the idea of informed consent evolved, discussion of appropriate guidelines moved increasingly from a narrow focus on the physician's or researcher's obligation to disclose information to the quality of a patient's or subject's understanding of information and right to authorize or refuse a biomedical intervention.

Early History of Associated Ideas

Prior to the late 1950s, there was no firm ground in which a commitment to informed consent could take root. This is not to say, however, that there is no relevant history of the physician's or researcher's management of information in the encounter with patients and subjects. The major writings of prominent figures in ancient, medieval, and modern medicine contain a storehouse of information about commitments to disclosure and discussion in medical practice. But it is a disappointing history from the perspective of informed consent. Beginning with the classic text of ancient medicine, the Hippocratic Corpus, the primary focus of medical ethics became the obligation of physicians to provide medical benefits to patients and to protect them from harm. The purpose of medicine as expressed in the Hippocratic oath was to benefit the sick and keep them from harm and injustice. Managing information in interactions with patients was portrayed as a matter of prudence and discretion. The Hippocratic writings did not hint even at obligations of veracity.

Throughout the ancient, medieval, and early modern periods, medical ethics developed predominantly within the profession of medicine. With few exceptions, no serious consideration was given to issues of either consent or self-determination by patients and research subjects. The proper principles, practices, and virtues of truthfulness in disclosure were occasionally discussed, but the perspective was largely one of maximizing medical benefits through the careful management of medical information. The central concern was how to make disclosures without harming patients by revealing their condition too abruptly and starkly. Withholding information and even outright deception were regularly justified as morally appropriate means of avoiding such harm. The emphasis on the principle "First, do no harm" even promoted the idea that a healthcare professional is obligated not to make disclosures because to do so would be to risk a harmful outcome.

Eighteenth and Nineteenth Centuries

Benjamin Rush and John Gregory are sometimes cited for their enlightened views about disclosure and public education in the eighteenth century. However, neither was advocating informed consent; they wanted patients to be sufficiently educated so that they could understand physicians' recommendations and therefore be motivated to comply. They were not even optimistic that patients would form their own opinions and make appropriate medical choices. For example, Rush advised physicians to "yield to [patients] in matters of little consequence, but maintain an inflexible authority over them in matters that are essential to life" (p. 323). Gregory (1772) was quick to underscore that the physician must be keenly aware of the harm that untimely revelations might cause. There is no assertion of the importance of respecting rights of self-determination for patients or of obtaining consent for any purpose other than a medically good outcome. Gregory and Rush appreciated the value of information and dialogue from the patient's point of view, but the idea of informed consent was not foreshadowed in their writings.

Thomas Percival's historic *Medical Ethics* (1803) continues in this same tradition. It makes no more mention of consent solicitation and respect for decision making by patients than had previous codes and treatises. Percival did, however, struggle with the issue of truth-telling. He held that the patient's right to the truth must yield to the obligation to benefit the patient in cases of conflict, thereby recommending benevolent deception. Percival maintained that

> [T]o a patient … who makes inquiries which, if faithfully answered, might prove fatal to him, it would be a gross and unfeeling wrong to reveal the truth. His right to it is suspended, and even annihilated; because its beneficial nature being reversed, it would be deeply injurious to himself, to his family, and to the public. And he has the strongest claim, from the trust reposed in his physician, as well as from the common principles of humanity, to be guarded against whatever would be detrimental to him …. The only point at issue is, whether the practitioner shall sacrifice that delicate sense of veracity, which is so ornamental to, and indeed forms a characteristic excellence of the virtuous man, to this claim of professional justice and social duty. (pp. 165–166)

Percival was struggling against the arguments of his friend, the Rev. Thomas Gisborne, who opposed practices of giving false assertions intended to raise patients' hopes and lying for the patient's benefit: "The physician … is invariably bound never to represent the uncertainty or danger as less than he actually believes it to be" (Gisborne, p. 401). From Percival's perspective, the physician does not lie or act improperly in beneficent acts of deception and falsehood, as long as the objective is to give hope to the dejected or sick patient.

The American Medical Association (American Medical Association) accepted virtually without modification the Percival paradigm in its 1847 "Code of Medical Ethics." Many of the above passages appear almost verbatim in this code as the AMA position on the obligations of physicians in regard to truth-telling (American Medical Association, 1847). This code and most codes of medical ethics before and since do not include rules of veracity although many codes today do contain rules for obtaining an informed consent. For more than a century thereafter, American and British medical ethics developed under Percival's vision.

There was, however, a notable nineteenth-century exception to the consensus that surrounded Percival's recommendations. Connecticut physician Worthington Hooker was the first champion of the rights of patients to information, in opposition to the model of benevolent deception that had reigned from Hippocrates to the AMA (Hooker). He and Harvard professor of medicine Richard Clarke Cabot were the best known among physicians who championed this model prior to the second half of the twentieth century. Moreover, there may never have been a figure who, in regard to truth-telling, swam so much against the stream of indigenous medical tradition as Hooker.

Hooker's arguments are novel and ingenious but do not amount to a recommendation of informed consent. Hooker was concerned with "the general effect of deception" on society and on medical institutions. He thought the effect disastrous. But in Hooker no more than in the AMA Code is there a recommendation to obtain the permission of patients or to respect autonomy for the sake of autonomy. Hooker's concerns were with expediency in disclosure and truth-telling rather than with the promotion of autonomous decision making or informed consent. The idea that patients should be enabled to understand their situation so that they are able to participate with physicians in decisions about medical treatment was an idea whose time was yet to come.

Although the nineteenth century saw no hint of a rule or practice of informed consent in clinical medicine, consent practices were not entirely absent. Evidence exists in surgery records of consent-seeking practices and rudimentary rules for obtaining consent since at least the middle of the nineteenth century (Pernick). However, the consents thus obtained do not appear to have been meaningful informed consents, because they had little to do with the patient's right to decide after being appropriately informed. Practices of obtaining consent in surgery prior to the 1950s were pragmatic responses to a combination of concerns about medical reputation, malpractice suits, and practicality in medical institutions. It is at best physically difficult and interpersonally awkward to perform surgery on a patient without obtaining the patient's permission. Such practices of obtaining permission, however, do not constitute practices of obtaining informed consent, although they did provide a modest nineteenth-century grounding for this twentieth-century concept.

The situation is similar in research involving human subjects. Little evidence exists that, until recently, requirements of informed consent had a significant hold on the practice of investigators. In the nineteenth century, for example, it was common for research to be conducted on slaves and servants without acquiescence or consent on the part of the subject. By contrast, at the turn of the century, American army surgeon Walter Reed's yellow-fever experiments involved formal procedures for obtaining the consent of potential subjects. Although deficient by contemporary standards of disclosure and consent, these procedures recognized the right of the individual to refuse or authorize participation in the research. The extent to which this principle became ingrained in the ethics of research by the mid-twentieth century is a matter of historical controversy. Although it has often been reported that the obtaining of informed and voluntary consent was essential to the ethics of research and was commonplace in biomedical investigation, it is unclear that consent seeking on the part of investigators was standard practice. Anecdotal evidence suggests that biomedical research often proceeded without adequate consent at least into the 1960s.

Early Twentieth-Century Legal History

The legal history of disclosure obligations and rights of self-determination for patients evolved gradually. It is the nature of legal precedent that each decision, relying on earlier court opinions, joins a chain of authority that incorporates the relevant language and reasoning from the cited cases. In this way, a few early consent cases built on each other to eventuate in a legal doctrine. The best known and ultimately the most influential of these early cases is *Schloendorff* v. *New York Hospital* (1914). *Schloendorff* used rights of *self-determination* to justify imposing an obligation to obtain a patient's consent. Subsequent cases that followed and relied upon *Schloendorff* implicitly adopted its justifactory rationale. In this way, self-determination came to be the primary rationale or justification for legal requirements that consent be obtained from patients.

In the early twentieth century, the behavior of physicians was often egregious, and courts did not shrink from using ringing language and sweeping principles to denounce it. The same language was then applied as precedent in later cases in which physicians' behavior was less outrageous. As the informed-consent doctrine developed and problems grew more subtle, the law could have turned away from the language of self-determination but instead increasingly relied on this rationale as its fundamental premise. The language in the early cases suggests that rights of freedom from bodily invasion contain rights of medical decision making by patients.

The 1950s and 1960s: Law and Medicine

The emerging legal doctrine of informed consent first brought the concept of informed consent to the attention of the medical community. "The doctrine of informed consent" is a legal doctrine; and informed consent has often been treated as synonymous with this legal doctrine. A remarkable series of cases in the second half of the twentieth century brought informed consent to the attention of lawyers and physicians alike.

During the 1950s and 1960s, the traditional duty to obtain consent evolved into a new, explicit duty to disclose certain types of information and then to obtain consent. This development needed a new term; and so *informed* was added onto *consent*, creating the expression *informed consent*, in the landmark decision in *Salgo* v. *Leland Stanford, Jr. University Board of Trustees* (1957). The *Salgo* court suggested, without accompanying analysis, that the duty to disclose the risks and alternatives of treatment was not a new duty but a logical extension of the already established duty to disclose the treatment's nature and consequences. Nonetheless, *Salgo* clearly introduced new elements into the law. The *Salgo* court was not interested merely in whether a recognizable consent had been given to the proposed procedures. Instead, *Salgo* focused strongly on the problem of whether the consent had been adequately informed. The court thus created not only the language but the substance of informed consent by invoking the same right of self-determination that had heretofore applied only to a less robust consent requirement.

Shortly thereafter, two opinions by the Kansas Supreme Court in the case of *Natanson* v. *Kline* (1960) pioneered the use of the legal charge of negligence in informed-consent cases, rather than that of battery. The court established the duty of disclosure as the obligation "to disclose and explain to the patient in language as simple as necessary the nature of the ailment, the nature of the proposed treatment, the probability of success or of alternatives, and perhaps the risks of unfortunate results and unforeseen conditions within the body" (*Natanson* v. *Kline*, 1960). Thus, the *Natanson* court required essentially the same extensive disclosure—of the nature, consequences, risks, and alternatives of a proposed procedure—as had *Salgo*. After *Natanson*, battery and negligence appeared virtually identical in their disclosure requirements for informed consent.

Not surprisingly, the number of articles in the medical literature on issues of consent increased substantially following these and other legal cases. Typically written by lawyers, these reports functioned to alert physicians both to informed consent as a new legal development and to potential malpractice risk. How physicians reacted to these legal developments in the 1950s and 1960s is not well documented, but a handful of empirical studies of informed consent in clinical medicine provides some insights. A study done in the early to mid-1960s indicates that a preoperative consent form was not yet a ubiquitous feature of the practice of surgery. Surgeons at several hospitals refused to participate in this study precisely because they were not using a consent form for surgery.

This indifference to consent procedures seems to have changed by the late 1960s, when most physicians appear to have come to recognize both a moral and a legal duty to obtain consent for certain procedures and to provide some kind of disclosure. There is also evidence, however, that physicians' views about proper consent practices even in the late 1960s differed markedly from the consensus of opinion and convention today. For example, in one study, half of the physicians surveyed thought it medically proper, and 30 percent ethically proper, for a physician to perform a mastectomy with no authorization from the patient other than her signature on the blanket consent form required for hospital admission; more than half the physicians thought that it was ethically appropriate for a physician not to tell a cancer patient that she had been enrolled in a double-blind clinical trial of an experimental anti-cancer drug.

On the basis of the volume of commentary in the medical literature, many physicians before the 1970s were at least dimly aware of informed consent. Empirical studies conducted at the time suggest that there was at least enough documentable consent seeking in such areas as surgery, organ donation, and angiography to warrant empirical investigation. Also during this period, the procedure-specific consent form was gaining acceptance, although it was not yet universally in use. Whether in the 1960s physicians generally regarded informed consent as a legal nuisance or as an important moral problem is unclear, but an explosion of commentary on informed consent emerged in the medical literature in the early 1970s. Much of this commentary was negative: Physicians saw the demands of informed consent as impossible to fulfill and—at least in some cases—inconsistent with good patient care. In tone the articles ranged from serious critique to caustic parody. Predictions were voiced that fearful patients would refuse needed surgery after disclosure. In much of this literature, only the legal, not the moral dimensions of informed-consent requirements were recognized. This began to change in the 1970s, with the ascendancy of an interdisciplinary approach to medical ethics. Gradually, informed consent became a moral as well as a legal issue.

The 1950s and 1960s: Biomedical Research

The histories of informed consent in research and in clinical medicine have developed largely as separate pieces in a larger mosaic of biomedical ethics, and these pieces have never been well integrated even when they developed side by side. Research ethics prior to World War II was no more influential on research practices than the parallel history of clinical-medicine ethics was on clinical practices. But one event that unquestionably influenced thought about informed consent was the Nuremberg trials. The Nuremberg military tribunals unambiguously condemned the sinister political motivation of Nazi experiments in their review of "crimes against humanity." A list of ten principles constituted the Nuremberg Code. Principle One of the code states, without qualification, that the primary consideration in research is the subject's voluntary consent, which is "absolutely essential" (Germany [Territory Under Allied Occupation], 1947).

The Nuremberg Code served as a model for many professional and governmental codes formulated in the 1950s and 1960s, but several other incidents involving consent violations subsequently moved the discussion of post-Nuremberg problems into the public arena. Thus began a rich and complex interplay of influences on research ethics: scholarly publications, journalism, public outrage, legislation, and case law. In the United States, one of the first incidents to achieve notoriety in research ethics involved a study conducted at the Jewish Chronic Disease Hospital (JCDH) in Brooklyn, New York. In July 1963, Dr. Chester Southam of the Sloan-Kettering Institute for Cancer Research persuaded the hospital's medical director, Emmanuel E. Mandel, to permit research involving injection of a suspension of foreign, live cancer cells into twenty-two patients at the JCDH. The objective was to discover whether a decline in the body's capacity to reject cancer transplants was caused by the cancer or by debilitation. Patients without cancer were needed to supply the answer. Southam had convinced Mandel that although the research was nontherapeutic, such research was routinely done without consent. Some patients were informed orally that they were involved in an experiment, but it was not disclosed that they were being given injections of cancer cells. No written consent was attempted, and some subjects were incompetent to give informed consent. The Board of Regents of the State University of New York later censured Southam and Mandel for their role in the research. They were found guilty of fraud, deceit, and unprofessional conduct (*Hyman v. Jewish Chronic Disease Hospital*, 1964).

Another major controversy about the ethics of research in the United States developed at Willowbrook State School, an institution for "mentally defective" children in Staten Island, New York. Beginning in 1956, Saul Krugman and his associates began a series of experiments to develop an effective prophylactic agent for infectious hepatitis. They deliberately infected newly admitted patients with isolated strains of the virus based on parental consents obtained under controversial circumstances that may have been manipulative. The issues in the Willowbrook case are more complex than those in the Jewish Chronic Disease Hospital case, and today there are those who still defend, at least in part, the ethics of these experiments. Krugman's research unit was eventually closed, but closure on the debate about the ethics of the studies conducted in the unit was never achieved (New York University).

The most notorious case of prolonged and knowing violation of subjects' rights in the United States was a Public Health Service (PHS) study initiated in the early 1930s. Originally designed as one of the first syphilis-control demonstrations in the United States, the stated purpose of the Tuskegee syphilis study, as it is now called, was to compare the health and longevity of an untreated syphilitic population with a nonsyphilitic but otherwise similar population. These subjects, all African-American males, knew neither the name nor the nature of their disease. That they were participants in a nontherapeutic experiment also went undisclosed. They were informed only that they were receiving free treatment for "bad blood," a term local African-Americans associated with a host of unrelated ailments, but which the white physicians allegedly assumed was a local euphemism for syphilis (Jones).

Perhaps the most remarkable thing about Tuskegee was that, although the study was reviewed several times between 1932 and 1970 by PHS officials and medical societies as well as reported in thirteen articles in prestigious medical and public-health journals, it continued uninterrupted and without serious challenge. It was not until 1972 that the U.S. Department of Health, Education and Welfare (DHEW) appointed an ad hoc advisory panel to review the study and the department's policies and procedures for the protection of human subjects. The panel found that neither DHEW nor any other government agency had a uniform or adequate policy for reviewing experimental procedures or securing subjects' consents.

The 1970s and 1980s

Although the Jewish Chronic Disease Hospital case, the Willowbrook study, and the Tuskegee study had a profound effect on public consciousness with respect to the ethics of research and medicine, these events are insufficient to explain why informed consent became the focus of so much attention in both case law and biomedical ethics between the late 1960s and the late 1980s. Many hypotheses can be invoked to explain this phenomenon. Perhaps the most accurate explanation is that law and ethics, as well as medicine itself, were all affected by issues and concerns in the wider society about individual liberties and social equality, made dramatic by an increasingly technological, powerful, and impersonal medical-care system. It seems likely that increased legal interest in the right of self-determination and increased philosophical interest in the principle of respect for autonomy and individualism were instances of the new rights orientation that various social movements had introduced. The issues raised by civil rights, women's rights, the consumer movement, and the rights of prisoners and the mentally ill often included healthcare components and helped reinforce public acceptance of rights applied to healthcare. Informed consent was swept along with this body of social concerns, which propelled the new bioethics throughout the 1970s.

Three 1972 court decisions are widely recognized as informed consent landmarks: *Canterbury* v. *Spence, Cobbs* v. *Grant,* and *Wilkinson* v. *Vesey. Canterbury* had a massive influence. In its most significant and dramatic finding, the *Canterbury* court moved in the direction of a more patient-oriented standard of disclosure:

> The patient's right of self-decision can be effectively exercised only if the patient possesses enough information to enable an intelligent choice. The patient should make his own determination on treatment. Informed consent is a basic social policy for which exceptions are permitted (1) where the patient is unconscious or otherwise incapable of consenting, and harm from failure to treat is imminent; or (2) when risk-disclosure poses such a serious psychological threat of detriment to the patient as to be medically contraindicated. Social policy does not accept the paternalistic view that the physician may remain silent because divulgence might prompt the patient to forego needed therapy. Rational, informed patients should not be expected to act uniformly, even under similar circumstances, in agreeing to or refusing treatment. (*Canterbury* v. *Spence,* 1972)

As the impact of *Canterbury* filtered down to medical practice, the U.S. National Commission for the Protection of Human Subjects of Biomedical and Behavioral Research began in 1974 what would be a four-year struggle with a variety of concerns about informed consent in research involving human subjects. The commission developed an abstract schema of basic ethical principles for research ethics that gave informed consent a major role (U.S. National Commission, 1978):

Principle of	applies to	Guidelines for
Respect for Persons		Informed Consent
Beneficence		Risk/Benefit Assessment
Justice		Selection of Subjects

Under this schema, the purpose of consent provisions is not protection from risk, as some earlier federal policies had implied, but rather the protection of autonomy and personal dignity, including the personal dignity of incompetent persons incapable of acting autonomously (for whose involvement a third party must consent). This conclusion develops an explicit philosophical position on informed consent for the first time in a government-sponsored document.

Among the most important publications in the medical literature to appear during this period was a statement by the Judicial Council of the American Medical Association in 1981. For the first time, the AMA recognized informed consent as "a basic social policy" necessary to enable patients to make their own choices even if the physician disagrees. The AMA's statement is a testament to the impact of the law of informed consent on medical ethics: The AMA's position closely followed the language of *Canterbury* v. *Spence* (Judicial Council, 1981).

The U.S. President's Commission for the Study of Ethical Problems in Medicine and Biomedical and Behavioral Research provides further evidence regarding the status informed consent had achieved by the 1980s. The commission was first convened in January 1980, with informed consent as a main item on its agenda. In 1982 it produced a three-volume report that dealt directly with informed consent: *Making Health Care Decisions: The Ethical and Legal Implications of Informed Consent in the Patient-Practitioner Relationship.* The commission argued that although informed consent has emerged primarily from a history in law, its requirements are essentially moral and policy-oriented. It held that informed consent is ultimately based on the principle that competent persons are entitled to make their own decisions from their own values and goals, but that the context of informed consent and any claim of "valid consent" must derive from active, shared decision making. The principle of self-determination was described as the "bedrock" of the commission's viewpoint.

In addition to the efforts of the U.S. President's Commission and the statement of the AMA, the 1980s saw the publication of several books devoted to the subject of informed consent, as well as hundreds of journal articles, and the passage of procedure-specific informed-consent laws and regulations. These events provide powerful testimony of the importance of informed consent in moral and legal thinking about medicine in the United States. By themselves, however, they tell us little about physicians' or researchers' actual consent practices or opinions or about how informed consent was viewed or experienced by patients and subjects.

As might be expected, the empirical evidence on this subject is mixed, although it is clear that procedures of informed consent have taken a firm hold in some parts of medical practice. For example, routine practice encourages the obtaining of signatures on consent forms and the disclosing of information about alternative treatments, risks, and benefits. The best data on this subject are the findings of a national survey conducted for the U.S. President's Commission by Louis Harris and Associates in 1982. Almost all of the physicians surveyed indicated that they obtained written consent from their patients before in-patient surgery or the administration of general anesthesia. At least 85 percent said they usually obtained some kind of consent—written or oral—for minor office surgery, setting of fractures, local anesthesia, invasive diagnostic procedures, and radiation therapy. Only blood tests and prescriptions appear to have proceeded frequently without patient consent, although about half of the physicians reported obtaining oral consent (1982).

The overall impression conveyed by this survey is that the explosion of interest in informed consent in the 1970s had a powerful impact on medical practice. However, evidence from the Harris survey and other sources questions the meaningfulness of the increase in consent-related activity. The overwhelming impression from the empirical literature and from reported clinical experience is that the actual process of soliciting informed consent often falls short of a serious show of respect for the decisional authority of patients. As the authors of one empirical study of physician-patient interactions put it, "despite the doctrine of informed consent, it is the physician, and not the patient, who, in effect, makes the treatment decision" (Siminoff and Fetting, p. 817).

The history of informed consent, then, indicates that medicine has undergone widespread changes under the influence of legal and moral requirements of informed consent, but it also remind us that informed consent is an evolving process, not a set of events whose history has passed.

TOM L. BEAUCHAMP
RUTH R. FADEN (1995)

SEE ALSO: *Autonomy; Competence; Information Disclosure, Ethical Issues of; Professional-Patient Relationship;* and other *Informed Consent* subentries

BIBLIOGRAPHY

American Medical Association. 1847. "Code of Medical Ethics." In *Proceedings of the National Medical Conventions, Held in New York, May 1846, and in Philadelphia, May 1847.* Adopted May 6 and submitted for publication in Philadelphia. Philadelphia: Author.

American Medical Association. Judical Council. 1981. *Current Opinions of the Judicial Council of the American Medical Association.* Chicago: Author.

Canterbury v. *Spence.* 464 F.2d 772 (D.C. Cir. 1972), *cert. denied* 409 U.S. 1064.

Cobbs v. *Grant.* 104 Cal. Rptr. 505, 502 P.2d 1 (1972).

Faden, Ruth R.; Beauchamp, Tom L.; and King, Nancy M. P. 1986. *A History and Theory of Informed Consent.* New York: Oxford University Press.

Germany (Territory Under Allied Occupation, 1945–1955: U.S. Zone) Military Tribunals. 1947 "Permissible Military Experiments." In vol. 2 of *Trials of War Criminals Before Nuremberg Tribunals Under Control Law No. 10,* pp. 181–184. Washington, D.C.: U.S. Government Printing Office.

Gisborne, Thomas. 1794. *A Enquiry into the Duties of Men in the Higher and Middle Classes of Society in Great Britain, Resulting from Their Respective Stations, Professions, and Employments.* London: B. and J. White.

Gregory, John. 1772. *Lectures on the Duties and Qualifications of a Physician,* New edition. London: Strahan & Cadell.

Harris, Louis, and Associates. 1982. "Views of Informed Consent and Decisionmaking: Parallel Surveys of Physicians and the Public." In vol. 2 of *Making Health Care Decisions,* pp. 17–316. Washington, D.C.: U.S. President's Commission for the Study of Ethical Problems in Medicine and Biomedical and Behavioral Research.

Hooker, Worthington. 1849. *Physician and Patient; or, A Practical View of the Mutual Duties, Relations and Interests of the Medical Professions and the Community.* New York: Baker and Scribner.

Hyman v. *Jewish Chronic Disease Hospital.* 251 N.Y. 2d 818 (App. Div. 1964): 206 N.E. 2d 338 (1965).

Jones, James H. 1981. *Bad Blood: The Tuskegee Syphilis Experiment.* New York: Free Press.

Katz, Jay. 1984. *The Silent World of Doctor and Patient.* New York: Free Press.

Natanson v. *Kline.* 186 Kan. 393, 350 P.2d 1093 (1960), opinion on denial of motion for rehearing, 187 Kan. 186, 354 P.2d 670.

New York University. Post-Graduate School. 1972. *Proceedings of the Symposium on Ethical Issues in Human Experimentation: The Case of Willowbrook State Hospital Research, May 4.* New York: New York University Medical Center.

Percival, Thomas. 1803. *Medical Ethics; or, A Code of Institutes and Precepts, Adapted to the Professional Conduct of Physicians and Surgeons.* Manchester, England: S. Russell.

Pernick, Martin S. 1982. "The Patient's Role in Medical Decisionmaking: A Social History of Informed Consent in Medical Therapy." In vol. 2 of *Making Health Care Decisions.* Washington, D.C.: U.S. President's Commission for the Study of Ethical Problems in Medicine and Biomedical and Behavioral Research.

Rush, Benjamin. 1786. *An Oration … Containing an Enquiry into the Influence of Physical Causes upon the Moral Faculty.* Philadelphia: Charles Cist.

Salgo v. *Leland Stanford, Jr. University Board of Trustees.* 317 P.2d 170 (Cal. 1957).

Schloendorff v. *Society of New York Hospital.* 211 N.Y. 125, 129, 105 N.E. 92 (1914).

Siminoff, L. A. and Fetting, J. H. 1991. "Factors Affecting Treatment Decisions for a Life-Threatening Illness: The Case of Medical Treatment of Breast Cancer." *Social Science and Medicine* 32(7): 813–818.

U.S. President's Commission for the Study of Ethical Problems in Medicine and Biomedical and Behavioral Research. 1982. *Making Health Care Decisions: A Report on the Ethical and Legal Implications of Informed Consent in the Patient-Practitioner Relationship.* 3 vols. Washington, D.C.: Author.

Wilkinson v. *Vesey.* 295 A.2d 676 (R.I. 1972).

II. MEANING AND ELEMENTS

Appropriate criteria must be identified to define and classify an act of informed consent properly. If overdemanding criteria such as "full disclosure and complete understanding" are adopted, an informed consent becomes impossible to obtain. Conversely, if underdemanding criteria such as "the patient signed the form" are used, an informed consent becomes too easy to obtain and the term loses all moral significance. Many interactions between a physician and a patient or an investigator and a subject that have been called informed consents have been so labeled only because they rest on underdemanding criteria; they are inappropriately referred to as informed consents. For example, a physician's truthful disclosure to a patient has often been declared the essence of informed consent, as if a patient's silence following disclosure could constitute an informed consent. The existence of such inadequate understandings of informed consent can be explained in part by empirical information about physicians' beliefs about informed consent.

Contemporary Assumptions in Medicine

Data about the relevant beliefs of physicians in the United States were gathered in a 1982 survey of physicians conducted by Louis Harris and Associates. One question of this survey asked physicians, "What does the term informed consent mean to you?" In their answers, only 26 percent of physicians indicated that informed consent has something to do with a patient's giving permission, consenting, or agreeing to treatment. In a related question, only 9 percent indicated that it involves the patient's making a choice or stating a preference about his or her treatment (Harris and Associates; U.S. President's Commission, 1982). Similar results were found in a survey of Japanese physicians (Hattori et al.).

The majority of these physicians appear to regard disclosure as the primary (and perhaps sole) element of informed consent. That is, they conceive of informed consent as explaining to patients the nature of their medical conditions together with a recommended treatment plan. But if physicians regard informed consent as nothing more than an event of conveying information to patients, rather than a process of discussion with and obtaining permission from the patient, then claims that they regularly "obtain consents" from their patients before initiating medical procedures are both vague and unreliable.

Other polls conducted in the United States indicate that the majority of physicians understand an informed consent to be either a signed consent form or a disclosure. Some also conclude that no evidence exists that informed-consent practices are widespread in clinical medicine and that many agreements by patients that are called informed consents in some clinical settings fall far short of being meaningful informed consents (Lidz and Meisel).

The Elements of Informed Consent

Literature of bioethics often analyzes informed consent in terms of the following elements: (1) disclosure; (2) comprehension; (3) voluntariness; (4) competence; and (5) consent (see U.S. National Commission, 1978, U.S. President's Commission, 1982; Meisel and Roth, 1981). This analysis is sometimes joined with a corresponding thesis that these elements collectively define informed consent. The postulate is that a person gives an informed consent to an intervention if and only if the person receives a thorough disclosure about the procedure, comprehends the disclosed information, acts voluntarily, is competent to act, and consents.

This definition is attractive because of its consistency with standard usage of informed consent in medicine and law. However, medical convention and malpractice law have special orientations that tend to distort the meaning of informed consent in ways that need correction. Analyses that use the five elements listed above, as well as conventional usage in law and medicine, are best suited for cataloguing the analytical parts of informed consent and for delineating moral and legal requirements of informed consent, not for conceptually analyzing the meaning of informed consent. Neither requirements nor parts amounts to a definition.

The U.S. Supreme Court addressed the definition of informed consent in *Planned Parenthood of Central Missouri* v. *Danforth* as follows: "One might well wonder ... what 'informed consent' of a patient is.... We are content to accept, as the meaning, the giving of information to the patient as to just what would be done and as to its consequences ..." (*Planned Parenthood of Central Missouri* v. *Danforth,* 1976, p. 67). The essential element or part of informed consent, as described here, is disclosure, an analysis that recalls the assumptions made by physicians in the Harris poll (Harris and Associates). However, as we will see, nothing about an informed consent requires disclosure as part of its meaning, and this element does not amount to a definition. Moreover, to make disclosure the sole or even the major condition of informed consent incorporates questionable assumptions about medical authority, physician responsibility, and legal liability. These norms delineate an obligation to make disclosures so that a consent can be informed, rather than a meaning of informed consent. Even all five of the above elements merged as a set do not satisfactorily capture the meaning of informed consent.

Both the elements and the meaning of informed consent, then, need a more comprehensive treatment. The following seven categories express the analytical components of informed consent more adequately than the above five categories—although this sevenfold list does not adequately express the meaning of informed consent either (Beauchamp and Childress):

I. Threshold elements (preconditions)
    1. Competence (to understand and decide)
    2. Voluntariness (in deciding)
II. Information elements
    3. Disclosure (of material information)
    4. Recommendation (of a plan)
    5. Understanding (of terms 3 and 4)
III. Consent elements
    6. Decision (in favor of a plan)
    7. Authorization (of the chosen plan)

The language of material information in (3) is pivotal for an adequate analysis of the elements of disclosure (3) and understanding (5). Critics of legal requirements of informed consent have often held that procedures sometimes have so many risks and benefits that they cannot be disclosed and explained in a reasonable period of time or in an understandable framework. The demands in this misreading of the nature and requirements of informed consent must be pruned, as many courts have pointed out. Material risks are the risks a reasonable patient needs to understand in order to decide among the alternatives; only these risks and benefits need to be disclosed and understood.

Corresponding to each of the above elements, one could construct informed-consent requirements. That is, there could be disclosure requirements, comprehension requirements, noninfluence requirements, competence requirements, authorization requirements, and so forth. These requirements would specify the conditions that must be satisfied for a consent to be valid.

Two Meanings of Informed Consent

Translating the above seven elements directly into a definition or meaning of informed consent invites confusion, because the term *informed consent* has subtleties not captured by these elements. A subtlety that has generated considerable misunderstanding is that two very different meanings of informed consent operate in current literature and social practices.

In the first meaning, an informed consent is an autonomous authorization of a medical intervention or of involvement in research by individual patients or subjects. An autonomous authorization requires more than merely acquiescing in, yielding to, or complying with an arrangement or a proposal made by a physician or investigator. A person gives an informed consent in this first sense if and only if the person, with substantial understanding and in substantial absence of control by others, intentionally authorizes a health professional to do something. A person who intentionally refuses to authorize an intervention but otherwise satisfies these conditions gives an informed refusal. This first sense derives from the philosophical premises that informed consent is fundamentally a matter of protecting and enabling autonomous or self-determining choice by patients and subjects and that final authority for making decisions about medical treatment or research participation properly rests with patients and subjects, not physicians or research scientists.

In the second meaning, informed consent is analyzed in terms of institutional and policy rules of consent. This sense expresses the mainstream conception in the regulatory rules of federal agencies and in healthcare institutions. Here *informed consent* refers only to a legally or institutionally effective approval by a patient or subject. An approval is therefore effective or valid if it conforms to the rules that govern specific institutions, whatever the operative rules may be. In this sense, unlike the first, conditions and requirements of informed consent are relative to a social and institutional context and need not be autonomous authorizations. This meaning is driven by demands in the legal and healthcare systems for a generally applicable and efficient consent mechanism by which responsibilities and violations can be readily and fairly assessed (Faden et al.).

Under these two contrasting understandings of informed consent, a patient or subject can give an informed consent in the first sense, but not in the second sense, and vice versa. For example, if the person consenting is a minor and therefore not of legal age, he or she cannot give an effective or valid consent under the prevailing institutional rules; a consent is invalid even if the minor gives the consent autonomously and responsibly. ("Mature minor" laws do sometimes make an exception and give minors the right to authorize medical treatments in a limited range of circumstances.)

The Relationship between the Two Meanings

Rules governing effective authorization have often not been premised on a carefully delineated conception of autonomous decision making, but current literature in bioethics suggests that any justifiable analysis of informed consent must be rooted in autonomous choice by patients and subjects. An act is increasingly recognized in this literature as an informed consent only if (1) a patient or subject agrees to an intervention based on an understanding of material information; (2) the agreement is not controlled by influences that engineer the outcome; and (3) an authorization for an intervention is given by the patient or subject with the understanding that it is an authorization.

In principle, although less clearly in practice, these conditions of informed consent (in the sense of an individual's autonomous authorization) can function as model standards for fashioning the institutional and policy requirements for effective consent. The model of autonomous choice would then serve as the benchmark against which the moral adequacy of prevailing rules and practices should be evaluated. The postulate that policies governing informed consent in the second sense should be formulated to conform to the standards of informed consent in the first sense is grounded in the premise that the primary goal of informed consent in medical care and in research is to enable potential subjects and patients to make autonomous decisions about whether to grant or refuse authorization for medical and research interventions (Katz).

It does not follow that institutional policies regarding informed consent are justifiable only if they rank the protection of decision making above all other values. Consent requirements imposed by institutions should be formulated and evaluated against a range of social and institutional considerations. The preservation of autonomous choice is the first but not the only consideration. For example, a patient's need for education and counseling in order to achieve a substantial understanding of a medical situation must be balanced against the interests of other patients and of society in maintaining a productive and efficient healthcare system. Accordingly, institutional policies must consider what is fair and reasonable to require of healthcare professionals and researchers and what the effect would be of alternative consent requirements on efficiency and effectiveness in the delivery of healthcare and the advancement of science.

TOM L. BEAUCHAMP
RUTH R. FADEN (1995)
BIBLIOGRAPHY REVISED

SEE ALSO: *Autonomy; Competence; Information Disclosure, Ethical Issues of; Professional-Patient Relationship;* and other *Informed Consent* subentries

BIBLIOGRAPHY

Appelbaum, Paul S.; Lidz, Charles W.; and Meisel, Alan. 1987. *Informed Consent: Legal Theory and Clinical Practice.* New York: Oxford University Press.

Beauchamp, Tom L., and Childress, James F. 1994. *Principles of Biomedical Ethics,* 4th edition. New York: Oxford University Press.

Berg, Jessica W. 1996. "Legal and Ethical Complexities of Consent with Cognitively Impaired Research Subjects: Proposed Guidelines." *Journal of Law, Medicine and Ethics* 24(1): 18–35.

Berg, Jessica W.; Appelbaum, Paul S.; Parker, Lisa S.; Lidz, Charles W., eds. 2001. *Informed Consent: Legal Theory and Clinical Practice.* New York: Oxford University Press.

Biros, M. H.; Lewis, R. J.; Olson, C. M.; et al. 1995. "Informed Consent in Emergency Research. Consensus Statement from the Coalition Conference of Acute Resuscitation and Critical Care Researchers." *Journal of the American Medical Association* 273(16): 1283–1287.

Committee on Bioethics, American Academy of Pediatrics. 1995. "Informed Consent, Parental Permission, and Assent in Pediatric Practice." *Pediatrics* 95(2): 314–317.

Doyal, Len, and Tobias, Jeffrey S., eds. 2001. *Informed Consent in Medical Research.* London: BMJ Books.

Faden, Ruth R.; Beauchamp, Tom L.; and King, Nancy M. P. 1986. *A History and Theory of Informed Consent.* New York: Oxford University Press.

Faden, Ruth. 1996. "Informed Consent and Clinical Research." *Kennedy Institute of Ethics Journal* 6(4): 356–359.

Gostin, Laurence O. 1995. "Informed Consent, Cultural Sensitivity, and Respect for Persons." *Journal of the American Medical Association* 274(10): 844–845.

Harris, Louis, and Associates. 1982. "Views of Informed Consent and Decisionmaking: Parallel Surveys of Physicians and the Public." In vol. 2 of *Making Health Care Decisions,* pp. 17–316. Washington, D.C.: U.S. President's Commission for the Study of Ethical Problems in Medicine and Biomedical and Behavioral Research.

Hattori, Hiroyuki; Salzburg, Stephan M.; Kiang, Winston P.; Fujimiya, Tatsuga; Tejima, Yutaka; and Furuno, Junji. 1991. "The Patient's Right to Information in Japan—Legal Rules and Doctor's Opinions." *Social Science and Medicine* 32(9): 1007–1016.

Katz, Jay. 1984. *The Silent World of Doctor and Patient.* New York: Free Press.

Levine, Robert J. 1988. *Ethics and Regulation of Clinical Research.* 2nd edition. New Haven, CT: Yale University Press.

Lidz, Charles W., and Meisel, Alan. 1982. "Informed Consent and the Structure of Medical Care." In vol. 2 of *Making Health Care Decisions,* pp. 317–410. Washington, D.C.: U.S. President's Commission for the Study of Ethical Problems in Medicine and Biomedical and Behavioral Research.

McConnell, Terrance C. 2000. *Inalienable Rights: The Limits of Consent in Medicine and the Law.* New York: Oxford University Press.

Meisel, Alan, and Roth, Loren H. 1981. "What We Do and Do Not Know About Informed Consent." *Journal of the American Medical Association* 246(21): 2473–2477.

Merz, Jon F., and Fischoff, Baruch. 1990. "Informed Consent Does Not Mean Rational Consent: Cognitive Limitations on Decision-Making." *Journal of Legal Medicine* 11(3): 321–350.

Planned Parenthood of Central Missouri v. *Danforth.* 423 U.S. 52 (1976).

Quill, Timothy E., and Brody, Howard. 1996. "Physician Recommendations and Patient Autonomy: Finding a Balance between Physician Power and Patient Choice." *Annals of Internal Medicine* 125(9): 763–769.

U.S. National Commission for the Protection of Human Subjects of Biomedical and Behavioral Research. 1978. *The Belmont Report: Ethical Principles and Guidelines for the Protection of Human Subjects of Biomedical and Behavioral Research.* DHEW Publication (OS) 78–0012. Washington, D.C.: Department of Health, Education, and Welfare.

U.S. President's Commission for the Study of Ethical Problems in Medicine and Biomedical and Behavioral Research. 1982. *Making Health Care Decisions: A Report on the Ethical and Legal Implications of Informed Consent in the Patient-Practitioner Relationship.* 3 vols. Washington, D.C.: Author.

Wear, Stephen. 1999. "Enhancing Clinician Provision of Informed Consent and Counseling: Some Pedagogical Strategies." *Journal of Medicine and Philosophy* 24(1): 34–42.

Wear, Stephen; Engelhardt, H. Tristam; and Wildes, Kevin W., eds. 1997. *Informed Consent: Patient Autonomy and Clinician Beneficence Within Health Care (Clinical Medical Ethics Series).* Washington, D.C.: Georgetown University Press.

III. CONSENT ISSUES IN HUMAN RESEARCH

"The voluntary consent of the human subject is absolutely essential." This, the first sentence of the Nuremberg Code, signals the centrality of the consent requirement in research involving human subjects (Germany [Territory under Allied Occupation], p. 181). Before the Nuremberg Code was written in 1947 as a response to the atrocities committed in the name of science by Nazi physician-researchers, statements of medical and other professional organizations apparently made no mention of the necessity of consent. Ironically, the only nations known to have promulgated regulations that established a requirement for consent to research were Prussia and Germany (Perley et al.). Subsequently, the tendency to focus on informed consent has been reinforced by public outcry over the inadequacy of consent in certain landmark cases in the United States, such as the Willowbrook Studies (1963–1966), Jewish Chronic Disease Hospital Study (1963), Tea Room Trade Study (1970), and Tuskegee Syphilis Study (1932–1972) (Katz, Capron, and Swift; Levine). Indeed, the issue of informed consent has so dominated recent discussion of the ethics of research that one might be led to think erroneously that other ethical issues (e.g., research design, selection of subjects) are either less important or more satisfactorily resolved.

This entry is concerned with the conceptual aspects of informed consent. For an extensive review of empirical studies of informed consent, see the 1999 article written by Jeremy Sugarman and Douglas C. McCrory.

Grounding of Informed Consent

The requirement for informed consent has philosophical, religious, and legal foundations.

PHILOSOPHICAL BASIS. The philosophical foundations of the requirement for informed consent may be found in several lines of reasoning (Veatch 1981; Faden, Beauchamp, and King; Brock 1987). Based on the Hippocratic admonition "to help, or at least, to do no harm," one can justify seeking consent for the benefit of the patient; to do so provides a mechanism for ascertaining what the patient would consider a benefit. Allowing individuals to decide what they consider beneficial is consistent with the perspective affirmed in U.S. public policy that competent persons are generally the best protectors of their own well-being (Brock 1987). A focus solely on patient benefit, however, would allow physicians and scientists not to seek consent when they judge that doing so might harm patients or subjects. Thus this justification alone does not suffice to establish a requirement to seek consent.

The requirement can also be justified on grounds of social benefit: The practice of seeking consent may contribute to producing the "greatest good for the greatest number" by forestalling suspicion about research, thus ensuring a subject population and increasing the efficiency of the research enterprise. Again, however, the justification fails to stand alone, because it can also be used to justify not seeking consent; the social good might be better served by avoiding the inefficient and frequently time-consuming consent process. Some commentators express concern that, carried to its extreme, the social-benefit argument might support the use of unwilling subjects, as in Nazi Germany; such a position would necessarily rest on a very limited vision of the relevant social consequences.

The firmest grounding for the requirement to seek consent is the ethical principle *respect for persons,* which according to the U.S. National Commission for the Protection of Human Subjects of Biomedical and Behavioral Research (hereafter, U.S. National Commission) "incorporates at least two basic ethical convictions: first, that individuals should be treated as autonomous agents, and second, that persons with diminished autonomy and thus in need of protection are entitled to such protection" (U.S. National Commission, p. 4). Although this term suggests a Kantian or deontological (a foundational ethical principle holding that the moral rightness of an action resides in the action itself without regard to its consequences) grounding of the principle, this was not the intent of the commission; a substantially similar principle, self-determination, may be grounded in rule utilitarianism deontological (a foundational ethical principle holding that the moral rightness of an action must be evaluated in terms of its consequences) (Brock, 1987). In a legal context, American jurist Benjamin Cardozo stated in 1914 that "every human being of adult years and sound mind has a right to determine what shall be done with his own body" (Katz, p. 51). To return to the Kantian approach that will be used often in this entry, this principle of respect for persons, autonomy or self-determination ensures that the research subject will be treated as an end and not merely as a means to another's end (Beauchamp and Childress). Thus the purpose of the consent requirement is not only to minimize risk but also to give persons the right to choose.

RELIGIOUS BASIS. Several fundamental tenets of the Judeo-Christian and other traditions also provide grounding for the requirement to seek consent. This tradition affirms that each human life is a gift from God and is of infinite and immeasurable worth (the "sanctity of life"). The infinite worth of the individual requires that persons treat each other with respect and not interfere in each other's lives without consent. The consent requirement can also be grounded explicitly in the notion of covenant. Seeking consent is an affirmation of the basic faithfulness or care required by the fundamental covenantal nature of human existence (Ramsey, 1970).

LEGAL BASIS. The legal grounding for the requirement for consent to research (Annas, Glantz, and Katz) is based on the outcome of litigation of disputes arising almost exclusively in the context of medical practice. There is virtually no case law on which to define the basis of the legal standards for consent to research, as distinguished from consent to practice (there is one Canadian case, *Halushka v. University of Saskatchewan* [1965]). The law defines, in general, the circumstances under which a patient, or by extension, a subject, may recover damages for having been wronged or harmed as a consequence of failure to negotiate adequate consent.

The legal bases for the consent requirement—which also shed light on the ethical dimensions of consent—are twofold (Annas, Glantz, and Katz). First, failure to obtain proper consent was traditionally treated as a battery action. Closely related to the principles of respect for persons and self-determination, the law of battery makes it wrong to touch, treat, or do research upon a person without the person's consent. Whether or not harm befalls the patient/subject is irrelevant: It is the unconsented-to touching that is wrong.

The modern trend in malpractice litigation is to treat cases based on failure to obtain proper consent as negligence rather than battery actions. The negligence doctrine combines elements of patient benefit and self-determination. To bring a negligence action, a patient/subject must prove that the physician had a duty toward the patient, that the duty was breached, that damage occurred to the patient, and that the damage was caused by the breach. In contrast to battery actions, negligence actions remove as a basis for the requirement for consent the simple notion that unconsented-to touching is a wrong. Rather, such touching is wrong (actionable) only if it is negligent and results in harm; otherwise, the patient/subject cannot recover damages. Under both battery and negligence doctrines, consent is invalid if any information is withheld from the patient/subject that might be considered material to the decision to give consent.

Functions of Informed Consent

In their 1975 book, *Catastrophic Diseases: Who Decides What?* Jay Katz and Alexander Morgan Capron identified the following functions of informed consent: promoting individual autonomy, encouraging rational decision making, avoiding fraud and duress, involving the public, encouraging self-scrutiny by the physician-investigator, and reducing the civil and/or criminal liability of the investigator and her institution.

In general, the negotiations for informed consent are designed to safeguard the rights and welfare of the subject, while documentation that the negotiations have been conducted properly safeguards the investigator and institution (Levine). The net effect of the documentation may, in fact, be harmful to the interests of the subject. Retaining a signed consent form tends to give the advantage to the investigator in any adversarial proceeding. Moreover, the availability of such documents in institutional records may lead to violations of privacy and confidentiality. Consequently, federal regulations permit waivers of the requirement for consent forms when the principal threat to the subject would be a breach of confidentiality and "the only record linking the subject and the research would be the consent document" ("Documentation of Informed Consent," pt. 46.117c).

Those who are interested in making operational the requirement for consent have a tendency to focus nearly all of their attention on the consent form. Federal regulations prescribe what information must be included in and excluded from these forms. Members of institutional review boards and researchers collaborate in a struggle to create reproachless forms. This seems to reflect an assumption that the consent form is an appropriate instrumentality through which researchers might fulfill their obligation not to treat persons merely as means. Most commentators on informed consent disagree, however, seeing consent as a continuing process rather than an event symbolized by the signing of a form; for example, Robert J. Levine (1986) characterized informed consent as a discussion or negotiation, while Katz (1984) envisioned consent as a searching conversation.

Whether or not negotiations for informed consent to research should be conducted according to different standards than consent to practice is controversial. In a 1974 article, Alvan R. Feinstein observed that it is the custom to adhere to a double standard: "An act that receives no special concern when performed as part of clinical practice may become a major ethical or legal issue if done as part of a formally designed investigation" (p. 331). In his view there is less need for formality in the negotiations for informed consent in a relationship in which the interests of research and practice are conjoined—for example, as in research conducted by a physician-investigator who has the aim of demonstrating the safety and/or efficacy of a nonvalidated therapeutic maneuver—than when the only purpose of the investigator–subject relationship is to perform research. Capron, on the other hand, asserted in a 1972 publication: "Higher requirements for informed consent should be imposed in therapy than in investigation, particularly when an element of honest experimentation is joined with therapy" (p. 574). Levine (1986) concluded that patients are entitled to the same degree of thoroughness of negotiations for informed consent as are subjects of research. Patients, however, may be offered the opportunity to delegate some (but not all) decision-making authority to a physician, whereas subjects should rarely be offered this option. The most important distinction is that the prospective subject should be informed that in research, in contrast with practice, the subject will be at least in part a means and perhaps primarily a means to an end identified by someone else.

Two Interpretations of the Consent Requirement

Interpretations of the meaning and application of informed consent reflect a tension between respecting the autonomy of persons and protecting them from harm. Hans Jonas (1970) and Paul Ramsey (1970) have developed a covenantal model in which subjects are respected and protected by ensuring that they give truly informed consent. Benjamin Freedman (1975) stressed the legally competent individual's freedom of choice, whether or not the choice is informed.

For Jonas and Ramsey, the consent requirement is derived from the duty to treat persons as ends, not merely as means. In research, subjects are *used* as means to the end of acquiring knowledge. (In Jonas's terms, they are "sacrificed" for the collective good.) Such *use* of persons is justified only if the subjects so identify with the purposes of the research that they will those purposes as their own ends. Only then are they not being *used*, but instead they have become, in Ramsey's term, "co-adventurers." The consent requirement thus affirms a basic covenantal bond between the researcher and the subject and ensures respect for the subject as an end, not merely a means.

To establish a true covenant, the subject's consent must be informed. Only subjects who genuinely know the purposes and appreciate the risks of research can assume those risks and adopt those purposes as their own ends. Ideal subjects, therefore, would be researchers themselves (Jonas). The less one understands the risks and identifies with the purposes of research, the less valid is one's consent. Jonas therefore established a "descending order of permissibility" for the recruitment ("conscription") of volunteers. Both Ramsey and Jonas restrict the use of subjects unable to consent or to understand what is involved, permitting the use of such subjects only in research directly related to their own condition (Jonas) or their own survival and well-being (Ramsey).

This interpretation reflects certain assumptions that can be challenged. First, while neither Jonas nor Ramsey focused exclusively on patients as subjects, their approach appears to be influenced largely by the medical practice model. That approach may not be adequate to deal with research not based on the medical practice model—for example, social-science research.

Second, while Ramsey argued that it is wrong to use a person in research without consent irrespective of risk (because one can be *wronged* without being *harmed*), he nonetheless appears to share with Jonas the assumption that most research is risky and involves *sacrifice* on the part of the subject. In fact, most research does not present risk of physical or psychological harm; rather, it presents inconvenience (e.g., of urine collection) and discomforts (e.g., of needle sticks) (Levine). Even Phase I drug testing, which involves the first administration of new drugs to humans and is usually assumed to be highly risky, has been estimated to present subjects with *risks* slightly greater than those involved in secretarial work and substantially less than those assumed by window washers and miners (Levine).

But the most important challenge is Freedman's (1975) alternative interpretation and use of the basic principles. Like Jonas and Ramsey, Freedman derived the consent requirement from the duty to have respect for persons. Unlike Jonas and Ramsey, however, he interpreted the requirement of respect for competent persons to allow the possibility of a "valid but ignorant" consent.

Freedman proposed that striving for *fully informed consent* is generally undesirable and that what is required is *valid consent,* not necessarily *informed consent.* To be valid, consent must be responsible and voluntary. Thus valid consent "entails only the imparting of that information which the patient/subject requires in order to make a responsible decision" (Freedman, p. 34). A choice based on less or other information than another responsible person might consider essential is not necessarily a sign of irresponsibility. Overprotection is a form of dehumanization and lack of respect; for example, to classify persons as incompetent to protect them from their own judgment is the worst form of abuse.

This approach also has several weaknesses. Much hinges on what is taken to be a responsible choice. Freedman suggested that responsibility is a dispositional characteristic and is to be judged in terms of the person, not in terms of a particular choice. There can be still, however, an element of paternalism introduced in judging another to be an irresponsible person. Moreover, this approach may not provide sufficient protection for those subjects who tend too readily to abdicate responsibility for choice, or who lack sufficient capacity or information to choose prudently.

It is clear that debates over the interpretation of informed consent depend on interpretations of the basic ethical principle of respect for persons and the extent to which that principle requires protection from harm or respect for autonomy.

Informed Consent: Conditions and Exceptions

According to the Nuremberg Code, to consent to participate in research one must:

1. be "so situated as to be able to exercise free power of choice";
2. have the "legal capacity" to give consent;
3. have "sufficient ... comprehension" to make an "enlightened" decision; and
4. have "sufficient knowledge" on which to decide (Germany [Territory under Allied Occupation], p. 181).

More recent discussion emphasizes the knowledge or information component of consent—hence the term "*informed consent*" (Katz). The Nuremberg Code's focus on freedom of choice rather than on the quantity or quality of information transmitted is represented by its use of the term *voluntary consent,* instead of *informed consent.* It is worth recalling that a demand for informed consent at the expense of other styles of self-determination such as Freedman's responsible choice is not necessarily respectful of persons. Most commentators agree that compromise on any one of the four conditions specified by the Nuremberg Code jeopardizes the ethical acceptability of the consent.

"FREE POWER OF CHOICE." The Nuremberg Code proscribes "any element of force, fraud, deceit, duress, overreaching, or other ulterior forms of constraint or coercion" (Germany [Territory under Allied Occupation], p. 181) in obtaining consent. Any flagrant coercion—for instance, when competent, comprehending persons are forced to submit to research against their expressed will—clearly renders consent invalid. There may be more subtle or indirect "constraints" or "coercions" when prospective subjects are highly dependent, impoverished, ignorant, or "junior or subordinate members of a hierarchical group" (CIOMS, p. 65). Some argue that consent obtained from such persons violates the intent of the Nuremberg Code. This argument has been posed most sharply with respect to prisoners and other institutionalized populations, because institutionalization often involves both dependency and impoverishment. (Biomedical research involving prisoners as subjects has become quite rare since 1976 when the U.S. National Commission recommended very stringent standards for its justification [Dubler and Sidel 1989].) Some argue that consent to participate in research is not valid when it is given (1) to procure financial reward in situations offering few alternatives for remuneration; (2) to seek release from an institution either by evidencing "good behavior" or by ameliorating the condition for which one was confined; or

(3) to please physicians or authorities on whom one's continued welfare depends (Branson).

But in his contribution to a 1976 U.S. National Commission report, Cornel R. West argued that such indirect forms of constraint do not constitute coercion in a strict sense and thus do not render consent involuntary. "Coercion," says West, consists in a threat to render one's circumstances worse if one does not do something. Hence, a threat to withdraw basic necessities of existence, or in some other way to render a prison inmate's situation worse if he declines to participate in research, would constitute coercion and render consent invalid. Similarly, to condition release from prison upon participation would constitute coercion, because it would make the inmate's situation worse by removing normal alternatives for seeking release. But the provision of better living conditions in exchange for participation in research does not constitute a threat to make conditions worse; rather, it is an enticement to make conditions better. While enticement and bribery can invalidate consent by undermining the rational grounds for choice, they do not undermine the voluntariness of the choice (Cohen). Similarly, a desire to *get well* or to favorably influence institutional authorities is not an *ulterior* constraint in the strict sense of the Nuremberg Code, though it may be a very real psychological constraint.

Other commentators, however, are less concerned with a sharp distinction between coercion and other forms of constraint or undue influence (Levine; CIOMS). Even outside such total institutions as prisons there are many situations in which junior or subordinate members of hierarchical groups may be exploited or manipulated. Such persons may assume that their willingness to consent to research may be rewarded by preferential treatment or that their refusals could provoke retaliation by those in positions of authority in the system. Whether or not such assumptions are justified, it is the assumptions themselves that make such persons susceptible to manipulation. Examples of such persons are medical or nursing students, subordinate hospital and laboratory personnel, employees of pharmaceutical firms, and members of the military services. Other persons whose dependency status can be exploited include residents of nursing homes, people receiving welfare benefits, patients in emergency rooms, and those with incurable diseases.

Apart from those populations identified by regulations and ethical codes as requiring *special protection*—fetuses, children, prisoners, and those who are incompetent by reason of mental incapacity—there is no clear consensus about how to respond to the problems presented by those whose capacity to consent may be limited by virtue of their dependency status. For example, whereas some medical schools have policies that forbid the involvement of medical students as research subjects, others have required investigators to invite them to participate in certain complex projects, reasoning that their highly sophisticated understanding of the risks, benefits, and purposes of such projects ensures a high quality of consent (Levine). Involvement of medical students, it is further argued, is consistent with Jonas's "descending order of permissibility" and contributes to their socialization into the medical profession.

While most regulations and ethical codes proscribe undue material inducements, there is no consensus on what this means. Some commentators argue that in most cases in which competent adults are recruited to serve as subjects in research that presents only slight increases above minimal risk, the role of the research subject is similar to that of an employee (Levine). Consequently, the amounts of cash payments or other material inducements can be determined by ordinary market factors. Others protest that because participation in research entails *selling one's body* as opposed to *selling one's labor* the role of the research subject might be considered more akin to commercial sex work than to any other type of employment (Wartofsky). According to this view, research subjects should not be paid at all; rather, they should be motivated by altruism.

Attempts to regulate the amounts of permissible material inducements are inevitably problematic (Levine). Setting the rates at a low level results in inequitable distribution of the burdens of participation among those who have no opportunities to earn more money for each unit of their time. Higher rates may overwhelm the capacity of the impoverished to decline participation.

In multinational research it is essential to evaluate the ethical acceptability of material inducements in the light of the gift-exchange traditions of the culture or community in which the research is to be carried out (CIOMS).

COMPETENCE AND COMPREHENSION. The Nuremberg Code requires both "legal capacity" to consent (often called *competence*) and "sufficient understanding" to reach an "enlightened" decision. Definitions of competence often include elements of comprehension, for example, to evaluate relevant information, to understand the consequences of action, and to reach a decision for rational reasons (Stanley and Stanley).

ASSESSMENTS OF INCOMPETENCE. The various standards employed for assessing competence are variations of four basic themes (Appelbaum, Lidz, Meisel):

1. *Reasonable outcome of choice.* This is a highly paternalistic standard in that the individual's right to self-determination is respected only if she makes the "right" choice—that is, one that accords with what the competency reviewer either considers reasonable or presumes a reasonable person might make.

2. *Factual comprehension.* The individual is required to understand, or at least be able to understand, the information divulged during the consent negotiation.

3. *Choice based on rational reasons.* Individuals must demonstrate a capacity for rational manipulation of information. They may, for example, be required to show that they not only understand the risks and benefits but also have weighed them in relation to their personal situations.

4. *Appreciation of the nature of the situation.* Individuals must demonstrate not only comprehension of the consent information but also the ability to use the information in a rational manner. Furthermore, they must appreciate that they are being invited to become research subjects and what that implies.

While there is disagreement as to the grounds for assessing incompetence, most commentators agree that such assessments are limited in several ways (Faden, Beauchamp, and King). First, a judgment of incompetence may apply to only certain areas of decision making, for example, to one's legal but not to one's personal affairs. Second, confinement to a mental institution is not in itself equivalent to a determination of incompetence. Third, some people are legally competent but functionally incompetent, whereas others are legally incompetent but functionally competent.

The Nuremberg Code does not permit the use of subjects lacking legal capacity or comprehension. Most subsequent codes and discussions allow their use with certain restrictions: for example, that mentally competent adults are not suitable subjects, that the veto of a legally incompetent but minimally comprehending subject is binding, and that consent or permission of the legal guardian must be obtained (Levine).

In its 1982 report, *Making Health Care Decisions,* the U.S. President's Commission for the Study of Ethical Problems in Medicine and Biomedical and Behavioral Research (hereafter, U.S. President's Commission) wrote that "decisionmaking capacity requires, to a greater or lesser degree: (1) possession of a set of values and goals; (2) the ability to communicate and understand information; and (3) the ability to reason and deliberate about one's choices" (p. 57). Moreover, individuals may have sufficient capacity to make some decisions but not others (Brock; Kopelman). In the words of the U.S. President's Commission:

Since the assessment [of capacity] must balance possibly competing considerations of well-being and self-determination, [one should] take into account the potential consequences of the patient's decision. When the consequences for well-being are substantial, there is a greater need to be certain that the patient possesses the necessary level of capacity.... Thus a particular patient may be capable of deciding about a relatively inconsequential medication, but not about the amputation of a gangrenous limb. (U.S. President's Commission, p. 60)

PROXY CONSENT. The debate between Paul Ramsey and Richard A. McCormick over the legitimacy of proxy consent to authorize the participation of an incompetent person in research is one of the classics in the brief history of bioethics. Adopting the battery argument, Ramsey claimed that the use of a nonconsenting subject is wrong whether or not there is risk, simply because it involves an unconsented touching. Unconsented touching is not wrongful, however, when the guardian judges it is for the good of the incompetent individual. Hence, proxy consent may be given for the use of nonconsenting subjects in research only when it includes therapeutic interventions related to the subject's own recovery (Ramsey, 1970).

Ramsey acknowledged, however, that benefit does not always justify unconsented touching; such touching of a competent adult is wrong even if it benefits that person. Why, then, can benefit be presumed to justify such touching for a child (or other subject unable to give consent)? McCormick proposed that the validity of such interventions rests on the presumption that the child, if capable, would consent to therapy. This presumption in turn derives from a child's obligation to seek therapy, an obligation that the child possesses simply as a human being (McCormick, 1974). Because children have an obligation to seek their own well-being, it is presumed that they would consent if they could, and thus presumed also that proxy consent on their behalf would not violate respect for them as persons.

By analogy, McCormick suggested that, as members of a moral community, children have other obligations to which one would presume their consent and give proxy consent on their behalf. One such obligation is to contribute to the general welfare when such contribution requires little or no sacrifice. Hence, nonconsenting subjects may be used in research not directly related to their own benefit so long as the research fulfills an important social need and involves no discernible risk. Ramsey countered this argument with respect to children, claiming that McCormick's position fails to recognize that children are not adults with a full range of duties and obligations. Instead, they have rights that must be protected by adults (Ramsey, 1976).

Adopting this premise about the nature of the child as a moral being, Freedman drew different conclusions. Because a child is not a moral being in the same sense as an adult, he argued, the concept of wrongful touching does not apply. The child has no right to be left alone but only a right to be protected. Hence, Freedman concluded that the only relevant moral issue is the risk involved in the research, and, like McCormick, that children could be used in research unrelated to their therapy, provided it presents them no discernible risk. Thus, the debate centers on the status of the child (a paradigmatic incompetent) as a moral being and on interpretations of the requirements of respect for persons.

Although disagreements persist over both standards of competence and the use of incompetent subjects, one issue seems to have been settled by the U.S. National Commission in several of its reports (Levine). Parents, guardians, and, in some cases, other *responsible relatives* may give *permission* (a term that often replaces "proxy consent") to involve an incompetent in research if there is no more than minimal risk, if incompetents who are capable of giving their *assents* (knowledgeable agreements that do not meet the legal standards for informed consent) do so, and if certain other criteria are satisfied. If there is more than minimal risk, the standards for ethical justification of the involvement of incompetents are more stringent.

DISCLOSURE OF INFORMATION. The Nuremberg Code requires that the subject be told "the nature, duration, and purpose of the experiment; the method and means by which it is to be conducted; all inconveniences and hazards reasonably to be expected; and the effects upon his health or person which may possibly come (Germany, [Territory under Allied Occupation], p. 182)." These requirements have been modified by subsequent codes and regulations. U.S. federal regulations require:

1. a statement of the purpose of the research and a description of its procedures;
2. a description of foreseeable risks and discomforts;
3. a description of benefits;
4. disclosure of appropriate alternatives, if any;
5. a statement of the extent of confidentiality;
6. an explanation of the availability of medical treatment for injury and compensation for disability;
7. an explanation of whom to contact for answers to questions; and
8. a statement that participation is voluntary and that neither refusal to participate nor withdrawal at any time will result in a loss of benefits to which the subject is otherwise entitled ("General Requirements" 1993).

The regulations further specify six additional elements of information to be provided when appropriate:

1. additional risks to the subject or to the fetus if the subject becomes pregnant;
2. circumstances in which a subject's participation may be terminated without his consent;
3. additional costs to the subject that may result from participation;
4. the consequences of a subject's decision to withdraw and procedures for orderly termination of participation;
5. a commitment to divulge significant new findings developed during the research that may relate to the subject's continued willingness to participate; and
6. the approximate number of subjects in the study.

Finally, the regulations forbid use of any exculpatory language through which the subject or her representative is made to waive any of their legal rights or that releases of the investigator, sponsor, or institution from liability for negligence.

While these requirements have the force of law, they are by no means exhaustive of possible standards for disclosure. To them one might add the following: a clear invitation to participate in research, distinguishing maneuvers required for research purposes from those necessary for therapy; an explanation of why the particular person is invited (selected); a suggestion that the prospective subject might wish to discuss the research with another person; and an identification of the source of funding for the research. Robert M. Veatch (1978) would add the names of members of any review boards that had approved the research and an explanation of the right, if any, to continue receiving treatments found useful. In short, there is no universal agreement on standards for disclosure of information or on what it takes for a person to have *sufficient knowledge* to give *informed* consent.

Those who agree on the need for disclosure of information in a particular category—the risks, for example—often disagree on the nature of the information that must be made known. The Nuremberg Code requires explication of hazards "reasonably" to be expected. Does this include a very slight chance of a substantial harm, or a substantial chance of a very slight harm? Neither the quality nor the probability of the risks to be divulged has been clearly determined legally.

Disagreements over particulars arise in part from disagreements about underlying standards: Is disclosure to be determined by (1) general medical practice or opinion, (2) the requirements of a *reasonable person,* or (3) the idiosyncratic judgment of the individual? While the legal trend may be shifting from the first to the second, it may be argued that only the third, the *subjective standard,* is truly compatible with the requirement of respect for the autonomy of the individual person (Faden, Beauchamp, and King; Veatch, 1978).

Yet even those who adopt the subjective standard disagree as to its implications. As noted earlier, Freedman (1975) held that the idiosyncratic judgment of the individual is overriding, to the point that the prospective subject can choose to have less information than a "reasonable" person might require. Veatch (1978), however, argued that anyone refusing to accept as much information as would be expected of a "reasonable person" should not be accepted as a subject.

In the context of medical practice, two exceptions to the requirement for informed consent are recognized—*emergency exception* and *therapeutic privilege.* The former, which permits the doctor to proceed without delay to administer urgently required therapy in emergencies, is reflected in a limited form in two provisions of the regulations of the U.S. Food and Drug Administration: (1) In some "life-threatening" emergencies in which informed consent is "infeasible," physician-investigators are authorized to employ investigational drugs and devices for therapeutic purposes (Levine). (2) In carefully defined circumstances, research designed to evaluate the safety and efficacy of investigational drugs or devices in emergency conditions may be carried out without the consent of the patient-subjects or the permission of their representatives. In such protocols either consent or permission must be obtained within a reasonable period of time after the initiation of the research; this entails authorization of the research participation already completed as well as the continuing participation of the subject in the research (Biros et al.).

The therapeutic-privilege exception to the informed-consent rule permits the doctor to withhold information when, in her judgment, disclosure would be detrimental to the patient's interests or well-being (Levine). Most commentators agree that invoking the doctrine of therapeutic privilege to assure a subject's cooperation in a research project is almost never appropriate; it gives the investigator entirely too much license to serve vested interests by withholding information that might be material to a prospective subject's decision. U.S. federal regulations do not explicitly endorse the use of the therapeutic-privilege exception in research, although some authors have suggested that they could be interpreted as an implicit endorsement (Levine).

The success of some research activities is contingent upon withholding from the subjects information about the purposes or procedures of the activities or, in some cases, upon deliberate deception (providing false information).

U.S. federal regulations permit *waivers and alterations* of consent requirements if there is no more than minimal risk; if the waiver or alteration will not adversely affect subjects' rights or welfare; if without the waiver or alteration the research "could not practicably be carried out"; and if the subjects will be debriefed (given a full and accurate explanation afterward) when appropriate ("General Requirements," pt. 46.116d).

There are some categories of research which, until recently, have been customarily carried out without individual informed consent; waiver of the requirement for informed consent in these categories was generally considered justified according to the *waivers and alterations* provisions of the regulations. Such activities included most research involving medical records and "leftover" specimens of tissues and body fluids obtained for either clinical or research purposes. Institutional patient information brochures generally contained notices of such routine research activities (Levine). Such routine uses of medical records without consent have had to be reconsidered in the light of the requirements of the Health Insurance Portability and Accountability Act of 1996 (DHHS). Similarly, routine use by researchers of specimens of tissue, without informed consent, have had to be reevaluated in the light of rapidly evolving standards (Clayton et al.); there is general agreement that such research is permissible without informed consent if the specimens are anonymous.

In a 1979 article, Diana Baumrind expressed her opposition to deceptive practices, arguing not only that they violate the principle of respect for persons but also that in the long run they will invalidate research on scientific grounds. Various proposals have been made to minimize the need for and harmful effects of deceptive practices: Subjects might be invited to consent to incomplete disclosure with a promise of full disclosure at the termination of the research; subjects might be told as much as possible and asked to consent for specified limits of time and risk; or approval of the plans to withhold information from or to deceive subjects might be sought from *surrogate* populations that resemble the actual intended subject populations in relevant respects (Levine).

"Secondary" Research Subjects

U.S. federal regulations define a human subject as "a living individual about whom an investigator … conducting research obtains (1) data through intervention or interaction with the individual, or (2) identifiable private information." (45 CFR 46.102f). Until 1999 it was generally assumed that this definition applied only to those individuals who were the targets of the researcher's interest and that part (2) of the definition was intended to cover the use of records and

specimens of tissue and body fluids. In 2000, however, the federal Office for Protection from Research Risks (now the Office for Human Research Protections, part of the Department of Health and Human Services) issued a novel interpretation: Questions asked of research subjects calling upon them to report on private information of their relatives, friends, or associates had the effect of turning these friends, relatives, and associates into *secondary* research subjects. If the private information solicited could be considered *sensitive,* then it would be required that the informed consent of the *secondary* subjects be obtained. This is a highly controversial matter, a full discussion of which is beyond the scope of this entry (Botkin).

Conclusions

The use of a person as a research subject can be justified only if that person, or one authorized to speak on the person's behalf, consents to such use. The legal and ethical requirement for consent is grounded in fundamental tenets of the Judeo-Christian religious tradition as well as in basic ethical principles that create the universal obligation to treat persons as ends and not merely as means to another's end. The consent requirement also reflects the perspective that competent persons are generally the best protectors of their own well-being. Most major disagreements over the form and substance of the consent requirement derive from conflicting interpretations of one or more of the basic principles.

A widespread tendency among researchers to focus on consent forms seems to reflect an assumption that the consent form is an appropriate instrumentality through which they might fulfill their obligation not to treat persons merely as means. Most commentators on informed consent disagree, however, seeing consent as a continuing process rather than a single event consummated by the signing of a form. Moreover, whereas the primary purposes of informed consent are to foster self-determination and to empower prospective subjects to protect their own well-being and other interests, the primary purpose of its written documentation is to protect the investigator, the institution, and the research sponsor from legal liability.

ROBERT J. LEVINE (1995)
REVISED BY AUTHOR

SEE ALSO: *Children: Healthcare and Research Issues; Competence; Coercion; Holocaust; Human Rights; Information Disclosure, Ethical Issues of; Minorities as Research Subjects; Placebo; Race and Racism; Research Policy: Risk and Vulnerable Groups; Students and Research Subjects;* and other *Informed Consent* subentries

BIBLIOGRAPHY

Annas, George J.; Glantz, Leonard H.; and Katz, Barbara F. 1977. *Informed Consent to Human Experimentation: The Subject's Dilemma.* Cambridge, MA: Ballinger.

Appelbaum, Paul S.; Lidz, Charles W.; and Meisel, Alan. 1987. *Informed Consent: Legal Theory and Clinical Practice,* pp. 83–89. New York: Oxford University Press.

Baumrind, Diana. 1979. "IRBs and Social Science Research: The Costs of Deception." *IRB: A Review of Human Subjects Research* 1(6): 1–4.

Beauchamp, Tom L., and Childress, James F. 2001. *Principles of Biomedical Ethics,* 5th edition. New York: Oxford University Press.

Biros, Michelle H.; Runge, Jeffrey W.; Lewis, Roger J.; and Doherty, Christopher. 1998. "Emergency Medicine and the Development of the Food and Drug Administration's Final Rule on Informed Consent and Waiver of Informed Consent in Emergency Research Circumstances." *Academic Emergency Medicine* 5(4): 359–368.

Botkin, Jeffrey. 2001. "Protecting the Privacy of Family Members in Survey and Pedigree Research." *Journal of the American Medical Association* 285(2): 207–211.

Branson, Roy. 1977. "Prison Research: National Commission Says 'No, Unless ... '" *Hastings Center Report* 7(1): 15–21.

Brock, Dan W. 1987. "Informed Consent." In *Health Care Ethics: An Introduction,* ed. Donald VanDeVeer and Tom Regan. Philadelphia: Temple University Press.

Capron, Alexander Morgan. 1972. "The Law of Genetic Therapy." In *Experimentation with Human Beings: The Authority of the Investigator, Subject, Professions, and State in the Human Experimentation Process,* ed. Jay Katz, Alexander Morgan Capron, and Eleanor Glass Swift. New York: Russell Sage Foundation.

Clayton, Ellen Wright; Steinberg, Karen K.; Khoury, Muin J.; et al. 1995. "Informed Consent for Genetic Research on Stored Tissue Samples." *Journal of the American Medical Association* 274(22): 1786–1796.

Cohen, Carl. 1978. "Medical Experimentation on Prisoners." *Perspectives in Biology and Medicine* 21(3): 357–372.

Council for International Organizations of Medical Sciences (CIOMS), in collaboration with the World Health Organization. 2002. *International Ethical Guidelines for Biomedical Research Involving Human Subjects.* Geneva, Switzerland: Author.

"Documentation of Informed Consent." 1993. *Code of Federal Regulations* Title 45, Pt. 46.117.

Dubler, Nancy N., and Sidel, Victor W. 1989. "On Research on HIV Infection and AIDS in Correctional Institutions." *Milbank Memorial Quarterly* 67(2): 171–207.

Faden, Ruth R.; Beauchamp, Tom L.; and King, Nancy M. P. 1986. *A History and Theory of Informed Consent.* New York: Oxford University Press.

Feinstein, Alvan R. 1974. "Clinical Biostatistics. XXVI: Medical Ethics and the Architecture of Clinical Research." *Clinical Pharmacology and Therapeutics* 15(3): 316–334.

Freedman, Benjamin. 1975. "A Moral Theory of Informed Consent." *Hastings Center Report* 5(4): 32–39.

"General Requirements for Informed Consent." 1993. *Code of Federal Regulations* Title 45, Pt. 46.116.

Germany (Territory under Allied Occupation, 1945–1955: U.S. Zone) Military Tribunals. 1947. "Permissible Medical Experiments." In *Trials of War Criminals before the Nuremberg Tribunals under Control Council Law No. 10.* Washington, D.C.: U.S. Government Printing Office.

Halushka v. University of Saskatchewan. 52 W.W.R. 608 (Sask. Ct. App. 1965).

Ingelfinger, Franz J. 1972. "Informed (but Uneducated) Consent." *New England Journal of Medicine* 287(9): 465–466.

Jonas, Hans. 1970. "Philosophical Reflections on Experimenting with Human Subjects." In *Experimentation with Human Subjects,* ed. Paul A. Freund. New York: George Braziller.

Katz, Jay. 1984. *The Silent World of Doctor and Patient.* New York: Free Press.

Katz, Jay, and Capron, Alexander Morgan. 1975. *Catastrophic Diseases: Who Decides What? A Psychosocial and Legal Analysis of the Problems Posed by Hemodialysis and Organ Transplantation.* New York: Russell Sage Foundation.

Katz, Jay; Capron, Alexander Morgan; and Swift, Eleanor Glass, eds. 1972. *Experimentation with Human Beings: The Authority of the Investigator, Subject, Professions, and State in the Human Experimentation Process.* New York: Russell Sage Foundation.

Kopelman, Loretta M. 1990. "On the Evaluative Nature of Competency and Capacity Judgments." *International Journal of Law and Psychiatry* 13(4): 309–329.

Levine, Robert J. 1986. *Ethics and Regulation of Clinical Research,* 2nd edition. Baltimore: Urban and Schwarzenberg.

McCormick, Richard A. 1974. "Proxy Consent in the Experimentation Situation." *Perspectives in Biology and Medicine* 18(1): 2–20.

McCormick, Richard A. 1976. "A Reply to Paul Ramsey: Experimentation in Children: Sharing in Sociality." *Hastings Center Report* 6(6): 41–46.

Perley, Sharon; Fluss, Sev S.; Bankowski, Zbigniew; and Simon, Françoise. 1992. "The Nuremberg Code: An International Overview." In *The Nazi Doctors and the Nuremberg Code: Human Rights in Human Experimentation,* ed. George J. Annas and Michael A. Grodin. New York: Oxford University Press.

Ramsey, Paul. 1970. *The Patient as Person: Explorations in Medical Ethics.* New Haven, CT: Yale University Press.

Ramsey, Paul. 1976. "A Reply to Richard McCormick: The Enforcement of Morals: Nontherapeutic Research on Children." *Hastings Center Report* 6(4): 21–30.

Stanley, Barbara H., and Stanley, Michael. 1982. "Testing Competency in Psychiatric Patients." *IRB: A Review of Human Subjects Research* 4(8): 1–6.

Sugarman, Jeremy, and McCrory, Douglas C. 1999. "Empirical Research on Informed Consent: An Annotated Bibliography." *Hastings Center Report* 29(1): S1–S42.

U.S. Department of Health and Human Services (DHHS). 2002. "Standards for Privacy of Individually Identifiable Health Information." *Federal Register* 67(157): 53182–53273.

U.S. National Commission for the Protection of Human Subjects of Biomedical and Behavioral Research. 1978. *The Belmont Report: Ethical Principles and Guidelines for the Protection of Human Subjects of Research.* Bethesda, MD: Author.

U.S. President's Commission for the Study of Ethical Problems in Medicine and Biomedical and Behavioral Research. 1982. *Making Health Care Decisions: A Report on the Ethical and Legal Implications of Informed Consent in the Patient–Practitioner Relationship.* Washington, D.C.: U.S. Government Printing Office.

Veatch, Robert M. 1978. "Three Theories of Informed Consent: Philosophical Foundations and Policy Implications." In *The Belmont Report: Ethical Principles and Guidelines for the Protection of Human Subjects of Research,* Appendix, vol. 2. Bethesda, MD: U.S. National Commission for the Protection of Human Subjects of Biomedical and Behavioral Research.

Veatch, Robert M. 1981. *A Theory of Medical Ethics.* New York: Basic.

Wartofsky, Marx W. 1976. "On Doing It for Money." In *Report and Recommendations: Research Involving Prisoners,* Appendix. Bethesda, MD: U.S. National Commission for the Protection of Human Subjects of Biomedical and Behavioral Research.

West, Cornel R. 1976. "Philosophical Perspective on the Participation of Prisoners in Experimental Research." In *Report and Recommendations: Research Involving Prisoners,* Appendix. Bethesda, MD: U.S. National Commission for the Protection of Human Subjects of Biomedical and Behavioral Research.

INTERNET RESOURCE

U. S. Code of Federal Regulations, Protection of Human Subjects. 45 CFR 46. 2003. Available from <http://ohrp.osophs.dhhs.gov/humansubjects/guidance/45cfr46.htm/>

IV. CLINICAL ASPECTS OF CONSENT IN HEALTHCARE

Decision making is an everyday event in healthcare, not only for doctors and patients, but also for nurses, psychologists, social workers, emergency medical technicians, dentists, and other health professionals. Since the 1960s, however, the cultural ideal of how these decisions should be made has changed considerably. The concept that medical decision making should rely exclusively on the physician's expertise has been replaced by a model in which healthcare professionals share information and discuss alternatives with patients who then make the ultimate decisions about treatment.

The concept of informed consent gained its initial support as part of the general societal trend toward broadening access to decision making during the 1960s. Thus, the initial support for informed consent came from legal and philosophic circles rather than healthcare professionals. In the legal arena, informed consent has been used to develop minimal standards for doctor–patient interactions and clinical decision making (Berg et al.). Although there are some

differences by jurisdiction, widely accepted legal standards require that healthcare professionals inform patients of the risks, benefits, and alternatives of all proposed treatments, and then allow the patient to choose among acceptable therapeutic alternatives.

In academia, informed consent has served as a cornerstone for the development of the discipline of bioethics. Based on the importance of autonomy in moral discourse, philosophers have argued that healthcare professionals are obligated to engage patients in discussions regarding the goals of therapy and the alternatives for reaching those goals, and that patients are the final decision makers regarding all therapeutic decisions.

While many physicians would express some support to the concept of shared decision making, this support is largely theoretical and does not seem to have made its way into routine medical practice. Physicians typically think of informed consent as a legal requirement for a signed piece of paper that is at best a waste of time, and at worst a bureaucratic, legalistic interference with their care for patients. Rather than seeing informed consent as a process that promotes good communication and patient autonomy, many healthcare professionals view it as a complex, legally prescribed recitation of risks and benefits that only frightens or confuses patients.

Objections to Informed Consent

There are various objections to informed consent that clinicians often make, and it will be useful to review those objections here.

CONSENT CANNOT BE TRULY "INFORMED." Many practicing clinicians report that their patients are unable to understand the complex medical information necessary for a fully rational weighing of alternative treatments. There is considerable research support for this view. A variety of studies document that patients recall only a small percentage of the information that professionals present to them (Meisel and Roth); that they are not as good decision makers when they are sick as at other times (Sherlock; Cassell, 2001); and that they often make decisions based on medically trivial factors. Informed consent thus appears either to promote uninformed—and thus suboptimal—decisions, or to encourage patients to blindly accept healthcare professionals' recommendations. In either case informed consent appears to be a charade, and a dangerous one at that.

However, the fact that patients often do have difficulty understanding important aspects of medical decisions does not mean that healthcare professionals are the best decision makers about the patient's treatment. Knowledge about medical facts is not enough. Wise house buyers will have a structural engineer check over an old house, but few would be willing to allow the engineer to choose their house for them. Just as structural engineers cannot decide which house a family should buy—because they lack knowledge about the family's pattern of living, personal tastes, and potential family growth—healthcare professionals cannot scientifically deduce the best treatment for a specific patient simply from the medical facts. What matters to individuals about their health depends on their lifestyles, past experiences, and values, so choosing the *optimal therapy* is not a purely objective matter (U.S. President's Commission). Thus, patients and healthcare professionals both contribute essential knowledge to the decision-making process: patients bring their knowledge of their personal situation, goals, and values; and healthcare professionals bring their expertise on the nature of the problem and the technology that may be used to meet the patient's goals (see Brock).

Informed-consent disclosures, even if they are well done, may not lead to what clinicians might consider optimal decisions. Most people make major life decisions, such as whom to marry and which occupation to take up, based on faulty or incomplete information. Patients' lack of understanding of medical information in choosing treatment is probably no worse than their lack of information in choosing a spouse, nor are medical decisions more important than spousal choice. Respecting patient autonomy means allowing individuals to make their own decisions, even if the healthcare professional disagrees with them. The informed-consent process can improve patient decisions, but it cannot be expected to lead to perfect decisions.

Moreover, although sick persons have defects in their rational abilities, so do healthcare professionals. In fact, some of the most famous research on the difficulties individuals have with the rational use of probabilistic data involves physicians (Dawson and Ackes). Health professionals must be careful not to be too pessimistic about patients' ability to become informed decision makers. Patients may not be able to become as technically well-informed as professionals, but they clearly can understand and make decisions based on relevant information. One study, for example, showed that patients' decisions regarding life-sustaining treatment changed when they were given accurate information about the therapy's chance of success and that patients, when given increased information about screening tests for prostate cancer, were less likely to have the test change their decision on having the test (Murphy et al.). Moreover, what seems to be an irrational decision may turn out to be, from the patient's point of view, rational. Thus, a patient may turn down a recommended treatment because

of personal experience with surgery or because the long-term benefit is not seen as being worth the short-term risk.

Most important, the difficulty of educating sick persons does not justify unilateral decision making. Rather, it places a special obligation on healthcare professionals to communicate clearly with patients. Using technical jargon, trying to give all of the available information in one visit, and not asking what the patient wants to know is a recipe for confusing even the most intelligent patient. A growing literature deals with informational aides—ranging from question prompt-sheets to giving patients audiotapes of the interaction and formal decision aides—that can be used to promote patient understanding and shared decision-making. New technologies like interactive DVD offer patients the opportunity to participate more fully in shared decision making at their own rate. A limitation of many of these aides is that they are limited helping with specific decisions and need to be updated frequently (Barry). Healthcare professionals also need to become more familiar with different cultural patterns of communication in order to talk with patients from different cultural backgrounds. For example, although a simple, factual discussion of depression and its treatment may be acceptable to most middle-class Americans, it would be seen as inappropriate by a first-generation Vietnamese male, whose culture discourages viewing depression as a disease (Hahn). There is no reason, in principle, why a person who makes decisions at home and work cannot, with help, understand the medical data sufficiently to become involved in medical decisions. Healthcare professionals must learn how best to present that help and involve patients in the decision-making process.

PATIENTS DO NOT WISH TO BE INVOLVED IN DECISION MAKING. Many healthcare professionals believe that it is unfair to force patients to make decisions regarding their medical care. After all, they argue, patients pay their healthcare professionals to make medical decisions. The empirical literature partially supports the view that patients want professionals to make treatment decisions for them (Steel et al.). For example, in a study of male patients' preferences about medical decision making regarding hypertension, only 53 percent wanted to participate at all in the decision-making process (Strull et al.). More recent data suggest that sicker patients are less interested in information about their disease and more willing to have doctors make decisions (Butow 1997; 2002).

There is no reason to force patients to be involved in decisions if they do not want to be. However, unless the health professional asks, he or she cannot know how involved a patient wants to be. Studies suggest that doctors' ability to predict their patients' interest in information, or their desire to be involved in decision making, is no better than flipping a coin (Butow 1997, 2002). In addition, roughly two-thirds of patients want to be involved in decision making, either by being the primary decision maker (the minority) or in shared decision making with the physician.

Patients may not always want to be involved in decision making, since many have been socialized into believing that "the doctor knows best." This is particularly true for poorer patients. Studies have shown that physicians wrongly assume that because patients with fewer socioeconomic resources ask fewer questions, they do not want as much information. These patients may in fact want just as much information, but they have been socialized into a different way of interacting with healthcare professionals (Waitzkin, 1984).

Patients may choose to allow someone else to make the decision for them. However, when a patient asks, "What would you do if you were me?" the underlying question may be, "As an expert in biomedicine, what alternative do you think will best maximize my values or interest?" If this is the case, the healthcare professional should respond by making a recommendation and justifying it in terms of the patient's values or interests. More frequently, the patient is asking, "If you had this disease, what therapy would you choose?" This question presumes that the professional and patient have the same values, needs, and problems, which is often not the case. Healthcare professionals should respond by pointing this out and emphasizing the importance of the patients' values in the decision-making process.

Although many patients do not want to be actively involved in decision making, they almost always want more information concerning their illness than the healthcare professional gives them. Healthcare professionals should not assume that just because patients do not wish to choose their therapy, they do not want information. Patients may desire information so as to increase compliance or make modifications in other areas of their lives, as well as to make medical decisions.

THERE ARE HARMFUL EFFECTS OF INFORMING PATIENTS. Healthcare professionals often justify withholding information from patients because of their belief that informing patients would be psychologically damaging and therefore contrary to the principle of nonmaleficence. Many healthcare professionals, however, overestimate potential psychological harm and neglect the positive effects of full disclosure (Faden et al.). Some discussions that physicians assume are stressful, such as advance care-planning, have been shown to decrease patient anxiety and increase the patient's sense of control. Moreover, bad news can often be communicated in a way that ameliorates the psychological effects of the

disclosure (Quill and Townsend). Truth-telling must be distinguished from "truth dumping." Explanation of the care that can be provided, and empathic attention to the patient's fears and uncertainties can often prevent or mitigate otherwise more painful news. Finally, sometimes the harm associated with bad news is unavoidable. It is normal to be sad after finding out that one has an incurable cancer, for example. That does not mean that one should not convey the information, only that it should be done in as sensitively and supportively as possible.

INFORMED CONSENT TAKES TOO MUCH TIME. Respecting autonomy and promoting patient well-being—the values served through informed consent—are fundamental to good medicine. However, adhering to the ideals of medical practice takes time—time to help patients understand their illness and work through their emotional reactions to stressful information, to discuss each party's preconceptions and to clarify the therapeutic goals, to decide on a treatment plan, and to elicit questions about diagnosis and treatment.

In U.S. healthcare, time is money. As many commentators have noted, physicians are less well reimbursed for talking to patients than for performing invasive tests. This may discourage doctors from spending enough time discussing treatment options with patients. This, along with the pressures of managed care has decreased the average outpatient encounter, allowing even less time for doctor–patient communication. The ultimate justification for spending time to facilitate patient decisions is the same as that for spending any time in medical care: that patients will be better cared for. Moreover, some of the new decision aides, such as question prompts, may in fact decrease the time spent in the patient visit, while simultaneously increasing patient understanding.

Clinical Approaches to Informed Consent

Many of the problems in implementing informed consent result, at least in part, from the way informed consent has been implemented in clinical practice. Informed consent has become synonymous with the *consent form,* a legal invention with a legitimate role in documenting that informed consent has taken place, but hardly a substitute for the discussion process leading to informed consent (Andrews).

A PRO FORMA APPROACH: AN EVENT MODEL OF IN-FORMED CONSENT. In many clinical settings, consent begins when *it is time to get consent,* typically just prior to the administration of treatment. The process of getting the patients' consent consists of the recitation by a physician or nurse of the list of material risks and benefits and a request that the patient sign for the proposed treatment. This "conversation" is a very limited one that emphasizes the transfer of information from the physician or nurse to the patient. While it does meet the minimal legal requirements for informed consent efficiently, it does not meet the higher ethical goal of informed consent, which is to empower patients by educating and involving them in their treatment plans. Instead, it imposes an almost empty ritual on an unchanged relationship between provider and patient (Katz).

The procedure just described assumes that care involves a series of discrete, circumscribed decisions. In fact, much of clinical medicine consists of a series of frequent, interwoven decisions that must be repeatedly reconsidered as more information becomes available. When "it is time to get consent," there may be nothing left to decide. Consider the operative consent form obtained the evening prior to an operation. After patients have discussed with their families whether to be admitted to the hospital, rearranged their work and child-care schedules, and undergone a long and painful diagnostic workup, the decision to have surgery seems preordained. The evening before the operation, patients do not seriously evaluate the operation's risks and benefits, so consent is pro forma. No wonder some healthcare professionals feel that *consent* is a waste of time and energy.

The event model for gathering informed consent falls far short of meeting the ethical goal of ensuring patient participation in the decision-making process. Rather than engaging the patient as an active participant in the decision-making process, the patient's role is to agree to or veto the healthcare professionals' recommendations. Little attempt is made to elicit patient preferences and consider how treatment might address them.

A DIALOGICAL APPROACH: THE PROCESS MODEL OF INFORMED CONSENT. Fortunately, it is possible to fulfill legal requirements for informed consent while maximizing active patient participation in the clinical setting. An alternative to the event model described above, which sees informed consent as an aberration from clinical practice, the process model attempts to integrate informed consent into all aspects of clinical care (Berg et al). The process model of informed consent assumes that each party has something to contribute to the decision-making process. The physician brings technical knowledge and experience in treating patients with similar problems, while patients bring knowledge about their life circumstances and the ability to assess the effect that treatment may have on them. Open discussion makes it possible for the patient and the physician to examine critically their views and to determine what might be optimal treatment.

The process model also recognizes that medical care rarely involves only one decision made at a single point in time. Decisions about care frequently begin with the suspicion that something is wrong and that treatment may be necessary, and they end only when the patient leaves follow-up care. Decisions involve diagnostic as well as therapeutic interventions. Some decisions are made in one visit, while others occur over a prolonged period of time. Although some interactions between provider and patient involve explicit decisions, decisions are made at each interaction, even if the decision is only to continue treatment. The process model also recognizes that various healthcare professionals may play a role in making sure that the patients' consent is informed. For example, a woman deciding on various breast cancer treatments may talk with an oncologist and a surgeon about the risks of various treatments, with a nurse about the side effects of medication, with a social worker about financial issues in treatment, and with a patient-support group about her husband's reaction to a possible mastectomy.

Ideally, then, informed consent involves shared decision making over a period of time; it a dialogue throughout the course of the patient's relationship with various healthcare professionals. Such a dialogue aims to facilitate patient participation and to strengthen the therapeutic alliance.

Tasks Involved in Informed Consent

Consent is a series of interrelated tasks. First, the patient and professional must agree on the problem that will be the focus of their work together (Eisenthal and Lazare). Most nonemergency consultations involve complex negotiations between healthcare professional and patient regarding the definition of the patient's problem. The patient may see the problem as a routine physical examination for a work release, the need for advice, or the investigation of a physical symptom. If professionals are to respond effectively to the patients' goals, they must find out the reason for the visit. Whereas physicians typically focus on biomedical information and its implications, patients typically view the problem in the context of their social situation (Fisher and Todd). The differences between the patient's perceptions of the problem and the professional's perceptions must be explicitly worked through, since agreement regarding the focus of the interactions will lead to increased patient satisfaction and compliance with further treatment plans (Meichenbaum and Turk).

Even when the professional and patient have agreed on what the problem is, substantial misunderstandings may arise regarding the treatment goals. Patients may expect the medically impossible, or they may expect outcomes based on knowledge of life circumstances about which the physician is unaware. Since assessing the risks and benefits of any treatment option depends on therapeutic goals, the professional and patient must agree on the goals the therapy aims to accomplish.

Finding out what the patient wants is more complicated than merely inquiring, "What do you want?" A patient typically does not come to the professional with well-developed preferences regarding medical therapy except "to get better," with little understanding of what this may involve (Cassell, 1985). As a patient's knowledge and perspective change over the course of an illness, so too may the patient's views regarding the therapeutic goals.

Because clinicians provide much of the medical information needed to ensure that the patient's preferences are grounded in medical possibility, healthcare professionals play a significant role in how a patient's preferences evolve. It is important that they understand that patients may reasonably hold different goals from those their practitioners hold. This is particularly true when they come from different economic strata. For example, a physician's emphasis on the most medically sophisticated care may pale in the light of the patient's financial problems. Therapeutic goals, like the definition of the problem, require ongoing clarification and negotiation.

After agreeing upon the problem and the therapeutic goals, the healthcare professional and the patient must choose the best way to achieve them. If patients have been involved in the prior two steps, the decision about a treatment plan will more likely reflect their values than if they are merely asked to assent to the clinician's strategy.

Healthcare professionals often ask how much information they must supply to ensure that the patient is an informed participant in the decision-making process (Mazur). There is, however, a more important question: Has the information been provided in a manner that the patient can understand? While the law only requires that healthcare professionals inform patients, morally valid consent requires that patients understand the information conveyed. Ensuring patient understanding requires attention to the quality as well as the quantity of information presented (Faden).

A great deal of empirical data has been collected concerning problems with consent forms. These forms have been criticized, for example, as being unintelligible because of their length and use of technical language (Berg et al.) Healthcare professionals thus need to be aware of, and facile in using, a variety of methods to increase patients' comprehension of information, including verbal techniques, written information, and interactive videodiscs (Stanley et al.).

Still, the question of how much information to present remains. The legal standards regarding information disclosure—what a reasonable patient would find essential to making a decision or what a reasonably prudent physician would disclose—are not particularly helpful. Howard Brody has suggested two important features: (1) the physician must disclose the basis on which the proposed treatment or the alternative possible treatments have been chosen; and (2) the patient must be encouraged to ask questions suggested by the the physician's reasoning—and the questions need to be answered to the patient's satisfaction (Brody). Healthcare professionals must also inform patients when controversy exists about the various therapeutic options. Similarly, patients should also be told the degree to which the recommendation is based on established scientific evidence rather than personal experience or educated guesses.

Two other factors will influence the amount of information that should be given: the importance of the decision (given the patient's situation and goals) and the amount of consensus within the healthcare professions regarding the agreed-upon therapy. For example, a low-risk intervention, such as giving influenza vaccines to elderly patients, offers a clear-cut benefit with minimal risk. In this case, the professional should describe the intervention and recommend it because of its benefits. A detailed description of the infrequent risks is not needed unless the patient asks or is known to be skeptical of medical interventions. Interventions that present greater risks or a less clear-cut risk-benefit ratio require a longer description—for example, the decision to administer AZT to an HIV (human immunodeficiency virus)-positive, asymptomatic woman with a CD4 cell count of 350. In this situation, the data regarding starting medications are unclear and a patient's preference is critical. In this situation, one would need to talk about the major side effects of the medicines, the burden of taking medicines daily, the immunological benefit of anti-virals, etc. In neither case is a discussion of pathophysiology or biochemistry necessary. It must be emphasized that there is no formula for deciding how much a patient needs to be told or the length of time this will take. The amount of information necessary will depend on the patient's individual situation, values, and goals.

Finally, an adequate decision-making process requires continual updating of information, monitoring of expectations, and evaluation of the patient's progress in reaching the chosen or revised goals. Thus, the final step in informed consent is follow-up. This step is particularly important for patients with chronic diseases for which modifications of the treatment plan are often necessary.

The process model of informed consent has many advantages. Because it assumes many short conversations over time rather than one long interaction, it can be more easily integrated into the professional's ambulatory practice than the event model. It also allows patients to be much more involved in decision making and ensures that treatment is more consistent with their values. Furthermore, the continual monitoring of patients' understanding of their disease, the treatment, and its progress is likely to reduce misunderstandings and increase their investment in, and adherence to, the treatment plan. Thus, the process model of informed consent is likely to promote both patient autonomy and well-being.

Unfortunately, there are situations in which this approach is not very helpful. Some healthcare professionals, anesthesiologists, or emergency medical technicians, for example, are not likely to have ongoing relationships with patients. In emergencies, there is not time for a decision to develop through a series of short conversations. In these cases, informed consent may more closely approximate the event model. However, since most medical care is delivered by primary-care practitioners in an ambulatory setting, the process model of informed consent is more helpful.

ROBERT M. ARNOLD
CHARLES W. LIDZ (1995)
REVISED BY AUTHORS

SEE ALSO: *Autonomy; Clinical Ethics: Elements and Methodologies; Competency; Information Disclosure, Ethical Issues of; Hospital, Contemporary Ethical Problems; Law and Bioethics; Life, Quality of: Quality of Life in Clinical Decisions; Paternalism; Patients' Rights: Origin and Nature of Patients' Rights;* and other *Informed Consent* subentries

BIBLIOGRAPHY

Andrews, Lori B. 1984. "Informed Consent Status and the Decision-making Process." *Journal of Legal Medicine* 5(2): 163–217.

Barry, M. 2000. "Involving Patients in Medical Decisions: How Can Physicians Do Better?" *Journal of the American Medical Association* 282(24): 2356–2357.

Berg, Jessica; Appelbaum, Paul S.; Lidz, Charles W.; et al. 2001. *Informed Consent: Legal Theory and Clinical Practice,* 2nd edition. New York: Oxford University Press.

Brock, Dan W. 1991. "The Ideal of Shared Decision Making Between Physicians and Patients." *Kennedy Institute of Ethics Journal* 1(1): 28–47.

Braddock, C. H.; Fihn, S. D.; Levinson, W., et al. 1997. "How Doctors and Patients Discuss Routine Clinical Decisions: Informed Decision Making in the Outpatient Setting." *Journal of General Internal Medicine* 12(6): 339–345.

Brody, Howard. 1989. "Transparency: Informed Consent in Primary Care." *Hastings Center Report* 19(5): 5–9.

Butow, P. N.; Dowsett, S.; Hagerty, R.; et al. 2002. "Communicating Prognosis to Patients with Metastatic Disease: What Do They Really Want to Know?" *Supportive Care in Cancer* 10(2): 161–168.

Butow, P. N.; Maclean, M.; Dunn, S. M.; et al. 1997. "The Dynamics of Change: Cancer Patients' Preferences for Information, Involvement, and Support." *Annals of Oncology* 8: 857–863.

Cassell, Eric J. 1985. *Talking with Patients.* 2 vols. Cambridge, MA: MIT Press.

Cassell, Eric J. 2001. "Preliminary Evidence of Impaired Thinking in Sick Patients." *Annals of Internal Medicine* 134(12): 1120–1123.

Dawson, Neal V., and Arkes, Hal R. 1987. "Systematic Errors in Medical Decision Making: Judgment Limitations." *Journal of General Internal Medicine* 2(3): 183–187.

Eisenthal, Sherman, and Lazare, Aaron. 1976. "Evaluation of the Initial Interview in a Walk-In Clinic." *Journal of Nervous and Mental Disease* 162(3): 169–176.

Faden, Ruth R. 1977. "Disclosure and Informed Consent: Does It Matter How We Tell It?" *Health Education Monographs* 5(3): 198–214.

Faden, Ruth R.; Beauchamp, Tom L.; and King, Nancy M. P. 1986. *A History and Theory of Informed Consent.* New York: Oxford University Press.

Fisher, Sue, and Todd, Alexandra D., eds. 1983. *The Social Organization of Doctor–Patient Communication.* Washington, D.C.: Center for Applied Linguistics.

Gadow, Sally. 1980. "Existential Advocacy: Philosophic Foundation of Nursing." In *Nursing: Images and Ideals: Opening Dialogue with the Humanities,* ed. Stuart F. Spicker and Sally Gadow. New York: Springer.

Hahn, Robert A. 1982. "Culture and Informed Consent: An Anthropological Perspective." In *Making Health Care Decisions: The Ethical and Legal Implications of Informed Consent in the Patient–Practitioner Relationship,* vol. 2. Washington, D.C.: U.S. President's Commission for the Study of Ethical Problems in Medicine and Biomedical and Behavioral Research.

Katz, Jay. 1984. *The Silent World of Doctor and Patient.* New York: Free Press.

Lidz, Charles W.; Meisel, Alan; Zerubavel, Eviatar; et al., eds. 1984. *Informed Consent: A Study of Decision-Making in Psychiatry.* New York: Guilford.

Mazur, Dennis J. 1986. "What Should Patients Be Told Prior to a Medical Procedure? Ethical and Legal Perspectives on Medical Informed Consent." *American Journal of Medicine* 81(6): 1051–1054.

Meichenbaum, Donald, and Turk, Dennis. 1987. *Facilitating Treatment Adherence: A Practitioner's Guidebook.* New York: Plenum Press.

Meisel, Alan, and Roth, Loren H. 1981. "What We Do and Do Not Know About Informed Consent." *Journal of the American Medical Association* 246(21): 2473–2477.

Murphy, Donald J.; Burrows, David; Santilli, Sara; et al. 1994. "The Influence of the Probability of Survival on Patients'

Preferences Regarding Cardiopulmonary Resuscitation." *New England Journal of Medicine* 330(8): 545–549.

Quill, Timothy E., and Townsend, Penelope. 1991. "Bad News: Delivery, Dialogue, and Dilemmas." *Archives of Internal Medicine* 151: 463–468.

Sherlock, Richard. 1986. "Reasonable Men and Sick Human Beings." *American Journal of Medicine* 80(1): 2–4.

Stanley, Barbara; Guido, Jeannine; Stanley, Michael; et al. 1984. "The Elderly Patient and Informed Consent: Empirical Findings." *Journal of the American Medical Association* 252(10): 1302–1306.

Steel, David J.; Blackwell, Barry; Gutmann, Mary C.; et al. 1987. "The Activated Patient: Dogma, Dream, or Desideratum." *Patient Education and Counseling* 10(1): 3–23.

Strull, William M.; Lo, Bernard; and Charles, Gerard. 1984. "Do Patients Want to Participate in Medical Decision-Making?" *Journal of the American Medical Association* 252(21): 2990–2994.

U.S. President's Commission for the Study of Ethical Problems in Medicine and Biomedical and Behavioral Research. 1982. *Making Health Care Decisions: A Report on the Ethical and Legal Implications of Informed Consent in the Patient–Practitioner Relationship.* Washington, D.C.: Author.

Waitzkin, Howard. 1984. "Doctor–Patient Communication: Clinical Implications of Social Scientific Research." *Journal of the American Medical Association* 252(17): 2441–2446.

Waitzkin, Howard. 1991. *The Politics of Medical Encounters: How Patients and Doctors Deal with Social Problems.* New Haven, CT: Yale University Press.

West, Candace. 1984. *Routine Complications: Troubles with Talk between Doctors and Patients.* Bloomington: Indiana University Press.

V. LEGAL AND ETHICAL ISSUES OF CONSENT IN HEALTHCARE

This article, by Jay Katz, is reprinted from the first edition, where it carried the title "Informed Consent in the Therapeutic Relationship: II. Legal and Ethical Aspects." It is followed immediately by a "Postscript," prepared by Angela R. Holder for purposes of updating the original article.

The doctrine of informed consent, introduced into U.S. case law in 1957, represents judges' groping efforts to delineate physicians' duties to inform patients of the benefits and risks of diagnostic and treatment alternatives, including the consequences of no treatment, as well as to obtain patients' consent (*Salgo v. Stanford University*, 1957). The doctrine's avowed purpose was to protect patients' right to "thorough-going self-determination" (*Natanson v. Kline*, 1960). The legal implications of informed consent, however, remain unclear. The doctrine is in fact more of a slogan, which

judges have been too timid or too wise to translate into law, at least as yet. It has been employed with little care but great passion to voice a dream of personal freedom and individual dignity. Though its legal impact in protecting patients' right to self-decision making has been scant, the threat of informed consent has opened profound issues for the traditional practice of medicine.

The Medical Framework

It has been insufficiently recognized, particularly by judges, that disclosure and consent, except in the most rudimentary fashion, are obligations alien to medical practice. Hippocrates' admonitions to physicians are still followed today: "Perform [these duties] calmly and adroitly, concealing most things from the patient while you are attending to him. Give necessary orders with cheerfulness and serenity, turning his attention away from what is being done to him; sometimes reprove sharply and emphatically, and sometimes comfort with solicitude and attention, revealing nothing of the patient's future or present condition." Thus it is not surprising that the Hippocratic oath is silent on the duty of physicians to inform, or even converse with, patients. Similarly Dr. Thomas Percival, whose 1803 book *Medical Ethics* influenced profoundly the subsequent codifications of medical ethics in England and the United States, commented only once on the discourse between physicians and patients, restricting his remarks to "gloomy prognostications." Even in that context he advised that "friends of the patient" be primarily informed, though he added that the patient may be told "if absolutely necessary" (Percival, p. 91). The Code of Ethics of the American Medical Association, adopted in 1847, and the Principles of Medical Ethics of the American Medical Association, adopted in 1903 and 1912, repeat, in almost the same words, Percival's statement. The AMA Principles of Medical Ethics, endorsed in 1957, delete Percival's wording entirely and substitute the vague admonition that "physicians … should make available to their patients … the benefits of their professional attainments." The pertinent sections of the *Opinions of the Judicial Council* of the AMA, interpreting the principles, note only the surgeon's obligation to disclose "all facts relevant to the need and performance of the operation" and the experimenter's obligation, when using new drugs and procedures, to obtain "the voluntary consent of the person" (American Medical Association Judicial Council). Nine years later, the AMA House of Delegates in endorsing, with modifications, the Declaration of Helsinki, asked that investigators, when engaged "in clinical [research] primarily for treatment," make relevant disclosures to and obtain the voluntary consent of patients or their legally authorized representative.

Thus in the context of therapy no authoritative statement encouraging disclosure and consent has ever been promulgated by the medical profession. The AMA's tersely worded surgical exception was compelled by the law of malpractice. Its experimental exception represented primarily an acquiescence to the U.S. Public Health Service and the U.S. Department of Health, Education, and Welfare requirements, which in turn were formulated in response to congressional concerns about research practices. When disclosure and consent prior to the conduct of therapeutic research were endorsed by the AMA, it did not extend those requirements to all patient care but limited the exception to "clinical [research] primarily for treatment."

Two significant conclusions can be drawn: (1) *Informed consent* is a creature of law and not a medical prescription. A duty to inform patients has never been promulgated by the medical profession, though individual physicians have made interesting, but as a rule unsystematic, comments on this topic. Judges have been insufficiently aware of the deeply ingrained Hippocratic tradition against disclosure and, instead, seem to have assumed that individual physicians' lack of disclosure was aberrant with respect to standard medical practice, and hence *negligent,* in the sense of *forgetful* or *inadvertent,* conduct. (2) When judges were confronted with claims of lack of informed consent, no medical precedent, no medical position papers, and no analytic medical thinking existed on this subject. Thus physicians were ill prepared to shape judges' notions on informed consent with thoughtful and systematic positions of their own.

The Legal Framework

With the historical movement from feudalism to individualism, consent, respect for the dignity of human beings, and the right of individuals to shape their own lives became important principles of English common law and, in turn, of American common law. Yet, as these principles gained greater acceptance, questions arose in many areas of law about the capacity of human beings to make their own decisions and about the need to protect them from their own "folly." The tug of war between advocates of thoroughgoing self-determination and those of paternalism has continued unabated. The informed-consent doctrine manifests this struggle. While in physician-patient interactions the legal trend during the past two decades has been to increase somewhat the right of patients to greater freedom of choice, the informed-consent doctrine has not had as far-reaching an impact on patients' self-determination as many commentators have assumed. This fact has been insufficiently appreciated and has led to confusion, further compounded by the courts' rhetoric that seemed to promise more than it delivered.

Consent to medical and surgical interventions is an ancient legal requirement. Historically an intentional touching without consent was adjudicated in battery. The law has not changed at all in this regard, and a surgeon who operates on a patient without permission is legally liable, even if the operation is successful. In such instances any inquiry into medical need or negligent conduct becomes irrelevant, for what is at issue is the disregard of the person's right to exercise control over his body. The jurisprudential basis of these claims is personal freedom:

> ... under a free government at least, the free citizen's first and greatest right, which underlies all others—the right to himself—is the subject of universal acquiescence, and this right necessarily forbids a physician or surgeon, however skillful or eminent ... to violate without permission the bodily integrity of his patient by ... operating on him without his consent.... (*Pratt v. Davis,* 1906)

But what does consent mean? In battery cases it means only that the physician must inform the patient what he proposes to do and that the patient must agree. Medical emergencies and patients' incompetence are the only exceptions to this requirement.

In mid-twentieth century, judges gradually confronted the question whether patients are entitled not only to know what a doctor proposes to do but also to decide whether the intervention is advisable in the light of its risks and benefits and the available alternatives, including no treatment. Such awareness of patients' informational needs is a modern phenomenon, influenced by the simultaneous growth of product liability and consumer law.

The law of fraud and deceit has always protected patients from doctors' flagrant misrepresentations, and in theory patients have always been entitled to ask whatever questions they pleased. What the doctrine of informed consent sought to add is the proposition that physicians are now under an affirmative duty to offer to acquaint patients with the important risks and plausible alternatives to the proposed procedure. The underlying rationale for that duty was stated in *Natanson v. Kline*:

> Anglo-American law starts with the premise of thorough-going self-determination. It follows that each man is considered to be master of his own body, and he may, if he be of sound mind, expressly prohibit the performance of life-saving surgery, or other medical treatment. A doctor might well believe that an operation or form of treatment is desirable or necessary but the law does not permit him to substitute his own judgment for that of the patient by any form of artifice or deception. (*Natanson v. Kline*)

The language employed by the *Natanson* court in support of an affirmative duty to disclose derives from the language of the law of battery, which clearly makes the patient the ultimate decision maker with respect to his body. Thus the courts reasoned, with battery principles very much in mind, that significant protection of patients' right to decide their medical fate required not merely perfunctory assent but a truly *informed consent,* based on an adequate understanding of the medical and surgical options available to them.

Yet in the same breath judges also attempted to intrude as little as possible on traditional medical practices. In doing so their impulse to protect the right of individual self-determination collided with their equally strong desire to maintain the authority and practices of the professions. Law has always respected the arcane expertise of physicians and has never held them liable if they practiced "good medicine." The law of consent in battery represented no aberration from this principle since most physicians agree that patients at least deserve to know the nature of the proposed procedure. However, the new duty of disclosure that the law, in the name of self-determination, threatened to impose upon physicians was something quite different. For the vast majority of physicians significant disclosure is not at all part of standard medical practice. Most doctors believe that patients are neither emotionally nor intellectually equipped to be medical decision makers, that they must be guided past childish fears into *rational* therapy, and that disclosures of uncertainty, gloomy prognosis and dire risks often seriously undermine cure. Physicians began to wonder whether law was now asking them to practice "bad" medicine.

In the early informed-consent cases, judges simply did not resolve the conflict between self-determination and professional practices and authority. The result was distressing confusion. In obeisance to the venerable ideal of self-determination, courts purported to establish, as a matter of law, the physician's

> ... obligation ... to disclose and explain to the patient in language as simple as necessary the nature of the ailment, the nature of the proposed treatment, the probability of success or of alternatives, and perhaps the risks of unfortunate results and unforeseen conditions within the body. (*Natanson v. Kline*)

The threat of such an obligation greatly disturbed the medical profession. It recognized that serious implementation of such a standard would significantly alter medical practice. Physicians argued that in order fully to serve patients' best interests, they must have the authority to exercise medical judgment in managing patients. Courts likewise bowed to this judgment. In the very sentence that introduced the ambiguous but exuberant new phrase "informed consent," the court showed its deference to medical judgment and its hesitancy to disturb traditional practice:

> ... in discussing the element of risk a certain amount of discretion must be employed consistent with the full disclosure of facts necessary to an informed consent. (*Salgo v. Stanford University*)

Thus the extent to which evolving case law, under the banner of individualism, was challenging traditional medical practice—which for millennia has treated patients paternally as children—remained confusing. In those earlier cases (*Salgo v. Stanford University, Natanson v. Kline*) judges were profoundly allegiant to both points of view, but the balance was soon tipped decisively in favor of protecting medical practices.

BATTERY OR NEGLIGENCE. The striking ambivalence of judges toward the doctrine of informed consent manifested itself in the competition between battery and negligence doctrines as a means of analyzing and deciding the claims of lack of informed consent. Battery offered a more rigorous protection of patients' right to self-determination. The inquiry into disclosure and consent would not be governed by professional practices but instead would rest on the question: Has the physician met his expanded informational responsibility so that the patient is able to exercise a choice among treatment options? A negative answer to this question would show that the physician's actions constitute trespass, rendering him liable for an unauthorized and *offensive* contact (*Dow v. Kaiser Foundation*).

However, in virtually every jurisdiction judges resolved the competition in favor of negligence law. In doing so, judges were able to defer to medical judgment by evaluating the adequacy of disclosure against the medical professional standard of care, asserting that this standard will govern those duties as it does other medical obligations. As a consequence, physicians remain free to exercise the wisdom of their profession and are liable only for failure to disclose what a reasonable doctor would have revealed. Furthermore, negligence theory does not redress mere dignitary injuries, irrespective of physical injuries, and requires proof that the patient, fully informed, would have refused the proposed treatment. Interferences with self-determination, standing alone, are not compensated.

In rejecting battery, judges made much of the fact that such an action required *intent,* while negligence involved *inadvertence*; it was the latter, they believed, that accounted for the lack of disclosure. They overlooked that the withholding of information on the part of physicians is generally quite intentional, dictated by the very exercise of medical judgment that the law of negligence seeks to respect. In stating that the nondisclosures were *collateral* to the central information about the nature of the proposed procedure and hence not required for a valid consent, judges discarded the very idea of informed consent—namely, that absence of expanded disclosure vitiates consent. They refused to extend the inquiry to the total informational needs of patients, without which patients' capacity for self-decision making remains incomplete. At bottom, the rejection of an expanded battery theory and of its proposed requirement of informed consent followed from the threat they posed to the authority of doctors and traditional medical practice.

Thus informed consent, based on patients thoroughgoing self-determination, was a misnomer from the time the phrase was born. To be sure, a new cause of action has emerged for failure to inform of the risks of, and in most jurisdictions alternatives to, treatment. Some duty to disclose risks and alternatives, the courts were willing to say, exists; the extent of that duty is defined by the disclosure practice of a reasonable physician in the circumstances of the case. The new claim is firmly rooted in the law of negligent malpractice, in that plaintiffs are still required to prove the professional standard of care by means of medical expert witnesses. In these, the majority of jurisdictions, traditional medical practice—which generally opposes disclosure—has scarcely been threatened at all in legal reality. The legal life of informed consent, except for dicta about self determination and the hybrid negligence law promulgated in a handful of jurisdictions, was almost over as soon as it began. Judges had briefly toyed with the idea of patients' self-determination and then largely cast it aside. Good medicine, as defined by doctors, remains good law almost everywhere.

MODIFICATIONS IN PROFESSIONAL STANDARD OF CARE. In a few jurisdictions, beginning in 1972 in the District of Columbia with the decision in *Canterbury v. Spence,* the new cause of action for failure to inform combined elements of battery with negligence, creating a legal hybrid. The court purported to abandon the professional standard of care with respect to disclosure, asserting that

> … respect for the patient's right of self-determination on particular therapy demands a standard set by law for physicians rather than one which physicians may or may not impose upon themselves. (*Canterbury v. Spence*)

Thus the court laid down a judge-made rule of disclosure of risks and alternatives, which for all practical purposes resembled an expanded battery standard of disclosure.

The preoccupation with risk disclosure, however, continued unabated. From the very beginning, despite all the talk about *informed consent,* judges did not lay down any rules for a careful inquiry into the nature and quality of consent, which on its face any meaningful implementation of the doctrine required. Instead major emphasis was placed on risk disclosures. Since in the cases before courts plaintiff-patients only complained of the injurious results of treatment, this emphasis is understandable. Yet to focus solely on risks is to bypass the principal issue of self-determination—namely, whether the physician kept the patient from arriving at his own decision. The *Canterbury* court, too, restricted its concerns largely to risk disclosures and added the requirement that

> an unrevealed risk that should have been made known must materialize for otherwise the omission, however, unpardonable, is legally without consequence. (*Canterbury v. Spence*)

Thus the court foreclosed legal redress for the patient who, fully informed of the potential effects of, for example, a maiming operation, would have chosen an alternative medical course, even though some of the risks did not materialize.

But to the extent these jurisdictions have abandoned the professional standard of disclosure, traditional medical practice has been challenged; "good medicine," in the eyes of the profession, may no longer be a sufficient defense. Seemingly, in these jurisdictions self-determination has begun to encroach upon the province of medical paternalism. That encroachment, however, may be substantially an illusion, for the touted abandonment of the professional standard of disclosure in *Canterbury* was far from complete. Medical judgment to truncate full disclosure must be "given its due," the court said, when "it enters the picture." The court left ambiguous when the plaintiff must establish the appropriate standard of disclosure by an expert witness, or when he must produce such a witness in order to rebut a defendant-physician's claim that good medical judgment was exercised.

What is clear is that the physician has a *therapeutic privilege* not to disclose information where such disclosure would pose a threat to the *well-being* of the patient. But the ambit of this privilege as well as the relationship of its invocation to a directed verdict is not clear, and this for "good" reasons: Even in these most liberal jurisdictions with respect to patients' rights, courts still cannot face squarely the question of how much they are willing to challenge the traditional medical wisdom of nondisclosure. The law remains ambiguous with respect to this, the core issue of informed consent.

TENSIONS BETWEEN SELF-DETERMINATION AND PATERNALISM. Beyond its allegiance to medical paternalism, noted above, the *Canterbury* court showed its preference for paternalism in another way. Under negligence law, the courts have stated that lack of disclosure cannot be said to have caused the patient's injury unless the patient, if adequately informed, would have declined the procedure; this is the crucial problem of causation in informed-consent cases. Such an approach to causation is quite appropriate where law seeks not to compensate interference with self-determination, but only physical injuries resulting from inadequate disclosure. Yet the *Canterbury* court, and every court that has considered the matter subsequently, held that the decision whether or not to undertake therapy must be examined not from the point of view of the patient-plaintiff but from that of a "prudent person in the patient's position," limiting the inquiry to whether a "reasonable patient" would have agreed to the procedure. This substitution of a community standard of a "reasonable" person cuts the heart out of the courts purported respect for individual self-determination. Questions of the influence of hindsight and bitterness are familiar to juries, as is the problem of self-serving testimony generally. While those are delicate problems, they do not justify abrogating the very right at issue in cases of informed consent: the right of individual choice, which may be precisely the right to be an "unreasonable" person.

EPILOGUE ON LAW. Thus law has proceeded feebly toward the objective of patients' self-determination. While a new cause of action, occasionally hybridized with battery, has emerged for the negligent failure to disclose risks and alternative treatments, it remains a far cry from the avowed purpose of the informed-consent doctrine, namely, to secure patients' autonomy and right to self-determination. In not tampering significantly with the medical wisdom of nondisclosure, yet creating a new cause of action based on traditional disclosure requirements, courts may have accomplished a different result, very much in line with other purposes of tort law—namely, to provide physically injured patients with greater opportunities for seeking compensation whenever it can be argued that disclosure might have avoided such injuries. In doing so judges may have hoped, through the anticipatory tremors of dicta, to urge doctors to consider modifying their traditional disclosure practices. But judges have been unwilling, at least as yet, to implement earnestly patients' right to self-determination.

Whither Informed Consent?

The disquiet that the doctrine of informed consent has created among physicians cannot be fully explained by the small incremental step courts have taken to assure greater patient participation in medical decision making. More likely it was aroused by the uncertainty over the scope of the doctrine and by an appreciation that medical practice, indeed all professional practice, would be radically changed if fidelity to thoroughgoing self determination were to prevail. In what follows, some of the issues raised by the idea of an informed-consent doctrine, based on a premise of self-determination, will be discussed.

PATIENTS. Traditionally patients have been viewed as ignorant about medical matters, fearful about being sick, child-like by virtue of their illness, ill-equipped to sort out what is in their best medical interest, and prone to make decisions detrimental to their welfare (Parsons). Thus physicians have asserted that it makes little sense to consult patients on treatment options: far better to interact with them as beloved children and decide for them. In the light of such deeply held convictions, many physicians are genuinely puzzled by any informed-consent requirement. Moreover, its possible detrimental impact on compassion, reassurance, and hope—ancient prescriptions for patient care—has raised grave ethical questions for the medical profession.

Those concerns should not be dismissed lightly. What may be at issue, however, is not an intrinsic incapacity of patients to participate in medical decision making. For not all patients, and probably not even most, are too uneducated, too frightened, or too regressed to understand the benefits and risks of treatment options available to them. Moreover, their capacities for decision making are affected to varying degrees, for example, by the nature of the disease process, its prognosis, acuteness, painfulness, etc., as well as by the personality of patients. The medical literature is largely silent on the question of who—under what circumstances and with what conditions—should or should not be allowed to participate fully in medical decision making.

But why has not the sorting-out process, distinguishing between those patients who do and those who do not have the capacity for decision making, been undertaken long ago? One answer suggests itself: Once those patients have been identified who, in principle, can make decisions on their own behalf, physicians would be compelled to confront the questions of whether to interact with them on a level of greater equality; whether to share with them the uncertainties and unknowns of medical diagnosis, treatment, and prognosis; and whether to communicate to them their professional limitations as well as the lack of expert consensus about treatment alternatives. Such an open dialogue would expose the uncertainties inherent in most medical interventions; and to the extent medicine's helpful and curative power depends on the faith and confidence which the physician projects, patients may be harmed by disclosure and consent.

Physicians' objections to informed consent, therefore, may have less to do with the incompetence of patients as such than with un unrecognized concern of the doctrine's impact on the dynamics of cure. Put another way, the all too sweeping traditional view of patients has misled doctors into believing that medicine's opposition to informed consent is largely based on patients' incompetence, rather than on an apprehension, however dimly perceived, that disclosure would bring into view much about the practice of medicine that physicians seek to hide from themselves and their patients; for example, the uncertainties and disagreements about the treatments employed; the curative impact of physicians' and patients' beliefs in the unquestioned effectiveness of their prescriptions rather than the prescriptions themselves; the difficulty in sorting out the contributions that *vis medicatrix naturae* ("the healing power of nature") makes to the healing process; the impact of patients' suggestibility to cure, etc. Thus the question: When does informed consent interfere with physicians' effectiveness and with the dynamics of cure?

Little attention has been paid to the fact that the practice of Hippocratic medicine makes patients more incompetent than they need be. Indeed patients' incompetence can become a self-fulfilling prophecy as a consequence of medical practices. That the stress of illness leads to psychological regression, to chronologically earlier modes of functioning, has been recognized for a long time. Precious little, however, is known about the contributions that physicians' attitudes toward and interactions with their patients make to the regressive pull. Also, little is known about the extent to which regression can be avoided by not keeping patients in the dark, by inviting them to participate in decision making, and by addressing and nurturing the intact, mature parts of their functioning. This uncharted territory requires exploration in order to determine what strains will be imposed on physicians and patients alike, if Anna Freud's admonition to students of the Western Reserve Medical School is heeded:

> … you must not be tempted to treat [the patient] as a child. You must be tolerant toward him as you would be toward a child and as respectful as you would be towards a fellow adult because he has only gone back to childhood as far as he's ill. He also has another part of his personality which has remained intact and that part of him will resent it deeply, if you make too much use of your authority. (quoted in Katz, p. 637)

PHYSICIANS. Traditionally physicians have asserted that their integrity, training, professional dedication to patients' best medical interests, and commitment to "doing no harm" are sufficient safeguards for patients. The complexities inherent in medical decision making, physicians maintain, require that trust be patients' guiding principle. The idea of informed consent does not question the integrity, training, or dedication of doctors. Without them, informed consent would be of little value. What the idea of informed consent does question is the necessity and appropriateness of physicians' making all decisions for their patients; it calls for a careful scrutiny of which decisions belong to the doctor and which to the patient.

Physicians have preferences about treatment options that may not necessarily be shared by patients. For example, no professional consensus exists about the treatment of breast cancer. The advantages and disadvantages of lumpectomy, simple mastectomy, radical mastectomy, radiation therapy, chemotherapy, and various combinations among these are subject to much controversy. Dr. Bernard Fisher, chairman of the National Surgical Adjuvant Breast Cancer Project, has said that we simply do not know which method is best (Fisher). Thus the question must be answered: How extensive an opportunity must patients be given to select which alternative? Informed consent challenges the stereotypical notion that physicians should assume the entire burden of deciding what treatment *all* patients, *whatever* their condition, should undergo. Indeed, can the assumption of this burden be defined purely on medical grounds in the first place? Is not the decision in favor of one treatment for breast cancer over another, like many other treatment decisions, a combination of medical, emotional, aesthetic, religious, philosophical, social, interpersonal, and personal judgments? Which of these component judgments belong to the physician and which to the patient?

Much needs to be investigated in order to learn the practical human limits of any new obligations to disclose and to obtain consent:

1. Informing patients for purposes of decision making requires learning new ways of interacting and communicating with patients. Such questions as the following will have to be answered: What background information must patients receive in order to help them formulate their questions? How should physicians respond to *precipitous* consents or refusals? How deeply should doctors probe for understanding? What constitutes irrelevant information that only tends to confuse? What words and explanations facilitate comprehension? Physicians have not been in the habit of posing such questions.

2. Underlying informed consent is the assumption that physicians have considerable knowledge about their

particular specialties, keep abreast of new developments, and are aware of what is happening in other fields of medicine that impinge on their area of professional interest. This is not so; indeed, it may be asking too much. Moreover, since physicians have their preferences for particular modes of treatment, can they be expected to present an unbiased picture of alternative treatments?

3. Physicians have consistently asserted that informed consent interferes with compassion (Silk). Doctors believe that, in order to maintain hope or to avoid the imposition of unnecessary suffering, patients in the throes of a terminal illness, and other patients as well, should not be dealt with honestly. But the evidence for such allegations is lacking. When physicians are asked to support them with clinical data, they are largely unable to do so (Oken). Indeed, the few studies that have been conducted suggest that most patients do not seem to yearn for hope based on deception, but for hope based on a reassurance that they will not be abandoned, that everything possible will be done for them, and that physicians will deal truthfully with them. Moreover, evidence is accumulating that informed patients become more cooperative, more capable of dealing with discomfort and pain, and more responsible. Whether the often alleged conflict between *compassionate* silence and *cruel* disclosure is myth or reality remains to be seen. Disclosure may turn out to be a greater burden to those who have to interact with patients than to the patients themselves.

4. Informed consent confronts the role of faith in the cure of disease and the complex problems created by the uncertainties inherent in medical practice. To some extent the two issues are intertwined. The effectiveness of a therapeutic program, it has often been said, depends on three variables: the "feeling of trust or faith the patient has in his doctor and therefore in his therapy … the faith or confidence the physician has in himself and in the line of therapy he proposes to use … and the therapy [itself]" (Hoffer, p. 124). Informed consent could interfere with the first two variables and thus undermine the effectiveness of treatment. Precisely because of the uncertainties in medical decision making, the physician, to begin with, defends himself against those uncertainties by being more certain about what he is doing than he realistically can be. There is perhaps some unconscious wisdom in what he has been doing since Hippocrates' days, for the unquestioned faith the doctor has in his own therapy is also therapeutic in its own right. Thus, to be a more effective healer, a physician may need to defend himself against his uncertainties by believing himself to be more powerful than he is. That defense will be threatened by informed consent, for

it would now require him to be more aware of what he does not know, and therapeutic effectiveness in turn might suffer. Finally, patients' response to treatment also depends on faith in the physician and his medicines. Knowing of the *ifs* and *buts* may shake patients' faith and undermine the therapeutic impact of suggestibility, which contributes so much to recovery from illness.

Physicians' traditional counterphobic reaction to uncertainty, adopting a sense of conviction that what seems right to them is the only correct thing to do, has other consequences as well. Defensive reactions against uncertainty have led to overenthusiasm for particular treatments that have been applied much more widely than an unbiased evaluation would dictate. The ubiquitous tonsillectomies performed to the psychological detriment of untold children is a classical example. Moreover, by not acknowledging uncertainty to themselves, doctors cannot acknowledge it to their patients. Thus consciously and unconsciously physicians avoid the terrifying confrontation of uncertainty, particularly when associated with poor prognosis. As a result, communications with patients take the form of an evasive monologue. The dialogue that might reveal these uncertainties is discouraged (Davis).

While disclosure of information would reduce patients' ignorance, it would also diminish doctors' power within the physician-patient relationship. As Waitzkin and Stoeckle have observed, the "physician enhances his power to the extent that he can maintain the patient's uncertainty about the course of illness, efficacy of therapy, or specific future actions of the physician himself" (p. 187). Thus new questions arise: What consequences would a diminution of authority have on physicians effectiveness as healers? How would patients react to less powerful doctors? Would they accept them or turn to new faith healers?

LIMITS OF SELF-DETERMINATION. Patients' capacity for self-determination has been challenged on the grounds that neither total understanding nor total freedom of choice is possible (Ingelfinger). This of course is true. Any informed-consent doctrine, to be realistic, must take into account the biological, psychological, intellectual, and social constraints imposed upon thought and action. But those inherent constraints, which affect all human beings, do not necessarily justify treating patients as incompetents. Competence does not imply total understanding or total freedom of choice.

What needs to be explored is the extent to which medicine, like law, should presume competence rather than incompetence, in interactions with patients. Neither presumption comports fully with the psychobiology of human beings; both of them express value judgments on how best to interact with human beings. Once the value judgment is made, one can decide on the additional safeguards needed to avoid the harm that any fiction about human behavior introduces.

The idea of informed consent asks for a presumption in favor of competence. If that is accepted, it may also follow that human beings should be allowed to strike their own bargains, however improvident. The then Circuit Judge Warren E. Burger, in commenting on a judicial decision to order a blood transfusion for a Jehovah's Witness, had this to say: "Nothing in [Justice Brandeis's `right to be let alone' philosophy, suggests that he] thought an individual possessed these rights only as to sensible beliefs, *valid* thought, *reasonable* emotions or *well-founded* sensations. I suggest he intended to include a great many foolish, unreasonable and even absurd ideas which do not conform such as refusing medical treatment even at great risk" (*Application of President of Georgetown College*). A physician may wish, and even should try, to persuade his patients to agree to what he believes would serve their medical interests best; but ultimately he may have to bow to his patients' decision, however "senseless" or "unreasonable," or withdraw from further participation. The alternatives, deception or coercion, may be worse, for either would victimize not only patients but physicians as well.

Conclusion

The narrow scope that courts have given to the informed-consent doctrine may reflect a deeply held belief that the exercise of self-determination by patients is often against the best interests of otherwise responsible adults and that those interests deserve greater protection than personal freedom. It may also reflect a judicial recognition of law's limited capacity to regulate effectively the physician-patient relationship. Therefore, once having suggested that patients deserve at least a little openness in communication, courts may have concluded that they had gone as far as they could. Judges, at least for the time being, have largely left it up to the medical profession to confront the question of patients' greater participation in medical decision making.

Despite their snail's pace, the courts' approach may have merit. Implementing a right of self-determination has tremendous consequences for medical practice. Many difficult problems, each with vast ethical implications, need to be considered by the medical profession. Thus introspection and education, responsive to the legal and professional problems that new patterns of physician-patient interaction will create, may ultimately provide firmer foundations for new patterns of physician-patient interactions than forced change through outside regulation. The latter, however,

may increase if the profession does not rise to the challenge of addressing these long-neglected problems.

JAY KATZ (1995)

American Medical Association. Judicial Council. 1969. "Principles of Medical Ethics." In *Opinions and Reports of the Judicial Council,* pp. vi–vii. Chicago: Author.

Application of President of Georgetown College. 331 F. 2d 1010 (D.C. Cir., 1964). Certiorari denied. 377 U.S. 978. 12 L. Ed. 2d 746. 84 S. Ct. 1883.

Burger, Warren E. 1968. "Reflections on Law and Experimental Medicine." *UCLA Law Review* 15: 436–442.

Canterbury v. Spence. 464 F.2d 772 (D.C.C.A. 1972).

Cobbs v. Grant. 104 Cal. Rptr. 505. 502 P.2d 1 (1972).

Davis, Fred. 1960. "Uncertainty in Medical Prognosis: Clinical and Functional." *American Journal of Sociology* 66: 41–47.

Dow v. Kaiser Foundation. 12 Cal. App.3d 488. 90 Cal. Rptr. 747 (Ct. App. 1970).

Estate of Brooks, in re. 32 Ill. 2d 361. 205 N.E.2d 435 (1965).

Fisher, Bernard. 1970. "The Surgical Dilemma in the Primary Therapy of Invasive Breast Cancer: A Critical Appraisal." *Current Problems in Surgery,* October, pp. 1–53.

Glass, Eleanor S. 1970. "Restructuring Informed Consent: Legal Therapy for the Doctor-Patient Relationship." *Yale Law Journal* 79: 1533–1576.

Henderson, L. J. 1935. "Physician and Patient as a Social System." *New England Journal of Medicine* 212: 819–823.

Hippocrates. 1923. "Decorum." In *Hippocrates,* tr. W. H. S. Jones. Loeb Classical Library. London: William Heinemann.

Hoffer, A. 1967. "A Theoretical Examination of Double-Blind Design." *Canadian Medical Association Journal* 97: 123–127.

Ingelfinger, F. J. 1972. "Informed (but Uneducated) Consent." *New England Journal of Medicine* 287: 465–466.

Katz, Jay, ed. 1972. *Experimentation with Human Beings: The Authority of the Investigator, Subject, Professions, and State in the Human Experimentation Process.* New York: Russell Sage Foundation.

Katz, Jay, and Alexander Morgan Capron. 1975. *Catastrophic Diseases: Who Decides What? A Psychosocial and Legal Analysis of the Problems Posed by Hemodialysis and Organ Transplantation.* New York: Russell Sage Foundation.

McCoid, Allan H. 1957. "A Reappraisal of Liability for Unauthorized Medical Treatment." *Minnesota Law Review* 41: 381–434.

Mohr v. Williams. 104 N.W. 12 (Minn. 1905).

Natanson v. Kline. 186 Kan. 393. 350 P.2d 1093. 187 Kan. 186. 354 P.2d 670 (1960).

Oken, Donald. 1961. "What to Tell Cancer Patients: A Study of Medical Attitudes." *Journal of the American Medical Association* 175: 1120–1128.

Parsons, Talcott. 1951. *The Social System.* Glencoe, IL: Free Press.

Percival, Thomas. 1927. *Medical Ethics,* ed. Chauncey D. Leake. Baltimore: Williams & Wilkins.

Plante, Marcus L. 1968. "An Analysis of 'Informed Consent.'" *Fordham Law Review* 36: 639–672.

Pratt v. Davis. 118 Ill. App. 161 (1905). Aff. 224 Ill. 300. 79 N.E. 562 (1906).

Salgo v. Stanford University. 317 P.2d 170 (Cal. 1st Dist. Ct. App. 1957).

Schloendorff v. New York Hospital. 105 N.E. 92 (N.Y. 1914).

Silk, Arthur D. 1976. "A Physician's Plea: Recognize Limitations of Informed Consent." *American Medical News,* April 12, p. 19.

Waitzkin, H., and J. D. Stoeckle. 1972. "The Communication of Information About Illness: Clinical, Sociological, and Methodological Considerations." *Advances in Psychosomatic Medicine* 8: 180–215.

Wilkinson v. Vesey. 295 A.2d 676 (R.I. 1972).

POSTSCRIPT

Courts have broadened the doctrine of informed consent well beyond its initial construct. For example, informed consent was, in a few states, applicable only to physical touching, as courts held that a failure to obtain informed consent was a claim for battery, not for negligence (e.g., *Morgan v. MacPhail,* 1997; *Gray v. Grunnagle,* 1966). This meant, for example, that a physician who failed to warn a patient about the risks of a prescribed medication before the patient had life–threatening consequences would not have violated the patient's right to informed consent. The clear trend by the beginning of the twenty–first century, however, was to treat any claim for informed consent as one in negligence, so no *touching* is required (*Matthies v. Mastromonaco,* 1999; Hanson). Of course, if a procedure is performed without any consent (i.e., a surgeon performs a different or additional procedure from the one to which the patient had consented while the patient is under anesthesia) an action for battery is still appropriate (*Montgomery v. Bazaz–Sehgal,* 2002).

Several court cases broadened the doctrine of informed consent, establishing that in order to give informed consent, the patient must understand the risks of refusing the proposed therapy (*Truman v. Thomas,* 1980; *Battenfield v. Gregory,* 1991; *Arato v. Avedon,* 1993).

Informed consent jurisprudence at the turn of this century also explored whether the patient is entitled to some information about the physician's abilities as well as about the contemplated procedure. Does the patient have a right to know that the surgeon has never performed the procedure

on anyone else? Does the patient have the right to know that the Health Maintenance Organization to which she belongs will reward her physician economically at the end of the year if he does not refer patients to specialists, even if her disease should be treated by specialists? Most cases in which disclosure of fiscal issues have arisen have imposed liability, if at all, on the HMO and not on the physician (Kurfirst; Potter; Simmons).

In one case from Illinois, the intermediate appellate court held that the physician had breached his fiduciary duty when he did not disclose to the patient that he made more money if the patient was not referred to a specialist. The Illinois Supreme Court held that since the failure to refer the patient to a cardiologist constituted malpractice, the reason the physician did not do so was irrelevant (*Neade v. Portes,* 2000). If a physician knows or should have known that he should refer a patient to a specialist or other more qualified physician and does not do so, if the patient's condition becomes worse, the failure constitutes malpractice even if the patient never raises the issue of informed consent (*Johnson v. Kokemoor,* 1996). The earliest case to this effect was decided in 1898, decades before there was any concept of *informed consent* (*Logan v. Field,* 1898).

Other informed consent cases involved a physician's failure to disclose inexperience with performing the procedure. Most courts take the position that the doctrine of informed consent applies only to the risks of the procedure or treatment itself, and not to information about the physician (*Ditto v. McCurdy,* 1997; *Duttry v. Patterson,* 2001). This was even true in one case where the surgeon failed to inform a child–patient's parents that he was an alcoholic and unlicensed (*Kaskie v. Wright,* 1991). A 2002 decision by the New Jersey Supreme Court, however, held that outright misrepresentation of experience or credentials (as opposed to failure to disclose) does constitute failure to obtain informed consent (*Howard v. University of Medicine and Dentistry,* 2002).

Special Situations

Some situations involving particular groups of patients create unusually complex problems in providing information or obtaining consent.

PREGNANT PATIENTS. During the 1980s there was a series of cases in which pregnant women were subjected to blood transfusions to which they had religious and other objections and, in some cases, court–ordered cesarean sections when they had refused the procedure. In the infamous case of A.C. (*In re A.C.,* 1990), the woman and her premature infant both died following her court–ordered cesarean, and professional organizations began to issue statements urging that such refusals be respected (George Washington University, 1991). Since that ruling, although there has been one reported case of a court–ordered cesarean (*Pemberton v. Tallahassee Memorial Regional Medical Center,* 1999), there have been many more cases in which the courts rejected such requests by hospitals (*In re Baby Boy Doe,* 1994; Levine, 1994; Oberman, 2000). Several states have also held that a pregnant woman may not be transfused against her will, even to save her fetus (*The Stamford Hospital v. Vega,* 1996; *Harrell v. St. Mary's Hospital,* 1996).

During the 1990s, several states attempted to decrease drug abuse among pregnant women by criminalizing it as *child abuse.* While these statutes are still being enforced in a few states, the Supreme Court has ruled that testing women for drugs without their knowledge or consent when they come to a clinic for prenatal care is a violation of their constitutional rights against search and seizure and, of course, in violation of any concept of informed consent (Barton; *Ferguson v. City of Charleston,* 2001). Moreover, many medical groups issued statements that they feared that the threat of prosecution would drive away from medical care the women who needed it most (see, for example, the 1990 statement of the American Medical Association's Board of Trustees; Annas).

Women have been increasingly successful in informed consent suits alleging that they were not told during prenatal care about diagnostic tests that would have revealed serious handicaps in time to abort their fetuses (*Quinn v. Blau,* 1997; *Kassama v. Magat,* 2001). Since many states refuse to permit *wrongful birth* cases, an action for failure to obtain informed consent may be the patient's only recourse (Gantz). In other cases, women have successfully sued when physicians refused to respect their wishes on such matters as Cesarean sections and the newborns had handicaps as the result. All of these cases allege obstetrical malpractice as well as an absence of informed consent (*Schreiber v. Physicians Insurance Co.,* 1998).

MINORS. Minors over age fourteen are increasingly able to make medical decisions for themselves, although many states in which a minor by herself could make decisions about major surgery or other serious interventions have abortion statutes that restrict the same young woman from deciding to have a first–trimester abortion. The standards of informed consent—the patient's capacity to understand the nature of the procedure and the risks (including foregoing treatment) and benefits—is the same for adolescent as it is for an adult (English).

Parents occasionally ask a physician not to tell their adolescent child his or her diagnosis. Although it may be negotiable in some illnesses, if an adolescent is HIV positive or has another serious communicable condition, the physician must tell him or her and make sure the patient understands safe sex and other means to keep others from contracting the infection. The physician can be found liable if the uninformed adolescent patient infects a third party (*Reisner v. Regents of the University of California,* 1995; Committee on Pediatric AIDS, American Academy of Pediatrics).

While minors may refuse treatment in many situations, courts rarely allow them to refuse life–saving therapies. In a few cases (*In re E.G.,* 1989, rehearing denied,1990 *Belcher v. Charleston Area Medical Center,* 1992), judges have allowed minors to refuse life–saving therapy, but most courts have ruled that minors do not have "the right to die." (*In re Application of Long Island Jewish Medical Center,* 1990; *Novak v. Cobb County–Kennestone Hospital Authority,* 1996). In no state is a minor permitted to create a valid Living Will or Durable Power of Attorney (Hawkins; McCabe). When the minor is dying, however, the fact that she or he cannot make a legally binding decision does not mean that the physician should not be the patient's advocate in arguing for that perspective if the parents wish to "try one more thing" (Leiken, 1993; Evans, 1995).

If the diagnosis and treatment of a minor is undertaken without the involvement or knowledge of the parent, the young patient is entitled to the same degree of confidentiality accorded an adult patient (Council for Scientific Affairs, American Medical Association; Sigman, Silber, English, et al.; American College of Obstetrics and Gynecology).

PSYCHIATRIC PATIENTS. Admission to a psychiatric hospital, even if a patient has been involuntarily committed, does not preclude a person's ability and right to consent to many aspects of his or her care, including agreeing to or refusing medication (Berg, Appelbaum, and Grisso; Wirshing, Wirshing, and Marder). In order to medicate a patient over his or her objections, the patient must be found incompetent to make that decision by a court (*In re Qawi,* 2001; *Hamilton County v. Steele,* 1999). Moreover, a psychiatric patient may consent to participate in research to the same extent that she or he may consent to treatment (Carpenter; Dunn and Jeste; Roberts; Capron, 1999).

Limits on Self-Determination

A patient is not always entitled to whatever care he or she wishes. A physician who does not think a therapy would be beneficial does not have to offer it to a patient, although if it is a treatment which a minority of physicians find acceptable, the physician may have the duty to refer the patient to such a practitioner. Therapies which have no adherents in mainstream medicine—for example, laetrile to treat cancer—do not impose a requirement of referral.

The physician does not have the right to discontinue a therapy he or she believes is *futile* over a family's objection as long as a patient is not brain dead (Jecker and Schneiderman; Blake, Maldondo, and Reinhardt; Capron, 1991; Cantor; Council on Judicial and Ethical Affairs, American Medical Association). Conversely, if an adult patient has made clear to his or her physician that he or she wishes to forego further treatment, the physician has the obligation to support the patient's decision, even if the family objects.

ANGELA RODDEY HOLDER (1995)
REVISED BY AUTHOR

BIBLIOGRAPHY

A.C., In re 573 A 2d 1235, DC App. (1990).

American College of Obstetrics and Gynecology. 1998. "Confidentiality in Adolescent Health Care." *International Journal of Gynecology & Obstetrics* 63: 295.

Annas, George J. 2001. "Testing Poor Pregnant Women for Cocaine: Physicians as Police Investigators." *New England Journal of Medicine* 344(22): 1729.

Application of Long Island Jewish Medical Center, In re. 147 Misc 2nd 724, 557 NYS 2d 239 (1990).

Arato v. Avedon. 5 Cal 4th 1172, 858 P 2d 598 (1993).

Baby Boy Doe, In re. 260 Ill App 3d 392, 632 NE 2d 326 (1994).

Barton, Erin F. 2001. "What About My Right to Privacy? Where the Court Went Wrong in *Ferguson v. City of Charleston*." *Brooklyn Law Review* 67: 261.

Battenfield v. Gregory. 247 NJ Super 538, 589 A. 2d 1059 (1991).

Belcher v. Charleston Area Medical Center. 422 SE 2d 827, WV (1992).

Berg, Jessica; Appelbaum, Paul S.; and Grisso, Thomas. 1996. "Constructing Competence: Formulating Standards of Legal Competence to Make Medical Decisions." *Rutgers Law Review* 48: 345.

Blake, David C.; Maldonado, L.; and Meinhardt, R.A. 1993. "Bioethics and the Law: The Case of *Helga Wanglie—Medically Futile Treatment v. Patient Autonomy*." *Whittier Law Review* 14: 119.

Board of Trustees, American Medical Association (Helene M. Cole, ed.). "Legal Interventions During Pregnancy: Court-Ordered Medical Treatment and Legal Penalties for Potentially Harmful Behavior By Pregnant Women." *Journal of the American Medical Association* 264(20): 2663.

Cantor, Norman L. 1996. "Can Healthcare Providers Obtain Judicial Intervention Against Surrogates Who Demand 'Medically Inappropriate' Life Support for Incompetent Patients?" *Critical Care Medicine* 24: 883.

Capron, Alexander M. 1991. "In re Helga Wanglie." *Hastings Center Report* 21(5): 26.

Capron, Alexander M. 1999. "Ethical and Human Rights Issues in Research on Mental Disorders that May Affect Decision–Making Capacity." *New England Journal of Medicine* 340(18): 1430.

Carpenter, William T., Jr.; Gold, James M.; and Lahti, Adrienne; et al. 2000. "Decisional Capacity for Informed Consent in Schizophrenia Research." *Archives of General Psychiatry* 57(6): 533.

Committee on Pediatric AIDS, American Academy of Pediatrics. 1999. "Disclosure of Illness Status to Children and Adolescents with HIV Infection." *Pediatrics* 103(1): 164.

Council for Scientific Affairs, American Medical Association. 1993. "Confidential Health Services for Adolescents." *Journal of the American Medical Association* 269(11): 1420.

Council on Ethical and Judicial Affairs, American Medical Association. 1999. "Medical Futility in End-of-Life Care: Report of the Council on Ethical and Judicial Affairs." *Journal of the American Medical Association* 281(10): 937–941.

Ditto v. McCurdy. 86 Hawaii 84, 947 P 2d 952 (1997).

Dunn, Laura B., and Dilip V. Jeste. 2001. "Enhancing Informed Consent for Research and Treatment." *Neuropsychopharmacology* 24: 595.

Duttry v. Patterson. 565 Pa 130, 771 A 2d 1255 (2001).

E.G., In re 133 Ill 2nd 98, 549 NE 2d 322 (1989).

English, Abigail. 1990. "Treating Adolescents: Legal and Ethical Considerations." *Med Clinics of North America* 74: 1097.

Evans, Janet L. 1995. "Are Children Competent to Make Decisions about Their Own Deaths?" *Behavioral Sciences and the Law* 13: 27.

Ferguson v. City of Charleston. 532 US 67 (2001).

Gantz, Julie. 1997. "State Statutory Preclusion of Wrongful Birth Relief: A Troubling Rewriting of a Woman's Right to Choose and the Doctor–Patient Relationship." *Virginia Journal of Social Policy & Law* 4: 795.

George Washington University. 1991. "Policy on Decision Making With Pregnant Patients at the George Washington University Hospitals." *BioLaw* 2(52): S:607.

Gray v. Grunnagle. 423 Pa 144, 223 A 2d 663 (1966).

Hamilton County v. Steele. 1999 WL 632925, Ohio App (1999).

Hanson, Laurel R. 2001. "Informed Consent and the Scope of a Physician's Duty of Disclosure." *North Dakota Law Review* 77: 71.

Harrell v. St. Mary's Hospital. 678 So 2d 455, Fla. App (1996).

Hawkins, Lisa Ann. 1992. "Living Will Statutes: A Minor Oversight." *Virginia Law Review* 78: 1581.

Howard v. University of Medicine and Dentistry. 2002 WL 1333646, NJ Supreme Ct, June 18 (2002).

Jecker, Nancy S., and Schneiderman, Lawrence J. 1995. "When Families Request that 'Everything Possible' Be Done." *Journal of Medicine & Philosophy* 20(2): 145.

Johnson v. Kokemoor. 199 Wisc 2d 615, 545 NW 2d 495 (1996).

Kaskie v. Wright. 403 Pa Super 334, 589 A 2d 213 (1991).

Kassama v. Magat. 136 Md App 637, 767 A 2d 348 (2001).

Kurfirst, Leonard S. 2001. "The Duty to Disclose HMO Physician Incentives." *Health Lawyer* 13(3): 18.

Leiken, Sanford. 1993. "The Role of Adolescents in Decisions Concerning Their Cancer Therapy." *Cancer* 71: 3342.

Levine, Eric M. 1994. "The Constitutionality of Court-ordered Cesarean Surgery: A Threshold Question." *Albany Law Journal of Science & Technology* 4: 229.

Logan v. Field. 75 Mo App 594 (1898).

Matthies v. Mastromonaco. 160 NJ 26, 733 A 2d 456 (1999).

McCabe, Mary Ann, et al. 1996. "Implications of the Patient Self–Determination Act: Guidelines for Involving Adolescents in Medical Decision-Making." *Journal of Adolescent Health* 19: 319.

Montgomery v. Bazaz-Sehgal. 2002 WL 1331774, Pa, June 18 (2002).

Morgan v. MacPhail. 550 Pa 202, 704 A 2d 617 (1997).

Neade v. Portes. 193 Ill 2d 433, 739 NE 2d 496 (2000).

Novak v. Cobb County-Kennestone Hospital Authority. 74 F 3d 1173, CCA 11 (1996).

Oberman, Michelle. 2000. "Mothers and Doctors' Orders: Unmasking the Doctor's Fiduciary Role in Maternal–Fetal Conflicts." *Northwestern University Law Review* 94: 451.

Pemberton v. Tallahassee Memorial Regional Medical Center. 66 F Supp 2d 1247, DC Fla (1999).

Potter, Lori. 2000. "Failure to Disclose HMO Incentives and the Breach of Fiduciary Duty: Is a New Cause of Action Against Physicians the Best Solution?" *University of San Francisco Law Review* 34: 733.

Qawi, In re. 109 Cal Rptr 523, 90 Cal App 4th 1192 (2001).

Quinn v. Blau. 1997 WL 781874, Conn Super (1997).

Reisner v. Regents of the University of California. 31 Cal App 4th 1195, 37 Cal Rptr 2d 518 (1995).

Roberts, Laura W. 2000. "Evidence-Based Ethics and Informed Consent in Mental Illness Research." *Archives of General Psychiatry* 57: 540.

Schreiber v. Physicians Insurance Co. 217 Wisc 2d 94, 579 NW 2d 730 (1998).

Sigman, Garry; Silber, Tomas J.; English, Abigail; and Epner, Jet E. Gans. 1997. "Confidential Health Care for Adolescents: Position Paper of the Society for Adolescent Medicine." *Journal of Adolescent Health* 21: 408.

Simmons, Jessica. 2000. "*Neade v. Portes:* A Physician's Fiduciary Duty to Disclose Financial Incentives." *University of Toledo Law Review* 31: 323.

The Stamford Hospital v. Vega. 236 Conn 646, 674 A 2d 821 (1996).

Truman v. Thomas. 165 Cal Rptr 308, 611 P 2d 902 (1980).

Wirshing, Donna A.; Wirshing, William C.; Marder, Stephen R.; et al. 1998. "Informed Consent: Assessment of Comprehension." *American Journal of Psychiatry* 155(11): 1508.

VI. ISSUES OF CONSENT IN MENTAL HEALTHCARE

Since the 1970s informed consent has been at the center of an evolving doctor-patient relationship whose characterization has shifted from strict paternalism to information exchange, shared decision making, and patient-centered care. In research, informed consent operates in concert with research regulations to protect human subjects while enabling research participation that is regarded, alternatively, as a burden or potential benefit to subjects. Concerns about informed consent in mental health treatment and research touch upon all of these issues.

Informed Consent in Mental Healthcare

The dual ethical goals of informed consent are the protection of the welfare and promotion of the autonomy of patients. As a legal doctrine, informed consent guarantees certain rights of patients in determining their treatment. Informed consent's legal history can be traced to the Supreme Court case of *Schloendorff v. Society of New York Hospitals* (1914), in which Justice Benjamin Cardozo declared that "every human being of adult years and sound mind has a right to determine what shall be done with his body" (*Schloendorff,* p. 126). The questions of what constitutes a sound mind and the rights of those with *unsound* minds remain central to discussion of informed consent in the context of mental healthcare.

At the beginning of the twentieth century, in the earliest stage of what would become the informed consent doctrine, battery provided the legal theory for a cause of action; physicians were required to obtain consent to invasive treatment (Katz). Informed consent's second stage was marked by increasing judicial pressure for consent to be not only free, but also informed; physicians were to disclose treatment alternatives and the risks of the proposed treatment, and then to obtain consent. Still, the California court in *Salgo v. Leland Stanford Junior University Board of Trustees* (1957), which ushered in this second stage, failed to articulate precisely the type of information that was required by this duty to disclose. The decision in *Canterbury v. Spence* (1972) initiated the third stage of informed consent doctrine by articulating a patient-oriented standard of disclosure that required physicians to disclose to patients what a reasonable person would find material to making treatment decisions. Since 1972, the literature on informed consent has burgeoned (e.g., Appelbaum, Lidz, and Meisel; Berg, Appelbaum, and Lidz; Faden and Beauchamp; Meisel, Roth, and Lidz).

Informed consent serves to protect individual autonomy, respect the patient's status as a human being, avoid fraud or duress, encourage doctors to carefully consider their treatment decisions, foster rational decision making by the patient, and involve the public in medicine (Capron). The law of informed consent is based on guaranteeing patients the right to receive sufficient information to make informed choices about treatment, and the right to accept or decline the physician's recommendations. As a process, informed consent involves active exchange of information between patient and physician. Elements fundamental to this process are *disclosure* of the risks and potential benefit of treatment options (or of participation in a research protocol), *comprehension* by the patient (or subject) of such information, *competence* of the decision maker, *voluntariness* of the decision, and the consent (or refusal) itself (Beauchamp and Childress). Competence and voluntariness have special import in the mental health context.

COMPETENCE. Determination of competence functions as a gatekeeping mechanism for informed consent in any healthcare context, because a decision maker's competence is a prerequisite for being able to give informed consent and thus have his/her treatment preferences or decisions respected. In bioethical analyses, competence pertains to a specific task (e.g., making a particular decision); it is not a general quality of persons (Buchanan and Brock). Conceived as decision-relative, competence is a variable or sliding-scale standard; in other words, the greater the degree of risk to patient welfare associated with a particular decision (e.g., to refuse likely life-saving treatment), the higher the standard of competence required of the patient choosing that option (Buchanan and Brock). Nevertheless, determination of competence is based on evaluation of the patient's process of decision making, not the acceptability or reasonability of its outcome. The capacities requisite for competent decision making are the ability to understand and appreciate the risks and benefits of treatment options, the ability to reason and deliberate about those options, and the ability to weigh options against a relatively stable set of values (Buchanan and Brock).

The difference between *competence* and *capacity* can be confusing, and the terms are often used interchangeably (Wolpe, Moreno, and Caplan). Medical or mental health professionals determine patient capacity, whereas incompetence is a legal construct, a legal determination that a patient is incapable of making decisions. The standards for determining incompetence are vague given the lack of judicial consensus. Although courts are available to make the determination, it is typically made by the attending physician. Whether the final determination of incompetence must be made by a court or in the clinical setting with judicial consideration remains unsettled (Berg, et al.; Berg and

Appelbaum). Despite attempts to establish standardized means for assessing decisional capacity and competence, in clinical practice such judgments are still highly dependent on individual psychiatric evaluations (and attending physicians' judgments). Competence assessment remains difficult, especially when a patient's decision seems contrary to his/her ostensible best interests.

In mental health contexts, competence determinations may be especially complicated. Although an ethical, legal, and medical consensus now exists that a competent adult's voluntary informed choices must be respected in the course of treatment and research, it is not entirely clear how to proceed when a person's decision-making capacity may be compromised by mental illness. Historically there has been an erroneous presumption that mental illness obviates the patient's ability to make competent decisions and that either professional paternalism or surrogate decision making is therefore warranted. While some mental disorders may impair the cognitive faculties upon which the capacities for competent decision making rest, a blanket generalization regarding such an adverse effect of mental illness on decision-making capacity is unwarranted. A person with Alzheimer's disease or late life dementia, for example, may be incapable of making some decisions at some times, but at other times may ably comprehend information and weigh options; a patient with bipolar disorder may be quite capable of decision making while medication controls his/her illness, but be incapable if such medication becomes inadequately adjusted to control symptoms of depression or mania. In reality, many people with mental illness may be competent to make medical decisions at least much of the time (Buchanan and Brock; NBAC).

Responses to patient incompetence—specifically, decision making by a surrogate (or proxy) or by a court—serve as an exception to the usual process of informed consent. Nevertheless, surrogate decision making pursues the dual ethical goals of informed consent: the promotion of patient autonomy and protection of patient welfare. Customarily, the surrogate decision-making process involves obtaining informed consent for treatment (or its refusal) from a surrogate named by the patient in an advance directive, or in the absence of such a directive, by the patients' family members. In the absence of such family members, or in the case of irresoluble conflict among them, courts may appoint a guardian to make healthcare decisions on behalf of an incompetent patient. Advance directives for psychiatric treatment allow for a currently competent person to make plans for a future period during which he/she may lose decision-making capacity due to mental illness. These advance directives may include choices about treatment (including electroconvulsive therapy and emergency interventions), medications, hospitalization, research participation (discussed below), and, through the vehicle of a durable power of attorney, the appointment of a surrogate decision maker. Persons who have reason to think they may lose decisional capacity or be subject to involuntary psychiatric commitment may complete such advance directives to guide their psychiatric care and even to help arrange such necessities as temporary custody for their children.

VOLUNTARINESS. In order to constitute an informed consent (or refusal), a competent patient's decision must be both informed and voluntary. Legal discussions of conditions that would impugn the voluntariness, and thus validity, of informed consent focus on undue pressures, threats, and coercion imposed by external factors. However, the medical setting is replete with pressures stemming from the experience of illness (e.g., pain, discomfort, and fear), as well as physicians' recommendations and family dynamics. These situational factors may be especially intense in mental health settings, especially inpatient psychiatric settings, and their effect on the voluntariness of patient decision making must be examined. Philosophical accounts of voluntariness differ, but for the purposes of the informed consent process, a decision is considered voluntary if it is made in the absence of substantially controlling influences (Faden and Beauchamp).

The practice of involuntary psychiatric commitment presents a unique challenge to the doctrine of informed consent, as it entails involuntary hospital admission, while consent to admission is usually sought in other (at least, non-emergency) contexts. The ethical and legal justification of the practice of involuntary commitment resides in balancing the patient's right of self-determination, the patient's well-being, and the protection of third parties from harm. Although statutes may differ, most states permit at least temporary involuntary commitment when there is reason to believe that a patient poses a danger to him/herself or to others, or is unable to take care of him/herself as a result of profound mental illness.

Historically, the involuntary commitment and treatment of mentally ill patients was an exception to the theory of informed consent (Appelbaum). Prior to the 1960s, involuntary commitment to psychiatric facilities on the basis of a mental disorder was considered *ipso facto* a determination of mental incompetence. As the grounds for psychiatric commitment evolved in the 1960 and 1970s from criteria based on the perceived need for treatment to criteria based on perceived dangerousness to self or others, the grounds for commitment came to be distinguished from the justification

for treatment. Judicial scrutiny of involuntary hospitalization has led to the widespread opinion that institutionalization is not always in the service of treatment, that it is certainly not equivalent to a determination of incompetence, and that therefore at least some involuntarily committed patients have the right to refuse treatment (Berg, et al.). In short, some individuals who meet criteria for involuntary commitment—to prevent harm to themselves or others—may nevertheless be competent to refuse (or consent to) treatment for their symptoms and/or underlying condition. Even if competent to refuse treatment, however, involuntarily committed patients may feel substantial pressure to agree to the recommendations of healthcare providers. The context of their treatment may unduly pressure them to consent in the (sometimes accurate) belief that only by agreeing to and undergoing treatment will they be permitted to leave and remain outside the institution. Further complicating this issue is the fact that some courts recognize a state interest in reducing the danger a patient poses to others and in restoring a patient sufficiently to warrant his/her discharge from the hospital. In some jurisdictions, then, treatment may be imposed without the patient's consent, although some jurisdictions at least require legal review of the medical appropriateness of the proposed intervention or the patient's competence, or both (Berg, et al.).

Informed Consent for Research in the Mental Health Context

Reflecting the Belmont Report's 1979 articulation of the ethical principles underlying research ethics and human subjects' protections, as well as provisions of the Nuremberg Code (1947) and the Declaration of Helsinki (1964, subsequently revised), federal regulations governing federally-funded research with human subjects consistently give priority to research subjects' rights and welfare over the pursuit of scientific and social interests (Title 45, Code of Federal Regulations). Informed consent's goal of welfare protection assumes prominence in research, because the right to refuse participation functions as an ultimate line of (self-) protection, in concert with other human subjects protections, or in the event that other protections prove inadequate. "Legally effective informed consent" is required of all research subjects (or their legally authorized representatives [LAR]).

Eight informational elements must be disclosed: a statement that the study involves research, as well as a description of the research and its purposes; a description of reasonably foreseeable risks; a description of reasonably expected benefits; disclosure of appropriate alternatives; a statement about maintenance of confidentiality; for research involving more than minimal risks, an explanation about possible compensation if injury occurs; information about how the subject can have pertinent questions answered; and a statement that participation is voluntary (i.e., the refusal to participate involves no penalties or loss of benefits). Subjects should also be given information regarding: unforeseeable risks; circumstances under which the subject's participation will be terminated; additional costs that the subject may incur; the consequences of a subject's decision to withdraw; the dissemination of findings developed during the study that relate to a subject's willingness to continue; and the approximate number of total subjects (Berg, at al.; Title 45, Code of Federal Regulations). Because the consent must be in writing, there has been a tendency to equate giving informed consent with signing a consent form; in reality, informed consent is a legally-mandated process that is merely documented by signing the consent form. During the informed consent process, care must be taken to prevent the therapeutic misconception (Appelbaum, Roth, and Lidz) or institutional and psychosocial factors from undermining subjects' understanding and voluntariness.

One of Belmont Report's principles is that individuals should be respected as autonomous agents and that those with diminished autonomy should be afforded additional protection in research. Mental health research is conducted on a diverse range of mental health conditions, and only some of these conditions diminish autonomy by impairing the decision-making capacity requisite for the informed consent process.

Guidelines that have been developed to protect *mentally or cognitively impaired* research participants—whether in mental health research projects or not—are relevant for understanding aspects of informed consent in mental health research. Simultaneously, the conflation of mental illness or impairment with incapacity or incompetence must be avoided, not only for conceptual clarity and ethical appropriateness, but also to avoid further stigmatizing those with mental illness. Indeed the 1998 report of the National Bioethics Advisory Commission (NBAC), "Research Involving Subjects with Mental Disorders That May Affect Decision-Making Capacity" has been criticized for perhaps perpetuating discriminatory attitudes by focusing on persons with mental disorders rather than selecting all incapacitated persons as the focus of concern (Oldham, Haimowitz, and Delano, 1999a).

Perhaps recognizing that special protections may themselves be stigmatizing, the Federal Code or "Common Rule" does not identify the mentally ill as a vulnerable group in need of such protections. Special guidelines do address research with children (considered a vulnerable group) and on substance abuse (Office for Protection From Research Risks). As part of the informed consent process, researchers

must be prepared to address, perhaps with federal certificates of confidentiality (Title 42, Code of Federal Regulations), and at least in disclosure of the psychosocial and economic risks of participation (McEnvoy and Keefe), the stigma that attaches to mental illness and to substance abuse (Gorelick, Rickens, and Bonkovsky). Because substance abuse and mental illness may impugn both decisional capacity and behavior control (and thus voluntariness), researchers may need to turn to surrogate decision makers in the consent process. Further, researchers must be cognizant that parents of children with mental disorders are also frequently stigmatized (Jensen, Fisher, and Hoagwood).

Thus, informed consent for mental health research is complicated, first, by the need to determine when mental illness or impairment renders patients incapable of giving informed consent (or refusal) and when it does not; second, by the institutional contexts of much psychiatric research and the myriad pressures that may impugn the voluntariness of such decisions; third, by the need for research to develop effective treatment for mental illness to alleviate the suffering it causes; and finally, by the difficulty that surrogates might have in appreciating the situation of those with mental illness so that they may decide as prospective subjects would if they were competent to do so.

Recognizing that some research potentially benefiting the *mentally infirm* cannot be conducted with any other group, the National Commission for the Protection of Human Subjects of Biomedical and Behavioral Research, created in 1974, sought ethical means to include in research subjects incapable of giving consent. In two reports (1977 and 1978), the Commission recommended that research involving children and the institutionalized mentally infirm be placed in three categories according to level of risk presented: minimal risk, minor increase over minimal risk, and more than a minor increase. Contrary to provisions in both the Nuremberg Code and the Declaration of Helsinki, the Commission concluded that subjects incapable of giving informed consent could be enrolled in both studies that offered the potential of direct benefit and studies that did not offer such a prospect, so long as the burdens and risks of participation did not exceed a certain level. Also proposed were provisions for incapable participants to assent or object to study participation (i.e., to say "yes" or "no" when asked about willingness to participate); such a recommendation is in keeping with the current Council for International Organizations of Medical Sciences (CIOMS) comment that incapable subjects' objections to participation must be respected except in the rarest instance involving direct therapeutic benefit to the subject and the absence of alternative therapy. The Commission also recommended that institutional review boards (IRBs) appoint an auditor to assure the adequacy of the consent process for research involving more than minimal risk, and that informed consent be obtained from the incompetent patient's legal guardian, which parallels provisions of the current version of the Declaration of Helsinki. While a substantial number of the Commission's recommendations regarding research with children were adopted as part of the Common Rule, due to a lack of consensus and concerns about auditing the informed consent process, its recommendations regarding the *mentally infirm* were not adopted.

Concerns about review and audit of research also plagued reception of the 1998 NBAC report, including its recommendations that a qualified expert "independent of the research team" assess subjects' decision-making capacity and that an "independent consent auditor" observe and approve the informed consent process with decisionally-impaired subjects. Most contentious, however, was the NBAC's proposed categorization of research based on risk levels, coupled with its recommendation that a Special Standing Panel (SSP) be created at the Department of Health and Human Services to which IRBs could submit some protocols for prospective review and authorization.

NBAC proposed adhering to a two-tier categorization of risks for research involving decisionally-incapacitated subjects: (1) minimal risk and (2) greater than minimal risk. NBAC recommended that IRBs approve protocols involving minimal risk, or greater than minimal risk that is potentially beneficial to the subject, only if the subject gives informed consent, or has given prospective authorization and his/her LAR also gives permission, or if the subject's LAR gives permission, and if there is no dissent by the subject. (IRBs may also waive the consent requirement for some minimal risk protocols.) LARs are to make decisions about participation based on "a best estimation of what the subject would have chosen if capable of making a decision," and must monitor the subject's participation to make decisions about continuing or withdrawing from participation. Patients with mental illness or with other conditions that may at some time(s) impair their decision-making capacities may execute research advance directives giving *prospective authorization* to research participation and naming a LAR (Sunderland and Dukoff). Prospective authorization cannot be a *blanket* authorization and must be limited to specific classes of research about which the (then capable) subject understood the relevant risks, potential benefits, and other conditions (NBAC). The degree of specificity of the prior prospective authorization must increase as the risk presented by a particular protocol increases. For research presenting greater than minimal risk and not holding out the prospect of direct medical benefit, NBAC recommended that IRBs approve such protocols under the same conditions, or if the protocol is approved by the SSP or falls within its guidelines and the potential subject's LAR gives permission for participation. This final provision drew criticism from two sides.

Recognizing that research involving greater than minimal risk and not presenting the prospect of direct benefit to subjects may nevertheless promise "significant increases in understanding their conditions," and thus warrant further review, the NBAC envisioned that IRBs could refer such protocols to a SSP for case-by-case review through an *open consensus process* with the prospect that, over time, guidelines for conducting such research would emerge. NBAC viewed its recommendations as consistent with the two-tier risk-level scheme found in the majority of the Common Rule (and the National Institutes of Health Clinical Center Policy on the Consent Process in Research Involving Impaired Human Subjects), and stated that the SSP could evaluate research protocols that could not be approved otherwise under provisions of its 1998 report while providing patients, their families, and advocates with confidence that such protocols were receiving independent review (NBAC).

Some critics, however, argue that the NBAC's approach would greatly hamper valuable moderate-risk research that would otherwise be categorized as minor increase over minimal risk research (Miller and Fins; Oldham, et al., 1999a, 1999b). They argue that if federal regulations result from the NBAC recommendations, relatively low-risk research, including routine medical procedures such as positron emission tomographic scans and magnetic resonance imaging with sedation, would be subject to the same restrictions as research that is categorized at the highest level of risk (such as internal organ biopsies). In a statement appended to the NBAC report, similar concerns are voiced by two NBAC commissioners (Lo and Flynn). Some of these critics advocate a tri-level risk classification including an intermediary category of research presenting "a minor increase over minimal risk" derived from the National Commission's 1978 report and the Common Rule's regulations governing research involving children (Miller and Fins). Responding to these concerns, NBAC commissioners suggest that a SSP would only review those protocols involving persons incapable of giving informed consent and who have not provided advanced authorization (Childress and Shapiro). Yet, argue John M. Oldham and his coauthors, the number of protocols involving low-risk procedures that would require SSP review would be large, given the infrequency of advance directives for research and the inclusion of so many different protocols based upon the two-tier categorization of risk (1999b).

Although the majority of concerns expressed about the NBAC's recommendations take issue with allegedly unnecessary and cumbersome layers of oversight for research involving subjects with impaired capacity, a second line of criticism urges the opposite. Beverly Woodward argues that human research subjects are now threatened by increased research-related risks as a result of pressures to reduce restrictions on research involving subjects with impaired decision-making capacity. She charges that by downplaying the conflict between the progress of science and the protection of human subjects, and in departing from protections afforded by the Nuremberg Code and the Declaration of Helsinki to those who cannot give informed consent, the NBAC has endorsed the primacy of scientific interests over human subject welfare. Woodward finds particularly troubling NBAC's recommendation that would "permit a waiver of the consent requirement for research involving greater than minimal risk" that is without the prospect of direct benefit, so long as the subject's surrogate consents and the SSP also "grants permission based on a finding that the research 'offers the possibility of substantial benefit to the population under study'" and that the risks presented to subjects are commensurate with this possible benefit (p. 1948). Woodward believes that in some of the NBAC's recommendations, the "rapid march of science" is being advanced over the interests of individual research subjects, which, if true, would constitute a serious departure from the consensus that has grounded research ethics and the requirements for informed consent in research since the Nuremburg Code. Much remains to be examined—both at the level of drafting regulations and at the point of their implementation—to determine whether any such shift is indeed occurring.

ALAN P. BROWN
TROYEN A. BRENNAN (1995)
REVISED BY LISA S. PARKER
KAMRAN SAMAKAR

SEE ALSO: *Autonomy; Competence; Institutionalization and Deinstitutionalization; Mental Health Services; Mental Health Therapies; Mentally Disabled and Mentally Ill Persons; Patients' Rights: Mental Patients' Rights;* and other *Informed Consent* subentries

BIBLIOGRAPHY

Appelbaum, Paul S. 1994. *Almost a Revolution: Mental Health Law and the Limits of Change.* New York: Oxford University Press.

Appelbaum, Paul S.; Lidz, Charles W.; and Meisel, Alan. 1987. *Informed Consent: Legal Theory and Clinical Practice.* New York: Oxford University Press.

Appelbaum, Paul S.; Roth, Loren H.; and Lidz, Charles W. 1982. "The Therapeutic Misconception: Informed Consent in Psychiatric Research." *International Journal of Law and Psychiatry* 5: 319–329.

Beauchamp, Tom L., and Childress, James. F. 2001. *Principles of Biomedical Ethics,* 5th edition. New York: Oxford University Press.

Berg, Jessica W., and Appelbaum, Paul S. 1999. "Subjects' Capacity to Consent to Neurobiological Research." In *Ethics in Psychiatric Research: A Resource Manual for Human Subjects Protection,* ed. Harold A. Pincus, Jeffrey A. Lieberman, and Sandy Ferris. Washington, D.C.: American Psychiatric Association.

Berg, Jessica W.; Appelbaum, Paul S.; Lidz, Charles W.; et al. 2001. *Informed Consent: Legal Theory and Clinical Practice,* 2nd edition. New York: Oxford University Press.

Buchanan, Allen E., and Brock, Dan W. 1990. *Deciding for Others: The Ethics of Surrogate Decision Making.* New York: Cambridge University Press.

Canterbury v. Spence. 1972. 464 F.2d 772 (D.C. Cir. 1972).

Capron, Alexander. 1974. "Informed Consent in Catastrophic Disease Research and Treatment." *University of Pennsylvania Law Review* 340: 365–76.

Childress, James F., and Shapiro, Harold T. 1999. "Almost Persuaded: Reactions to Oldham, et al." *Archives of General Psychiatry* 56: 697–698.

Council for International Organizations of Medical Sciences (CIOMS). 1993. *International Ethical Guidelines for Biomedical Research Involving Human Subjects.* Geneva: Office of the General Secretary of CIOMS.

Department of Health and Human Services. Title 42, Code of Federal Regulations (CFR), Part 2.

Department of Health and Human Services. 1983. Title 45, Code of Federal Regulations (CFR), Part 46. "Protection of Human Subjects." 48 *Federal Register (FR)* 9818; March 8, 1983. 56 *FR* 28032; June 18, 1991.

Faden, Ruth R., and Beauchamp, Tom L. 1986. *A History and Theory of Informed Consent.* New York: Oxford University Press.

Gorelick, David A.; Rickens, Roy W.; and Bonkovsky, Frederick O. 1999. "Clinical Research in Substance Abuse: Human Subjects Issues." In *Ethics in Psychiatric Research: A Resource Manual for Human Subjects Protection,* ed. Harold A. Pincus, Jeffrey A. Lieberman, and Sandy Ferris. Washington, D.C.: American Psychiatric Association.

Jensen, Peter S.; Fisher, Celia B.; and Hoagwood, Kimberly. 1999. "Special Issues in Mental Health/Illness Research with Children and Adolescents." In *Ethics in Psychiatric Research: A Resource Manual for Human Subjects Protection,* ed. Harold A. Pincus, Jeffrey A. Lieberman, and Sandy Ferris. Washington, D.C.: American Psychiatric Association.

Katz, Jay. 1984. *The Silent World of Doctor and Patient.* New York: Free Press.

McEvoy, Joseph P., and Keefe, Richard S.E. 1999. "Informing Subjects of Risks and Benefits." In *Ethics in Psychiatric Research: A Resource Manual for Human Subjects Protection,* ed. Harold A. Pincus, Jeffrey A. Lieberman, and Sandy Ferris. Washington, D.C.: American Psychiatric Association.

Meisel, Alan; Roth, Loren H.; and Lidz, Charles W. 1977. "Toward a Model of the Legal Doctrine of Informed Consent." *American Journal of Psychiatry* 134: 285–289.

Miller, Franklin G., and Fins, Joseph J. 1999. "Protecting Vulnerable Research Subjects Without Unduly Constraining Neuropsychiatric Research." *Archives of General Psychiatry* 56: 701–702.

National Commission for the Protection of Human Subjects of Biomedical and Behavioral Research. 1977. "Report and Recommendations: Research Involving Children." Washington, D.C.: U.S. Government Printing Office.

National Commission for the Protection of Human Subjects of Biomedical and Behavioral Research. 1978. "The Belmont Report: Ethical Principles and Guidelines for the Protection of Human Subjects of Research." Washington, D.C.: U.S. Government Printing Office.

National Commission for the Protection of Human Subjects of Biomedical and Behavioral Research. 1978. "Report and Recommendations: Research Involving Those Institutionalized As Mentally Infirm." Washington, D.C.: U.S. Government Printing Office.

National Institutes of Health Clinical Center Policy on the Consent Process in Research Involving Impaired Human Subjects. 1987. In *Ethics in Psychiatric Research: A Resource Manual for Human Subjects Protection (1999)*, ed. Harold A. Pincus, Jeffrey A. Lieberman, and Sandy Ferris. Washington, D.C.: American Psychiatric Association.

Office for Protection From Research Risks (OPRR), Department of Health and Human Services, National institutes of Health. 1993. *Protecting Human Research Subjects: Institutional Review Board Guidebook.* Washington, D.C.: Government Printing Office.

Oldham, John M.; Haimowitz, Stephan; and Delano, Susan J. 1999a. "Protection of Persons with Mental Disorders From Research Risk: A Response to the Report of the National Bioethics Advisory Commission." *Archives of General Psychiatry* 56: 688–693.

Oldham, John M.; Haimowitz, Stephan; and Delano, Susan J. 1999b. "Commentary." *Archives of General Psychiatry* 56: 703–704.

Salgo v. Leland Standford Jr. Univ. Bd. of Trustees. 317 P.2d 170 (Cal. Ct. App. 1957).

Schloendorff v. Society of New York Hospital. 105 N.E. 92 (N.Y. 1914).

Sunderland, Trey, and Dukoff, Ruth. 1999. "Surrogate Decision Making and Advance Directives With Cognitively Impaired Research Subjects." In *Ethics in Psychiatric Research: A Resource Manual for Human Subjects Protection,* ed. Harold A. Pincus, Jeffrey A. Lieberman, and Sandy Ferris. Washington, D.C.: American Psychiatric Association.

Wolpe, Paul W.; Moreno, Jonathan; and Caplan, Arthur L. 1999. "Ethical Principles and History." In *Ethics in Psychiatric Research: A Resource Manual for Human Subjects Protection,* ed. Harold A. Pincus, Jeffrey A. Lieberman, and Sandy Ferris. Washington, D.C.: American Psychiatric Association.

Woodward, Beverly. 1999. "Challenges to Human Subjects Protections in U.S. Medical Research." *Journal of the American Medical Association* 282: 1947–1952.

INTERNET RESOURCE

National Bioethics Advisory Commission (NBAC). 1998. "Research Involving Persons With Mental Disorders That May Affect Decision-Making Capacity: Volume 1, Report and Recommendations of the National Bioethics Advisory Commission, Rockville, Maryland." National Bioethics Advisory Commission. Available from <http://www.georgetown.edu/research/nrcbl/>.

INJURY AND INJURY CONTROL

• • •

The factual assertions used to demonstrate the importance of injuries as a public-health problem are well known: Injuries are the leading cause of death for the majority of the human life span; injuries deprive people of more potential years of life than any single disease; and the cost of injuries, whether measured in dollars or in human suffering, is staggering (Rice et al.). Injuries are generally defined by those working in the field of injury prevention as human damage due to the acute transfer of energy or the lack of essentials such as oxygen (as in asphyxiation) or heat (as in hypothermic injuries) (National Committee for Injury Prevention and Control).

Actions taken to control injury provide prototypical clashes between the personal liberty of the individual and the goals of public health. These conflicts—referred to in ethical terminology as conflicts between paternalistic beneficence and individual autonomy—are experienced in such public interventions as those that mandate helmet use by motorcyclists or that require the wearing of seat belts by drivers and passengers in automobiles. However, injury control also illuminates how public health makes progress by redefining the nature of the problem—in this case, by shifting from the term *accident* (which points to the individual who is injured or an "act of God" as the responsible agent) to *injury* (which suggests that equipment, environment, and those responsible for equipment and environment share responsibility).

Historical Development

Although injuries have plagued the human race since its earliest times, it is only in the twentieth century that science has been applied to this public-health problem. For most of history, and to some extent up to the present, injuries have been misperceived as the equivalent of accidents; that is, chance occurrences that are basically unpredictable, and therefore unpreventable. The notions that some people are accident-prone, and therefore we should expect them to be injured, and that people are injured as punishment for a prior moral offense, have substantially retarded the ability to approach injuries and injury prevention scientifically.

A turning point in the historical development of injury control occurred in the early 1960s, when scientists first recognized that injuries, like diseases, had agents that interacted with hosts in specific environments to produce human damage (Gibson; Haddon). By modifying the agent (which was recognized as transferred energy), the human host, or the environment, one could substantially reduce the likelihood and/or the severity of an injury. William Haddon is generally recognized as the individual who most clearly "moved injury prevention into the mainstream of public health research and policy" (Baker). He developed the conceptual tools for the analyses of injury etiology and prevention that form the foundation of modern injury control.

In the decades that followed, scientists applied epidemiologic methods to the investigation of injuries and developed a new body of knowledge on how, when, where, and to whom injuries occur. Data are now available to dispel definitively the notion that injuries occur at random. The clear patterns of injury, which include identified high-risk groups (e.g., elderly persons at risk for hip fractures), geographic patterns (e.g., the distribution of firearm fatalities in the United States), and temporal trends (e.g., the increasing rate of adolescent suicide), make injuries both predictable and, more important, preventable (Baker et al.). Interventions can be focused on high-risk persons and sites, and the effects of the interventions can be scientifically evaluated by comparisons of injury rates.

Shifting Conceptions: Environmental and Product Modification

Notwithstanding these significant advances in the science of injury control, the field remains troubled by popular misconceptions that impede effective prevention programs. The reduction of injuries is still considered a matter of common sense by many. Unlike disease prevention, which is generally recognized to depend upon expert knowledge, injury prevention is commonly misperceived as a matter of an individual's responsibility rather than of public policy, and the importance of expert advice in preventing injuries is often not acknowledged. Thus the false orientation that the only way to prevent injuries is to teach people to be careful

remains a popular bias, even among key decision makers who are in a position to protect millions from injury. The exclusive focus on the behavior of individuals for the prevention of injuries characterizes what was once known as accident prevention. Accidents were understood as the result of imprudent behavior; the remedy was to teach people to be constantly careful and vigilant. An example of this is the early approach to reducing highway fatalities. The method relied upon was improvement of drivers' skills through education and frequent reminders to be careful delivered in public service announcements. By the mid-1960s, however, there was a growing awareness that lives could be saved by shifting the focus of attention from the driver to the highway and the automobile. Crashes were recognized as foreseeable events. By altering the construction of vehicles and highways, the human cargo of the vehicles would not have to suffer serious injuries if and when a crash occurred.

The U.S. Congress took notice of the increasing number of highway fatalities and the opportunity to reduce this toll by mandating "crashworthy" vehicles. In 1966, Congress passed the National Traffic and Motor Vehicle Safety Act, which provided for the creation of motor vehicle safety standards. These standards, which anticipated driver error and provided a more forgiving environment within the vehicle, have saved tens of thousands of lives (Robertson).

The idea of paying attention to products as well as behaviors has not been restricted to highway safety. Efforts to prevent childhood scald injuries from hot tap water provide an example of this trend toward product alteration. Hot water coming out of faucets in homes is often at a temperature that can cause a severe burn injury to a child's skin in a matter of a few seconds. Rather than relying on parents to keep young children away from faucets, efforts have been made to direct the parents to turn down the setting on their water heaters so that water will not be discharged at temperatures greater than 125°F (Katcher et al.). This prevention strategy, however, still relies upon motivating parents to reset the water heater. An even more effective strategy has been to influence appliance manufacturers to set the heaters at the proper level before they leave the factory, thus eliminating the need to modify parental behavior.

A general principle of injury control, illustrated by the prevention of scald injuries, is to shift the focus of prevention from the individual to the community (Beauchamp; Barry). Legislation and regulation that require safer products and environments are more effective in preventing injuries than are efforts to have individuals control their own behaviors. When safety legislation or regulation has been difficult to accomplish because of strongly resistant political influences, litigation has been used. An example of this is product liability litigation, which transfers the cost of injuries from a dangerous product back to the manufacturer, thus giving the manufacturer a strong incentive to improve the safety aspects of its product (Teret).

Altering Behaviors: Paternalism and Prevention

Sometimes product modification is not available to achieve a desired prevention strategy, and reliance upon altering behaviors is necessary. Such is the case with motorcycle helmet use. The effectiveness of helmet use in preventing or reducing the severity of head injuries is well established, but helmet use is not universally accepted by motorcyclists. Legislation requiring helmet use is effective both in increasing the use rates and in decreasing motorcyclist death rates. These laws, however, have been bitterly fought by some motorcyclists, and most states have passed and then repealed mandatory helmet use laws.

The debate over motorcycle helmet laws has raised many issues that apply to other areas of mandating safe behaviors. The propriety of governmental paternalism, the relevance of who pays the costs of injuries, and the constitutionality of laws that interfere with personal decisions are all included in the helmet issue. Assuming a definition of paternalism as institutional interference with individual action for the sake of some greater good, motorcyclists question whether their enforced safety is a good substantial enough to deny them their freedom of choice to ride without a helmet.

Opponents of helmet laws categorize such laws as *hard* legal paternalism, in that the laws regulate voluntary behavior that can harm only the motorcyclist (see Feinberg, p. 12, for distinction between *hard* and *soft* legal paternalism). Proponents of the laws point out that the increased harm inflicted on a helmetless motorcyclist eventually affects the public as a whole. The public pays about 85 percent of the costs of motorcyclists' injuries; helmet laws would reduce the human capital costs by about $400 million per year in the United States (Rice et al.). Arguments have been raised that the solution to the cost-of-injury problem is to require adequate medical insurance of those who choose to assume risks, but the flaws of this argument are apparent. Some motorcyclists will not purchase insurance, through lack of money or indifference; and it would be unacceptable to have the injuries of these motorcyclists go without medical attention (Dworkin).

The motorcycle helmet issue illustrates a problem that permeates the field of injury prevention. As a society, Americans will still permit the manufacture and marketing of some inherently dangerous products, and then rely upon limited efforts to control the behavior of the individuals to whom these products are distributed. Guns provide a striking example. There are about 38,000 firearm fatalities each year in the United States, and most of the policy to reduce this toll focuses on modifying the behavior of the individual who possesses a gun. There are few effective regulations governing the number and types of guns that can be manufactured in the United States (Webster et al.).

The future success of injury prevention appears to be highly dependent upon the willingness of government to regulate business. The products people use and the built environments in which they place themselves are highly determinative of the risk of injury. Since people do not always act in a prudent fashion, and since government is unwilling and unable to mandate such behavior, the greatest opportunity to reduce the incidence and severity of injury rests in the regulation of products and environments.

STEPHEN P. TERET
MICHAEL D. TERET (1995)
BIBLIOGRAPHY REVISED

SEE ALSO: *Autonomy; Paternalism; Public Health: History; Public Health Law*

BIBLIOGRAPHY

Baker, Susan P. 1989. "Injury Science Comes of Age." *Journal of the American Medical Association* 262(16): 2284–2285.

Baker, Susan P.; O'Neill, Brian; Ginsberg, Marvin J.; and Li, Guohua. 1991. *The Injury Fact Book,* 2nd edition. New York: Oxford University Press.

Barry, Patricia Z. 1975. "Individual Versus Community Orientation in the Prevention of Injuries." *Preventive Medicine* 4(1): 47–56.

Barss, Peter; Smith, Gordon; Baker, Susan; and Mohan, Dinesh. 1998. *Injury Prevention: An International Perspective: Epidemiology, Surveillance, and Policy.* New York: Oxford University Press.

Beauchamp, Dan E. 1989. "Injury, Community and the Republic." *Law, Medicine and Health Care* 17(1): 42–49.

Berger, Lawrence R., and Mohan, Dinesh, eds. 1996. *Injury Control: A Global View.* New York: Oxford University Press.

Bonnie, Richard J.; Fulco, Carolyn; and Liverman, Catharyn T., eds. 1999. *Reducing the Burden of Injury: Advancing Prevention and Treatment.* Washington, D.C.: National Academy Press.

Dworkin, Gerald. 1983. "Paternalism." In *Paternalism,* pp. 19–34, ed. Rolf E. Sartorius. Minneapolis: University of Minnesota Press.

Feinberg, Joel. 1986. *Harm to Self: The Moral Limits of the Criminal Law.* New York: Oxford University Press.

Gibson, James J. 1961. "The Contribution of Experimental Psychology to the Formulation of the Problem of Safety—A Brief for Basic Research." In *Behavioral Approaches to Accident Research,* pp. 77–89. Conference on Research in Accident Prevention. New York: Association for the Aid of Crippled Children.

Haddon, William, Jr. 1963. "A Note Concerning Accident Theory and Research with Special Reference to Motor Vehicle Accidents." *Annals of the New York Academy of Sciences* 107: 635–646.

Katcher, Murray L.; Landry, Gregory L.; and Shapiro, Mary Melvin. 1989. "Liquid-Crystal Thermometer Use in Pediatric Office Counseling About Tap Water Burn Prevention." *Pediatrics* 83(5): 766–771.

Mohan, Dinesh, and Tiwari, Geetam. 2000. *Injury Prevention and Control.* New York: Taylor & Francis.

National Committee for Injury Prevention and Control. 1989. *Injury Prevention: Meeting the Challenge.* New York: Oxford University Press.

Rice, Dorothy P.; MacKenzie, Ellen J.; Jones, Alison S.; et al. 1989. *Cost of Injury in the United States: A Report to Congress,* ed. Ida V. S. W. Red. San Francisco: Institute for Health and Aging, University of California, and Injury Prevention Center, Johns Hopkins University.

Rivara, Frederick P.; Koepsell, Thomas; and Maier, Ronald V., eds. 2000. *Injury Control: Research and Program Evaluation.* New York: Cambridge University Press.

Robertson, Leon S. 1981. "Automobile Safety Regulations and Death Reductions in the United States." *American Journal of Public Health* 71(8): 818–822.

Teret, Stephen P. 1986. "Litigating for the Public's Health." *American Journal of Public Health* 76(8): 1027–1029.

Widome, Mark D. 1997. *Injury Prevention and Control for Children and Youth.* Elk Grove Village: American Academy of Pediatrics.

INSANITY AND THE INSANITY DEFENSE

• • •

A defendant's legal responsibility for his or her criminal conduct is a controversial issue that continually draws public attention, particularly after highly publicized crimes. The insanity defense relates to the defendant's mental condition at the time of the crime rather than at the time of the trial. The latter issue, which is discussed as the defendant's competency to stand trial, is not the subject of this entry. The insanity defense deals with the criminal competency of an individual at a time in the past rather than at the time of the trial and sentencing.

Legal insanity is by definition a legal issue and should be distinguished from *clinical insanity,* which is not a term that is recognized by mental health professionals. The term *temporary insanity* sometimes is used by the general public to refer to a brief episode of mental illness and abnormal behavior that was present only at the time of the offense rather than before or after it. Legal insanity, however, is always temporary in the sense that it refers only to the defendant's behavior at the precise time of the alleged offense.

The insanity defense represents a special defense to a criminal offense. Although the prosecution generally has the responsibility of proving the defendant guilty beyond a reasonable doubt, a defendant is legally entitled to raise defenses to the charge, whether self-defense, alibi, misidentification, insanity, or another defense.

The insanity defense is one of many issues subsumed under the rubric of criminal responsibility. Although this entry reviews several of the important issues related to the special defense of insanity, it excludes several related issues, such as diminished mental capacity, diminished responsibility, guilty but mentally ill, and the sentencing of a mentally ill defendant after conviction.

There are public misperceptions about the insanity defense. That defense is used infrequently in criminal trials in the United States and is rarely successful. Empirical research has revealed that it is introduced in less than 1 percent of felony trials and is successful in fewer than one-quarter of those trials. Many insanity acquittals occur through a stipulation between the prosecution and the defense rather than as a result of a contested trial. There is substantial variation among the states in the use and success of the insanity defense, with some states having more than seventy-five acquittals each year and many others having fewer than five. After acquittal insanity acquittees can remain hospitalized longer than they would have been imprisoned if they had been convicted of the same criminal offense and incarcerated. Generally, the public is not sympathetic to defendants who use the insanity defense for serious violent crimes except in cases of infanticide by severely depressed or mentally ill women.

Purpose of the Insanity Defense

The contemporary insanity defense had its origins more than 2,500 years ago, when it was recognized that certain categories of individuals, such as children, the mentally ill, and the developmentally disabled, could not be considered to be at fault for their offenses. A twentieth-century judge in the United States, David Bazelon, noted in the 1954 court decision *Durham v. United States,* "Our collective conscience does not allow punishment where it cannot impose blame." Generally, however, the criminal law posits that individuals act with *free will* should be held responsible for their behavior. Mentally ill individuals can be excused from moral, and sometimes legal, blameworthiness when they act in ignorance, under compulsion, or irrationally.

Many people in the lay community mistakenly believe that a crime is defined by the perpetrator's behavior so that a homicide is a homicide. In contrast, most criminal offenses require the presence of a physical element and a mental element. The physical element, the *actus rea,* refers to the actual behavior of the perpetrator, such as aiming and firing a weapon at the victim. The mental element, the *mens rea,* or guilty mind, addresses the state of mind of the perpetrator at the time of the offense. There are, for instance, several types and degrees of criminal homicide, and they usually are distinguished by the intent of the perpetrator, such as the presence of malice, criminal intent, or advance deliberation. In many states murder is charged in several degrees. Criminal homicides may be charged as involuntary manslaughter, voluntary manslaughter, third-degree murder, second-degree murder, or first-degree murder. The most serious homicide charge requires the presence of premeditation and deliberation by the defendant at the time of the crime. Each homicide crime has different mental elements, although all involve the killing of a victim by a defendant, and the punishments vary considerably among them.

The special defense of insanity builds on this inclusion of a mental element in the offense but advances it further to inquire about the defendant's state of mind beyond criminal intent. A defendant who makes detailed advanced preparations and then kills a person upon hearing voices from God commanding that act has criminal intent but may lack criminal responsibility for that offense, depending on the legal definition of insanity in the jurisdiction.

A handful of state jurisdictions in the United States have eliminated the legal defense of insanity. In those jurisdictions evidence regarding the defendant's mental illness at the time of the offense sometimes still can be introduced at trial to attempt to prove that the defendant did not have the requisite mental element or intent to commit the offense. Thus, if the defendant was so mentally ill that he or she could not have intended to commit the offense, then evidence of that illness and mental state is admissible at trial.

Legal Standards of Criminal Responsibility

Elements of the insanity defense are defined in different ways. The definition of the underlying mental disorder and the specific components of the defense are defined by state and federal statute but sometimes are defined by case (judge-made) law. The states vary widely in the definition, implementation, and outcome of the insanity defense.

Statutes and case law also describe the applicable procedural issues related to evaluations of criminal responsibility, such as the right of the defense and the prosecution to request an examination, the court appointment and payment of forensic experts to conduct the examination, and the extent of the waiver, if any, of the attorney client-privilege in conjunction with the examination.

For centuries courts, legislators, and policy makers have struggled to articulate an appropriate threshold and definition of legal insanity to exculpate a criminal defendant. The concept of a "wild beast" test was introduced centuries ago, excusing only individuals who did not know what they were doing because they resembled infants or wild beasts in their intellectual function. A New Hampshire court decision in 1868 (*State v. Pike,* 49 N.H. 399) offered the "product test" of insanity, stating, "No man shall be held accountable, criminally, for an act which was the offspring and product of mental disease." The product test subsequently was adopted in 1954 for the federal courts in the Washington, D.C., Federal Circuit. The product test was abandoned because of its breadth and concerns about abuse in light of the fact that symptoms of many mental disorders not deemed exculpatory can be expressed as criminal acts.

The contemporary legal standards for the insanity defense are composed of two principal factors: cognitive standards and volitional standards. Cognitive standards relate to the defendant's cognitive ability or actual knowledge of the criminality, illegality, or wrongfulness of his or her conduct at the time of the crime. Cognitive abilities include the ability to perceive reality accurately and make rational decisions that are based on that reality. Originating in the United Kingdom in 1843, the M'Naghten standard, for example, asks whether the defendant was suffering from a "defect of reason, from disease of the mind, as not to know the nature and quality of the act he was doing; or if he did know it, that he did not know he was doing what was wrong." *Wrong* is defined variously as legally wrong (the defendant knew his or her action to be illegal) or morally wrong (the defendant knew his or her action to be morally wrong in his or her own eyes or in those of the public). As a symptom of severe mental illness, a command hallucination from God instructing a defendant to kill someone could be accompanied by an impairment in the defendant's cognitive ability or knowledge regarding wrongfulness. Cognitive tests of legal insanity are the most common test in the United States and characterize the legal insanity test used by the federal courts since 1984.

The alternative insanity defense standard is concerned with the defendant's ability to control his or her behavior at the time of the offense as a result of a mental disease or disorder. This volitional test asks whether the defendant lacked partial or total capacity to control the behavior that led to the offense independent of cognitive knowledge or appreciation of the offense and its wrongfulness. This standard originally was described as an "irresistible impulse test" in which the individual's desires were so strong that he or she could not help acting on them. The individual was in effect compelled to perform the criminal acts. Mental disorders such as bipolar disorder, with a euphoric mood, elevated energy, insomnia, impulsive behavior, and racing thoughts, can reduce an individual's ability to control his or her behavior.

There are several specific variations of the cognitive and volitional tests of insanity. A cognitive test that employs the language of the defendant's ability to appreciate the wrongfulness of his or her conduct is significantly different from one that relates to the defendant's ability to know its wrongfulness. Appreciation is a broader mental ability than simple knowledge and encompasses emotional as well as cognitive or intellectual abilities. Similarly, the test that asks whether a defendant lacks substantial capacity to conform her or his conduct to the requirements of the law is a looser or broader test than one that asks whether the defendant was unable to control herself or himself because of the mental illness.

The federal test of criminal responsibility, which was enacted by Congress in 1984 after the acquittal of John Hinckley, Jr., by reason of insanity for the attempted assassination of President Ronald Reagan, applies to federal crimes. It states: "It is an affirmative defense to a prosecution under any federal statute that, at the time of the commission of the acts constituting the offense, the defendant, as a result of severe mental disease or defect, was unable to appreciate the nature and quality or wrongfulness of his acts" (18 u.s.c. section 17a).

Some states use both a cognitive prong and a volitional prong. The American Law Institute (ALI) proposed a model test in 1962 through the Model Penal Code. The ALI test states: "A person is not responsible for criminal conduct if at the time of such conduct as a result of mental disease or defect he lacks substantial capacity either to appreciate the criminality of his conduct or to conform his conduct to the

requirements of law." This test had been adopted by approximately half the states before the Hinckley trial and the subsequent reforms.

Post-Hinckley Reforms of the Insanity Defense

After John Hinckley, Jr.'s, acquittal by reason of insanity in federal court many states as well as the federal government enacted changes to the insanity defense. Those changes included altering the test by making it stricter and changing certain procedures for its use. Some states and the federal courts eliminated the volitional test. Some states and the federal courts shifted the burden of proof at trial from the prosecution having the burden of proving that the defendant was not legally insane (beyond a reasonable doubt) to the defense, which must prove that the defendant was legally insane (by clear and convincing evidence). Other states added a guilty but mentally ill verdict to their criminal laws, offering a jury an alternative verdict to the insanity acquittal for mentally ill defendants who failed to satisfy the insanity defense requirements at trial.

Other statutory changes implemented stricter controls and supervision over individuals acquitted by reason of insanity, such as initial automatic hospitalization at least for psychiatric evaluation, with tighter procedures to prevent the premature release of dangerous individuals. Connecticut and Oregon have established special security review boards that intensively monitor insanity acquittees even on an outpatient basis, similar to criminal probation. Acquittees can be rehospitalized involuntarily if they are deemed to be too mentally ill or dangerous to remain in the community.

Clinical Evaluation

Statutes and case law variously use and define the terms *mental disease, mental disorder, mental illness,* and *mental defect* as the condition underlying a defendant's loss of cognitive or volitional function. The evaluator must be familiar with the legal definition of the term *mental disease* and the precise language of the criminal responsibility test in the defendant's jurisdiction. Statutes may or may not clearly define a mental disease or defect and usually do not employ accepted psychiatric nomenclature. Severe mental disorders such as schizophrenia, schizoaffective disorder, bipolar disorder, and other mood disorders with psychotic features generally qualify as mental diseases or defects for purposes of the insanity defense. Impulse control disorders such as kleptomania, pyromania, paraphilia, and pathological gambling may or may not be grounds for an insanity defense under the law. Other conditions not formally recognized as mental disorders by the mental health community, such as *battered woman syndrome,* may not constitute a mental disease or defect for purposes of the insanity defense.

The criminal responsibility evaluation is a retrospective evaluation of a defendant's criminal competency and is readily distinguished from an evaluation for treatment purposes. Therefore, forensic evaluators must have adequate training, experience, and forensic knowledge to conduct such evaluations properly. Evaluators typically attempt to interview the defendant about his or her thinking, behavior, and emotional controls at the time of the offense. However, evaluators cannot rely exclusively on the defendant's account of the crime because of the possibility of feigned mental illness and also must review crime scene data such as police reports, autopsies, witness accounts, and other information that can lead more objectively to an understanding of the events. Psychiatric treatment records of the defendant also are made available to the evaluator. Collateral interviews with family members or friends of the defendant, current treatment personnel, coworkers, and victims and witnesses also can be conducted. Psychological or neurological testing can be helpful in establishing a psychiatric diagnosis but cannot provide direct evidence that the defendant satisfies the insanity test standard. Evaluators may not be able to interview a defendant until months or years after the crime. Thus, reconstructing the defendant's mental state at that earlier time is a challenging task.

Clinical Issues

After the forensic mental health evaluator has obtained the necessary data regarding the defendant's mental health history and the defendant's state of mind at the time of the offense, the evaluator must provide to the retaining attorney or court an opinion about the defendant's psychiatric diagnosis and address the insanity defense standard. There are no biological tests that can prove directly whether a defendant had a mental disorder at the time of the crime or met the insanity defense standard, and the evaluator uses clinical judgment to reach conclusions in this regard. A defendant's assertion of a severe mental disorder at the time of the crime is more credible when there is a previous history of that disorder and documented treatment for it.

The evaluator must attempt to exclude mental conditions that are not deemed to be exculpatory by the applicable law. Personality disorders and intoxication by alcohol and drugs at the time of an offense are typically not exculpatory, and so the effects of those disorders on a defendant must be considered but separated from those of disorders that are potentially exculpatory. In other words, the evaluator must

establish the relationship between the mental disorder present at the time of the offense and the criminal behavior.

There are many challenges in determining whether a defendant meets the legal insanity standard. The evaluator focuses on the defendant's thoughts, feelings, and behavior at the time of the crime but also inquires about those issues before and after the crime. If the defendant is charged with multiple crimes, the evaluator performs the analysis for each of those crimes. The evaluator must analyze the defendant's thoughts, feelings, and behavior carefully to determine whether the specific cognitive or volitional criteria for the applicable insanity defense are satisfied. It is likely that a defendant will satisfy the criteria for one insanity defense test but not for another.

If a jurisdiction uses a volitional insanity defense test, the evaluator must determine whether the defendant lacked the ability to control his or her behavior as a result of a severe mental disorder or simply failed to control his or her behavior because of anger, revenge, greed, envy, sexual arousal, or another condition unrelated to a severe mental disorder. The fact that a defendant acted on an impulse or desire does not mean that that impulse was irresistible; most, if not all, impulses can be resisted in certain circumstances. Volitional assessments involve a determination of whether the defendant attempted to delay or resist the impulse, pursued alternatives to gratifying the impulse, and planned or prepared for the crime while avoiding apprehension.

The insanity defense has been a complex yet compelling subject for centuries, attracting extraordinary public attention, especially after well-publicized crimes. The defense has survived many attempts to abolish it, with only a few states having done that. Although there are moral and legal bases for excusing an individual's criminal activity, most societies have struggled to adopt exculpatory rules that are politically acceptable and fair to mentally disordered individuals. Increasing attention has been paid in the United States to adopting postacquittal treatment and monitoring procedures to maximize the treatment of insanity acquittees while providing for the public safety.

ROBERT M. WETTSTEIN

SEE ALSO: *Autonomy; Behaviorism; Competence; Conscience; Freedom and Free Will; Mental Illness; Mentally Disabled and Mentally Ill Persons; Responsibility*

BIBLIOGRAPHY

American Academy of Psychiatry and the Law. 2002. "Practice Guideline: Forensic Psychiatric Evaluation of Defendants

Raising the Insanity Defense." *Journal of the American Academy of Psychiatry and the Law* 30: S1–S40.

American Law Institute, Model Penal Code, section 4.01, 1962.

Bloom, Joseph, and Williams, Mary. 1994. *Management and Treatment of Insanity Acquittees: A Model for the 1990s.* Washington, D.C.: American Psychiatric Press.

Cirincione, Carmen. 1996. "Revisiting the Insanity Defense: Contested or Consensus?" *Bulletin of the American Academy of Psychiatry and the Law* 24: 165–176.

Cirincione, Carmen, and Jacobs, Charles. 1999. "Identifying Insanity Acquittals: Is It Any Easier?" *Law and Human Behavior* 23: 487–497.

Durham v. United States, 214 F. 2d 862 (D.C. Circuit 1954).

Elliott, Carl. 1996. *The Rules of Insanity.* Albany: State University of New York Press.

Harris, Victoria. 2000. "Insanity Acquittees and Rearrest: The Past 24 Years." *Journal of the American Academy of Psychiatry and the Law* 28: 225–231.

Heilbrun, Kirk. 2001. *Principles of Forensic Mental Health Assessment.* New York: Kluwer Academic Press.

Lymburner, Jocelyn, and Roesch, Ronald. 1999. "The Insanity Defense: Five Years of Research (1993–1997)." *International Journal of Law and Psychiatry* 22: 213–240.

Melton, Gary; Petrila, John; and Poythress, Norman. 1997. *Psychological Evaluations for the Courts,* 2nd edition. New York: Guilford Press.

Meyer, Cheryl, and Oberman, Michelle. 2001. *Mothers Who Kill Their Children.* New York: New York University Press.

Palmer, Carleton, and Hazelrigg, Mark. 2000. "The Guilty but Mentally Ill Verdict: A Review and Conceptual Analysis of Intent and Impact." *Journal of the American Academy of Psychiatry and the Law* 28: 47–54.

Perlin, Michael. 1994. *The Jurisprudence of the Insanity Defense.* Durham, NC: Carolina Academic Press.

Queen v. Daniel McNaughton, 4 St. tr. 847 (1843).

Rogers, Richard, and Shuman, Daniel. 2000. *Conducting Insanity Evaluations,* 2nd edition. New York: Guilford Press.

Simon, Rita, and Aaronson, David. 1988. *The Insanity Defense.* New York: Praeger Press.

Simon, Robert, and Shuman, Daniel, eds. 2002. *Retrospective Assessment of Mental States in Litigation: Predicting the Past.* Washington, D.C.: American Psychiatric Press.

Simon, Robert, and Wettstein, Robert. 1997. "Toward the Development of Guidelines for the Conduct of Forensic Psychiatric Examinations." *Journal of the American Academy of Psychiatry and the Law* 25: 17–30.

State v. Pike, 49 N.H. 399 (1869).

Steadman, Henry; McGreevy, Margaret; and Morrissey, Joseph. 1993. *Before and after Hinckley: Evaluating Insanity Defense Reform.* New York: Guilford Press.

Wettstein, Robert. 2002. "Ethics and Forensic Psychiatry." *Psychiatric Clinics of North America* 25: 623–633.

Williams, Christopher; Lees-Haley, Paul; and Djanogly, Stacy. 1999. "Clinical Scrutiny of Litigants' Self-Reports." *Professional Psychology: Research and Practice* 30: 361–367.

INSTITUTIONALIZATION AND DEINSTITUTIONALIZATION

• • •

Deinstitutionalization, the mass exodus of mentally ill persons from state hospitals into the community, was accomplished in the United States during the seventh and eighth decades of the twentieth century. The process has taken away from persons with long-term, severe mental illness the almost total asylum from the pressures of the world and the care, however imperfect, that they received in these institutions. The central ethical question is: Does society not have an obligation to provide the care and treatment that they need in the community? The fact that a significant proportion of the severely and persistently mentally ill population is now living in the streets, in jails, and in other squalid conditions is evidence that adequate community care has not been provided. Moreover, it may be that some mentally ill persons who cannot be effectively treated in the community have been deinstitutionalized. Does society not have an obligation to correct this situation as well?

Before the current era of deinstitutionalization, persons with long-term, severe mental illness were usually institutionalized for life in large state mental hospitals. This institutionalization often began after a first acute mental breakdown in adolescence or early adulthood. Sometimes these patients went into remission in the hospital and were discharged, but at the point of their next psychotic episode were rehospitalized, often never to return to the community.

In the 1960s, British social psychiatrist John Wing and others observed that persons who spent long periods in mental hospitals developed what has come to be known as *institutionalism,* a syndrome characterized by lack of initiative, apathy, withdrawal, submissiveness to authority, and excessive dependence on the institution (Wing and Brown). Sociologist Erving Goffman argued that in what he called *total institutions,* such as state mental hospitals, impersonal treatment can strip away a patient's dignity and individuality and foster regression. The deviant person is locked into a degraded, stigmatized, deviant role. Goffman and others believed that the social environment in institutions could strongly influence the emergence of psychotic symptoms and behavior.

Other investigators, however, observed that institutionalism may not be entirely the outcome of living in dehumanizing institutions; at least in part, it may be characteristic of the schizophrenic process itself. With deinstitutionalization, these researchers observed that many persons with long-term, severe mental illness who were liable to institutionalism seemed to develop dependence on any other way of life that provided minimal social stimulation and allowed them to be socially inactive. They gravitated toward a lifestyle that allowed them to remain free from symptoms and painful and depressive feelings.

Is this dependent, inactive lifestyle bad? For many deinstitutionalized persons, it may lead to unnecessary regression and impede their social and vocational functioning; thus, for these patients it should be discouraged. However, this restricted lifestyle may meet the needs of many deinstitutionalized individuals and help them stay in the community. Mental-health professionals and society at large need to recognize the crippling limitations of mental illness that do not yield to current treatment methods. They also need to be clear about the importance of providing adequate care for this vulnerable group of severely mentally ill persons so that the end result is not like the fate of the mentally ill in the back wards of state hospitals—neglect, abysmal conditions, extreme regression, and marked deterioration of their mental states. For those persons who can be restored to social and vocational functioning only to a degree, many mental-health professionals advocate lowered expectations and the provision of reasonable comfort and a dignified, undemanding life.

The Origins of Deinstitutionalization

In 1955, the number of persons in state hospitals in the United States reached its highest point: 559,000 persons were institutionalized in state mental hospitals out of a total national population of 165 million. In 1998, there were approximately 57,000 institutionalized persons out of a population of 275 million. In 43 years, the United States reduced its number of occupied state hospital beds from 339 per 100,000 population to 21 per 100,000. Some individual states have gone even further: in California in 2000, for example, there were 9 state hospital beds per 100,000 population, including forensic patients (committed through the legal system); nonforensic beds numbered only 3 per 100,000.

Until the deinstitutionalization movement, state mental hospitals had fulfilled the function for society of keeping the mentally ill out of sight and thus out of mind. At the same time, before the advent of modern psychoactive medications, the controls and structure provided by the state hospitals—as well as the granting of asylum—may have been necessary for many of the long-term mentally ill. Unfortunately, the ways in which structure and asylum were achieved, and the everyday abuses of state hospital life such as neglect, abysmal living conditions, and deterioration of the patients' mental states, left scars on the mental-health professions and on the reputation of state hospitals, as well as on the patients. Periodic public outcries about these deplorable conditions, documented by journalists such as Albert Deutsch in his influential book *The Shame of the States* (1948), set the stage for deinstitutionalization. These concerns, shared by mental-health professionals, led to the formation by Congress of the Joint Commission on Mental Illness and Health (1961), which issued recommendations for community alternatives to state hospitals. When psychoactive medications appeared in the 1950s, along with a new philosophy of social treatment, the majority of the long-term psychotic population seemed to have been left in an institutional environment that was no longer necessary or even appropriate.

Other factors also came into play. First, the conviction that mental patients receive better and more humanitarian treatment in the community than in state hospitals far away from home was a philosophical keystone of the community mental-health movement. Another motivating force was concern that the system of indefinite commitment and institutionalization of psychiatric patients deprived them of their civil rights. Finally, many financially strapped state governments wished to shift some of the fiscal burden for these patients to federal and local governments, that is, to federal Supplemental Security Income (SSI) and Medicaid, and to local law-enforcement and emergency-health and mental-health services.

Two developments at the federal level accelerated the process of deinstitutionalization in 1963. Under the provisions of categorical Aid to the Disabled (ATD), the Secretary of Health, Education, and Welfare issued an administrative order making the mentally ill eligible for federal financial support in the community. Moreover, Congress passed legislation to facilitate the establishment of community mental-health centers. With ATD, psychiatric patients and mental-health professionals acting on their behalf now had access to federal grants-in-aid, in many places supplemented by funding from the state. This enabled patients to support themselves or be supported either at home or in such facilities as board-and-care homes (boarding homes) or old hotels, at little cost to the state. ATD is now the Supplemental Security Income referred to above, and is administered by the Social Security Administration. Instead of maintaining patients in a state hospital, the states, even those that provided generous ATD supplements, found the cost of maintaining these patients in the community to be far less than the cost of maintaining them in state hospitals. Although the amount of money available to patients under ATD was not a princely sum, it was sufficient to pay for a board-and-care home or to maintain a low standard of living elsewhere in the community.

Many individuals in the community discovered that they could earn substantial additional income by taking former mental patients into their homes, even at the rates allowed by the ATD grants. Some entrepreneurs set up board-and-care homes holding as many as one hundred persons or more in large, old houses and converted apartment buildings and rooming houses. Although these board-and-care-home operators were not skilled in the management of psychiatric patients, they were able to accommodate tens of thousands of persons who had formerly been in state hospitals and who did not now have major behavior problems (primarily because they were being treated with the antipsychotic drugs).

In 1963, too, Congress passed the Mental Retardation Facilities and Community Mental Health Centers Construction Act, amended in 1965 to provide grants for the initial costs of staffing newly constructed centers. This legislation was a strong incentive to the development of community programs with the potential to treat people whose main recourse previously had been the state hospital. However, although rehabilitative services and pre-care and aftercare services were among the ten services eligible for funding, an agency did not have to offer them in order to qualify for funding as a comprehensive community mental-health center. Many community mental-health centers chose to focus on persons with neuroses and problems of living—the healthy but unhappy. Persons with long-term, severe mental illness were often just as neglected in the community as they had been in the hospitals.

Sweeping changes in the commitment laws of the various states also contributed to deinstitutionalization. In California, for instance, the Lanterman-Petris-Short Act of 1968 provided further impetus for the movement of patients out of hospitals. Underlying this legislation was a concern for the civil rights of the psychiatric patient. (Much of this concern came from civil rights groups and individuals outside the mental-health professions.) The act made the involuntary commitment of psychiatric patients a much more complex process, and holding psychiatric patients indefinitely against their will in mental hospitals became much more difficult. Thus, the initial stage of what had formerly been the career of the long-term hospitalized patient—namely, an involuntary, indefinite commitment—became a thing of the past.

Deinstitutionalization in Practice

One of the most important lessons to be drawn from the experience with deinstitutionalization was almost totally unforeseen by its advocates. The most difficult problem is not the fate of those patients discharged into the community after many years of hospitalization. Rather, the problem that has proved most vexing and that has presented the most difficult ethical dilemmas has been the treatment of the generation that has grown up since deinstitutionalization. It is largely from this generation that the homeless mentally ill are drawn. The large homeless population with major mental illness—that is, schizophrenia, schizoaffective disorder, bipolar illness, and major depression with psychotic features—tends to be young.

Why is this so? In the older generation of long-stay, hospitalized patients, chances were that most of those who were least appropriate for discharge—because of their propensity to physical violence, very poor coping skills, or marked degree of manifest pathology—were not discharged, or if they were discharged and failed in the community, were be sent into the community again.

Those who have been hospitalized for long periods have been institutionalized to passivity. For the most part, they have come to do what they are told. This is not presented as a beneficial effect of long-term hospitalization, but simply as a clinical observation. When those for whom discharge from the hospital is feasible and appropriate are placed in a community living situation with sufficient support and structure, most (though by no means all) tend to stay where they are placed and to accept treatment.

Long-term, severely mentally ill persons of the new generation, however, have not been institutionalized to passivity. Not only have they not spent long years in hospitals, they have probably had difficulty just getting admitted to an acute hospital, whether or not they wanted to be admitted, and even greater difficulty staying there for more than a short period on any one admission. Acute psychiatric inpatient care is extremely expensive, and there is a great reluctance to use scarce mental-health funds to provide it.

Existential Problems in the Community

A young person just beginning to deal with life's demands struggles to achieve some measure of independence, to choose and succeed at a vocation, to establish satisfying interpersonal relationships and attain some degree of intimacy, and to acquire some sense of identity. Lacking the abilities to withstand stress and to form meaningful interpersonal relationships, the mentally ill person's efforts often lead only to failure. The result may be a still more determined, often frantic effort with a greatly increased level of anxiety and desperation. Ultimately, this may lead to another failure accompanied by feelings of despair. For a person predisposed to retreat into acute mental breakdowns, the result is predictably stormy, with acute psychotic breaks, and repeated—and usually brief—hospitalizations often related to these desperate attempts to achieve. The situation becomes even worse when such persons are in an environment where unrealistic expectations emanate not just from within themselves, but also from families and mental-health professionals.

Before deinstitutionalization, these *new long-term patients* would have been institutionalized, often from the time of their first mental breakdown in adolescence or early adulthood. After their initial failures in trying to cope with the vicissitudes of life and of living in the community, such patients would have been exposed no longer to these stresses, but given a permanent place of asylum from the demands of the world.

Such an approach now tends to be the exception, not the rule; since large-scale deinstitutionalization began, hospital stays tend to be brief. In this sense, the majority of *new* long-term patients are the products of deinstitutionalization. To observe this is not to imply that society should turn the clock back and return to a system of total institutionalization for all persons with long-term, severe mental illness. In the community, most of these patients can have something very precious—their liberty, to the extent they can handle it. Furthermore, if the resources are provided, they can realize their potential to pass some of life's milestones successfully. Nevertheless, it is this new generation of long-term, severely mentally ill persons that poses the greatest ethical challenge to deinstitutionalization and the most difficult clinical problems in community treatment, and that has swelled the ranks of the homeless and the incarcerated mentally ill.

Problems in Treatment

As recently as 1950, there were no psychoactive drugs to bring long-term, severely mentally ill persons out of their world of autistic fantasy and help them return to the community. Even today, many patients fail to take psychoactive medications because of disturbing side effects, denial of illness, or, in some cases, the desire to avoid the depression and anxiety that result when they see their reality too clearly; grandiosity and a blurring of reality may make

their lives more bearable than a drug-induced relative normality.

A large proportion of the new long-term patients tends to deny the need for mental-health treatment and to eschew the identity of the long-term mental patient. Admitting mental illness seems to many of these persons to be admitting failure. Becoming part of the mental-health system seems to them like joining an army of misfits. Many of these persons also have substance-abuse disorders and/or medicate themselves with street drugs. Another contributing factor is the natural rebelliousness of youth.

The problem becomes worse for those whose illnesses are more severe. These persons' problems are again illustrated by the problems of the homeless mentally ill. Evidence is beginning to emerge that the homeless mentally ill are more severely ill than the general mentally ill population. At Bellevue Hospital in New York City, for example, approximately 50 percent of inpatients who were homeless on admission are transferred to state hospitals for long-term care as a result of the severity of their illnesses, as opposed to 8 percent of other Bellevue psychiatric inpatients.

Functions of the State Hospital

Valid concerns about the shortcomings and antitherapeutic aspects of state hospitals in the United States often overshadowed the fact that the state hospitals fulfilled some crucial functions for persons with long-term, severe mental illness. The term *asylum* was in many ways appropriate: these imperfect institutions did provide asylum and sanctuary from the pressures of the world with which, in varying degrees, most of these persons were unable to cope. They also provided medical care, patient monitoring, respite for the patient's family, and a social network for the patient, as well as food, shelter, and needed support and structure.

Furthermore, in the state hospitals, the treatment and services that did exist were in one place and under one administration. In the community the situation is very different. Services and treatment are under various administrative jurisdictions and in various locations. Even the mentally healthy have difficulty dealing with a number of bureaucracies, both governmental and private, and having their needs met. Patients can easily get lost in the community. In a hospital, they may have been neglected, but at least their whereabouts were known.

These problems have led to the recognition of the importance of case management. Many of America's homeless mentally ill would not be on the streets if they were on the caseload of a professional or paraprofessional trained to deal with the problems of persons with long-term, severe mental illness, monitor these persons (with considerable persistence when necessary), and facilitate their receiving services.

The fact that persons with long-term, severe mental illness have been deinstitutionalized does not mean they no longer need social support, protection, and relief, either periodic or continuous, from external stimuli and the pressures of life. In short, they need asylum and sanctuary in the community. Unfortunately, because the old state hospitals were called asylums, the word *asylum* took on an almost sinister connotation. Only in recent years has the word again become respectable, signifying the function of providing asylum, rather than asylum as a place.

The concept of asylum and sanctuary in the community becomes important in post-discharge planning because, while some long-term, severely mentally ill persons eventually attain high levels of social and vocational functioning, others have difficulty meeting simple demands of living on their own, even with long-term rehabilitative help. Whatever degree of rehabilitation is possible for each patient cannot take place unless support and protection in the community—from family, treatment program, therapist, family-care home, or board-and-care home—are provided at the same time. Moreover, if the need for asylum and sanctuary within the community is not taken into account, many persons with long-term, severe mental illness may find it impossible to live in the community.

Ingredients of a System of Community Care

Has community care in the United States been better than institutionalized care for persons with long-term, severe mental illness? The answer appears to be both yes and no. With deinstitutionalization, for instance, some long-term dysfunctional and mentally disordered individuals gradually, over a period of years, succeed in their strivings for independence, a vocation, intimacy, and a sense of identity. For them, deinstitutionalization has indeed been a success. The deinstitutionalization movement has also taught administrators much about what good community care should be: a comprehensive and integrated system of care, with designated responsibility, accountability, and adequate fiscal resources.

More specifically, such care requires an adequate number and ample range of graded, stepwise, supervised community-housing settings; adequate, comprehensive, and accessible psychiatric and rehabilitative services provided assertively and through outreach services when necessary; and available and accessible crisis services. A system of responsibility for persons with long-term, severe mental illness living in the community should ensure that each patient has one case manager, a mental-health professional or paraprofessional who is responsible for seeing that the appropriate psychiatric and medical assessments are carried out. This case manager should formulate, in collaboration with the patient, an individualized treatment and rehabilitation plan, including the proper pharmacotherapy; monitor the patient; and assist him or her in receiving services. Respite care, a period when families can be relieved of the responsibilities of caring for their mentally ill relatives, is needed for the more than 50 percent of the long-term, severely mentally ill population in the United States who live with their families, so that the family is better able to provide a support system. The entire burden of deinstitutionalization should not be allowed to fall on families, as it sometimes has.

Setting up such a comprehensive and integrated system of care for persons with long-term, severe mental illness in the United States has proven far more difficult to accomplish than was envisioned. A large proportion of the many hundreds of thousands of persons with long-term, severe mental illness has not been well served in the community. In addition, some patients who cannot be effectively treated in the community have been deinstitutionalized. Probably only a relatively small minority of long-term mentally ill persons requires a highly structured, locked, twenty-four-hour setting for adequate intermediate or long-term management. But for members of this small minority, such institutional management may be critical—for their sake and for the sake of the community. Attempts to treat persons characterized by such problems as assaultive behavior; severe, overt major psychopathology; grossly inappropriate social behavior; reluctance to take psychoactive medications; inability to adjust to open settings; problems with drugs and alcohol; and self-destructive behavior in the community have required an inordinate amount of time and effort from mental-health professionals, various social agencies, and the criminal-justice system. Many patients have been lost to the mental-health system because their treatment needs have not been met, and these people, for the most part, are on the streets or in jail.

The result has often been seen as a series of failures on the part of both mentally ill persons and mental-health professionals. As a consequence, a number of long-term mentally ill persons have become alienated from the system that has not met their needs, and some mental-health professionals have become disenchanted with the treatment of these persons. The heat of the debate in the United States over the issue of whether or not to provide intermediate and long-term hospitalization has tended to obscure the benefits of community treatment for the great majority of the long-term mentally ill, who do not require such highly structured, twenty-four-hour care.

Where to treat—hospital versus community—should not be an ideological issue; it is a decision best based on the clinical needs of each person. Unfortunately, efforts to deinstitutionalize have, in practice, too often confused locus of care with quality of care. Where mentally ill persons are treated has been seen as more important than how they are treated. Care in the community has often been assumed by definition to be better than hospital care. In actuality, poor care can be found in both hospital and community settings.

Independence

For many long-term mentally ill persons, nothing is more difficult to attain and sustain than independence. The issue of supervised versus unsupervised housing provides an example. Professionals would like to see their patients living in their own apartments and managing on their own, perhaps with some outpatient support. But, as described in the 1992 American Psychiatric Association Task Force's report on the homeless mentally ill, the experience of deinstitutionalization has shown that most long-term, severely mentally ill persons living in unsupervised mainstream housing in the community find the ordinary stresses of managing on their own more than they can handle. After a while they tend to not take their medications and to neglect their nutrition. Their lives unravel; eventually they find their way back to the hospital or to the streets.

Mentally ill persons value independence highly, but they often underestimate their dependency needs and their needs for structure—for instance to have a living situation where their medication is dispensed to them and their meals are provided. Professionals need to be realistic about their patients' potential for independence, even if the patients are not.

Freedom

What about the issue of freedom? Persons with long-term, severe mental illness enjoy much more liberty than when they were institutionalized; in most cases, as was discussed earlier, this is appropriate. But that freedom may well be damaging to some patients if they are given more than they can handle. Many of those on the streets and in the jails suffer from the lack of structure and organization in their lives; they need, because of their illnesses, to have these elements imposed upon them.

However, involuntary treatment presents an extremely difficult ethical dilemma. Beliefs about civil liberties come into conflict with concerns for the welfare of persons with long-term, severe mental illness. A basis for facing this dilemma is provided by the belief that the mentally ill have a fundamental right to treatment, even if at times the treatment must be involuntary when, because of severe mental illness, they present a serious threat to their own welfare or that of others and are not able to make a rational decision about accepting treatment. Reaching out to patients and working with them to accept help on a voluntary basis is certainly a mandatory first step. But if this fails and the patient is at serious risk, professionals with direct responsibility for patients usually see that ethically they cannot simply stop there.

In such cases, humane commitment laws facilitate a prompt return to acute inpatient treatment when such treatment is needed. Ongoing measures, such as conservatorship or guardianship, court-mandated outpatient treatment, and appointing a payee for the person's disability check are components of a treatment philosophy and practice that recognizes that external controls such as these are a positive therapeutic approach for mentally ill persons who lack the internal controls to deal with their impulses and to cope with life's demands. Such external controls may help interrupt a self-destructive, chaotic life on the streets and in and out of jails and hospitals.

Conclusion

Further deinstitutionalization must be preceded by careful planning and the establishment of community services. In fact, community services set up in the United States have in most cases been swamped by the number of patients coming out of the hospitals or who are already in the community and in need of care. Clearly, deinstitutionalization should be implemented only to the extent that each long-term, severely mentally ill person in the community can be properly and adequately housed and treated. This should also be done for those mentally ill persons already in the community. Those who implement a policy of deinstitutionalization must take into account not only those still in hospitals but those mentally ill persons who are reaching an age where their mental illness is becoming manifest and who will never be long-term hospitalized mental patients.

For this latter group, it is essential that there be a system of case management with staff who understand their problems and their needs, as well as a range of supervised housing in the community that is sufficiently structured to accommodate those who require it. Although adequate case management, appropriate housing, and treatment should greatly decrease the need for involuntary treatment, there should still be a willingness to use it when it becomes necessary. It also needs to be recognized that there is a significant subpopulation of persons with long-term, severe mental illness who should not be deinstitutionalized.

Having dismantled such a large proportion of the institutions for the mentally ill, society surprisingly continues to face the grave ethical and clinical question of whether there is still an obligation to provide care and treatment in the community for the mentally ill persons who used to inhabit these institutions. It is a matter of priorities among the various social needs of our society. Mental-health professionals, at least those in public service, are coming around to giving this population the highest priority. With regard to legislators and the general public, there is much more ambivalence, and persons with long-term, severe mental illness often fare poorly in the struggle over setting priorities and allocating funds.

H. RICHARD LAMB (1995)
REVISED BY AUTHOR

SEE ALSO: *Autonomy; Beneficence; Coercion; Mental Health Services; Mental Health Therapies; Mentally Disabled and Mentally Ill Persons: Healthcare Issues; Paternalism; Patients' Rights: Mental Patients' Rights; Psychiatry, Abuses of*

BIBLIOGRAPHY

American Psychiatric Association. 1992. *Treating the Homeless Mentally Ill: A Task Force Report of the American Psychiatric Association,* ed. H. Richard Lamb, Leona L. Bachrach, and Frederic I. Kass. Washington, D.C.: Author.

Bachrach, Leona L. 1984. "Asylum and Chronically Ill Psychiatric Patients." *American Journal of Psychiatry* 141(8): 975–978.

Baum, Alice S., and Burnes, Donald W. 1993. *A Nation in Denial: The Truth About Homelessness.* Boulder, CO: Westview.

Curson, David A.; Pantelis, Christos; Ward, Jan; and Barnes, Thomas R. E. 1992. "Institutionalism and Schizophrenia 30 Years On: Clinical Poverty and the Social Environment in Three British Mental Hospitals in 1960 Compared with a Fourth in 1990." *British Journal of Psychiatry* 160 (February): 230–241.

Deutsch, Albert. 1948. *The Shame of the States.* New York: Harcourt, Brace.

Goffman, Erving. 1961. *Asylums: Essays on the Social Situation of Mental Patients and Other Inmates.* New York: Doubleday.

Isaac, Rael Jean, and Armat, Virginia C. 1990. *Madness in the Streets: How Psychiatry and the Law Abandoned the Mentally Ill.* New York: Free Press.

Joint Commission on Mental Illness and Health. 1961. *Action for Mental Health: Final Report.* New York: Basic Books.

Lamb, H. Richard. 1982. *Treating the Long-Term Mentally Ill.* San Francisco: Jossey-Bass.

Lamb, H. Richard, ed. 1984. *The Homeless Mentally Ill: A Task Force Report of the American Psychiatric Association.* Washington, D.C.: American Psychiatric Association.

Lamb, H. Richard, and Bachrach, Leona L. 2001. "Some Perspectives on Deinstitutionalization." *Psychiatric Services* 52(8): 1039–1045.

Lamb, H. Richard, and Weinberger, Linda E. 1998. "Persons with Severe Mental Illness in Jails and Prisons: A Review." *Psychiatric Services* 49(4): 483–492.

Manderscheid, Ronald W., and Henderson, Marilyn J., eds. 2000. *Mental Health, United States 2000.* Washington, D.C.: U.S. Government Printing Office.

Marcus, Luis R.; Cohen, Neal L.; Nardacci, David; and Brittain, Joan. 1990. "Psychiatry Takes to the Streets: The New York City Initiative for the Homeless Mentally Ill." *American Journal of Psychiatry* 147(11): 1557–1561. at Bellevue Hospital.

Thornicroft, Graham, and Bebbington, Paul. 1989. "Deinstitutionalization—From Hospital Closure to Service Development." *British Journal of Psychiatry* 155(December): 739–753.

Torrey, E. Fuller. 1988. *Nowhere to Go: The Tragic Odyssey of the Homeless Mentally Ill.* New York: Harper & Row.

Torrey, E. Fuller. 1997. *Out of the Shadow: Confronting America's Mental Illness Crisis.* New York: Wiley.

Wing, John K. 1990. "The Functions of Asylum." *British Journal of Psychiatry* 157(December): 822–827.

Wing, John K., and Brown, George W. 1970. *Institutionalism and Schizophrenia: A Comparative Study of Three Mental Hospitals 1960–1968.* Cambridge, Eng.: Cambridge University Press.

INSTITUTIONAL REVIEW BOARDS (IRBs)

SEE *Research Ethics Committees*

INTERNATIONAL HEALTH

• • •

The term *international health* has a variety of meanings that depend on the context in which it is used. In a geopolitical sense the term is used in regard to the numerous governmental and nongovernmental organizations (NGOs) throughout the world that are concerned with human health and disease. Those organizations broadly deal with health issues that involve both economically advanced and less developed nations, although the focus is frequently on impoverished populations in both settings. Examples include the World Health Organization (WHO); the United Nations (UN) and its various agencies, such as UNDP (United Nations

Development Programme), UNICEF (United Nations International Children's Emergency Fund), and UNHCR (United Nations High Commission on Refugees); the World Bank; and NGOs supported by philanthropy, such as the Wellcome Trust, the Rockefeller Foundation, and Médicin Sans Frontières. Those organizations work with national and regional health authorities to address operational and research issues. The creation and maintenance of those groups have resulted from moral, social, and financial obligations and altruism (Basch; Merson et al.).

International health also relates to biomedical research and health policy issues that cross national boundaries and increasingly involve the participation of people who live in developing countries. Bioethical issues arising from the conduct of research on people in economically depressed regions have received much attention over the last several years. This entry deals with ethical issues that have been sources of controversy and debate in the context of international health.

History of Bioethical Principles and International Health

Bioethical guidelines for the conduct of research involving humans originally were put forth formally in the Nuremberg Code, a document that was generated after World War II, when atrocities conducted by physicians under the Nazi government became widely known. In 1964 the World Medical Association Declaration of Helsinki elaborated on those principles. The Declaration of Helsinki was concerned primarily with medical experimentation involving persons in economically advanced developed countries and made a distinction between *therapeutic* and *nontherapeutic* research. Bioethical issues concerned specifically with research that involved vulnerable populations and people in developing countries were addressed by the Council for the International Organization of Medical Sciences (CIOMS), which was last revised in 1993. Controversies about the interpretation of those documents have been commented on by several authorities in the field of bioethics (Levine; Singer and Benatar; Zion et al.).

When it became public knowledge that treatment for neurosyphilis was withheld deliberately from African-American men in Tuskegee, Alabama, to examine the natural course of the disease, a commission was organized to outline the principles of conducting research involving human subjects. This resulted in the publication of the Belmont Report, which built on the Declaration of Helsinki. The Belmont Report emphasized the notion that individual autonomy, beneficence, and justice were central to the ethical conduct of research involving humans (National

Commission for the Protection of Human Subjects of Biomedical and Behavioral Research). Committees in the United States (National Bioethics Advisory Commission) and the United Kingdom (Nuffield Council for Bioethics) later addressed bioethical aspects of research in the international setting. Those principles are being refined by organizations and people from developing countries where the research is being conducted (Bhotta).

Major Issues in Biomedical Research Ethics in Developing Countries

Research involving human subjects implies a wide range of responsibilities on the part of the participants and their communities, the investigator, and funding agencies. In the context of international health those issues generally have been viewed from the perspective of the cultural and legal norms of developed countries, which historically have been interpreted by institutional review boards (IRBs) (Shuklenk and Ashcroft).

Issues issues of recent debate and controversy in international health are illustrated by a clinical trial that tested the efficacy of the antiretroviral drug zidovudine in limiting maternal-infant transmission of human immunodeficiency virus (HIV). A study conducted in East Africa in the mid-1990s involved randomization of HIV-infected pregnant women to either short-duration therapy with zidovudine or inert placebo. The lack of any treatment with an antiretroviral drug was the normal standard of care in Africa at that time. When it became widely known that earlier research conducted in developed countries (AIDS clinical trial group protocol 076) showed that a longer course of zidovudine therapy reduced the risk of transmission of HIV from mothers to their offspring from approximately 25 percent to 8 percent (Connor et al.), several highly cited publications in the lay and professional press suggested that the African study was unethical because it denied therapy of known efficacy to participants who were randomized to the placebo group (Lurie and Wolf, 1997, 1998; Angell et al).

Moreover, on the basis of the concept that the *best available therapy* should be made available to HIV-infected women, it was suggested that the duration of a course of zidovudine in developing countries be as long as the course given in developed countries (Angell et al.). The cost of the longer course of the antiretroviral drug at that time was $800, an amount that far exceeded the annual per capita financial allocation for healthcare in African countries where the HIV pandemic was present.

This controversy highlights several bioethical concepts that are germane to research in international health, including (1) local standards of care and achievement of equipoise,

(2) informed consent, (3) incentives and benefits of biomedical research and clinical trials to the individual and the community, and (4) disparities in global health between developed and developing countries.

LOCAL STANDARDS OF CARE AND EQUIPOISE. It is a central tenet of clinical research trials involving humans that hypotheses generated to evaluate new therapies be compared with the established standard; that is, the design of a trial must achieve equipoise. The controversy cited above is paradigmatic of the differing perceptions of this issue as it applies to a disease that affects resident populations of both the developed world and the developing world. The standard of care for HIV-infected pregnant women in Uganda at the time the study was conducted—no treatment with an antiretroviral drug—was strikingly different from that for residents of the United States, who had reasonable access to long-duration zidovudine despite its cost.

Acknowledgment of differences based on economic and cultural differences is important in the design and implementation of international research studies so that real or perceived issues that imply ethical imperialism can be avoided (Mbidde). This constitutes a broad rather than a narrow interpretation of the concept that the best therapy be made available to participants in research studies and their local community. A stricter interpretation inadvertently may led to a situation that, ironically, some may consider unethical because clinical research not performed in developing countries cannot possibly benefit the local population; that is, the efficacy of short-term zidovudine would not be known unless the African study were performed. Tensions arising from the fact that financial support for research studies conducted in developing countries comes mainly from governmental organizations and NGOs based in developing countries undoubtedly will continue to raise these issues. It is thus a positive development that training in the bioethical aspects of international research is receiving greater emphasis in both developed and developing countries, for example, through programs supported by the Fogarty International Center of the National Institutes of Health in the United States.

Bioethical aspects of international health research have been focused on disease and health issues that affect the inhabitants of both developed and developing countries, such as HIV infection. With increasing attention to research on health issues that primarily or exclusively affect residents of developing countries, such as the global health initiatives of the Gates Foundation, it is important that investigators and IRBs with different backgrounds come together to develop study designs that are acceptable in a broad cultural context.

It is critical that a study have potential benefit to the local population and not entail exclusively the care or prevention of a disease in persons in developed countries. For example, the development of a vaccine against blood-stage infection with the parasite *Plasmodium falciparum* has advanced to clinical trials in Africa and other areas in the tropics. The need for such a vaccine is great because falciparum malaria is estimated to kill approximately one million African infants per year. Residents of developed countries, where funding for the development and testing of vaccines comes from, are at minimal risk of malaria unless they visit endemic areas and do not take appropriate chemoprophylaxis. At the extreme, some diseases, such as lymphatic filariasis, do not exist in economically advanced countries, yet global initiatives for research and treatment of those health problems will benefit impoverished residents of developing countries exclusively.

On the one hand, investigators engaged in these research activities are largely from developed countries and stand to benefit from the conduct of clinical trials through increased scientific stature and competitiveness for additional funding and fame. On the other hand, agreement to participate in clinical trials by local populations may be motivated by the perceived short-term health benefit for oneself and one's family, community, or nation. It is therefore important that the topic of the research study and the details of its design address the health needs that are important in the local context. Moreover, participants in such studies need to understand how and in what time frame the research ultimately will benefit them and their community (Participants in the 2001 Conference on Ethical Aspects of Research in Developing Countries).

INFORMED CONSENT. European and North American concepts of informed consent generally are aimed at preserving the integrity and autonomy of the individuals who are recruited to participate in a research study. Excessive financial or other types of incentives are considered coercive. In the case of the United States the litigious nature of the interaction between the research subject and the investigator is also a significant factor in the process of obtaining and documenting informed consent.

Informed consent in many developing countries is an equally complex process with important variables that distinguish it from the process in developed countries. Community participation and educational sessions that include an ongoing dialogue with the researchers before, during, and after the completion of clinical research studies are prominent features, especially when the disease or health issue being studied has great significance for public health. Because many studies in international health involve investigators who are not residents of the area where the participants live, it is prudent and appropriate that scientists, public health officials, and community leaders be involved in developing methods of obtaining informed consent that are culturally appropriate. For example, although documentation of consent by signing a piece of paper that describes the risks and benefits of participation generally is done in developed countries, the residents of many rural areas of sub-Saharan Africa and developing countries in Asia and Latin America may not have achieved a literate status that enables them to be competent to appraise such a document critically. An extreme example would be to ask an illiterate individual to mark a piece of paper that contains information that that person cannot read. In this scenario oral informed consent obtained from local persons trained for this purpose is appropriate. Attention to this process is especially important for vulnerable populations in developing countries who may feel pressured to cooperate because of gender or economic biases that are prevalent in developed as well as developing countries (London 2001, 2002).

INCENTIVES AND HEALTH BENEFITS. Financial incentives to participate in clinical trials have been the subject of debate. Some have argued that financial incentives are coercive, especially in populations that are considered vulnerable because of extreme poverty. Reasonable financial inducements that account for time spent away from normal daily activities, for example, farming in populations in which subsistence agriculture is common, may be appropriate. In the international health setting, in which village and neighborhood life is common, inducements in the form of community improvements may be considered not coercive at the individual level and as representing reasonable "payment" for participation by community members. For example, financial support for a local health center may benefit populations that participate in malaria vaccine trials. Thus, although the benefit of a malaria vaccine may not materialize until years after the completion of a specific clinical trial, education of mothers in recognizing the symptoms of malaria in infants and improved access to antimalarial drugs will improve the local standard of care.

EQUITY AND GLOBAL DISPARITIES IN INTERNATIONAL HEALTH. Consideration of bioethical principles in international health must be seen in the context of the moral dilemma that more than 87 percent of the annual global health budget is devoted to 16 percent of the world's population in the most affluent developed countries (Iglehart). As the amount of money and scientific talent committed to the examination of health issues associated with the changing demography of developed countries, such as Alzheimer's disease and other dementias associated with old age, is increasing, infectious diseases that are rampant in developing countries continue to perpetuate the cycle of poverty and high childhood mortality and morbidity. This inequity may increase as the servicing of debt limits the economic advancement of developing countries and the internationalization of industrial and agriculture markets influences research priorities (Benatar). In the long term political advocacy on the part of those who conduct international biomedical research is needed to change this power disparity and increase research capacity training in developing countries (Nchinda).

JAMES W. KAZURA

SEE ALSO: *AIDS; Bioterrorism; Environmental Ethics; Epidemics; Health and Disease: History of the Concepts; Human Dignity; Human Rights; Minorities as Research Subjects; Pharmaceutical Industry; Population Ethics; Population Policies; Public Health; Race and Racism; Research, Multinational; Responsibility*

BIBLIOGRAPHY

Angell, M.; Kliger, C. H.; Germain, A.; and Martin, W. G. 1997. "AIDS Studies Violate Helsinki Rights Accord." *New York Times,* February 19, p. A26.

Basch, P. F. 1999. *Textbook of International Health.* New York: Oxford University Press.

Benatar, S. R. 1998. "Global Disparities in Health and Human Rights: A Critical Commentary." *American Journal of Public Health* 88: 295–300.

Bhutta, Z. A. 2002. "Ethics in International Health Research: A Perspective from the Developing World." *Bulletin of the World Health Organization* 80: 114–120.

Connor, E. M.; Sperling, R. S.; Gelber, R.; Kiselev, P.; Scott, G.; O'Sullivan, M. J.; VanDyke, R.; Bey, M.; Shearer, W.; Jacobson, R. L., et al. 1994. "Reduction of Maternal-Infant Transmission of Human Immunodeficiency Virus Type 1 with Zidovudine Treatment: Pediatric AIDS Clinical Trials Group Protocol 076 Study Group." *New England Journal of Medicine* 331: 1173–1180.

Iglehart, J. K. 1999. "The American Health Care System—Expenditures." *New England Journal of Medicine* 340: 70–76.

Levine, R. J. 2000. "Some Recent Developments in the International Guidelines on the Ethics of Research Involving Human Subjects." *Annals of the New York Academy of Sciences* 918: 170–178.

London, A. J. 2001. "Equipoise and International Human-Subjects Research." *Bioethics* 15: 312–332.

London, L. 2002. "Ethical Oversight of Public Health Research: Can Rules and IRBs Make a Difference in Developing Countries?" *American Journal of Public Health* 92: 1079–1084.

Lurie, P., and Wolfe, S. M. 1997. "Unethical Trials of Interventions to Reduce Perinatal Transmission of the Human Immunodeficiency Virus in Developing Countries." *New England Journal of Medicine* 337: 853–856.

Lurie, P., and Wolfe, S. M. 1998. "Ethics of HIV Trials." *Lancet* 351: 220.

Mbidde, E. K. 1998. "Ethics of Placebo-Controlled Trials of Zidovudine to Prevent the Perinatal Transmission of HIV in the Third World." *New England Journal of Medicine* 338: 837. Author reply 831–840.

Merson, M. H.; Black, R.; and Mills, A. J. 2001. *International Public Health: Diseaes, Programs, Systems, and Policies.* Gathersburg, MD: Aspen.

National Commission for the Protection of Human Subjects of Biomedical and Behavioral Research. 1988. *Belmont Report: Ethical Principles and Guidelines for the Protection of Human Subjects of Research.* Washington, D.C.: U.S. Government Printing Office.

Nchinda, T. C. 2002. "Research Capacity Strengthening in the South." *Social Science and Medicine* 54: 1699–1711.

Participants in the 2001 Conference on Ethical Aspects of Research in Developing Countries. 2002. "ETHICS: Fair Benefits for Research in Developing Countries." *Science* 298: 2133–2134.

Schuklenk, U., and Ashcroft, R. 2000. "International Research Ethics." *Bioethics* 14: 158–172.

Singer, P. A., and Benatar, S. R. 2001. "Beyond Helsinki: A Vision for Global Health Ethics." *British Medical Journal* 322: 747–748.

Zion, D.; Gillam, L.; and Loff, B. 2000. "The Declaration of Helsinki, CIOMS and the Ethics of Research on Vulnerable Populations." *Nature Medicine* 6: 615–617.

ISLAM, BIOETHICS IN

• • •

Islam, the last of the Abrahamic religions (literally meaning "submission [to God's will]"), was proclaimed by Muhammad (born ca. 570 C.E.), the prophet of Islam and the founder of Islamic public order in the seventh century C.E. in Arabia. This article will focus on the historical development of Islam, its fundamental teachings, Islamic legal thought, the Islamic theological and ethical tradition, Islamic mysticism, and Islam and modernity. Throughout the article an attempt will be made to relate religious-moral belief to practice, thereby indicating implications of the tradition in molding attitudes toward maintenance and preservation of life, including ways of dealing with suffering, pain, illness, death, and connected issues.

Historical Development

Seventh-century Arabia was socially and politically ripe for the emergence of new leadership. When Muhammad was growing up in Mecca, a city that had become an important center of a flourishing trade between Byzantium and nations on the Indian Ocean, he was aware of the social inequities and injustices that existed in the tribal society dominated by a political oligarchy made up of a few powerful chiefs. Monotheistic traditions like Judaism and Christianity were known to the Arabs; but they had persisted in worshiping their pagan deities, who dwelt in sanctuaries in and around Mecca. The most important shrine in Mecca was the Kaaba, a rectangular building, to which tribes made annual pilgrimage, using the occasion to trade with people who came from all over Arabia.

Religious practices and attitudes before Islam, then, were determined by the tribal aristocracy who also upheld tribal values: "bravery in battle, patience in misfortune, persistence in revenge, protection of the weak, defiance of the strong," generosity, and hospitality as part of their moral code (Watt, p. 20). The growth of Mecca as a commercial center where individuals acted more freely in their own private interest than in the interest of the tribe, had weakened this tribal ethic to the extent that weaker members of a tribe and those who had been marginalized were left without security. Islam emerged in the midst of a serious socioeconomic imbalance between the rich and the poor, between extreme forms of individualism and tribal solidarity.

Muhammad was born into the Hashimite clan of the powerful Quraysh tribe in Mecca. His father died before he was born, and his mother died when he was six years old. In accordance with Arab tribal norms, he was brought up first by his grandfather, then, following the grandfather's death, by his uncle, with whom he traveled on trade missions to Syria. As a young man he was employed by a wealthy Meccan woman, Khadija, as her trade agent. He was twenty-five when he accepted a marriage offer from Khadija, who was fifteen years his senior. When Muhammad received his prophetic call at the age of forty, Khadija was the first person to become *muslim* ("believer in Islam").

This was the beginning of Islam as a struggle to establish a monotheistic faith and create an ethical public order embodying divine justice and mercy. Meccan leadership resisted Muhammad and persecuted him and his followers, who were drawn mainly from among the poor and disenfranchised. Under unbearable conditions, Muhammad decided to emigrate to Medina, an oasis town in the north, where two warring Arab tribes had invited him to arbitrate their affairs. This emigration in 622 C.E. marks the beginning of the Muslim calendar and the genesis of the first Islamic polity: Muhammad as a statesman instituted a series of reforms to create his community, umma, on the basis of religious affiliation. It also established a distinctive feature of Islamic faith, which does not admit the separation between the religious and temporal spheres of human activity, and has insisted on the ideal unity of civil and moral authority under the divinely ordained legal system, the *shari'a*.

Muhammad died in 632 C.E., having brought the whole of Arabia under the Medina government. However, he had left no explicit instructions regarding succession to his religious-political authority. The early Muslim leaders who succeeded him as caliphs exercised Muhammad's political authority, making political and military decisions that led to the expansion of Muslim domains beyond Arabia. The community leaders were convinced that the Islamic domain, and not necessarily Islamic faith, was to prevail over all other nations. This conviction, in addition to the political need to consolidate the Muslim polity threatened by internal tribal strife, became the driving force behind the early territorial expansion. Within a century Muslim armies had conquered the region from the Nile in North Africa to the Oxus in Central Asia and as far as India. This vast empire required an Islamic legal system for the administration of the highly developed political systems of the conquered Persian and Byzantine regions. Muslim jurists formulated a comprehensive legal code, using the ethical and legal principles set forth in the Qur'an, the collected revelations of Muhammad, and the precedents set by the Prophet and the early community, in addition to the customary law in the conquered regions.

Differences of opinion on certain critical issues emerged as soon as Muhammad died. The question of succession to Muhammad was one of the major issues that divided the community into the Sunni and the Shia. Those supporting the candidacy of Abu Bakr (d. 634), an elderly associate of the Prophet, as caliph (political successor) formed the majority of the community, who gradually came to be known as the Sunnis; those who acclaimed 'Ali (d. ca. 660), Muhammad's cousin and son-in-law, as the imam (religious and political leader) designated by the Prophet, formed the minority group, known as the Shia ("partisans").

The dispute had profound implications beyond the political. The ideal nature of prophetic prestige in the community, established both in the Qur'an through persistent admonition to obey the prophet and through the prophet's personal exercise of discretionary power in shaping the public order, meant acknowledgment of an authority whose decisions in all spheres affecting Muslim life would be binding on posterity.

The early years of military victories over the Persians and the Byzantines were followed by the civil wars that broke out in 656 C.E. under Muhammad's third successor, 'Uthman. The tension occasioned by the existence of political and social injustices in the Muslim polity gave rise to two distinct, and in some ways contradictory, attitudes among Muslims: quietist and activist. The supporters of a quietist posture supported authoritarian politics, which feigned unquestioning and immediate obedience to almost any *de facto* Muslim authority who publicly promised to uphold Islamic norms. The exponents of an activist posture supported radical politics and taught that under certain circumstances, it was imperative to remove an unjust authority from power. Gradually the quietist and authoritarian stance became associated with the majority of the Sunnite Muslims. The activist and radical stance came to be associated with Shiite Islam.

By the end of the third Islamic century (ninth–tenth C.E.), these two distinct responses to the question of political-religious authority were expounded by the Sunni and Shia schools of thought. Despite the disintegration of the caliphal authority in the thirteenth century C.E., the Muslim community has continued to live in the shadow of the idealized history of early Islam, when the religious and secular authority was united under the divinely guided caliph.

Fundamental Teachings

The two authoritative sources of Islamic teachings are the Qur'an, regarded by Muslims as the book of God, and the *sunna,* the exemplary conduct of the Prophet. The Qur'an consists of the revelations Muhammad received intermittently from the time of his call as prophet in 610 C.E. until his death in 632. Muslims believe that the Qur'an was directly communicated to the Prophet by God through the archangel Gabriel; accordingly, it is regarded as inerrant and immutably preserved. It has served as the source for ethical and theological doctrines and principles for the public organization. The *sunna* (meaning "trodden path") has functioned as the elaboration of the Qur'anic revelation, providing details about each and every precept and deed purportedly traced back to the Prophet's own precedent. The narratives that carried such information were designated as *hadith.* In the ninth century, Muslim scholars developed an elaborate system for the theological and legal classification of these *hadith* to deduce certain beliefs and practices.

The *hadith* literature describes the Muslim creed and practice as "the Five Pillars of Islam." The First Pillar is the *shahada,* the profession of faith: "There is no deity but God, and Muhammad is the messenger of God." Belief in God constitutes the integrity of human existence, individually and as a member of society. The Qur'an speaks about God as the being whose presence is felt in everything that exists; everything that happens is an indicator of the divine. God is the "knower of the Unseen and the Visible; ... the All-Merciful, the All-compassionate, ... the Sovereign Lord, the All-holy, the Giver of peace, the Keeper of faith, the All-preserver, the All-mighty, the All-powerful, the Most High" (Qur'an, 59:23). Faith in God results in being safe, well integrated, sound, and at peace.

Life is the gift of God, and the body is the divine trust given to humankind to enable it to serve God as completely and fully as the wonderful creation of God has made that serving possible. The humble origin of humans is established by the Qur'anic reference to their creation from "dry clay of black mud formed into shape" (15:26). Through the well-proportioned creation of the human body and the perpetual guidance provided to perfect it both spiritually and morally, human beings have been given the trusteeship of their body. On the Day of Resurrection, all parts of the human body will have to account for the actions of the person whose bodily organs they formed. God has set limits on what human beings may do with their own bodies. Suicide, homicide, and torturing one's body in any form are regarded as transgressions.

The Qur'anic affirmation of bodily resurrection has determined many religious-moral decisions regarding cadavers. Dead bodies should be buried reverently, as soon as possible. Islamic law prohibits mutilation of the cadaver and, thus, cremation. Under certain circumstances, in order to determine the cause of death, autopsy is permitted. Postmortem dissection is permitted, for instance, to retrieve a valuable object belonging to another person that might have been swallowed by a deceased person. There was doubt about the use of human cadavers for medical research until fairly recently.

The rulings are now well established in regard to the cadavers of non-Muslims, which do not require any monetary compensation for their mutilation (as required by the *shariʿa* for the cadaver of a Muslim). However, if the research for a cure of a disease is dependent on the dissection of a Muslim cadaver, then most Sunni and Shiʿite jurists rule it permissible and, as a precautionary measure, require the payment of compensation to the family of the deceased (*Fiqh al-tabib* [Islamic Laws for Physicians], pp. 159–180). Some recent rulings from Shiʿite jurists make no distinction between a Muslim and a non-Muslim cadaver, thereby permitting research and use of organs for transplantation (*Fiqh al-tabib* [Islamic Laws for Physicians]).

The Qur'an affirms reverence for human life in reference to a similar commandment given to other monotheists: "We decreed for the Children of Israel that whosoever killeth a human being for other than manslaughter or corruption in the earth, it shall be as if he had killed all humankind, and whoso saveth the life of one, it shall be as if he saved the life of all humankind" (5:32). This passage has provided modern Muslim jurists with religious documentation to legitimize medical advances in saving human lives. It has also served as an incentive to protect humanity against peril by choosing to save oneself and others from perdition and to serve humanity as service to God.

The corollary of the belief in God's guidance is human accountability to further divine purposes on earth. The purpose of creation is to allow human beings, created with cognition and volition, freely to accept the responsibility of perfecting their existence by working with the laws of nature grasped by the divinely endowed innate disposition (*fitra*) and by understanding principles of causality that regulate their well-being. The Qur'an emphasizes God's benevolence, all-forgivingness, and mercy. But it also accentuates God's justice, and stresses that humanity should develop moral and spiritual awareness (*taqwa*) in fulfilling everyday requirements of life.

Human existence is not free of tension and inner stresses caused by rejection of truth (*kufr*) and impairment of moral consciousness. To help humanity, God sends prophets "to remind" humanity of its covenant with God (Qur'an, 7:172). There have been 124,000 prophets from the beginning of history, of whom five (Noah, Abraham, Moses, Jesus, and Muhammad) are regarded as *messengers* sent to organize their people on the basis of the guidance revealed by God.

The Second Pillar is daily worship (*salat*), required five times a day: at dawn, midday, afternoon, evening, and night. These very short prayers entail bowing and prostrations. A Muslim may worship anywhere, preferably in a congregation, facing Mecca. Muslims are required to worship as a community on Fridays at midday and on two major religious holidays, celebrating the end of Ramadan and the completion of the pilgrimage in Mecca. The congregational prayer gives expression to the believer's religious commitment within the community. Women are exempt from the obligation of congregational participation, and the tradition recommends that they worship in the privacy of their homes. However, they have always worshiped at designated areas in the mosque, apart from men. The Qur'an prescribes physical purity for the worshiper through the performance of ablutions, and a full washing after sexual intercourse or a long illness, prior to undertaking worship. Women are required to perform a full washing after the menstrual cycle and childbirth, because blood is regarded as ritually unclean. Islamic law prescribes regular cleansing and physical hygiene as expressions of one's faith.

Prayer in Islam is regarded as therapeutic. Besides seeking medical treatment, Muslims are encouraged to seek healing, especially of psychological illnesses, by praying to God. Many illnesses, according to the teachings of the Prophet, are caused by psychological conditions like anxiety, sorrow, fear, loneliness, and so on. Hence, prayer restores the serenity and tranquillity of the soul.

The Third Pillar is the mandatory "alms levy" (*zakat*). The obligation to share what one possesses with those less fortunate is stressed throughout the Qur'an. The Muslim definition of the virtuous life includes charitable support of widows, wayfarers, orphans, and the needy. Islamic law includes technical regulations about how much *zakat* is due and upon what property it is to be levied. These legal rulings, which originated before the disintegration of the Islamic public order, do not necessarily prevail in contemporary Muslim nations. Although *zakat* has for the most part been left to the conscience of Muslims, the obligation to be charitable and contribute to the general welfare of the community continues to be emphasized. In a number of poor Muslim countries this benevolence, provided by wealthy individuals, has underwritten badly needed healthcare for those who cannot afford the rising cost of medical treatment. It has also led to the creation of private charitable foundations that compete with the cumbersome and poorly administered government welfare institutions.

The Fourth Pillar is the fast during the month of Ramadan. Since the Muslim calendar, which has been in use since the seventh century, is lunar, the month of fasting moves throughout the year over a period of time, because the lunar year is shorter than the solar. Ramadan is regarded as the holy month during which the Qur'an was revealed to Muhammad. During the fast, which lasts from dawn to dusk, Muslims are required to refrain not only from eating, smoking, and drinking but also from sexual intercourse and acts leading to sensual behavior. The fasting is meant to alter the pattern of life for a month, and Muslims are required to make necessary adjustments in their normal schedules of work and study. The end of the month is marked by a festival, 'Id al-fitr, after which life returns to normal.

Instituted to cultivate individual spiritual and moral self-control, Ramadan also provides a community experience in which families and friends share both fasting and evening meals in the spirit of thanksgiving. Like prayer, fasting possesses therapeutic value. Prophetic medical tradition prescribes fasting for various kinds of ailments, including psychological problems caused by fear and anxiety. It was regarded as a remedy for excessive sexual drive.

The Fifth Pillar is the pilgrimage, the *hajj*, which all Muslims are required to undertake once in their lives, provided they have the financial means. The rituals of the pilgrimage at Mecca are a collective commemoration of the sacrifice story of Abraham and of lessons to be derived from it. Its spiritual objective is to inculcate a form of asceticism accompanied by renunciation of worldly desires (sexual intercourse, use of perfumes, and so on) and concern with the hereafter. The experience brings together Muslims of diverse cultures and nationalities to achieve a purity of existence and a communion with God that will exalt the pilgrim for the rest of his or her life.

Islamic Legal Thought

Islamic jurisprudence (*fiqh*) was developed to determine normative Islamic conduct as detailed in the *shari'a*, the sacred law. The *shari'a*, the divinely ordained blueprint for human conduct, is inherently and essentially religious. The juridical inquiry that led to the *shari'a* code was comprehensive because it necessarily dealt with every case of conscience covering God-human relations, as well as the ethical content of interpersonal relations in every possible sphere of human activity. Most of the legal activity, however, went into settling more formal interpersonal activities that affected the morals of the community. These activities dealt with the obligation of doing good to Muslims and guarding the interests of the community.

Islamic legal theory recognized four sources for judicial decisions: the Qur'an, the *sunna*, consensus (*ijma'*) of the early community of the Muslims, and analogy (*qiyas*), a method of reasoning from data furnished by the Qur'an and the *sunna* in an attempt to estimate the unknown from the known ruling. Al-Shafi'i (d. 820), a rigorous legal thinker, systematically and comprehensively linked the four sources in order to derive the *shari'a* to cover all possible contingencies. The legal precedents and principles provided by the Qur'an and *sunna* were used to develop an elaborate system of rules of jurisprudence. Human conduct was to be determined in terms of how much legal weight was borne by a particular rule that rendered a given practice obligatory or merely recommended.

For instance, if it is deemed that by risking one's life, one may be able to save another person from impending death, then the law permits not only donation but also sale of a needed body part or an organ after a careful risk-benefit analysis. Vital organs like eyes are excepted in this ruling. Likewise, it had to be decided whether an obligatory act, because of its social relevance and the degree of applicability of a given rule or precedent, was to be enforced by penalties in the courts or left to God's judgment in the hereafter.

In family law, the rights of women, children, and other dependents were protected against the male head of the family, who, on the average, was stronger than a woman and more independent, being free of pregnancy and having to care for children. Islamic marital rules encouraged individual responsibility by strengthening the nuclear family. *Shari'a* protected the prerogative of the male because he was required to support the household; the woman was protected primarily by her family. Muslim jurists gave the husband one-sided divorce privileges because for a woman to divorce a man would mean to unsettle her husband's economic investment. Under these rules a husband could divorce a wife almost at will; a wife who wished to leave her husband had to show good reason.

The main legal check upon the man in divorce was essentially financial and a matter of contract between equal parties that included a provision about the bridal gift. Part of the gift, which might be substantial, was paid at the time of marriage; if a husband divorced his wife without special reason, he had to pay her the rest. The equality of women in the *shari'a* carried with it an important financial independence. The Muslim woman could own property that could not be touched by any male relative, including her husband, who was required to support her from his own funds. Moreover, she had a personal status that might allow her to go into business on her own. However, this potential female independence was curbed primarily by cultural means, keeping marriages within the extended family, so that property would not leave the family through women marrying out.

Muslim jurists, although tending to give the male an extensive prerogative, presupposed a considerable social role for women. The Qur'anic injunction to propriety was stretched by means of the *sunna* to impose seclusion. The veil was presented simply in terms of personal modesty; the female apartments, in terms of family privacy. It was not intended to become a form of social distinction, as it did with upper-class women living in rigorous segregation. Among the latter it became a mark of a woman of a quality that she was secluded from all men but those in her own family.

Segregation of the sexes as required by the *shari'a* has led to untold problems in the teaching and practice of medicine today. The problems cover such areas as closely examining and touching the reproductive organs (male-female, female-male, male-male, and female-female); looking at photographs of naked persons for studying physiology and anatomy; taking the pulse and other vital signs of patients of opposite sex. While the classical decisions were prohibitive in all these cases, the majority of the modern Muslim jurists have casuistically accommodated the need to carry out necessary medical training, research, and treatment.

In the patriarchal family structure, and not necessarily in the *shari'a*, women were assigned a subordinate role in the household and community. Through certain cultural practices women's reproductive capacity was controlled. In some parts of the Muslim world women are subjected to traditional practices that are often harmful to their well-being and that of their children. One of the controversial and persistent practices is female circumcision (*khafd* or *khifad*), without which it is believed that girls cannot attain the status of womanhood. Islamic views on female circumcision are ambiguous. While Islam does not condone the practice, neither does it forbid it. The operation was performed long before the rise of Islam. It is not a practice in many Muslim countries, including Saudi Arabia, Tunisia, Iran, and Turkey. There is nothing in the Qur'an that justifies female circumcision, especially its most severe form, infibulation. The Prophet opposed the custom as found among pre-Islamic Arabs, since he considered it harmful to women's sexual well-being. Yet the official juridical position among the majority of Sunni jurists is that female circumcision is sanctioned by the *sunna*. However, the *shari'a* does not regard it as obligatory. It is merely a recommended act.

As Islamic jurisprudence became highly technical, disputes about method and judicial opinions crystallized into legal schools designated by the names of prominent jurists. The legal school that followed the Iraqi tradition was called Hanafi, after Abu Hanifa (d. 767), the great imam (teacher) in Iraq. Those who adhered to the rulings of Malik ibn Anas (d. 795), in Arabia and elsewhere, were known as Malikis. Al-Shafi'i founded a legal school in Egypt whose influence spread widely to other regions of the Muslim world. Another school was associated with Ahmad ibn Hanbal (d. 855), who compiled a work on *hadith* reports that became the source for juridical decisions of those who followed him. Shiites developed their own legal school, whose leading authority was the imam Ja'far al-Sadiq (d. 765).

Normally, Muslims accepted one of the legal schools prevalent in their region. Most Sunnites follow Hanafi or Shafi'i; the Shiites follow the Ja'fari school. In the absence of an organized *church* and ordained *clergy* in Islam, determination of valid religious praxis was left to the qualified scholar of religious law. Hence, there emerged a living tradition, with different interpretations of the Qur'anic laws and prophetic traditions, giving rise to different schools of the *shari'a*.

The scope of *shari'a*, understood as the norm of the Muslim community as a community, was defined by two essential areas of human life: acts of worship, both public and private, connected with the pillars of faith; and acts of public order that ensure individual justice. The *shari'a* reflected Muslim endeavors to ensure that Islam pervaded the whole of life. However, many areas of human existence, including the ethical problems connected with the medical treatment of ailments, received little systematic attention in the classical formulations of the legal thought.

Islamic Theological and Ethical Tradition

In the first half of the eighth century, the debates about qualified leadership, the existence of injustices in the community, and the appropriate response to redress the situation, formed the rudiments of the earliest systematic theology of the group called Mu'tazilites. Before them, some Muslim thinkers had developed theological arguments, including a doctrine of God and human responsibility, in defense of the Islamic revelation and the prophethood of Muhammad when these were challenged by other monotheists. The Mu'tazilites undertook to show that there was nothing repugnant to reason in the Islamic revelation. Their theological system was worked out under five headings: (1) belief in God's unity, which rejected anything that smacked of anthropomorphism; (2) the justice of God, which denied any ascriptions of injustice to God's judgment of human beings, with the consequence that humans alone were responsible for all their acts, and thus punishable for their evil ones; (3) the impending judgment, which underscored the importance of daily righteousness and rejected laxity in matters of faith; (4) the middle position of the Muslim sinner, who, because of disobeying God's commandments was neither condemned to Hell nor rewarded with Paradise but was regarded as reformable; and (5) the duty to command the good and forbid the evil in order to ensure an ethical social order.

In defining God's creation and governance of the world, these early Muslim theologians sought to demonstrate the primacy of revelation. At the same time, their theology reflected Hellenic influences. From the ninth century on, translations of the full Greek philosophic and scientific heritage became available in Arabic. The result was the development of a technical vocabulary and a pattern of syntax that enriched theological terminology.

The Ash'arites, reacting to Mu'tazilite rationalism, limited speculative theology to a defense of the doctrines given in the *hadith* reports, which were regarded as more reliable than abstract reason in deducing individual doctrines. The Ash'arites emphasized the absolute will and power of God, and denied nature and humankind any decisive role. What humans perceive as causation, they believed, is actually God's habitual behavior. In their response to the Mu'tazilite view on the objective nature of good and evil, and in their effort to maintain the effectiveness of a God, at once omnipotent and omnibenevolent, who could and did intervene in human affairs, they maintained that good and evil are what God decrees them to be. Accordingly, they cannot be known from nature but must be discovered in the sources of revelation, like the Qur'an and the Prophet's example. There are no inherently unchanging essences and natural laws that self-subsistent reason can discern. God transcends the order of nature. Hence, the notion of free will is incompatible with the divine transcendence, which determines all actions directly.

Ash'arite theological views remained dominant well into modern times, and had a profound effect upon scientific (and particularly medical) theory and practice among the Sunnites. The attitude of resignation, a by-product of belief in predestination, is summed up in the Sunni creedal confession: "What reaches you could not possibly have missed you; and what misses you could not possibly have reached you" (*Fiqh akbar,* art. 3, in Wensinck, p. 103). This belief in overpowering destiny was bound to have negative implications for some Sunni Muslims encountering adversities caused by illness and other forms of suffering. The Shiite theological and ethical doctrines were based on the Mu`tazilite thesis about the justice of God and the objective nature of moral values.

Positive sciences, especially medicine and astronomy, emerged from the rationalism of Muslim theologians influenced by translations of the works on these subjects from Greek into Arabic. Nature studies in Islamic civilization were pursued by intellectuals who contributed to the Mu'tazilite and Shiite rational theology. Human nature was studied in order to deduce rational principles that could help direct human life to create an ideal society. Ethics and politics were regarded as rational knowledge necessary to harmonize human existence in the universe.

At the practical level, medicine involved the training necessary to apply techniques that demonstrated tact and insight in the treatment of patients. Medical practice was based on a tradition of clinical observation, which became the source for encyclopedic works like the *Canon* (*al-Qanun*) of Avicenna (d. 1037). Since dissection of human cadavers was impossible because of the prohibition in Islamic law against mutilation of the dead and the requirement of immediate burial, physicians treated their patients partly on the basis of their knowledge of anatomy and partly by relying on their understanding of the rationality and harmony of the cosmos. Diagnosis and prognosis were also based on their insights about psychological and environmental factors. Despite the disapproval of some orthodox Muslims, who rejected Greek medicine as not provided for in the Prophetic medical tradition, many of these Greek-influenced philosopher-physicians came to be known as the *hakim* (wise). Prophetic medicine (*al-tibb al-nabawi*) was believed to have arisen to counter the authority of Greek-based medical tradition by positing the notion that certainty in knowledge, including medicine, depended upon revealed sources. However, although seemingly based on the Qur'an and statements attributed to the Prophet, Prophetic medicine actually was the remnant of the medicine customarily practiced among the Arabs in the pre-Islamic age.

Islamic Mysticism

In the early days of the Islamic empire under the Umayyads (eighth century), the mysticism that began as an ascetic reaction to growing worldliness in the Muslim community became institutionalized. Sufism, as Islamic mysticism came to be known, aimed to interiorize the formally undertaken ritual acts, and emphasized rigorous self-assessment and self-discipline for the achievement of spiritual and moral perfection. In its early form Sufism was mainly a form of ascetic piety that involved ridding oneself of any dependence on satisfying one's desires, in order to devote oneself entirely to God. Mystical practices developed by the Sufi masters comprised a moral process to gain the relative personal clarity that comes at moments of retreat and reflection. A further dimension of this reflection was to cultivate an ability to face reality about oneself and to love any being capable of needing love. The mystic experienced more intense levels of awareness, which could take ecstatic forms, including ecstatic love of God.

This aspect of Sufism brought the mystics into direct conflict with orthodox Muslims. Sufi teaching that a symbolic and spiritual fulfillment of religious duties was as good as the actual rites was seen by orthodox Muslims as a kind of antinomian behavior within the community that considered literal adherence to the requirements of law as the valid form of religiosity. In general, Sufis increasingly tended to minimize religious differences among various faiths and cultivated humanism based on universalistic spiritual and moral qualities.

By the eleventh century the Sufi masters had developed a new form of religious orientation that brought about the acceptance of Sufism in many parts of the Islamic world. Near the end of the twelfth century, several formal Sufi brotherhoods or orders (*tariqa*), in which women also participated, were organized. Each order taught a pattern of invocation and meditation that used devotional practices to organize a group of novices under a master. Special controls of breath and bodily posture accompanied invocative words or syllables to make possible more intense concentration. The orthodox, who had been suspicious of early elitist Sufism, were now persuaded to accept the Sufism of the masses and to try to discipline it. The ultimate approval of

Sufism as a genuine form of Islamic piety was facilitated by Abu Hamid al-Ghazali (d. 1111), who taught Islamic law and theology in Baghdad. His writings in connection with his personal spiritual crisis at the height of his professional success demonstrated that Sufism could be a powerful discipline for curing doubt and experiencing truth.

A number of Sufi masters served as analysts for younger Sufis, helping them to understand their psychic states and making sense of their place in the universe. In the premodern Islamic world, where medical treatment was not generally available to an average person, some prominent Sufis practiced traditional medicine based on the theory of the four humors that kept the body functioning. Herb remedies were used to treat ailments caused by imbalance in the four qualities of the body (hot and cold, moist and dry), which led to an imbalance of the humors. Other Sufis treated physical and psychic disorders through the writing of talismans and amulets. Talismans, some using sections of the Qur'an, and exorcism are used in treating mental disorders even today in rural areas of the Islamic world.

Islam and Modernity

The modern age brought Islam and Muslims face to face with intellectual as well as political challenges both from within and from without. From within, Muslims faced the deterioration of Islamic religious life caused by centuries of stagnation and petrification of doctrines and beliefs. From without, the hegemony of the West since the mid-nineteenth century resulted in alien domination of Muslim societies. Since that time, Muslims have endeavored to strike a balance between the divine promise of earthly success to Muslims and their tenuous contemporary situation by introducing internal reforms to prevent further degeneration of Islamic life, and by resisting any form of domination of Muslim societies by the Western powers.

Islamic fundamentalism in modern times stems from the acute awareness among Muslims of a conflict between the religion that promises worldly as well as eternal prosperity to its followers, on the one hand, and the historical development of the Muslim world, which points to the breach of a divine promise, on the other. Muslim leaders call for a return to the original teachings of Islam in the Qur'an and the Prophet's exemplary life. To regain the power and prestige of early Islam, they propose fashioning the modern nation-state on ideals derived from the practices of the original Muslim community. Muslim brotherhoods throughout the Islamic world have joined forces to implement strictly religious reform in a modern society, requiring adherence to the restrictive traditional social-cultural norms.

Resistance to modern secular ideologies and their implications has posed a greater challenge to the Muslim leadership. It has meant providing an Islamic alternative to intentionally imported or externally imposed sociopolitical systems. Such an alternative entails creative interpretation of religious ideas and symbols. Thus far, the traditional Muslim leadership has not succeeded in providing such an alternative as the only viable solution to the multifarious problems faced by the Muslim societies.

A case in point is provided by enormous problems that have arisen with the technological advancement in medicine. Muslim jurists are faced with a crisis because, by its own standards, Islamic jurisprudence has ceased to progress toward some further stage of development. The methods of inquiry and the forms of argument have disclosed inadequacies to furnish solutions to concrete problems faced by the community. Hence, important questions connected with the role of female physicians and patients in a male-dominated profession; conflict between rigorous religious observance and medical education; state policy toward family planning; and social and cultural factors that affect women's health adversely are among numerous pressing issues that remain to be authoritatively resolved.

The judicial decisions issued so far in various Muslim countries, where conferences on bioethics have been held in the last three decades, are mostly in the form of supposition or opinion, and lack the intellectual rigor to become part of state-sponsored health policy.

The greatest challenge to Muslim leadership, both religious and political, remains that of correcting the social and political injustices endured by the common people, who encounter a modern, materialist world over which they have minimal control.

Muslims living as a minority outside the geographical sphere of Islam face the challenge of integration and assimilation in the non-Muslim social universe. Muslim communities belonging to various ethnocultural groups in the West, including North America, are engaged in working out socially interactive strategies that will enable them to establish their identity as Western Muslims. African-American Muslims in North America have reminded the immigrant Muslims of the difficult process of integrating ethnic-cultural and religious identities in modern secular society. African-American Muslims, having been part of American society for a long time, have emerged with a rare ability to combine the most relevant and applicable facets of the modern American social universe and their adopted religion, Islam.

ABDULAZIZ SACHEDINA (1995)

SEE ALSO: *Abortion, Religious Traditions: Islamic Perspectives; African Religions; Authority in Religious Traditions; Christianity, Bioethics in; Eugenics and Religious Law; Hinduism, Bioethics in; Judaism, Bioethics in; Medical Ethics, History of: Near and Middle East; Population Ethics, Religious Traditions: Islamic Perspectives; Sikhism, Bioethics in; Women, Historical and Cross-Cultural Perspectives*

BIBLIOGRAPHY

Assaad, Marie Bassili. 1979. *Female Circumcision in Egypt: Current Research and Social Implications.* Cairo: American University, Social Research Centre.

Bakar, Osman. 1986. "Islam and Bioethics." *Greek Orthodox Theological Review* 31(1–2): 157–179.

Burgel, J. Christoph. 1973. "Psychosomatic Methods of Cures in the Islamic Middle Ages." *Humaniora Islamica* 1: 157–172.

Burgel, J. Christoph. 1976. "Secular and Religious Features of Medieval Arabic Medicine." In *Asian Medical Systems: A Comparative Study,* pp. 44–62, ed. Charles M. Leslie. Berkeley: University of California Press.

Campbell, Donald Edward H. 1926. *Arabian Medicine and Its Influence on the Middle Ages.* 2 vols. Trubner's Oriental Series. London: K. Paul, Trench, Trubner.

Ebrahim, Abul Fadl Mohsin. 1991. *Abortion, Birth Control and Surrogate Parenting: An Islamic Perspective.* Indianapolis, IN: American Trust.

Elgood, Cyril. 1951. *A Medical History of Persia and the Eastern Caliphate from the Earliest Times Until the Year A.D. 1932.* Cambridge, Eng.: Cambridge University Press.

Elgood, Cyril. 1962. "Tibb-ul-Nabbi or Medicine of the Prophet: Being a Translation of Two Works of the Same Name. I. The Tibb-ul-Nabbi of al-Suyuti. II. The Tibb-ul-Nabbi of Mahmud bin Mohamed al-Chaghhayni, Together with Introduction, Notes and a Glossary." *Osiris* 14: 33–192.

Fiqh al-tabib [Islamic Laws for Physicians]. 1993, comp. Mustafa Najafi, Mas`ud Salihi, and Mas`ud Firdawsi. International Congress on Medical Ethics. Tehran, July 14–16.

Giorgis, Belkis Wolde. 1981. *Female Circumcision in Africa.* Addis Ababa: U.N. Economic Commission for Africa.

Hodgson, Marshall G. S. 1974. *The Venture of Islam: Conscience and History in a World Civilization,* vol. 1. Chicago: University of Chicago Press.

Islam and Family Planning. 1974. International Islamic Conference (Rabat, Morocco, 1971). 2 vols. Beirut: International Planned Parenthood Federation, Middle East and North Africa Region.

Islamic Medical Wisdom: The Tibb al-A'imma. 1991, tr. Batool Ispahany, ed. Andrew J. Newman. London: Muhammadi Trust.

Masoom, Seyed Hossein Fattahy. 1992. *Collection of Articles from the Seminar on Islam's Views in Medicine.* Mashhad: Ferdowsi University Press. In Persian.

Musallam, Basim F. 1983. *Sex and Society in Islam: Birth Control Before the Nineteenth Century.* Cambridge, Eng.: Cambridge University Press.

Plessner, Martin. 1974. "The Natural Sciences and Medicine." In *The Legacy of Islam,* 2nd edition, ed. Joseph Schacht with C. E. Bosworth. Oxford: Clarendon Press.

Rahman, Fazlur. 1980. *Major Themes of the Qur'an.* Minneapolis, MN: Bibliotheca Islamica.

Rahman, Fazlur. 1989. *Health and Medicine in the Islamic Tradition: Change and Identity.* New York: Crossroad.

Rispler-Chaim, Vardan. 1993. *Islamic Medical Ethics in the Twentieth Century.* Leiden, Netherlands: E. J. Brill.

Rosenthal, Franz. 1969. "The Defence of Medicine in the Medieval Muslim World." *Bulletin of the History of Medicine* 43(6): 519–532.

Sachedina, Abdulaziz A. 1988. "Islamic Views on Organ Transplantation." *Transplantation Proceedings* 20(1 (Supp. 1)): 1084–1088.

Watt, W. Montgomery. 1968. *Muhammad at Mecca.* Oxford: Clarendon Press.

Wensinck, A. J. 1965 (1932). *The Muslim Creed: Its Genesis and Historical Development.* London: Frank Cass.

J

JAINISM, BIOETHICS IN

• • •

The Jaina religious tradition originated in India. Its adherents currently number approximately seven million, most of them living in India. According to tradition, the founders of the faith were not emissaries or embodiments of a supreme being, but were human beings who through their own efforts reached an elevated spiritual state called Kevala, characterized as blissful, omniscient solitude free from all karmic suffering and hence liberated from rebirth. According to Jaina lore, twenty-four persons known as Tīrthaṇkaras crossed over the river of rebirth and conquered the influences of negative karma. They then established and promulgated the Jaina religion. Their stories extend back into the prehistory of India. Historical records exist for the two most recent Tīrthaṇkaras: Parśvanatha, who lived around 850 B.C.E., and Vardhamāna Mahāvīra, the Jina or Conqueror, whose approximate dates are 599–527 B.C.E. The term *Jaina* means "follower or disciple of the Jina."

The belief structure and lifestyle of the Jainas are closely linked. In Jainism, there is no creator God. Rather, the Jaina religion is rooted in a unique respect for all life forms that serves as the basis for a sophisticated system of ethics based on the observance of nonviolence (*ahiṃsā*).

According to the Jainas, there are two categories of reality: one possesses life (*jīva*); the other is lifeless (*ajīva*). However, unlike Western definitions of life, which require "metabolism, growth, response to stimulation, and reproduction," the Jainas regard even seemingly inanimate objects as possessing life. The universe is said to be suffused with countless life forces grouped in five categories: earth, water, fire, and air bodies; microorganisms (*nigoda*); plants; animals; and humans. These *jīva* take the shape of their particular life form, whether it be large as a whale or small as a pebble. Each of these life forces is involved in a process of transmigration, moving after death into a new form.

According to Jaina tradition, sticky particles of nonliving matter called karmas adhere to *jīvas* when acts of desire, passion, or violence are committed. Though not visible to the naked eye, six subtle color distinguish this karma. Black, blue, and gray are associated with sinful or brutish karma, and yellow with less serious offenses. Pink and white indicate that one's karmic burden is being lessened. Through unethical passionate or violent behavior, one increases the inhibiting influence of darker, heavier karma. Through adherence to the Jaina code of ethics, one can expel the negative karma and cultivate the purer forms. Eventually, the goal of Jainism entails breaking free from all karmic influence. In this state, referred to as Kevala, one gains omniscience and freedom from rebirth, dwelling eternally in energy, consciousness, and bliss.

Jaina ethics consists of taking vows (*vrata*) designed to eliminate karma. Both lay Jainas and members of monastic orders are expected to observe these vows, though the rules for nuns and monks are much more stringent. Earliest Jaina tradition lists four vows: nonviolence (*ahiṃsā*), truthfulness (*satya*), not stealing (*asteya*), and nonpossession (*aparigraha*). Vardhamāna Mahavīra is credited with adding a fifth vow, chastity (*brahmacarya*). Scriptures such as the *Acārāṇga Sūtra* serve as authoritative sources for religious life.

From ancient times to the present, Jaina monks and nuns have served as preceptors and living symbols of this tradition. Though there are many "lineages" within the Jaina tradition, all modern Jainas can be classified as belonging to either the Śvetāmbara (White Clad) or the Digambara (Sky Clad) group. In the former group, all monks and nuns wear white robes. In the latter group, the highest order of monks renounces all possessions, including clothing. Both sects allow women to take advanced religious vows, though only the Śvetāmbara allow women to take final vows.

Jaina monks and nuns wander throughout India, teaching the lay community about the lives of earlier saints, advocating the practice of nonviolence, and discussing such topics as the all-pervasiveness of life forms and the karmic effects of behavior. Depending upon the rules of their particular subsect, they may cover their mouths with cloth to avoid injuring insects and microorganisms, or gently sweep the path in front of them to remove insects. In 1949, Ācārya Tulsi, head of the Terāpanthi Śvetāmbara monastic order, began teaching a twelvefold system of vows, including modern adaptations such as "not to resort to unethical practices in elections" and "to avoid contributing to pollution."

Although these vows are most intently observed by members of monastic communities, the Jaina lay community has developed a culture anchored in the practice of nonviolence. Lay Jainas generally enter professions in which they can avoid violent action that would increase the depth and darkness of one's karma. Many Jainas engage in trade and commerce, provided that animal products and weaponry are not involved. All Jainas, both laypersons and members of religious orders, are lacto vegetarians.

Although the Jaina system was originally conceived as outlining a path of personal liberation and spiritual enlightenment, many of the practices inspired by a desire to avoid the accumulation of karma have found new relevance in the modern ethical context, especially vegetarianism, animal protection, attitudes toward death, and the Jaina ideal of tolerance.

Jainas regard vegetarianism as a way to ensure that one does not accumulate the negative karmas associated with animal slaughter. In modern medical terms, it also purifies one's body, minimizing the violence done to the body that is often associated with the consumption of meat. Jaina eating habits, rooted in the ancient doctrine of nonviolence, are compatible with modern, scientific concerns about enhancing personal health through a low-fat, low-cholesterol diet.

Respect for animals has long been a mainstay of Jaina tradition. Throughout Indian history Jainas have lobbied for animal protection, building shelters and providing food for lost or wounded animals, and successfully campaigning to ban animal sacrifice in most parts of India. The Mogul emperor Akbar (1556–1605), influenced by Jaina monks, proclaimed days of restraint from hunting and renounced

the consumption of several types of meat. Jaina laypersons periodically visit slaughterhouses and purchase animals for release and protection. In India, pharmaceutical companies owned by Jainas, though required to test medicines on animals, rehabilitate their test animals and then release them.

Jaina tradition regards the death of an older person to be both natural and an opportunity for spiritual advancement. For many centuries, Jainas of advanced age or infirmity have engaged in a practice known as *sallekhanā,* referred to by modern Therāpanthi Śvetāmbara Jainas as *santhārā.* Rather than prolonging death when the process of decline becomes irreversible, some Jainas obtain permission from their religious preceptor to engage in a fast unto death. This final ritual is deemed in Samantabhadra's *Ratnakarandaśrāvakācāra,* a Jaina text of the second century, as acceptable only in "calamity, severe famine, old age, or illness from which there is no escape." One first renounces food, then milk, then water, and is encouraged to "depart from the body repeating the *nammokkāra mantra* [prayer] until the last." The Jainas assert that such a fast is neither suicide, which is done out of despair or hopelessness, nor euthanasia, which requires the assistance of a second party and a violent act. This practice, associated with a quest for spiritual freedom, embodies the Jaina ideal of encountering and embracing death without fear.

In a more philosophical vein, the Jainas have developed an ethic of debate, according to which each position or opinion is given provisional status. Any statement or perspective is said to be perhaps true or partially true, including the religious views held by non-Jainas. This ethic both reflects and fosters an attitude of tolerance for which the Jainas have become well known. Mahatma Gandhi, Albert Schweitzer, and Leo Tolstoy were all influenced by Jaina principles.

Technology and modernity present new challenges to the Jaina tradition in that they have spawned new forms of violence not discussed in the original Jaina texts. At Jaina Viśva Bhārati, a university dedicated to the teaching of Jainism located in western India, a curriculum has been developed to help apply Jaina principles to contemporary life, to minimize conflict among groups of people, and to encourage sensitivity to ecological issues.

The Jaina worldview sees the world as a biocosmology, a reality suffused with life. From the perspective of bioethics, this religion is unique in its advocacy of vegetarianism, animal protection, tolerance of multiple perspectives, and philosophical approach to the inevitability of death.

CHRISTOPHER KEY CHAPPLE (1995)

SEE ALSO: *Animal Welfare and Rights: Ethical Perspectives on the Treatment and Status of Animals; Animal Welfare and Rights: Vegetarianism; Death: Eastern Thought; Harm; Hinduism, Bioethics in; Medical Ethics, History of: South and East Asia: India*

BIBLIOGRAPHY

Chapple, Christopher Key. 1993. *Nonviolence to Animals, Earth, and Self in Asian Traditions.* Albany: State University of New York Press.

Jacobi, Hermann, tr. 1884–1895. *Jaina Sutras.* 2 vols. Oxford: Oxford University Press.

Jaini, Jagomanderlal. 1916. *Outlines of Jainism.* Cambridge: Cambridge University Press.

Jaini, Padmanabh S. 1979. *The Jaina Path of Purification.* Berkeley: University of California Press.

Jaini, Padmanabh S. 1991. *Gender and Salvation: Jaina Debates on the Spiritual Liberation of Women.* Berkeley: University of California Press.

Tatia, Nathmal. 1951. *Studies in Jaina Philosophy.* Banaras: Jain Cultural Research Society.

Tobias, Michael. 1991. *Life Force: The World of Jainism.* Berkeley: Asian Humanities Press.

JEHOVAH'S WITNESS REFUSAL OF BLOOD PRODUCTS

• • •

Jehovah's Witnesses are members of a biblically based, semi-Christian religious denomination that forbids its adherents from accepting transfusions of blood and blood products. This religious tenet is based on a literal interpretation of specific passages in the Bible. As a result of this doctrine, most baptized Jehovah's Witness *believers* refuse blood transfusions in their pursuit of medical treatment and healthcare. Some nonblood, transfusion-like replacement techniques and agents derived from minor blood fractions are left to individual believers to accept or reject. Jehovah's Witnesses do not subscribe to "faith healing," and thus seek the assistance of modern medicine as needed, excluding blood transfusions. This belief creates ethical questions and dilemmas related to patient autonomy, informed consent, advance directives, decisional capacity, surrogate decision making, professional integrity and promotion of patients' best interests, medical treatment for children, maternal–fetal conflicts, and the use of healthcare resources.

Historical Development and Organizational Structure

Jehovah's Witnesses trace their historical roots to Charles Taze Russell (1852–1916) and the nineteenth-century North American Adventist movement (a group of Christians who predicted an imminent "second coming" of Jesus Christ). In 1881, as a result of his teaching and writings, Russell founded the Zion's Watch Tower Tract Society. Russell had calculated and predicted that Jesus Christ would return in 1914, when God's direct rule would be established on earth and humanity would be restored to perfection. At the time of Russell's death, he had not appointed a successor.

Russell's religious movement floundered and fractionated until 1931, when Joseph Franklin Rutherford (1869–1942), a lawyer from Missouri, took over leadership. At a meeting of the renamed Watchtower Bible and Tract Society in Columbus, Ohio, in 1931, the name *Jehovah's Witnesses* was adopted and Rutherford became the group's president. Rutherford believed that because the Hebrew name for God was Jehovah, God's people should be known by the same name. In addition to authoring twenty books and numerous pamphlets that greatly influence the denomination's evolving belief system, Russell focused the lives of Jehovah's Witnesses on local congregations and places of assembly known as *Kingdom Halls,* which were established throughout the United States. A principle tenet of Jehovah's Witnesses is to inform the world about Jehovah's reign and kingdom via missionary activity, including door-to-door evangelization.

Nathan H. Knorr (1905–1977) succeeded Rutherford as the society's president in 1942. During Norr's term, the belief about the divine mandate to refuse blood transfusions was first introduced and promulgated in one of the Society's official publications, *The Watchtower* (July 1, 1945). By 2002, there were 6 million Jehovah's Witnesses participating in over 90,000 congregations in 230 countries.

Similar to other religious groups, Jehovah's Witnesses have developed a theologically justified organizational structure with accompanying degrees of hierarchical authority. God's will and direction are revealed primarily through the Bible, and secondarily through the leadership at the international headquarters of the Watchtower Bible and Tract Society, based in Brooklyn, New York. The teaching and organizational authority of the Society is composed of a president and a governing body of seventeen members who head up various committees.

Educational and instructional resources, including printed materials such as official publications (e.g., *The Watchtower,* and *Awake!*) are primarily written, produced, and published at the Brooklyn headquarters. Distribution of materials takes place through branch offices, districts, and circuits, the last consisting of approximately twenty congregations. Districts and circuits have overseers appointed by the society's governing body. Local Kingdom Halls, where individual congregations are centered, are presided over by elders responsible for worship, training, and evangelization.

Biblical Beliefs about Blood

As noted above, the Jehovah's Witness belief system is biblically based. The exegetical method used to interpret biblical texts is a literal, or fundamentalist, method (what the words literally state or do not state), rather than a historical-critical method (taking into consideration the human author's intention and the cultural and historical milieux of the text). Jehovah's Witnesses view the sixty-six books of the Bible as inspired by God and historically accurate. As a result of this literal exegesis of the scriptures, Jehovah's Witnesses find biblical support for pacifism; the practice of adult baptism by immersion; the practices of not saluting national flags and not celebrating birthdays or Christmas (because such celebrations are not mentioned or mandated in the Bible); a belief that the reign of God will be established on the earth, where people will live forever; and the belief that the number of the "spiritual sons of God" who will rule with Jesus Christ in heaven is limited to 144,000. The literal interpretation of the "Christian Greek Scriptures" (their official name for the New Testament) has led Jehovah's Witnesses to conclude that Jesus Christ is God's son, but is inferior to God and was the first of God's creations. This last set of beliefs about Jesus Christ technically places Jehovah's Witnesses outside of mainstream Christian denominations, which profess God as a trinity of "equal persons," including Jesus Christ as God incarnate.

A literal interpretation of the Bible helps to explain why, in 1945, the governing body of the Watchtower Bible and Tract Society determined that accepting blood or blood products for medical purposes violated the biblical word of God. Pertaining to blood, there are at least three scriptural passages that have great significance for Jehovah's Witness belief and practice. These passages are:

> Every moving animal that is alive may serve as food for you. As in the case of green vegetation, I do give it all to you. Only flesh with its soul—its blood—you must not eat (Gen. 9:3–4).

> As for any man of the house of Israel or some alien resident who is residing as an alien in their midst who eats any sort of blood, I shall certainly set my face against the soul that is eating the blood, and I shall indeed cut him off from among his people (Lev. 17:10).

> The holy spirit and we ourselves have favored adding no further burden to you, except these necessary things, to keep abstaining from things sacrificed to idols and from blood and from things strangled and from fornication (Acts 15:28).

Viewed as inspired by God and to be interpreted literally, these three scriptural texts forbid the eating or ingestion of blood. An important step in the reasoning and interpretive process for Jehovah's Witnesses is that the relatively recent medical practice of intravenous blood transfusion is seen as a way of nourishing or feeding the human body. With this understanding and perception of blood transfusions, a literal interpretation and application of the cited biblical texts becomes clear: Through God's inspired and literal word contained in the Bible, he has expressly forbidden the eating of blood, and, when applied to modern medical practice, this means that God has forbidden the nourishing of the human body with blood transfusions. This divine prohibition applies in all circumstances, including emergency and life-threatening situations. Jehovah's Witnesses who knowingly and willfully accept transfusions of blood or blood products violate God's commandment and disassociate themselves from the congregation of believers.

What Is Forbidden and Permitted

Because of medicine's increasing abilities and techniques to collect, store, dissect, develop, infuse, and salvage blood and blood-based products, numerous and specific questions about what is forbidden and permitted have arisen among Jehovah's Witnesses, as well as among healthcare professionals who treat them. For example, can a Jehovah's Witness accept the use of an intraoperative cell-saver technique or the administration of albumin, erythropoietin, bone marrow, stem cells, or clotting factors for hemophilia?

Jehovah's Witnesses are officially and specifically prohibited from receiving whole blood, packed red blood cells, white blood cells, plasma, and platelets. This explicit prohibition remains the same regardless of the source of the blood, that is, whether the donation is autologous (derived from the same individual) or donated by someone else. Once blood has left the body and the body's circulatory system, it cannot be transfused into a Jehovah's Witness patient. Some techniques and blood-based agents, however, are left to the discretion and conscience of the individual believer. One example is an intraoperative cell-saver procedure that involves salvaging blood from a surgical field (e.g., a body cavity), cleansing the blood, and then returning the blood to the patient. If during this process a continuous, closed circulation of the blood is maintained as it moves from the body of the patient through the tubing of the salvaging machine and then back into the body, this external circulatory process can be viewed as an extension of the body's own circulation system, consequently the procedure can be acceptable. Also left to the individual believer's conscience and decision are the use of agents derived from minor fractions of blood components, such as immune globulins, albumin, clotting factors for hemophilia, as well as bone marrow and stem cells.

Medical Management of Jehovah's Witnesses

With the exception of transfusions of blood and blood products, Jehovah's Witnesses do not have religious objections to any other medical treatment or procedure that promotes the patient's health. In fact, seeking medical treatment for disease and the promotion of health are seen as concrete ways for believers to respond appropriately to God's gift of life. Thus, as long as blood transfusions are not involved, and when medical necessity arises, Jehovah's Witnesses will seek solid organ transplantation, surgery (including coronary artery bypass grafting, dialysis, and various life-sustaining measures such as intubation and ventilatory support), and medically supplied nutrition and hydration.

When blood loss is a likely risk with an accompanying decrease of hematocrit, hemoglobin, and blood pressure (such as during many surgeries), Jehovah's Witnesses hope for and encourage the medical team to engage in a variety alternative medical and surgical methods that obviate the need for blood transfusions. These methods include limiting phlebotomies or using pediatric needles for blood draws; inducing hormonal suppression of menstruation; stimulating red-blood-cell production through administration of recombinant (synthetic) erythropoietin; utilizing proven and published techniques to reduce surgical blood loss (e.g., cooling a patient to lessen oxygen needs; electrocautery; using laparoscopic and minimally invasive instruments; administration of desmopressin, aprotinin, antifibrinolytics); or preventing shock (from inadequate blood flow to the body's peripheral tissues) by use of nonblood volume expanders such as saline solution, lactated Ringer's solution, and dextran.

To promote respect for their beliefs and help educate healthcare professionals, many Jehovah's Witness congregations and circuits have formed Hospital Liaison Committees to educate healthcare professionals and hospital administrators about the nuances of what is forbidden and permitted, according to Jehovah's Witness beliefs. Committee members have available current literature and bibliographies, usually from prestigious peer-reviewed clinical journals, that reference bloodless management and blood-substitute treatment techniques that have had successful outcomes.

Most of this medical reference material is also available from the Brooklyn headquarters. Hospital Liaison Committees also strives to identify physicians, especially surgeons and anesthesiologists, who are willing to treat Jehovah's Witness patients while respecting their beliefs about blood. Of special significance for Jehovah's Witnesses are hospitals and surgery centers that are willing to develop and advertise bloodless surgery programs (deCastro). Hospital Liaison Committees promote a five-step protocol addressed to healthcare professionals treating Jehovah's Witnesses:

1. Review nonblood medical alternatives and treat the patient without using homologous blood.
2. Consult with other doctors experienced in nonblood alternative management at the same facility.
3. Contact the local Hospital Liaison Committee for locating experienced and cooperative doctors at other facilities to consult on alternative care.
4. Transfer the patient, if necessary, to a cooperative doctor or facility before the patient's condition deteriorates.
5. In a rare situation, if the above steps have been exhausted and governmental or court intervention is deemed necessary, the patient, the parents, or the guardian should be notified as soon as possible of such intended action.

Ethical Evaluation and Analysis

In general, informed adult patients with decisional capacity have an ethically supported right to refuse medically recommended treatment, including treatment that is life-sustaining and death-preventing. This is true regardless of the patient's motive or rationale and whether the refusal is religiously based or not. The American Hospital Association's "Patient's Bill of Rights" echoes this ethical and legal consensus when it states: "The patient has a right to make decisions about the plan of care prior to and during the course of treatment and to refuse a recommended treatment or plan of care to the extent permitted by law and hospital policy" (Right # 3). Some ethical and legal limitations on this right have been argued when the adult refusing treatment has dependent minor children; that is, when there are *innocent third parties* who will be affected by the adult's refusal.

Thus, adult Jehovah's Witnesses with decisional capacity have the right to refuse blood transfusions, even in life-threatening situations. Although the recommended treatment of a blood transfusion can be presumed in most situations to be in the patient's best interests, a patient's right to self-determination (i.e., autonomy) and the corresponding norm of informed consent, ethically and legally "trump" a physician's or medical team's recommendations and perception of the patient's best interests.

This right to refuse can be extended to include patients who once had, but no longer have, decisional capacity, if such patients have indicated their wishes through an advance directive. In anticipation of such situations, many Jehovah's Witnesses sign and carry a specially prepared, wallet-size *medical directive/release* card indicating their wishes not to receive blood transfusions "even though physicians deem such vital to my health or life." In general, such an advance directive should be honored unless there is clear evidence that the patient revoked the advance directive or completed it when coerced or inadequately informed.

An adequate informed-consent process has great ethical significance for Jehovah's Witnesses' refusals of blood products. In the usual fashion for informed consent, the nature, purpose, risks, benefits, and alternatives associated with consenting to or refusing blood products should be explained to Jehovah's Witnesses. This proactive process is even more important prior to medical and surgical interventions that risk significant blood loss. Many hospitals and surgery centers have informed-consent forms that specifically address the use of blood transfusions. However, a form signed by a patient is less important than the conversation and education between physician and patient, which can be triggered by the presentation of a form to be signed.

Unless there has been an acute event or an emergency situation, there is usually time for physicians to present sensitively and clearly the likely outcomes should blood be needed and not provided, and for patients to be queried about their willingness, for each projected outcome, to consent to blood, blood products, agents partially derived from blood, and nonblood alternatives. Also, during such discussions, physicians should communicate their willingness (or unwillingness) to honor Jehovah's Witnesses' refusals of blood transfusions. Because physicians' professional integrity should be protected and respected as much as possible, the transfer of a Jehovah's Witness patient to another qualified physician, who is willing to limit treatment according to the patient's religious beliefs, might become necessary and is ethically supportable as long as continuity of the patient's care is preserved.

When Jehovah's Witness patients have lost decisional capacity and healthcare decisions must be made, the healthcare team may need to involve surrogate decision makers (often family members or someone specifically designated by the patient through a medical-power-of-attorney document). The surrogate should provide a substituted judgement on behalf of the patient; that is, consent to or refuse a specific treatment in accord with the patient's wishes, values, and beliefs. Providing a substituted judgement may be especially difficult for a surrogate who does not share the patient's beliefs and if the outcome could be death or serious debilitation (e.g., a stroke) if blood is not transfused.

When the interests of *innocent third parties* will be affected by a refusal of treatment, additional cautions and considerations are in order. Such situations occur when a pregnant woman refuses life-sustaining treatment, or when a parent's refusal of treatment will likely result in death or serious and permanent disability and any dependent children will subsequently be abandoned or lose parental support and nurturing. An analysis of the latter situation should include whether support is available from other family members or the community. In such instances, some courts have intervened in the decision process in favor of preserving life (*Raleigh-Fitkin Hospital v. Anderson; Werth v. Taylor*), while other courts have supported the patient's refusal (*Fosmire v. Nicoleau; Norwood Hospital v. Munoz; Stamford Hospital v. Vega*). Because neither a consistent ethical nor legal consensus exists for such *third party* circumstances, in actual cases of this kind professionals should seek the guidance and support of institutional ethics committees, hospital legal counsel, or the courts.

When the Patient Is a Child

Jehovah's Witnesses who are parents generally refuse to give permission for blood transfusions for their children when transfusions are needed. Members of healthcare teams usually experience such refusals as much more troublesome and problematic than when adult patients refuse recommended treatments for themselves. With treatment decisions involving children, it is usually not a situation of patient autonomy clashing with medical perception of best interests, but rather parental perception of best interests (based on parental religious beliefs) clashing with medical perception of best interests.

At least for younger children who have not achieved a level of cognitive and emotional development to make their own decisions, most ethicists and legal commentators echo the sentiments of the 1944 U. S. Supreme Court conclusion that, "Parents may be free to make martyrs of themselves.

But it does not follow [that] they are free, in identical circumstances, to make martyrs of their children before they have reached the age of full and legal discretion when they can make that choice for themselves" (*Prince v. Massachusetts*). Especially in life-threatening situations, there is ethical support (based primarily on a best interest standard) for providing needed blood transfusions for patients who have never had decisional capacity.

The American Academy of Pediatrics (AAP) supports such a stance: "The AAP ... advocates that children, regardless of parental religious beliefs, deserve effective medical treatment when such treatment is likely to prevent substantial harm or suffering or death" (AAP, 1997). This position can be extended to include patients with severe mental retardation, regardless of chronological age. However, outside of life-threatening situations, and when nonblood alternatives have a reasonable likelihood of being effective, physicians should give serious consideration to honoring the parent's religious tenets that the child not be given transfusions. If a decision is made to seek a court order to permit blood transfusions, the parents should be informed about this decision before it is carried out.

More ethically complex are cases of adolescent Jehovah's Witness patients who have not reached the legal age of majority or adulthood (usually age 18), or who have not been declared emancipated minors by a court, and who refuse blood transfusions. Some of these adolescents may have the requisite cognitive skills to give an informed consent or refusal (Leikin; Weir; Weithorn). From an ethical perspective, healthcare professionals should use the same criteria for assessing decisional capacity (Grisso) and the same process of informed consent and information disclosure as is used for legal adults. Some courts in North America have affirmed this judgement, specifically if adolescent patients can demonstrate sufficient cognitive skills to consent to or refuse medical treatment (Robb).

Use of Resources

From one perspective, Jehovah's Witnesses could be accused of increasing medical expenses and the use of scarce medical resources because of their idiosyncratic beliefs. Although there have not been comprehensive studies comparing and calculating costs for medically managing Jehovah's Witness patients versus non–Jehovah's Witness patients with similar diseases, many physicians and hospitals caring for Jehovah's Witness patients could likely provide individual case reports demonstrating a greater use of resources for some specific patients. A few published reports have claimed an increase in expenses because the usual *standard of care* could not be

followed due to patient wishes (Busuttil). As healthcare teams work for good medical outcomes while honoring patients' refusals of blood transfusions in some individual cases, there can be increases in hospital lengths-of-stay, occupancies of intensive-care beds, time in operating rooms, and costs for medications.

But from another perspective, Jehovah's Witnesses could argue that respect for their religious beliefs has occasioned discoveries and developments that conserve a scarce resource—blood products—while benefiting all patients. Jehovah's Witnesses can make the claim that their refusals of blood have accelerated research and the adoption of innovative practices that reduce, eliminate or substitute for the use of blood transfusions. Further, because transfusions of blood and blood products always involve some risk to recipients, any reduction of transfusion therapy by using safe and effective nonblood alternatives and techniques decreases potential medical risks for all patients.

Treating some Jehovah's Witnesses within the context of their beliefs about blood may indeed increase costs and the use of resources in comparison to the general population. But without sufficient comparative studies, such claims remain hypothetical. Even if it can be shown that Jehovah's Witness beliefs increase healthcare costs, would that be sufficient justification for either not honoring refusals of blood therapy or expecting Jehovah's Witnesses to contribute more financially for their healthcare (e.g., in the form of higher insurance premiums)? Such a conclusion seems to fail, based on fairness, until such time as all or most individual behaviors and decisions that increase demands on healthcare resources (e.g., smoking, routinely eating foods high in fat, not wearing seat belts) result in those individuals being either denied treatment or paying more for their healthcare as well.

Conclusion

In general, there is strong ethical and legal support for honoring Jehovah's Witnesses' informed refusals of blood transfusions. Some exceptions to this general principle do exist, however. Because persons can have varying degrees of commitment to religious beliefs, and because the Jehovah's Witness leadership leaves some issues for individual judgement and decision, physicians and healthcare professionals should explore the limits and desires for specific treatments with each Jehovah's Witness. For this patient population, as much as possible, safe and effective nonblood alternatives should be used to promote restoration of health and preserve life. Healthcare professionals and others do not need to agree with Jehovah's Witnesses' beliefs and biblical exegesis in order to show them respect, honor their religiously based refusals of transfusion therapy, and provide them with high-quality care.

MARTIN L. SMITH

SEE ALSO: *Authority in Religious Traditions; Autonomy; Children: Rights of Children; Competence; Coercion; Conscience; Conscience, Rights of; Infants*

BIBLIOGRAPHY

American Academy on Pediatrics, Committee on Bioethics. 1995. "Informed Consent, Parental Permission, and Assent in Pediatric Practice." *Pediatrics* 95: 314–317.

American Academy of Pediatrics, Committee on Bioethics. 1997. "Religious Objections to Medical Care." *Pediatrics* 99: 279–281.

Busuttil, David, and Adrian Copplestone. 1995. "Management of Blood Loss in Jehovah's Witnesses: Recombinant Human Erythropoietin Helps But Is Expensive." *British Medical Journal* 311: 1115–1116.

Cumberland, William H. 1986. "The Jehovah's Witness Tradition." In *Caring and Curing: Health and Medicine in the Western Religious Traditions,* edited by Ronald L. Numbers and Darrel W. Amundsen. New York: Macmillan.

deCastro, Roberto M. 1999. "Bloodless Surgery: Establishment of a Program for the Special Medical Needs of the Jehovah's Witness Community—The Gynecologic Surgery Experience at a Community Hospital." *American Journal of Obstetrics and Gynecology* 180: 1491–1498.

Fosmire v. Nicoleau. 551 N.E.2d 77, N.Y. (1990).

Grisso, Thomas, and Appelbaum Paul S. 1998. *Assessing Competence to Consent to Treatment, A Guide for Physicians and Other Health Professionals.* New York: Oxford University Press.

Leikin, Sanford L. 1983. "Minors' Assent or Dissent to Medical Treatment." *Journal of Pediatrics* 102: 169–176.

Norwood Hospital v. Munoz. 409 MA 116,564 N.E.2d 1017 (1991).

Prince v. Massachusetts. 321 US 158 (1944).

Raleigh-Fitkin Hospital v. Anderson. 201 A2d 537, New Jersey (1964).

Robb, Nancy. 1994. "Ruling on Jehovah's Witness Teen in New Brunswick May Have 'Settled the Law' for MDs." *Canadian Medical Association Journal* 151: 625–628.

Smith, Martin L. 1997. "Ethical Perspectives on Jehovah's Witnesses' Refusal of Blood." *Cleveland Clinic Journal of Medicine* 64: 475–481.

Stamford Hospital v. Vega. 674 A.2d 821, Conn (1996).

Thomas, J. Mervyn. 1994. "The Worldwide Need for Education in Nonblood Management in Obstetrics and Gynaecology." *Journal of the Society of Obstetricians and Gynaecologists of Canada* 16: 1483–87.

Watchtower Bible and Tract Society of New York. 1992. *Family Care and Medical Management for Jehovah's Witnesses.* New York: Watchtower Bible and Tract Society of New York.

Watchtower Bible and Tract Society of Pennsylvania. 1990. *How Can Blood Save Your Life?* New York: Watchtower Bible and Tract Society of New York.

Weir, Robert F, and Charles Peters. 1997. "Affirming the Decisions Adolescents Make about Life and Death." *Hastings Center Report* 27(6): 29–40.

Weithorn, Lois A., and Susan B. Campbell. 1982. "The Competency of Children and Adolescents to Make Informed Treatment Decisions." *Child Development* 53: 1589–1598.

Werth v. Taylor. 475 N.W.2d 426, 427, Mich. Ct. App (1991).

INTERNET RESOURCES

American Hospital Association. 1992. "A Patient's Bill of Rights." Available from <http://www.hospitalconnect.com/aha>.

Watchtower Bible and Tract Society of New York. 2003. Available from <http://www.watchtower.org/>.

JUDAISM, BIOETHICS IN

• • •

As a specific discipline, bioethics is as new to Judaism as it is to human culture in general. To be sure, every cultural tradition throughout history has developed various ethical norms or rules to govern the different areas of human action. But it is only with the great innovations in biomedical science and technology during the second half of the twentieth century that there has been a need for a distinct schematization of traditional rules, and even the formulation of new ones, for this increasingly complex area of human action.

Judaism is no exception to this general cultural phenomenon. Indeed, Jewish ethicists have been particularly eager to make a Jewish contribution to bioethics, not least of all because of the great interest Jews have always taken in medical practice throughout history, and because many Jewish scholars maintain that there is no area of human action, however unprecedented, to which the rules formulated in the Jewish tradition do not somehow apply. Furthermore, the increasingly cross-cultural context of bioethics gives Jewish ethicists a much larger audience of interested parties than they have had heretofore.

Origins and Development of Jewish Bioethics

Historically, Judaism has seen the normative authority of Jewish life, both communal and individual, as stemming from a twofold teaching (Torah): Scripture and Tradition, or the Written Torah and the Oral Torah. The Written Torah consists of the divinely mandated precepts of the first five books of the Hebrew Bible. The Oral Torah consists largely of the legislation of the rabbis of the Talmudic period (first century B.C.E. to the sixth century C.E.) along with a few ancient traditions (*halakhot*) accepted as having been revealed to Moses at Mount Sinai. Regarding many ethical (as opposed to ritual) norms, moreover, especially those dealing with basic human questions of life and death, Judaism has seen the Torah's commandments as binding on all humankind, at least in theory. This area of the law has been designated as *Noahide Law,* the descendants of Noah being the name for humankind. Since it has long been accepted that there cannot be a double standard differentiating between Jews and non-Jews in questions of life and death (*Sanhedrin* 59a; *Tosafot* s. v. "leika"), and since virtually all medical treatment and so much contemporary Jewish discussion of bioethical issues is conducted in the context of a pluralistic society, this universal aspect of Jewish law has become the most prevalent standard for the formulation of most Jewish views on the subject.

Scriptural law is subject to human interpretation, but it cannot be amended or repealed (Num. 15:23; Deut. 4:2; *Kiddushin* 29a; cf. *Sotah* 9.9) because it is taken to be the direct word of God. Because rabbinic law is considered human-made law only, although legislated by authority sanctioned by Scripture (*Shabbat* 23a), it has been much easier to change and adapt than scriptural law. Rabbinic legislation, at least in theory, admits of amendment and repeal (*Eduyot* 1.5), but since the demise of the *Sanhedrin* as the central Jewish legislative authority, reinterpretation of already existing norms has been the method of changing rabbinic law. Since the actual practical rules of any area of Jewish law—certainly those pertaining to bioethics—are much more rabbinic than scriptural, the authorized range for the exercise of human reason is the widest.

Within the immediate confines of the traditional Jewish community, the method of judgment employed in Jewish bioethics is not different from the method employed in any other area of Jewish law. The basic scriptural norm is located, its rabbinic elaborations are traced through the Talmud and related literature, its authoritative structure is determined, relevant precedents (if there are any) are culled from the vast literature of legal responsa by individual rabbinical authorities, and finally the person accepted by a community of Jews as their legal authority frequently seeks the counsel of learned colleagues. This process involves the ordering and application of rules to apply adequately to a case at hand, and occasionally the recognition of more basic principles behind the rules as well as procedures that direct their application. More and more frequently, in the cases posed by the new medical technology we see a greater role for principles. It is often much more difficult to find appropriate rules for the novel situations at hand, and principles must more directly guide the formulation of rather tenuous analogies from existing rules. Also, in the context of cross-cultural discussion of bioethical issues, the general guidance suggested by principles is sought much more than the governance of the rules of a singular tradition.

Theological and Moral Principles in Jewish Bioethics

A number of theological-moral principles operate in Jewish discussions of bioethics. The most prominent of these principles are God as creator, God as covenanter, the sanctity of human life, human benevolence, the authority of medical expertise, and the personal prerogatives of the patient.

GOD AS CREATOR. All the great Jewish theologians throughout history have emphasized that the first principle of Judaism is that God is the creator and Lord of the entire universe, who maintains its perpetual order (*ma'aseh beresheet*), its "nature." Accordingly, God is considered to be the only possessor of absolute property rights. All creatures are the subjects of varying privileges granted by their divine creator. In accordance with its exalted status as the image of God, the human creature is given duties (*mitsvot;* Gen. 2:16) as well as the highest privileges (Gen. 1:26). However, whatever powers humans have are legitimate only when they are seen as from God for the sake of God, and not as the possessions of the individual or the community in any way. "Indeed, all lives are Mine" (Ezek. 18:4).

This principle is at the very heart of the differences between Jewish law and the secular norms based on the primacy of human autonomy or utility. This is especially apparent in the current intense debates concerning the beginning of human life in relation to abortion, and concerning the end of human life in relation to euthanasia. Arguments insisting upon a *right* to abortion or a *right* to euthanasia, be that *right* the individual's or the community's, essentially deny divine creatorship and lordship as the fundamental norm, which is contrary to what Judaism teaches. Therefore, one can see that the most intense debates in bioethics are quite often more about theological principles than ethical precepts as such.

GOD AS COVENANTER. God is not only the creator of the universe and its perpetual Lord but is also in intimate historical relationship with the people of Israel. This relationship is called the "covenant" (*berit*). According to Moses Maimonides (1135–1204) and other Jewish theologians, Christians and Muslims, who also see themselves as related to this covenantal God, share in some of this covenantal intimacy (*Mishneh Torah: Melakhim*, chap. 11, uncensored ed.). This theological principle impinges upon the main issues of bioethics because it largely determines the status of human personhood as the "image of God" (*tselem Elohim*), a term that seems to designate the essential human capacity for a direct personal relationship with God. Accordingly, human persons are not seen as being primarily defined by innate capacities such as intelligence or freedom of choice, because these qualities vary too much from person to person and are not possessed by everyone born into the human race. Thus, according to the first-century sage Ben Azzai, the most all-encompassing principle of the entire Torah is expressed in the verse "This is the book of the human generations" (Gen. 5:1; quoted in *Palestinian Talmud: Nedarim* 9.3/41c). This means that full personhood is gained solely by one's birth to human parents, and not by less comprehensive criteria based on such capacities as rationality or freedom of choice.

The principle of God as covenanter is also at the heart of the issue of care for the sick. If the sick have the privilege of making special claims upon those able to care for them, claims that translate into the duties of caretakers, then these privileges and duties are rooted in God's care for his creation, care that is epitomized by God's covenantal involvement with Israel. This is clearly seen in the role of prayer in the treatment of illness, both the special privilege of the prayers of the sick themselves (*Shabbat* 12b) and the duty of those who care for them to pray for them as well (*Nedarim* 40a). In fact, the Talmud interprets the scriptural command that the sufferer from the disease tsara῾at (mistranslated as *leprosy*—but actually a skin disease with symptoms close to those of eczema or psoriasis) publicly declare himself "unclean! unclean!" (Lev. 13:45)—to be a cry to those hearing these words of anguish to pray for the sufferer (*Mo῾ed Qatan* 5a). In another Talmudic text this requirement is extended to include prayer for the plight of anyone suffering from any other illness of calamity (*Sotah* 32b). Those with whom God has covenanted must show genuine sympathy to one another. The extension of this sympathy is, finally, seen as reaching even to nonmembers of the covenant in the interest of peace and general goodwill (*Gittin* 61a).

THE SANCTITY OF HUMAN LIFE. The term *sanctity of human life* does not appear in the classical Jewish sources but is an accurate expression of the principle that "one human life is not pushed aside for another" (*Ohalot* 7.6; see also *Tosefta: Terumot* 7.20), that is, that one human life has no more inherent value than another, that the blood of one person "is not redder than someone else's" (*Pesahim* 25b; cf. *Sefer Hasidim*, ed. Parma, no. 252; Luria, *Yam shel Shlomoh: Baba Kama*, 8.59). The underlying assumption of the basic sanctity of each individual human life is expressed by the Mishnah: "Whoever saves even one human life, it is as if he saved an entire world" (*Sanhedrin* 4.5; *Palestinian Talmud: Sanhedrin* 4.5/22a).

However, this does not mean that the value of any human life is infinite. In certain cases Judaism demands martyrdom, especially when continued life requires that the God of Israel be denied (*Sanhedrin* 74a). Moreover, at times, priorities are assigned when only one life in a particular situation can be saved as opposed to all lives in that same situation being lost (*Horayot* 3.7–8; *Tosefta: Terumot* 7.20; *Baba Metsia* 62a; *Sanhedrin* 72b). It is in the realm of ritual practice that the sanctity of human life and the duty to rescue are paramount (*Yoma* 85b). Any doubt is to be resolved in favor of human life; thus the practice of any ritual act that endangers human life is proscribed (*Shabbat* 129a). The classic example of this is the rule that rescue efforts are to be conducted on the Sabbath or on the Day of Atonement, irrespective of whatever labors are involved, as long as there is any chance that human life might be saved (*Yoma* 85a). But once the death of the person endangered is ascertained, all ritual restraints are in effect once more (*Tosefta Shabbat* 17.19; *Shabbat* 30b, 151b).

The principle of the sanctity of human life can be seen most clearly operating in cases of nonviability, that is, when there is no reasonable expectation of survival. Thus a child born so defective as to be considered nonviable is still to be nursed by its mother (*Yevamot* 80b, *Rashi* and *Bach* thereto; also, *Tosefta: Ketubot* 5.5; *Tosefta: Niddah* 2.5), that is, not abandoned to die, as was the case in many ancient cultures. And a human life in the very last stages of its existence, in its death throes, is not to be extinguished on the assumption that death is inevitable (*Shabbat* 151b).

There is debate among later authorities as to what measures may or may not be taken to extend the death throes called goses (Isserles's note on *Shulhan Arukh: Yoreh De῾ah* 339.1; cf. *Bach* on Tur: *Yoreh De῾ah* 339). This debate anticipates current ones as to whether one can distinguish between active and passive euthanasia. Those authorities who argued that not extending the death agony automatically shortens the life of the patient would seem to support the view that no cogent distinction can be made in euthanasia: either one must permit it per se (as Judaism clearly does not) or one must prohibit it per se (as Judaism seemingly does). This is based on a rejection in the Talmud of any *double effect* rationale (*Shabbat* 75a).

However, the treatment of pain is something that may be done as an end in itself as long as it is not simultaneous with the actual death of the patient (*Avodah Zarah* 18a). Moreover, one is allowed to pray for the death of the patient in cases where agony is extreme and there is no real hope for recovery (*Ran* on *Nedarim* 40a re *Ketubot* 104a). Yet this is always an appeal for divine action and not an endorsement of humans acting in place of God. Even in cases of extreme suffering, the taking of human life is never to be the purpose of any intervention (*Avodah Zarah* 18a). Whereas a cure cannot always be effected, care is always mandated until the very end of human life. That is why, for example, a dying person is not to be left alone even when there is very little time left (*Shulhan Arukh: Yoreh De'ah* 339.4).

HUMAN BENEVOLENCE. The duty to care for the sick, and to heal them whenever possible (*biqur holim*, literally, "visitation of the sick"), is derived from two different sets of biblical and rabbinic sources. The difference in the selection of the sources indicates two distinct approaches to the issue of medical treatment in general.

Maimonides, who was the prototypical rabbi-physician for later generations, categorized the specific duty to care for the sick as a rabbinically mandated act stemming from the general duty of benevolence commanded in Scripture: "You shall love your neighbor as yourself" (Lev. 19:18), which, undoubtedly basing himself on earlier rabbinic sources (*Shabbat* 31a; *Targum Jonathan* on Lev. 19:18), he paraphrased as "Everything you want others to do for you, you do" (Mishneh Torah: Evel 14.1). As for the duty actually to save a human life, Maimonides based this directly on the scripturally mandated act: "Do not stand idly by your neighbor's blood" (Lev. 19:16), that is, whoever can save a life and does not do so has violated a negative commandment (*Mishneh Torah: Rotseah* 1.13).

Finally, he located the specific duty to heal the sick by those competent to do so in the scriptural command concerning the duty to return lost property to its owner (Deut. 22:2). He reasoned, as the Talmud had earlier (*Sanhedrin* 73a), that if one is to return someone else's lost property, then certainly one is to return someone else's *lost body* to him or her—namely, the bodily function lost through illness or injury (*Mishnah Commentary: Nedarim* 4.4). All of this is quite consistent with Maimonides's high regard for the regularity of the natural order and the role of medicine as part of the general human attitude of respect for that order and cooperation with its inherent teleology (*Guide of the Perplexed,* 2.40). Any special role for medicine, by separating it from the commandment of general benevolence, might

very well lead to its being considered a magical function. This would contradict the essentially scientific role of medicine insisted on by Maimonides (*Mishnah Commentary: Pesahim* 4.10).

Many commentators wondered why Maimonides never quoted the most direct Talmudic source for the duty to heal the sick: "It was taught in the School of Rabbi Ishmael that from the words of Scripture 'he shall surely provide for his healing' (Exod. 21:19) we derive permission for a physician to heal" (*Baba Kama* 85a). Perhaps he did not think that the verse itself supported this inference, since the text refers directly to the duty of an assailant to pay the medical bills of his or her victim, not the duty of the physician to heal. Also, the use of the word "permission" (*reshut*) might have seemed to him too weak to ground a duty, since it seems only to allow an option.

Nevertheless, Moses Nahmanides (1194–1270) does use this Talmudic text, reflecting his entirely different approach to the practice of medicine. He sees this use of the word "permission" as being an answer to those who might say that medicine is an unwarranted interference with divine healing. Just as a judge is not interfering with God's dispensing justice, he argued, so is a physician not interfering with God's dispensing healing. Both judge and physician have the exalted role of participating directly in acts that are seen as essentially divine (*Torat Ha'Adam,* ed. Chavel, 41–43). Both roles are forms of *imitatio dei.* This follows from Nahmanides's emphasis that medicine is needed by those in less than a full state of grace, who are within the confines of nature alone, and that the truly righteous will not need any such human intervention, being assured of direct divine attention (*Torah Commentary:* Lev. 26:11).

Nahmanides's connection of medical treatment with what the rabbis called "following after God's attributes" (*middotav*) has a precedent in the rabbinic location of the duty to attend to the sick in God's visitation of Abraham immediately after his circumcision (*Sotah* 14a re Gen. 18:1; also *Baba Metsia* 30b re Exod. 18:20; 86b). Indeed, attending to the needs of the sick has been seen in Jewish tradition as being more than general benevolence; it is an act having even mystical connotations. This appears in the many biblical texts that see illness and healing as specifically supernatural interventions (e.g., Gen. 18:14, 25:21–22; Exod. 15:26; Lev. 26:16; Num. 5:21; Deut. 28:20–22, 32:39; 2 Kings 5:7–8, 20:1–5; Jer. 17:14; Ps. 103:1–3; 2 Chron. 16:12). The rabbis, too, saw any affliction as being God's special visitation that calls for a special human response (*Berakhot* 5a re Isa. 53:10; cf. *Shabbat* 55a–b).

PROTECTION OF THE HUMAN CONDITION. The human condition is always to be the subject of care, and its infirmities are to be cured if possible. The question of the relation between care and cure is especially acute today, when the new means to extend life provided by advances in medical technology are seen by many as simultaneously compromising care by extending the agony of the terminally ill. Contemporary Jewish bioethicists certainly struggle with this problem as much as any other group. One can find no sufficient body of rules on this subject in the tradition, because the death agony in the past was seen as being quite brief (*Mordecai: Mo*ʿ*ed Qatan* no. 864). There do not seem to be any rules at hand for dealing with persons in irreversible comas lasting weeks, months, or even years.

Some precedent for this dilemma, however, can be found in an eighteenth-century responsum by Rabbi Jacob Reischer. He asked whether one may risk one's life by undergoing surgery that has a chance to prolong it, but also a chance to terminate it sooner than would be the case if nothing were done and nature were left to run its course. Reischer permitted such surgery if there was reasonable consensus of medical opinion that there was a good chance for success (*Shevut Ya*ʿ*agov: Yoreh De*ʿ*ah* no. 75). But without this consensus, it seems that the patient might have the right to refuse what is in effect an unwarranted invasion of his or her body.

The most immediate phenomenon that medicine treats is pain. Whereas the patient knows he or she is alive by inference from consciousness, one is immediately conscious of the presence of pain. Pain is a primary datum for all sentient beings (Maimonides, *Guide of the Perplexed,* 3.48). Jewish tradition mandates the treatment of unbearable pain in much the same way it mandates the treatment of mortal danger to human life. This can be seen by looking at the laws pertaining to the Sabbath, which is the most important religious observance in Judaism (*Palestinian Talmud: Nedarim* 3.9/38b). Just as the Sabbath is to be violated in case of a threat to human life (*sakkanat nefesh*), so may medical procedures normally prohibited on the Sabbath be performed when they can alleviate bodily pain. Such procedures as lancing a painful boil (*Shabbat* 107a; *Tosafot* s.v. "u-memai") and a woman removing by hand milk from her engorged breasts (*Shabbat* 135a; *Tosafot* s.v. "mipnei") are mentioned in the Talmud.

The great public-health problem of AIDS entails another challenge to Jewish tradition and its ability to rule in the interest of protecting the human condition of all sufferers from any disease whatsoever. That challenge arises when it must be determined what is to be done with those who have contracted AIDS through acts that the normative tradition regards as sinful. Most AIDS sufferers have contracted the disease through male homosexual acts and intravenous drug use. These acts are proscribed by Scripture and Jewish tradition (Lev. 18:22; Maimonides, *Mishneh Torah: Ishut,* 1.4; *De*ʿ*ot* 4.1). Furthermore, one Talmudic text minimally prescribes neglect for those who are seen to be "habitual sinners" (*Avodah Zarah* 26b). Nevertheless, the important twentieth-century authority Rabbi Abraham Isaiah Karelitz contended that this harsh law no longer applies because its intention is to dissuade sinners, and in this day and age such harshness would be counterproductive (*Hazon Ish: Yoreh De*ʿ*ah* sec. 2). His opinion has rarely been contested, for it is not unprecedented (*Teshuvot Ha-Rosh* 17.1). This legal opinion is important because it removes the one main impediment in the tradition for treating AIDS patients with the same concern as those suffering from any illness not contracted through acts the tradition considers illicit.

MEDICAL EXPERTISE. Jewish tradition has long recognized that a trained medical profession is a requirement of a humanly sufficient society. This can be seen in the Talmud's ruling (*Sanhedrin* 17b; cf. *Baba Batra* 21a; *Bach* on *Tur: Hoshen Mishpat* 156) that no educated Jew should live in a locality where there is no physician (*rofe*). Because of this, members of the medical profession have special duties and special privileges connected with these duties.

The first duty of medical professionals is to attend to whoever requires their attention. The centrality of this duty is seen in the interpretation by *Rashi*, the great eleventh-century commentator on the Bible and the Talmud, of the rather bizarre statement in the *Mishnah* that "the best of the physicians are destined for hell" (*Kiddushin* 4.14). Rashi takes this to be an indictment of persons who are physicians rather than of the institution of medicine as such (Nahmanides, *Torat Ha'Adam,* ed. Chavel, 43). He emphasizes the frequent carelessness and arrogance of physicians, and that they often refuse to treat the poor. This final indictment presupposes that lack of funds should not be an impediment to a person's right to medical treatment (*Tur: Yoreh De*ʿ*ah* 336; see also *Ketubot* 67b re Deut. 15:8).

Medical practitioners are considered to be "experts" (*beqi'im*), and thus have a professional status (*Yoma* 8.5). Hence they are to be publicly licensed (*Avodah Zarah* 26b–27a). Publicly licensed medical professionals are exempt from paying damages to their patients unless it can be proven that they were grossly negligent or actually malicious in performing their medical duties (*Tosefta: Baba Kama* 9.11, 6.17; *Gittin* 3.8). Based on the analogy between physicians and judges, Nahmanides (*Torat Ha'Adam,* ed. Chavel, 41) sees the basis of this unusual dispensation from civil and even criminal liability in the Talmud's acceptance of the inherent subjectivity of judgment in even the most precise human activities: "The judge only has what his eyes see" (*Sanhedrin* 6b). However, this dispensation applies only to licensed personnel and does not extend to unlicensed personnel, even if they are otherwise "expert" (*Sanhedrin* 44).

Because medical professionals are engaged in an activity commanded by the Torah (*mitsvah*), they are not to be paid directly for their services because no one is to receive direct monetary benefit for the performance of a commandment (*Sanhedrin* 44 re *Bekhorot* 29a; see also *Rosh Hashanah* 28a). In this respect they are like Torah scholars, who are to study and teach the Torah for its own sake and not for the sake of any monetary benefit (*Avot* 4.5; *Nedarim* 37a). Nevertheless, based on this analogy, one cannot be expected regularly to deplete his or her own income when benefiting someone else. If this were the case, only those of independent wealth could possibly function either as scholars or as physicians, or in any other necessary communal function. For this reason, then, both scholars and medical personnel, being deemed necessary for a well-functioning Jewish community, are to be paid, not for what they actually do but for what they do not do—in other words, what they would be paid if they were making a living doing something else. This legal fiction is called "payment for idleness" (*sekhar betalah*).

Medical personnel are exposed to the danger of contagion in treating persons suffering from diseases. The question arises of how much danger they are required to expose themselves to in the course of their work, and how much danger is considered to be above and beyond the call of duty. This question has become especially acute today with the proliferation of a number of highly contagious diseases, such as hepatitis B.

In cases of clear and direct danger to one's own life, Jewish tradition mandates the priority of one's own life (*Baba Metsia* 62a re Lev. 25:36) irrespective of whether one is a layperson or a professional. Acts above and beyond the call of duty are considered forms of supererogatory piety. Such acts cannot be seen as being derived from a universal rule applicable to everyone and anyone, however meritorious they might be to the person performing them (*Palestinian Talmud: Terumot* 8.4/46b). However, the real moral problem arises in cases where there is possible danger (*safeq sakkanah*) to those involved in treating the sick. There is a passage in the Talmud that states, "When there is a plague in the city, gather up your legs" (*Baba Kama* 60b re Isa. 26:20; Deut. 32:25), which implies that one should save oneself in the face of possible danger.

Nevertheless, the sixteenth-century commentator Rabbi Solomon Luria argued that in the absence of clear and direct danger to oneself, one ought to remain in the city if one is able to save other lives there. He also indicates that those who had already suffered from "the plague" (he probably meant smallpox) were in no danger of further recurrence and so should remain in the city to help others in distress (*Yam shel Shlomoh: Baba Kama* 6.26). Earlier, Rabbi Joseph Karo (1488–1575) had ruled that one was to expose oneself to possible danger if this enabled one to save other human lives (*Kesef Mishneh* on Maimonides, *Mishneh Torah: Rotseah* 1.14; *Bet Yosef* on Tur: *Hoshen Mishpat* 426; cf. Rabbi David ibn Zimra, *Teshuvot Ha-Radbaz* 3, no. 627). Of course, the difference between certain possible danger can be decided only on an ad hoc basis. Nevertheless, the distinction must always be kept in mind, that is, one can rule neither that healthcare personnel must treat every patient nor that they may absolve themselves from treating any patient whom they consider at all dangerous to their well-being.

Medical professionals are to keep abreast of scientific developments that affect their ability to treat patients. Along these lines, the tenth-century authority Sherira Gaon argued that the medical opinions of the rabbis of the Talmud, unlike their legal opinions, had no inherent value and should be accepted or rejected solely on the basis of whether they are actually effective (Jakobovits). Maimonides made the same point two centuries later (*Mishnah Commentary: Yoma* 8.4). In cases where human viability is to be determined, Maimonides ruled that current medical opinion is the criterion to rely on (*Mishneh Torah: Rotseah* 2.8; cf. *Shehitah* 10.13). As in all scientific questions, it is irrelevant whether those offering the accepted opinion are Jews (*Pesahim* 94b; Maimonides, *Shemonah Peraqim,* intro.).

However, other authorities were more conservative in their treatment of the medical counsels of the rabbis of the Talmud. Some of them held that the cures prescribed by the Talmud are ineffective in later times because human nature has changed significantly (*Mo'ed Qatan* 11a; *Tosafot* s.v. "kavra"; Isserles's note on *Shulhan Arukh: Even Ha'Ezer* 156.4). This view denies that earlier sages were deficient in any knowledge whatsoever, a point in keeping with the general rabbinic tendency to consider past sages always to have been wiser than present sages (*Shabbat* 112b). Thus, present sages are taken to be incapable of making some of the fine scientific distinctions that were made by past sages in medical issues pertaining to the law (Isserles's note on *Shulhan Arukh: Orah Hayyim* 330.5).

Nevertheless, whether one accepts changed medical practice on the more radical grounds suggested by Sherira Gaon and Maimonides, or on the more conservative grounds suggested by the tosafists (medieval Franco-German glossators on the Talmud) the Isserles, the fact is that no Jewish authority sees the medical remedies from the Talmud or any other classical source as being valid in the present. This has enabled the most religiously traditional Jewish medical professionals to take advantage of all the current and future advances in medical technology.

PERSONAL PREROGATIVES OF THE PATIENT. Current bioethics has stressed the personal prerogatives of those who are ill so that they can take a more active and responsible role in their own treatment and not simply be the passive *patients* of medical professionals. Most advocates of patient activism in medical treatment have looked to the modern principle of autonomy for grounding—namely, that human individuals are essentially their own masters. Clearly, the theocentric Jewish tradition does not underwrite autonomy in this strong sense of the term. However, it does supply the basis for allowing patients to take an active role for other reasons.

Pain, for example, is to be treated immediately, and the patient is considered the final authority in determining just how much pain he or she can stand, even if that personal determination contradicts expert opinion. It is assumed that the person is the best judge of his or her own condition at this most elementary level of experience (*Yoma* 83a re Prov. 14:10; see also *Baba Kama* 8.1). This judgment by the suffering person can exempt that person from the same ritual obligations (such as fasting) as an expert's judgment concerning a life-threatening condition can. Unbearable pain is considered worse than death, and to escape it, anything short of direct killing is exonerated (*Ketubot* 33a; *Shir Ha-Shirim Rabbah* 2.18; Rabbi Tsvi Hirsch Chajes, *Tiferet Yisrael,* beg.).

A second personal prerogative of the patient is the right to be told the exact nature of his or her illness and the opinion of the experts about whether death is imminent. Thus the Talmud rules that when it is determined that one's death is imminent, one is to be told so that there may still be time for the patient to offer the deathbed confession known as *vidui* (*Shabbat* 32a). This is considered extremely important because whether one dies in a state of repentance could very well affect whether one merits the life of the world to come (*Sanhedrin* 6.2). If the life in this world is considered a preparation for the unending life of the world to come (*Avot* 4.16), and if no one but the person himself or herself can make the proper preparation, then it follows that one may not be kept in ignorance about the gravity of one's condition. Only persons considered too emotionally unstable to be able to make proper use of this information are to be spared (Nahmanides, *Torat Ha'Adam,* ed. Chavel, 46).

The Stages of Human Life

Judaism is concerned with the human condition from conception to death. Especially at the edges of life, where there is much public dispute, Jewish teachings have been very much in the forefront of current debate.

ABORTION. The abortion debate has usually centered on the question of when human personhood begins. Those on the *pro-life* side of the issue argue that human personhood begins at conception, and abortion is therefore murder. Those on the *pro-choice* side of the issue argue that human personhood begins at birth, and abortion is therefore not murder and ought to be the option of the individual pregnant woman.

In Jewish tradition there seem to be two differing views as to when human personhood begins. One view (*Sanhedrin* 57b re Gen. 9:6; see also *Sanhedrin* 91b re Job 10:12) is that it begins at conception; another view (*Ohalot* 7.6; *Sanhedrin* 72b; *Rashi* s.v. "yatsa rosho") is that it begins at birth. Nevertheless, these views are more statements of principle than actual rules. Rules are not directly derived from principles in Jewish law (*Baba Batra* 130b). Instead, principles are formulated to explain rules, coordinate them with other rules, and guide their application. Therefore, one should not automatically deduce from principles defining human personhood just what the rule concerning abortion is to be.

The rule proscribes abortion unless there is a threat to the life or health of the mother. Those who hold that personhood begins at conception thus see abortion as being akin to murder (although, on technical legal grounds, not literally murder that is liable for capital punishment; see *Niddah* 5.3; *Niddah* 44b re Lev. 24:17). They would tend to be more conservative in judging what constitutes a threat to the life or health of the mother. Yet even they would judge some abortions (however few) to be mandated. Those who hold that personhood begins at birth, and who are thus likely to be more liberal in judging just what constitutes a threat to the mother's life or health, still hold that abortion is usually proscribed because even fetal life has enough rights of its own (*Yoma* 82a; *Rashi* s.v. "ubar"). It may not be destroyed unless it is a threat (*rodef*) to the mother's life or health. Even assuming that the fetus is still considered part of the mother's body in utero (*Sanhedrin* 80b) does not lead to permission for elective abortion because self-mutilation is proscribed (*Baba Kama* 91b).

Hence traditionalist authorities, however they might view the actual beginnings of human personhood in principle, all regard abortion as generally proscribed, and permitted only under specific conditions. Their practical debates all center on the interpretation of the exceptions to the general proscription of abortion. In that sense, the more conservative authorities are no more absolutely *pro-life* than the more liberal authorities are absolutely *pro-choice*. In fact, abortion is not an option at all. Either it is proscribed in most cases, or it is prescribed in some exceptional cases. Nonetheless, less traditionalist Jewish feminists have argued that the whole issue of abortion must be reconsidered inasmuch as it most directly affects women, and women's voices have been absent from the legal debates about it in the Jewish community heretofore (see Davis).

DEFINITION OF DEATH. The question of precisely when human life ends is an issue of much current debate among contemporary Jewish bioethicists. Some of the more conservatively inclined have insisted that the traditional criteria for determining death be literally interpreted: the cessation of spontaneous reflexes, heartbeat, and breath (*Yoma* 85a; Teshuvot Hatam Sofer: *Yoreh De'ah* no. 338). Yet other Jewish bioethicists, more liberally inclined, or more influenced by current scientific trends, have argued that *brain death* can constitute a ground for taking a patient off a respirator, inasmuch as breathing in this case is not being done by the patient, but by a machine (Task Force on Death and Dying). In fact, not doing this might constitute a violation of Jewish law, the prohibition against leaving the dead unburied (*Sanhedrin* 46b re Deut. 21:23). However, the motive behind this innovation, whether stated or not, is that the interpreters of Jewish law must accept growing medical consensus on any major issue if their rulings are to be taken seriously in the general society, where even the most pious Jews receive their medical treatment.

DAVID NOVAK (1995)
BIBLIOGRAPHY REVISED

SEE ALSO: *Abortion, Religious Traditions: Jewish Perspectives; Authority in Religious Traditions; Christianity, Bioethics in; Death, Definition and Determination of: Philosophical and Theological Perspectives; Death: Western Religious Thought; Eugenics: History of; Eugenics and Religious Law: Judaism; Genetics and Racial Minorities; Holocaust; Islam, Bioethics in; Medical Ethics, History of, Near and Middle East: Israel; Population Ethics, Religious Traditions: Jewish Perspectives; Research, Unethical; Women, Historical and Cross-Cultural Perspectives*

BIBLIOGRAPHY

Biblical, rabbinic, and medieval sources are cited in the text.

MODERN RESPONSA

Feinstein, Moses. 1959–1973. *Igrot Mosheh.* 7 vols. New York: M. Feinstein.

Waldenberg, Eliezer. 1945–1992. *Sefer Sheelot u-teshuvot: Tsits Eliezer.* 19 vols. Jerusalem: E. Waldenberg.

Weinberg, Yechiel. 1961–1969. *Seride Esh: Sheelot u-te shuvot, hidushim u-veurim.* 4 vols. Jerusalem: Mosad ha-Rav Kuk.

Yosef, Ovadia. 1986. *Yabia omer: ... sheelot u-teshuvat,* 2nd edition. 6 vols. Jerusalem: Mosad ha-Rav Kuk.

GENERAL WORKS

Cohen, Jonathan R. 1999. "In God's Garden: Creation and Cloning in Jewish Thought." *Hastings Center Report* 29(4): 7–12.

Davis, Dena S. 1991. "Beyond Rabbi Hiyya's Wife: Women's Voices in Jewish Bioethics." *Second Opinion* 16(March): 10–30.

Dorff, Elliot N., and Newman, Louis E. eds. 1997. *Contemporary Jewish Ethics and Morality: A Reader.* New York: Oxford University Press.

Feldman, David M. 1968. *Birth Control in Jewish Law: Marital Relations, Contraception, and Abortion as Set Forth in the Classic Texts of Jewish Law.* New York: New York University Press.

Feldman, David M. 1986. *Health and Medicine in the Jewish Tradition.* New York: Crossroad.

Freedman, Benjamin.1999. *Duty and Healing: Foundations of a Jewish Bioethic (Reflective Bioethics).* London: Routledge.

Friedenwald, Harry. 1944. *The Jews and Medicine.* 2 vols. Baltimore: Johns Hopkins University Press.

Jakobovits, Immanuel. 1975. *Jewish Medical Ethics: A Comparative and Historical Study of the Jewish Religious Attitude to Medicine and Its Practice.* New York: Bloch.

Klein, Issac. 1979. *A Guide to Jewish Religious Practice.* New York: Jewish Theological Seminary of America.

Levin, Mark, and Birnbaum, Ira. 2000. "Jewish Bioethics?" *Journal of Medicine and Philosophy* 25(4): 469–484.

Mackler, Aaron L., ed. 2000. *Life and Death Responsibilities in Jewish Biomedical Ethics.* New York: The Louis Finkelstein Institute.

Novak, David. 1974–1976. *Law and Theology in Judaism.* 2 vols. New York: KTAV.

Novak, David. 1985. *Halakah in a Theological Dimension.* Chico, CA: Scholars Press.

Pellegrino, Edmund D., and Faden, Alan I., eds. 2001. *Jewish and Catholic Bioethics: An Ecumenical Dialogue (Moral Traditions & Moral Arugments).* Washington, D.C.: Georgetown University Press.

Rosner, Fred. 2001. *Biomedical Ethics and Jewish Law.* New York: KTAV Publishing House.

Rosner, Fred, and Bleich, J. David, eds. 1978. *Jewish Bioethics.* New York: Hebrew Publishing.

Rosner, Fred; Bleich, J. David; and Brayer, Menachem M., eds. 1999. *Jewish Bioethics.* New York: KTAV Publishing House.

Task Force on Death and Dying of the Institute of Society, Ethics, and Life Sciences. 1972. "Refinements in Criteria for the Determination of Death: An Appraisal." *Journal of the American Medical Association* 221(1): 48–53.

Wahrman, Miryam Z. 2002. *Brave New Judaism: When Science and Scripture Collide.* Waltham, MA: Brandeis University Press.

Wolpe, Paul Root. 1997. "If I Am Only My Genes, What Am I? Genetic Essentialism and a Jewish Response." *Kennedy Institute of Ethics Journal* 7(3): 213–230.

Zimmels, Hirsch Jacob. 1952. *Magicians, Theologians, and Doctors: Studies of Folk-Medicine and Folklore as Reflected in the Rabbinical Responsa, 12th–19th Centuries*. London: E. Goldston.

Zohar, Noam J. 1997. *Alternatives in Jewish Bioethics (Suny Series in Jewish Philosophy)*. Albany: State University of New York Press.

Zoloth-Dorfman, Laurie. 1994. "One of These Mornings I'm Going to Rise Up Singing: The Necessity of the Prophetic Voice in Jewish Bioethics." *Journal of Clinical Ethics* 5(4): 348–52.

JUSTICE

• • •

At some time or another, virtually all of us become involved in disputes about justice. Sometimes our involvement in such disputes is rooted in the fact that we believe ourselves to be victims of some form of injustice; sometimes our involvement is rooted in the fact that others believe us to be the perpetrators or at least the beneficiaries of some form of injustice affecting them. Sometimes the injustice at issue seems to require for its elimination a drastic reform, or even a revolutionary change in the political system. Sometimes it seems to require only some electoral pressure or administrative decision, as may be required in ending a war. Whatever the origin and whatever the practical effect, such disputes about justice are difficult to avoid, especially when one is dealing with issues, like the distribution of income or healthcare resources, that have widespread social effects.

Reasonable resolutions of such disputes require a critical evaluation of the alternative conceptions of justice available to us. In philosophical debate at the end of the twentieth century, five major conceptions of justice are defended:

(1) a libertarian conception, which takes liberty to be the ultimate political ideal;

(2) a socialist conception, which takes equality to be the ultimate political ideal;

(3) a welfare liberal conception, which takes contractual fairness or maximal utility to be the ultimate political ideal;

(4) a communitarian conception, which takes the common good to be the ultimate political ideal; and

(5) a feminist conception, which takes a gender-free society to be the ultimate political ideal.

All these conceptions of justice have certain features in common. Each regards its requirements as belonging to the domain of obligation rather than to the domain of charity; they simply disagree about where to draw the line between these two domains. Each is also concerned with giving people what they deserve or should rightfully possess; they simply disagree about what it is that people deserve or rightfully possess. These common features constitute a generally accepted core definition of justice. What we need to do, however, is examine the aspects of each of these conceptions of justice over which there is serious disagreement in order to determine which conception, if any, is most defensible.

Libertarian Justice

Libertarians frequently cite the work of Friedrich A. Hayek, particularly *The Constitution of Liberty* (1960), as an intellectual source of their view. Hayek argues that the libertarian ideal of liberty requires "equality before the law" and "reward according to market value," but not "substantial equality" or "reward according to merit." Hayek further argues that the inequalities due to upbringing, inheritance, and education that are permitted by an ideal of liberty actually tend to benefit society as a whole.

In basic accord with Hayek, contemporary libertarians define "liberty" as "the state of being unconstrained by other persons from doing what one wants." Libertarians go on to characterize their moral and political ideal as requiring that each person have the greatest amount of liberty commensurate with the same liberty for all. From this ideal, libertarians claim that a number of more specific requirements—in particular a right to life; a right to freedom of speech, press, and assembly; and a right to property—can be derived.

The libertarians' right to life is not a right to receive from others the goods and resources necessary for preserving one's life; it is simply a right not to be killed. So understood, the right to life is not a right to receive welfare. In fact, there are no welfare rights in the libertarian view. Accordingly, the libertarian's understanding of the right to property is not a right to receive from others the goods and resources necessary for one's welfare but, rather, a right to acquire goods and resources either by initial acquisition or by voluntary agreement.

By defending rights such as these, libertarians can support only a limited role for government. That role is simply to prevent and punish initial acts of coercion—the only wrongful acts for libertarians.

Libertarians do not deny that it is a good thing for people to have sufficient goods and resources to meet their basic nutritional needs and basic healthcare needs, but they do deny that government has a duty to provide for such needs. Some good things, such as the provision of welfare and healthcare to the needy, are requirements of charity rather than justice, libertarians claim. Accordingly, failure to make such provisions is neither blameworthy nor punishable.

A basic difficulty with the libertarian's conception of justice is the claim that rights to life and property, as the libertarian understands these rights, derive from an ideal of liberty. Why should we think that an ideal of liberty requires a right to life and a right to property that excludes a right to welfare? Surely it would seem that a right to property, as the libertarian understands it, might well justify a rich person's depriving a poor person of the liberty to acquire the goods and resources necessary for meeting basic nutritional needs. How, then, could we appeal to an ideal of liberty to justify such a deprivation of liberty? Surely we could not claim that such a deprivation is justified for the sake of preserving a rich person's freedom to use the goods and resources he or she possesses to meet luxury needs. By any neutral assessment, it would seem that the liberty of the deserving poor not to be interfered with when taking from the surplus possessions of the rich what they require to meet their basic needs would have priority over the liberty of the rich not to be interfered with when using their surplus possessions to meet their luxury needs. But if this is the case, a right to welfare—and possibly a right to equal opportunity as well—would be grounded in the libertarian's own ideal of liberty.

Socialist Justice

In contrast with libertarians, socialists take equality to be the ultimate political ideal. In the *Communist Manifesto* (1848), Karl Marx and Friedrich Engels maintained that the abolition of bourgeois property and bourgeois family structure is a necessary first requirement for building a society that accords with the political ideal of equality. In the *Critique of the Gotha Programme* (1891), Marx provided a much more positive account of what is required to build a society based on the political ideal of equality. In such a society, Marx claimed, the distribution of social goods must conform, at least initially, to the principle "from each according to his ability to each according to his contribution." But when the highest stage of communist society has been reached, Marx added, distribution will conform to the principle "from each according to his ability to each according to his need."

At first hearing, this conception might sound ridiculous to someone brought up in a capitalist society. The obvious objection is, how can you get people to contribute according to their ability if income is distributed on the basis of their needs and not on the basis of their contributions?

The answer, according to a socialist conception of justice, is to make the work that must be done in a society as enjoyable, in itself, as possible. As a result, people will want to do the work they are capable of doing because they find it intrinsically rewarding. For a start, socialists might try to get people to accept currently existing intrinsically rewarding jobs at lower salaries—top executives, for example, to work for $300,000 rather than $900,000 a year. Yet ultimately, socialists hope to make all jobs as rewarding as possible, so that after people are no longer working primarily for external rewards while making their best contributions to society, distribution can proceed on the basis of need.

Socialists propose to implement their ideal of equality by giving workers democratic control over the workplace. They believe that if workers have more to say about how they do their work, they will find their work intrinsically more rewarding. As a consequence, they will be more motivated to work, because their work itself will be meeting their needs. Socialists believe that extending democracy to the workplace will necessarily lead to socialization of the means of production and the end of private property. Socialists, of course, do not deny that civil disobedience or even revolutionary action may be needed to overcome opposition to extending democracy to the workplace.

However, even with democratic control of the workplace, some jobs, such as collecting garbage or changing bedpans, probably cannot be made intrinsically rewarding. Socialists propose to divide such jobs up in some equitable manner. Some people might, for example, collect garbage one day per week and then work at a more rewarding job for the rest of the week. Others would change bedpans or do some other menial work for one day per week and then work at a more rewarding job the other days of the week. Socialists believe that by making jobs intrinsically as rewarding as possible, in part through democratic control of the workplace and an equitable assignment of unrewarding tasks, people will contribute according to their ability even when distribution proceeds according to need.

Another difficulty raised concerning the socialist conception of justice is in the proclaimed necessity of abolishing private property and socializing the means of production. It seems perfectly possible to give workers more control over their workplace while the means of production remain privately owned. Of course, private ownership would have a somewhat different character in a society with democratic control of the workplace, but it need not cease to be private ownership. After all, private ownership would also have a somewhat different character in a society where private holdings, and hence bargaining power, were distributed more equally than they are in most capitalist societies, yet it would not cease to be private ownership. Accordingly, we could imagine a society where the means of production are privately owned but where—because ownership is so widely dispersed throughout the society and because of the degree of democratic control of the workplace—many of the criticisms socialists make of existing capitalist societies would no longer apply.

Welfare Liberal Justice: The Contractarian Perspective

Finding merit in both the libertarian's ideal of liberty and the socialist's ideal of equality, welfare liberals attempt to combine both liberty and equality into one political ideal that can be characterized as contractual fairness or maximal utility.

A classic example of the contractual approach to welfare liberal justice is found in the political works of Immanuel Kant, who claimed that a civil state ought to be founded on an original contract satisfying the requirements of freedom (the freedom to seek happiness in whatever way one sees fit as long as one does not infringe upon the freedom of others to pursue a similar end), equality (the equal right of each person to restrict others from using his or her freedom in ways that deny equal freedom to all), and independence (which is necessarily presupposed for each person by the free agreement of the original contract).

According to Kant, the original contract, which ought to be the foundation of every civil state, does not have to "actually exist as a fact." It suffices that the laws of a civil state are such that people would agree to them under conditions in which the requirements of freedom, equality, and independence obtain. Laws that accord with this original contract would then, Kant claimed, give all members of society the right to reach any degree of rank that they could earn through their labor, industry, and good fortune. Thus, the equality demanded by the original contract would not, in Kant's view, exclude a considerable amount of economic liberty.

The Kantian ideal of a hypothetical contract as the moral foundation for a welfare liberal conception of justice has been further developed by John Rawls in *A Theory of Justice* (1971). Rawls, like Kant, argues that principles of justice are those that free and rational persons who are concerned to advance their own interests would accept in an initial position of equality. Yet Rawls goes beyond Kant by interpreting the conditions of his "original position" to explicitly require a "veil of ignorance." This veil of ignorance, Rawls claims, has the effect of depriving persons in the original position of the knowledge they would need to advance their own interests in ways that are morally arbitrary.

According to Rawls, the principles of justice that would be derived in the original position are the following: (1) Special conception of justice, involving (a) A principle of equal political liberty; (b) A principle of equal opportunity; and (c) A principle requiring that the distribution of economic goods work to the greatest advantage of the least advantaged. (2) General conception of justice: a principle requiring that the distribution of all social goods work to the greatest advantage of the least advantaged.

The general conception of justice differs from the special conception of justice by allowing trade-offs between political liberty and other social goods. According to Rawls, persons in the original position would want the special conception of justice to be applied in place of the general conception of justice whenever social conditions allow all representative persons to benefit from the exercise of their political liberties.

Rawls holds that these principles of justice would be chosen in the original position because persons so situated would find it reasonable to follow the conservative dictates of the "maximin strategy" and maximize the minimum, thereby securing for themselves the highest minimum payoff.

Rawls's defense of a welfare liberal conception of justice has been challenged in a variety of ways. Some critics have endorsed Rawls's contractual approach while disagreeing with him over what principles of justice would be derived from it. These critics usually attempt to undermine the use of a maximum strategy in the original position. Other critics, however, have found fault with the contractual approach itself. Libertarians, for example, have challenged the moral adequacy of the very ideal of contractual fairness because they claim that it conflicts with their ideal of liberty.

This second challenge to the ideal of contractual fairness is potentially the more damaging because, if valid, it would force its supporters to embrace some other political ideal. This challenge, however, would fail if it were shown that the libertarian's own ideal of liberty, when correctly interpreted, leads to much the same practical requirements as are usually associated with the welfare liberal ideal of contractual fairness.

Welfare Liberal Justice: The Utilitarian Perspective

One way to avoid the challenges that have been directed at a contractarian defense of welfare liberal justice is to find some alternative way of defending it. Historically, utilitarianism has been thought to provide such an alternative defense. It has been claimed that the requirements of a welfare liberal conception of justice can be derived from considerations of utility in such a way that following these requirements will result in the maximization of total happiness or satisfaction in society. The best-known classical defense of this utilitarian approach is certainly that presented by John Stuart Mill in *Utilitarianism* (1861).

In Chapter 5 of this work, Mill surveyed various types of actions and situations that are ordinarily described as just or unjust and concluded that justice simply denotes a certain class of fundamental rules, the adherence to which is essential for maximizing social utility. Thus Mill rejected the idea that justice and social utility are ultimately distinct ideals, maintaining instead that justice is in fact derivable from the ideal of social utility.

Nevertheless, a serious problem remains for the utilitarian defense of welfare liberal justice. There would appear to be ways of maximizing overall social utility that do injustice to particular individuals. Think of the Roman practice of throwing Christians to the lions for the enjoyment of all those in the Colosseum. Did this unjust practice not maximize overall social utility?

John Rawls (1971) makes the same point somewhat differently. He criticizes utilitarianism for regarding society as a whole as if it were just one person, and thereby treating the desires and satisfactions of separate persons as if they were the desires and satisfactions of just one person. In this way, Rawls claims, utilitarianism fails to preserve the distinction between persons. But is Rawls right? It may well be that a proper assessment of the relative merits of the contractual and utilitarian approaches to welfare liberal justice will turn on this very issue.

Communitarian Justice

Another prominent political ideal defended by contemporary philosophers is the communitarian ideal of the common good. Many contemporary defenders of a communitarian conception of justice regard their conception as rooted in Aristotelian moral theory. In the *Nicomachean Ethics* (332 B.C.E.), Aristotle distinguished between different varieties of justice. He first distinguished between justice as the whole of virtue and justice as a particular part of virtue. In the former sense, justice is understood as what is lawful, and the just person is equivalent to the moral person. In the latter sense, justice is understood as what is fair or equal, and the just person is the one who takes only a proper share. Aristotle focused his discussion on justice in the latter sense, which further divides into distributive justice, corrective justice, and justice in exchange. Each of these varieties of justice can be understood to be concerned with achieving equality. For distributive justice, it is equality between equals; for corrective justice, it is equality between punishment and the crime; and for justice in exchange, it is equality between whatever goods are exchanged. Aristotle also claimed that justice has both its natural and conventional aspects: this twofold character of justice seems to be behind his discussion of equity, in which equity, a natural standard, is described as a corrective to legal justice, a conventional standard.

Few of the distinctions Aristotle made seem tied to the acceptance of any particular conception of justice. One could, for example, accept the view that justice requires formal equality, but then specify the equality that is required in different ways. Even the ideal of justice as giving people what they deserve, which has its roots in Aristotle's account of distributive justice, is also subject to various interpretations. An analysis of the concept of desert would show that there is no conceptual difficulty with claiming, for example, that everyone deserves to have his or her needs satisfied or that everyone deserves an equal share of the goods distributed by society. Consequently, Aristotle's account is helpful primarily for clarifying the distinctions belonging to the concept of justice that can be made without committing oneself to any particular conception of justice.

Yet rather than draw out the particular requirements of their own conception of justice, contemporary communitarians have frequently chosen to defend their conception by attacking other conceptions of justice; by and large, they have focused their attacks on the welfare liberal conception of justice. Alasdair MacIntyre, for example, argues in "The Privatization of the Good" (1990a) that virtually all forms of liberalism attempt to separate rules defining right action from conceptions of the human good. MacIntyre contends that these forms of liberalism not only fail but must fail because the rules defining right action cannot be adequately grounded apart from a conception of the good. For this reason, MacIntyre claims, only a version of a communitarian theory of justice that grounds rules supporting right action in a complete conception of the good can ever hope to be adequate.

But why cannot we view most forms of liberalism as attempting to ground moral rules on part of a conception of the good—specifically, that part of a conception of the good that is more easily recognized, and needs to be publicly recognized, as good? For Rawls, this partial conception of the good is a conception of contractual fairness, according to which no one deserves his or her native abilities or initial starting place in society. If this way of interpreting liberalism is correct, in order to evaluate welfare liberal and communitarian conceptions of justice properly, we would need to do a comparative analysis of their conceptions of the good and their practical requirements. Moreover, there is reason to think that once the practical requirements of both liberal and communitarian conceptions of justice are compared, they will be found to be quite similar.

Feminist Justice

Defenders of a feminist conception of justice present a distinctive challenging critique to defenders of other conceptions of justice. In *The Subjection of Women* (1869), John Stuart Mill, one of the earliest male defenders of women's liberation, argued that the subjection of women was never justified but was imposed on women because they were physically weaker than men; later this subjection was confirmed by law. Mill argued that society must remove the legal restrictions that deny women the same opportunities enjoyed by men. However, Mill did not consider whether, because of past discrimination against women, it may be necessary to do more than simply removing legal restrictions: he did not consider whether positive assistance may also be required.

Usually it is not enough simply to remove unequal restrictions to make a competition fair among those who have been participating. Positive assistance to those who have been disadvantaged in the past may also be required, as would be the case in a race where some were unfairly impeded by having to carry ten-pound weights for part of the race. To render the outcome of such a race fair, we might want to transfer the ten-pound weights to the other runners in the race for an equal period of time. Similarly, positive assistance, such as affirmative-action programs, may be necessary if women who have been disadvantaged in the past are going to be able to compete fairly with men.

In *Justice, Gender and the Family* (1989), Susan Okin argues for the feminist ideal of a gender-free society, that is, one in which basic rights and duties are not assigned on the basis of a person's sex. Being male or female is not the grounds for determining what basic rights and duties a person has in a gender-free society. Since a conception of justice is usually thought to provide the ultimate grounds for the assignment of rights and duties, we can refer to this ideal of a gender-free society as *feminist justice*.

Okin goes on to consider whether Rawls's welfare liberal conception of justice can support the ideal of a gender-free society. Noting Rawls's failure to apply his original position-type thinking to family structures, Okin is skeptical about the possibility of using a welfare liberal ideal to support feminist justice. She contends that in a gender-structured society like that of the United States, male philosophers cannot achieve the sympathetic imagination

required to see things from the standpoint of women. In a gender-structured society, Okin claims, male philosophers cannot do the original position-type thinking required by the welfare liberal ideal because they lack the ability to put themselves in the position of women. According to Okin, original position-type thinking can really be achieved only in a gender-free society.

Yet, at the same time that Okin despairs of doing original position-type thinking in a gender-structured society, she purportedly does a considerable amount of just that type of thinking. For example, she claims that Rawls's principles of justice "would seem to require a radical rethinking not only of the division of labor within families but also of all the nonfamily institutions that assume it" (Okin, p. 104). She also claims that "the abolition of gender seems essential for the fulfillment of Rawls's criterion of political justice" (Okin, p. 104). So Okin's own work would seem to indicate that we can do such thinking, and that her reasons for thinking we cannot are not persuasive. To do original position-type thinking, it is not necessary that everyone be able to put themselves imaginatively in the position of everyone else. All that is necessary is that some people be able to do so. Some people may not be able to do original position-type thinking because they have been deprived of a proper moral education. Others may be able to do original position-type thinking only after they have been forced to mend their ways and live morally for a time.

Of course, even among men and women in a gender-structured society who are in a broad sense capable of a sense of justice, some may not be able to do such original position-type thinking with respect to the proper relationships between men and women; these men and women may be able to do so only after the laws and social practices in our society have significantly shifted toward a more gender-free society. But this inability of some to do original position-type thinking does not render it impossible for others, who have effectively used the opportunities for moral development available to them, to achieve the sympathetic imagination necessary for original position-type thinking with respect to the proper relationships between men and women.

Drawing Conclusions

What conclusion should we draw from this discussion of libertarian, socialist, welfare liberal, communitarian, and feminist conceptions of justice? Should we draw the conclusion defended by Alasdair MacIntyre in *After Virtue* (1981) that such conceptions of justice are incommensurable and, hence, there is no rational way of deciding between them? Many philosophers have challenged this view, and even

MacIntyre, in *Three Rival Versions of Moral Enquiry* (1990b), has significantly qualified it, now claiming that it is possible to argue across conceptions of justice.

Another conclusion that we might draw from this discussion of conceptions of justice is that if the ideal of liberty of libertarian justice can be shown to require the same rights to welfare and equal opportunity that are required by the welfare liberal conception of justice, and if the communication critique of welfare liberalism can be rebutted, it may be possible to reconcile, at a practical level, the differences between welfare liberal justice, socialist justice, and feminist justice. If this can be done, all that would be necessary to reasonably resolve disputes about justice would be to clarify what the shared practical requirements of these conceptions of justice are and simply to act on them.

The Provision of Just Healthcare

Assuming that it is possible to show that libertarian, welfare liberal, socialist, communitarian, and feminist conceptions of justice have the same practical requirements as a right to welfare and a right to equal opportunity, then in order to determine the morally appropriate level of healthcare, it would be necessary to determine what provision of healthcare would be required by these rights. Since a right to welfare and a right to equal opportunity are usually associated with a welfare liberal conception of justice, it would seem reasonable to use Rawls's original position decision procedure—a procedure favored by welfare liberals—to determine what level of healthcare would be required by a right to welfare and a right to equal opportunity.

In *Just Health Care* (1985) and *Am I My Parents' Keeper?* (1988), Norman Daniels develops just such an account of healthcare. Daniels imagines people behind a veil of ignorance trying to determine how they should allocate healthcare services over their lifetimes. Behind this veil of ignorance, people are to imagine themselves ignorant of their actual age so that they could be young or old. Daniels claims that people using this Rawlsian decision procedure would reserve certain life-extending technologies for their younger years and thus maximize their chances of living a normal life span, even if that meant reducing the medical resources that would be available in their old age.

The consequences of using a Rawlsian decision procedure to determine the morally appropriate level of healthcare required by a right to welfare and a right to equal opportunity are (1) a focus on death-preventing level of healthcare for the young, (2) a focus on a life-enhancing healthcare for both young and old, and (3) a willingness to cut back on death-preventing healthcare for the old to some extent when it conflicts with (1) and possibly when it conflicts with (2) as well.

Yet these consequences remain indeterminate until we can specify the amount of resources that are to be devoted to healthcare rather than to meeting the various other needs and wants that people have. It will not do simply to have each person choose the level of healthcare that he or she prefers, because we cannot assume that everyone will have sufficient income to purchase whatever level of healthcare he or she wants or needs. Rather, there seem to be two options.

One option is to specify an optimal and affordable level of healthcare and then guarantee this level of healthcare to all legitimate claimants. The other option is to specify a decent minimal level of healthcare and guarantee that level of healthcare to all legitimate claimants, but then allow higher levels of healthcare to be purchased by whoever has the income and desire to do so. Of course, both these options will leave some people dissatisfied. The equal-healthcare option will leave dissatisfied people who would have preferred and could have afforded a higher level of healthcare that would have been available under the multi-tiered healthcare option. The multi-tiered healthcare option will leave dissatisfied people who would receive only the decent minimum level of healthcare under that option but who want or need more healthcare than they will be receiving. Is there any just resolution of this conflict?

Assuming again that we are trying to determine the morally appropriate level of healthcare required by a right to welfare and a right to equal opportunity, it is surely the case that nothing less than a guaranteed decent minimum level of healthcare to all legitimate claimants would be morally acceptable. But is a multi-tiered option for healthcare morally permissible, or is the option of an equal level of healthcare morally required?

To answer this question, we must take into account all the morally legitimate claimants to our available resources. They include not only the members of the particular society to which we happen to belong but also distant peoples and future generations as well. Once we recognize how numerous are the morally legitimate claimants on the available resources, it becomes clear that all that we can hope to do is provide a decent minimal level of healthcare to all claimants. Given the morally legitimate claims that distant peoples and future generations make on our available resources, it is unlikely that we will have sufficient resources to allow people to purchase higher levels of healthcare (the multi-tiered option). Morally, we would seem to have no other choice than to favor the same level of healthcare for everybody (the equal-healthcare option).

In preferring the equal-healthcare option, we appealed not to the ideal of equality itself but, rather, to the goal of providing all legitimate claimants with a decent minimum level of healthcare. Given that available resources are limited, to meet the goal of providing a decent minimum of healthcare to all legitimate claimants, equality of healthcare for all legitimate claimants is required. In this context, no one can have more than equality if everyone is to have enough. This choice would clearly be favored by people behind a Rawlsian veil of ignorance, assuming that the hypothetical choosers are understood to represent all morally legitimate claimants.

Nor could one reasonably object to the ideal of including distant peoples and future generations within the class of morally legitimate claimants, because each of the five conceptions assumes that each human being has the same basic rights. So if these basic rights that each human being has include a right to welfare and a right to equal opportunity, the requirements to provide each human being with a decent minimum of healthcare would clearly follow.

Nevertheless, there remains the question of how to specify this minimum level of healthcare that all legitimate claimants are to receive. The problem here is how to specify how much of the available resources should go to providing everyone with a decent minimum of healthcare rather than providing for the satisfaction of people's other needs and wants. Yet here, too, the question seems resolvable with the aid of a Rawlsian hypothetical choice procedure. We simply need to introduce behind the veil of ignorance the knowledge of the relevant technology for meeting people's basic needs and the knowledge of available resources to decide how much of the resources should be devoted to providing a decent minimum level of healthcare and how much should be devoted to meeting the other needs and wants that people have.

In this way, we should be able to determine what specific requirements of just healthcare are grounded in a right to welfare and a right to equal opportunity. Moreover, these specific requirements of just healthcare would be further supported if it can be shown that the rights from which these healthcare requirements are derived are themselves the shared practical requirements of libertarian, welfare liberal, socialist, communitarian, and feminist conceptions of justice.

JAMES P. STERBA (1995)
REVISED BY AUTHOR

SEE ALSO: *Aging and the Aged: Societal Aging; Children: Rights of Children; Communitarianism and Bioethics; Economic Concepts in Healthcare; Ethics: Social and Political Theories; Future Generations, Reproductive Technologies and Obligations to; Healthcare Resources, Allocation of; Human Rights; Health Insurance; Health Policy in International Perspectives; Health Policy in the United States; Just Wages and Salaries; Managed Care; Medicaid; Medicare; Utilitarianism and Bioethics; Warfare: Introduction*

BIBLIOGRAPHY

Aristotle. 1962 (332 B.C.E.). *Nicomachean Ethics,* tr. Martin Ostwald. Indianapolis, IN: Bobbs-Merrill.

Brody, Baruch A. 1981. "Health Care for the Haves and Have Nots: Toward a Just Basis of Distribution." In *Justice and Health Care,* ed. Earl E. Shelp. Dordrecht, Netherlands: D. Reidel.

Buchanan, Alan E. 1984. "The Right to a Decent Minimum of Health Care." *Philosophy and Public Affairs* 13(1): 55–78.

Daniels, Norman. 1985. *Just Health Care.* Cambridge, Eng.: Cambridge University Press.

Daniels, Norman. 1988. *Am I My Parents' Keeper? An Essay on Justice Between the Young and the Old.* New York: Oxford University Press.

Gibbard, Alan. 1982. "The Prospective Pareto Principle and Equity of Access to Health Care." *Milbank Memorial Fund Quarterly/Health and Society* 60(3): 399–428.

Gutmann, Amy. 1981. "For and Against Equal Access to Health Care." *Milbank Memorial Fund Quarterly/Health and Society* 59(4): 542–560.

Hayek, Friedrich A. 1960. *The Constitution of Liberty.* Chicago: University of Chicago Press.

Jaggar, Alison M. 1983. *Feminist Politics and Human Nature.* Totowa, NJ: Rowman and Allanheld.

MacIntyre, Alasdair C. 1981. *After Virtue: A Study in Moral Theory.* Notre Dame, IN: University of Notre Dame Press.

MacIntyre, Alasdair C. 1990a. "The Privatization of the Good: An Inaugural Lecture." *Review of Politics* 52(3): 344–361.

MacIntyre, Alasdair C. 1990b. *Three Rival Versions of Moral Enquiry: Encyclopaedia, Genealogy, and Tradition.* Notre Dame, IN: University of Notre Dame Press.

Marx, Karl. 1977 (1891). *Critique of the Gotha Programme,* ed. C. P. Dutt. New York: International Publishers.

Marx, Karl, and Engels, Friedrich. 1992 (1848). *The Communist Manifesto,* ed. David McLellan. Oxford: Oxford University Press.

Mill, John Stuart. 1979. (1861). *Utilitarianism.* Indianapolis, IN: Hackett.

Mill, John Stuart. 1988 (1869). *The Subjection of Women.* Indianapolis, IN: Hackett.

Nielson, Kai. 1985. *Liberty and Equality: A Defense of Radical Egalitarianism.* Totowa, NJ: Rowman and Allanheld.

Nozick, Robert. 1974. *Anarchy, State, and Utopia.* New York: Basic Books.

Okin, Susan M. 1989. *Justice, Gender and the Family.* New York: Basic Books.

Rawls, John. 1971. *A Theory of Justice.* Cambridge, MA: Harvard University Press.

Reiss, Hans, ed. 1970. *Kant's Political Writings,* tr. H. B. Nisbet. New York: Cambridge University Press.

Sommers, Christina. 1989. "Philosophers Against the Family." In *Person to Person,* ed. George Graham and Hugh LaFollette. Philadelphia: Temple University Press.

Sterba, James P. 1998. *Justice for Here and Now.* New York: Cambridge University Press.

U.S. President's Commission for the Study of Ethical Problems in Medicine and Biomedical and Behavior Research. 1983. *Securing Access to Health Care: A Report on the Ethical Implications of Differences in the Availability of Health Services,* vol. 1. Washington, D.C.: U.S. Government Printing Office.

JUST WAGES AND SALARIES

• • •

The ethics of just compensation are informed by the continual effort to balance three powerful principles; several other considerations contest and limit the reach of these ethical principles.

Overview of Ethical Dimension of Just Compensation

The first ethical principle is that every working person possesses an inherent dignity and deserves respect. All workers, no matter how high or low their skills or compensation, are important and valued members of the institution. In fact, ethically, each person, no matter what job they perform, is entitled to the same amount of respect as any other worker.

The second ethical principle is that each working person has the right to be able to support themselves and their families by the fruits of their work. Few argue with the proposal that people who work full-time should earn enough to support themselves and their families. That means people who work full-time should earn at least a living wage. How much constitutes a living wage is open to discussion, but most people of goodwill agree that part of being a good employer involves paying workers a living wage. While an employer has many obligations and paying fair wages is not their only duty, it is certainly one of the most important.

The third ethical principle is that economic considerations and the health of the employer are also important. Without an economically healthy employer, opportunities for jobs paying living wages are limited. Wages are an important part of the overall budget of all healthcare providers and must be set with the economic health of the institution in mind. If an employer is in a precarious financial situation, then the obligation to pay a living wage must be adjusted accordingly. Ethically, however, the employer is obligated to pay living wages to workers before spending money on other, less important matters. For example, corporations have a duty to produce returns for shareholders. But the corporate duty of employers to shareholders is not as compelling ethically as the duty to pay living wages to employees. Healthcare institutions often present themselves as, and are expected by the public to be, community resources. As community resources, healthcare employers are viewed differently than, for example, the local food and beverage industry or other retail businesses. This creates different and legitimately higher justice expectations for the healthcare employer. Unlike other corporations, healthcare institutions are expected to operate with a commitment to the common good and not just for private gain.

Several countervailing arguments are used to attempt to limit these ethical considerations in determining just compensation. The first and most pervasive argument is that economic market forces alone set ranges of compensation. To many, these market forces are apart from and unaffected by ethical principles. From this perspective, the ethical duty of employers to pay each and every worker at least a living wage is a discussion that philosophers may engage in, but is not realistic enough to engage business decision-makers.

A second argument, which arises out of the first, is that the labor of some people is inherently worth more than the labor of others. In this perspective, considerations of productivity, educational achievement, difficulty of replacement, and competition from other institutions are the real standards for determining compensation. Considerations of human dignity and the right to a living wage are at best peripheral. The determination of what is just compensation is analyzed, evaluated, and decided in the continual contest between these considerations.

Just Compensation

Justice demands that all compensation decisions start with the recognition that each worker has a fundamental human dignity and worth that is equal to every other worker. People work to support themselves and their family members. Thus, at a minimum, each worker must earn enough to support themselves and their family as a result of their labor. Justice does not demand, however, that all persons earn the same amount.

Compensation decisions involving individuals engaged in the same type of occupation are often based on considerations of ability to perform the task assigned, demonstrated and consistent effort, overall quality of work performed, and special skills, ability, or training that allow the person to perform tasks that coworkers do not or cannot. Compensation decisions involving allocation of funds between different categories of workers are often based on principles of productivity, scarcity, comparative effort, and market forces.

Justice demands that the basic needs of all workers be respected as a first principle, and that the decisions about how to apportion the surplus be made in a manner which is fair in both process and result. Fair process for determining compensation in a healthcare institution means that the needs of all workers, the needs of the recipients of healthcare, and the economic needs of the institution are given fair opportunity to be heard and balanced in decision making. To be fair, the process of determining just compensation must be transparent, inclusive, responsible, and participatory. The ability of workers to bargain collectively if they choose to do so must be protected and respected. Fair results in determining compensation are difficult to define, because there are so many competing needs. At a minimum, fair results require decisions that are rational, explainable, and non-discriminatory. Even when fair results are achieved, rapidly changing circumstances can undermine the appropriateness of prior decisions.

Lowest-Paid Workers

A critically important part of the ethical evaluation of any institution is how it compensates its lowest-paid workers. This is the point where the contest between living wages and market forces is played out.

Living wages are the ethical goal of all responsible employers, but as noted above, there are considerations opposed to living wages for the lowest-paid worker. The need to keep overall lower-skilled labor costs down is a constant concern of management. Part of the determination of what is fair compensation is the answer to the question of "what is everyone else, at least those in the surrounding community, paying for similar work?" Employers who pay less than prevailing wages will find it hard to attract and retain a full complement of good workers. Employers who pay a living wage when others pay less will be faced with internal and institutional criticism that there is an overpayment of wages that may harm the financial health of the

institution. And, in some lower-wage communities, healthcare institutions need not pay a living wage to attract and retain entry level or lower-skilled employees.

What is a living wage? While there are many definitions of what constitutes a living wage, all involve the worker earning enough to be able to be self-sufficient and to have enough income to support their family. While the precise amount needed to be self-supporting varies by locale, it is always significantly higher than the federal minimum wage. Some living wage laws have calculated the amount of living wages as the amount necessary for a full-time worker to lift a family of four over the federal poverty guidelines, roughly twice the federal minimum wage. The living wage is sometimes even called the family wage.

Highest-Paid Workers

While ethics indicates that all persons are entitled to be treated with human dignity and respect, there is also general agreement that just compensation does not mean that all people must earn the same amount. Once the basic needs of all workers have been met, justice recognizes that more educated and skilled workers have first claim to higher compensation out of the surplus that remains. This recognizes that higher pay is a partial motivation for people to continue education and to defer other work opportunities while learning higher skills.

Higher compensation is particularly called for in healthcare, where many of the higher-skilled workers have developed their expertise by accumulating substantial educational debt and where the risks associated with their practice require significantly higher insurance costs. People who invest more in their education, who continually improve their skills, who sacrifice more, who are more difficult to attract to provide needed work, and who risk more to provide needed services to others, are ethically deserving of extra compensation.

Compensation for higher-skilled workers should be calculated after consideration of many factors: the overall economic health of the institution, the provision of quality care to those who seek healthcare, and the needs of the lower-paid workers to receive living wages.

There is an ethical caution in the actual calculation of compensation for higher-paid workers: the duty to provide fair and adequate compensation for low-wage workers is ethically more important than the goal of providing competitive compensation for the highest-paid workers. Where there is a conflict within an institution between providing more attractive compensation for higher-wage workers versus paying a living wage to lower-wage workers, the needs of the lower-wage workers ethically trumps the wants of the higher-salaried workers.

Pay Equity Considerations

Equity issues in determining just compensation are aimed at eliminating the effects of gender-, race-, age-, and disability-based wage discrimination. While these types of wage discrimination are now illegal, the effects of discrimination remain. For example, a quick look at most institutions will show that occupations dominated by women and people of color usually pay less than others within the same institution. Gains have been made toward removing the barriers of intentional discrimination. Most people of goodwill agree that intentional acts of discrimination are wrong and should be immediately corrected. But discrimination is not confined to overt acts of prejudice on the part of individuals. Discrimination continues in many institutions as the structural effects of past practices continue to have a negative impact. Differences in education, experience, and time in the workforce form a part of the legitimate criteria for determining compensation. However, concerns for pay equity require the institution to continually question and readjust the institutional respect for the value of work performed by lower-paid workers. Action should be taken to upgrade lower-paying jobs and to correct unjust wage discrimination based on gender, race, age, and disability.

Another equity issue is the large income gap between the highest-paid workers and the lowest-paid workers found in many institutions. Economic inequality within an institution often reflects an uneven participation in the decision-making process within the institution. Further, income disparity within institutions usually becomes a heightened source of concern in times of economic trouble and transition. While some accept this disparity as inevitable, it is not. Like all economic decisions, wage and salary scales are set by people in an ethical, legal, economic, and community context.

Role of Government

The government has an obligation to provide the legal and economic framework necessary for employers and workers to engage in fair and just compensation relationships. Government has a duty to help citizens secure basic justice and to protect the civil and human rights of those without the power to secure those rights for themselves.

The government exists to protect the common good. Just compensation of all members of the community is certainly in the common good. Government must protect the rights of the employer and all workers to fair and just determinations of compensation. Where there are unequal power relationships between workers and employers, the government should participate in leveling the playing field. Government has a role in securing fair labor practices that lead to just compensation.

If the government assists the common good, it acts justly; when individuals or institutions prompt the government to assist the common good, they act justly. When the actions of government are contrary to the common good, they are unethical and unjust; when private individuals or institutions attempt to prevent government from regulating for the common good, their actions are unjust. The government has an important role to promote fairness and equity in the continual process of securing just compensation, particularly for lower-paid workers and those who have been the victims of pay inequity.

WILLIAM QUIGLEY

SEE ALSO: *Healthcare Management Ethics; Justice; Labor Unions in Healthcare; Organizational Ethics in Healthcare*

BIBLIOGRAPHY

Adler, Mortimer J. 1992. *The Great Ideas: A Lexicon of Western Thought.* New York: Scribner.

Galbraith, John K. 1998. *Created Unequal: The Crisis in American Pay.* New York: The Free Press.

Hart, Vivien. 1994. *Bound by Our Constitution: Women, Workers and the Minimum Wage.* Princeton, NJ: Princeton University Press.

National Conference of Catholic Bishops. *Economic Justice for All: Pastoral Letter on Catholic Social Teaching and the U.S. Economy.* 1986. Washington, D.C.: Author.

Pollin, Robert, and Luce, Stephanie. 1998. *The Living Wage: Building a Fair Economy.* New York: The New Press.

Quigley, William. 2003. *Ending Poverty as We Know It: Guaranteeing a Right to a Job at a Living Wage.* Philadelphia: Temple University Press.

Rawls, John. 1999. *A Theory of Justice,* revised edition. Cambridge, MA: Harvard University Press.

L

LABOR UNIONS IN HEALTHCARE

• • •

The relationship between unions, employers, and employees in healthcare raises a wide range of ethical issues at the levels of policy, strategy, and practice. From initial attempts at employee organization, through union elections, contractual negotiations, and interactions over the life of the contract, to strikes, lockouts and union decertification activities, all have an ethical dimension. But the ethical stance taken at the level of policy, strategy and practice depends upon the way three fundamental questions are answered: Do employees have a right to *self-organization;* and, if so, what does that right mean? Do healthcare employees have a right to strike? Do healthcare employees through their self-organization have broader social responsibilities?

The term *self-organization* refers to the shared means employees establish to have a voice in the terms and conditions of their employment. It includes joining a union, forming a union, and developing other types of concerted effort.

In addressing the ethical dimensions of self-organization in healthcare, two points need to be made. First, self-organization in healthcare and other human service organizations is different from self-organization in other forms of employment not because it is completely distinct but because it adds the further component of responsibility to the public served. Second, in considering employee self-organization as a right from an ethical perspective, it is important also to look at that right from a legal perspective. Within the United States, labor law is based on a specific ethical understanding of that right; and often little distinction is made between ethics and law, with the legal being accepted as the ethical.

Self-Organization as a Right

HISTORICAL BACKGROUND. At the beginning of the twenty-first century, the right of employees to organize is widely accepted. Even libertarians acknowledge the right of individuals to choose what groups they wish to join. But getting that right accepted was difficult and costly in human suffering. The experience in the United States is instructive. While the U.S. Constitution guarantees "the right of the people peaceably to assemble," the courts found early attempts by employees to establish permanent organizations to achieve improvements in wages and working conditions through concerted action to be criminal conspiracies in constraint of trade. Later judges granted injunctions against strikes and picketing. Following World War I, unions were branded as *un-American* and *Bolshevic.* Employers used intimidation and violence to break up unionizing efforts and strikes.

In 1935 President Roosevelt signed the National Labor Relations Act (Wagner Act) which recognized employees's right to organize. According to Section 7 of the Act, "Employees shall have the right to self-organization, to form, join or assist labor organizations, to bargain collectively through representatives of their own choosing, and to engage in concerted activities for the purpose of collective bargaining or other mutual aid or protection." Two years later, in *National Labor Relations Board v. Jones & Laughlin Steel Corp.,* the U.S. Supreme Court termed this right a *fundamental right,* stating that labor unions grew "out of the necessities of the situation; that a single employee was helpless in dealing with an employer; … that union was essential to give laborers opportunity to deal on an equality with their employer" (p. 33).

In 1947 in the face of problems in labor-management relations following World War II, Congress passed the Taft-Hartley Act which restricted union powers, adding to the employee rights set out in the Wagner Act the right to *refrain from* self-organization and concerted activities. While the Taft-Hartley Act exempted not-for-profit hospitals, denying those employees the right to organize, this exemption was lifted in 1974. Employees of public hospitals cannot organize under the National Labor Relations Act. In 1987 the National Labor Relations Board (NLRB) established the number of separate bargaining units within a healthcare institution as eight (Lichtenstein).

CIVIL RIGHT. Terming self-organization a right within the United States generally means interpreting it in light of the rights set out in the U.S. Bill of Rights. Those rights, known as civil rights, which include freedom of speech and freedom of assembly, focus on the individual and emphasize freedom. They allow the individual freely to pursue self-interest, protecting the individual against external coercions. While legally the rights contained in the Bill of Rights pertain only to the relation of the individual to the government, an ethic embodying this perspective views the protections of individual freedom broadly.

From the perspective of self-organization as a civil right, the right of the individual to choose freely is a primary focus. This focus has played an important role in addressing the racism and sexism which have marked the history of unions in the United States, upholding the right of each and all to join unions regardless of gender or race. But emphasizing individual choice also has implications for the effectiveness and even the future of unions. The right to choose includes the right to forego. As a result, interpreting the right to self-organization from a civil rights perspective often leads to the conclusion that individuals not only should have a say on whether a unit within a healthcare facility is unionized but also should have a right to refuse to join a union. This has led to so-called *right to work* legislation which supports such a refusal. But, bargaining collectively and engaging in concerted action require a cohesiveness that can be undercut by individual free choice. Allowing an individual to exercise a right of refusal with regard to union membership also opens the possibility that the individual will enjoy the benefits from union activity while bearing none of the costs.

Equally important from a civil rights perspective is the right of freedom of speech. As this right relates to and impacts employees's right to self-organization, there are ethical concerns about what limits, if any, should be placed on the right to free speech of the various parties with an interest in the self-organization process. In the years immediately following the Wagner Act, the NLRB took the position that employers should remain neutral while employees were determining their form of self-organization. By 1941, however, employers's free-speech right to voice their opinion and take sides on employees's self-organization was recognized. In exercising that right, employers, according to the National Labor Relations Act, were not allowed to "interfere with, restrain, or coerce employees in the exercise of their right" to self-organization. That raises questions about what counts as interference, restraint, and coercion. The greater the emphasis on freedom of speech, the greater the latitude employers have to express through word and deed their negative reaction to unionization. Allowing employers to voice their opinion about unionization recognizes their right to free speech; but it can also have the effect of shifting the focus of the exercise of the right to self-organization from the efforts of employees to the interaction between union and employer. The self-organization process can move from one of deliberation among employees to one of antagonism between employer and union.

As the right to free speech of employees, employers and unions comes more to the fore, the danger is that the differentials of power existing between employers and individual employees will be lost to sight, and employers and employees will be treated simply as individuals with different and competing interests, each struggling to achieve their own ends. The right to self-organization then becomes primarily a matter of self-determination. Employees can choose to exercise or not exercise this right; and, even after exercising it, they can retreat from their decision through decertification of the union.

Employees's ability to deal with an employer from a position of equality is especially important in healthcare. In addition to their proper concern about wages and working conditions, healthcare employees have a responsibility as advocates for their patients. Without the power from collective bargaining and concerted action made possible by self-organization, healthcare employees's ability to carry out that responsibility can be severely restricted (White).

SOCIAL RIGHT. Employee self-organization, however, can also be viewed as a social right. Unlike civil rights, which protect the individual against external intrusions and coercions, particularly by the government, social rights set out the basic elements each individual requires to participate within society. Participation here means more than just not being hindered from voting, assembling or speaking one's mind. Its focus are the basic resources needed to take one's place within society and interact substantively with one's fellow citizens to achieve personal and communal good. Social rights include the right to food, housing, education, and healthcare.

Self-organization can be understood as a social right. Then, the right to self-organization, just like the right to food, education, housing, and healthcare, is not treated as a right in conflict with civil rights. It is a basic need that must be met to achieve and ensure social participation for individuals, to establish the foundation needed for exercising civil rights. For example, from this perspective, to say that a person who is homeless or without an education has the right of freedom of expression is formalistic and empty.

Understood as a social right, employees's right to self-organization is not in competition with an employer's right to self-expression. Employees need to exercise their right to self-organization in order to make use of their right of freedom of expression with regard to their working conditions and, in the case of healthcare, with regard to their responsibility for patient care. Thus, in 1999, the American Medical Association (AMA) announced its intention to develop an affiliated national labor organization to represent employed physicians to help them advocate more effectively on behalf of their patients.

Clearly employers have an interest in the results of employees's self-organization; but employees also have an interest in their employer's self-organization. Employees of course are free to make comments about an employer's self-organization. But, because of the power differentials between employers and employees, those comments have neither the power nor the possibility of interference and hindrance that an employer's words have during employees's self-organization.

Viewing employees's right of self-organization from the perspective of social rather than civil rights also has implications for employees's exercise of individual freedom. An approach emphasizing civil rights focuses on the individual as the fundamental element within society and the exercise of freedom as a primary defining factor for the individual. An approach emphasizing social rights looks to the community as the basic building block of society and emphasizes participation as a primary defining activity of the individual. From the latter perspective, freedom is mainly concerned with the way an individual participates, not whether one participates. Applying that to employees's right to self-organization understood as a social right, employees's exercise of freedom goes toward determining the form of their self-organization, not whether there will be some form of

self-organization. Loss of a union election does not remove the discussion of employee self-organization from the table; it simply moves the discussion to other possible forms that self-organization might take. Underlying this is an understanding that, given the differentials of power between employees and employer and given the right and responsibility of healthcare employees to advocate for their patients, healthcare employees can exercise freedom only through self-organization (Hirschl).

Ultimately, these two categories, the right to employee self-organization as a civil right and as a social right, are points on either end of a continuum. Where one comes down on the continuum affects the policies, strategies and actions of the parties involved. For example, as already noted, the stronger the emphasis on self-organization as a civil right, the greater the stress on employer freedom of self-expression and on employee individualism; the stronger the emphasis on self-organization as a social right, the greater the stress on seeing employees's self-organization activity as fundamental for, and thus a prelude to, their exercise of freedom of speech. Regardless of where one is on the continuum, it is important not to lose sight of the fact that the employees are the center focus. When union organizing efforts are underway, events can easily escalate to what can best be described as a war where the focus shifts from the employees's attempts at self-organization to antagonism between the employer and the union. It is also important not to forget the differentials of power that exist between employees and employer.

Right to Strike

A second issue, closely related to the right to self-organization, is whether healthcare employees can strike. Those replying in the negative often base their response on the adverse effect such an action would have on the community at large, taking away a basic resource, and/or on the patients at the healthcare facility, depriving them of needed immediate care. Those replying in the positive often add a qualifier, indicating that in any strike action healthcare employees have a responsibility to ensure that immediate, emergent care is available.

Differences between human service organizations such as healthcare facilities and other organizations involving employees, while they exist, should not be exaggerated, because doing so often leads to the conclusion that healthcare employees should be denied the right to strike. In healthcare, as in other organizations, employee interests differ from, and at times clash with, employer interests in all areas, including patient or resident care. In healthcare, as in other organizations, a power differential exists between employees and employer that always has the potential of hindering employees from pressing their case for proper benefits and working conditions and (in healthcare) proper patient care. The power to strike is essential in light of that power differential.

While a strike can have a negative effect on patient care and the availability of medical care to the community, this result can be the consequence of employer as well as employee action. If, for example, the managers of a healthcare facility have developed policies that result in less than proper benefits, working conditions, or patient care and refuse to bargain fairly with employees, their responsibility for a strike cannot be overlooked. Actions must be evaluated in light of the totality of the circumstances. In addition, during a strike, managers share with employees responsibility for ensuring that basic healthcare resources continue to be available.

Employees's right to strike should not be undercut by the hiring of permanent replacement workers. Such action takes away from managers any incentive to address the concerns employees have about benefits, working conditions and patient care (Gibson; Lauer; Muyskens, 1982a, 1982b; Priest; Weber).

Social Responsibility of Unions

Third, the right to self-organization carries with it social responsibilities. This is especially true when the right to self-organization is seen as a social right. But even civil rights, which, although not created by society, require social promotion and protection, must be exercised in a socially responsible manner and at times give way to the good of the whole. The social responsibilities attendant to healthcare employees's exercise of their right of self-organization require that they take into account the effects their actions (seeking greater benefits, demanding better working conditions, striking) have on the care of patients and the ability of the community to access healthcare. At the same time, employee action in this regard should not be termed *self-interest* and placed in opposition to the common good of the community. Adequate salary and benefits, proper working conditions, and a voice in one's work are all as much social rights as is access to healthcare. At issue is appropriately allotting the resources of society so that each and all can meet their needs and participate in society. Moreover, the responsibility for working to provide access to healthcare to the community rests with management as well as employees.

Finally, healthcare employees have a duty to use the power they achieve through self-organization to actively advocate for better and broader access to healthcare. The dedication of healthcare employees to care for the injured and diseased should not stop with their ministrations to those seeking help at their facility. Through the power self-organization gives healthcare employees, they should be a voice for those lacking adequate healthcare and work to address the stark inequities in the United States where the only access to healthcare for too many is through emergency departments or through healthcare providers willing to offer *charity care* as well as to address the stark inequities worldwide with so many people lacking access (Muyskens, 1986).

THOMAS F. SCHINDLER

SEE ALSO: *Healthcare Management Ethics; Just Wages and Salaries; Organizational Ethics in Healthcare; Profession and Professional Ethics; Responsibility*

BIBLIOGRAPHY

Gibson, Mary. 1989. "The Right to Strike." In *Ethical Issues in the Professions,* ed. Peter Y. Windt; Peter C. Appleby; Margaret P. Pattin; et al. Englewood Cliffs, NJ: Prentice-Hall.

Hirschl, Ran. 2000. "*Negative* Rights vs. *Positive* Entitlements: A Comparative Study of Judicial Interpretations of Rights in an Emerging Neo-Liberal Economic Order." *Human Rights Quarterly* 22: 1060–1098.

Lauer, Eugene. 1986. *Human Service Strikes: A Contemporary Ethical Dilemma.* St. Louis, MO: The Catholic Health Association of the United States.

Lichtenstein, Nelson. 2002. *State of the Union: A Century of American Labor.* Princeton, NJ: Princeton University Press.

Muyskens, James L. 1982a. "Nurses' Collective Responsibility and the Strike Weapon." *Journal of Medicine and Philosophy* 7: 101–112.

Muyskens, James L. 1982b. *Moral Problems in Nursing: A Philosophical Investigation.* Totowa, NJ: Rowman and Littlefield.

Muyskens, James L. 1986. "Collective Responsibility and the Nursing Profession." In *Biomedical Ethics,* ed. Thomas Mappes and Jane S. Zembaty. New York: McGraw Hill.

National Labor Relations Board v. Jones & McLaughlin Steel Corp., 301 U.S. 1 (1937).

Priest, William. 1995. "Collective Bargaining for Nurses under the National Labor Relations Act." *Journal of Legal Medicine* 16: 277–310.

Weber, Leonard. 2001. *Business Ethics in Healthcare: Beyond Compliance.* Bloomington: Indiana University Press.

White, Mary E. 2001. "Nurses and Hospitals Battling: Hospitals Protect Profits; Nurses Advocate for Quality patient Care

While Turning to Unions as a Solution." *Ohio Northern University Law Review* 27: 285–296.

LAW AND BIOETHICS

• • •

Bioethics began as, and remains, an interdisciplinary field. If developments in biology and medicine have fueled the bioethics train and philosophy has laid down the tracks on which it has run, then law has been the engineer at the controls of the locomotive and statutes and court decisions have thrown the switches that guided the train through the rail yards. Law's influence on bioethics has been so pronounced as to be unmistakable, yet so pervasive as sometimes to be unnoticed.

It might be argued that law's role was pronounced for purely historical reasons: Bioethics began as an American phenomenon and hence was shaped by certain aspects of American culture. Lacking an established church or a single heritage of values, though committed to the rule of law and to the equality of all persons, Americans have a habit of turning to courts to resolve moral conflicts. Moreover, other features of the terrain also indicated a major role for the law. Bioethics frequently presents central civic issues, among them these: When does a human entity first become (or cease being) a legal person? What conduct of healthcare professionals treating incurably ill patients would constitute murder? May parents be paid for transferring to other persons the rights of custody and control over their children? Does the prospect of gaining knowledge of potential benefit to the community ever justify using people without their consent or even their knowledge?

Dependence on the legal system to settle many ethical and social issues generated by medicine and the life sciences does more than merely provide a means for resolving disputes. Reliance on the legal system denotes that an issue should be understood as having two opposing sides that will do battle for their respective rights to act in a particular fashion or to restrain the other side from acting in a contrary fashion. Moreover, as a means of discovering and articulating principles, the law favors certain implicit and explicit values.

The relationship of law and bioethics has not, however, been unidirectional: Bioethics has also affected the law. While much of law is concerned with commerce and institutions, both public and private, bioethics is essentially about people and about the fundamental choices that determine and even define their lives. If the law has brought to bioethical cases an attention to rights and procedure, bioethics has enriched legal analysis with life-and-death dramas. It would strain the point to say that medicine saved the law, as Stephen Toulmin observed medicine did for philosophy. But the ethical dilemmas arising from medicine and its associated scientific disciplines have helped to humanize the law, providing a setting in which the central struggles of our times—of individual rights and the collective good, of liberty as against equity and equality, of justice and fairness, of personal wishes versus expert judgment or the will of the majority—are played out with unparalleled urgency and vitality. When the question is whether a life is worth living, for example, the answer is consequential. And when legal institutions falter in answering such questions, then lawyers and others are reminded that perfect legal solutions may not exist for all bioethical dilemmas. Bioethics raises fundamental challenges for theorists as well as practitioners of the law about the harm that society may impose upon a minority in order to uphold values believed to be of fundamental importance to the majority, or the limits of the law as a guide to human conduct. Yet the focus of this essay is not the theoretical connection between morality and law, but rather the law as a practical force in shaping and defining bioethics.

What Is the Law?

SOURCES OF LAW. The term *law* carries a number of meanings. In ordinary speech, it usually refers to specific criminal or regulatory provisions ("It's against the law to …"). This usage also reflects the common equation of law with statutes, denoting not just criminal statutes but also those governing civil or procedural matters, such as the ownership of property or how one is called for jury duty. A fuller understanding of the law would emphasize other important sources. Of particular prominence today are the detailed and voluminous regulations issued by governmental departments and administrative agencies to implement the powers and carry out the duties conferred on them by statutes. Although statutes are sometimes quite detailed, many areas of human activity (especially of an industrial or commercial nature) are so complex that the legislature must almost of necessity confine itself to framing the basic legal structure, while delegating the task of supplying all the details to those with greater time and expertise at the administrative level, subject to various degrees of public, executive, legislative, and judicial oversight.

Especially in countries, including the United States, whose legal systems are derived from the English model, judicial decisions are a source of law at least as important as statutes. In some decisions, judges interpret statutes and hence give meaning and shape to them; while in others, judges decide issues not directly addressed by statutes and effectively make new law. At one time, when statutory rules covered only a small portion of human affairs, most of English law consisted of judicial resolution of individual disputes, collectively known as "the common law." To this day, many areas of law have a strong common-law flavor, which is constantly reinforced and renewed by judges' decisions about novel issues. Even in countries with civil-law systems based on Roman law or the Napoleonic Code, judges participate in the crafting of the law by their interpretation of code provisions.

Finally, in legal systems that follow the model of the United States, in which all activities of the government—including making and interpreting the law—are subject to limits specified in a constitution, no statement of the law would be complete without reference to the text of that supreme law, as well as the authoritative interpretations of its provisions by the courts.

Even these sources—statutes, regulations, judicial decisions, and the constitutions—do not exhaust the meaning of *the law,* which also connotes the legal system, the institutions, and the processes through which the law is applied. In this sense, the law encompasses the processes and rules of courts and administrative bodies (for example, on admission of evidence), as well as the more informal standards or practices that are reflected in the action of those law-applying people and institutions (such as public prosecutors or bureaucrats) who have wide discretion in administering statutes and regulations. Within their sphere of authority, the law is what they say it is. Indeed, to the extent they are not expressly forbidden, the customs and practices of people in any field may properly be described as part of the law, though those customs and practices may formally be denominated *law* only when explicitly incorporated into a judicial opinion, statute, or regulation.

Seen in this way, the law is a basic framework for society; it is a system not only for promulgating official policies and procedures and for administrating prosecutorial, judicial, and regulatory affairs but also for providing explicit or implicit sanction for the private arrangements through which activities and relationships are ordered. Of course, many people would not identify the law as the source for the way they conduct their affairs. Instead, they would point to the influence of family and community customs or values, as well as to explicit moral or religious teachings. But as members of society, they must still operate within the law; this means that if their private arrangements run afoul of the expectations of society as embodied in the law, these arrangements may be limited or nullified. For example, in a number of U.S. jurisdictions, legislatures or judges have declared contracts for women to bear children for couples (so-called surrogate motherhood) to be null and void, as against public policy, even though a purported contract is freely and knowingly agreed to by all parties.

The existence of such private ordering as an important but often overlooked source of lawmaking also serves as a reminder that even in a society, such as the United States, with a high proportion of lawyers, lawmaking is not restricted to lawyers. From the local to the national level, many members of the legislative and executive branches of government are not lawyers; indeed, the federal constitution does not even require that judges be legally trained. Law is one of the three traditional learned professions (along with medicine and the clergy). Its members are licensed by the state and admitted "as officers of the court" to practice "at the bar of justice." Accordingly, like physicians, they are governed by ethical standards articulated by their profession through its associations as well as through the decisions of judges passing on cases of alleged transgression of professional obligations.

Around the world, most legal education occurs in schools affiliated with universities. Characterizing legal education in the early twentieth century as akin to a trade school, Thorstein Veblen opined that "the law school belongs in the modern university no more than a school of fencing or dancing" (p. 211); but this complaint is no longer justified, if indeed it ever was. Today, schools provide much more than mere vocational training, and scholarship is not limited to exegesis of doctrine; it encompasses empirical, normative, and theoretical work. Nonetheless, the law is a practical field, not simply one of the liberal arts and sciences.

DIVISIONS OF THE LAW. Traditionally, for purposes of basic study and classification, law has been divided along such doctrinal lines as tort law, criminal law, contract law, constitutional law, equitable remedies, property law, wills and trusts, and civil and criminal procedure. Each of these areas is characterized by prototypical relationships among parties and a set of analytic and practical devices for structuring those relationships and determining the outcomes of disputes. In recent years, legal scholarship has taken on several additional layers.

One is an enrichment of the tools brought to the law's tasks by combining with another discipline: legal anthropology, law and economics, legal history, law and literature, law and philosophy, law and psychology or psychoanalysis, sociology of law, and law and religion, to mention prominent examples. Each of these combined subdisciplines has not only a methodology but also its own theories and assumptions. Furthermore, additional schools of thought have arisen—such as legal realism, critical legal studies, feminism, and critical race studies—that provide perspectives on the law by combining the tools of several disciplines and a set of attitudes toward legal, social, economic, and personal relationships. Plainly, a person working in an interdisciplinary field may bring one of the analytic perspectives to bear—for instance, a feminist approach to legal history or a legal-realist perspective on law and economics.

A third way of dividing the domain of law is by focusing on its application to specialized types of personal, commercial, institutional, and sociopolitical activities. (The range of specialized areas of the law seems virtually limitless; attorneys now practice antitrust law, art law, bankruptcy law, civil-rights law, commercial law, education law, employment and labor law, entertainment law, family law, insurance law, intellectual-property law, juvenile and dependency law, media and broadcast law, mental-health law, probate law, public and private international law, regulated industries law, sports law, securities law, and even space law, to name a few.) Whether from an academic or a practice vantage point, specialized fields of law usually link traditional doctrinal categories with information and methods derived from the disciplinary and analytic approaches just described. For example, people working in family law will draw not only on legal doctrines from remedies, from property law, from wills and trusts, and from criminal and civil law and procedure, but also on psychological, sociological, or feminist analyses and perspectives; while those pursuing antitrust law will draw not only on various aspects of business law and criminal and civil law but also on law and economics studies and perhaps historical and sociological analysis as well.

HEALTH LAW. Traditionally, medicine and law intersected in civil or criminal cases in which proof of medical facts was at issue. From the medical side, those involved were usually pathologists, who became specialists in "forensic medicine," as the field was known to prosecutors and criminal-defense attorneys; on the legal side, torts specialists who handled a large proportion of malpractice cases (and some of whom held degrees in both law and medicine) described their expertise as encompassing "medical law." With the tremendous growth in healthcare and research beginning in the mid-1960s, healthcare law—or more simply health law—emerged as a new field that includes these areas and more. It is one of the fastest-growing, most diverse, and most exciting legal specialties.

Health law draws on practically the entire corpus of traditional doctrinal fields—civil, criminal, constitutional, property, and procedural—as well as many other specialized areas, such as labor, insurance, antitrust, and government regulation. Practitioners represent hospitals and other healthcare providers; academic research centers; physicians, nurses, and other healthcare professionals and nonprofessional employees; insurance carriers and employers that provide health insurance as an employee benefit; manufacturers and distributors of drugs and medical devices; patients and their families; and governmental departments and agencies that finance and regulate the individuals and institutions providing healthcare. Although cases involving ethical dilemmas are the ones that draw public attention, they are the exception for most health lawyers, who are more likely to spend their time drafting contracts for the purchase of goods and services; bargaining about insurance reimbursement; preparing staff bylaws, checking professional peer activities, or handling other issues that arise in accreditation, credentialing, or certification of practitioners or institutions; negotiating with government agents about licensing, taxation, and environmental controls; or litigating a case of professional malpractice (Macdonald et al.).

The Impact of Law on Bioethics

The relationship of law and bioethics is complex and multifaceted. One need not share the view of a leading legal commentator—"American law, not philosophy or medicine, is primarily responsible for the agenda, development, and current state of American bioethics" (Annas, 1993, p. 3)—to conclude that the law has strongly influenced the methodology of bioethics, the central focus of bioethics, and the values of bioethics. "And—to the considerable extent that bioethics is an American invention and export—the influence of American law has been felt even in societies in which legal institutions play a less pronounced role than they do in the United States" (Capron, p. 43). Law's role in shaping bioethics has at least five facets.

FAMOUS LEGAL CASES. Notable cases have played a major role not merely in the development of bioethics but also in making it, by the 1990s, a prominent part of private reflection and public discourse. Difficult ethical issues are nothing new to the health professions. Yet until recently, issues were examined largely behind closed doors by physicians and nurses and an occasional theologian. In democratic societies, legal proceedings are usually open (though sometimes parties are permitted to use fictitious names, to help preserve their privacy). Consequently, the media are able not merely to report about a difficult decision that must be taken but also to put a human face on it by recounting the drama as it unfolds in the hearing room.

And bioethics cases are often very dramatic. A familiar example: As Karen Quinlan's parents argued during

1975–1976 in the New Jersey courts for authority to order her ventilator turned off, her photograph appeared so often in the media that it was probably more familiar to most Americans than the faces of their local members of Congress. Likewise, bioethical breaches—particularly scandalous ones, such as the Nazi physicians' experiments on concentration camp prisoners and the Tuskegee syphilis study—not only generate landmark judicial rulings but also provoke adoption of new statutory or administrative law.

METHODOLOGY. Related to the addressing of bioethical cases through the law is a second facet, the law's largely inductive methodology. This method is especially associated with the common law, the process through which judges render decisions specific to the facts of the individual cases before them that are grounded in, or justified by, the decisions in prior cases whose facts are sufficiently analogous. Not only do judges often apply the same methodology when interpreting statutes, but legislatures, in drafting statutes, usually operate concretely and incrementally, building on court decisions and existing legislation (or borrowing from other jurisdictions) rather than attempting to operationalize grand principles. The law's fact-based, inductive method provides a counterpoint to the "principlism" that characterizes much philosophically oriented analysis in bioethics. Of course, this approach is not unique to the law, but it reinforces other case-based traditions in ethics, such as casuistry and Jewish ethics.

PROCEDURAL EMPHASIS. Third, recognizing that midlevel ethical principles such as autonomy, beneficence, justice, and nonmaleficence cannot solve most bioethical dilemmas (which arise precisely when conflict occurs among these unranked principles), and that pluralistic societies do not necessarily hold enough moral views in common to agree upon the correct resolution of most controversies, many bioethicists have welcomed "a procedural ethic, based on respect of the freedom of the moral agents involved, even without establishing the correctness of any particular moral sense" (Engelhardt, p. 45). This emphasis on procedure is familiar to lawyers, though the suggestion that bioethics should concentrate on acceptable decision-making processes rather than substantive rules draws objections from some legal scholars who see in proceduralism the risk of a slide into "the arbitrary exercise of power" (Annas, 1988, p. xiii).

Even when they have mandated that procedures be followed, the courts have not insisted that bioethical disagreements outside court employ all the procedural niceties that attach to judicial proceedings. Indeed, judges, legislators, and administrators alike have not always been very clear about the mandate and membership, much less the process,

of institutional committees to make judgments about medical treatment and research. For example, in its landmark *Quinlan* decision, the New Jersey Supreme Court held that the guardians of unconscious patients could order life-sustaining treatment forgone with the agreement of the treating physician, provided a multiprofessional committee at the hospital concurred; yet it said nothing about how that committee should gather, hear, or evaluate evidence or otherwise reach conclusions (*In re Quinlan,* 1976).

RIGHTS ORIENTATION. The issues in bioethics are some of the most sensitive and most divisive confronted by our society, not least because of the rapid development of the life sciences. In both the laboratory and the clinic, novel problems are constantly generated by new capabilities for organ transplantation and mechanical replacement, for genetic diagnosis and therapy, for assisting reproduction, for sustaining life, for modifying human behavior, and for myriad other means of altering nature; such problems also arise out of major changes in the way health services are organized and financed. These developments and changes challenge existing social and professional norms; where those challenges are substantial and intractable, the people involved not infrequently turn to courts, legislatures, or executive agencies to protect their rights. "The concept of rights ... has its most natural use when a political society is divided, and appeals to cooperation or a common goal are pointless" (Dworkin, 1977, p. 184).

Concern over abuses of patients and research subjects has been a major theme in bioethics, reinforced repeatedly by instances in which healthcare professionals and institutions have acted—sometimes from good motives and occasionally not—to the detriment of people in their care. The law has offered bioethics not just a procedural response but also a long tradition of protecting people from harm by assertion of their rights; indeed, a rights orientation seems inherent in the law's perspective on the relationship of the healthcare system to patients and research subjects.

Certain risks to patients arise from the imbalance inherent in this relationship—the vulnerability and dependence that illness creates, physicians' superior knowledge and technical mastery, and the way the organization of healthcare enhances professionals' power and prestige. From ancient times, medical ethics proclaimed the duties of beneficence and fidelity to patients' interests in order to guard against harm to patients. Yet, as bioethicists have pointed out from the first, this traditional view of medical ethics is problematic because physicians not only promised to serve their patients' interests but often took it upon themselves to define those interests. Lawyers aided this assault on medical paternalism with concepts borrowed from civil-rights law, such as political liberty and equality of treatment. From the 1960s onward, bioethicists adopting this stance "had much in common with the new roster of rights agitators" for consumers, racial and sexual minorities, and women (Rothman, p. 245).

The increase in the rights orientation coincided with the increasing effectiveness of medical interventions. Armed with wonder drugs, high-tech surgery, and new methods of resuscitation and intensive care, physicians saw their power to influence their patients' futures increase dramatically from the middle of the twentieth century; and that power became the subject of disputes concerning how it was to be distributed in the physician–patient relationship. Legal commentators suggested—and most bioethicists embraced—a reformulation of that relationship in terms of patients' rights (Annas and Healy). The dominance of the rights orientation dismays many healthcare professionals, who lament the adversarial tone they feel law has introduced into the practice of medicine. There may be a legitimate complaint here, but physicians have historically denied that they are making anything but medical decisions for patients. It has taken bioethicists to point out that once alternatives become available, the choice between them is usually based on value judgments, not medical judgments, and doctors have no special expertise that justifies their values taking precedence over patients' values. Rights are crucial to dealing with power inequality, even where one might prefer to conceive of relationships in terms of caring and connection. This tension remains a recurring theme in law and bioethics.

Although the incorporation of such central legal doctrines as informed consent into the core of bioethics can hardly be doubted, the transformative effects of law on medical practice are less clear. Commentators such as George Annas, who take a patients' rights approach, find many instances where those rights are still abused (1988); whereas scholars such as Jay Katz, who look at physicians' behavior, emphasize that powerful factors in physicians' training and psychology have prevented them from adopting a stance of open discussion and shared decision making. At the same time, other critics argue that the authority the law took from physicians is often transferred to lawyers and judges, not to patients; and that moreover, by replacing professional discretion with legal rules, the law has given physicians the unintended message that they need not exercise ethical judgment (Hyman). Even if physicians do not react in this fashion, the law's inclination to view relationships in terms of rights changes the way bioethical issues are analyzed and potentially displaces other forms of moral discourse traditionally associated with medicine. For example, by emphasizing what one has the right to do without helping to define what is the right thing to do, the law may have undermined

the specifically moral aspects of bioethics (Schneider, 1994). "[N]othing but confusion of thought can result," as Justice Oliver Wendell Holmes observed, "from assuming that the rights of man in a moral sense are equally rights in the sense of the Constitution and the law" (p. 172).

SPECIFIC VALUES. Besides leading toward a rights orientation, the reliance upon the legal system imports specific values. These values are not unique to the legal system, though they tend to be associated with it, nor are they controversial, though they are not without consequence. That is, when one of these values is given preference in the resolution of a problem, other values, such as those that may be favored by medicine or by other philosophical systems, are likely to be overridden. The values usually associated with the law include justice, as opposed to progress or efficiency; equality, as opposed to inherent differences or measures of quality; due process, as opposed to scientific proof; and individual self-determination over one's life and body, as opposed to beneficence, psychological interdependence, or communal welfare. The law's values are generally those of liberal society: personal autonomy within a setting of ordered liberty in which individuals have wide but not unlimited freedom. Especially in pluralistic democracies, the law sets boundaries on the enforcement of majoritarian morality, thereby protecting many individual choices from interference.

Not all liberal societies treat the values involved in the same way. For example, although revolutions in France and the United States in the late eighteenth century drew on the same sources in articulating basic rights, the Declaration of the Rights of Man and the Citizen in France in 1789—unlike the Declaration of Independence in the United States in 1776—emphasized that individuals have duties as well as rights (Glendon). This difference between the American and European views of rights, which persists to this day, has important implications as bioethicists attempt to address such issues as self-risking behavior and limits on the allocation of scarce community resources to healthcare.

Law and Bioethics as a Field

As a field of study, law and bioethics can be viewed from several perspectives. First, from the vantage point of a nonlawyer doing bioethics—whether at a policy level or in individual clinical situations—one needs at least some understanding of the law and legal institutions. Moreover, institutional ethics committees usually include at least one lawyer, who can provide analytic abilities as well as expertise on statutory, regulatory, and case law.

Second, "law and bioethics" is a subject of increasing interest to students, scholars, and practitioners of law. In one view, law and bioethics can be seen as a subset of health law that deals with medical decision making, genetic and reproductive technology, human subjects research, and the like. In fact, health-law casebooks today typically include chapters or sections on bioethics. But this view does not fully capture the way in which bioethics is generally conceived. By the early 1960s, long before health law emerged as a separate field, courses dealing with bioethics were being taught at American law schools, although the first casebook with the title *Cases, Materials, and Problems in Bioethics and Law* was not published until 1981 (Shapiro and Spece). That volume, like other legal books dealing with bioethical issues, not only describes "the new biology" and recounts the dilemmas engendered by modern medicine and biotechnology; it also discusses ethical theories and concepts, such as proportionality and personhood, that have crept from ethics into legal opinions. Nonetheless, law and bioethics is not just a subset of law and philosophy (or law and religion), since attention is usually focused on philosophical concepts not for their own sake but as they relate to understanding society's appropriate responses to technical developments that deeply affect people's lives and relationships. Most of the text of such books is drawn from reports of medical and scientific developments and from the rich array of relevant cases, statutes, and regulations, as well as commentaries about them (Capron and Michel).

In addition to academic attention, law and bioethics has been examined through commissions established by national and state governments through statutes and executive orders. These bodies have advanced bioethical analysis and promulgated legislative and administrative proposals (U.S. Congress).

Although people looking at the topic "law and bioethics" from the perspective of the latter field are likely to view it as a legitimate area of scholarship and practice, it is largely unrecognized among lawyers at large, who treat it neither as one of the distinctive "law and ..." interdisciplinary fields nor as a distinct special application of law ("bioethics law") akin to employment law, sports law, and the like. The Association of American Law Schools does not categorize courses or teachers under such a heading, nor does the *Index to Legal Periodicals,* despite the existence in law journals of bioethics symposia as far back as the late 1960s (Capron and Michel). The literature of law and bioethics is not found only in law reviews or, for that matter, in scholarly journals of other disciplines such as philosophy. It also appears in medical and health-policy journals and in bioethics publications, such as the *Hastings Center Report,* the *Kennedy*

Institute of Ethics Journal, and the *Journal of Law, Medicine, and Ethics.*

One important aspect of legal scholarship that can legitimately be said to be part of the "law and bioethics" literature is abortion. Recent treatments of this subject have been enriched by feminist legal analysis, which itself is greatly influenced by theorists such as Carol Gilligan and Nel Noddings, whose work concerns moral development and the different ways in which women and men may resolve moral dilemmas. This influence is perceptible not only in subjects dealing directly with women, such as abortion, maternal-fetal issues, and reproductive technology, but also in less obvious places such as analyses of ethics committees. Since feminist analysis emphasizes relationships and nurturance, it is not surprising to see that as the literature of law and bioethics moves beyond the rights orientation, feminist insights become important in developing a better legal understanding of the relationship between patients and health caregivers (Capron and Michel).

Conclusion

Scholars differ on the precise influence the law has had in shaping the content, methods, and focus of the interdisciplinary field of bioethics, but all would agree that the influence has been significant. Both those who applaud and those who bemoan the law's influence seem to agree that the law has done more than merely allow the enforcement of, or provide redress for breach of, existing moral rights possessed by participants in the healthcare system. Rather, the law has—through its orientation toward rights and through the values implicit in the processes it has fostered—established new rights and preferred certain values over others. On the positive side, this has helped promote the autonomy of patients and subjects, the openness of the processes by which decisions are reached, and equality of respect and concern for all participants. On the negative side, it has diminished the sense of community and of duties that attach to rights, while increasing many providers' sense of adversariness in their relationship to patients.

In a society in which ethical standards were sufficiently complete to address even novel technical problems, widely enough shared to be accepted without question by all or nearly all persons, and consistent and coherent enough never to lead to uncertain or contradictory results, bioethics might operate with little reference to the law. As Grant Gilmore observed, "A reasonably just society will reflect its values in a reasonably just law. The better the society, the less law there will be. In Heaven there will be no law and the lion will lie down with the lamb" (p. 1044). Until that time, the law will continue to play a large role in bioethics—not only providing a relatively neutral means through which troubling issues can be addressed and contended points resolved in a manner that is socially sanctioned, but also shaping bioethics through its concerns for justice and fair procedures, equality, and personal self-determination.

ALEXANDER MORGAN CAPRON (1995)
BIBLIOGRAPHY REVISED

SEE ALSO: *Animal Research: Law and Policy; Death, Definition and Determination of: Legal Issues in Pronouncing Death; Disability: Legal Issues; Environmental Policy and Law; Human Rights; Informed Consent: Legal and Ethical Issues of Consent to Healthcare; Insanity and the Insanity Defense; Maternal-Fetal Relationship: Legal and Regulatory Issues; Medical Futility; Organ Tissue and Procurement: Ethical and Legal Issues Regarding Living Donors; Public Health Law; Right to Die: Policy and Law*

BIBLIOGRAPHY

Annas, George J. 1988. *Judging Medicine*. Clifton, NJ: Humana Press.

Annas, George J. 1993. *Standard of Care: The Law of American Bioethics*. New York: Oxford University Press.

Annas, George J., and Annas, Julia. 1997. *Standard of Care: The Law of American Bioethics*. New York: Oxford University Press.

Annas, George J., and Healy, Joseph M., Jr. 1974. "The Patient Rights Advocate: Redefining the Doctor-Patient Relationship in the Hospital Context." *Vanderbilt Law Review* 27: 243–269.

Capron, Alexander Morgan. 1994. "Why Law and the Life Sciences?" *Hastings Center Report* 24(3): 42–44.

Capron, Alexander Morgan. 1996. "Morality and the State, Law and Legalism." *Hastings Center Report* 26(6): 35–37.

Capron, Alexander Morgan. 1999. "What Contributions Have Social Science and the Law Made to the Development of Policy on Bioethics?" *Daedelus* 128(4): 295–325.

Capron, Alexander Morgan, and Michel, Vicki. 1993. "Law and Bioethics." *Loyola of Los Angeles Law Review* 27 (November):25–40.

Engelhardt, H. Tristram, Jr. 1986. *The Foundations of Bioethics*. New York: Oxford University Press.

Dworkin, Roger B. 1996. *Limits: The Role of the Law in Bioethical Decision Making (Medical Ethics Series)*. Bloomington: Indiana University Press.

Dworkin, Ronald. 1977. *Taking Rights Seriously*. London: Gerald Duckworth.

Furrow, Barry R.; Greaney, Thomas L.; Johnson, Sandra H.; and Jost, Timothy. 2001. *Bioethics: Health Care Law and Ethics*. Belmont, CA: West Wadsworth.

Gilmore, Grant. 1975. "The Storrs Lectures: The Age of Anxiety." *Yale Law Journal* 84(5): 1022–1044.

Glendon, Mary Ann. 1991. *Rights Talk: The Impoverishment of Political Discourse*. New York: Free Press.

Holmes, Oliver Wendell. 1920. "The Path of the Law." In *Collected Legal Papers*. New York: Harcourt, Brace.

Hyman, D. A. 1990. "How Law Killed Ethics." *Perspectives in Biology and Medicine* 34: 134–151.

Katz, Jay. 1984. *The Silent World of Doctor and Patient*. New York: Free Press.

Macdonald, Michael G.; Kaufman, Robert M.; Capron, Alexander Morgan; and Birnbaum, Irwin M., eds. 1991. *Treatise on Health Care Law*. New York: Matthew Bender.

Minikoff, Jerry. 2002. *Law and Bioethics: An Introduction*. Washington, D.C.: Georgetown University Press.

Quinlan, In re. 70 N.J. 10, 355 A.2d 747, cert. denied sub nom. (1976). *Ginger v. New Jersey*. 429 U.S. 922.

Robinson, John H.; Berry, Roberta M.; and McDonnell, Kevin, eds. 1999. *A Health Law Reader: An Interdisciplinary Approach*. Durham, NC: Carolina Academic Press.

Rothenberg, Karen H. 1996. "Feminism, Law, and Bioethics." *Kennedy Institute of Ethics Journal* 6(1): 69–84.

Rothman, David J. 1991. *Strangers at the Bedside: A History of How Law and Bioethics Transformed Medical Decisionmaking*. New York: Basic Books.

Schneider, C. 1996. "Moral Discourse, Bioethics, and the Law." *Hastings Center Report* 26(6): 37–39.

Schneider, Carl E. 1994. "Bioethics in the Language of the Law." *Hastings Center Report* 24(4): 16–22.

Shapiro, Michael H., and Spece, Roy G., Jr. 1981. *Cases, Materials, and Problems in Bioethics and Law*. St. Paul, MN: West.

Toulmin, Steven. 1982. "How Medicine Saved the Life of Ethics." *Perspectives in Life and Medicine* 25: 736–750.

U.S. Congress. Office of Technology Assessment. 1993. *Biomedical Ethics in U.S. Public Policy*. Washington, D.C.: Author.

Van der Burg, Wibren. 1997. "Bioethics and Law: A Developmental Perspective." *Bioethics* 11(2): 91–114.

Veblen, Thorstein. 1965 (1918). *The Higher Learning in America: A Memorandum on the Conduct of Universities by Business Men*. New York: B. W. Huebsch.

LAW AND MORALITY

• • •

Bioethical problems are often discussed in legal as well as in moral contexts. Lawyers as well as ethicists are involved with such questions as abortion, euthanasia, and experimentation upon human beings. This is not surprising; the law is seriously concerned with protecting such basic rights as life, bodily integrity, and privacy—the rights involved in these ethical questions.

The overlap between law and morality has been a source of the substantial debate about the relation between law and morality, a debate not confined to the bioethical context. It is best divided into two main issues, although the discussion of these issues often overlaps: (1) What, if any, bearing does the moral status of a rule have on its status as a law? (2) To what extent, if any, should the legal system be used to enforce moral perspectives?

Moral Status and Legal Status

Western legal thought has been dominated by a natural-law tradition. There are many variants of this tradition, and the differences among them will be discussed below; what they have in common is a belief in a body of laws governing all people at all times, and in a source for those laws other than the customs and institutions of a given society. Such beliefs are frequently accompanied by the additional beliefs that no society is authorized to create laws that conflict directly with natural laws, and that any such conflicting laws may therefore be invalid. In short, the natural-law tradition asserts the existence of a set of laws whose status as laws is based upon their moral status.

The beginning of this tradition lies in the ancient world. Aristotle (384–322 B.C.E.) drew a distinction between the part of justice that is natural and should have the same force everywhere, and the part that is legal and has its force only in those places where it has been adopted by the people who live there. That distinction was developed extensively by the Stoics, who emphasized two further points about natural justice: that it is based upon right reason and that it is in agreement with nature. Cicero (106–43 B.C.E.), whose legal writings are based upon the Stoic tradition, emphasized the claim that no legislation can alter the validity of natural laws, which remain binding on all people. Some of these ideas were incorporated into Roman law, and the later Roman lawyers probably identified *jus naturale* (the philosophical notion of natural law) with *jus gentium* (a system of laws that had developed in the Roman world and governed the relations among free men independently of their nationality). This identification strengthened the idea of natural law as universal law.

These classical ideas gave rise to a number of different natural-law traditions, the two most important of which are the religious tradition culminating in the writings of Saint Thomas Aquinas (1224–1274) and the secular tradition, exemplified by Hugo Grotius (1583–1645) and John Locke (1632–1704).

Saint Thomas Aquinas defined a law as an ordinance of reason for the common good, promulgated by the individual who has the care of the community. He then distinguished four types of laws: eternal laws, natural laws, human laws, and divine laws. The eternal laws are laws promulgated by God on the basis of divine reason. The natural laws are the eternal laws implanted by God in human beings, in that human beings are naturally inclined toward their proper acts and ends. In short, Saint Thomas postulated an eternal, unchanging set of laws implanted by God in human beings and knowable by reason. Human laws are valid only insofar as they do not conflict with divinely promulgated, unchanging laws. Valid human laws either are conclusions drawn from the basic natural laws or are determinations of details left undetermined by the natural laws.

The natural-law theories of Grotius and Locke also contain theological references, and Saint Thomas does emphasize the rational basis of natural law. Nevertheless, Grotius and Locke represent a different tradition of natural law, one that puts more emphasis on natural law as rationally derivable than on natural law as divinely ordained. In addition, their tradition, especially in the writings of Locke, puts great emphasis on the natural law's protection of natural rights, rights that all human beings have independently of the state and its laws. Locke explicitly drew the conclusion that a state loses its legitimacy insofar as its laws are in violation of natural rights, such as the right to life or liberty.

These natural-law traditions continue to influence discussions about the relation between the law and bioethics. Writers influenced by the theological version of the natural-law tradition continue to argue that any valid law must be in conformity with the divinely ordained natural law. Thus, many Roman Catholic writers (e.g., Grisez and Boyle) argue that there must be civil laws prohibiting abortion and euthanasia because those procedures are in conflict with the natural law. To those who would object that this is an illegitimate use of the law to enforce morality, these writers reply that it is the very nature of legitimate law to prohibit such activities. The most important recent reiteration of this view is found in the 1987 statement from the Congregation for the Doctrine of the Faith titled *Instruction on Respect for Human Life in its Origin and on the Dignity of Procreation*. Having argued that abortion from the moment of conception and various forms of assisted reproduction are immoral, the Congregation goes on to claim that there must be laws prohibiting both because "The task of the civil law is to ensure the common good of people through the recognition of and the defence of fundamental rights and through the promotion of peace and of public morality" (p. 35).

Writers influenced by the ideas of natural-rights thinkers like Locke continue to argue that no purported law is legitimate if it allows the violation of the basic rights of human beings. This type of argumentation is particularly prevalent in countries such as the United States, where the courts possess the ability to declare laws unconstitutional when they infringe upon basic human rights. U.S. Supreme Court decisions from *Griswold v. Connecticut* (1965), in which the Supreme Court ruled that a Connecticut law prohibiting the use of contraceptives is unconstitutional, to *Roe v. Wade* (1973), in which the Supreme Court ruled that women have a constitutional right to abortions at least in the first two trimesters, have indicated that jurists are prepared to extend those rights to include ones not explicitly mentioned in the Constitution, suggesting to many—but by no means all—commentators that they are implicitly invoking some natural-law theory of rights.

The natural-law tradition has not been universally accepted. There has also been a long tradition of thinkers, dating back to antiquity, who have insisted that the only laws that exist are those adopted by a given society, and that there is no necessary connection between the legal status of a law and its moral status. Defenders of this position, the position of legal positivism, are not opposed to the moral criticism of individual laws and of whole legal institutions; positivists often advocate changes in the law on the basis of moral considerations. But the positivists insist that an immoral law, however much it should be changed, remains valid as a law until it is repealed by the society's appropriate social mechanisms.

Jeremy Bentham (1748–1832) and John Austin (1790–1859) were the two most influential proponents of this view, although earlier figures like Jean Bodin (1530–1596) and Thomas Hobbes (1588–1679) should also be mentioned. The basic thesis of positivism has often been conflated with another of Austin's theories, the imperative theory of law, which held that law is the command of the sovereign. Since this latter theory has not survived critical examination, it is crucial to distinguish it from the basic theme of positivism: that what the law is, is a separate question from what the law ought to be. H. L. A. Hart, the most influential contemporary positivist, placed particular emphasis on drawing this distinction.

Some legal positivists have taken their view to mean that laws must be obeyed no matter how immoral they are. But the most important positivists, Bentham and Austin, clearly argued that there are circumstances in which an immoral law should be violated despite its status as a law; this of course weakens the force of the claim that a law retains its status as a law despite its immorality.

In any case, legal positivists insist that questions about the relation between law and morality must be settled independently of questions about what the law is. The legal status of a rule is independent of its moral status. This leads us, therefore, to the second of our questions: When ought the law to be used to enforce certain moral positions?

Use of the Legal System to Enforce Morality

The law is clearly used on some occasions to enforce moral viewpoints. We believe that murder is wrong and that the coercive mechanism of the law should be used to prevent murders. However, even if we believe that euthanasia is wrong or that one should come to the aid of others in distress, should the law be used to enforce these beliefs?

John Stuart Mill (1806–1873), in his classic *On Liberty* (1859), advocated the liberal answer to that question—that society should use the coercive mechanisms of the law only to prevent actions that harm someone other than the performer or another who has consented to the performance of the action. In other words, Mill argued that the social enforcement of morality was inappropriate when only the agent or others who had consented would be harmed. In his elaboration of this position in *The Moral Limits of the Criminal Law* (1984–1988), the most important elaboration of the liberal position in the twentieth century, Joel Feinberg has argued that actions might be criminalized if they were profoundly offensive, even if not harmful, to others. Mill's followers have therefore opposed the existence of laws creating "victimless crimes," among which they have included laws against suicide and voluntary euthanasia, unless such laws are required to protect against mistake and abuse. They have also approved of court decisions that allow rational adults to refuse medical treatment on religious or on other grounds, even though the refusal would result in their dying.

A number of points must be kept in mind about the liberal position. First, it does not require legislation prohibiting all actions that harm others. Whether there should be legislation will depend upon such factors as the existence of harmful consequences and the possibility of enforcement. All that the liberal position entails is that such actions, because they harm others, are candidates for appropriate legal prohibition.

Second, actions that harm others may be prohibited legally, even when others consent, if their consent is not valid. This point is extremely important in connection with legislation governing medical experimentation. Consider, for example, the problem of experiments on children, where the experiments are not primarily intended to aid in their therapy and where there are potential hazards. Given that the consent of the children may not count if they are young enough, and given that the relevance of parental consent is unclear, Mill's principles could allow for enforcing some socially determined moral standards in this area. In fact, the 1993 U.S. regulations on research involving children enforce a very strict moral standard; the risks must represent only a minor increase over minimal risk, and the information must be of vital importance.

Third, this liberal position is not identical either with the English common-law tradition or with American constitutional law. Both have allowed for legal prohibitions that are unacceptable in the liberal framework. For example, the consent of the person killed in an act of voluntary euthanasia has been, at least until the early 1990s, no defense against a charge of murder in either legal system. Some of the language in the U.S. Supreme Court case *Cruzan v. Missouri Department of Health* (1990) suggests that many judges are now prepared to say that the right of a competent adult to refuse life-preserving therapy is a protected constitutional right, a result that liberals would applaud. Nothing in the text of this decision, however, suggests the extension of that view to assisted suicide or voluntary active euthanasia.

Adherents of the liberal approach have in recent years expanded upon it and modified it in a number of ways. One question that has received considerable attention is determining whose consent is valid. The current understanding of mental illness makes it very difficult to accept a sharp dichotomy between those competent to consent and those incompetent, since there are many degrees of mental disturbance. Some (including Buchanan and Brock) have responded that the standard for competency must be more demanding when the decision is more momentous. Others (including Brody) insist that we must recognize that competent decisions may be overridden when the costs to the individual are great and the person's decision making is impaired, even if he or she is somewhat competent.

Another question that has received considerable attention is the extent to which society can legitimately use the law temporarily to prevent an individual from carrying out certain decisions, to see whether the individual will change his or her mind or whether the choice is truly voluntary. Within the liberal framework, could we legally require, for example, a period between a request for voluntary euthanasia and the implementation of that request? Following Joel Feinberg, many liberal authors have allowed for this form of weak or soft paternalism.

A third question that has received considerable attention is the legitimacy of legally imposing certain positive moral duties. Mill was primarily concerned with challenging the legitimacy of laws prohibiting immoral actions; it is unclear how he would have dealt with Good Samaritan laws—laws that would, for example, require trained medical personnel to come to the aid of accident victims. Would such laws that require positive actions, and not mere forbearances, be a legitimate legal enforcement of morality? A final question that has received considerable attention is whether society can pass laws designed to prevent harm to animals. If it could, this would markedly change the liberal attitude toward laws governing experimentation on animals. Peter Singer and Tom Regan are two liberal authors who have advocated the extension of the liberal tradition in this way.

From its very beginning, the liberal tradition has had its critics. Writers in the natural-law tradition objected, of course, to the liberal presupposition that the moral and legal status of rules could be separated. But even some of those who agreed with positivism have argued that there is a wider scope for legislating morality than the scope allowed by Mill.

James Fitzjames Stephen (1829–1894), in his influential *Liberty, Equality, Fraternity,* argued that one of the purposes of both the criminal and the civil law is to promote and encourage virtue while discouraging vice. Stephen conceded that certain areas of morality could not be dealt with by the law because the relevant laws could not be enforced without destroying privacy and individual rights; he claimed, however, that there are many areas of morality that should be treated by the law despite Mill's strictures. This point of view has been extended by Patrick Devlin, a distinguished English jurist. Devlin contends that the continued existence and strength of a society require a common moral code. There is, therefore, a social interest in the preservation of such a code, and it is at least sometimes appropriate to enforce part of the code through the use of the law. Devlin limits his conclusions to cases where this enforcement of morality will not violate human rights. He applied this approach to English abortion legislation in the 1960s. He argued that the severe punishment of the illegal abortionist cannot be justified on the grounds that such a person poses a threat to the health of the mother, since that threat exists primarily because the abortionist's activities are illegal. Instead, such laws can be explained and justified only as an attempt by society to protect its fundamental views on sexuality and on human life.

A number of recent authors (Bellah et al.; MacIntyre; Sandel) have emphasized, in different ways, the importance of communities and a sense of community values, and they have seen this as standing in opposition to the liberal account. This new communitarianism no doubt has significant implications for the legislation of morality in areas related to bioethics, but those implications have not yet been studied systematically. There are, then, a number of differing systematic approaches to the question of which aspects of morality should be enforced legally. In addition to those systematic approaches, various authors and courts have suggested additional considerations that must be weighed in deciding whether legally to enforce moral standards. Among the most prominent of the considerations are the following.

1. Respect for differing views in a pluralistic society. In the 1973 discussion of abortion statutes in *Roe v. Wade,* the U.S. Supreme Court suggested that legislation enforcing a moral viewpoint is inappropriate when those who are experts in the relevant area disagree as to the legitimacy of that viewpoint. This principle is in keeping with a wider movement against legislating disputed moral positions. A number of important considerations support this mode of thought. To begin with, people seem to have a right to follow their own conscience rather than to be compelled to follow the conscience of the rest of society. Moreover, there are tremendous detrimental consequences for a society when many of its citizens feel that the law is being used to coerce them into following the moral views of others. Such considerations are even more important in societies where there are substantial moral disagreements among the citizens. One author who has particularly stressed the importance of respecting differing views in a pluralistic society is H. Tristram Engelhardt, Jr.

2. Respect for privacy. There are laws that cannot be enforced without infringing the privacy of the citizens involved. Following a long tradition that appealed to this point, the U.S. Supreme Court suggested (in *Griswold v. Connecticut,* 1965), that such laws are illegitimate because of the inability to enforce them in an acceptable fashion. For that reason, the Court declared unconstitutional a Connecticut law prohibiting the use (and not merely the production) of contraceptive devices. It has also been argued that laws regulating the patient–doctor relation are inappropriate because they can be enforced only by the state's entering into and examining a relation that must be private. Many authors have criticized the U.S. "Baby-Doe" law (P.L. 98–457, 1984), which limits on moral grounds the decision-making authority of parents and physicians with regard to severely disabled newborns, because it involves state intrusion into a private relation.

3. The consequences of passing such a law. It is sometimes argued that certain moral positions ought not to be enforced legally because the laws that codify them will be violated anyway, and their surreptitious violation will lead to many tragic results. Thus, it has been argued that laws prohibiting abortion only result in women seeking unsafe, illegal, and very dangerous abortions. Again, it has been argued that laws prohibiting voluntary euthanasia or allowing to die only result in surreptitious acts of voluntary euthanasia and in informal decisions to "let the patient die," acts and decisions that can be abused. Many studies of such abuses (by, e.g., Bedell and Delbanco; Evans and Brody) led in the 1980s to more formal policies governing such decisions.

Considerations 1–3 are reasons why certain actions should not be illegal, whether or not they are immoral. Most authors would agree that these legitimate considerations must be balanced against others that argue for the criminalization of the acts in question. These include the extent of the harmful consequences of the actions in question and the extent to which they involve infringements of the rights of others. There are, in addition, considerations for making actions illegal even if they are not immoral. Two deserve special notice:

4. The difficulty of distinguishing between fraudulent and legitimate cases. Suppose that there are no moral objections to voluntary euthanasia. Some have argued that it would be wise legally to prohibit such killings because it is difficult to distinguish cases of honest requests from cases of consent obtained by subtle fraud or duress. Again, some have argued that despite the moral permissibility of experimenting upon consenting adults, there should be laws prohibiting experiments conducted upon prison inmates, because one cannot tell when the consent of such inmates is truly voluntary.

5. Slippery-slope arguments. It is often argued that legalizing certain morally acceptable actions would later lead to irresistible pressures for legalizing immoral actions, and that the only way to avoid sliding down this slippery slope is to prohibit even the acceptable actions. Thus, it has been argued that voluntary euthanasia should be illegal, even if morally acceptable, as a way of ensuring against the later legalization of involuntary euthanasia. Naturally, both of these factors must be weighed against the possible desirable results of legalizing the morally acceptable actions.

Conclusion

It is clear, then, that there are no easy answers to questions about the relation between law and morality. There are strong considerations favoring legal positivism, but there are other considerations favoring a natural-law doctrine. And even if one is a legal positivist, there are conflicting considerations that one has to weigh in deciding on the appropriate relation between one's moral code and society's legal code.

BARUCH A. BRODY (1995)
BIBLIOGRAPHY REVISED

SEE ALSO: *Conscience; Conscience, Rights of; Consensus, Role and Authority of; Contractarianism and Bioethics; Ethics; Human Dignity; Human Rights; Justice; Law and Bioethics; Moral Status; Natural Law; Paternalism*

BIBLIOGRAPHY

Aquinas, Thomas. 1945. *Summa theologica,* I–II, 90–95. *Basic Writings of Saint Thomas Aquinas,* 2: 747–789, ed. Anton C. Pegis. New York: Random House.

Austin, John. 1832. *The Province of Jurisprudence Determined.* London: J. Murray.

Bedell, Susanna, and Delbanco, Thomas. 1984. "Choices about Cardiopulmonary Resuscitation in the Hospital: When Do Physicians Talk with Patients?" *New England Journal of Medicine* 310(17): 1089–1093.

Bellah, Robert; Madsen, Richard; Sullivan, William; et al. 1985. *Habits of the Heart: Individualism and Commitment in American Life.* Berkeley: University of California Press.

Brody, Baruch. 1988. *Life and Death Decision Making.* New York: Oxford University Press.

Buchanan, Allen, and Brock, Dan. 1989. *Deciding for Others.* New York: Cambridge University Press.

Congregation for the Doctrine of the Faith. 1987. *Instruction on Respect for Human Life in Its Origin and on the Dignity of Procreation: Replies to Certain Questions of the Day.* Vatican City: Author.

Cotterrell, Roger. 2000. "Common Law Approaches to the Relationship between Law and Morality." *Ethical Theory and Moral Practice.* 3(1): 9–26.

Devlin, Patrick. 1965. *The Enforcement of Morals.* London: Oxford University Press.

Engelhardt, H. Tristram, Jr. 1986. *The Foundations of Bioethics.* New York: Oxford University Press.

Duff, Antony, ed. 1998. *Philosophy and the Criminal Law: Principle and Critique.* New York: Cambridge University Press.

Evans, Andrew, and Brody, Baruch. 1985. "The Do-Not-Resuscitate Order in Teaching Hospitals." *Journal of the American Medical Association* 253(15): 2236–2239.

Feinberg, Joel. 1984–1988. *The Moral Limits of the Criminal Law.* 4 vols. New York: Oxford University Press.

Friedrich, Carl Joachim. 1958. *The Philosophy of Law in Historical Perspective.* Chicago: University of Chicago Press.

Fuller, Lon L. 1964. *The Morality of Law.* Storrs Lectures on Jurisprudence, 1963. New Haven, CT: Yale University Press.

Gierke, Otto Friedrich von. 1957. *Natural Law and the Theory of Society, 1500 to 1800: With a Lecture on the Ideas of Natural Law and Humanity by Ernest Troeltsch,* tr. Ernest Barker. Boston: Beacon Press.

Gomez-Lobo, Alfonso. 2002. *Morality and the Human Goods: An Introduction to Natural Law Ethics.* Washington, D.C.: Georgetown University Press.

Grisez, Germain, and Boyle, Joseph M. 1979. *Life and Death with Liberty and Justice: A Contribution to the Euthanasia Debate.* Notre Dame, IN: University of Notre Dame Press.

Grotius, Hugo. 1925. *De jure belli ac pacis,* vol. 2, *The Translation,* tr. Francis W. Kelsey. Oxford: Clarendon Press.

Hart, Herbert L. A. 1958. "Positivism and the Separation of Law and Morals." *Harvard Law Review* 71(4): 593–629.

Hart, Herbert L. A. 1963. *Law, Liberty, and Morality: The Harry Camp Lectures.* Stanford, CA: Stanford University Press.

Heller, Agnes. 2000. "The Complexity of Justice—A Challenge to the 21st Century." *Ethical Theory and Moral Practice.* 3(3): 247–262.

Kramer, Matthew H. 2000. "How Moral Principles Can Enter into the Law." *Legal Theory.* 6(1): 83–108.

Locke, John. 1960. *Two Treatises of Government,* ed. Peter Laslett. Cambridge, Eng.: Cambridge University Press.

MacIntyre, Alasdair. 1981. *After Virtue: A Study in Moral Theology.* Notre Dame, IN: University of Notre Dame Press.

Mill, John Stuart. 1859. *On Liberty.* London: J. W. Parker.

Morris, Christopher W. 2000. "Morals, Manners, and Law." *Journal of Value Inquiry* 34(1): 45–59.

Packer, Herbert L. 1968. *The Limits of the Criminal Sanction.* Stanford, CA: Stanford University Press.

Passerin d'Entrèves, Alessandro. 1951. *Natural Law: An Introduction to Legal Philosophy.* London: Hutchinson.

Peach, Lucinda Joy. 2002. *Legislating Morality: Pluralism and Religious Identity in Lawmaking.* New York: Oxford University Press: New York.

Regan, Tom. 1983. *The Case for Animal Rights.* Berkeley and Los Angeles: University of California Press.

Sandel, Michael. 1982. *Liberalism and the Limits of Justice.* Cambridge, Eng.: Cambridge University Press.

Singer, Peter. 1979. *Practical Ethics.* Cambridge, Eng.: Cambridge University Press.

Stephen, James Fitzjames. 1873. *Liberty, Equality, Fraternity.* London: Smith, Elder.

Williams, Glanville. 1957. *The Sanctity of Life and the Criminal Law.* New York: Alfred A. Knopf.

INTERNET RESOURCES

U. S. Code of Federal Regulations, Protection of Human Subjects. 45 CFR 46. 2003. Available from <http://ohrp.osophs.dhhs.gov/humansubjects/guidance/45cfr46.htm/>

the definitional issues, raised by the concept of life itself, that remain subject to dispute and ongoing transformation.

LIFE

• • •

Like many of the concepts foundational to the field of bioethics, life is a subject about which there is both long-standing conviction and increasing uncertainty. The beginnings and endings of life, as well as its creation, have become subject to greater technological modification, particularly through the rise of the modern biological sciences and new reproductive and genetic technologies. In the late twentieth century, increasing technological control over the management, regulation, and production of life and lifelike systems, as well as the accelerating commodification of life forms, raise questions about the limits of what can or should be done to life itself. Hence, seemingly timeless and universal human attitudes toward life, such as mourning in the wake of its loss and joy in its creation, are today accompanied by profound ambiguities concerning the meaning, value, and definition of life.

Some commentators have claimed that even a few decades ago life was more often understood as an absolute value—for example, among medical professionals, for whom the protection of life was an unquestioned moral duty (Parsons et al.). Related arguments hold that the technologization of life has produced a shift away from an understanding of life as an absolute value, and toward more relative assessments of the quality of life (Parsons et al., pp. 405–410). The appearance of an entry entitled "Life" in an encyclopedia of bioethics would support the position that life itself has become the object of increased management in the form of decision making.

In contrast to the urgent call for guidelines concerning the subject of life is the difficulty of defining this term. Neither philosophers, theologians, nor scientists can offer a clear understanding of life. This is in part due to the wide-ranging uses of the term. Not only does life have many meanings as a noun, it is a key term within a wide range of systems of thought from religion to science. In all of the many senses in which the word is used, definitions of it have varied historically in relation to changing social forces and cultural values. Contemporary moral, legal, theological, and scientific uncertainty attends the origins of life, the relative importance of human versus other forms of life, the beginnings and endings of life, the creation and destruction of life, and the nature of life. These and other concerns follow from

Historical and Cultural Variations

To be animate or vital is a condition for which cross-culturally and transhistorically there exists a range of modes of recognition. Broadly speaking, notions of life, or of a vital force, are often connected to beliefs about the supernatural, divinity, and sacredness. It is also generally the case that understandings of life are often made most explicit in relation to death (Bloch and Parry; Huntington and Metcalf). These features characterize both Judeo-Christian and classical understandings of life, the two predominant sources of its definition in the Euro-American tradition prior to the rise of modern science.

According to the Judeo-Christian tradition, life is interpreted and valued as a gift from God. The Old Testament relates that God created man (Adam) in his own likeness, with dominion over all living things. In the Garden of Eden, life was everlasting; and Adam and Eve's expulsion, through which they became mortal, was both a sign of divine displeasure and a partial rescinding of the gift of life. According to the New Testament, the gift of everlasting life was restored through the sacrifice of God's only begotten son, Jesus, and his resurrection to the kingdom of Heaven. Consequently, only those who believe in the resurrection of Christ have "life" in the Christian sense. When Jesus states "I am life" (or "I am the way, the truth, and the life"), it is the resurrection promised to believers in the life, death, and salvation of Christ that is invoked. The historian Barbara Duden notes:

> In most of the New Testament and in two thousand years of ecclesiastical usage, to "have life" means to participate as a believing Christian in the life of Christ.… Even the dead live in Christ, and only those who live in Christ can have life in this world. Of those who exist outside this relationship, the Church has consistently spoken of those who "live" under conditions of death. (p. 102)

Blood is a key symbol of life in the Christian tradition as well as in much secular culture, most notably medicine. To give the "gift of life" is more literally possible today than ever before in the context of organ donation, whereby a body part of a deceased person may "live on" in the body of another person, or a living donor may sacrifice a body part (such as a kidney) on behalf of a relative. The capacity to donate not only blood and vital organs but also egg and sperm cells, and the increasing availability of bodily tissues through a service sector and a marketplace, complicate the understanding of life as a "gift" (Parsons et al.; Titmuss). The sacrificial importance of the body and the blood of Christ makes the exchange of body tissue a potent symbolic practice, as does the definition of kin ties in terms of "blood relations."

The association between the flow of blood and the flow of life anticipates the notion of germ plasm (the hereditary material of the germ cells) as the basis for heredity; this in turn gives rise to the modern scientific concept of the gene, which is today described as the essence of life. While the gene in some senses represents the triumph of mechanistic explanations of life itself, the most reductionist accounts of genes as "selfishly" reproducing entities defined by the attainment of their own inbuilt "ends" may seem not dissimilar from that of the most influential proponent of vitalism, Aristotle. Aristotelian definitions of life were predominant for nearly two millennia, in part because Aristotle was among the few philosophers of antiquity to pay significant attention to the problem of defining life. According to Aristotle, life is defined by the possession of a soul, or vital force, through which an entity is rendered animate and given shape. The attainment of a predetermined end point is seen as the purpose of life in Aristotelian terms, a purpose that is contained in itself, independent of any external causal agent. This view is known as *entelechy*—a *telos,* an ultimate end that is self-defined as the achievement of a final form.

Although the Aristotelian view was based on close observations of the natural world and eschewed any notion of divine creation, it is strongly criticized by modern scientists for its *teleologism* (conflation of an endpoint with a cause) and *essentialism* (predeterminism), which are dismissed as metaphysical and therefore insufficiently empirical. Cartesian accounts of animation, which defined life in terms of the organization instead of the essence of matter, succeeded Aristotelian vitalism in the seventeenth century. From the perspective of mechanism, which explained motion or aliveness purely in terms of the articulation among parts of a whole (as in the ticking of a watch), Aristotelian vitalism came to be seen as mystical, nonobservable, and therefore unscientific.

The history of the concept of life in Western science, from which many of the most authoritative contemporary definitions of it are derived, underscores the importance of change and variation in the meanings of this term (Canguilhem; Schrödinger). Eighteenth-century natural historians employed a horizontal ordering strategy to classify diverse life forms into taxonomies of kind or type. A vertical ranking of the value of these life forms (known as the great chain of being, descending from God to humanity and

thence to other living entities) was based on their proximity to the divine. According to this conceptual framework, *life* comprised a diverse array of animate entities classified epistemologically and ranked theologically in terms of proximity to God. The sacred act of divine creation that brought life into being was, in this schema, paralleled by the secular production by natural philosophers, such as Carolus Linnaeus (1707–1778), of a classification system through which life forms were named, defined, and ordered according to their perceived nature, which was seen to be immutable.

The stability of these vertical ranking and horizontal classifying axes was irrevocably shaken by the gradual acceptance of the evolutionary model of life, in particular the work of Charles Darwin, which, over the latter half of the nineteenth century, gained acceptance in Europe and America. With the rise of Darwinian theories of evolution came a radical new understanding of life: as an underlying connectedness of all living things. It was the evolutionary view of life as a distinct object of study in its own right that gave rise to the modern notion of *life itself*; not until this time could such a thing have been conceived. Many of the current dilemmas in bioethics demanding our attention came to be understood as a direct result of the emergence of this particular conceptualization of life.

As the historian Michel Foucault points out, life itself did not exist before the end of the nineteenth century; it is a concept indebted to the rise of the modern biological sciences.

> Historians want to write histories of biology in the nineteenth century; but they do not realise that biology did not exist then, and that the pattern of knowledge that has been familiar to us for a hundred and fifty years is not valid for a previous period. And that if biology was unknown, there was a very simple reason for it: *that life itself did not exist.* All that existed was living beings, which were viewed through a grid of knowledge constituted by natural history. (p. 128; emphasis added)

Life, in the sense of life itself, is thus a concept linked closely to the rise of the modern life sciences, founded on notions of evolutionary change, the underlying connectedness of all living things, and a biogenetic mechanism of heredity through which life reproduces itself. As the foundational object of the modern life sciences, the concept of life itself does not exist as a thing, as something visible or tangible. Only its traces are accessible, through the forms in which life manifests itself. Like Newtonian gravity, Darwinian life is a principle or force subject to an orderliness decipherable by science, such as the process of natural selection by which evolution is understood to proceed.

Life as Defined by Modern Science

From the vantage point of the modern life sciences, life itself has come to be associated with certain qualities, including movement, the ability to reproduce and to evolve, and the capacity for growth and development. Other criteria for defining life as opposed to nonlife include the capacity to metabolize, in particular through the possession of cells. These characteristics of aliveness in turn comprise key areas in the study of life forms, and in the forms of connectedness and interrelatedness among them. Whereas the comparative anatomy or morphology of animals and plants was the definitive technique for the classification of life forms during the classical period of natural history, it is molecular biology that today provides the primary analytic perspective on the essence of life, which is seen to be DNA, or the genetic code. It is DNA, composed of nucleotide chains that guide the manufacture of essential proteins, that all living beings are said to have in common. Thus DNA is the substance and mechanism of heredity intrinsic to the neo-Darwinian notion of life itself. (For a historical account of Darwinian notions of life itself, see Jacob. For a contemporary view, see Pollack.)

The most definitive accounts of life itself today rely on evolutionary and genetic models. "The possession of a genetic program provides for an absolute difference between organisms and inorganic matter," claims the biologist Ernst Mayr, one of the great twentieth-century exponents of evolution as a unifying theme in modern biological thought (p. 55). "Life should be defined by the possession of those properties which are needed to ensure evolution by natural selection," states John Maynard Smith, one of the leading evolutionary biologists in Britain (p. 7).

In addition to offering the most definitive accounts of life, the modern life sciences provide the most detailed and substantive information on the subject. In the article "Life" written for the *Encyclopaedia Britannica*, Carl Sagan notes: "A great deal is known about life…. Anatomists and taxonomists have studied the forms and relations of more than a million separate species of plants and animals." A range of biological specialties have together compiled "an enormous fund of information" on the origin, diversity, interaction, and complexity of living organisms and the principles that order their existence (p. 985).

Yet even such definitive accounts of life from established scientific figures are often admittedly provisional. Both within and outside the scientific community there is considerable uncertainty about what is being studied when the subject is life itself. As Sagan notes perfunctorily, "There is no generally accepted definition of life" (p. 985).

Problems in Defining Life

The definition of life is not only contested from within the scientific community; it is also troubled by the proximity of lifelike systems, especially those that are computer-generated, to the requisite features of animate existence. There may well be, as Stephen Levy notes in his account of artificial life, a "particular reluctance to grant anything synthetic or man-made the exalted status of a life-form" (p. 6). Yet insofar as the biogenetic definition of life itself relies on an informational model, of DNA as a message or a code, the distinction between life and nonlife is readily challenged by complex informational systems that are to a degree self-regulating and that have the capacity both to replicate themselves and to evolve. If, as some have claimed (Oyama), information is the modern equivalent of form, then life is transformed from an absolute property into a receding horizon merging with artificial, synthetic, or virtual *life*. (see also Langton, and Levy).

Today, both the border between human and nonhuman life and the distinction between life and death are increasingly blurred. Genetic science offers the possibility of transspecies recombinations effecting a merging of human and animal body parts. Artificial-life scientists using information technology distinguish computer-generated organisms, which live, evolve, reproduce, and die, from the "wet" life forms they imitate (Levy). Health professionals distinguish degrees of death: dead (in the sense of brain-dead); double dead (respiratory failure); and triple dead (no body parts suitable for donation). Such distinctions indicate the increasing difficulties of establishing the parameters of life and death.

In sum, life itself may be charted along the course of its four-billion-year history to its estimated point of origin, and along this path may be classified and analyzed scientifically according to established principles, such as the operation of natural selection, and specific qualities, such as the possession of DNA. It is from the perspective of the modern life sciences that the most elaborate and definitive accounts of life are constructed, and from these in turn that the concept of life itself emerges. Yet the instability of these definitional parameters, like those of previous eras that they replaced, ensures their continued transformation.

Life as a Moral Issue

Despite the ubiquity and authority of biological definitions of life, they are also reductionist and materialist, relying upon mechanistic and objective terms that are ultimately most meaningful to professional specialists. Most people, when asked "What is life?" do not appeal to Darwinian principles.

Many of the more everyday definitions of life can be classed as processual or phenomenological, referring to the course of events comprising the life of an individual or other entity (including inanimate objects, as in the expression "shelf life"). Expressions such as *c'est la vie* ("that's life") invoke the fortuitous and inexplicable dimensions of life, very much in contrast to scientific accounts, which emphasize order and predictability even while admitting great uncertainty. Such expressions convey a sense of limits to the capacity for rational understanding, and especially prediction or control, in relation to the vicissitudes of life and living.

The lengthy debate in early modern science concerning *mechanism* (the presumption that animate and inanimate entities alike are composed of matter, which can be explained through inherent principles of structure and function) versus *vitalism* (the presumption of an inherently inexplicable vital force differentiating the quick from the dead) opposes the ancient association of lifelike properties with mystery and the sacred to their accessibility through instrumental reason (see Merchant). In relation to the moral questions concerning life—whether as a process, a possession, or a right—the vitalistic notion of life as something inexplicable and deserving of reverence and protection is far more prevalent than the more mechanistic and instrumental account dominant within science. In both secular and religiously derived accounts, life does not need to be fully explicated or rational to be seen as uniquely deserving of protection, especially human life.

The Protection of Life

In his discussion of abortion and euthanasia, two of the most controversial areas of debate concerning human life, philosopher Ronald Dworkin emphasizes the importance of recognizing that life is not exclusively or even primarily understood by many people in terms of scientific explanations, but rather in terms of a value more akin to sacredness. In relation to moral dilemmas, he claims, life does not present itself as a question of objective fact, but rather as a truth, or a "quasi-religious" principle held to be self-evident through "primitive conviction."

Dworkin's approach thus differs from the more utilitarian arguments about the beginnings and endings of life propounded by philosophers and other commentators who use rights or interest-based approaches to questions of the meaning and value of life. In demarcating the value of life as a "quasi-religious" one, something essentially felt rather than reasoned, Dworkin returns the question of the value of life to an older, more traditional paradigm linked to notions of divinity or a vital force.

Social scientists have shown the value of life to be a key symbolic resource in struggles of many kinds, including both ways of life (as in the preservation of ethnic traditions or indigenous cultures) and life forms (such as endangered species). Anthropologist Faye Ginsburg's study of the abortion debate in a midwestern American community, for example, demonstrates the symbolic dimensions of life as a subject of dispute extending to notions of citizenship, nationalism, and the sexual division of labor. Precisely because the preservation of human life may be seen as an absolute moral value, it proves readily amenable to the social function of grounding other beliefs and practices.

Abortion is one of the best-known arenas of controversy in which both definitions of life and the value of human life are paramount and explicitly formulated. Opponents of abortion argue that life begins at conception and therefore that the deliberate termination of a pregnancy is the taking of a human life, which is seen to be immoral or even comparable to murder. Proponents of a woman's right to control her own fertility, including the choice to terminate an unwanted pregnancy, often argue on the basis of consequentialism, that is, that the moral value of an act should be measured in reference to its outcome. Rights-based claims are used by both sides, antiabortionists stressing the right to life of the fetus, which they argue to be paramount, and pro-choice advocates stressing a woman's right to control her own reproduction, on which they, in turn, place primary importance.

Current legislation on abortion in many industrialized countries, including the United States, invokes a combination of rights-based arguments and biologically based distinctions. Hence, for example, the 1973 U.S. Supreme Court decision in *Roe v. Wade,* which currently determines abortion law in the United States, combines protection of the individual right to privacy with a biologically based definition of fetal viability as the determinant of the upper time limit for abortion. The same standard holds in Great Britain.

Both the notion of biological viability and the definition of the person to whom rights are ascribed invoke a particular construction of life. Viability, for example, is strictly biologically determined: It is measured by the ability of a fetus to survive biologically. The question of the social viability of a child's life, such as its likelihood of receiving adequate nurture, shelter, protection from disease, or sustenance is not considered part of the criteria valid in determining the morality of a decision to terminate a pregnancy. Feminists have been prominent in the challenge to the notion of the *person* often used by antiabortionists on similar grounds. It is undeniably the case that an embryo is human, that it is a being, and that it is a form of life. That it is a living human being is therefore undeniable. Yet it is no more or less a living human being in this sense than an egg or sperm cell, or for that matter a blood cell, none of which is considered a person or seen as entitled to civil rights. Increasingly, antiabortionists have used biologically based arguments to support their position, even when it is derived from religious principles. Hence, it is the potential for an embryo—unlike an egg, a sperm, or a blood cell—to develop into a human being that is often stressed. This argument is based on an embryo's possession of a unique genetic blueprint, which some established theologians claim is evidence of ensoulment (see Ford).

Hence, arguments against abortion based on fetal viability, or those that stress the genetic potential of the fetus to develop into a person, are based on a particular model of life, according to which its sanctity may be represented in biogenetic terms. Historian Barbara Duden has called this historically recent turn toward biology as an arbiter of moral decision making the "sacralisation of life itself." Life, in this sense, is not a biological fact but a cultural value, an essentialist belief, or even a fetish.

The Geneticization of Life Itself

Similar claims have been made regarding the biogenetic definition of life as possession of a genetic blueprint. Critical biologists have argued against the genetic reductionism or genetic essentialism such definitions risk (see Hubbard). Social scientists also have warned of the dangers of eugenicism implicit in such a view (Nelkin and Lindee); other scholars have minimized such risks (Kevles).

Advocates of a "strong" genetic essentialism argue not only that genes are the essence of life but that life itself is consequently based on the selfish desire to reproduce itself. From this vantage point, humans are mere epiphenomena of a primordial genetic drive to self-replicate, and human moral or ethical systems are a complex admixture of altruism motivated by strategic sacrifice, which benefits one genetic trajectory or another (Dawkins).

The belief that life processes will one day be subject to much greater control through instrumentalized understandings of their genetic code is the basis for a major expansion in the biotechnology industry, and corresponding scientific research, since the early 1980s. International scientific projects, such as the attempt to map the human genome by sequencing all of the DNA in the twenty-three pairs of human chromosomes, reflect the increasing importance of genes and genetic processes to the understanding of life itself (for a description of the Human Genome Project, see British Medical Association, and Cook-Deegan; for an account of

the ethical dimension, see Kevles and Hood; for a critical account, see Hubbard and Wald). In turn, increasing information about the role of genes in heredity will pose new choices and decisions, as well as dilemmas, for many. On the one hand, new diagnostic procedures utilizing genetic screening to detect severe, chronic, degenerative, and often terminal disorders caused by a single gene are claimed to offer greater reproductive choice and control, and the potential to alleviate human suffering and disease. On the other hand, the identification of gene "defects" poses worrisome questions, especially when linked to notions of individual predisposition, genetic selection, and the elimination of "undesirable" traits. Controversies such as that attending the putative discovery of a "gay gene" underscore the dangers of social prejudice wedded to genetic determinism in the name of greater reproductive choice and control.

Altering the genetic code of an individual entity, be it human, plant, or animal, is most controversial when the alteration has the potential to be replicated in subsequent generations, therefore resulting in irreversible and cumulative hereditary effects. Although a distinction is currently maintained between somatic cell gene therapy (genetic alteration of nonreproductive bodily tissue) and germ-line gene therapy (genetic modification of the egg or sperm cells, or the early embryo), this boundary is known to be unstable. Considerable ethical concern therefore surrounds the advent of human gene therapy, now practiced in both Great Britain and the United States (for further discussion, see British Medical Association). The release of genetically engineered organisms into the environment, largely in the form of plants and microorganisms, has also attracted controversy, in particular concerning the labeling of foodstuffs and the limits of acceptable risk.

It is the biogenetic definition of life, then, that informs many of the moral debates about the protection of life, whether human, animal, or environmental—the latter category denoting the ecosystem as a complex "living whole" (for a discussion of protecting life as "biodiversity," see Wilson; also Kellert and Wilson). Confusions about when life begins, for example, as in debates about fetal rights, derive from a biogenetic definition of life, which is continuous: each life form has its origin in the lives of those preceding it, and their connectedness underscores the interrelation of life itself. Given such a definition of life, clear demarcations concerning the beginnings and endings of life, of a life, or of life itself are understandably subject to dispute.

Artificial Life

New techniques for technologically assisting the creation of life (e.g., assisted conception) and for prolonging life or redesigning life (genetic engineering) add to the difficulties of establishing a clear basis for decision making by health professionals, relatives, policymakers, or legislators. Technology now enables the production, extension, and even redesign of life forms, including humans, animals, plants, and microorganisms. Increasingly sophisticated medical technology has affected both the beginning and the ending of human life. Life-support technologies can artificially sustain human life in the context of severely restricted life functions both at the beginning of life (perinatal support) and toward the end of life, in cases where the individual becomes fully dependent on technology for respiration. Cases of prolonged "vegetative" human existence raise difficult questions as a result of the availability of technologically maintained biological viability. Insofar as a person is more than a biological life, difficult decisions concerning continued treatment for a person who is only minimally alive are the inevitable result of modern technology's capacity to sustain baseline survival functions indefinitely.

Technology also affects the creation of life itself. As medical scientists acquire ever greater command of genetic structure, the question of the ethical acceptability of the creation of life forms such as the Harvard "oncomouse," genetically engineered to develop cancer so it can be used in the design of new drugs for the treatment of human disease, must be addressed. The subject of a major patent dispute in the European Parliament, and removed from the market in 1993 by its manufacturer, DuPont, the oncomouse was among the first higher life forms to be defined as a technology, comparable to other forms of laboratory apparatus. As both a mammal and a scientific instrument, the oncomouse inhabits a domain subject to increasing ethical, commercial, and political controversy (Haraway).

Most significant, the oncomouse raises the question of ownership of life, which is established as an inviolable right for humans within the liberal democratic tradition and was described by humanist philosopher John Locke as "ownership of one's person." This principle, used in arguments favoring the emancipation of women and the abolition of slavery (both women and slaves being considered chattels), is more recently evident in disputes concerning body parts. In the landmark case of *John Moore v. California Regents*, conflict over the use of Moore's body tissue in the design of a drug, through production of an immortal cell line derived from his spleen cells, culminated in a U.S. Supreme Court decision prohibiting the individual ownership of bodily tissue. Ownership of human life in this case was declared not subject to extracorporeal extension.

The question is again different in the case of the "right to life" of the oncomouse, or the "geep," the transspecies hybrid of a goat and a sheep produced through genetic manipulation. Here, the question concerns the deliberate production of a life that brings great suffering to the resultant organism. Only the greater good to humans of such developments can justify their deliberate creation by scientists. But the basis for ethical decision making in such an instance remains indeterminate.

Conclusion

Many of the ethical questions addressed to life itself concern the degree of protection it requires. These questions in turn depend on how life is defined. Whether they concern the beginnings or endings of life, its creation, redesign, or sustenance under technological conditions, the underlying definition of life itself is a fundamental force shaping ethical decision making. Scientifically, life is defined according to the modern life sciences in a biogenetic idiom, which constructs it as a continuous and connected force unto itself, manifested by the self-replicating properties of DNA. In the liberal humanist tradition, human life is also seen as a possession, and the persistent association of life with sacredness is well established. The rights to life, the protection of life, and the quality of life are extended to some degree to other life forms, on the principle of avoiding cruelty and suffering. In none of these areas are definitive boundaries or limits available upon which to base ethical practice. Instead, as definitions of both life and death are subject to ongoing transformation, so are the ethical frameworks brought to bear on the creation, management, and protection of all life forms.

SARAH FRANKLIN (1995)
BIBLIOGRAPHY REVISED

SEE ALSO: *Abortion; Animal Welfare and Rights: Ethical Perspectives on the Treatment and Status of Animals; Cloning; Embryo and Fetus; Environmental Ethics; Human Nature; Life Sustaining Treatment and Euthanasia; Life, Quality of; Moral Status; Palliative Care and Hospice; Value and Valuation*

BIBLIOGRAPHY

Agar, Nicholas. 2001. *Life's Intrinsic Value.* New York: Columbia University Press.

Bloch, Maurice, and Parry, Jonathan, P., eds. 1982. *Death and the Regeneration of Life.* Cambridge: Cambridge University Press.

British Medical Association. 1992. *Our Genetic Future: The Science and Ethics of Genetic Technology.* Oxford: Oxford University Press.

Canguilhem, Georges. 1994. *A Vital Rationalist: Selected Writings from Georges Canguilhem,* tr. Arthur Goldhammer, ed. Francois Delaporte. New York: Zone.

Carson, Thomas L. 2000. *Value and the Good Life.* South Bend, IN: University of Notre Dame Press.

Cook-Deegan, Robert M. 1993. *The Gene Wars: Science, Politics, and the Human Genome.* New York: Norton.

Davis, Dena S. 2001. "Is Life of Infinite Value?" *Kennedy Institute of Ethics Journal* 11(3): 239–246.

Dawkins, Richard. 1989. *The Selfish Gene,* new edition. Oxford: Oxford University Press.

Dorman, Peter. 1996. *Markets and Mortality: Economics, Dangerous Work, and the Value of Human Life.* New York: Cambridge University Press.

Duden, Barbara. 1993. *Disembodying Women: Perspectives on Pregnancy and the Unborn.* Cambridge, MA: Harvard University Press.

Dworkin, Ronald M. 1993. *Life's Dominion: An Argument about Abortion and Euthanasia.* New York: HarperCollins.

Ford, Norman M. 1988. *When Did I Begin? Conception of the Human Individual in History, Philosophy and Science.* Cambridge: Cambridge University Press.

Foucault, Michel. 1970. *The Order of Things: An Archaeology of the Human Sciences.* New York: Vintage.

Fox, Michael W., and Rollin, Bernard E. 2001. *Bringing Life to Ethics: Global Bioethics for a Humane Society.* Albany: State University of New York Press.

Ginsburg, Faye D. 1989. *Contested Lives: The Abortion Debate in an American Community.* Berkeley: University of California Press.

Haraway, Donna. 1992. "When Man Is on the Menu." In *Incorporations,* pp. 36–43, ed. Jonathan Crary and Sanford Kwinter. New York: Zone.

Hubbard, Ruth. 1990. *The Politics of Women's Biology.* New Brunswick, N.J.: Rutgers University Press.

Hubbard, Ruth, and Wald, Elijah. 1993. *Exploding the Gene Myth: How Genetic Information Is Produced and Manipulated by Scientists, Physicians, Employers, Insurance Companies, Educators, and Law Enforcers.* Boston: Beacon Press.

Huntington, Richard, and Metcalf, Peter. 1979. *Celebrations of Death: The Anthropology of Mortuary Ritual.* Cambridge, Eng.: Cambridge University Press.

Jacob, François. 1973. *The Logic of Life: A History of Heredity,* tr. Betty E. Spillman. Princeton, NJ: Princeton University Press.

Kass, Leon R. 2002. *Life, Liberty and the Defense of Dignity: The Challenge for Bioethics.* Encounter Books.

Kellert, Stephen R., and Wilson, Edward O., eds. 1993. *The Biophilia Hypothesis.* Washington, D.C.: Island.

Kevles, Daniel J. 1986. *In the Name of Eugenics: Genetics and the Uses of Human Heredity.* Berkeley: University of California Press.

Kevles, Daniel J., and Hood, Leroy E., eds. 1992. *The Code of Codes: Scientific and Social Issues in the Human Genome Project.* Cambridge, MA: Harvard University Press.

Langton, Christopher G., ed. 1989. *Artificial Life: Proceedings of an Interdisciplinary Workshop on the Synthesis and Stimulation of Living Systems, Held September, 1987, in Los Alamos, New Mexico.* Santa Fe Institute Studies in the Sciences of Complexity, vol. 6. Redwood City, CA: Addison-Wesley.

Langton, Christopher G.; Taylor, Charles J.; Farmer, J. Doyne; and Rasmussen, Steven, eds. 1992. *Artificial Life II: Proceedings of the Workshop on Artificial Life Held February, 1990, in Santa Fe, New Mexico.* Santa Fe Institute Studies in the Sciences of Complexity, vol. 10. Redwood City, CA: Addison-Wesley.

Levy, Stephen. 1992. *Artificial Life: The Quest for a New Creation.* New York: Pantheon.

Maynard Smith, John. 1986. *The Problems of Biology.* Oxford: Oxford University Press.

Mayr, Ernst. 1982. *The Growth of Biological Thought: Diversity, Evolution, and Inheritance.* Cambridge, MA: Harvard University Press.

McMahan, Jeff. 2002. *The Ethics of Killing: Problems at the Margins of Life.* New York: Oxford University Press.

Merchant, Carolyn. 1980. *The Death of Nature: Women, Ecology, and the Scientific Revolution.* San Francisco: Harper & Row.

Nelkin, Dorothy, and Lindee, Susan. 1995. *Supergene: DNA in American Popular Culture.* New York: W. H. Freedman.

Oyama, Susan. 1985. *The Ontogeny of Information: Developmental Systems and Evolution.* Cambridge: Cambridge University Press.

Parsons, Talcott; Fox, Renée C.; and Lidz, Victor M. 1972. "The 'Gift of Life' and its Reciprocation." *Social Research* 39(3): 367–415.

Pollack, Robert. 1994. *Signs of Life: The Language and Meanings of DNA.* Boston: Houghton Mifflin.

Popper-Lynkeus, Josef. 1995. *The Individual and the Value of Human Life.* Totowa, NJ: Rowman & Littlefield.

Reiman, Jeffery H. 1999. *Abortion and the Ways We Value Human Life.* Totowa, NJ: Rowman & Littlefield.

Sagan, Carl. 1992. "Life." In *Encyclopaedia Britannica,* 15th edition, vols. 10 and 22, pp. 893 and 979–996. Chicago: Encyclopaedia Britannica.

Schrödinger, Erwin. 1956 (1944). *What is Life? and Other Scientific Essays.* New York: Doubleday.

Titmuss, Richard M. 1971. *The Gift Relationship: From Human Blood to Social Policy.* New York: Pantheon.

Wilkie, Tom. 1993. *Perilous Knowledge: The Human Genome Project and Its Implications.* Berkeley: University of California Press.

Wilson, Edward O. 1992. *The Diversity of Life.* New York: Norton.

LIFE, QUALITY OF

• • •

I. QUALITY OF LIFE IN CLINICAL DECISIONS

Quality of life is one of the most important but controversial issues in clinical ethics. The contemporary development of the concept and its use as a normative criterion in clinical decision making date from the period after World War II, when advances in medical technology increased tremendously. Along with other ethical criteria—for example, a medical indications policy (Meilaender; Ramsey; U.S. Department of Health and Human Services); the ordinary-extraordinary means criterion (Connery; Johnstone; Reich, 1978a); or the reasonable person standard (Veatch)—quality of life is used in conflict situations to help make clinical decisions about whether or not to forgo or to withdraw medical treatment from patients.

Modern medicine has the capacity through the application of technology to save lives that until relatively recently would have been lost to acute disease or accident. As a consequence, some of these lives either are shaped by severe disabilities or chronic illness or continue to exist only at the biological level (for example, infants born with multiple congenital abnormalities; elderly patients who suffer chronic illnesses after recovery from an acute illness; and patients in a persistent vegetative state (PVS). Quality of life is frequently proposed as a criterion in making treatment decisions about these patients, whose lives might be saved only to be lived out in severely impaired conditions.

Quality-of-life considerations arise in several key areas of clinical ethics: termination or shortening of human life, including issues of abortion and euthanasia; limiting human reproduction, such as through contraception, sterilization, or abortion; interventions that alter the genetic and biological nature of humans, such as embryo cloning or eugenic engineering; and public policy areas, including economics, ecology, and cultural development (Reich, 1978a). This article will focus principally on the first issue.

Quality-of-life considerations raise a number of important questions that bear specifically on clinical ethics: (1) Given the tremendous advances in medical technology and the implicit imperative to use it, what are the goals and limits of medicine? (2) What is normatively human, and thus, what is it that we value about life? (3) Are quality-of-life judgments purely subjective, or are there objective criteria that guide them? (4) Can there be a life that is so burdened by pain or disability that it can be judged not worth living? (5) Who should decide to terminate treatment? (6) Is it morally legitimate to include considerations of the patient's prior medical condition in a decision about forgoing future medical interventions? and (7) Is it morally legitimate to include in treatment decisions the potential burdens on affected others who will have to care for a severely handicapped patient?

The following sections will provide some preliminary clarifications and conceptual frameworks for understanding quality of life; define quality of life and identify the spectrum of positions that come under the general heading of this normative criterion; articulate the evaluative status of life that is adopted in the various quality-of-life positions and compare the so-called quality-of-life ethic with the sanctity-of-life ethic; and analyze both the normative dimensions of quality-of-life judgments and the normative theories that justify these judgments.

Preliminary Clarifications

Statements or claims about a "quality" or "qualities" of life can be either evaluative or morally normative (Reich, 1978a; Walter). Evaluative claims or statements indicate that some value or worth is attached either to a characteristic of the person (for example, capacity to choose) or to a type of life that is lived (for example, free of pain and handicap). Thus, evaluative statements assess that the quality, and by implication the life that possesses the quality, is desired, appreciated, or even considered sacred. These statements, however, do not establish whether an action to support or to terminate life is morally right or wrong, nor do they specify which action would be morally obligatory. On the other hand, morally normative or prescriptive claims about a quality of life always involve a moral judgment on the valued quality and, by implication, a judgment on the life that possesses the quality. These latter statements, then, not only presume that a quality—for example, cognitive ability—is valued, but they also entail judgments about whether, and under which conditions, one must or ought to protect and preserve a life that possesses the valued quality or qualities. Thus, one could formulate a prescriptive claim that "any life that has cognitive abilities always ought to be given all medical treatment." Evaluative statements about quality of life do bear on clinical decisions, but the more important and controversial issues are concerned with the validity and use of the normative claims about quality of life, especially with regard to patients who lack any ability to participate in the clinical decision.

Many different perspectives could be used in establishing, defending, and assessing evaluative and normative claims in the area of quality of life. A feminist perspective could be used to analyze and critique an evaluative claim that proposes the discursive quality of rationality to be superior to a rationality based on the qualities of affectivity and caring (e.g., Gilligan; Sichel). A perspective from the elderly (Kilner) or the disabled community could be used to assess the normative claim that the qualities of youth, physical beauty, independence, and athletic ability—qualities that are extolled and prized in modern Western culture—are necessary for one to live well. Sociological perspectives could be used to study the cultural patterns of commitment to quality of life (e.g., Gerson), or legal perspectives to study the jurisprudential implications of these claims on the disabled (e.g., Destro). Each of these perspectives, and more, would be important to consult in adequately assessing both evaluative and normative claims about quality of life. However, the remainder of this article will use only the philosophical and theological perspectives that have been developed in the literature on quality of life vis-à-vis treatment decisions.

Definitions of Quality of Life

There is much ambiguity about what *quality of life* means, and consequently there is little agreement about the definition of this criterion. First, there is the word *life*. It can refer to two different realities in this context: (1) vital or metabolic processes that could be called *human biological life*; or (2) *human personal life* that includes biological life but goes beyond it to include other distinctively human capacities, for example, the capacity to choose or to think. Anencephalic infants and PVS patients have biological life, but they do not possess human personal life.

Similarly, *quality* can refer to several different realities. Sometimes the word refers to the idea of excellence. So defined, its meaning is bounded only by the horizons of our imaginations and desires. It is difficult to discover any objective criteria to assess quality-of-life judgments under this definition. Consequently, one may fear that patients whose lives cannot achieve the expected level of imagined or desired excellence, such as the handicapped or the dying, will either not be offered any life-sustaining treatment or will be actively killed.

Another possible definition is to understand *quality* as an attribute or property of either biological or personal life.

Most proponents of quality of life subscribe to this general definition. Some authors identify quality of life with a single valued property of life, while others identify it with a cluster of valued properties. Thus, this definition represents a spectrum of positions. At one end of the spectrum is the original position of Richard McCormick, who isolated only one quality or attribute to be considered as the minimum for personal life: the potential for human relationships (1974). For McCormick, a Down syndrome baby would possess the potential for human relationships, but an anencephalic infant would not. At the other end of the spectrum, Joseph Fletcher originally defined the indicators of "humanhood" by reference to fifteen positive qualities, among them self-awareness, concern for others, curiosity, and balance of rationality and feeling, and five negative properties, among them, that humans are not essentially parental (1972). He believed that many, if not all, severely handicapped children would not possess the attributes necessary to live a life of quality. Between these two ends a number of "median" positions exist that identify quality of life with valued properties of life. For example, Earl Shelp has proposed minimal independence as the central property in his quality-of-life position. He includes in this basic property the abilities to relate to others, to communicate, to ambulate, and to perform the basic tasks of hygiene, feeding, and dressing. From this perspective, many, but not all, Down syndrome children would possess the necessary attributes to live a life of quality.

James Walter has suggested that the word *quality* should not primarily refer to a property or attribute of either physical or personal life. Rather, the quality that is at issue is the quality of the relationship that exists between the medical condition of the patient, on the one hand, and the patient's ability to pursue human purposes, on the other. These purposes are understood as the material, social, moral, and spiritual values that transcend physical, biological life. The quality referred to is the quality of a relation and not a property or attribute of life. Thus, for patients to judge that they possess a quality of life means that the patients themselves would evaluate that, based on their medical condition, they are able to pursue values important to them at some qualitative or acceptable level.

Evaluative Status of Life

When quality of life is defined by reference to a property or attribute of physical life, then some basic questions are raised about the value of physical life itself. What is it that we value about our physical lives? Do we value biological existence in and for its own sake, or because of the presence of some property or attribute in that life, for example, cognitive ability? What theological or philosophical justifications can be offered for one's evaluations of life?

Many who define quality of life basically by reference to a property do not attribute intrinsic value to physical life. For example, in some of his writings McCormick has suggested that physical life does not possess inherent value but is a good to be preserved precisely as the condition of other values (1981, 1984). Based on his theological convictions that physical life is a created, limited good and that the ability to relate to others is the mediation of one's love of the divine, McCormick resists attributing to physical life itself the status of an absolute value. Kevin O'Rourke and Dennis Brodeur have stated that physiological existence as such is not a value if that life lacks any potential for a mental-creative function. Other quality-of-life proponents such as David Thomasma and his colleagues have described physical life as only a conditional value. According to these positions, what is valuable or worthwhile about physical life is either the properties that inhere in life or the values that transcend biological existence but whose pursuit is conditioned on the presence of physical life.

When quality of life is not defined as a property or attribute but rather as a qualitative relation between the patient's medical condition and his or her ability to pursue human values, then a different evaluative status is accorded to physical life. Walter has argued that physical life, as a created reality, is an ontic value, that is, a true and real value that does not depend on some property to give it value. He has tried to acknowledge that physical life is objectively a value in itself, though it may not always be experienced as such by some patients. Thus, physical life is not simply a useful or negotiable good; on the other hand, neither is it an absolute value that must be preserved in every instance.

Some commentators have attempted to address questions about the evaluative status of life by contrasting the quality-of-life ethic with the sanctity-of-life ethic (e.g., Johnstone; Reich, 1978b; Weber). Most proponents of a sanctity-of-life ethic (e.g., Connery; Johnstone; Meilaender; Reich, 1978a) do not argue that physical life itself is an absolute value. In this regard, at least, they agree with all proponents of the quality-of-life ethic. However, these authors frequently claim that when quality of life is understood as a property of life, either no value or only varying degrees of value is accorded to physical life. Possessing no intrinsic worth, physical life must receive its value based on whether it possesses one or more of the valued qualities, for example, neo-cortical function.

The sanctity-of-life position argues that this view is intolerable on several counts. First, quality of life does not acknowledge the equality of physical lives and the equality of persons because it assigns only relative or unequal value to physical lives and persons when certain valued qualities are only partially present or totally absent. Second, quality of life denies that all lives are inherently valuable, and so it leaves open the possibility that some lives can be deemed "not worth living." Finally, it is charged that the quality-of-life position adopts a two-level anthropology committed to protecting physical life only as an instrumental value (Reich, 1978b). Consequently, it is argued that the sanctity-of-life position is far superior because it affirms the equality of life on the basis that physical life is truly a value or good in itself. Life is not merely a useful or negotiable value, dependent on some other intrinsically valuable property.

In conclusion, it is not always clear how useful it may be to contrast sanctity of life with quality of life, as if each position could be represented by an individual and distinct "ethic." Because there are many positions that fit under each one of these "ethics," the terms and results of the comparison really depend on which two positions are selected.

Normative Considerations of Quality of Life

The most important issues related to quality of life in clinical decisions are those concerned with the normative dimensions of the criterion. This level involves several considerations: (1) assessments about what is considered normatively human, or what reasons can be adduced to consider a certain trait or property of life decisive in making a clinical decision to treat or not to treat; (2) the normative moral theory that grounds and justifies moral obligations; and (3) the limits or exceptions to moral obligations to preserve life and the moral justifications for these limits or exceptions. The first issue is definitional in nature, although it also entails some normative features. The second issue relates to the debate over deontology, which determines the rightness of actions by reference to moral rules or the doing of one's duty, and teleology, which determines moral rightness by reference to the ends or consequences of actions. The third issue involves a discussion of the nature and degree of obligation in moral duties to preserve life.

Before turning to actual positions and their normative implications, it is important to distinguish cases where quality-of-life judgments are made by patients who possess decision-making capacity, and those cases where patients— for example, PVS patients, neonates, or severely mentally handicapped adults from birth—lack the capacity to decide. Many issues need to be faced once patients with decision-making capacity are permitted to make treatment choices based on their own assessments of quality of life. However, these problems may pale in comparison to the application of the quality-of-life criterion to situations where a proxy or surrogate must make a decision to terminate treatment.

Some authors (e.g., Ramsey) argue that quality-of-life judgments should never be permitted in treatment decisions for patients who lack decision-making capacity. Only competent patients can make these judgments for themselves; no one may morally substitute his or her quality-of-life judgments for those of someone else. Thus, the moral criterion that applies in treatment decisions for patients who lack decision-making capacity is whatever is medically indicated. However, quality-of-life proponents argue that the medical indications policy could be devastating for these patients. If surrogates do not apply some measure of the quality-of-life criterion, these patients may be condemned to lives of pain, suffering, or burden that no person with decision-making capacity would reasonably choose (Hastings Center). Most of the following considerations will be concerned with the use of quality-of-life judgments in cases involving patients who lack decision-making capacity.

When some proponents of this criterion define quality of life as a property or attribute that gives value to physical life, they are either implicitly or explicitly defining what is normatively human, that is, how personhood ought to be defined. For example, when Fletcher originally defined the fifteen positive and five negative indicators of humanhood, he was defining the nature of personhood, and therefore, who is morally entitled to medical care. If a handicapped neonate or adult lacked a number of the indicators of humanhood but needed medical treatment to survive, in Fletcher's view (1972), the patient should not be treated.

The moral obligation to treat or not to treat patients is derived from the objective presence or absence of a valued property that gives worth and moral standing to the patient's life. When the properties that define humanhood are absent, the patient is not considered a moral subject who possesses any rights to healthcare. The moral theory that Fletcher adopts in his quality-of-life position is a form of teleology called consequentialism. In this theory, any moral claim about the value of a patient's life or any moral duty to provide medical treatment is almost entirely based on predictable qualitative consequences for the patient or for others whose interests are involved in the situation.

In a similar position on quality of life, Earl Shelp has sought to articulate the quality or property that defines the normatively human for handicapped neonates and the extent to which parents and the medical community have moral obligations to these never-competent patients. He adopts a quality-of-life position that corresponds to the main features of a property-based theory of personhood. A property-based theory, as opposed to a genetic-based theory, seeks to designate a desired quality or property that must be present before one can consider a particular human life to be an unqualified member in the moral community.

Shelp has argued that any neonate must possess the possibility of attaining a "minimal independence" before the child can be considered a person in a full sense. If the newborn will never have the capacity of minimal independence, even with the help of modern medicine, then the parents can decide on the basis of quality-of-life considerations that their child, who is in need of medical treatment, should not be treated.

The normative position that underlies Shelp's quality-of-life criterion is a type of a socially weighted calculus. Because he believes that no newborn, whether normal or impaired, is a full member of the moral community (person), he maintains that there is no compelling reason why a severely defective newborn's interests should take priority over those of the parents or siblings who are already persons in a moral sense. In fact, the interests of the ill newborn can be weighed against the independent interests of those whom the child will affect. Thus, if the burden imposed on others is unreasonable or disproportionate, then a decision to forgo or terminate all treatment for the imperiled child is morally legitimate.

What may be problematic in both Fletcher's and Shelp's versions of quality of life, and certainly what worries all opponents of quality-of-life positions, is that their views appear to define and prescribe the "good life" in terms of the quality or qualities necessary to live a minimal moral existence. Their positions then become entrapped within what William Aiken has called the "exclusionary" use of quality of life. The lack of certain valued qualities in a patient's life is a way of positively excluding potential patients from the normal standards of medical and moral treatment.

Other versions on the spectrum of quality-of-life positions do not limit the meaning of quality of life merely to a property of life and then establish moral obligations on the basis of the presence or absence of the property. In addition, these positions do not define the normatively human by reference to a valued attribute and then identify it with quality of life. For them, quality of life functions as a way to include in the clinical decision what they believe are morally relevant factors that are often excluded by other criteria. In other words, some proponents of this normative position hold that quality of life is a patient-centered way of discovering the best interests of a patient.

These authors (e.g., Sparks) argue that in the clinical situation for noncompetent patients, we should be trying to discover what is in their best interests. They recognize that other criteria, such as the ordinary-extraordinary means criterion, have also been used to determine the patient's best interests, and that these criteria have been used to ground moral duties to patients in treatment decisions. However, they argue that these criteria often exclude some morally relevant factors needed to make an adequate and informed moral judgment, for example, the experienced burdens of the patient's prior medical condition in cases of spina bifida.

A comparison of the quality-of-life criterion with the ordinary-extraordinary means criterion might be helpful in illustrating the point that these authors are making. Those who subscribe to the ordinary-extraordinary means criterion argue that all ordinary means of preserving life are morally obligatory, but extraordinary means are morally optional. They do permit surrogates to use what could be called a limited version of the quality-of-life criterion. Surrogates can legitimately include quality-of-life considerations in their treatment decisions, but these considerations are only valid where the treatment itself would cause either excessive harm or leave the patient in a debilitated state (Connery; Reich, 1978b). For example, a surrogate could morally refuse quadruple amputation because the surgery itself would leave the patient with such an extremely low quality of life that the patient would have no duty to undergo the surgery.

All too often, however, the use of this criterion excludes all quality-of-life considerations that cannot be directly connected to the treatment itself or to its application. For example, the fact that a child who is born with Lesch-Nyhan syndrome will have a very poor quality of life is not considered relevant in the clinical decision to treat the child for a life-threatening condition. Lesch-Nyhan is an incurable genetic disease that causes its victims to suffer uncontrollable spasms and mental retardation. Once the young patients of this disease develop teeth, they gnaw their hands and shoulders, and they often bite off a finger or mutilate other parts of their bodies.

Some proponents of the quality-of-life criterion (e.g., McCormick, 1986; Sparks) identify this criterion with the category of "patient's best interests." They adopt what they believe is a patient-centered, teleological assessment of the best interests of the patient. If a patient in a life-threatening condition does possess at least a minimal ability to relate to others, then it can be presumed that the patient would want treatment; thus, treatment should be provided. This form of the quality-of-life criterion maintains that physical life itself is the ground of a prima facie duty to preserve it.

However, other factors—for example, the patient's prior medical condition, which might include permanent loss of all sentient and cognitive abilities, or the financial cost to the family and society of caring for these patients—also come to bear in determining the actual moral duty these patients have to preserve their own lives. Proponents of this version of the criterion argue that medical interventions to continue the lives of accurately diagnosed PVS patients and neonates born with anencephaly or hydranencephaly are unwarranted. These patients have reached the limits of their moral obligations to preserve their own lives, based on an assessment of their best interests. Any medical intervention to save their lives would only perpetuate a condition that most people who possess decision-making capacity would judge burdensome and intolerable. These authors do not judge that some patients' lives are not worth living; however, they do argue that the experienced burdens on patients' lives prior to treatment must be considered in determining the patient's best interests, and thus whether the patient himself or herself has a moral obligation to preserve life.

One of the more difficult questions involved in the debate over the use of quality-of-life judgments is whether one can include in the assessment of best interests of the patient any of the burdens that accrue to affected others. For example, when a family must face the tragic situation of financially and psychologically caring for a severely handicapped child, many would find such a lifelong commitment quite burdensome. Must one discount in treatment decisions the burdens experienced by the family and society in caring for these children, and focus only on the burdens imposed on the child either by the disease or by the treatments themselves? Or is it morally legitimate to include at least some of the burdens imposed on the family and society in assessing the patient's best interests? In other words, how broadly should one interpret the category of "best interests of the patient"? And finally, should the interests of others be considered in their own right? These are some of the questions that the proponents of quality of life regularly ask in clinical situations.

Richard Sparks (1988) is critical of any position that tries to understand the proportionality of benefits and burdens in a way that weighs a severely handicapped child's claims against the interests, claims, and rights of others who are affected, whether within the family or in society. He is also critical of quality-of-life proponents like McCormick, whom he sees as too narrowly defining the range of burdens in these cases. Sparks suggests the phrase "total best interests" as a way not only of including the burden experienced by the patient but also of including the broader social factors, for example, the financial cost, psychic strain, and inconvenience borne by others. He reasons that the patient's social nature must be taken into account, not only in calculating benefits (for example, the benefit to the patient derived from his or her ability to relate to others), but also in calculating burdens (for example, psychic strain to the family or financial cost to society).

Sparks's version of the quality-of-life criterion rejects a socially weighted calculus similar to the one Shelp adopts in determining the best interests of the patient. He judges that such a calculus denies the inherent worth of each individual patient, and that it weighs the benefits and burdens experienced by the patient against those of affected others. Although he argues that the burden to others should be included in assessing the total best interests of the patient, this burden is only one factor among many that must be considered. What is essential is that one not construe the burden to the patient and the burden to affected others as being in competition with one another when making decisions to terminate medical treatment.

By trying to construe the social burdens from the patient's perspective, Sparks believes one can avoid the competitive atmosphere that is part of the socially weighted position. His version of quality of life seems to imply that the child would not, and perhaps should not, want to be treated if it were an excessive social burden because the child's best interests would not be served if these burdens were placed on those who must care for him or her.

The spectrum of definitions and positions representing quality of life makes it difficult to identify any one quality-of-life ethic for analysis or critique. Though there are some shared features among the various positions, in the end it is necessary to assess the validity or invalidity of each position on its own merits.

JAMES J. WALTER (1995)
BIBLIOGRAPHY REVISED

SEE ALSO: *Abortion; Aging and the Aged; Death; Ethics: Normative Ethical Theories; Family and Family Medicine; Genetic Testing and Screening; Life Sustaining Treatment and Euthanasia; Long-Term Care; Mentally Disabled and Mentally Ill Persons; Narrative; Pain and Suffering; Palliative Care and Hospice; Rehabilitation Medicine; Virtue and Character;* and other *Life, Quality of* subentries

BIBLIOGRAPHY

Aiken, William. 1982. "The Quality of Life." *Applied Philosophy* 1 (Spring): 26–36.

Breck, John. 1995. "Euthanasia and the Quality of Life Debate." *Christian Bioethics* 1(3):322–337.

Connery, John R. 1986. "Quality of Life." *Linacre Quarterly* 53 (February): 26–33.

Destro, Robert A. 1986. "Quality-of-Life Ethics and Constitutional Jurisprudence: The Demise of Natural Rights and Equal Protection for the Disabled and Incompetent." *Journal of Contemporary Health Law and Policy* 2: 71–130.

Fletcher, Joseph. 1972. "Indicators of Humanhood: A Tentative Profile of Man." *Hastings Center Report* 2(6): 1–4.

Fletcher, Joseph. 1974. "Four Indicators of Humanhood—The Enquiry Matures." *Hastings Center Report* 4(6): 4–7.

Gerson, Elihu M. 1976. "On 'Quality of Life.'" *American Sociological Review* 41: 793–806.

Gilligan, Carol. 1982. *In a Different Voice: Psychological Theory and Women's Development.* Cambridge, MA: Harvard University Press.

Hastings Center. 1987. *Guidelines on the Termination of Life-Sustaining Treatment and the Care of the Dying: A Report.* Briarcliff Manor, NY: Hastings Center.

Johnstone, Brian V. 1985. "The Sanctity of Life, the Quality of Life and the New 'Baby Doe' Law." *Linacre Quarterly* 52(August): 258–270.

Keyserlingk, Edward W. 1979. *Sanctity of Life; or, Quality of Life in the Context of Ethics, Medicine and Law: A Study.* Ottawa: Minister of Supply and Services.

Kilner, John F. 1988. "Age as a Basis for Allocating Lifesaving Medical Resources: An Ethical Analysis." *Journal of Health Politics, Policy and Law* 13(3): 405–423.

McCormick, Richard A. 1974. "To Save or Let Die." *America* 131(1): 6–10.

McCormick, Richard A. 1978. "The Quality of Life, the Sanctity of Life." *Hastings Center Report* 8(1): 30–36.

McCormick, Richard A. 1981. *How Brave a New World? Dilemmas in Bioethics.* Washington, D.C.: Georgetown University Press.

McCormick, Richard A. 1984. *Health and Medicine in the Catholic Tradition: Tradition in Transition.* New York: Crossroad.

McCormick, Richard A. 1986. "The Best Interests of the Baby." *Second Opinion* 2: 18–25.

Meilaender, Gilbert C. 1982. "If This Baby Could Choose …" *Linacre Quarterly* 49(November): 313–321.

Musschenga, Albert W. 1997. "The Relation between Concepts of Quality-of-Life, Health and Happiness." *Journal of Medicine and Philosophy* 22(1): 11–28.

O'Rourke, Kevin D., and Brodeur, Dennis. 1986. *Medical Ethics: Common Ground for Understanding.* St. Louis: Catholic Health Association of the United States.

Ramsey, Paul. 1978. *Ethics at the Edges of Life: Medical and Legal Intersections.* New Haven, CT: Yale University Press.

Reich, Warren T. 1978a. "Life: Quality of Life." In vol. 2 of *Encyclopedia of Bioethics,* pp. 829–840, ed. Warren T. Reich. New York: Macmillan.

Reich, Warren T. 1978b. "Quality of Life and Defective Newborn Children: An Ethical Analysis." In *Decision Making and the Defective Newborn: Proceedings of a Conference on Spina Bifida and Ethics,* pp. 489–511, ed. Chester A. Swinyard. Springfield, IL.: Charles C. Thomas.

Shelp, Earl E. 1986. *Born to Die? Deciding the Fate of Critically Ill Newborns.* New York: Free Press.

Sichel, Betty A. 1989. "Ethics of Caring and the Institutional Ethics Committee." *Hypatia* 4(2): 45–56.

Sparks, Richard C. 1988. *To Treat or Not to Treat: Bioethics and the Handicapped Newborn.* New York: Paulist Press.

Thomasma, David C.; Micetich, Kenneth C.; and Steineker, Patricia H. 1986. "Continuance of Nutritional Care in the Terminally Ill Patient." *Critical Care Clinics* 2(1): 61–71.

U.S. Department of Health and Human Services. 1985. "Child Abuse and Neglect Prevention and Treatment." *Federal Register* 50(72): 14887–14892.

Veatch, Robert M. 1976. *Death, Dying, and the Biological Revolution: Our Last Quest for Responsibility.* New Haven, CT: Yale University Press.

Walter, James J. 1988. "The Meaning and Validity of Quality of Life Judgments in Contemporary Roman Catholic Medical Ethics." *Louvain Studies* 13(Fall): 195–208.

Walter, James J., and Shannon, Thomas A., eds. 1990. *Quality of Life: The New Medical Dilemma.* New York: Paulist Press.

Weber, Leonard J. 1976. *Who Shall Live? The Dilemma of Severely Handicapped Children and Its Meaning for Other Moral Questions.* New York: Paulist Press.

Wildes, Kevin W. 1996. "Ordinary and Extraordinary Means and the Quality of Life." *Theological Studies* 57(3): 500–512.

II. QUALITY OF LIFE IN HEALTHCARE ALLOCATION

Issues concerning quality of life in healthcare allocation arise from three factors. First, there is an important project that a society wants to undertake: in this case, to provide access to healthcare for more of its citizens. Second, unlike the ordinary marketplace, in which individuals purchase what they want for their own reasons, with no need to seek anyone else's agreement about what to purchase, a society that collectively funds a community project such as healthcare must agree on what outcomes will count as fulfilling that goal. Third, resources are limited partly because taxpayers cannot be expected to forfeit an unlimited amount of their income, and partly because there are other important projects that command taxpayers' funds. Together, these three factors mean that a society needs reasonable assurance that expenditures will actually enhance health without wasting resources.

Prioritizing expenditures becomes urgent because healthcare is extraordinarily expensive, commonly consuming around 15 percent of the gross domestic product of the United States. The need is further dramatized by various cases in which families of patients with anencephaly or persistent vegetative state have insisted on unlimited medical support, regardless of the cost, on the grounds that all life is infinitely precious (*Matter of Baby K,* Miles). Many who have commented on such cases deem it wasteful to prolong the life of someone who will never be conscious while so many other social needs, from healthcare to education, are underfunded. More controversial examples point out the trade-offs between costly new technologies that benefit a few identified patients versus more routine kinds of care that benefit many more people whose identities may never be known (Eddy, 1992a, 1992b). Cases such as these raise the question of whether it is permissible, and if so in what way, to consider quality of life in healthcare resource allocation.

There are two ways to do so. Negatively, one might rule out certain kinds of expenditure on the grounds that they produce little or no benefit for the patient. This might be based on evidence that the treatment has not been shown to be effective, as when a treatment is highly experimental or when a patient is so close to death that no medical interventions can help. Positively, one might invoke quality-of-life judgments to give funding priority to health interventions that will produce the greatest overall benefit for the money spent. Since healthcare is intended to improve as well as prolong life, quality-of-life judgments could shape this quest for the greatest benefit.

It is important to identify some basic distinctions. To speak of the quality of life is not equivalent to making judgments about the value of that life. Persons suffering from a painful terminal illness might have a poor quality of life even though their value and dignity as human beings are every bit as precious as those of healthier persons. Similarly, the quality that someone's life has for himself or herself is not equivalent to the impact that the person has on another person's quality of life. A patient suffering from advanced Alzheimer's disease or other dementia, for instance, might be content and free of suffering, while posing serious burdens and sorrow for family members. Finally, judgments about the quality of an individual's life might come from the individual himself or herself, or from others. Several of the most commonly used instruments for measuring quality of life rely on views elicited from the public at large as they contemplate the life quality caused by certain illnesses or disabilities. However, these opinions may not match the views of people who actually experience these conditions.

Formulas for Measuring Health Benefits

A variety of instruments have been developed to measure the benefits of healthcare interventions. The *human capital* approach, for instance, measures the value of saving or prolonging a life by projecting that person's future earnings. This method is not widely accepted, mainly because it looks only at market valuation of economic contributions, and not at broader features of the person's experiences, relationships, and noneconomic contributions.

A more sophisticated instrument, the *willingness-to-pay* approach, hypothetically lets individuals determine what value they place on a prolongation or improvement of their lives by indicating how much they would actually be willing to pay in order to avoid a certain risk of mortality or morbidity, or to gain a chance at improving their lot. Though this approach permits individuals to make their own quality-of-life judgments, its main disadvantage is that it could represent wealth status rather than personal preferences, which may in turn reflect factors such as social injustices (Brock).

A still more sophisticated approach does not try to translate morbidity and mortality directly into cash equivalents, nor to count lives saved or the number of years saved by a particular healthcare intervention. Rather, it attempts to determine the effect that an intervention has on the quality as well as duration of life by computing Quality-Adjusted Life-Years (QALYs). Extending an extra year for a patient in a vegetative state, for instance, is presumably not as worthwhile as adding a year of vigorous, healthy function. This approach estimates the quality of life that may accompany a particular set of circumstances before and after a proposed intervention, such as a medical treatment or a course of physical therapy, and calculates how long the change is expected to last. The net value of that intervention can then be compared with the value of other healthcare interventions to determine which ones produce the greatest value.

Quality of Life Measurements: Application and Controversy

Various instruments have been used to measure quality of life. The Quality of Well-Being (QWB) Index defines twenty-four health or functional states from perfect health to death. Through questionnaires and community surveys, each QWB state is given a weight, from zero for death to one for perfect health (Kaplan, 1992, 1985; Kaplan et al.). Other scales, such as the Quality of Life Index or the Sickness Impact Profile, evaluate quality of life according to factors such as ability to perform daily activities, feelings of satisfaction with one's health status, and the like (Brock; Zeckhauser; Zeckhauser and Shepard; Wenger et al.).

The state of Oregon used the QALY approach in an effort to ensure, on the negative side, that it does not waste limited state dollars, and on the positive side, to maximize the good achieved by its Medicaid program by avoiding marginally valuable expenditures while expanding coverage to encompass numerous uninsured people. Initially, a series of town meetings and phone surveys elicited community opinions about the value of a variety of conditions, such as

perfect health, feeling depressed and upset, being burned over large areas of one's body, and so on. The value system thus generated was then combined with physicians' estimates of the magnitude and duration of effects produced by various medical interventions for those assorted conditions. After combining the QALY units derived for these treatment/condition pairs with their respective costs, a priority list was developed. Taking the prevalence and cost of treatment for each condition on that list, accountants were able to tell the legislature how much money would be required to fund the program as the next lower priority item was added. The legislature then set its Medicaid budget and identified a cutoff point: Eligible recipients would receive all services prioritized above that line, but not below it (Garland; Eddy, 1991; Hadorn; Kaplan, 1992). This first attempt yielded enough unexpected and unsatisfactory results that the priority list was significantly changed before the program was finally approved (Eddy, 1991).

The problems the Oregon process encountered illustrate the ethical challenges in using quality-of-life considerations in healthcare allocation. They begin with methodological problems. Oregon's plan, and QALY approaches generally, are criticized for ignoring the wide variations of severity that can characterize any medical condition, from broken bones to lupus, and the equally varying results that any given treatment can have for a particular condition. Further, it is not clear whose values should be attached to these factual descriptions. Opinions solicited from the public at large may be based on a poor understanding of the medical condition at stake. A one-sentence summary on a questionnaire, for instance, is hardly sufficient for understanding what it is like to live as a paraplegic. The Oregon plan, in particular, was criticized for eliciting values mainly from articulate, middle-class persons rather than from the poor and disabled, who would be most affected by the resulting distribution of healthcare resources. On the other hand, it is not always possible to discover patients' views on their own quality of life. Advanced dementia, infancy, stroke, retardation, and a host of conditions can prevent the individual from expressing his or her views or even, in some cases, from conceptualizing his or her quality of life. These and other methodological criticisms (Morreim, 1986, 1992) are important, because even if one can on principle justify allocating healthcare resources according to treatments' impact on life quality, it is morally more difficult to justify using measures that may not capture what they should.

Moral issues also concern the very idea of using quality of life as a basis on which to allocate care. Vitalists who believe that all life is infinitely valuable, regardless of its quality, simply reject the idea that interventions should be graded according to how well they enhance quality of life.

Others, however, insist that it is wasteful, if not unconscionable, to spend limited resources sustaining the lives of permanently unconscious or imminently dying patients.

A corollary objection insists that the cost of treatment is no reason for restricting it. Individuals should not suffer needlessly just because their care is costly. Rather, costs should be contained in other ways, such as by eliminating wasteful expenditures. In reply, it is argued that needs are always greater than resources, rendering rationing inevitable, and that overt public decisions are preferable to covert priorities.

A further critique holds that maximizing QALYs, somehow reified as a good in themselves, ignores the justice of the distribution. In one of the classic challenges to utilitarianism, critics point out that a pure cost–benefit approach can ignore terrible suffering, simply because some other intervention may be cheaper and help larger numbers of people. The first listing of Oregon's priorities, for instance, ranked dental caps for pulp exposure higher than surgery for ectopic pregnancy, and splints for temporomandibular joints higher than appendectomies for appendicitis. Although some people might reply that only the methodology needs to be adjusted (Eddy, 1991), others would argue that this approach is inherently incapable of honoring the preciousness that attaches to the lives and well-being of individual people (Hadorn). Severely disabled persons may not be capable of enjoying as great a benefit as healthy persons snatched from the jaws of death, but their comfort and personhood are not necessarily less important.

Another controversy concerns whose values should shape estimates of life quality. If the purpose of medical interventions is to help individuals, perhaps patients should be permitted to define for themselves what constitutes a benefit. Studies indicate that persons afflicted with a particular malady often rate their quality of life higher than observers do (Evans et al.). On the other hand, a broader kind of fairness might require recognizing that sometimes individual preferences are costly and idiosyncratic, and acknowledging that the community paying for care should be permitted to use its own community values to determine monetary allocation (Morreim, 1986, 1992).

A related concern points out that the QALY approach inherently discriminates against the elderly and the disabled, whose prognoses and initial quality of life are typically lower than average. In reply, it is argued that the elderly at least have had the opportunity to complete their life's biography (Callahan), and that while methods to value the comfort and improved function of the disabled can be developed, aggressive medical interventions may not serve the most severely compromised patients well.

Conclusion

The issues cannot be resolved here, but a few comments seem pertinent. First, society is not required to fund every expenditure that each citizen might find worthwhile. Vitalists should arguably be permitted to seek life support for permanently unconscious loved ones, but this does not entail that a society that does not share this belief must pay for their quest (Morreim, 1992). Second, the moral character of a society is at least partly reflected by the ways it treats its weakest members. The fact that someone is not useful to others does not entail that his or her sensibilities are insignificant or undeserving of help. Third, those obligations are not unlimited. There is a virtually endless variety of ways in which society can arrange its resource priorities, and none of them is the single morally correct approach. What is probably most important is to implement procedures that are fair and open to wide participation, are sensitive to varying viewpoints, and embrace a respect for citizens as persons (Brock, Engelhardt).

E. HAAVI MORREIM (1995)
REVISED BY AUTHOR

SEE ALSO: *Chronic Illness and Chronic Care; Communitarianism and Bioethics; Consensus, Role and Authority of; Economic Concepts in Healthcare;* and other *Life, Quality of* subentries

BIBLIOGRAPHY

Baby K, In re. 1993. 832 F.Supp. 1022 (E.D.Va.), 16 F.3d 590 (4th Cir. 1994).

Brock, Dan W. 1993. *Life and Death: Philosophical Essays in Biomedical Ethics.* Cambridge, Eng.: Cambridge University Press.

Brown, Johathan B.; Boles, Myde; Mullooly, John Pl.; Levinson, Wendy. 1999. "Effect of Clinician Communication Skills Training on Patient Satisfaction: A Randomized, Controlled Trial." *Annals of Internal Medicine* 131: 822–829.

Callahan, Daniel. 1987. *Setting Limits: Medical Goals in an Aging Society.* New York: Simon and Schuster.

Eddy, David M. 1991. "Oregon's Methods: Did Cost-Effectiveness Analysis Fail?" *Journal of the American Medical Association* 266(15): 2135–2141.

Eddy, David M. 1992a. "Clinical Decision Making: From Theory to Practice. Applying Cost-Effectiveness Analysis: The Inside Story." *Journal of the American Medical Association* 268(18): 2575–2582.

Eddy, David M. 1992b. "Clinical Decision Making: From Theory to Practice. Cost-Effectiveness Analysis: Is It Up to the Task?" *Journal of the American Medical Association* 267(24): 3342–3348.

Engelhardt, H. Tristram, Jr. 1992. "Why a Two-Tier System of Health Care Delivery Is Morally Unavoidable." In *Rationing America's Medical Care: The Oregon Plan and Beyond*, ed. Martin A. Strosberg, Joshua M. Wiener, Robert Baker, et al. Washington, D.C.: Brookings Institution.

Evans, Roger W., Manninen, Diane L.; Garrison, Louis P.; et al. 1985. "The Quality of Life of Patients with End-Stage Renal Disease." *New England Journal of Medicine* 312(9): 553–559.

Garland, Michael J. 1992. "Rationing in Public: Oregon's Priority-Setting Methodology." In *Rationing America's Medical Care: The Oregon Plan and Beyond*, ed. Martin A. Strosberg, Joshua M. Wiener, Robert Baker, et al. Washington, D.C.: Brookings Institution.

Goodwin, Pamela J.; Leszcz, Molyn; Ennis, Marguerite; et al. 2001. "The Effect of Group Psychosocial Support on Survival in Metastatic Breast Cancer." *New England Journal of Medicine* 345: 1719–1726.

Hadorn, David C. 1991. "Setting Health Care Priorities in Oregon: Cost-Effectiveness Meets the Rule of Rescue." *Journal of the American Medical Association* 265: 2218–2225.

Kaplan, Robert M. 1985. "Quality-of-Life Measurement." In *Measurement Strategies in Health Psychology*, ed. Paul Karoly. New York: Wiley.

Kaplan, Robert M. 1992. "A Quality-of-Life Approach to Health-Resource Allocation." In *Rationing America's Medical Care: The Oregon Plan and Beyond*, ed. Martin A. Strosberg, Joshua M. Wiener, Robert Baker, et al. Washington, D.C.: Brookings Institution.

Kaplan, Robert M.; Bush, J. W.; and Berry, Charles C. 1976. "Health Status: Types of Validity and the Index of Well-Being." *Health Services Research* 11(4): 478–507.

Lüderitz, Berndt, and Jung, Werner. 2000. "Quality of Life in Patients with Atrial Fibrillation." *Archives of Internal Medicine* 160: 749–757.

Miles, Steven H. 1992. "Interpersonal Issues in the Wanglie Case." *Kennedy Institute of Ethics Journal* 2: 61–72.

Morreim, E. Haavi. 1986. "Computing the Quality of Life." In *The Price of Health*. Dordrecht, Netherlands: D. Reidel.

Morreim, E. Haavi. 1992. "The Impossibility and the Necessity of Quality of Life Research." *Bioethics* 6(3): 218–232.

Morreim, E. Haavi. 1994. "Profoundly Diminished Life: The Casualties of Coercion." *Hastings Center Report* 24(1): 33–42.

Steneck, Gunner; Helgesen, Fred; Adolfsson, Jan; et al. 2002. "Quality of Life after Radical Prostatectomy, or Watchful Waiting." *New England Journal of Medicine* 347: 790–796.

Wenger, Nanette Kass; Mattson, Margaret E.; Furberg, Curt D.; et al. 1984. "Overview: Assessment of Quality of Life in Clinical Trials of Cardiovascular Therapies." In *Assessment of Quality of Life in Clinical Trials of Cardiovascular Therapies*, ed. Nanette Kass Wenger. New York: LeJacq.

Zeckhauser, Richard. 1975. "Procedures for Valuing Lives." *Public Policy* 23(4): 419–464.

Zeckhauser, Richard, and Shepard, Donald. 1976. "Where Now for Saving Lives?" *Law and Contemporary Problems* 40(4): 5–45.

III. QUALITY OF LIFE IN LEGAL PERSPECTIVE

Law has addressed quality-of-life issues primarily in the context of the withholding or withdrawal of life-sustaining medical intervention. The legal dilemma arose when medical technology became capable of keeping alive persons with gravely debilitating and potentially fatal afflictions long beyond the point that most people would wish to live. The questions became: Under what circumstances is the removal of life support lawful? Can decisions to remove life support be grounded on quality-of-life factors?

Many sources contend that deteriorated quality of life—in the sense of a patient's mental and physical debilitation—is a natural and inevitable element in shaping the bounds of medical intervention in the dying process. Most people, faced with a prolonged and debilitated dying process for themselves or a loved one, prefer that life support be withdrawn at some stage of deterioration. Decisions about life support for formerly vital people are therefore often grounded on factors such as extreme mental dysfunction, immobility, and helplessness.

The opponents of using quality-of-life factors in ending people's lives cite numerous concerns. The most common is that judicial or legislative sanctioning of quality-of-life considerations will undermine the traditional focus of both criminal and tort law on preserving and protecting all human life, regardless of quality. One asserted hazard is that quality of life will be measured in terms of utilitarian elements such as cost of care, social productiveness of the patient, and burdens imposed upon the people caring for the patient. Such a utilitarian calculus would place the lives of the weak and vulnerable—the very young, the developmentally disabled, and the elderly—at particular risk (Destro).

Even if quality-of-life considerations are confined to factors that, from the patient's own perspective, make existence intolerable, some observers find moral hazards. If dismal quality of life focuses on physical and mental dysfunction, a concern is that the lives of disabled persons generally might be devalued and their morale eroded. Surrogate decision makers for incompetent patients might also be insensitive to the true quality of life as a disabled person, so that vulnerable populations would be endangered by arbitrary determinations. Some sanctity-of-life proponents prefer to protect and support all human existence even in the face of fatal afflictions and severe degeneration.

This tension between sanctity of life and quality of life has surfaced in a number of legal settings. Each of the following sections discusses the resolution of that tension in a particular legal context.

Patients Competent to Make Their Own Decisions

Current law, rooted in concepts of self-determination and bodily integrity, establishes that competent patients are entitled to reject life-sustaining medical intervention. The relevant cases recognize that patients can and often do base their rejection of life-sustaining treatment on quality-of-life factors. That fact emerges most clearly in cases involving severely disabled persons who reject treatment capable of preserving their existences for many years.

The typical situation involves a quadriplegic person dependent on mechanical life support who finds the debilitated existence so painful or demeaning that he or she orders the cessation of life-sustaining measures (*McKay v. Bergstedt,* 1990; *State v. McAfee,* 1989; *Bouvia v. Superior Court,* 1986). Courts uniformly uphold the patient's decision. These courts recognize that patient self-determination encompasses personal values and preferences about whether a prospective medical state is intolerably painful or degrading— that is, constitutes an unacceptable quality of life. A California court explained:

> Since death is the natural conclusion of all life, the precise moment may be less critical than the quality of time preceding it. Especially when the prognosis for full recovery from serious illness or incapacity is dim, the relative balance of benefit and burden must lie within the patient's exclusive estimation: "That personal weighing of values is the essence of self-determination." (*Thor v. Superior Court,* 1993, p. 384)

These same courts reject any notion that judicial acceptance of debilitated patients' fatal decisions weakens respect for life generally or devalues the lives of the disabled. The judges view their decisions as upholding individual autonomy and thereby promoting a critical element of human dignity, rather than as denigrating the sanctity of life.

Incompetent Patients

Many medical patients lack the capacity to make their own decisions about life-sustaining treatment. A surrogate must then act on the patient's behalf. Some commentators oppose the use of quality of life—determining whether a patient's life is "worth" preserving—in decision making for incompetent patients (see Wicclair, pp. 56–60). Again, the concerns include use of utilitarian factors such as economic costs and social unproductivity of the patient. Beyond that, sanctity-of-life proponents fear arbitrary decisions by surrogates who are insensitive to the value of disabled persons' lives or motivated by self-interest.

In some instances, the now-incompetent patient has exercised personal autonomy by previously, when competent, issuing written or oral instructions about terminal medical care. Both courts and legislatures accept in principle this prospective autonomy (though some state legislatures have confined their endorsement of advance medical directives to situations in which the patient is in a "terminal" state). Through advance instructions, people can seek to discontinue medical intervention at a point when their existence becomes intolerable according to their own previously expressed definitions of quality of life.

The situation is more complicated when a now-incompetent patient facing a potentially fatal affliction has never clearly articulated personal values and preferences about life-sustaining medical intervention (Cantor, 2001). Courts in a few states disallow any terminal decision on behalf of an incompetent patient who has never issued advance instructions that clearly and convincingly express the patient's desire to forgo life support in the medical circumstances at hand (*In re Westchester County Medical Center,* 1988; *Cruzan v. Harmon,* 1990; *Mack v. Mack,* 1993; *DeGrella v. Elston,* 1993). A few state courts insist on clear and convincing evidence of the now-incompetent patient's prior wishes only when the patient is still conscious (*Spahn v. Eisenberg,* 1997; *In re Martin,* 1995; *Matter of Wendland,* 2001). These courts all express grave apprehension about allowing surrogates to determine that another person's life is not worth preserving. To foreclose end-of-life decisions grounded on the surrogate's values rather than the patient's, they insist either upon the patient's personal prior assessment of an intolerable quality of life or upon legislative guidance concerning what kinds of deteriorated existence are so undignified as not to be worth preserving.

Insistence upon clear-cut prior instructions as a prerequisite for withdrawal of life support from an incompetent patient disregards certain interests of people who have simply neglected to address the issue of terminal care (as well as those of people who have never been competent). The hazard is that such persons, once afflicted with debilitating medical conditions, will be indefinitely maintained in a status that the patients themselves would deem intolerably painful or demeaning, were they able to express their wishes. In the words of one judge, invariable preservation of life without regard to the incompetent patient's prospective deteriorated status "transforms human beings into unwilling prisoners of medical technology" (*In re Guardianship of L.W.,* 1992, p. 74). To avoid this unfortunate consequence, most courts that have spoken to the issue allow some surrogate decisions to reject life support even in the absence of prior instructions.

Courts subscribing to this position usually articulate a best-interests-of-the-patient standard to guide the surrogate decision maker (*In re Conroy,* 1985; *In re Grant,* 1987). This normally means that in order to justify removal of life support, the "burdens" to the patient must clearly outweigh the "benefits," with irremediable suffering being the primary burden and pleasure being the primary benefit. The relevant cases carefully exclude "social utility" or "personal worth" as factors in the best interests calculus (*Conroy,* pp. 1232–1233). However, the role of quality of life (in the sense of a severely deteriorated and undignified patient status) is uncertain. Quality of life or dignity of the patient is often mentioned as an element within the best-interests formula (*Rasmussen v. Fleming,* 1987; *Grant,* 1987). Indeed, in 1983 the President's Commission for the Study of Ethical Problems in Medicine and Biomedical and Behavioral Research listed "quality as well as the extent of life sustained" as a major component within the best-interests standard. But in application in the reported cases, quality of life has been a determinative factor primarily in the context of permanently unconscious patients.

A few commentators have suggested that the concept of "medically inappropriate" or "futile" treatment ought to fix the bounds of life support for gravely debilitated patients (e.g., Jecker). Futile treatment, in the sense of medical intervention that cannot achieve a particular physiological goal, may be a meaningful and useful concept. But when medical intervention can extend life, albeit debilitated life, the futility concept is much less helpful. A determination that life-sustaining medical intervention is futile really represents a judgment that the quality of life is so dismal that life support ought to be withdrawn as inconsistent with the best interests of the incompetent patient or as contrary to the patient's likely preferences. That determination may be appropriate for surrogate decision makers (in conjunction with medical staff), but it cannot be the province of medical personnel alone (Cranford and Gostin; Veatch and Spicer, 1992).

Patients in a Permanent Vegetative State

A permanently unconscious patient cannot experience suffering or sense the bodily invasions that normally constitute "burdens" to be assessed under a best-interests-of-the-patient standard. At the same time, permanent unconsciousness represents a dehumanizing condition, with the patient indefinitely devoid of sensation, emotion, or human interaction. The vast majority of people contemplating such a status deem it so degrading that they would not want to be medically sustained in that insensate condition. (Some commentators even argue that the legal definition of death should be changed to include permanently vegetative beings, a suggestion that has not yet been adopted [Schrode].)

The clear majority of state court decisions regarding permanently unconscious patients have permitted surrogate decision makers to end life support. Still undecided is the precise legal rationale for this result and whether this line of cases represents use of quality of life as a determinative factor in surrogate decision making.

In some instances, the courts upholding removal of life support rely on prior expressions (whether written or oral) by the now unconscious patient. Those courts simply respect the patient's self-determination and accept the patient's own declaration of permanent unconsciousness as an unacceptable quality of life. These cases sometimes disclaim any surrogate's prerogative to define another person's quality of life as unacceptable (e.g., *DeGrella,* 1993).

A number of cases, however, uphold removal of life support from a permanently unconscious patient even in the absence of prior expressions. Some of these cases include never-competent patients, such as infants. None of the cases relies on the burdens placed upon society or surrounding family by having to care for the insensate patient. Rather, the judges articulate diverse rationales. Some courts use the substituted judgment rationale and accept that the patient, if competent, would have wanted removal of life support (*In re Fiori,* 1995; *Matter of Tavel,* 1995; *In re Guardianship of Jane Doe,* 1992). Other courts purport to apply a best-interests standard but rely on the patient's dismal existence without cognitive function as warranting removal of life support (*In re Guardianship of Crum,* 1992).

Most courts confronting the fate of permanently unconscious patients recognize, either explicitly or implicitly, that the patient's status is so dehumanizing that it represents what most people would regard as an unacceptable quality of life. These courts sometimes demand that the surrogate decision maker not rely on his or her personal views about the value of an unconscious person's life (*Guardianship of L.W.,* 1992). But they do allow for surrogates' reliance on the common judgment that most people wish to avoid a permanently unconscious state (because it lacks dignity and is devoid of value from the perspective of the unconscious patient), as long as the patient's ostensible preferences did not deviate from that norm (*Guardianship of Jane Doe,* 1992).

By contrast, courts in a few jurisdictions have refused to endorse removal of life support from a permanently unconscious patient in the absence of clear-cut prior expressions from that patient (*Cruzan,* 1990; *Mack,* 1993; *DeGrella,* 1993). These courts see the removal decision as a quality-of-life determination that should be made, if at all, pursuant to legislative directions. Some judges also fear that permission to remove life-sustaining medical intervention from the permanently unconscious would ultimately endanger vulnerable populations, such as the severely retarded (*Mack*, 1993; *Guardianship of Jane Doe*, 1992, dissent).

Infants and Young Children

Some congenital anomalies entail a foreshortened lifespan, as well as neurological impairment, physical incapacity, repeated bodily invasion, and suffering so severe that the affected infant is arguably better off dead than alive. As patient autonomy cannot function in this setting, the question becomes whether parents, in conjunction with medical sources, can withhold life support on the basis that the child's life would be so burdened or devoid of personal value that death is preferable. Some commentators oppose this surrogate option, fearing that decisions would be based on prejudice or ignorance about life as a disabled person or concern for parental burdens, rather than burdens upon the child (Field).

Only a small number of cases have been litigated, and the legal picture concerning removal of infants' life support is murky. A few cases use a best-interests standard and rely on likely physical suffering to uphold parental decisions involving withholding of life-sustaining intervention (*In re C.A.*, 1993; *Newmark v. Williams*, 1991). A few cases purport to apply a substituted judgment rationale (reasoning that the child, if competent, would choose death) in order to uphold removal of life support from a permanently vegetative child (*In re L.H.R.*, 1984; *In re Guardianship of Barry*, 1984). In a 2001 case, a court declared that Texas law prohibits any parental effort to remove life support from a newborn (*Miller v. Hospital Corporation of America*).

The best-interests approach seems most plausible, allowing consideration of irremediable suffering and continuous bodily intrusions (Weir). An unresolved issue is the extent to which a dismal quality of life—in the sense of total helplessness and minimal potential for human relationships—can be used legitimately in this best-interests calculus. As a practical matter, it is hard for decision makers to exclude extreme debilitation in applying a best-interests standard. Extreme disability is commonly associated with hardship for the affected child. This element apparently emerges in decision making not only in the United States but also in Australia, Canada, and Great Britain (Charlesworth).

At the same time, stereotypes about disabled persons might prompt inappropriate terminal decisions. This happened in one case involving an infant afflicted with Down syndrome (*Baby Doe v. Hancock County Board of Health*,

1982). One possible limitation appears in U.S. federal statutes and regulations prohibiting hospital discrimination against the disabled and requiring states to protect the interests of disabled infants (see *In re Baby K*, 1993; *Johnson v. Thompson*, 1993). (Note that quality of life issues arose under the Americans with Disabilities Act in the context of state funding priorities under Medicaid.) The effect of these antidiscrimination measures is still unclear. U.S. federal regulations purport to bar quality-of-life considerations in decisions about infants' medical treatment (Clark). Those regulations are applicable to states participating in certain child abuse prevention programs and do not directly apply to individual hospitals. Moreover, decisions about medical treatment ineluctably involve consideration of the hardship and debilitation to be encountered by the patient after treatment. Where a patient's disability is intertwined with the contemplated medical service (as in spina bifida), a nontreatment decision cannot be deemed unlawful discrimination if the decision is grounded on a reasonable assessment of the suffering and hardship to be encountered by the affected individual. The disabled infant's fate is being determined by the same criteria—overall best interests— applicable to any child under treatment.

Conclusion

Diminished quality of life, in the sense of grievous bodily deterioration, is a frequent consideration in shaping the bounds of medical intervention in the dying process. The current challenge for law and medicine is to fix quality-of-life criteria for surrogate decision makers that avoid arbitrariness and abuse toward vulnerable, incapacitated patients. The key, for previously competent patients without advance instructions, should be assessment of which levels of deterioration the great majority of competent persons would consider (for their own dying processes) to be so undignified that they would prefer that life support be withdrawn (Cantor, 1996).

By using this shared vision of dignity as a guideline, decision makers will better replicate the likely wishes of now-incompetent patients, thus ultimately attaining results as consistent as possible with personal preferences. Empirical data for measuring common notions of dignity can be gleaned from public surveys as well as from scrutiny of patterns in advance medical directives. Anyone whose preferences diverge from common notions of dignity can provide individualized instructions reflecting those preferences.

NORMAN L. CANTOR (1995)
REVISED BY AUTHOR

SEE ALSO: *Death, Definition and Determination of: Legal Issues in Pronouncing Death; Disability: Legal Issues; Environmental Policy and Law; Human Rights; Informed Consent: Legal and Ethical Issues of Consent to Healthcare; Medical Futility; Organ Tissue and Procurement: Ethical and Legal Issues Regarding Living Donors; Public Health Law; Right to Die: Policy and Law*

BIBLIOGRAPHY

Baby Doe v. Hancock County Board of Health. 436 N.E.2d 791 (Ind. 1982).

Baby K, In re. 832 F. Supp. 1022 (E.D. Va. 1993) aff'd 16 F.3d 590 (4th Cir. 1994).

Bouvia v. Superior Court (Glenchur). 225 Cal. Rptr. 297 (Dist. Ct. App. 1986).

Buchanan, Allen E., and Brock, Dan W. 1989. *Deciding for Others: The Ethics of Surrogate Decision Making.* New York: Cambridge University Press.

C.A., In re. 1992. 603 N.E. 2d 1171 (Ill. App.); cert. denied, 610 N.E. 2d 1264 (Ill. 1993).

Cantor, Norman L. 1987. *Legal Frontiers of Death and Dying.* Bloomington: Indiana University Press.

Cantor, Norman L. 1990. "The Permanently Unconscious Patient, Non-Feeding, and Euthanasia." *American Journal of Law and Medicine* 15(4): 381–437.

Cantor, Norman L. 1996. "Toward a Constructive Preference Standard for Dying, Previously Competent Patients without Advance Directives." *Rutgers Law Review* 48: 1193–1272.

Cantor, Norman L. 2001. "Twenty-five Years after *Quinlan*: A Review of the Jurisprudence of Death and Dying." *Journal of Law, Medicine, and Ethics* 29(2): 182–196.

Charlesworth, Max. 1993. "Disabled Newborn Infants and the Quality of Life." *Journal of Contemporary Health Law and Policy* 9: 129–137.

Clark, Frank I. 1993. "Withdrawal of Life-Support in the Newborn: Whose Baby Is It?" *Southwestern University Law Review* 23(1): 1–46.

Conroy, In re. 1985. 486 A.2d 1209 (N.J.).

Cranford, Ronald, and Gostin, Lawrence. 1992. "Futility: A Concept in Search of a Definition." *Law, Medicine, and Health Care* 20(4): 307–309.

Cruzan v. Harmon. 760 S.W.2d 408 (Mo. 1988), aff'd 497 U.S. 261 (1990).

DeGrella v. Elston. 858 S.W.2d 698 (Ky. 1993).

Destro, Robert A. 1986. "Quality-of-Life Ethics and Constitutional Jurisprudence: The Demise of Natural Rights and Equal Protection for the Disabled and Incompetent." *Journal of Contemporary Health Law and Policy* 2(2): 71–130.

Dresser, Rebecca S. 1990. "Relitigating Life and Death." *Ohio State Law Journal* 51(2): 425–437.

Dresser, Rebecca S., and Robertson, John A. 1989. "Quality of Life and Non-Treatment Decisions for Incompetent Patients: A Critique of the Orthodox Approach." *Law, Medicine, and Health Care* 17(3): 234–244.

Field, Martha A. 1993. "Killing 'the Handicapped'—Before and after Birth." *Harvard Women's Law Journal* 16(1): 79–138.

Fiori, In re. 1995. 673 A.2d 905 (Pa.).

Grant, In re. 1987. 747 P.2d 445 (Wash.).

Guardianship of Barry, In re. 1984. 445 So. 2d 365 (Fla. Dist. Ct. App.).

Guardianship of Crum, In re. 1991. 580 N.E. 2d 876 (Ohio P. Ct. [Franklin County]).

Guardianship of Jane Doe, In re. 583 N.E.2d 1263 (Mass. 1992); cert. denied sub nom. *Doe v. Gross,* 112 S. Ct. 1512.

Guardianship of L.W., In re. 482 N.W.2d 60 (Wis. 1992).

Jecker, Nancy S. 1991. "Knowing When to Stop: The Limits of Medicine." *Hastings Center Report* 21(3): 5–8.

Johnson v. Thompson. 971 F.2d 1487 (10th Cir. 1992); cert. denied, 113 S. Ct. 1255 (1993).

L.H.R., In re. 1984. 321 S.E.2d 716 (Ga.).

Mack v. Mack. 618 A.2d 744 (Md. 1993).

Martin, In re. 538 N.W.2d 399 (Mich. 1995).

McKay v. Bergstedt. 801 P.2d 617 (Nev. 1990).

Miller v. Hospital Corporation of America. #14–98–00582 (Tex. Civ. App. 2001).

Newmark v. Williams. 588 A.2d 1108 (Del. 1991).

President's Commission for the Study of Ethical Problems in Medicine and Biomedical and Behavioral Research. 1983. *Deciding to Forego Life-Sustaining Treatment: A Report on the Ethical, Medical, and Legal Issues in Treatment Decisions.* Washington, D.C.: Author.

Rasmussen v. Fleming. 741 P.2d 674 (Ariz. 1987).

Rhoden, Nancy K. 1985. "Treatment Dilemmas for Imperiled Newborns: Why Quality of Life Counts." *Southern California Law Review* 58(5): 1283–1347.

Rhoden, Nancy K. 1988. "Litigating Life and Death." *Harvard Law Review* 102(2): 375–446.

Schrode, Kristin. 1995. "Life in Limbo: Revising Policies for Permanently Unconscious Patients." *Houston Law Review* 31: 1609–1679.

Spahn v. Eisenberg. 543 N.W.2d 485 (Wis. 1997).

State v. McAfee. 385 S.E.2d 651 (Ga. 1989).

Strasser, Mark. 1995. "Incompetents and the Right to Die: In Search of Meaningful Standards." *Kentucky Law Journal* 83: 733–791.

Tavel, Matter of. 661 A.2d 1061 (Del. 1995).

Thor v. Superior Court. 855 P.2d 375 (Cal. 1993).

Veatch, Robert M. 1989. *Death, Dying, and the Biological Revolution: Our Last Quest for Responsibility,* rev. edition. New Haven, CT: Yale University Press.

Veatch, Robert M., and Spicer, Carol M. 1989. *Abating Treatment with Critically Ill Patients: Ethical and Legal Limits to the*

Medical Prolongation of Life. New York: Oxford University Press.

Veatch, Robert M., and Spicer, Carol M. 1992. "Medically Futile Care: The Role of the Physician in Setting Limits." *American Journal of Law and Medicine* 18(1–2): 15–36.

Weir, Robert F. 1984. *Selective Treatment of Handicapped Newborns: Moral Dilemmas in Neonatal Medicine.* New York: Oxford University Press.

Wendland, Matter of. 2001. 28 P.3d 181 (Calif.).

Westchester County Medical Center (O'Connor), In re. 1988. 531 N.E.2d 607 (N.Y.).

Wicclair, Mark. 1993. *Ethics and the Elderly.* New York: Oxford University Press.

Yuen, Michele. 1992. "Letting Daddy Die: Adopting New Standards for Surrogate Decisionmaking." *University of California at Los Angeles Law Review* 39(3): 581–632.

LIFE, SANCTITY OF

• • •

The sanctity of life is the theological or philosophical understanding that all human life has an inherent dignity, worth and sacredness that sets it apart from all other beings within the world. This perspective does not assert that human life is sacred in the sense of being divine, but that its very essence is distinct within the biological world and of incalculable worth, thus warranting protection throughout the course of its entire existence. The sanctity of life as a doctrine has both religious and philosophical roots and is applied to a wide range of bioethical issues such as abortion, euthanasia, genetic engineering, and cadaver organ transplants. Advocates often consider this understanding of human life to be the foundation of moral civilization, and have applied it to issues outside of bioethics such as human rights, suicide, and care for the poor and weak in society.

Religious Foundations

Various religious traditions have articulated and defended a concept of human sanctity in reference to their overarching worldview conceptions. In the Hebrew tradition the doctrine is rooted in human creation in the image of God: "Then God said, 'Let us make humankind in our image, according to our likeness; and let them have dominion over the fish of the sea, and over the birds of the air, and over the cattle, and over all the wild animals of the earth, and over

every creeping thing that creeps upon the earth.' So God created humankind in his image, in the image of God he created them; male and female he created them" (Genesis 1:26–27, NRSV). The creation in God's image became then for the Hebraic tradition the foundation for protecting human life and for justice when it was de-sacralized (Genesis 9:6). The duty to protect human life extended to the necessities for life, such as food and clothing (Deuteronomy 24:6,12–13), and especially to justice for the poor and disenfranchised (Leviticus 19:15, 33–34).

Within the Jewish tradition the taking or defacing of human life is morally wrong because it violates a sacredness that "inheres in life itself, and that life, by its very being calls forth an appropriate human response, whether of veneration or restraint" (Kass, p. 235). The tradition does not teach that humans are God, but rather, "To be an image is also to be different from that of which one is an image. Man is, at most a mere likeness of God" (Kass, p. 242).

Jakobovits notes that in Jewish law and moral teaching, "The value of human life is infinite and beyond measure, so that any part of life—even if only an hour or a second—is of precisely the same worth as seventy years of it" (Jakobovits, p. 380). In contrast to Roman Catholic thinking and some Protestants, this intrinsic value does not extend to the life in the womb. "An unborn fetus in Jewish law is not considered a person … until it has been born" (Rosner, p. 136). For most Jewish scholars this does not give automatic sanction to abortion, for as Rosner points out, "The destruction of the unborn fetus, although legally not considered murder, can be considered to constitute 'moral murder'. The unborn baby has a heartbeat, a brain, arms, legs, and nearly everything with which a healthy newborn baby is endowed" (Rosner, p. 146). Within the various branches of Judaism there is wide variation on the issue of abortion, though fairly uniform agreement that a person is not present until birth. At the other end of life, Jewish moral teaching repudiates active euthanasia or assisted suicide on the grounds that it cheapens life and constitutes murder.

The Christian tradition, incorporating and building from the Hebrew Scriptures, similarly articulates the sanctity of human life on the basis of creation in God's image. This has not only been a warrant for rejecting the willful taking of human life, but also for treating every human life with respect and dignity. Thus, the epistle of James calls for restraint of the human tongue on the basis of this foundation: "No one can tame the tongue—a restless evil, full of deadly poison. With it we bless the lord and Father, and with it we curse those who are made in the likeness of God" (James 3:8–9). The application of human dignity rooted in the *imago dei* is often extended more broadly to social realities, in that it forms the foundation and the ideal of inalienable rights and intrinsic human values that have long been articulated in Western cultures.

The Christian church has also grounded the sanctity of human life in the doctrine of the incarnation, God taking on human flesh in the person of Jesus Christ. As theologian Karl Barth put it, "The respect of life which becomes a command in the recognition of the union of God with humanity in Jesus Christ has an incomparable power and width" (Barth, p. 339). Barth and other theologians argue that the very fact that God became human in Jesus of Nazareth and then died for human beings is an affirmation that human life has great worth and value.

The sanctity of life tradition stemming from Judeo-Christian sources has historically argued that the value of human life is not dependent upon its being valued by others or by the presence of certain functional capabilities such as rationality or relationality. Rather, sanctity and dignity inhere within the human person. Thus, with regard to bioethical issues of life and death the late Protestant ethicist Paul Ramsey argued against a benign neglect of infants with severe physiological handicaps on the grounds that their value is not dependent on extrinsic characteristics. He noted, for example, that a Tay-Sachs baby is born destined to die, but their dying is no different from our own dying. "For about the first six months it is like any other baby; living and growing and presumably enjoying human existence as any other infant would. In religious perspective there is no reason for saying those six months are a life span of lesser worth to God than living seventy years before the onset of irreversible degeneration" (Ramsey, p. 191).

The Roman Catholic Church has been without doubt the most consistent voice in defense of the sanctity of life. In the words of the Church's catechism, "Human life is sacred because from its beginning it involves the creative action of God and it remains forever in a special relationship with the Creator.... No one can under any circumstance claim for himself the right directly to destroy an innocent human being" (*Catechism*, p. 544). As Pellegrino and Thomasma put it, "The person is to be affirmed as a person, possessing dignity simply because he or she is a person. Man is a personal being, created and loved by a personal God and destined to be united face-to-face with the Creator" (Pellegrino and Thomasma, p. 143).

The Roman Catholic application of this doctrine extends not only to abortion and euthanasia, but also to matters such as research on human subjects. "Research or experimentation on the human being cannot legitimate acts that are in themselves contrary to the dignity of persons and to the moral law. The subjects' potential consent does not justify such acts" (*Catechism*, p. 553).

The sanctity of human life is by no means only found in the Jewish/Christian traditions, though these traditions have given the most explicit renditions of the doctrine due to their common theology of creation. Traditional and contemporary Islamic teaching does not generally use the language "sanctity of human life," but there is a conception of the sacredness of human life: "And do not kill anyone whom Allah has made sacred, except for a just cause" (Qur'an 17:33). In the contemporary setting the Islamic Code of Medical Ethics states that "Human life is sacred...and should not be willfully taken except upon the indications specified in Islamic jurisprudence, all of which are outside the domain of the medical profession" (van Bommel, p. 211). A sense of sanctity seems to be implied in the teaching that humankind is granted a vice-regency (*khalifa*) by Allah, but that role must be carried out consistent with the commandments of Islamic moral law. In the Islamic tradition ensoulment or becoming a person takes place at 120 days in the gestation period. Thus, "It can be said that although abortion in the first 120 days of gestation is morally wrong in Islamic law, it is not considered to be murder or even killing. Rather, abortion in this early period would fall into the categories of bodily injury or breaking of an oath, both of which require some type of penance" (Rogers, p. 129).

Philosophical Foundations

The sanctity of life doctrine is not limited to religious foundations. Various philosophers have attempted to articulate the unique, intrinsic value of human beings on the basis of experience and/or reason. Immanuel Kant, for example, argued that a person should be treated as an end, not as means to an end. The foundation for this assertion is that humans are rational and autonomous beings who thus possess a freedom which must be protected. Human freedom for Kant is not a license to do with life as we please, but rather a warrant for maintaining and protecting human dignity as an absolute inner worth. The problem in Kant's account, for those who today affirm the sanctity of life, is his insistence on rationality as its foundation; for if rationality is no longer present it would seem that human sanctity or personhood is no longer present, if indeed rationality is its foundation and primary indicator.

In the contemporary scene Arthur Dyck has argued for the sanctity of life on the grounds that it is a necessary prerequisite for communal life in society. As Dyck sees it, "Our lives did not and could not originate and persist because we valued it but because someone else valued it, parents to begin with, but also a whole network of individuals and groups. Our lives depended upon and continue to depend on the persistence of the moral behavior that makes life, and the communal protection of it, possible at all" (p. 52). Killing, including oneself, is thus morally wrong because it undermines mutual moral responsibilities which are necessary for human life to exist.

Humans throughout history, says Dyck, have had a natural love of life that has been enshrined even in law as a protection of the sanctity of human life. He notes, for example, that the U.S. Supreme Court in 1997 rejected the individual's right to exercise control over one's life to the point of seeking assistance in suicide. In rejecting the right to assisted suicide the Court appealed to the American Bar Association's Model Penal Code: "The interests in the sanctity of life are represented in the criminal homicide laws" (p. 59). Dyck, therefore, concludes that there is a moral structure for life's worth and protection, which is based legally, not on religious doctrines, but on the necessary requirements for communal life in society. "If laws were permitted to embody the idea that in some circumstances life loses its worth, or that some people lack sufficient worth to have their lives protected, individuals would no longer enjoy equal protection of the law so far as their lives are concerned" (p. 60).

Challenges to the Sanctity of Life

There have been various challenges to the sanctity of life doctrine from both religious and philosophical frameworks. These challenges have invariably led to different conclusions on a host of bioethical issues.

One set of challenges has been metaphysical, arguing that the human person is not inherently different in nature from the rest of biological life. Thus, there is no warrant for a notion of exclusive human sanctity. Peter Singer, for example, argues against speciesism, the view that *Homo sapiens* life is to be valued above all others. "The wrongness of inflicting pain on a being cannot depend on the being's species, nor can the wrongness of killing it. The biological facts upon which the boundary of our species is drawn do not have moral significance" (p. 128). Thus, he contends that the sanctity of life doctrine is false, for there is no special value to a being by virtue of its species identity.

In contrast to the sanctity of life doctrine, Singer argues that the primary moral criterion for determining the protection of life is its ability to experience pain and pleasure. There are many beings that are capable of experiencing pain and pleasure who do not fit the ordinary conception of personhood (i.e., animals), and there are beings who are

often considered persons that are not capable of experiencing pain and pleasure (i.e., some newborn infants and severely mentally disabled adults). Thus, says Singer, "If we value our own pleasures ... then the universal aspect of ethical judgments requires us to extend our positive evaluation of our own experience of these pleasures to the similar experiences of all who can experience them" (p. 139). This leads Singer to a strong affirmation of animal rights on the one hand, and to a belief that in some cases deformed children may be euthanized.

Peter Singer utilizes a utilitarian framework for his ethical judgments, but his ethics, including his rejection of the sanctity of life doctrine, ultimately rests on metaphysical commitments about the nature of life. Sanctity of life adherents note that the root difference between Singer and themselves is distinct foundational world views.

A second challenge to the sanctity of human life commitment is theological in nature. Some have argued that the conception overstates the nature of human essence and is idolatrous in its insistence that human life is sacred, an attribute reserved only for God. Margaret Mohrmann believes that the notion of sanctity of life is intrinsically idolatrous. "Theologically speaking there can be no argument based on a purported 'sanctity of life', both because there is no 'life' as such and because we are on very shaky ground when we speak of anything or anyone but God as unqualifiedly sacred" (Mohrmann, p. 22). She notes that "Christians do not believe that God is somehow generically present in something called 'life'. We believe that God is present in individual human persons" (p. 30). And God alone is sacred.

Adherents of the sanctity of life perspective generally counter that such conceptions are caricatures of their understanding. They believe that sanctity of life in no way implies that human life is sacred in the sense of being divine, but rather is set apart by God and hence distinct within the created order.

A third challenge to sanctity of life thinking is the charge of medical vitalism, the notion that all means must be utilized to keep a human being alive in the face of death. Vitalism is the view that because human life has incalculable worth, there must be a commitment to keeping patients alive at all costs. Many critics of the sanctity of life perspective have assumed that vitalism is an inherent part of the tradition.

But advocates of human dignity and worth respond that vitalism is not implied in the commitment to human sacredness, for there is natural cycle to human life, even under divine providence, that must be accepted. Gilbert Meilaender, a strong advocate of the sanctity of human life, notes that "we indefinitely transcend our historical location. But it is as embodied creatures that we do so, and our person cannot be divorced from the body and its natural trajectory. This is not vitalism; it is the wisdom of the body" (Meilaender, p. 22).

A fourth challenge to sanctity of life formulations is the emphasis on quality of life as an ethical criterion. In contrast to the assumption that all human life has an inherent value and dignity, a number of bioethicists have suggested that quality of life measures ought to be determinative in ethical dilemmas throughout the course of life. Joseph Fletcher a number of years ago argued that for one to be considered a person, four functional traits must be present: neocortical function, self-awareness, relational ability, and happiness (1974, pp. 4–7). There is a clear rational bias in this formulation of personhood, as he questions whether one with an IQ below 40 is a person and concludes that those below 20 are clearly not persons. As Fletcher sees it, "Mere biological life, before minimal intelligence is achieved or after it is lost irretrievably, is without personal status" (1972, p. 1).

Other bioethicists and philosophers have argued similarly for quality of life indices over against sanctity of life. Mary Anne Warren, for example, believes that we can never get away from some notion of speciesism (contra Singer), but she does believe that we must make distinctions within humans on the basis of their capacities. Warren sees two ways in which we speak of humans: humans in the genetic sense, and humans in the moral sense. Being a member of the human species does not ensure that one is human in the moral sense. Warren believes that inclusion in the moral community of humanity entails qualities such as consciousness, reason, self-motivated activity, self-awareness, and the ability to communicate (pp. 457–458).

Sanctity of life advocates counter that while quality of life may be a medical category used to determine when treatment is futile, it is not an ethical category to determine human dignity or personhood.

Applications of Sanctity of Life

The sanctity of human life is not the only ethical norm utilized by its advocates. Nonetheless, they claim, it is a foundational assumption for bioethical issues surrounding life, death, and human treatment.

One of the applications of the doctrine is in the ethics of abortion. Sanctity of human life does not automatically imply that a human or person is present from the moment of conception, but its advocates tend in that direction because human value and dignity is not dependent on functionality. Continuity in human life is usually emphasized, and thus the protection of a fetus or human embryo is just as important as protecting a healthy, mature adult. As a result, most advocates of the sanctity of human life reject abortion on demand and the use of embryonic stem cells in research and therapy.

Sanctity of life is also applied to death and dying issues. Advocates, as noted above, do not generally espouse vitalism and the necessity of futile treatment, but they do raise strong ethical objections to euthanasia or assisted suicide, contending that allowing to die and causing to die are not identical. Sanctity of human life proponents emphasize the role of palliative medicine and compassionate presence as is provided by hospice care in the face of pain and impending death.

Other applications of the sanctity of human life include organ transplants and genetic engineering. In transplantation one of the crucial issues is triage, the allocation of scare resources. Advocates of human sanctity argue that justice in this realm should not depend on merit or the way one is valued in society, but rather must entail a blind-folded egalitarian justice which gives equal opportunity to all potential candidates. With regard to genetic engineering, human sanctity usually means not transgressing one's essential humanness and not utilizing experimental measures for the sake of knowledge, at the expense of human dignity.

In summary, the doctrine of the sanctity of human life teaches that "all human beings possess equal dignity and worth regardless of the level of maturity they have achieved.… Thus, all humans—not just those who are rational or self-conscious—retain the right to life" (Hui, p. 148).

DENNIS HOLLINGER

BIBLIOGRAPHY

Barth, Karl. 1961. *Church Dogmatics*, III-4. Edinburgh: T&T Clarke.

Catechism of the Catholic Church, 2nd edition. 1997. Washington, D.C.: United States Catholic Conference.

Dyck, Arthur J. 2002. *Life's Worth: The Case Against Assisted Suicide*. Grand Rapids: Eerdmans Press.

Fletcher, Joseph. 1972. "Indicators of Humanhood: A Tentative Profile of Man." *Hastings Center Report* 2(5): 1–3.

Fletcher, Joseph. 1974. "Four Indicators of Humanhood: The Inquiry Matures." *Hastings Center Report* 4(6): 4–7.

Harris, John. 1999. "The Concept of the Person and the Value of Life." *Kennedy Institute of Ethics Journal* 9(4): 293–308.

Hui, Edwin C. 2002. *At the Beginning of Life: Dilemmas in Theological Bioethics.* Downers Grove, IL: InterVarsity Press.

Jakobovits, I. 1979. "Medical Experimentation on Humans in Jewish Law." In *Jewish Bioethics,* ed. Fred Rosner and J. D. Bleich. New York: Hebrew Publishing Co.

Kass, Leon R. 2002. *Life, Liberty and the Defense of Dignity: The Challenge for Bioethics.* San Francisco: Encounter Books.

Meilaender, Gilbert. 1995. "Terra es Animata: On Having a Life." In *Politics and the Human Body,* ed. Jean Bethke Elshtain, and Cloyd, J. Timothy. Nashville: Vanderbilt University Press.

Mohrmann, Margaret E. 1995. *Medicine as Ministry: Reflections on Suffering, Ethics, and Hope.* Cleveland: The Pilgrim Press.

Pellegrino, Edmund, and Thomasma, David. 1996. *The Christian Virtues in Medical Practice.* Washington, D.C.: Georgetown University Press.

Ramsey, Paul. 1978. *Ethics at the Edges of Life: Medical and Legal Intersections.* New Haven: Yale University Press.

Rogers, Therisa. 1999. "The Islamic Ethics of Abortion in the Traditional Islamic Sources." *The Muslim World* LXXX(2): 122–129.

Rosner, Fred. 1991. *Modern Medicine and Jewish Ethics,* 2nd edition. New York: Yeshiva University Press.

Singer, Peter. 2000. *Writings on an Ethical Life.* New York: Harper Collins.

von Bommel, Abdulwahid. 1997. "Quality or Sanctity of Life?" In *Holy Scriptures in JudaismChristianity and Islam: Hermeneutics, Values, and Society,* ed. Hendrik M. Vroom and Jerald D. Gort. Atlanta: Ropodi.

Walters, James W. 1997. *What is a Person?: An Ethical Exploration.* Urbana, IL: University of Illinois Press.

Warren, Mary Anne. 2001. "On the Moral and Legal Status of Abortion." In *Biomedical Ethics,* 5th edition, ed. Thomas A. Mappes, and David Degrazia. New York: McGraw-Hill.

LIFESTYLES AND PUBLIC HEALTH

• • •

The people of every nation would be healthier if they adopted healthier lifestyles. Ninety percent of those who die of lung cancer would not have contracted the disease if they had not smoked. Exercise, sensible diet, and compliance with treatment for high blood pressure can, and do, prevent countless episodes of cardiovascular disease. Practicing safe sex reduces the risk of contracting AIDS. Use of seat belts and motorcycle helmets lowers the chance of injury from accidents on the road.

The prospect of improving health and reducing illness through changes in living habits rather than through curative healthcare is attractive on a number of grounds. Since it is preventive, it avoids the distress of disease; side effects and iatrogenic consequences may be fewer; cost may be lower; and the healthier ways of living may be rewarding in their own right. For these reasons, any government that failed to promote healthy lifestyles could be faulted on ethical grounds.

Nevertheless, the encouragement of healthier lifestyles has drawn moral criticism in the literatures of bioethics and health policy. The chief concern is that governmental (and even private) attempts to bring about changes in living habits will encroach on personal liberty or privacy. A second complaint is that lifestyle-change programs may have the wrong motives, and may have undesirable social and psychological effects.

Health versus Liberty

INTERVENTION: WHAT JUSTIFICATION? Nearly everything we do affects health in some way, if only because the time spent could be devoted to exercise or other health-enhancing behavior. The notion of unhealthy lifestyles, however, is typically associated with a small number of habits. Smoking, the leading killer in the United States, always takes first place, closely followed by alcohol and other drug abuse, lack of exercise, and being overweight. Other risk factors affected by individual choice veer toward the medical, including behavioral change intended to control serum cholesterol and hypertension, perhaps including compliance with doctors' orders. Construed still more broadly, a "healthy lifestyle" would include living in a region not plagued by pollution or recurring natural disasters; avoidance of unsafe jobs; and purchasing the safest cars and appliances.

Attempts to change unhealthy behavior through education and exhortation are relatively unproblematic from the moral point of view. But these measures are less likely to be effective than programs that seek to influence behavior more directly through penalties, taxes, restrictions, or prohibitions. These, however, involve or border on coercion, and in some cases, as with sexual behavior, they necessarily intrude into a person's most private domains.

The fact that good health may be valued by every person does not by itself justify these interventions, since for some people the health risks seem to be less important than the benefits derived from the risk-taking behavior. Few would seriously assert that eating rich ice cream or smoking falls within the category of fundamental human rights, but each encroachment on individual autonomy is commonly regarded as standing in need of justification, especially in the United States, which has a cultural history marked by an ideology of individualism. Three kinds of justification have been offered for programs aiming to change lifestyles: (1) paternalist concern for the person's good; (2) protection of others from burdens involuntarily imposed by the risk-taking behavior; and (3) the public's stake in the nation's health.

PATERNALIST JUSTIFICATIONS. In the United States, paternalist justifications are rarely provided as such. Though exceptions and counterexamples abound, lip service is still paid to the tradition of John Stuart Mill's *On Liberty*. It is easier to argue for motorcycle helmet laws as a means of reducing the costs of medical care than as a means of protecting human life, despite the greater importance of the latter. When paternalism is explicitly defended, however, it is usually on the grounds that the choices the paternalistic policy prohibits are not fully voluntary ones: Bad habits, such as smoking and overeating, may be sustained by addiction or genetic predisposition. This "soft" paternalism avoids the need to argue for the "hard" paternalist view that even fully voluntary choices may be overruled if the state concludes that the individual might benefit.

For many unhealthy habits, the argument that the behavior is not fully voluntary is easy to make. The individual choice may be determined by chemical, psychological, or social causes. Once a person is addicted to nicotine, it is extremely difficult to stop smoking, as millions of unhappy smokers know; the same holds true for alcoholics and those addicted to legal or illegal drugs. The original decision to try cigarettes, alcohol, or drugs is often made during adolescence, when the individual's ability to resist peer pressure is typically weak.

Nevertheless, the soft paternalist argument faces a number of objections. Not all unhealthy choices are obviously involuntary. The decision to engage in unprotected sex, for example, may be the result of partner coercion, or inner compulsion or denial, but it may also stem from the individual's dislike of condoms or not having a condom. Moreover, even the person whose behavior is shaped by an addiction may be capable of deciding to seek professional help in breaking the addiction. The decision to forgo seeking help, a "second-order" choice about choice, is not necessarily rendered involuntary by the "first-order" addiction. In these instances, paternalistic intervention will be of the hard variety, which involves the authorities acting on the principle that their goals for the individual should be imposed on the individual's own goals.

Intervention aimed at altering lifestyle choices on paternalist grounds may overemphasize the goal of health at the expense of other goals. If the paternalist justification is strongest when the unhealthy choices are least voluntary, these may also be the occasions when the choices are most difficult to influence, and the degree of coercion required may be objectionable in itself. Smokers subjected to very high excise taxes, for example, may suffer from the taxes without giving up cigarettes. Finally, the behavior in question may be difficult to change without considerable meddling in the individual's culture and milieu, whether these champion "wine, women, and song," or risk taking and violence, or quiet (and unathletic) contemplation. The life of the fitness-loving moderate is not for everyone, even if it is most conducive to long life and good health.

FAIR DISTRIBUTION OF BURDENS. Mill's principle of liberty sought to limit intervention to the protection of others from the effects of one's own actions; "self-regarding" behavior is thus the domain of the individual, while others have a say in the regulation of "other-regarding" behavior. Critics have long noted that the boundary is indistinct; nearly everything we do has effects on others. Sexual behavior, the most private of acts, is not at all self-regarding in the era of the AIDS epidemic. And since few people pay all their healthcare bills out of pocket, any behavior that necessitates care will impose a financial burden on other parties.

If these behavioral choices are to be protected, they will have to find some shelter other than Mill's principle. In the case of AIDS, an argument might be made that intrusive regulation would violate a right of privacy, where "private" does not mean "self-regarding" (AIDS transmission is anything but that) but "intimate" or "personal." This right might not be defensible in light of the seriousness of the AIDS epidemic, however; and in any case, other unhealthy habits and choices—for example, smoking, which incurs risks to others through passive smoke inhalation—fall outside of this personal zone. Since there is no general right of liberty when our choices affect the lives of others, the individual's prerogative to maintain unhealthy practices must be decided on other grounds.

Paternalist arguments aim at justifying interventions that seek to curb unhealthy behavior. Arguments that point to the burden of unhealthy behavior for other people, however, may or may not share this aim. They may indeed seek to justify curbs on the behavior in order to forestall the imposition of burdens. But this can also be accomplished by requiring the individual to pay his or her own way, perhaps through excise taxes, without any diminution of the unhealthy behavior. Finally, the individual whose choices result in illness may be made to pay for his or her own healthcare, or to forfeit any claim on the resources of others, or, at the least, to be placed at the end of the line when resources are scarce.

These steps represent a particular understanding of distributive justice. They seek to impose the true costs of choices on the one who chooses, so that these costs will be taken into account at the moment of choice. Those who believe that the welfare state should assist its citizens in meeting their basic needs, in this view, should not regard all needs as equal. Unhealthy lifestyles create avoidable needs, and individuals should be held responsible for these choices. Those who refuse to take care of themselves, in this view, forfeit at least some of the liberties (to individual choice) and the entitlements (to help, on an equal footing, in time of need) that others deserve.

As with the paternalist justification for intervention in lifestyle choices, this argument concerning the fair sharing of burdens faces a number of objections. One might argue that distinguishing between patients with similar healthcare needs on the basis of personal responsibility for illness introduces a concept of fault more at home in the legal world than in the system of healthcare. Treating all patients according to need, without regard to such factors as status, ability to pay, or fault, is a powerful way of affirming the importance of those aspects of people in virtue of which they are equal, relative to those that divide, distinguish, and rank us. This equality is important both to us as patients and to doctors and other healthcare providers, whose first instinct should be compassionate response to human suffering.

On more technical grounds, the burden-sharing argument rests the case for intervention into unhealthy lifestyles on the outcome of an economic calculation: that the habit in question incurs a net cost. The problem is that those who die prematurely because of unhealthy habits avoid burdening others with the cost of maintaining them in their old age. Economists have long debated whether smokers burden others or relieve others of a financial burden of care; the answer may vary by country, depending on such variables as the cost of healthcare and the cost of living. If there are places in which smokers actually save society money, the burden-sharing argument would entail penalties for those who do not smoke.

Care must be taken, moreover, in stating the burden-sharing argument. Insurance, including health insurance, protects against risk, but it also can make risk taking less unwise. Those Americans who play football, for example, can regard America's healthcare system as a partial safety net; the sport would be too dangerous for many without it. In this light, the burden-sharing argument might succeed in justifying special and higher insurance premiums for risk takers, but unless the risk takers refused to pay these fees, it would not justify curbs on the actual risk taking. Even the special fees would be unjustified if there were rough equivalence in the degree of risk taken by a large number of coinsureds, one person's motorcycle riding offsetting another's sedentary library dwelling.

PUBLIC HEALTH. The third justification for intervention on behalf of healthier lifestyles points to the collective health of the public as a common good. In material terms, a healthy population enhances economic productivity and the nation's capacity to defend itself. General health also provides some degree of protection from the spread of infectious disease. Theorists of public health have contended, moreover, that the *public health,* meaning the sum of each person's health, constitutes a further goal of public policy that can be distinguished from both the paternalist and the burden-sharing arguments.

Another feature of the public-health perspective is the "prevention paradox," the observation that many critical prevention policies affecting lifestyles produce large aggregate savings in lives but little demonstrable benefit to each individual. For example, seat-belt policies may save thousands of lives nationally but only marginally reduce the risk for each individual who drives. Similarly, changes in fat intake will strongly reduce the number who die prematurely from heart disease but affect the chances of each individual only slightly.

The prevention paradox thus arises from the fact that even small changes in the behaviors of tens of millions of individuals involved in low to moderate lifestyle risks avert thousands of deaths. The prevention paradox further underscores the emphasis in public health on rates of disease and deaths averted, and the difficulty of producing mass changes in behaviors through voluntary measures alone.

Far more important than the government's stake in a healthy work force is the centuries-old tradition of governmental responsibility to protect the health and safety of the public, construed as a public or common good. The public-health perspective is rooted in the democratic and constitutional tradition of assigning to elected officials and members of executive agencies responsibilities for protecting the common good, where this has been interpreted by courts as involving the protection of health and safety (and morals as well, which accounts for the long entanglement of public health and moralism). The public-health or regulatory power of government has long been justified on the grounds that reasonable restrictions on liberty and property, as weighed by the legislature, to promote the common good are the very essence of the regulatory power. This tradition is rooted in theories of government and the duties of citizens that antedate the rise of concerns with paternalism and Mill's famous essay.

Motives and Effects of Intervention Programs

The preceding discussion of arguments for intervention in unhealthy lifestyles has taken the arguments at face value. Critics, however, have suggested that the real motivations for these policies are usually unannounced. The actual motivation, in this view, is moral—or, to be more precise, moralistic, proceeding from a rarely examined and rarely defended set of moral premises. Once these are made explicit, according to the critics, both the motive and the policies are rendered less attractive.

One sign that lifestyle intervention has a moralistic motive, according to critics, is the selectivity of targets. Many kinds of behavior have negative health effects that are not equally addressed. Promiscuity, lack of exercise, and being overweight are merely the medieval vices of lust, sloth, and gluttony. These habits have negative effects on health, to be sure; but so do other kinds of behavior not viewed as vices. Childbirth, for example, presents a certain level of risk to every woman and a decided risk for some; but because it is socially approved, there is no thought of penalizing, taxing, or discouraging the behavior. The burden-sharing argument presents itself as a neutral act of accounting; but, in the critics' view, it is actually concerned with the costs of behavior deemed undesirable on moral grounds while it tolerates behavior of which it approves, no matter how costly.

The moral perspective from which lifestyle intervention is urged, moreover, has been criticized as *healthism,* a parochial view that elevates health from a self-interested goal to a virtue. In this light, "personal responsibility for health" stems not from the need to avoid burdening others with the costs of one's care but from the conviction that healthy people (at least, those who choose health) are better people, morally speaking. This perspective is also said to be linked to an ideology that emphasizes the degree to which one's state of health is a function of choices one makes, rather than the whims of nature or the safety of one's environment and workplace.

One of the most frequent complaints about the lifestyle debate is that it is used to "blame the victim" and undercut the justification for collective action. Thus, those who wish to restrict in various ways the availability of alcohol or tobacco, to limit overall use of these risky products, meet counterclaims that these are not problems of regulation but of individual responsibility and education. The advocates for regulation, in effect challenging the motivation of this view, argue that their opponents do not really want to see a well-financed campaign against smoking and drinking but want no official action at all. Instead, they want wider acceptance of the view that these are problems that will be resolved only when people take more responsibility for their own health and safety.

Conclusion

Though this entry has dwelt on the difficulties in making a convincing case for intervening in unhealthy lifestyles, the collective weight of such lifestyles should not be exaggerated. Much of the bioethical literature on lifestyles indicates that the choices posing the greatest problem for public-health authorities are those which involve personal or intimate behavior, are entirely self-regarding, and represent fully voluntary behavior. Little in our behavioral repertoire falls in this narrowly defined category, however, and those who wish to pursue this promising avenue to health can enter the argument on an even footing.

DANIEL WIKLER
DAN E. BEAUCHAMP (1995)
BIBLIOGRAPHY REVISED

SEE ALSO: *AIDS; Autonomy; Coercion; Economic Concepts in Healthcare; Freedom and Free Will; Healthcare Resources, Allocation of; Justice; Paternalism; Public Health Law; Responsibility*

BIBLIOGRAPHY

Alibhai, S. M. 1995. "Caring for Unhealthy Lifestyles." *Canadian Medical Association Journal* 152(4): 469–470.

Beauchamp, Dan E. 1985a. "Community: The Neglected Tradition of Public Health." *Hastings Center Report* 15(6): 28–36.

Beauchamp, Dan E. 1985b. *The Health of the Republic: Epidemics, Medicine, and Moralism as Challenges to Democracy.* Philadelphia: Temple University Press. See especially chaps. 3 and 4.

Beauchamp, Dan E., and Steinbock, Bonnie, eds. 1999. *New Ethics for the Public's Health.* New York: Oxford University Press.

Berkman, Lisa F., and Kawachi, Ichiro, eds. 2000. *Social Epidemiology.* New York: Oxford University Press.

Buchanan, David Ross. 2000. *An Ethic for Health Promotion: Rethinking the Sources of Human Well-Being.* New York: Oxford University Press.

Buve, A.; Laga, M.; Remes, P.; Padian, N.; and Morison, L. 2000. "Ethics of Mass STD Treatment." *Lancet* 356(9235): 1115–1116.

Darragh, Martina, and McCarrick, Pat Milmoe. 1998. "Public Health Ethics: Health by the Numbers." *Kennedy Institute of Ethics Journal* 8(3): 339–358.

Feinberg, Joel. 1986. *Harm to Self.* New York: Oxford University Press.

Gostin, L. O., and Javitt, G. H. 2001. "Health Promotion and the First Amendment: Government Control of the Informational Environment." *Milbank Quarterly* 79(4): 547–578, iv.

Hodgson, Thomas A. 1992. "Cigarette Smoking and Lifetime Medical Expenditures." *Milbank Quarterly* 70(1): 81–125.

Laumann, Edward O., and Michael, Robert T. 2000. *Sex, Love, and Health in America: Private Choices and Public Policies.* Chicago: University of Chicago Press.

Leichter, Howard M. 1991. *Free to Be Foolish: Politics and Health Promotion in the United States and Great Britain.* Princeton, NJ: Princeton University Press.

O'Rourke, A. 2001. "Dealing with Prejudice." *Journal of Medical Ethics* 27(2): 123–125.

Panter-Brick, C., and Worthman, C. M., eds. 1999. *Hormones, Health, and Behavior: A Socio-Ecological and Lifespan Perspective.* New York: Cambridge University Press.

Perkins, Elizabeth R.; Wright, Linda; and Simnett, Ina, eds. 1999. *Evidence-Based Health Promotion.* Hoboken, NJ: John Wiley & Son Ltd.

Poland, Blake D.; Rootman, Irving; and Green, Lawrence W., eds. 1999. *Settings for Health Promotion: Linking Theory and Practice.* Thousand Oaks, CA: Sage Publications, Inc.

Rippe, James M., ed. 1999. *Lifestyle Medicine.* Boston, MA: Blackwell Science Inc.

Rose, Geoffrey. 1985. "Sick Individuals and Sick Populations." *International Journal of Epidemiology* 14(1): 32–38.

Rothstein, Mark A. 2002. "Rethinking the Meaning of Public Health." *Journal of Law, Medicine and Ethics* 30(2): 144–149.

Thorogood, Margaret, and Coombes, Yolande, eds. 2002. *Evaluating Health Promotion: Practice and Methods.* New York: Oxford University Press.

Veatch, Robert M. 1980. "Voluntary Risks to Health: The Ethical Issues." *Journal of the American Medical Association* 243(1): 50–55.

Wikler, Daniel I. 1978. "Persuasion and Coercion for Health: Ethical Issues in Government Efforts to Change Lifestyles." *Milbank Memorial Fund Quarterly/Health and Society* 56(3): 303–333.

LIFE-SUSTAINING TREATMENT AND EUTHANASIA

• • •

I. Ethical Aspects

II. Historical Aspects

I. ETHICAL ASPECTS

Ethical and legal norms exist in virtually all societies to help protect human life and regulate when taking or not prolonging life is ethically permissible. In most Western societies, the Judeo-Christian religious tradition has given great importance to the sanctity of life. Modern medicine has also gained extraordinary new powers to prolong life. Within the last few decades, medical treatments such as kidney dialysis, cardiopulmonary resuscitation, organ transplantation, respirator support, and provision of food and water by artificial means have become common in hospitals.

While these new treatments often benefit patients, restoring them to well-functioning lives, they also can be employed in circumstances where they may be neither a benefit to nor wanted by patients. Where once pneumonia was the "old man's friend," the way in which "nature" ended a life that had become seriously debilitated, now the time and manner of death has been brought increasingly under human control. In coming to grips with sustaining, taking, or not prolonging life, medicine has drawn on both its own ethical traditions and society's broader ethical and religious traditions.

This entry will first develop an ethical framework for life-sustaining-treatment decisions around which a considerable, though hardly universal, consensus has developed, and contrast it with the distinction between ordinary and extraordinary care. It will then consider broad alternative positions on the morality of taking life and some of their implications for care of the dying. Focusing on more specific controversies, it will then address the intentional taking of life versus pain relief that hastens death, killing and allowing to die, not starting versus stopping treatment, and four prominent examples of end-of-life treatment—resuscitation, artificially administered food and water, terminal sedation and futile treatment. Finally the entry will conclude with discussions of life-sustaining treatment and suicide and of physician-assisted suicide and voluntary euthanasia.

An Ethical Framework for Life-Sustaining-Treatment Decisions

An ethical framework for life-sustaining-treatment decisions should be sufficiently general to apply to all forms of such decisions and to both competent and incompetent patients.

COMPETENT PATIENTS. In the United States in the twentieth century, healthcare-treatment decision making came increasingly under the dominion of the ethical and legal doctrine of informed consent. This doctrine requires that treatment not be administered without the informed and voluntary consent of a competent patient. From a paternalistic and authoritarian tradition, in which the physician made almost all treatment decisions and the patient's role was to follow the doctor's orders, a new ideal emerged that involves shared treatment decision making between physicians and patients. Physicians use their knowledge, experience, and training to determine the patient's diagnosis and prognosis with different possible alternative treatments, including the alternative of no treatment, and the risks and benefits of each. Patients, on the other hand, use their own aims and values to discern and decide which option is best for them. Shared decision making is based on the recognition that sound, individualized-treatment decision making requires both contributions.

The principal ethical values that underlie shared decision making involve promoting the well-being of patients while respecting their self-determination or autonomy. The term *well-being* is meant to signal that what is best for a particular patient depends not only on the "medical facts" but also on the patient's own aims and values. It is also meant to signal the extremely important point that preserving or sustaining life is not always a benefit to patients; whether it is depends on the nature of the life sustained and whether the patient values that life. Self-determination is the interest ordinary persons have in making important decisions about their lives for themselves and according to their own values or conception of a good life. The capacity for self-determination allows people to take control over and responsibility for their lives and the kind of persons they become. The fundamental importance of self-determination has consistently been the central appeal in the United States both in the long line of informed-consent legal cases going back at least as far as the 1914 case *Schloendorf v. Society of New York Hospital,* and in the more recent life-sustaining-treatment cases.

On the basis of these two values, as well as the ideal of shared decision making and the requirement of informed consent they support, competent patients have the right to weigh the benefits and burdens of alternative treatments, including the option of no treatment, and to make their own selection. While this ethical framework applies to any treatment, it provides especially strong support for patients deciding about life-sustaining treatment. When forgoing life-sustaining treatment is seriously in question, the patient is often critically or terminally ill and near death and also often in a seriously debilitated state. Whether a particular patient will want to fight to stay alive as long as possible, or will instead at some point find continued life no longer a benefit but now a burden, is highly variable and unpredictable. Self-determination on so important a decision as when and in what ways one's life comes to an end or is sustained by medical treatment is of particular importance.

INCOMPETENT PATIENTS. When forgoing life-sustaining treatment is seriously in question, patients are often—probably usually—incompetent to make the decision for themselves, and so another person must decide for them. Bioethics and the law have given much attention to who should decide about life support for incompetent patients and what standards should be used. A number of ethical grounds support the common practice, employed by physicians and sanctioned by the courts, of turning to a close family member of the patient, when one is available. Most patients would want such a person to make these decisions for them when they are unable to do so; in most cases, then, turning to a close family member respects the patient's self-determination. Moreover, a close family member will usually know the patient best and will therefore be in the best position to determine what the patient would have wanted. This person is also likely to care most about doing what is best for the patient. Turning to a close family member thus promotes both the patient's self-determination and the patient's well-being. Finally, in most societies the family is the social unit in which important social bonds and responsibilities to care for dependent members are developed; one exercise of this responsibility is to serve as surrogate for an incompetent family member. These ethical grounds usually, but do not always, apply and so can be thought of as establishing an ethical presumption that a close family member is the appropriate surrogate to make life-sustaining-treatment decisions for an incompetent patient. When these reasons do not apply—for example, when there is evidence that the patient would have wanted someone else to serve as surrogate or there is a serious conflict of interest between the family member and surrogate—then the presumption in favor of the family member as surrogate can be rebutted and another should be selected to serve instead.

How should a surrogate make life-sustaining-treatment decisions for an incompetent patient? A significant consensus has developed, both in ethics and in law, that there are three standards for a surrogate's decisions. First, if the patient has made an advance directive (e.g., a "living will" or a "durable power of attorney for healthcare") that includes instructions about the individual's wishes as to the decision in question, then the patient's choice expressed in the advance directive should be followed, with only limited qualifications. Second, when most patients do not have an advance directive or their advance directive is too general to determine the actual treatment decision, the "substituted judgment" standard should be used. This directs a surrogate to attempt to make the decision that the patient would have made, in the circumstances that then obtain, if the patient were competent. More informally, the surrogate should use his or her knowledge of the patient and the patient's values and wishes to attempt to decide what the patient would have wanted. Third, when there is no knowledge available of the patient and the patient's values that bear on the decision at hand, the "best-interest" standard should be used. Here, the surrogate should determine what is in the patient's overall best interests by a more objective and communal conception of best interest. This often amounts to asking what most reasonable persons would want; in the absence of available evidence about how, in relevant respects, the patient is different from most people, this is justified. These three standards constitute a way to promote patient well-being and self-determination to the extent possible when the patient lacks capacity to make decisions.

These standards have not gone unchallenged (Meisel; Veatch; Dresser and Whitehead). For example, parents are given significant discretion, especially in the case of young children, in deciding what would be best for their child and are permitted to give some weight to the effects of different options on important interests of other family members. The authority of both advance directives and substituted judgment have also been challenged when following them would conflict with important interests of the now-incompetent patient or when the patient has undergone such profound mental changes that he or she appears to be a "new person" with new interests. Despite the substantial consensus on the ethical framework sketched above, it is not uncontroversial.

This ethical framework for life-sustaining-treatment decisions by competent and incompetent patients does give weight to a narrowly focused quality-of-life judgment: Is the best life possible for the patient with treatment sufficiently poor, according to the patient's evaluation of that quality, that it is worse than no further life at all? No weight is given, on the other hand, to the fact that the patient's quality of life may have diminished from what it once was or from most people's lives, or to any evaluation of the social worth or social value of the patient. The fundamental feature of this ethical framework is that it entitles the patient or surrogate to weigh the benefits and burdens of possible treatments, including the option of no treatment, according to the patient's aims and values, and to select from among available treatments or to refuse any treatment. This decision-making framework has now largely supplanted the distinction between ordinary and extraordinary treatment.

Ordinary versus Extraordinary Care

The distinction between ordinary and extraordinary care has its origins in Roman Catholic moral theology, where it is employed to distinguish between obligatory care—ordinary—and care that may be permissibly forgone—extraordinary. The two central issues about this distinction are: (1) What is the difference between ordinary and extraordinary care? and (2) Why should that difference determine whether care is morally obligatory or optional?

The distinction itself has been criticized as being unclear and resulting in confusion and controversy about how it should be applied (U.S. President's Commission). For example, it has been used to mark the difference between statistically usual and statistically unusual care (perhaps the most commonly held understanding of the terms), between noninvasive and highly invasive treatments, and between treatments that employ low- and high-technology interventions. Because the distinction has many different, natural understandings, confusion often arises about what it means. None of the possible meanings of the distinction explains why the difference itself should determine whether the treatment is morally obligatory or optional. For example, treatment that is statistically common or involves the use of low technology might be beneficial to a particular patient in particular circumstances, but not beneficial or, perhaps, even burdensome to another patient in different circumstances.

The correct understanding of the traditional distinction is the difference between treatment that is beneficial and treatment that is unduly burdensome (or without benefit) to a patient. Of course, treatment is unduly burdensome only when the benefits it provides are insufficient to warrant its burdens. Unlike the other interpretations noted above, this interpretation of the ordinary–extraordinary distinction does mark a morally significant difference. Understood in this way, however, no general list of kinds of treatments that would be consistently ordinary or consistently extraordinary is possible; any treatment may be beneficial in some circumstances but not in others. More important, when the distinction is understood in this way it ceases to be an alternative to the benefit–burden framework. The judgment that a treatment is "extraordinary" places a label on treatment already and independently determined to be without benefit or unduly burdensome to the patient. The benefit–burden assessment does the substantive work in assessing treatments. For this reason, most commentators have given up the ordinary–extraordinary analysis in favor of the clearer and more direct appeal to the assessment of the benefits and burdens of treatment to a particular patient.

Of course, no ethical framework of the sort sketched here can be applied mechanically to make decisions to forgo life-sustaining treatment easy and unambiguous; even with the best efforts and the clearest reasoning, many decisions will remain ethically problematic and emotionally wrenching. While this is also true of many decisions about treatment that is not life sustaining, decisions concerning whether to sustain or shorten life raise several special ethical issues. In the 1960s and 1970s, it was common to distinguish between "active" and "passive" euthanasia. Passive euthanasia was understood to include forgoing life-sustaining treatment, either by stopping it or by not starting it. Active euthanasia was understood to be a deliberate intervention to end a patient's life, for example, by administering a lethal injection. Because euthanasia is often understood to be only active euthanasia, it has become common to avoid the term passive euthanasia in favor of referring to forgoing life-sustaining treatment. Most of these additional ethical issues raised about life-sustaining treatment represent special constraints or limits to be considered regarding the ethical framework just discussed for decisions where life itself is at stake.

The Morality of Taking Life

Any view about the morality of forgoing life-sustaining treatment or of euthanasia will depend in large measure on the basic moral principle presupposed concerning the taking of human life. This principle will differ depending on the general moral theory or conception of which it is a part or from which it is derived. Moral conceptions regarding taking life and killing may be divided into those that are goal-based, duty-based, and rights-based. A goal-based position, of which utilitarianism is the best-known variant, prohibits taking life when doing so fails to maximize the goals or consequences the position holds to be valuable, for example, human happiness or the satisfaction of people's desires. In this view it is a factual matter whether any particular killing produces better consequences than any other available alternative. Because this position not only permits but requires taking an innocent person's life when doing so will produce the greatest balance of benefits over harms, it is in sharp conflict with the patient-centered, ethical framework, which does not permit sacrifice of the patient for the benefit of others.

In a duty-based view, taking life is wrong because it violates a fundamental moral duty not to take innocent human life intentionally. This view looks not to the consequences produced by a particular killing but to the action itself, which is prohibited by the duty not to kill. It is often found within religions that view life as a gift from God, and therefore subject only to God's decision about when to take it. Perhaps the most serious difficulty for this view is its failure to give moral weight to the consent of the person whose life may or may not be taken. In this view, a competent patient's free request that another take her life need not morally justify doing so; instead, it is a request or temptation to do evil and should be resisted by a moral person.

In a rights-based view, taking human life is morally wrong because it violates a basic moral right not to be killed. In this view, killing harms its victims because it denies them their future, together with all that they wanted to pursue or achieve in that future. It wrongs its victims by taking from them without their consent what is rightfully theirs—their lives. In contrast with the duty-based view, however, when a competent individual freely requests that another person take his or her life because that life has become a burden and no longer a good for the individual, that request would be understood to be a waiving of the individual's right not to be killed, and acceding to it would be morally permissible.

The most important, substantive moral difference between duty-based and rights-based views is whether an individual's free and informed consent can make taking the person's life permissible. The distinction between duty-based and rights-based views is a natural way in which this moral difference is often expressed. Nevertheless, the duty not to kill could be understood to apply only to individuals who wish to live, and the right not to be killed could be understood to be unwaivable, as many in the right-to-life movement understand it. The distinction between rights-based and duty-based accounts of the morality of killing is used in this entry only to distinguish whether an individual's consent to be killed does or does not make killing that individual morally permissible.

Which of these alternative positions is correct is controversial and raises general questions of moral theory that cannot be addressed here. An ethical position that gives fundamental ethical importance to individual self-determination—as the ethical framework for life-sustaining-treatment decisions sketched above does—is most naturally formulated as a rights-based position. Whichever basic view is adopted, however, there are two important questions: (1) What actions are included under the moral prohibition of taking life, broadly construed? and (2) Is this prohibition absolute or does it have exceptions? The duty-based view is sometimes understood to make absolute the prohibition on intentionally taking human life; but it also typically distinguishes acts that intentionally take life from acts in which death is a foreseen but unintended consequence. Both duty-based and rights-based views about the morality of taking life tend to share the position that allowing to die is a less serious wrong than taking a life by killing.

Intended versus Foreseen but Unintended Taking of Life

When caring for dying patients, health professionals sometimes take actions that may shorten the patient's life. They may, for example, provide larger and larger doses of morphine when necessary to relieve a patient's pain, and in doing so, risk bringing on respiratory depression and earlier death. When this is done with the patient's or surrogate's knowledge of the risk and consent, it is morally justified. For the rights-based moral view about taking life, consent to the risk is crucial. In many duty-based positions, however, the consent of the victim does not justify taking human life, and a distinction is drawn instead between whether the resulting death was intended and whether it was only foreseen but unintended.

This intended/foreseen distinction has a long history. Invoked in the thirteenth century by the Italian theologian and philosopher Thomas Aquinas to justify killing in self-defense, the distinction is central to the Roman Catholic doctrine of double effect. (Double effect here refers to actions that may have two effects, one that is directly intended and the other one only indirectly intended or foreseen.) In some form, it is also common in much secular thinking about the morality of taking life.

Two central questions must be answered in order to evaluate whether this distinction really can or should be used to distinguish some morally permissible from impermissible taking of life. First, what precisely is the nature of the difference between "intended" and "foreseen"? Second, why is this difference morally important? In treating a dying cancer patient's pain, it may seem clear that the physician's primary or direct intention is to treat the pain; the earlier death from respiratory depression caused by the morphine the physician prescribes to treat the pain is, at most, a secondary or indirect intention, or more accurately, a foreseen but unintended consequence. (It is also clinically rare, especially for patients who have been receiving morphine for a considerable period of time.) Many physicians would not give this same patient a lethal injection if all other means of pain relief had failed, because then the death would be intended. Yet the physician's primary intention in the case of

killing by lethal injection might also be to relieve the patient's pain, though then the means of doing so is to kill the patient. This distinction between what is intended as a means and what is a foreseen but unintended consequence, however, is not always clear. Killings that seem plainly wrong because they are an impermissible means to a good end can be redescribed as only a foreseen but unintended consequence of achieving the good end, and as, therefore, morally permissible. An extreme example will illustrate the point. Suppose a renowned transplant surgeon removes the heart and liver from a healthy person without the person's consent in order to transplant them in two patients who otherwise will die from heart and liver failure. Such killing is wrong even though it is a means of saving a greater number of persons. But suppose the surgeon denies that the killing is the means of saving other patients: The means of saving the other patients, he claims, was by removing the healthy person's organs and transplanting them, whereas the death of the healthy person was merely foreseen but not intended. Proponents of this distinction have not clarified it in a way that prevents such unwelcome misuse of it.

In many cases, such as giving morphine as opposed to a lethal injection, there is agreement about how to apply the intended-versus-foreseen-but-unintended distinction. The question then arises, what is its moral significance? Critics of the distinction note that in each case the physician's end is to relieve suffering, and that to gain such relief, both physician and patient are prepared to accept the risk of the patient's earlier death. Whether by morphine or a lethal injection, relieving the patient's suffering will bring about an earlier death. These similarities cast doubt on the moral importance of this difference. In the case of morphine, there may be only a risk of death, whereas in the case of a lethal injection the death is certain. But sometimes the amount of morphine necessary makes the likelihood of earlier death extremely high, and then this small difference in probabilities is too slim a foundation for the very great moral difference between permissible and impermissible killings. In any event, this is a difference in the certainty or risk of the outcome of death, not in whether it is intended or unintended.

Critics of the distinction between intended and foreseen deaths argue that physicians are morally responsible for all foreseen or reasonably foreseeable consequences of their actions, whether intended or foreseen but unintended, because foreseeability brings these consequences under the control of physicians and so makes physicians responsible for them. This disagreement in medical contexts about the moral importance of whether death is intended is often a particular instance of a broader disagreement between goal-based or utilitarian theorists who are concerned only with good results and duty- or rights-based theorists who place moral restrictions on how good results may be brought about.

Killing and Allowing to Die

Many moral theorists distinguish between duties not to kill, called negative duties, and duties to save or not to allow to die, called positive duties (Steinbock and Norcross). They argue that, unless this distinction is used to set reasonable moral limits, moral responsibilities will extend far beyond what they are usually thought to be and will deeply limit people's pursuit of their various life plans. Persons can usually satisfy the duty not to kill simply by pursuing their particular aims and purposes, although these goals may have to be altered if necessary to avoid killing. But if there is an equally stringent duty not to allow to die, it might seem that people must likewise set aside nearly all their usual aims and activities and devote their lives to saving those whose lives are in peril, such as victims of famines or extreme poverty. The implications of whether killing is morally worse than allowing to die are far-reaching both within and outside of medicine.

There are again two distinct issues. First, what makes one particular "doing," understood to include both acts and omissions, a "killing," and another, an "allowing to die"? Once the difference is clear, the second issue is whether and why this difference between killing and allowing to die is morally important. Killing is usually distinguished from allowing to die by establishing whether something was done, or not done, that resulted in death. A person who kills performs an action that causes a person to die in a way and at a time that the person would not otherwise have died. For example, two people are in a boat; Person 1 cannot swim. Knowing this, Person 2 pushes Person 1 out of the boat; Person 1 drowns.

A person who allows another to die knows that there is an action she could perform that would prevent another's death, but she does not take this action, and the person dies. For example, Person 1 accidentally falls out of the boat. Person 2 does not throw out an available life preserver, and Person 1 drowns. Some philosophers have argued that if the difference between killing and allowing to die is predicated on acting or not acting, killing is not morally worse than allowing to die.

The meaning of this claim has often been misunderstood. The claim is that the mere fact that one doing is a killing, while the other is an allowing to die, does not make one morally better or worse than the other, or make one morally justified or permissible when the other is not. This is compatible with saying that a particular killing, all things considered, is morally worse than, or not as bad as, a particular allowing to die because of other differences between the two, such as the motives of the agents or the presence or absence of the consent of the victim. This is also compatible with holding that most killing, all things considered, is morally worse than most allowing to die, but once again, that must be because of other morally important differences between them.

The usual argument for the position that killing is not in itself morally worse than allowing to die has consisted of comparing two cases that differ in no other morally relevant respect except that one is a killing, the other an allowing to die. Such a comparison helps focus on whether this difference by itself is morally important. James Rachels provided the following well-known example:

> In the first [instance], Smith stands to gain a large inheritance if anything should happen to his six-year-old cousin. One evening, while the child is taking his bath, Smith sneaks into the bathroom and drowns the child, and then arranges things so that it will look like an accident.

> In the second, Jones also stands to gain if anything should happen to his six-year-old cousin. Like Smith, Jones sneaks in planning to drown the child in his bath. However, just as he enters the bathroom Jones sees the child slip and hit his head, and fall face down in the water, Jones is delighted; he stands by, ready to push the child's head back under if it is necessary, but it is not necessary. With only a little thrashing about, the child drowns all by himself, "accidentally," as Jones watches and does nothing. (1975, p. 79)

Whereas Smith killed, Jones allowed to die. Rachels argued that there seems to be no basis for saying that what Smith did was any worse than what Jones did; there must be other factors in real cases that account for any moral differences. The conclusion that killing is not, in itself, morally worse than allowing to die remains controversial. Those who hold that there is a significant moral difference between the two argue that it is important to establish which of the two types of forgoing of life support, if either, comes under the stronger moral prohibition against killing. Because forgoing life support includes both not starting treatment and stopping treatment, the issue of whether either is equivalent to killing can be pursued by asking whether or not starting life support and stopping life support are morally different.

Not Starting Treatment and Stopping Treatment

When a decision is made not to initiate some form of life-sustaining treatment, such as kidney dialysis or respirator support, and the patient dies as a result, this is commonly understood to be an omission and so an allowing to die. Even if active killing is wrong, its prohibition does not apply to not initiating life support. But what of stopping life support—for example, stopping respirator support at the persistent, voluntary request of a clearly competent and respirator-dependent patient who is terminally ill and undergoing suffering that cannot be adequately relieved? If such action is taken by the physician with the intent of respecting the patient's right to decide about his or her treatment, most people would consider it a morally justified instance of allowing the patient to die. If only killing, but not allowing to die, is prohibited, then stopping life support and not starting it are both allowing to die and morally permitted.

But some philosophers have argued that stopping this patient's respirator is killing, not allowing to die (Brock). Suppose, for example, the patient has a greedy son who mistakenly believes that his mother will never decide to stop treatment and that even if she did, her physicians would not comply with her wishes. Afraid that his inheritance will be exhausted by a long hospitalization, he enters his mother's room while she is deeply sedated and removes her from the respirator, and she dies. If upon being found out, the son protested, "I didn't kill her; I merely allowed her to die; it was her disease that caused her death," this claim would be rejected. The son went into his mother's room and deliberately killed her.

Does the physician who did the same thing, performed the same physical action, kill the patient as well? Even if the physician in such a case does kill, other moral differences make the physician's killing morally justified, whereas the son's is morally wrong. The physician acts with a good motive, to respect the patient's wishes, with the patient's consent, and in a professional role in which the physician is socially and legally authorized to so act; the son acts with a bad motive, without consent, and with no social or legal authorization to do so. But these do not appear to be differences in whether either kills or allows to die: One can kill or allow to die with a good or bad motive, with or without consent, and in or not in a role that authorizes the action.

Those who reject this analysis and hold that stopping and not starting life support are both allowing to die usually have a different account of the kill/allow-to-die difference than the act/omission account offered in the last section. They hold that when a patient has a lethal illness such as lung disease, whose usual fatal outcome is being held off by a life-sustaining treatment such as a respirator, removing this artificial intervention amounts to allowing the patient to die by letting the disease process proceed unimpeded to death.

But this account is problematic, not least because it requires one to accept that the greedy son also allows to die, but does not kill.

Whether stopping life support is killing or allowing to die, some physicians and others have contended that it is an ethically graver matter to stop a life-sustaining treatment than not to start it, or that it is permissible not to start it in circumstances in which it would not be justified to stop it. But consideration of cases such as the following has led most persons to reject the argument that stopping life support is different from or more serious morally from not starting it:

> A gravely ill patient, Mr. S, arrives at the hospital in respiratory distress and is sent to the intensive care unit (ICU) to be intubated and placed on a respirator. Before he is intubated, his family and physician arrive at the ICU and inform the staff that while clearly competent Mr. S, after extensive consideration and because of his debilitated and terminal condition, had firmly rejected being put on a respirator under any circumstances. The ICU staff respect his wishes, keep him comfortable, and he dies of respiratory failure. Now suppose instead that heavy traffic had delayed the family and the physician and they arrive at the ICU just after Mr. S is put on the respirator. His treatment now must be stopped instead of not started as before. (Brock, p. 209)

It is hard to see why the same factors that morally justified not starting his treatment do not, equally, morally justify stopping it.

Those who hold that stopping life support is not different ethically from not starting it usually stress two bad effects of a greater reluctance to stop life support. First, it will result in continuing treatment beyond the point at which it is a benefit to or still wanted by the patient. Second, and less obvious but at least as important, the belief that it will be harder to stop life support once it is begun can make physicians, patients, and family members all reluctant to try treatment when the benefits are uncertain or unlikely, for fear that if the treatment proves not to be beneficial they will not be able to stop it and the patient will end up "stuck on machines." The result is to deny patients possibly beneficial life-sustaining treatment.

In fact, there is often better reason to stop a life-sustaining treatment than not to start it. Often, before a life-sustaining treatment is started, it is uncertain whether it will bring the hoped-for benefits to the patient. Once it has been tried, and it is clear that it does not produce the benefits sought, a reason exists for stopping it that did not exist for not starting it. This supports the use of time-limited trials of life-sustaining treatment, with the understanding that if the treatment does not prove to be beneficial it will be stopped.

Four Kinds of End-of-Life Treatment

Four forms of treatment of patients near death that have received special attention are resuscitation, artificial nutrition and hydration, terminal sedation, and so-called futile treatment.

RESUSCITATION. Life-sustaining-treatment debates in the United States during the 1970s and 1980s often focused on the use of cardiopulmonary resuscitation (CPR) for persons who suffer cardiac or pulmonary arrest. Because CPR, to be effective, must be administered immediately after a patient suffers an arrest, hospitals have developed policies generally requiring that CPR be administered to any such patient, unless there is a "do not resuscitate" (DNR) order already in effect for the patient. The presumption of these policies—that anyone in medical need of resuscitation should receive CPR unless there was a prior order not to use it—made CPR different from many other life-sustaining treatments, which required a physician's explicit order to start them.

CPR is the most prominent example of a class of emergency procedures for which consent is presumed unless the patient or the patient's surrogate has explicitly refused it beforehand. Because CPR in the hospital is usually not successful, is associated with significant morbidity for the patient even when it is successful, and often would, at best, extend the lives of dying patients only briefly, there is widespread consensus that forgoing it is often ethically justified so long as patients or their surrogates agree and explicitly withdraw the presumption of consent for it. As a result, resuscitation, or "code status," is probably the most frequently raised life-sustaining-treatment decision.

ARTIFICIAL NUTRITION AND HYDRATION. Those who seek to limit the life-sustaining treatments which it is ethically permissible for patients or their surrogates to decide to forgo have usually focused on the provision of nutrition and hydration by artificial means, such as intravenous, nasogastric, and other forms of tube feeding. Some people have argued that food and water are not medical treatment but are instead the most basic form of caring for dependent persons; all people, not just medical patients, need food and water. Others argue that when the patient's medical condition necessitates the artificial provision of food and water, and when this is done by medical personnel using medical means, there is not much difference between this situation and the provision of oxygen by respirators to patients with lung disease.

Other opponents of forgoing food and water focus not on the issue of whether it is medical treatment, but on the strong symbolic meaning and importance of feeding those in need. The usual symbolism of food and water, however, may be misleading in the circumstances in which the question arises in medicine. There the cultural and social symbolism and meaning associated with eating and feeding are largely absent, as is the suffering typically associated with starvation. Applying the benefits-and-burdens analysis, food and water should be forgone only if doing so would not cause significant suffering to the patient. The benefits-and-burdens analysis will support forgoing nutrition and hydration either when continued life itself is burdensome or not a benefit to the patient, or when providing nutrition and hydration increases, rather than decreases, the patient's suffering. For example, many patients in a persistent vegetative state—that is, those who have permanently and completely lost the capacity for any conscious experience—would not want nor consider it a benefit to have their lives continued. Consequently, treatment that sustains life is not beneficial, and its withdrawal cannot impose any burden on such a patient. In other cases, providing normal levels of nutrition and hydration may increase the awareness and suffering of some dying patients; for these patients, feelings of thirst can be assuaged, for example, with ice chips, without providing a level of hydration that would make their dying less peaceful and comfortable (Lynn). In still other cases, the benefits of continued life for seriously demented patients must be weighed against the burdens of physical restraints necessary to keep them from removing feeding tubes.

A different form of forgoing food and water can occur when a competent patient refuses them because the patient wishes to die. Some have argued that because competent patents always have not only the right to refuse artificially provided nutrition and hydration but also the right to refuse to eat or drink by ordinary means, physician-assisted suicide is an unnecessary option. Refusing to eat or drink will always result in the patient's death, and so a competent patient who wishes to die but who does not have any life-sustaining treatment to be forgone does not need access to physician-assisted suicide to do so. Stopping eating and drinking, however, can take considerable resolve on the patient's part and may not meet many patients' views of a humane and dignified death. Proponents argue that it still may be a better policy option than physician-assisted suicide if the latter has substantial risks that stopping eating and drinking does not have.

TERMINAL SEDATION. Related to stopping nutrition and hydration as an alternative to physician-assisted suicide is the use of terminal sedation (Quill, Lo, and Brock). This

typically involves sedating a patient with otherwise intractable pain to the point of unconsciousness and then withdrawing nutrition and hydration, with the inevitable result of the
patient's death. Terminal sedation is used by some hospices
and is defended as an acceptable practice because treating
patients' pain is an uncontroversial responsibility of physicians and withdrawing nutrition and hydration is within
patients' general right to refuse any treatment. The practice
remains controversial, however, both because it raises the
previously discussed problems with the distinction between
intended and foreseen but unintended consequences, and
because it is subject to abuse, especially if employed with
incompetent patients. Others argue that because it may take
up to a week or more for the patient to die, physician-
assisted suicide would usually provide the patient with a
preferable death.

FUTILE TREATMENT. A final recent controversy concerns
futile care. As physicians have come to accept patients' rights
to refuse treatment, they have increasingly encountered
patients, or more commonly the families of incompetent
patients, demanding treatment that the physicians judge to
be futile. The debate began with CPR but has expanded to
other forms of life-sustaining care. When physicians are
asked to actively provide a treatment, it has seemed to many
that the treatment should be acceptable both to the patient
and to the physician; typically, in any joint enterprise, such
as that between patient and treating physician, what is done
must be acceptable to both participants. This may help
account for the asymmetry many support between patients'
right to refuse any treatment but to choose only from among
medically acceptable alternative treatments.

A central issue in the futility debate has been how to
define futility. Some have tried to narrowly restrict it to only
those treatments known with certainty not to achieve their
goal. The attempt is to eliminate value judgments from
futility determinations and to make them only an empirical
matter about which the physician should be expert. But
others have pointed out that it is not possible to eliminate all
value judgments. How certain is certain enough, and what
are the legitimate goals of the treatment? Others have more
broadly characterized futility to include cases in which the
probability of benefit is considered too low, or the size of
benefit too small, to warrant the burdens of the treatment.
Here, the value judgment in determining futility is whether
the treatment's benefits are likely enough, or large enough,
to warrant its burdens. This value judgment seems in most
cases appropriately left to the patient or surrogate, not the
physician. The courts that have addressed futility cases have
largely sided with patients or surrogates seeking treatment
rather than with physicians who wish not to provide it.

Life-Sustaining Treatment and Suicide

Suicide is difficult to define precisely but is usually understood as the intentional taking of one's own life. In some
religious traditions, suicide has long been and continues to
be prohibited and considered a sin, and some important
moral philosophers such as Immanuel Kant (1724–1804)
have held that suicide is morally wrong (Battin). Historically, the law often reflected these views, although in the
United States no states now criminalize suicide or attempted
suicide, but a majority prohibit assisting in suicide.

The different, basic moral positions discussed earlier on
the morality of taking human life have different implications
for the morality of suicide. Despite these differences, most
people agree that a public policy of seeking to prevent most
suicide attempts is morally justified. Even strong defenders
of individual self-determination generally agree that most
suicide attempts are dramatic pleas for help and occur when
a person's decision-making capacity is seriously disordered
by such conditions as depression. These features justify
intervention to prevent the suicide, so as to determine if the
patient is competent and not subject to impaired decision
making, in which case, some believe, others should cease
coercive interference.

Because a patient's decision to forgo treatment correctly
believed to be life-sustaining will result in the patient's
death, the question arises whether this is suicide. In some
cases, the patient may not intend her own death, or seek
death, but only be unwilling to undergo the burdens of a
particular life-sustaining treatment. In other cases, however,
the patient's decision may also be made in the interest of
seeking an end to an excessively burdensome existence; in
such cases, therefore, there is an intent to cause one's
own death, making it hard to differentiate the decision
from suicide. Many legal decisions about life-sustaining
treatment, and most Western religious traditions, have
sought to distinguish forgoing life support from suicide,
often by characterizing the former as an exercise of self-
determination about one's medical treatment, not intentional self-destruction. (The courts may have sought to
distinguish forgoing life support from suicide to protect
participating physicians and others from potential prosecution under legal statutes prohibiting assisting in suicide.) Yet
the normative judgment a competent person makes justifying each act is often essentially the same: The best future life
possible for me (with life-sustaining treatment, in the case of
a decision to forgo treatment) is so bad that it is worse than
no further life at all. The principal difference between some
cases of forgoing life-sustaining treatment and suicide appears to be only a difference in the means a person uses to
bring about her death. Nevertheless, even if some or all
forgoing of life support is essentially suicide, it need not, for

that reason, be morally wrong, but might instead be considered a justified exercise of self-determination.

Physician-Assisted Suicide

In nearly all countries, neither professional practice nor the law permits physicians to grant patients' requests for physician-assisted suicide or voluntary euthanasia. An example of physician-assisted suicide is when a patient ingests a lethal substance provided by a physician for that purpose; voluntary euthanasia, by contrast, involves the physician administering the lethal substance. In both cases, the choice rests fully with the patient, and the patient can change his mind up until the moment the lethal process becomes irreversible. The only difference need be who performs the last physical action of administering the lethal dose, for example, placing potassium chloride in the patient's intravenous line. This small difference in the part played by the physician in the causal process leading to death does not seem to support a substantial moral difference between physician-assisted suicide and voluntary euthanasia.

Those who nevertheless believe that it is morally worse for physicians to perform voluntary euthanasia than physician-assisted suicide can argue that in the former, the physician kills the patient, whereas in the latter, the patient kills herself. But it may be more accurate to say that in physician-assisted suicide, the physician and the patient together kill the patient—a case of joint action for which both together bear responsibility. This suggests that physician-assisted suicide and voluntary euthanasia may not be substantially different morally.

Voluntary, Active Euthanasia

Considerable public and professional attention, spurred by publicity about the practice in the Netherlands (Van Der Maas, Van Delden, and Pijnenborg) and several notorious cases in the United States, such as those of Dr. Jack Kevorkian, has focused on voluntary, active euthanasia. In significant part, the public interest in euthanasia reflects fear of loss of control and dignity while dying. It also reflects recognition that the same values of patient self-determination and well-being that have been accepted as guiding treatment decision making in general, and decisions about life-sustaining treatment in particular, can in some cases support voluntary, active euthanasia as well. If this positive support for voluntary euthanasia is granted, opponents have in general offered two kinds of arguments against it.

The first argument is that any individual instance of euthanasia is morally wrong because it violates the duty not to kill innocent human beings. As noted earlier, in some duty-based accounts of the wrongness of killing, the consent of the one killed does not make the killing permissible. Nevertheless, given the centrality of the patient's consent in ethical accounts of the permissibility of forgoing life-sustaining treatment, some special argument is needed for why consent has no relevance for euthanasia. Moreover, if the argument in the earlier section on killing and allowing to die is correct—that some stopping of life support is justified killing—then euthanasia cannot be morally condemned simply because it is killing. Many duty-based moral accounts of the wrongness of killing either implicitly or explicitly depend on theological premises that give God sole dominion over life and death. However, in pluralistic societies that respect religious freedom, public policy should not be based on religious beliefs that many members of that society do not share. The rights-based account of the wrongness of killing, however, gives decisive weight to the consent and self-determination of the patient who seeks it.

The other general kind of argument against euthanasia is that although it may be morally permissible in some individual cases, it would nonetheless be bad public policy to permit voluntary, active euthanasia. This argument depends on an assessment of the likely good and bad consequences of permitting euthanasia, only a few of which can be noted here. Among the potential good consequences that proponents cite are: respecting the self-determination of those who request euthanasia but have not been able to get it; assuring the much larger number of people who believe it should be permitted so that should they request it, it would be available; ending the pain and suffering of dying patients that cannot be relieved by any other means; and providing for some patients a more humane and peaceful death than they would otherwise have.

Among the potential bad consequences opponents cite are: its apparent incompatibility with the aim of medicine of protecting life in all its frailty; the erosion of the trust of patients in their physicians as caregivers; the erosion of the social commitment to provide appropriate care to the dying if euthanasia, in an era of cost containment, is seen as an acceptable and cheaper alternative; and fear that permitting voluntary euthanasia would, over time, lead to involuntary euthanasia, or at least to nonvoluntary euthanasia of incompetent patients. Evaluating the likelihood and relative seriousness of these and other possible good and bad consequences of permitting either physician-assisted suicide or voluntary euthanasia is difficult and controversial. In 2003 in the United States, physician-assisted suicide is legal in the state of Oregon, and that state's accumulating experience with the practice is the basis for considerable debate (Sullivan, Hedberg, and Hopkins; Nuland). Whether either practice should be permitted remains one of the most deeply controversial issues in medical ethics.

Conclusion

Since the 1960s, the capacity of medicine to prolong patients' lives has steadily increased, making the time and circumstances of a person's death increasingly a matter of human choice and control. The debates considered and the ethical framework for life-sustaining-treatment decisions sketched in this entry have been responses to this new control over how and when humans die. Perhaps the central feature and accomplishment of the great public and professional attention to death and dying in recent decades has been securing the rights of patients or their surrogates to decide about care near the end of life together with focusing the medical profession's attention on improving care at the end of life. However, the deeply personal, emotionally complex, and ethically controversial nature of decisions about care at the end of life ensures that they will continue to be a prominent part of bioethics.

DAN W. BROCK (1995)
REVISED BY AUTHOR

SEE ALSO: *Advance Directives and Advance Care Planning; Anthropology and Bioethics; Autonomy; Clinical Ethics; Competence; Death; Death, Definition and Determination of; Dementia; Healthcare Resources, Allocation of; Holocaust; Informed Consent; Long-Term Care; Medical Codes and Oaths; Metaphor and Analogy; Palliative Care and Hospice; Right to Die: Policy and Law; Surrogate Decision-Making;* and other *Life Sustaining Treatment and Euthanasia* subentries

BIBLIOGRAPHY

Battin, Margaret Pabst. 1982. *Ethical Issues in Suicide.* Englewood Cliffs, NJ: Prentice-Hall.

Bole, Thomas J., ed. 1991. "Double Effect: Theoretical Function and Bioethical Implication." Special issue of *Journal of Medicine and Philosophy* 16(5).

Brock, Dan W. 1993. *Life and Death: Philosophical Essays in Biomedical Ethics.* Cambridge, Eng.: Cambridge University Press.

Brody, Baruch A., ed. 1989. *Suicide and Euthanasia: Historical and Contemporary Themes.* Dordrecht, Netherlands: Kluwer.

Buchanan, Allen E., and Brock, Dan W. 1989. *Deciding for Others: The Ethics of Surrogate Decision Making.* New York: Cambridge University Press.

Dresser, Rebecca, and Whitehead, Peter. 1994. "The Incompetent Patient on the Slippery Slope." *Hastings Center Report* 24(4): 6–12.

Glover, Jonathan. 1977. *Causing Death and Saving Lives.* New York: Penguin.

Hastings Center. 1987. *Guidelines on the Termination of Life-Sustaining Treatment and the Care of the Dying.* Bloomington: Indiana University Press.

Kamm, F. M. 1993. *Morality, Mortality,* vol. I: *Death and Whom to Save from It.* Oxford: Oxford University Press.

Kant, Immanuel. 1785 (reprint 1990). *Groundwork of the Metaphysic of Morals,* tr. and ed. Herbert James Paton. New York: Barnes and Noble.

Kuhse, Helga. 1987. *The Sanctity-of-Life Doctrine in Medicine: A Critique.* Oxford: Oxford University Press.

Kuhse, Helga, and Singer, Peter. 1985. *Should the Baby Live? The Problem of Handicapped Infants.* Oxford: Oxford University Press.

Lynn, Joanne, ed. 1986. *By No Extraordinary Means: The Choice to Forgo Life-Sustaining Food and Water.* Bloomington: Indiana University Press.

Meisel, Alan. 1992. "The Legal Consensus about Foregoing Life-Sustaining Treatment: Its Status and Its Prospects." *Kennedy Institute of Ethics Journal* 2(4): 309–345.

Nuland, Sherwin. 2000. "Physician-Assisted Suicide and Euthanasia in Practice." *New England Journal of Medicine* 342(8): 583–584.

Quill, Timothy E.; Lo, Bernard; and Brock, Dan W. 1997. "Palliative Options of Last Resort: A Comparison of Voluntarily Stopping Eating and Drinking, Terminal Sedation, Physician Assisted Suicide, and Voluntary Euthanasia." *Journal of the American Medical Association* 278(23): 2099–2104.

Rachels, James. 1975. "Active and Passive Euthanasia." *New England Journal of Medicine* 292(2): 78–80.

Rachels, James. 1986. *The End of Life: Euthanasia and Morality.* Oxford: Oxford University Press.

Schloendorf v. Society of New York Hospital. 211 N.Y. 125, 105 N.E. 92, 95 (1914).

Steinbock, Bonnie, and Norcross, Alistair, eds. 1994. *Killing and Letting Die,* 2nd edition. Englewood Cliffs, NJ: Prentice-Hall.

Sullivan, Amy; Hedberg, Katrina; and Hopkins, David. 2001. "Legalized Physician-Assisted Suicide in Oregon, 1998–2000." *New England Journal of Medicine* 344(8): 605–607.

Tomlinson, Tom, and Brody, Howard. 1990. "Futility and the Ethics of Resuscitation." *Journal of the American Medical Association* 264(10): 1276–1280.

U.S. President's Commission for the Study of Ethical Problems in Medicine and Biomedical and Behavioral Research. 1983. *Deciding to Forego Life-Sustaining Treatment: A Report on the Ethical, Medical, and Legal Issues in Treatment Decisions.* Washington, D.C.: Government Printing Office.

Van Der Maas, Paul J.; Van Delden, Johannes J. M.; and Pijnenborg, Loes. 1991. "Euthanasia and Other Medical Decisions Concerning the End of Life." *Lancet* 338(8768): 669–674.

Veatch, Robert M. 1993. "Forgoing Life-Sustaining Treatment: Limits to the Consensus." *Kennedy Institute of Ethics Journal* 3(1): 1–19.

Weir, Robert F. 1989. *Abating Treatment with Critically Ill Patients: Ethical and Legal Limits to the Medical Prolongation of Life*. New York: Oxford University Press.

II. HISTORICAL ASPECTS

The history sustaining and ending of human life in the West has three facets: a chronology of the meanings of euthanasia, the major cultural heritages that have influenced the beliefs and actions of physicians, and changing modes of medical practice. This entry explores this multifaceted history from its ancient Hebrew origins to the rise of the "right to die" and "death and dying" movements after the1960s.

The Meanings of Euthanasia

All the meanings of the term *euthanasia* can be related to the etymology of the Greek term *euthanatos*: *eu* meaning "good" and *thanatos* meaning "death." At the present time the word is used to denote a doctor's painlessly terminating the life of a suffering, terminally ill patient who wishes to die: physician produced or physician induced death (*Oxford English Dictionary*). Advocates for euthanasia often call it mercy killing.

The current meaning is actually the *second* way the term was used in Western history. The term's *first* and most long-standing use denoted a gentle and natural or noninduced death. The Roman historian Suetonius (c. 69–135 C.E.) described how Augustus Caesar was "blessed with an easy death" when he expired peacefully at age seventy-five: "For almost always on hearing that anyone had died swiftly and painlessly, [Augustus] prayed that he and his might have a like 'euthanasia'" [here *euthanatos* is inserted in the Latin text] (Suetonius, p. 281).

Francis Bacon (1561–1626) appears to have been the first scholar to maintain that the practice of medicine should include knowledge and skill that enable doctors to help patients to die easily and naturally. Bacon entitled this dimension of medicine *euthanasia exteriori* ("outward euthanasia") to distinguish it from "that euthanasia, or sweet calm dying, procured by a due preparation of the soul" in religious literature on consoling the dying (Bacon, pp. 124–125; Beaty). By saying that doctors should help patients "make a fair and easy passage out of life" Bacon meant that they should enable patients to die as Augustus Caesar had or like the aged Antoninus Pius, who died calmly "as though he were falling asleep" (Bacon; Bryant). This analysis of what Bacon proposed corrects the claim that he advocated doctor-induced death (Fletcher; Wilson; Emanuel).

For the next two centuries the term denoted physician-aided natural dying. The replacement of this meaning by the current understanding of euthanasia occurred between 1870 and the 1920s. A defense of doctor-induced peaceful death was made by Samuel D. Williams in 1870, after which heated debate ensued in Great Britain and the United States (Williams, 1872; Vanderpool, 1997). The fact that the debate has continued accounts for the current use of the term.

The meaning of euthanasia in its original sense continued into the 1920s, but its equation with mercy killing was so common by the turn of the century that some suggested that the original term should be replaced with the term *euphoria* ("Euphoria vs. Euthanasia"; Rosenberg and Aronstam). Later proponents of the duty of doctors to help patients die peacefully and naturally dropped such terminology in favor of phrases such as *caring for the dying* (Worcester; Alvarez).

Third, during the first four decades of the twentieth century the practice of extinguishing the lives of unwanted persons also was called euthanasia. Newspapers, films, books, physicians, professors such as Harvard's Charles Eliot Norton, clergy, scientists such as the Nobel laureate Alexis Carrel, and other eugenicists in the West called for euthanasia, that is, a painless extermination of various groups: "lunatics," "degenerates," "cripples," and others ("Dr. Norton on Euthanasia"; "The Right to Kill"; Pernick). That eugenics euthanasia movement played a complex role in Nazi ideology and the legitimization of Nazi genocide (Pernick).

Fourth, at times euthanasia was identified with the use of sedatives to "secure easy deaths" to the point of shortening life (South Carolina Medical Association, p. xvii). *Fifth,* the term occasionally was associated with what is now called assisted or physician-assisted suicide (Sperry, 1948), in part because some of the legislative bills sponsored by the Euthanasia Society of America were essentially assisted-suicide bills (Sperry, 1950).

Sixth, euthanasia became attached to the practice of withdrawing terminally ill persons from life-prolonging medical measures. After 1970 that practice commonly was termed *passive* or *indirect* euthanasia to distinguish it from *active* or *voluntary* euthanasia: doctor-produced death (Vanderpool, 1997). Although some authors disassociated the right to refuse life-sustaining measures from the term *euthanasia* (Pope Pius XII; Rynearson), the distinction between active and passive euthanasia made as early as 1884 ("Editorial: Permissive Euthanasia") had significant staying power.

An understanding of the major cultural heritages that informed and still inform the beliefs and actions of physicians sets the stage for the history of euthanasia and the sustaining of life in medical practice.

Hebraic and Jewish Perspectives

The Hebrew Scriptures proclaim an understanding of human life that has been immensely influential in Western history. Humans are created by God (Genesis 2:2–27), life and consciousness are gifts of God, and as Lord of life, God alone should determine when and how humans die (Job 1:21). As God's property, no individual has the right to destroy his or her life as if it were self-owned. It also is not lawful wantonly to take the life of another person (Exodus 20:13, Genesis 9:5–6).

On the basis of this legacy, Jewish tradition requires that when life is threatened by illness or injury, it must be sustained if possible. Because Jews were and are obligated to prolong their lives, they must not settle in communities where no physician is available. Obligations to save and extend life are drawn from Scripture: "You shall not stand idly by the blood of your neighbor" (Leviticus 19:16). Advanced medical interventions are urged for critically ill persons as long as it seems probable that those treatments will save or prolong life (Bleich). Rabbinic debate continues over situations in which life can be prolonged for a while, but at the expense of great pain and no hope for a real cure. Past and present, Jewish authorities have held that active pain relief can be undertaken at the risk of a patient's dying sooner (Jakobovits; Brody).

Doctors who induce death to spare patients from pain are considered murderers (Exodus 20:13, Carmi). Destroying those who are socially unwanted is absolutely prohibited. This includes neglecting or killing severely deformed newborns (Bleich).

Although it forbids mercy killing, Judaism defends the morality of letting fatally ill persons die naturally. The meaning of *honorable death* (*Mita Yafa*) in the Talmud centers on merciful dying, not mercy killing (Carmi). Each dying person should be comforted by relatives, friends, and physicians. Prayers for life to end are permissible. Once a patient is near death, treatments that interrupt dying should be discontinued (Bleich).

Greco-Roman Antiquity

By the fifth century B.C.E. Greek physicians and elite citizens were praising health as one of the greatest human goods. The goals of the physician's art were "to bring health in all cases of sickness [and] preservation of health to those who are well" (Hippocratic Corpus, "Regimen in Acute Diseases," p. 71). Greek physicians recognized the limitations of their art. Modestly conceived, their goals were "to do away with the sufferings of the sick, to lessen the violence of their diseases, and to refuse to treat those who are overmastered by their diseases" (Hippocratic Corpus, "The Art," p. 193). Physicians would abuse their art and ruin their reputations if they attempted to prolong the lives of the severely sick and injured. A terminally-ill patient's death would be blamed on the physician's lack of skill, so it behooved the physician to refuse even to try to treat at all. Galen (131–201 C.E.) and other Roman physicians adapted those values and goals to Roman life and its institutions.

Although the Greek heritage is unambiguous about the limits of life prolongation, it includes two traditions related to physician-aided death. Vastly influential in Western medicine, the Hippocratic Oath has physicians swear that they will not "give a deadly drug to anybody if asked for it" or even "make a suggestion" to that effect (Edelstein, p. 6). Debate continues over whether that oath reflects a Pythagorean origin or some other origin (Edelstein, Carrick, Anagnastopoulos). Insofar as it reflects opinions of the Pythagorean sect, it would oppose physician-assisted euthanasia in an almost Hebraic sense. With the gods as keepers and humans as their possessions, people sin against the gods if they seek to escape from their posts in life. Insofar as it is non-Pythagorean, the oath could reflect the philosophical logic of Plato (c. 427–348 B.C.E.) and Aristotle (384–322 B.C.E.): Because health is one of the greatest human goods and restoration of heath is the ultimate end of medicine, the termination of life is contrary to medical practice (Anagnastopoulos).

In contrast to the prohibition of physician-assisted death in the oath, Plato, Aristotle, and Stoic philosophers from Zeno (c. 336–264 B.C.E., Greece) to Seneca (4 B.C.E.–65 C.E., Rome) argued that incurably sick adults who consume vital resources of the city—the polis—should die from neglect or be put to death involuntarily (Carrick; Anagnastopoulos). Similarly, deformed and sickly infants should be exposed or drowned for the good of the community, the highest and greatest human end according to Plato and Aristotle. Exposure included taking newborns to rock caverns or casting them into the sea. By law in Sparta and Rome newborns were examined by nonparents for anatomic flawlessness and vigor to determine which ones should be exposed (Amundsen, 1987).

Seneca praised the ability of humans to choose when to end their lives. People should quit life nobly rather than await the cruel endings "either of disease or of man" (Seneca, quoted in Carrick, p. 145). Certain elite citizens, virgins, married women, slaves, common persons, and soldiers ended their lives when they were faced with humiliation, a fearful future, illness, or old age (Van Hooff).

Opposed to suicide in those instances, Aristotle held that death is "the most terrible of all things" (quoted in

Carrick, p. 51). Suicide also conflicted with Aristotle's theory of human virtue: the nobility of facing death bravely versus the cowardly quitting of life when one is faced with misfortune.

Christianity

Christianity emerged from Judaism and flourished in the Roman world. The early churches regarded Hebrew Scripture as the authoritative word of God even as they reinterpreted it as forecasting the life, death, and resurrection of Jesus. Christians thus inherited Hebraic and Jewish teachings about life and death.

EARLY CHRISTIANITY. Christians regarded God as the creator and sustainer of human life and opposed suicide in response to suffering or despair. Contrary to the myth that Christians were inclined to commit suicide to escape from life and be with God, Christ, and their departed loved ones, early Christians ardently opposed self-induced death (Amundsen, 1998).

With Jesus as their model, Christians added new themes to Jewish opposition to suicide and mercy killing. They accented the redemptive dimensions of suffering (2 Corinthians 12:7–10, Hebrews 12:5–11). Faced with pain and death, they too should exclaim, "Not my will, but thine be done" (Luke 22:42). Beginning with the early church (James. 5:10), Christians praised Job, who endured grave suffering steadfastly. Patience and steadfastness were valued all the more because of frequent persecutions (1 Peter 4:12–5:1).

Based on Jesus's teaching that all humans are the children of a loving Father (Luke 15), Christians also displayed mercy and offered care for sick, infirm, and dying persons (Luke 4:16–21, 6:36, 8:26–56, 10:29–37). Believing that no human group should be despised or considered unworthy of life, they condemned cruel executions, abortion, infanticide, and suicide by the second century (Amundsen, 1987).

AUGUSTINE. Augustine (354–430 c.e.) developed systematic criticisms of suicide. Like Aristotle, he argued that self-inflicted death was cowardly. He also viewed it as contrary to the Sixth Commandment, "Thou shall not kill." He regarded suicide as a mortal sin because it excluded the possibility of repentance (Amundsen, 1989). With the establishment of Christianity as the official religion of the Roman Empire after 325, self-killing was equated with homicide. In central and northern Europe the properties of suicides were confiscated, their corpses were desecrated, and they were excluded from Christian burial grounds.

THOMAS AQUINAS AND MODERN ROMAN CATHOLICISM. Thomas Aquinas (1225–1274) expanded on Augustine's arguments against suicide in ways that have shaped Catholic perspectives to the present time. Suicide and by extension induced euthanasia for sufferers were and are viewed as contrary to Christian tradition, natural law, the well-being of society, Christian compassion, and, most important, the dominion of God over human life (O'Malley; Sacred Congregation for the Doctrine of the Faith).

Through the centuries Catholics condemned physician-induced euthanasia as well as ending the lives of mentally or physically handicapped persons. At the same time, decades before the right to die movement began, Catholic authorities distinguished between "ordinary" and "extraordinary" medical treatments and argued that incurably ill persons in most circumstances had the right to refuse advanced medical interventions (Kelley; Pope Pius XII).

PROTESTANTISM. On issues involving life and death the Protestant reformers of the sixteenth century differed little from their early Christian and Roman Catholic predecessors. By the seventeenth century, however, certain Lutheran and Calvinist theologians were arguing that some self-inflicted deaths stemmed from mental imbalance. Holding that traditional arguments that cosigned the souls of suicides to eternal damnation were subject to human hubris, they also argued that the soul's eternal destiny was for God alone to decide (Ferngren). Directly countering the inclusive condemnation of Catholic heritage, the English poet and Anglican prelate John Donne (1572–1631) reasoned that some suicides did not violate natural law, human reason, Scripture, or the dominion of God over human life.

The lack of unanimity within seventeenth-century Protestantism increased in the ensuing centuries (Numbers and Amundsen 1998 [1986]). In the 1930s and afterward Anglican, Episcopalian, and Unitarian clergy played active roles in euthanasia societies in Great Britain and the United States. Beginning in the 1950s, a Protestant Episcopalian priest, Joseph Fletcher, became the most influential advocate of mercy killing in the United States (Fletcher; Vanderpool, 1997). Fletcher opposed the declaration against legalized mercy killing by his own denomination in 1952, by the Presbyterian General Assembly in 1951, and by the assertion of Willard L. Sperry, dean of the Harvard Divinity School, that legalized euthanasia cuts "against the whole basis and practice of medicine" (Sperry, 1948, p. 988).

Nevertheless, Jews, Catholics, and Protestants remained united about the virtue of helping persons die peacefully and naturally not by inducing death but by alleviating suffering and isolation through attentive care. The literature on consoling the dying that first flourished in Catholicism in the fifteenth century was adopted readily by Calvinists (Reformed Protestants) and Anglicans and transformed by Methodists and those in other denominations (Beaty; Vanderpool, 1998 [1986]). Francis Bacon rightly forecast how this literature harmonized with medical euthanasia in its original sense: special care of the dying.

The Law

Continental and Anglo-American law during the centuries following the advent of Christianity included a mixture of Roman law, the customs of various ethnic groups and communities, and canon laws developed and systematized by Roman Catholic jurists. Having inherited the Hebraic-Jewish conviction that God is the ultimate law-giver and judge and holding to the view that universal truths can be rationally discerned from the laws of nature, Catholic canonists sought systematically to adapt Roman law to Christian teaching (Plucknett). The cohesiveness, power, and geographical expansion of the Church enabled canon law to exert a profound influence on national laws, including the tradition of common law in England and its colonies.

Canon law was first adopted in England at the Council of Hereford in 673 C.E. Rooted in centuries of custom, canon law influenced the development of the common law from the time of the reforms of William the Conqueror (1027–1087 C.E.), to the vastly influential interpretations of the common law by Sir Edward Coke (1552–1654), to the present time (Plucknett; Williams, 1957). The canon laws adopted at the Council of Hereford included prohibition of suicide (*Washington et al. v. Glucksberg et al.*).

Savage penalties for suicide—bodily desecration, property forfeiture, and exclusion from Christian burial grounds—were set forth in common law by the thirteenth century and were rigorously enforced between 1500 and 1700. Coke wrote in 1644 that suicide is a category of murder and the property of suicides should be forfeited. In the middle of the sixteenth century, the Court at Common Bench—one of the pivotal councils of English sovereigns that developed and defined the common law—observed, as if it were taking a page from Thomas Aquinas, that suicide "is an Offence against Nature, against God, and against the King … To destroy one's self is contrary to Nature, and a Thing most horrible" (quoted in *Washington et al. v. Glucksberg et al.*)

Penalties against suicide were removed in England in 1823, followed by abolishment of suicide as a crime in 1961 (Markson). Beginning with Pennsylvania in 1701, the harsh common law penalties enacted in several American colonies were also abolished (*Washington et al. v. Glucksberg et al.*).

Nevertheless, laws in England, the majority of American states, and most western democracies associated assisted suicide with homicide and with suicide as a grievous wrong (MacDonald; Markson; *Washington et al v. Glucksberg et al.*). Considered a criminal offense ranging from second degree murder to manslaughter, laws against assisted suicide never contained exceptions for those who helped to end the lives of persons who were terminally ill, fatally wounded, or condemned to death (*Washington et al v. Glucksberg et al.*). American statutes that explicitly outlawed assisted suicide were first enacted in New York in 1828, then most other American jurisdictions. The Model Penal Code of the twentieth century, including its official 1980 draft, opposes anyone's "willingness to participate in taking the life of another, even though the act may be accomplished with the consent, or at the request, of the suicide victim" (quoted from *Washington et al v. Glucksberg et al.*).

Criminalization of assisted suicide was and is based on States' interests to protect and preserve human life, prevent suicides by persons who are young, elderly, or suffering from mental disorders, and protect the ethical integrity and healing roles of the medical profession (*Washington et al v. Glucksberg et al.*; Kamisar). The relatively high incidences of acquittals, suspended sentences, and reprieves of citizen- and doctor-induced euthanasia proves that, "The Law in Action is as malleable as the Law On the Books is [in almost every State] uncompromising" (Kamisar, p. 408).

Secular Legacies

As minority opinions in the dominant Christian culture, various humanists from the sixteenth through the eighteenth centuries spoke of the permissibility of suicide for seriously sick and injured persons. Enamored with Greco-Roman culture, Michel de Montaigne (1533–1592) voiced the unorthodox views that the "most voluntary death is the finest" and that "God gives us permission" to take our lives "when he reduces us to such a condition that living is worse than dying" (Montaigne, 1946 [1580], p. 338).

Skepticism, secular interests, and an emphasis on personal pleasure became more pervasive during the seventeenth and eighteenth centuries. English playwrights such as John Dryden (1631–1700) and Deists such as Charles Blount (1654–1693) defended certain suicides motivated by honor, suffering, lost love, or self-willed destiny (Ferngren). These themes informed the thought of one of the Enlightenment's most influential representatives, David Hume (1711–1776).

HUME. Hume began his essay "On Suicide" (1963 [1783]) with an attack on "superstition and false religion," which compel a person to prolong "a miserable existence … lest he offend his Maker" (pp. 252–253). He held that overwhelming suffering and wishes to die should be regarded as calling persons from life "in the clearest and most express terms" (p. 259). Like Socrates and Plato, Hume argued that persons plagued with suffering that negates social usefulness are not obligated to prolong their lives. He also held that each person's "native liberty" consists of carrying out an autonomous course of action in keeping with one's "chance for happiness" (p. 261).

Hume's critics included Immanuel Kant (1724–1824), who censured self-killing because it cannot be willed as a universal action without undermining the possibility of morality, that is, the existence of rational beings. Kant also viewed suicide as a violation of one's duty to God, the sovereign of all life. Unlike Kant, nineteenth-century thinkers such as Friedrich Nietzsche (1844–1900) adopted Hume's view that autonomous persons have the right to end their lives when disease extinguishes pleasure and social usefulness.

DARWINISM. Charles Darwin's (1809–1892) theory of evolution played a pivotal role in reshaping Western religion, science, literature, and political philosophy and policy (Vanderpool, 1973). The secular understanding of the world advanced by Darwin and Darwinians directly affected views of euthanasia. The Darwinian theme that human progress depends on the survival of the fittest through natural selection engendered a Westernwide eugenics movement that promoted active interventions to rid the world of the "unfit" (Vanderpool, 1973; Pernick). Other Darwinians argued that euthanasia in the form of doctor-induced painless death was permissible because "nature certainly knows nothing" of the sacredness of life ("Euthanasia," p. 91) and "the doctrine of evolution" justifies shortening the lives of sufferers in the face of outmoded religious opposition (South Carolina Medical Association, p. xv).

EXPERIMENTAL MEDICAL SCIENCE. Well before the Darwinian revolution physician scientists performed extensive laboratory experiments on the physiology of death and resuscitation from which they developed a mechanistic understanding of life and death. After describing his experiments on "the laws of the vital functions," the British doctor A. P. W. Philip concluded that human life is not "a subject of peculiar mystery" (p. 211).

That mechanistic understanding led to the dominant twentieth-century view that the human body is a physical-chemical and mechanical entity that can and should be salvaged with sufficient repair. Ivan Pavlov's (1849–1936)

vivisection experiments with dogs proved how severe and sequential injuries could be repaired one after the other to the point where a dog's death could be seen to represent a failure in technical mastery. This was the backdrop to ever greater attempts to sustain human life and to the neglect of care for dying patients after 1945.

Modes of Medical Practice to 1870

In keeping with the cultural heritages of Judaism, Christianity, and experimental medical science, physicians from the seventeenth century to 1870 focused on mitigating the effects of disease and the ultimate goals of saving and sustaining human life. In the eighteenth century the goal of saving life engendered a Western-wide movement to establish humane societies to rescue persons who appeared to be dead from drowning and other causes. Imbued with a sense of progress, physicians, human society members, and others discovered many means by which life could be restored and extended: manual breathing methods, ammonia, strychnine, bloodletting, tongue stretching, and electric shocks (Liss).

Nevertheless, in keeping with the admonition of Francis Bacon in the seventeenth century, a number of notable physicians lectured and wrote about the duty "to soothe the last moments of existence" (Ferriar, p. 392). Addressing his German faculty of medicine colleagues, Carl F. H. Marx termed the physician's "skilful alleviation of suffering" as "that science, called euthanasia, which checks oppressing features of illness, relieves pain, and renders the … inescapable hour a most peaceful one" (p. 405). Marx and others stressed shared themes: the painlessness of dying versus myths about "death agonies," the necessity of not disturbing dying patients, the comforting presence of physicians, expertise in symptom relief, the skilled use of opiates, the immorality of purposefully shortening life, and steadfast opposition to "dangerous and dubious treatment measures" to prolong life (p. 407).

These advocates of euthanasia in its original sense of helping patients to die naturally and peacefully appealed to moral, philosophical, and spiritual values: how close attention to the process of dying causes "the physical process of death [to lose] much of its horror" for patients and physicians alike (Ferriar, p. 392), the virtue of alleviating "the supreme anguish of the patient's mind" (Marx, p. 411), the humanity of caring for "a powerless and suffering creature" when "the scene of life is closing" (Dendy, p. 121), and the assurance that humane and steadfast care "will ever prove consolation to the hearts of attached friends" (Dendy, p. 124). Predicated on these values, end-of-life care was deemed "not unworthy of the attention of the most scientific physician" (Dendy, p. 124).

All these physicians strongly opposed futile life-prolonging measures utilized by inexperienced and uninformed practitioners. Physicians ought to be able to know "when any hope [of cure] has departed" (Marx, p. 405) and they should honor the moral principle of refraining from harm. John Ferriar criticized "ignorant practitioners" who "torment" dying patients with "liquors of different kinds" (pp. 393, 397). W. C. Dendy spoke of the cruelty of using stimulants such as brandy or ammonia "when hope is gone" (p. 122). Marx decried the use of caustics, "external irritants," "and other tortures" (p. 409).

In the first half of the nineteenth century when educated physicians were closing ranks against poorly trained and unorthodox practitioners, this tradition of terminal care was set forth as a profession. Thomas Percival's (1740–1804) widely published code of medical ethics shaped the codes of several U.S. medical societies and became the primary moral foundation for membership in the new American Medical Association (AMA). The AMA's Code of Ethics was unanimously adopted in 1847, and its sections on the care for dying patients were lifted verbatim from Percival's Medical Ethics. When doctors find that they cannot "revive expiring life," they should "soothe the bed of death" and not "abandon a patient because the case is deemed incurable, for [their] attendance may continue to be highly useful ... by alleviating pain ... and by soothing mental anguish" (Code of Medical Ethics of the American Medical Association p. 221).

Medical Practice and Turmoil: 1870–1945

SUSTAINING LIFE AND CARING FOR THE DYING. The ability to cure diseases and repair injuries increased exponentially between 1870 and 1945. The sophisticated advances in surgery and curative medicine during this time were symbiotic with the creation and explosive growth of modern hospitals. Increasing from 200 in 1873 to 4,438 in 1928, these hospitals were monuments to scientific medicine. They became and remain the central places in which an ever increasing number of medical specialists treat countless patients from all walks of life. Within these hospitals, new techniques for resuscitation and life prolongation were readily developed and adopted: "the struggle to reactivate the whole organism" with blistering benzine compresses (Jellinek, p. 216), injections of epinephrine via long hypodermic needles directly into the failing heart in the 1900s, open-chest message during cardiac surgery in the 1930s, and positive- and negative-pressure ventilation apparatuses and masks in the 1930s (Liss; Hermreck).

The resulting institutionalization of curative medicine and life-sustaining techniques detracted from care for dying patients. The increasing lack of concern is mirrored in revisions of the AMA Code of Ethics. The two paragraphs on care for the dying in the 1847 code were reduced to four lines in 1903, then to this part of a sentence in 1912: "a physician should not abandon or neglect the patient because the disease is deemed incurable" (Vanderpool, 1997, p. 40).

Only a few increasingly isolated physicians continued to explore and write about "the medical art" of "euthanasia" as "aid of an easy, gentle, and placid death" (Munk, pp. 4–5). By the late 1920s doctors were beginning to leave dying patients in care of nurses, clergy and sorrowing relatives. Alfred Worcester considered "this shifting of responsibility" to be "unpardonable" (p. 33). Worcester also lamented the lack of teaching about terminal care in medical schools and decried the increasing use of "modern methods of resuscitation" such as cardiac stimulation for dying patients. Worcester exclaimed that his peers "ought to know better" (p. 47). Beyond his criticisms, Worcester published a lengthy book chapter that outlined what medical students should be taught about care of the dying. Years later Walter C. Alvarez praised Worcester's "excellent little book" as one "every physician in the land should read and re-read" (Alvarez, p. 87).

DOCTOR-INDUCED DEATH FOR THE DESPERATELY ILL. Many factors contributed to the post-1870 turmoil over the morality of doctors' inducing the deaths of suffering and incurable patients. Several of these preceded the development of modern hospitals by a few decades, but included factors—such as the discovery of anesthesia—that made modern surgery in these hospitals possible. The factors underlying the debate included the resurgence of secular challenges to traditional Jewish and Christian understandings of human life and death in the second half of the nineteenth century, the discovery and refinements of anesthesia after 1846, the development the hypodermic syringe (introduced in the United States in 1856) by which morphine could be injected by physicians with quick and powerful results, paternalistic physician supervision of patients with dread disease in modern hospitals, and the public's increasing reliance on physicians to relieve their aches and pains (Vanderpool, 1997, p. 37).

Turmoil over the painlessly putting to death of incurable sufferers began after the speech by Samuel D. Williams before the Birmingham Speculative Club in 1870 was turned into a pamphlet and seized upon as newsworthy. Williams defended the proposition that in "all cases of hopeless and painful illness it should be the recognized duty of the medical attendant, whenever desired by the patient to administer chloroform ... or ... other anesthetic ... so as to destroy consciousness at once, and put the sufferer at once to a quick and painless death" ("Euthanasia," p. 90).

Williams's speech became newsworthy for several reasons. It directly challenged doctors who regularly used chloroform and hypodermic morphine and were responsible for dealing with catastrophic illness and determining when patients' conditions were incurable. It challenged lawyers because Williams's proposition was illegal. It alarmed the clergy because of the clergy's historical opposition to induced death. It engaged the American public because opiates were unregulated before 1920 and because dying persons often were cared for at home.

Through the years journals and newspapers perpetuated the debate and reported about euthanasia societies, attempts to legalize euthanasia, and individuals who admitted to ending the lives of desperately sick persons or were brought to trial for doing so ("Euthanasia"; Rosenberg and Aronstam; "Shakers Justify Killing Sister"; "Physician Admits to 'Mercy' Killings"). The arguments set forth in the early years of the debate became fixtures in the years to come (Vanderpool, 1997).

Proponents argued that euthanasia is merciful and that refusal to perform it is cruel. Doctors have the duty to alleviate pain as well as prolong life. Life racked with pain is hardly sacred, and evolution undermines the value of individual life ("Euthanasia"). The fact that some physicians were already practicing it surreptitiously attests to its moral acceptability. People deserve "at least as much kindness and sympathy" as animals that readily are put out of their misery (Wolbarst, p. 354).

Medical societies and most physicians found "insuperable objections" to the practice (Victor Robinson, 1913, p. 145). Intentionally ending the lives of suffering patients repeatedly was declared to be antithetical to the traditions of medicine. That "ghastly" practice would undermine the physician's premier goal of saving life and turn doctors into executioners ("The Moral Side of Euthanasia"). Euthanasia was a crime, and legalized euthanasia would be abused by devious physicians and nonphysicians. It would display cruelty to dying patients who would question their worth and fear for their lives rather than receive the care they deserved. It would devalue suffering, cheapen life, and undermine the dominion of God. Between 1906 and 1969 opponents of physician-caused death in Great Britain and the United States united to defeat the many attempts to legalize euthanasia.

KILLING UNWANTED HUMAN BEINGS. Advocacy to end the lives of unwanted human beings—euthanasia in the *third* sense—emerged in Europe and the United States toward the end of the nineteenth century. Those who promoted euthanasia for "defectives" often claimed that civilized sentimentality "nullified nature's methods of eliminating the unfit" ("Foreign Letters," p. 1617). Others spoke of the "benevolent extermination of degenerates," (Smith, p. 50) the "inhumanity" of not relieving a "gibbering driveling idiot" from his or her misery (William Robinson, p. 88), and the need to "liberate" retarded and insane persons from "tortured mentalities" (Wolbarst, 1935, p. 332). Those despised groups were thought to be interfering with the progressive evolution of the human race (Smith).

Devotees of eugenic euthanasia differed over which groups should be eliminated and how their lives should be ended: denying treatment to newborn "monstrosities" and/or actively ending the lives of insane persons and/or others. After Dr. J. J. Haiselden created a storm of controversy between 1915 and 1919 over his refusal to save the lives of several severely defective newborns and young children, eugenic euthanasia rhetoric continued, but its practice remained hidden and rare in the United States (Pernick).

In Germany proposals for exterminating unwanted persons became political policy. In 1868 Ernst Haeckel (1834–1919), a disciple of Darwin, argued that Germany's physical and mental incurables should be put to death painlessly. Haeckel praised the Spartans for killing their deformed and weak children, in contrast to the "antiselection" of Christian compassion for the infirm and sickly (Lifton).

Germany was considered the new polis. Each doctor should become a "physician to the Volk" for the "perfection of the health" of the people (Lifton, p. 30). The "biological body of the German people" should be invigorated through programs of physical fitness and the science of "race hygiene" (Ernst, p. 574). Preceded by the recommendation of a child-welfare pioneer Sigmund Engle that "cripples, high-grade cretins, idiots, and children with gross deformities" should be destroyed painlessly (quoted in Pernick, p. 23), a jurist Karl Binding and academic psychiatrist Alfred Hoche called for the elimination of mentally ill and retarded persons in their influential book titled *Release and Destruction of Lives Not Worth Living,* 1920.

Eugenic beliefs infused the thinking of mainstream physicians, academicians, and scientists in Germany well before their adoption by Adolf Hitler (1889–1945) as National Socialist (Nazi) policy (Shevell). Physicians played a critical role in creating the concept of racial hygiene, supporting the Nazi rise to power, and administering sterilization and extermination programs (Ernst; White).

Shortly before Germany's invasion of Poland in September 1939 Hitler directed that children with severe mongolism, hydrocephaly, paralysis, and deformities be registered. In thirty pediatric departments across Germany doctors supervised the registering, sorting out, and killing of 5,000 children (Lauter and Meyer). Within months Hitler issued a decree that mentally incurable adolescents and adults should "be granted a mercy death." That decree created an agency that orchestrated physician-directed killing of over 70,000 persons in gas chambers disguised as showers (Shevell).

When they were stereotyped as destructive to the health of the body politic, Jews, Gypsies, and others were consigned to a massive, bureaucratic doctor-run extermination program that was modeled on its medical predecessors. Those programs lasted only six years, but their horror is unforgettable. After World War II the World Medical Association (WMA) and several national medical associations condemned the Nazi extermination programs.

Medical Practice and Debate: 1945–1960s

MERCY KILLING. The revulsion against Nazi practices did not curtail campaigns to legalize mercy killing (Vanderpool, 1997). At the end of the war a new campaign to legalize euthanasia backed by 1,776 physicians and 54 eminent clergypersons began in New York, and from 1945 through 1969 petitions were signed and legislative attempts were made in the United States and Great Britain (Wilson). In spite of those efforts and the passionate defense of euthanasia by Joseph Fletcher, bills to legalize mercy killing were not introduced for a vote or were voted down. At its meeting in 1950 the World Medical Association resolved that national medical associations should "condemn the practice of euthanasia in any circumstances" ("Official Notes").

THE PREEMINENCE OF PROLONGATION. Effective and sophisticated ways to save life were developed during and after World War II, including penicillin and other antibiotics and methods to overcome cardiac arrests through the use of open-chest heart massage in the 1950s and closed chest defibrillators in the 1960s. The reversal of cardiac arrest was called "the restoration of life after death" in the media (Bains, p. 1346). The use of nasogastric feeding tubes and blood transfusions became widespread, and mechanical ventilators as a "complete substitution of the spontaneous ventilation of the patient" were refined (Petty, p. 2).

Along with these technological advancements, the physician's duty to sustain life achieved a preeminent status in hospitals from the 1940s through the 1960s. Lest they betray their training, many doctors felt that they should do everything possible to sustain life rather than "just let the patient die" (Glaser and Strauss, p. 196). Even in the face of dire prognoses heroic treatments often were continued until a patient's organ systems deteriorated, extensive pain was experienced, the patient's family reached "an advanced stage of grieving," or a doctor's colleagues intervened (Glaser and Strauss, p. 199).

Graphic accounts of attempts to prolong life became news in the 1950s. No story was more influential than that of a widow's anguish over her husband's treatment in a metropolitan hospital in 1957. "If you are very ill," the widow said, "modern medicine can save you. If you are going to die it can prevent you from so doing for a very long time." She lamented the use of "all the latest wonder drugs, the tricks and artificial wizardry" that "deprived death of its dignity." Upon begging a doctor to "cease this torture," she was told that "they had to maintain life" ("A Way of Dying," pp. 53–54). The reasons for the priority of prolongation included the equation of medical practice with mastery of the new technologies, death as the ultimate evil, the equation of death with defeat and medical failure, and lost concern with care for the dying. "Who causes these extraordinary measures to be continued indefinitely?" one doctor asked. "In most cases, it is the physician himself" (Rynearson, p. 86).

CARE FOR THE DYING. The few physicians who perpetuated the tradition of natural dying displayed despair. Describing how he was "bringing comfort to the slowly dying" in their homes, Walter C. Alvarez wrote that dying persons "should never be cast off and neglected simply because they cannot be 'cured'" (pp. 89–90). Alvarez observed that "rarely does anyone ever discuss the subject in medical schools, at medical meetings, or in the journals." Like his predecessors, he decried the abuses of prolongation:

> When I myself lie dying, I hope that I will have by me some wise and kindly physician who will keep interns from … puncturing my veins, or putting a tube down my nose, or giving me enemas and drastic medicines (p. 91).

Depicting his medical training between 1957 and 1960, Roger Bulger described how students were taught "the intricacies of every method or technique that might possibly bring someone back from *extremis* but no one has ever suggested that we ought to attempt to care" for the person beneath "the multiplicity of tubes that are entering him from every direction" (Bulger, pp. 23–24). In hospitals doctors probe and test, nurses are indifferent, and the dying "'crock' is a second class citizen" (Kohn, p. 1180).

SHORTENING LIFE AND ASSISTING IN SUICIDE. In the context of the preeminence of prolongation, instances of euthanasia in the *fourth* sense—painless death to the point of shortening life—were designated "invisible acts" by hospital personnel in the late 1950s (Glaser and Strauss, p. 198). At times, however, a patient's right to receive pain relief at the cost of abbreviating life was advocated openly (Fletcher; Ayd).

Euthanasia in the *fifth* sense—assisting patients to end their lives—was practiced even more surreptitiously. Suffering patients who begged to die at times were relegated to a "dying room" where overdoses of pills were left at the bedside and patients were unwatched for long periods so that they could "manage" their own deaths (Glaser and Strauss). Stories of doctors giving overdoses of opiates for patients to take at home were told to clergypersons and known by physicians (Sperry, 1948). The extent of the practice of shortening life and assisting suicide in medical practice remains unknown.

TWO IMPENDING REFORMS. Descriptions of dreadful and often futile attempts to prolong life increased in medical and popular journals in the 1950s and 1960s. Those descriptions identified two problems: how to curtail life-prolonging attempts so that patients could die naturally (passive euthanasia) and how to care for sick persons and aged individuals at the end of life.

Father Gerald Kelly wrote a sophisticated analysis of the first problem in 1950, and a way to resolve it was announced by Pope Pius XII seven years later: "The doctor … has no separate or independent right where the patient is concerned … he can take action only if the patient … gives him permission" (p. 285). Despite opposition, several physicians, including non-Catholics, citing the widow's story and the pronouncement of the Pope, agreed that "the decision concerning further treatment should be in terms of the patient's own interests" (Rynearson, p. 86). In their articles those doctors occasionally outlined "components of the care of the dying patient": death with "dignity, respect and humanity," minimal pain, and familiar surroundings that promote sharing with family and friends (Rynearson, p. 87).

In 1966 Charles Hofling observed that the problem of determining when to terminate life by withholding various medical interventions had "thus far received little thoughtful, and very little authoritative, attention" from his fellow practitioners. In fact, "the typical approach has been to arrive at a course of action with a minimum of discussion." Convinced that this approach "will force the whole matter on the public's attention," he called for "multidisciplinary consultations" on the part of physicians, lawyers, clergy, sociologists, and "quite possibly" philosophers (pp. 43–46).

Those authors were the prophets of two impending reforms: the "right to die" movement and the "death and dying" movement.

Conclusions

An untutored glance at the title of this entry could give the impression that it would be far more conceptually balanced—though less provocative—if it were entitled "Ending and Sustaining Life, Historical Aspects." In fact, due to the multiple meanings of euthanasia in medical history, this entry does balance the many ways doctors have dealt with ending human life on the one hand and sustaining and extending life on the other.

This history is filled with an intriguing combination of continuities and tensions. The continuities surface in the first cultural legacy explored in this entry—Hebraic and Jewish perspectives. Its major motifs forecast enduring themes for the ensuing three thousand years: a commitment to saving and extending life whenever possible, a mandate to display concern and care for dying persons, and, based on the sacredness and ultimate value of human life, an opposition to mercy killing of incurably sick persons, disabled children and others.

Christianity inherited these motifs from Judaism and embedded them within Western culture to the extent that they became moral givens. The cultural transformation that occurred over the centuries included the way canon law infused common law and the way those motifs shaped codes of conduct, common commitments, and the increasing power of the medical profession.

Historical tensions were both exterior to and inherent within these continuities. Exterior to them, Nazi programs of extinguishing unwanted and despised persons appealed to Greco-Roman precedent, but due to the depth of Western cultural transformation that had occurred, became equated with unspeakable moral deviance. The Nazi programs secured the loyalty of a number of German physicians enamored by Aryan supremacy and eugenic-based notions of evolutionary progress. These programs were condemned as betrayals of professional ethics that continued to uphold the moral mandates transmitted to Western culture through Judaism and Christianity. Euthanasia in its current meaning—a doctor's terminating the life of a terminally ill patient—began and remained contentious because it drew upon factors that were both inherent within and external to the reigning motifs of Western medicine. Advocates of mercy killing appealed to the themes of mercy for sufferers of fatal illnesses and the cruelty of not relieving persons from pain. At the same time, against the strictures of common law and in the name of naturalistic evolution and/or secular notions of self-ownership and autonomy, these advocates countenanced circumscribed forms of homicide and assisted suicide.

Within the historic continuities, tensions developed between the primacy of prolonging human life and humanitarian care for the bodily, emotional, and spiritual needs of persons who could not be cured. By the eighteenth century physicians devoted to this humanitarian ideal began opposing the sustaining of life by every available means for persons at the end of life. The last decades of history covered by this essay end when experimental science provided means by which to extend life in hitherto fore unimagined ways. Devoted to the prolongation of life, scientific medicine became entrenched in modern hospitals and the preoccupation of medical training.

The agonizing stories of patients, the troubled concerns voiced by a handful of physicians, and the voices of historical continuity from the Pope and physicians with similar concerns declared that modern medicine was losing its moral moorings. The seeds for the impending reforms regarding the rights to refuse advanced life-prolonging treatment and to receive attentive humane end-of-life care were sown in the late 1950s and 1960s. Their germinating power lay in the fact that they were gleaned from dominant cultural motifs that had shaped the practice of medicine through centuries of Western history.

HAROLD Y. VANDERPOOL (1995)
REVISED BY AUTHOR

SEE ALSO: *Advance Directives and Advance Care Planning; Clinical Ethics; Death; Death, Definition and Determination of; Holocaust; Informed Consent; Medical Codes and Oaths; Palliative Care and Hospice; Right to Die: Policy and Law; Surrogate Decision-Making; and other Life Sustaining Treatment and Euthanasia subentries*

BIBLIOGRAPHY

Albury, W. R. 1993. "Ideas of Life and Death." In *Companion Encyclopedia of the History of Medicine*, vol. 1, ed. W. F. Bynum and Roy Porter. London: Routledge.

Alvarez, Walter C. 1952. "Care of the Dying." *Journal of the American Medical Association* 150(2): 86–91.

Amundsen, Darrel W. 1987. "Medicine and the Birth of Defective Children: Approaches of the Ancient World." In *Euthanasia and the Newborn: Conflicts Regarding Saving Lives*, ed. Richard C. McMillan, H. Tristram Engelhardt, Jr., and Stuart F. Spicker. Dordrecht, Netherlands: D. Reidel.

Amundsen, Darrel W. 1989. "Suicide and Early Christian Values." In *Suicide and Euthanasia: Historical and Contemporary Themes*, ed. Baruch A. Brody. Dordrecht, Netherlands: Kluwer.

Amundsen, Darrel W. 1998. "The Ninth Circuit Court's Treatment of the History of Suicide by Ancient Jews and Christians." *Issues in Law and Medicine* 13(4): 365–423.

Anagnastopoulos, Georgios. 2000. "Euthanasia and the Physician's Role." In *Bioethics: Ancient Themes in Contemporary Issues,* ed. Mark G. Kuczewski and Ronald Polansky. Cambridge, MA: MIT Press.

Ayd, Frank J., Jr. 1962. "The Hopeless Case." *Journal of the American Medical Association* 181(13): 1099–1102.

Bacon, Francis. 1674 (1605). *Of the Advancement and Proficiency of Learning.* London: Thomas Williams.

Bains, Jatinder. 1998. "From Reviving the Living to Raising the Dead." *Social Science and Medicine* 47(9): 1341–1349.

Baldwin, Simeon. 1899. "The Natural Right to a Natural Death." *Journal of Social Science* 37: 1–17.

Beaty, Nancy Lee. 1970. *The Craft of Dying.* New Haven, CT: Yale University Press.

Beauchamp, Tom L. 1989. "Suicide in the Age of Reason." In *Suicide and Euthanasia: Historical and Contemporary Themes,* ed. Baruch A. Brody. Dordrecht, Netherlands: Kluwer.

Bleich, J. David. 1979. "The Obligation to Heal in the Judaic Tradition: A Comparative Analysis." In *Jewish Bioethics,* ed. Fred Rosner and J. David Bleich. New York: Sanhedrin Press.

Brody, Baruch A. 1989. "An Historical Introduction to Jewish Casuistry on Suicide and Euthanasia." In *Suicide and Euthanasia: Historical and Contemporary Themes,* ed. Baruch A. Brody. Dordrecht, Netherlands: Kluwer.

Bryant, E. E. 1895. *The Reign of Antoninus Pius.* Cambridge, Eng.: Cambridge University Press.

Bulger, Roger. 1960. "The Dying Patient and His Doctor." *Harvard Medical Alumni Bulletin,* April, pp. 23–25, 53–57.

Carmi, A. 1984. "Live Like a King: Die Like a King." In *Euthanasia,* ed. A. Carmi. New York: Springer-Verlag.

Carrick, Paul. 1985. *Medical Ethics in Antiquity: Philosophical Perspectives on Abortion and Euthanasia.* Dordrecht, Netherlands: D. Reidel.

Code of Medical Ethics of the American Medical Association. 1975 (1847). In *Percival's Medical Ethics,* ed. Chauncey D. Leake. New York: Robert E. Krieger Publishing.

Dendy, W. C. 1948. "On the Physiology of Death and the Treatment of the Dying." *Journal of Psychological Medicine and Mental Pathology* 1: 112–124.

"Dr. Norton on Euthanasia." 1906. *New York Times,* January 6, p. 8.

Edelstein, Ludwig. 1967. In *Ancient Medicine: Selected Papers of Ludwig Edelstein,* ed. Owsei Temkin and C. Lilian Temkin. Baltimore: Johns Hopkins Press.

"Editorial: Permissive Euthanasia." 1884. *Boston Medical and Surgical Journal* 110: 19–20.

Emanuel, Ezekiel J. 1994. "The History of Euthanasia Debates in the United States and Britain." *Annals of Internal Medicine* 121(10): 793–802.

Ernst, E. 1996. "50 Years Ago: The Nuremberg Doctors' Tribunal: The Descent towards Medicalised Murder." *Weiner Medizinische Wochensschrift* 146: 574–576.

"Euphoria vs. Euthanasia." 1899. *Journal of the American Medical Association* 32: 674.

"Euthanasia." 1873. *Popular Science Monthly* 3: 90–96.

Ferngren, Gary B. 1989. "The Ethics of Suicide in the Renaissance and Reformation." In *Suicide and Euthanasia: Historical and Contemporary Themes,* ed. Baruch A. Brody. Dordrecht, Netherlands: Kluwer.

Ferriar, John. 1816 (1798). "Of the Treatment of the Dying." In *Medical Histories and Reflections.* Philadelphia: Thomas Dobson.

Fletcher, Joseph. 1960 (1954). *Morals and Medicine.* Boston: Beacon Press.

"Foreign Letters: Social Progress and the Unfit." 1935. *Journal of the American Medical Association* 105: 1617.

Glaser, Barney G., and Strauss, Anselm L. 1965. *Awareness of Dying.* Chicago: Aldine.

Hermreck, Arlo S. 1988. "The History of Cardiopulmonary Resuscitation." *American Journal of Surgery* 156(6): 430–436.

Hippocratic Corpus. 1923a. "The Art." *Hippocrates,* vol. 2, tr. W. H. S. Jones. Cambridge, MA: Harvard University Press.

Hippocratic Corpus. 1923b. "Regimen in Acute Diseases." 1923. In *Hippocrates,* vol. 2, tr. W. H. S. Jones. Cambridge, MA: Harvard University Press.

Hofling, Charles K. 1966. "Terminal Decisions." *Medical Opinion and Review* October, pp. 40–49.

Hooker, Worthington. 1972 (1849). *Physician and Patient.* New York: Arno Press.

Hume, David. 1963 (1783). "On Suicide." In *David Hume on Religion,* ed. Richard Wollheim. New York: World Publishing.

Jakobovits, Immanuel. 1959. *Jewish Medical Ethics.* New York: Bloch.

Jellinek, Stefan. 1947. *Dying, Apparent Death and Resuscitation.* Baltimore: Williams and Wilkins.

Kamisar, Ya. 1977 (1958). "Some Non-Religious Views against Proposed 'Mercy-Killing' Legistation." In *Death, Dying, and Euthanasia,* ed. Dennis J. Horan and David Hall. Washington, D.C.: University Publications of America.

Kelley, Gerald. 1950. "The Duty of Using Artificial Means of Preserving Life." *Theological Studies* 16: 203–220.

Kohn, Lawrence A. 1961. "Thoughts on the Care of the Hopelessly Ill." *Medical Times* 89(11): 1177–1181.

Lauter, H., and Meyer, J. E. 1982. "Mercy Killing without Consent." *Acta Psychiatrica Scandinavica* 65(2): 134–141.

Lifton, Robert Jay. 1986. *The Nazi Doctors: Medical Killing and the Psychology of Genocide.* New York: Basic Books.

Liss, Howard P. 1986. "A History of Resuscitation." *Annals of Emergency Medicine* 15: 65–72.

MacDonald, Michael. 1989. "The Medicalization of Suicide in England: Laymen, Physicians, and Cultural Change: 1500–1870." *The Milbank Quarterly* 67: 69–91.

Markson, David S. 1969. "The Punishment of Suicide—A Need for Change." *Villanova Law Review* 14: 463–483.

Marx, Carl F. H. 1952 (1826). "Medical Euthanasia." *Journal of the History of Medicine and Allied Sciences* 7: 401–416.

Montaigne, Michel. 1946 (1580). "A Custom of the Island of Cea." In *The Essays of Montaigne,* tr. Emit Julius Trechmann. New York: Oxford University Press.

"The Moral Side of Euthanasia." 1885. *Journal of the American Medical Association* 5: 382.

Munk, William. 1977 (1887). *Euthanasia: Or, Medical Treatment in Aid of an Easy Death.* London: Longmans, Green.

Numbers, Ronald L., and Amundsen, Darrel W., eds. 1998 (1986). *Caring and Curing: Health and Medicine in the Western Religious Traditions.* Baltimore: Johns Hopkins University Press.

"Official Notes: The World Medical Association." 1950. *Journal of the American Medical Association* 13(6): 561.

O'Malley, Austin. 1917. "Euthanasia and the Quack." *America* 18: 6–8.

Pernick, Martin S. 1996. *The Black Stork.* New York: Oxford University Press.

Petty, Thomas L. 1988. "The Modern Evolution of Mechanical Ventilation." *Clinics in Chest Medicine* 9(1): 1–10.

Philip, A. P. W. 1834. *An Inquiry into the Nature of Sleep and Death.* London: Henry Renshaw.

"Physician Admits to 'Mercy' Killings." 1935. *New York Times,* November 8, p. l.

Plucknett, Theodore F. T. 1956. *A Concise History of the Common Law.* Boston: Little, Brown and Company.

Pope Pius XII. 1977 (1957). "The Prolongation of Life." In *Death, Dying, and Euthanasia,* ed. Dennis J. Horan and David Mall. Washington, D.C.: University Publications of America.

"The Right to Kill." 1935. *Time* 26: 53–54.

Robinson, Victor, ed. 1913. "A Symposium on Euthanasia." *Medical Review of Reviews* 19: 134–155.

Robinson, William J. 1913. "Euthanasia." *Medical Pharmacology Critic and Guide* 6: 85–90.

Rosenberg, Louis J., and Aronstam, N. E. 1901. "Euthanasia—A Medicolegal Study." *Journal of the American Medical Association* 36: 108–110.

Rynearson, Edward H. 1959. "You Are Standing at the Bedside of a Patient Dying of Untreatable Cancer." *CA: A Cancer Journal for Clinicians* 9: 85–89.

Sacred Congregation for the Doctrine of the Faith. 1980. "Vatican Declaration on Euthanasia." *Origins* 10(10): 154–157.

"Shakers Justify Killing Sister." 1991. *New York Times,* September 14, pp. 3–4.

Shevell, Michael I. 1999. "Neurosciences in the Third Reich: From Ivory Tower to Death Camps." *Canadian Journal of Neurological Sciences* 26: 132–138.

Smith, James LeRoy. 1909. "Shall Degenerates Be Condemned to Death?" *Physical Culture* 21: 49–52.

South Carolina Medical Association. 1879. *Transaction of the South Carolina Medical Association.* Charleston: Edward Perry.

Sperry, Willard L. 1948. "Moral Problems in the Practice of Medicine." *New England Journal of Medicine* 239(26): 986–990.

Sperry, Willard L. 1950. *The Ethical Basis of Medical Practice.* New York: Harper and Brothers.

Suetonius. 1944. *Suetonius,* vol. 1, tr. J. C. Rolfe, Cambridge, MA: Harvard University Press.

Vanderpool, Harold Y. 1973. *Darwin and Darwinism.* Lexington, MA: D.C. Heath.

Vanderpool, Harold Y. 1981. "The Responsibilities of Physicians toward Dying Patients." In *Medical Complications in Cancer Patients,* ed. Jean Klastersky and Maurice J. Staquet. New York: Raven Press.

Vanderpool, Harold Y. 1993. "Death and Dying: Euthanasia and Sustaining Life: I. Historical Aspects." *Encyclopedia of Bioethics,* rev. edition, ed. Warren T. Reich. New York: Simon & Schuster Macmillan.

Vanderpool, Harold Y. 1997. "Doctors and the Dying of Patients in American History." In *Physician-Assisted Suicide,* ed. Robert F. Weir. Bloomington: Indiana University Press.

Vanderpool, Harold Y. 1998 (1986). "The Wesleyan-Methodist Tradition." In *Caring and Curing: Health and Medicine in the Western Religious Traditions,* ed. Ronald L. Numbers and Darrel W. Amundsen. New York: Macmillan.

Van Hooff, Alton J. L. 1990. *From Autothanasia to Suicide.* London: Routledge.

"Voluntary Euthanasia: Debate in the House of Lords." 1936. *British Medical Journal* 2: 1232–1234.

Washington, et al. v. Glacksberg et al., 117 S.Ct 2258, 138 C. Ed. 2d 772 (1997), pp. 96–110.

"A Way of Dying." 1957. *Atlantic Monthly,* January, pp. 53–55.

White, Lawrence W. 1996. "The Nazi Doctors and the Medical Community." *Journal of Medical Humanities* 17(2): 119–135.

Williams, Glanville. 1957. *The Sanctity of Life and the Criminal Law.* New York: Alfred A. Knopf.

Williams, Samuel D. 1872. *Euthanasia.* London: Williams and Norgate.

Wilson, Jerry B. 1975. *Death by Decision.* Philadelphia: Westminster Press.

Wolbarst, Abraham L. 1935. "The Right to Die." *Forum* 94: 330–334.

Wolbarst, Abraham L. 1939. "The Doctor Looks at Euthanasia." *Medical Record* 149: 354–356.

Worcester, Alfred. 1935. *The Care of the Aged, the Dying and the Dead.* Springfield, IL.: Charles C. Thomas.

LITERATURE AND HEALTHCARE

• • •

If dialogue—sophisticated, passionate, often angry dialogue—is the mark of a lively field of inquiry, then the study of creative literature is thriving. Central to the dialogue has been the question of the relation, if any, of literature to the world outside itself—that is, to the so-called real world of culture, politics, and ethics. Some of the most influential philosophers of literature (e.g., Derrida; see also Belsey) have been warning readers that they can no longer go to the classics of literature to mine gold nuggets of knowledge about life. Ironically, all this has been happening at the same time that certain prominent ethicists have been rediscovering the moral value of literature while speaking of "virtue" (MacIntyre) and—most prominently—"narrative ethics" (Hauerwas and Burrell; Nelson, 1997; Chambers; Charon and Montello). Have literature and ethics passed each other in the night? This much is clear: Before anyone can speak responsibly of the relationship of bioethics to literature, it is necessary to understand the general terms of the literary professionals' fight about meaning.

Theoretical Contexts

Of course, the agitation is far more complicated than it will appear here in a nontechnical summary. But the commentators can fairly be divided into two loose groups called values-oriented and language-oriented theorists. This distinction is related to the ethics/aesthetics, art for life's sake/art for art's sake, and content/form divisions of the past in that the first term of each pair (values, ethics, life, content) encourages the use of literature as a tool for living a good life, and the second term (language, aesthetics, art, form) points to a view of literature as an important end in itself. But today's values/language debate, particularly the language side, is by no means strictly congruent with past positions. Values-oriented people can be taken to include those who believe that the relationship between literature and ethics can be richly productive of change in individuals and society; the language-oriented group includes those who believe that, given contemporary understandings of language, such a relationship is an illusion. Thus far, the language theorists have prevailed—if not in the classroom, then certainly in the scholarly conferences and journals as well as in the commercial reviews.

VALUES-ORIENTED THEORIES. The values side has nevertheless been accorded intelligent attention, too, and their side is showing strong signs of renewal (Booth, 2001). Using various technical terms for values in literature (e.g., *classic realism, hermeneutics, ethical criticism,* and *moral imagination*), literary commentators have: (1) suggested that, in the words of Mark Twain, the reports of their death have been greatly exaggerated and would, in any case, be disastrous for both literature and society (Graff); and (2) proclaimed that moralists may very well have died but should be resurrected and readmitted, within certain limits, to the practice of criticism (Booth, 1988). Influential endorsement for the values-oriented position has also come from outside literature. Most notably, the philosopher Martha C. Nussbaum has insisted in a string of influential books that literary narratives of ideas and emotions constitute an essentially—and, for her, sometimes the solely—adequate depiction of ethical dilemmas. Another philosopher, Geoffrey Galt Harpham, agrees. And psychiatrist Robert Coles has championed the traditional view of literature as balm for the human spirit.

The complete history of values-oriented critics must make space for the two towering figures who, in the first half of the twentieth century, took up the mantle of the English poet and critic Matthew Arnold (1822–1888) to proclaim that a commitment to individual and social morality was the mark of supreme writers. In 1967 F. R. Leavis wrote in *The Great Tradition* that the finest novelists "are all distinguished by a vital capacity for experience, a kind of reverent openness before life, and a marked moral intensity" (p. 9). And Lionel Trilling, whose influence in the United States was once as widespread as Leavis's in England, said in *The Liberal Imagination:* "For our time the most effective agent of the moral imagination has been the novel of the last two hundred years" (p. 209).

Today, the two men are ignored or reviled by many of the most famous critics of literature. To some of them, Leavis's and Trilling's classics-minded disciples share part of the blame for enthroning the traditional academic canon—largely produced, in the now infamous phrase, by "dead, white, male writers"—as opposed to a more flexible list that is open to writers of both sexes and those of multicultural origins. The followers of Leavis and Trilling are among those who have been tagged as "liberals" and "humanists" by self-proclaimed "radicals" of the Marxist, African-American, and feminist schools of literary criticism. But, if examined closely from the perspective of this entry, these arguments are all in the family—the family of literary critics whose guidelines promote discussions of values. So are the arguments of the so-called reader-response critics, such as Wolfgang Iser, who locate the meaning of literature in the interaction between the text and the reader, and, probably, even the "formalists" of various stripes (e.g., Mikhail Bakhtin), who emphasize form over—and occasionally at the expense of—content.

LANGUAGE-ORIENTED THEORIES. The true opposition to the values-oriented approach comes from the theorists who, under several different banners (most often "semiotics," "deconstruction," and, according to some definitions, "postmodernism"), deny that literary texts have an objective relationship to the world outside themselves. The founding father of these language-oriented thinkers is often said to be Ferdinand de Saussure, whose revolutionary book, *Course in General Linguistics,* was published in 1916 and is still being analyzed for its contributions to literary studies. Paul de Man, Roland Barthes, and Jacques Derrida are other influential writers whose theories undermine literature's direct contribution to ethics.

The basis of their position, which is introduced by Catherine Belsey, is roughly this: Contrary to the empiricist-idealistic tradition that language, and therefore literature, is a reflection of the real world of facts, objects, and transcendent states of being, language is arbitrary and constructed solely by cultural convention. Language does not name things that are already in existence, but is, instead, responsible for a person's recognition of distinctions in what would otherwise be a blurred continuum. If, for instance, our language recognizes a difference between the color blue and the color green, we will see a line on the horizon over land. If there is no such distinction, the sky will melt into the earth. In other words, the language-oriented literary critics say, we cannot experience the world except through language; there is no reality except for language. In effect, we are prisoners of the languages we understand, for language structures our world.

None of these ideas is remotely startling anymore. But trouble arises when they are logically extended, because, with these ideas in place, it is foolish to speak of a literary text as possessing any "truth" about ethical matters or about an empirical world in which ethical matters must be considered. Language is not related directly to the world, but only to other language, texts only to other texts. Does this post-Saussurean conclusion leave any room for ethicists seeking help from literature? For the most extreme of the language theorists, the answer is "very little." They would grant that literature might portray people making moral decisions or, at most, shame readers into feeling "a little ethical flutter, a little frisson" (Bly, p. xix). But they would add that because language by itself has no agency—that is, no power to bring anything about in the real world—then neither has literature.

For bioethicists, what is finally important about the maelstrom of contemporary literary/linguistic theory is that, first, whether they acknowledge it or not, people who think about bioethics and literature (e.g., Brody, 1987, 1992; Jones; Brock and Ratzan; Clouser and Hawkins) generally derive their theoretical justification from the values-oriented thinkers, and, second, these ethicists are thereby ignoring the dominant literary epistemology of recent decades.

The Ethics of Literary Form

To be sure, there have always been routes through literature to ethics that circumvent the entire values/language debate. A number of these routes are a matter of form as opposed to content.

THE STUDY OF NARRATIVE FORM. Chief among these routes is the form called "narrative" or "story." Narrative is not exclusively literary: Writers from nearly every academic discipline have asserted that human beings tend to perceive life not as isolated ideas, facts, or problems, but as stories—series of plotted events involving characters and told from certain perspectives. In literature, the study of narrative form has become highly sophisticated (Martin; Newton), and literature-and-medicine scholars have participated in its development (Hunter, 1991). Narrative ethicists use the narrative paradigm to counter, or at least to supplement, an ethics based solely on abstract principles (Reich; Clouser and Hawkins; Nelson, 1997; Charon and Montello). In other words, narrative ethics is an attempt to return ethical dilemmas to the messy, complicated lives from which they arose and to plumb those narrated dilemmas with other stories that are coherent and meaningful.

Narrative ethics usually stops there, and it should not. No one looking to literature for moral anecdotes should think that the task is complete when they are found, for the narrative form itself may present—or, more commonly, mask—ethical problems. Most ethical problems derive from questions about the adequacy and authority of what is called the "narrative point of view." Whether a story is oral or written, whether it is from life or art, the audience needs to know the narrator's angle of perspective. That is, who is telling a particular story, and what constitutes his or her authority for doing so? Did the narrator witness the events related or is the report secondhand? Is the narrator deeply involved with the events, distant from them, or perhaps not able to understand them? T. Hugh Crawford points out that one needs to determine the narrator's social privilege, which, in the case of physicians, may be so great that the truth of

their stories will go unchallenged. An ethicist should also realize that the narrator always functions as an editor and therefore inevitably omits some elements of the imaginary "complete story" that may have a substantial moral impact. A second set of questions should concern the audience to whom the narrator directs the story, for the tale will be adjusted accordingly.

The questions become more complicated when a story is written, more complicated still when it is part of literary art. For instance, the narrator must not be unthinkingly identified with the real man or woman who composed the story, especially when the story is written in the first person, or even when authors use their own names for the narrators. The doctor who narrates the William Carlos Williams stories about patients in Rutherford, New Jersey, where the author practiced medicine, is not the same person as the Dr. Williams who made house calls or the Bill Williams who was Floss's husband; for the simple truth is that the author is never precisely the same as the narrator. Medical ethicists, writing about paternalism in Williams's famous short story "The Use of Force" (1933), do not always make this distinction, and their conclusions are thereby less precise.

Nevertheless, most literary narratives are written in the third person (e.g., "Sid was thinking that the surgeon seemed unresponsive"). It is an ethical, as well as an aesthetic, question to ask whether the narrator is positioned inside Sid's head, as it were, and therefore knows authoritatively only what Sidney knows, or whether the narrator also knows that "the surgeon was thinking about Sid's gall bladder," that outside "the wind was pushing the fall leaves around the parking lot," and that in the world at large "it was the worst of times." The first kind of narrator is technically a "concealed narrator" or "center of consciousness," the second an "omniscient narrator." Fashion in the twentieth and early twenty-first centuries has favored the first kind for its epistemological and ethical qualities because the omniscient narrator's sweeping knowledge is suspect. In the United States, especially, people tend to balk at according anyone— a president, a spouse, a doctor, a narrator—that kind of power.

These sticky questions about narrators lie in wait for medical ethicists when they are using their favorite narrative form, the case history. When "participant–observer" David Barnard published an extended case history, his intentions were to broaden the social and temporal bases from which ethical decisions are made and to show that a given illness affects the caregivers as well as the patient. He achieved these goals, but literary critic Eric Rabkin challenged the form of the case, asserting that Barnard-as-narrator and the physician, Valerie Walsh, had unconsciously produced "a story in which each could be the hero" (Banks, et al., p. 52). The resultant furor, summarized by Barnard (1992), who later (2000) accepted the criticism as valid, has helped to clarify the ethics of narrative form, but some aspects are still underexplored.

THE IMPORTANCE OF GENRE. The study of narrative is only one of the important ways to understand how literary form affects ethics. In fact, an awareness of what genre a given work falls into—is it a story or a play, a comedy or a tragedy?—is almost always important for the ethicist. Because drama, for instance, is distinguished from other literary forms by virtue of its dialogue and conflict, perhaps ethical conflicts should be presented in dramatic form rather than in narrative case histories. Not only would the various positions on a problem be fully embodied in the individual language of each "character," the format would also encourage the greater objectivity for which drama has a reputation. An argument can also be made that great plays and their first cousins, films, ought to be studied by ethicists to sharpen their awareness of not only dialogue and conflict but also such matters as role, costume, setting, set speeches, and audience reaction, because all of these factors change the moral climate of any scene from life. It would not matter whether the play chosen was specifically about bioethics or not. Any good play would serve the ethical goals (Banks, 1990).

Genre also affects more pervasively and subtly, because genres are, finally, forms that cultures select to convey their deepest values. Granted, for language-oriented theorists, the traditional distinctions among the genres have blurred—even disintegrated. Texts are texts, no matter what the form. They refer solely to other linguistic productions in an endless line of what literary critics call "intertextuality" and "subjectivities." These are important concepts. Nevertheless, traditional genres yield valuable information for ethicists. For example, the form of Greek tragedy inevitably introduced certain ethical values. One of the most troublesome for modern individualists is the widespread attitude toward fate (often personified as the vengeful Erinyes, or, in Rome, the Furies), whereby the Greeks believed that once a sequence of events had been set into motion, human beings had no ability to prevent its outcome. Once Oedipus had unknowingly killed his father, he was destined to marry his mother. Furthermore, he had to be punished for these acts even though he had no evil intention. That is, in order for the good to triumph in the ultimate balance of the universe, all those who had done wrong, whether consciously or not, had to pay. Like all great artists, Sophocles (c. 496–406 B.C.E.) lived in creative tension with what conventional form forced upon him: His Oedipus sees himself as free enough to be blamed and to inflict his own punishment by blinding

himself. Nevertheless, a belief in what might be called the "Greek tragic plot" not only affected ethical decisions—in a sense, it precluded them. Though less confining, certain ethical perspectives are already inherent in modern authors' affinity for mixing the traditional genres, as in "tragicomedy" and "docudrama." We may be too sophisticated to separate the serious from the funny, the real from the make-believe; or—and here is the ethical issue—we may be too confused to understand the difference.

AN EXAMPLE FROM SHAW. If literary form may thus limit ethics, form may also free it. The British playwright George Bernard Shaw's *The Doctor's Dilemma* can serve as an efficient illustration of both capabilities. Next to Williams's "The Use of Force," Shaw's play is probably the most oft-cited example of medical ethics in literature (see, e.g., Brody, 1991, on teaching Shaw in an ethics class). Shaw, of course, was a first-rate comic writer: The pompous, ignorant, and fee-grabbing physicians in this play are squarely in the tradition of the hilariously unethical doctors created by the seventeenth-century French playwright Molieè. But Shaw was also a playwright of great moral passion, an unabashed didact who mounted theatrical soapboxes to preach his ideas about social reform. The play form simply did not give this second Shaw enough room. Therefore, to most plays he published, he attached an essay of polemical prose that allowed him to go over much of the same material in a different literary form. In the case of *The Doctor's Dilemma,* this material was medical ethics.

The two forms, preface and play, dictate two startlingly different takes on the same ideas. Whereas the preface requires precision, the play requires ambiguity, or, more accurately, encourages it. In the play, Sir Colenso Ridgeon, who has recently discovered a successful treatment for tuberculosis, is forced by limited resources into deciding whom to treat and whom to allow to die. Specifically, he must choose between a poor, worthy—and dull—doctor, and a poor, reprehensible—and uniquely brilliant—artist. The situation is complicated by Sir Colenso's amorous feelings for the artist's wife, whom he imagines as an available widow. That is the dilemma of the title. Sir Colenso resolves it by treating the doctor. His justification for this action is that because the artist has no moral integrity, he, Sir Colenso, is saving the wife from discovering her husband's deceit and killing herself, as she has threatened. When he reveals his reasoning to the wife, now the widow, she accuses him of murder. In reply, he justifies his actions by citing Arthur Hugh Clough's satiric poem, *The Latest Decalogue:* "Thou shalt not kill, but needst not strive / Officiously to keep alive."

Shaw's play raises more questions than it answers. When he writes polemical prose, Shaw argues easily, logically, and from an unshakable moral perspective. But when he takes ethics into the personal realm of drama, he cannot manage equally clear conclusions. So the play, as distinct from the preface, reverberates with moral ambiguity. Sir Colenso and an older, sensible physician soundly debate the central dilemma—but no conclusion is drawn by Shaw. Similarly, Sir Colenso's decision is padded with ethical red herrings. When, with no apology, he recommends as a physician for the artist a man of eminent reputation but shameful ignorance, Sir Colenso is behaving in a superficially licit manner that serves to distract him from the ethical problem. What the playwright does face directly is that ethical decisions in medicine are difficult to sort out logically; that no physician alone, or even in consultation with other professionals, can make them on objective grounds; that the results, when allocating limited medical resources, will be a type of murder; and that these burdens are too much for one person to bear.

For Shaw the playwright, then, the dilemma of who shall live and who shall die cannot be answered without dishonor and tragedy. (He calls this play, and this play only, a tragedy.) For Shaw the political philosopher, the same question is answered in terms that, by contrast to the subtleties of the play, are chillingly clear. He asserts in the preface that "invalids, meaning persons who cannot, beyond reason, expect to be kept alive by the activity of others," must be allowed for social reasons to die. "The theory," Shaw concludes firmly, "that every individual alive is of infinite value is legislatively impracticable … the man who costs more than he is worth is doomed by sound hygiene as inexorably as by sound economics" (pp. 86–87). And that's that.

Abortion and AIDS, among Others

Shaw, Williams, Molireè: These names are the beginning of a long, long list of first-rate creative writers who have narrated, dramatized, and, in general, illuminated specific topics of bioethics. Hundreds of other names and their works could be added. A partial roll call of the most useful would include Tobias Smollett's *The Adventures of Roderick Random* (1748), Herman Melville's *White-Jacket* (1850), Anthony Trollope's *Doctor Thorne* (1858), George Eliot's *Middlemarch* (1871–1872), Georg Büchner's *Woyzeck* (1836), Henrik Ibsen's *An Enemy of the People* (1882), Sinclair Lewis's *Arrowsmith* (1925), Albert Camus's *The Plague* (1948), Peter Nichols's *A Day in the Death of Joe Egg* (1967), Joyce Carol Oates's *Wonderland* (1971), and Peter Shaffer's *Equus* (1973).

In the first bibliography of literature and medicine (Trautmann and Pollard), which annotated about 1,400 literary works from classical to contemporary times under thirty-nine categories, ethicists can check for information not only under "medical ethics" but also under "abortion," "euthanasia," and "evil doctors." The years since the bibliography's publication have, of course, added more authors, and many more works, to the inventory of resources. It is intriguing that the years have also changed the categories. Among the bibliography's topics, "age," "handicaps," "mental retardation," "plague," "suicide," "venereal disease," and "women as patients" have taken on extensive political, and therefore ethical, implications. New categories have emerged too. "Cross-cultural," for instance, must be clearly distinguished from the old "poverty and health"; "AIDS" deserves its own category, having grown beyond "plague" and "venereal disease" (which itself has developed into "sexually transmitted diseases").

Bibliographic assembly for literature and healthcare has, since 1993, been under the direction of Felice Aull at the New York University (NYU) School of Medicine. Aull and a large board of editors and annotators have brought their subjective, interactive, and regularly revised bibliographic work where it needs to be—to the Internet. The NYU group has tripled the number of Trautmann and Pollard's subjects and mirrored the movement in literary criticism toward cultural studies, thereby broadening the definitions of text and literature to include, for example, film and the visual arts. Following the trend in ethics, medicine has also been broadened to include not only nursing but also all the newer healthcare professions.

Along with the expansion of creative work about bioethics, the field of literature and healthcare has seen an enormous growth of books *about* these works. The studies are generally about topics and people at some distance from U.S. culture's centers of power: the feminist body (Grosz); disabilities (Thomson); aging (Wyatt-Brown and Rossen); pain (Scarry; Morris); and caregivers (Poirier and Ayres).

To demonstrate precisely how literature illuminates bioethics, it might be helpful to analyze, first, a traditional work on an established ethics topic—in this case, abortion—and, second, a group of fiery works about a newer topic, AIDS.

ABORTION AND *THE CIDER HOUSE RULES*. One of the most important novels on U.S. medical ethics is John Irving's *The Cider House Rules*, which was made into an influential film that was released in 1999. Morality—the metaphorical "rules" of the title—is its central concern, specifically the morality of abortion before *Roe v. Wade*, the 1973 U.S. Supreme Court case that established abortion's constitutionality. One of the book's two main characters is

Dr. Wilbur Larch, who performs illegal abortions at the orphanage he has established in a remote area of Maine. He offers women a choice—an orphan or an abortion. The other character is Homer Wells, one of those orphans, who, as a young man, is an ardent antiabortionist, able to articulate arguments in opposition to Larch. But, in the end, breaking his own and society's rules, Homer assumes a medical identity that allows him to take over Dr. Larch's practice.

As is so often the case in life, Homer's position begins with an image rather than an idea. At the age of thirteen, Homer sees a dead, nearly nine-month-old entity, whom Dr. Larch wants to call a "fetus," but Homer feels compelled to call a "child." After that, Homer immediately links any argument from Larch about "the products of conception" before the quickening to the image of the dead baby. Now the pictures of even the eight-week-old fetuses in Gray's *Anatomy* strike Homer as having an "expression," or, the narrator tells us, what other people call a "soul."

Nor is Dr. Larch initially won over to abortion by arguments. As a medical student, Larch sees for himself the damage inflicted on women by the alleyway butchers and poisonous aborticides. He stares into the dead face of a woman to whom he had refused an abortion. He witnesses the deprivations of orphans. Later, Dr. Larch adds reason to his emotions. He has a large array of arguments at his command, including, for instance, his disgust at someone "who cares more for the misgivings suffered in his own frail soul than for the actual suffering of countless unwanted and mistreated children" (Irving, p. 260). He presents another argument that finally convinces Homer. Written in a letter, it reads: "If abortions were legal, you could refuse—in fact, given your beliefs, you *should* refuse. But ... how can you feel free to choose not to help people who are not free to get other help?" (p. 488).

These characters, these events, and these ethical concepts are all embedded in a form that must be described and its intimate connection to the ethical content made plain. Basically, the form is adapted from the nineteenth-century, realistic, English novel because it suits Irving's traditionalism—his sense that fiction has as its chief mission the examination of values. In that regard, his model is surely Charles Dickens. *The Cider House Rules* has Dickensian size. Like a Dickens novel, it is openly concerned with individual and social ethics. Every night, Homer reads Dickens's *David Copperfield* or *Great Expectations* to the boy orphans, who unquestioningly accept the novels as portals to morality.

To the girls, by the way, Homer reads Charlotte Brontë's *Jane Eyre,* whose orphan heroine is blatantly offered as a role model—and is sometimes blatantly rejected. Jane's

sweet optimism is too much for one angry, world-weary orphan. In a vividly comic instance of what scholars such as Wayne C. Booth and Nussbaum would be forced to call "ethical criticism," the hulking, teenaged orphan demonstrates the power of literature:

> "Even for me [chirped little Jane Eyre], life had its gleam of sunshine."
>
> "'Gleams of sunshine'!" Melony shouted in violent disbelief. "Let her come here! Let her show me the gleams of sunshine!" (Irving, p. 84).

From the nineteenth century, too, comes the novel's narrative voice. It is omniscience, moving freely in and out of any character's mind and making such general observations as: "Society is so complex that even [the little town of] Heart's Haven had a wrong part to it" (Irving, p. 125). The narrator knows everything in this created world. If he (let us say) can build an aesthetically convincing world, readers may believe he knows a great deal about the real world, too. Irving has tried to buttress the authority of his novel's narrator by appending the scholarly apparatus of endnotes. Tied to certain pages and narrative "facts," these notes assert that Irving has researched his material. He has read medical texts, both old and modern. He has consulted with physicians, including one of the canonical authors in literature and medicine, Richard Selzer. All the evidence points to this author being very serious about the real world, a values-oriented thinker as described earlier, rather than one for whom language is a closed system.

Irving writes tragicomedy. One distinguishing mark of an Irving novel (the most successful was *The World According to Garp* [1978]) is that, after much humor, someone innocent dies. This is Dickensian too: Think of Little Nell in *The Old Curiosity Shop.* As noted earlier, the mixed genre of tragicomedy is a favorite twentieth-century form, and cultural critics are still sorting out its implications. More and more, tragicomedy seems appropriate to the creative literature of medical ethics because the genre deals simultaneously with patients' tragic losses and caregivers' need to continue in spite of them. Tragedy ends something, but comedy always implies continuation, and the two are interdependent. Here is a literary lesson that bioethicists, whose "quandary ethics" proceeds from an exclusively tragic premise, have yet to learn. As that wily moralist, Shaw, has Dr. Ridgeon say in *The Doctor's Dilemma,* "Life does not cease to be funny when people die any more than it ceases to be serious when people laugh" (p. 185).

SEVERAL WORKS ABOUT AIDS. Literary writers have responded to AIDS faster and more often than to abortion. They have also tended to leap more aggressively from art to ethics. Taken as a group, the narratives, plays, poems, films, and critical essays about AIDS (see Nelson, 1992, for a bibliography) are fervently contesting the ethical boundaries of language itself. For a start, some of the creative writers and critics who write about AIDS are activists. Larry Kramer, author of *The Normal Heart,* was an early and loud voice. These activists insist that the first goal of AIDS literature must be to change the critical circumstances of the disease and its sufferers. They call for "stridently interventionist cultural practice" (Nelson, 1992, p. 8, citing Douglas Crimp). They say that to write about AIDS at all is automatically to be a moralist, for, in this battle, no sidelines exist. Demurrers about art for art's sake are irrelevant and themselves immoral. So one question about activist AIDS literature is: Does such work fit into the artistic genre called "social realism" or is it not art at all, but, instead, blatant propaganda whose first and last goal is social change? To the first category, literary historians have assigned, for instance, Ibsen's *An Enemy of the People,* which is an ardent piece about an idealistic doctor's crusade to warn tourists about his town's polluted public baths in the face of community pressure, as represented by his brother the mayor, to keep his mouth shut. The play is comparable to Kramer's *The Normal Heart,* in which another doctor battles to get money for AIDS research in a New York whose mayor seeks to prevent would-be tourists from knowing about the epidemic. But where do we draw the line between taking a stand and propaganda, wherein the end shapes, even justifies, the means?

What might any writer, activist or not, be excused for saying in order to bring about a desired end? What language—which images, which metaphors—may validly be used to inflame audiences with a just passion? One of the most common metaphors for the AIDS epidemic in the homosexual community is the Holocaust (e.g., Nelson, 1992), which was said in the early days of activism to be recurring through the establishment's lack of a plan to prevent the genocide of gay men. Is this horrifying image apt? Is it logical? Alternatively, are these questions themselves out of place in view of the absolute primacy, for some people, of subjective data about illness?—that is, "I have AIDS, and it feels as though I am living through another Holocaust. What do you know about it?"

The morality of metaphor is the territory famously covered by Susan Sontag in *Illness as Metaphor* (1978). There she argues that to substitute metaphors, especially negative metaphors, for the reality of bodily suffering is to impose a spurious meaning on illness and a sense of guilt on the patient. If cancer, in the common military metaphor, is a battleground, then the patient can be blamed for not winning. Sontag comes back to her point in *AIDS and Its*

Metaphors (1989), where she contends that "plague," the most common metaphor for AIDS, implies judgment on a corrupt society. In her own story about AIDS, "The Way We Live Now" (1987), there are no metaphors for the illness. Moreover, in what would seem to be a further attempt to free AIDS from contaminating linguistic associations, she does not even name it.

Sontag's reasoned approach to this crisis is similar to the theories of the German playwright Bertolt Brecht (1898–1956). Unlike the AIDS plays, most of which are designed to be deeply cathartic, Brecht's plays aimed for the "alienation effect" in order to limit his audience's emotional involvement in the work. He used various devices to remind audiences that they were watching illusion, not reality—a play, not life. This distancing, he hoped, would free their minds to reason clearly that humanitarian action was needed in the world outside the theater. A former medical student, Brecht wanted to achieve the theatrical equivalent of clinical objectivity. His goal, like that of AIDS activists, was to change society, but, unlike some of them, he thought it unethical to reach minds by manipulating emotions.

In arguing against metaphor, Sontag seeks to chip away at the use of language as a shield to protect people from difficult experience. Given the symbol-making nature of the human mind, she has chosen a position that finally may be impossible to defend. She seems to know that, and yet she thinks it eminently worthwhile to fight for the "thereness" of the human body, for the indisputable fact of its physical presence. So does literary and film critic James Morrison, who is worried that postmodernism (read: "language-oriented thinking") has infected criticism about AIDS literature. Defining allegory as "a series of metaphors arranged in sequence" (Nelson, 1992, p. 169), Morrison complains that the postmodern attraction to allegory—that is, to expressing experience as an abstract text that refers only to other language and not to the real world—has moved readers further away from the actual experience of AIDS. In his eyes, allegories dictate that both AIDS and the person with AIDS be classified as "other"—something, at any rate, that cannot be approached without the intervention of elaborate figures of speech. The allegory to which he objects most vehemently is the series of metaphors that describe the body as text. When logically extended, he says, such an allegory would allow someone to "read," as it were, "the lesions of Kaposi's sarcoma as indexical signs" of the body-book (Nelson, 1992, p. 171). This he thinks a ludicrously unsympathetic way to approach the body in pain.

Morrison may not realize it, but his challenge implicitly goes out to the scholars in the interdisciplinary field of literature and medicine for whom the patient-as-text is both metaphor and method. He might just as well challenge every one of us, because the process of abstracting that he condemns in the case of literary criticism and AIDS seems to be a universal human phenomenon. The combined evidence of the writers examined here suggests that all of us are trapped between our suffering bodies and our symbolizing minds—that is, between a world whose existence we can prove simply by stubbing a toe and the engrossing stories that we are constantly creating about that world. It would appear to be nearly useless to ask which level of experience, the physical or the imaginative, is more real; or to look to one, at the exclusion of the other, for ethical insight.

In a sense, this brings us back to the values/language split with which this entry began. In calling for a clear-sighted view of every specific person with AIDS, Morrison aligns himself with the values-oriented camp. He wants not only creative writers but also commentators on literature to write justly. So does Sontag. But, as she demonstrates in her own fictional works, language is a powerful and playful human trait that tends to seek its own ends, regardless of its possible relationship to the real world of ethical problems. Language, in fact, creates new worlds all the time. Consider only Tony Kushner's *Angels in America,* so magnificent an achievement that it transcends the category of AIDS play. In short, the values/language dichotomy is more properly seen not as a true division but as a perpetual ethical tension.

JOANNE TRAUTMANN BANKS (1995)
REVISED BY AUTHOR

SEE ALSO: *Bioethics; Ethics; Narrative*

BIBLIOGRAPHY

Banks, Joanne Trautmann. 1986. "A Controversy about Clinical Form." *Literature and Medicine* 5: 24–26.

Banks, Joanne Trautmann. 1990. "Literature as a Clinical Capacity: Commentary on 'the Quasimodo Complex.'" *Journal of Clinical Ethics* 1(3): 227–231.

Banks, Joanne Trautmann; Barnard, David; Rabkin, Eric; et al. 1986. "A Controversy about Clinical Form." *Literature and Medicine* 5: 24–57.

Barnard, David. 1986. "A Case of Amyotophic Lateral Sclerosis" *Literature and Medicine* 5: 27–42.

Barnard, David. 1992. "'A Case of Amyotrophic Lateral Sclerosis': A Reprise and a Reply." *Literature and Medicine* 11(1): 133–146.

Barnard, David. 2000. "Consider the Philosophers of the Field, How They Narrate; They Admit It Not, but Oh, Do They Spin." *Medical Humanities Review* 14(2): 83–88.

Belsey, Catherine. 1980. *Critical Practice.* New York: Routledge.

Bly, Carol. 1988. "Foreword." In *Full Measure: Modern Stories on Aging,* ed. Dorothy Sennett. St. Paul, MN: Graywolf.

Booth, Wayne C. 1988. *The Company We Keep: An Ethics of Fiction.* Berkeley: University of California Press.

Booth, Wayne C. 2001. "Literary Criticism and the Pursuit of Character." *Literature and Medicine* 20(2): 97–108.

Brock, D. Heyward, and Ratzan, Richard M., eds. 1988. "Literature and Bioethics." *Literature and Medicine* 7.

Brody, Howard. 1987. *Stories of Sickness.* New Haven, CT: Yale University Press.

Brody, Howard. 1991. "Literature and Bioethics: Different Approaches." *Literature and Medicine* 10: 98–110.

Brody, Howard. 1992. *The Healer's Power.* New Haven, CT: Yale University Press.

Chambers, Tod. 1999. *The Fiction of Bioethics: Cases as Literary Texts.* New York: Routledge.

Charon, Rita, and Montello, Martha, eds. 2002. *Stories Matter: The Role of Narrative in Medical Ethics.* New York: Routledge.

Clouser, K. Danner, and Hawkins, Anne Hunsaker, eds. 1996. "Literature and Medical Ethics." Special issue of *Journal of Medicine and Philosophy* 21(3).

Coles, Robert. 1989. *The Call of Stories: Teaching and the Moral Imagination.* Boston: Houghton Mifflin.

Crawford, T. Hugh. 1992. "The Politics of Narrative Form." *Literature and Medicine* 11(1): 147–162.

Derrida, Jacques. 1972. "Structure, Sign, and Play in the Discourse of the Human Sciences." In *The Structuralist Controversy: The Languages of Criticism and the Sciences of Man,* ed. Richard Macksey and Eugenio Donato. Baltimore: Johns Hopkins University Press.

Graff, Gerald. 1979. *Literature against Itself: Literary Ideas in Modern Society.* Chicago: University of Chicago Press.

Grosz, Elizabeth. 1994. *Volatile Bodies: Toward a Corporeal Feminism.* Bloomington: University of Indiana Press.

Harpham, Geoffrey Galt. 1992. *Getting It Right: Language, Literature, and Ethics.* Chicago: University of Chicago Press.

Hauerwas, Stanley, and Burrell, David. 1989. "From System to Story: An Alternative Pattern for Rationality in Ethics." In *Why Narrative? Readings in Narrative Theology,* ed. Stanley Hauerwas and L. Gregory Jones. Grand Rapids, MI: William B. Eerdmans.

Hunter, Kathryn Montgomery. 1991. *Doctors' Stories: The Narrative Structure of Medical Knowledge.* Princeton, NJ: Princeton University Press.

Hunter, Kathryn Montgomery, ed. 1994. "Narrative and Medical Knowledge." *Literature and Medicine* 13(1).

Irving, John. 1985. *The Cider House Rules: A Novel.* New York: Morrow.

Jones, Anne Hudson. 1987. "Literary Value: The Lesson of Medical Ethics." *Neohelicon* 14: 383–392.

Kramer, Larry. 1985. *The Normal Heart.* New York: Samuel French.

Kushner, Tony. 1993. *Angels in America.* New York: Theatre Communications Group.

Leavis, F. R. 1967. *The Great Tradition.* New York: New York University Press.

MacIntyre, Alasdair C. 1981. *After Virtue: A Study in Moral Theory.* Notre Dame, IN: Notre Dame University Press.

Martin, Wallace. 1986. *Recent Theories of Narrative.* Ithaca, NY: Cornell University Press.

Morris, David. 1991. *The Culture of Pain.* Berkeley: University of California Press.

Nelson, Emmanuel S., ed. 1992. *AIDS: The Literary Response.* New York: Twayne.

Nelson, Hilde Lindemann, ed. 1997. *Stories and Their Limits: Narrative Approaches to Bioethics.* New York: Routledge.

Newton, Adam Zachary. 1995. *Narrative Ethics.* Cambridge, MA: Harvard University Press.

Nussbaum, Martha C. 1990. *Love's Knowledge: Essays on Philosophy and Literature.* New York: Oxford University Press.

Poirier, Suzanne, and Ayres, Lioness. 2002. *Stories of Family Caregiving: Reconsiderations of Theory, Literature, and Life.* Indianapolis, IN: Center Nursing Publishing.

Rabkin, Eric. 1986. "A Case of Self Defense." *Literature and Medicine* 5: 43–53.

Reich, Warren Thomas. 1988. "Experiential Ethics as a Foundation for Dialogue between Health Communication and Health-Care Ethics." *Journal of Applied Communication Research* 16: 16–28.

Scarry, Elaine. 1985. *The Body in Pain: The Making and Unmaking of the World.* New York: Oxford University Press.

Shaw, George Bernard. 1906 (reprint 1954). *The Doctor's Dilemma: A Tragedy.* Baltimore: Penguin.

Smith, David H. 1986. "The Limits of Narrative." *Literature and Medicine* 5: 54–57.

Sontag, Susan. 1978. *Illness as Metaphor.* New York: Farrar, Straus and Giroux.

Sontag, Susan. 1987. "The Way We Live Now." In *The Best American Short Stories 1987.* ed. Ann Beattie and Shannon Ravenel. Boston: Houghton Mifflin.

Sontag, Susan. 1989. *AIDS and Its Metaphors.* New York: Farrar, Straus and Giroux.

Thomson, Rosemarie Garland, ed. 1996. *Freakery: Cultural Spectacles of the Extraordinary Body.* New York: New York University Press.

Trautmann, Joanne, and Pollard, Carol. 1982. *Literature and Medicine: An Annotated Bibliography,* rev. edition. Pittsburgh, PA: University of Pittsburgh Press.

Trilling, Lionel. 1978. *The Liberal Imagination: Essays on Literature and Society,* uniform edition. New York: Harcourt Brace Jovanovich.

Williams, William Carlos. 1961. "The Use of Force," In *The Farmers' Daughters: The Collected Stories of William Carlos Williams.* New York: New Directions Press.

Wyatt-Brown, Anne M., and Rossen, Janice, eds. 1993. *Aging and Gender in Literature: Studies in Creativity.* Charlottesville: University of Virginia Press.

INTERNET RESOURCE

Aull, Felice, et al. "The Literature, Arts, and Medicine Database." 2003. New York University School of Medicine. Available from <http://endeavor.med.nyu.edu/lit-med/>.

LIVING WILL

SEE *Advance Directives and Advance Care Planning*

LONG-TERM CARE

• • •

I. CONCEPT AND POLICIES

Long-term care (LTC) is an individualized mix of personal care, healthcare, and social services for persons whose functional impairments dictate that they need help with tasks of everyday living (Kane and Kane). Consumers of LTC may live in congregate residential settings such as nursing homes, assisted living settings, adult foster homes, or board-and-care homes, but most live in their own homes and are candidates for community-based LTC programs including home care, adult day care, home-delivered meals, emergency assistance, and home renovation. LTC may be provided by paid workers, but most often it is provided voluntarily by family and friends. The need for LTC is assessed by evaluating the person's ability to perform activities of daily living (ADL), such as bathing, dressing, using the toilet, getting in and out of bed, eating, and performing household and other practical tasks including cleaning, cooking, shopping, managing money, and transporting oneself. LTC services correspond directly to measured impairments in ADL performance and to other functional impairments. People may choose to purchase similar services for convenience alone, but a service is defined as LTC only if a measurable disability prevents the RAK (people receiving care) person from performing the given task.

Most LTC consumers are elderly and, indeed, well over age seventy-five. But many younger people also need and receive LTC. These include physically disabled adults with conditions such as multiple sclerosis, spinal-cord injuries, head injuries, and late-stage cancer; persons with late-stage acquired immunodeficiency syndrome (AIDS); technology-dependent, severely disabled children; and persons of all ages with developmental disabilities such as cerebral palsy. Anyone who needs and receives help with everyday functioning because of a disability may be considered to be receiving LTC. They may, of course, also receive preventive and curative acute medical care from time to time. Some disability activists prefer to replace the term LTC with a substitute such as "long-term services," both because LTC is often equated with nursing homes in the popular mind and because they prefer to distinguish the emotional and nurturing aspects of "care" from the concept of services.

The goals of LTC may be multiple and often are ambiguous. Sometimes the goal appropriately includes rehabilitation or improvement of the consumer's functional abilities, but frequently the most reasonable goal is to enable consumers to live as meaningfully as possible given their impairments, abilities, interests, and life-cycle stage and roles. Sometimes LTC providers treat the LTC services (e.g., bathing assistance and cooking, or any particular mix of services in the plan) as the actual goal of LTC. Other LTC programs promulgate ambitious goals, for example, that LTC consumers should be well satisfied with life and score well on absolute indicators of well-being or social adjustment. In either case, practitioners and policymakers struggle to attend to rehabilitation possibilities while avoiding grandiose or intrusive goals. For service providers to assume responsibility for global outcomes of someone's life along with their provision of routine services requires some hubris, and LTC professionals are perplexed about how comprehensively to cast their goals.

A number of other factors make LTC unique. LTC is an enterprise in which the services are diverse though often ordinary, the providers are diverse (including professionals, paraprofessionals, and family members), the clientele is diverse, and the goals are often unclear. Furthermore, much LTC, and most publicly subsidized LTC, takes place in nursing homes, where the functionally impaired consumer may have been involuntarily relocated, and the high cost of LTC in residential settings and in the community is of concern to private and public payers. Finally, LTC is a women's issue because the consumers, the family caregivers who are pressed into service, and the paid caregivers are predominantly female. Of course, husbands give care to their wives as needed, but the typical LTC consumer is a widow, and the typical family caregiver is a wife, a daughter, or a daughter-in-law.

Trends in the 1990s and Early 2000s

Several trends in the United States during and following the 1990s have also helped shape the key ethical issues involving LTC. In the United States, publicly funded LTC is usually offered on a means-tested basis and is a matter of state rather than federal policy (although the Medicaid program matches state funds and sets some broad program parameters). State governments expend most of their funds on care in nursing homes, although consumers prefer to live anywhere else. The magnitude of this disproportionate spending has receded somewhat since 1990, and a concomitant growth has occurred in what is called the home- and community-based services (HCBS) sector. Three elements are highlighted: the growth of assisted living, the promotion of consumer-centered approaches to care, and the pursuit of LTC as a civil right for persons with disabilities.

Assisted living is an umbrella term for a variety of residential settings that provide or arrange care and are not licensed as nursing homes. They have proliferated, partly because of consumer interest in alternatives to nursing homes. At their best, assisted living settings combine a high level of privacy and autonomy-enhancing architectural features with a capacity to provide substantial care to residents in their own assisted living apartments. At their worst, they fail to offer high privacy or high service or both, they are costly, and they evict residents when they have real care needs. The presence of almost a million assisted living units by 2002, and the coverage of the services provided or arranged by assisted living programs in most states (Mollica), has given rise to concerns about quality, punctuated by highly publicized scandals in the print media and a 1999 U.S. General Accounting Office study showing that consumers had poor and incomplete information prior to purchase. The extent to which the federal government should regulate assisted living programs and how they should be regulated is now a matter of spirited debate.

Consumer-directed care and consumer-centered care are slogans that reflect a growing sentiment that the users of services should as much as possible direct the nature of those services and that their views should be solicited for quality reviews and program development. At the extreme end of this view, advocates suggest that funds for services be provided directly to consumers or their agents, who would then hire, train, supervise, and dismiss care workers. Advocates of this view prefer the use of personal attendants or personal assistants to home care from agencies. In some European countries, notably Germany, cash is offered in lieu of services in LTC insurance programs, and the United States launched in the late 1990s a randomized trial of the effectiveness of cash with the cash amount established as somewhat less than the average cost of service plans versus services for HCBS under Medicaid. Care patterns that emphasize the authority of the consumer, however, raise problems about the rights of paid care workers, who themselves have been making strides toward collective bargaining.

Finally, the Americans with Disabilities Act (ADA) of 1990 provided leverage for social action related to LTC in a different vein than advocacy for better health and human service programs. In the closely watched *Olmstead v. L.C.* case, the U.S. Supreme Court in 1999 enunciated a right to care in the most integrated setting based on the ADA (although the right was circumscribed by vaguely stated requirements for "appropriateness"). This brought the Office of Civil Rights into the business of enforcing decisions related to quality of care (Rosenbaum; Rosenbaum, Teitelbaum, and Stewart). Younger persons with disabilities, even people with developmental disabilities and mental retardation, have made greater progress toward care outside of institutions than have older people. Comparisons between HCBS received by seniors and younger people with disabilities reveal sharp discrepancies; for example, the former often must be homebound to get publicly funded help at home, whereas the latter can use publicly funded personal attendants to help them leave their homes. Some argue that older people prefer the more secure; institutionally based services, but others suggest ageism is at work in the discrepancies. Also, older LTC consumers tend not to perceive themselves as being disabled and having rights under the ADA. Possibly the options and services would be better for seniors if pursued as a rights issue rather than as a healthcare quality issue.

Ethical Themes in LTC

Nine interrelated themes can be identified that give rise to ethical dilemmas for those who provide, administer, plan, or finance LTC.

INTIMACY OF LTC. Whether it is provided in consumers' own homes or in group residential settings, LTC is inextricably tied to daily routines. The way it is provided literally affects how LTC consumers live, where they live, whom they see, and how they spend their time. Ethical issues arise concerning the extent to which personal preferences and wishes should be honored, especially when they conflict with operating procedures of a caregiving organization or when they entail public costs. For example, should a person receiving home care be permitted to establish the timing for

getting up and going to bed, even if this requires an attendant to visit late in the evening? Because LTC plans can be so comprehensive and intrusive, many believe that the consumer should be given as much choice and control as possible. Further, George J. Agich suggested in his 1993 book, *Autonomy and Long Term Care,* that a legalistic ethic based narrowly on the right to noninterference ignores the existential reality of LTC. He argued that respect for autonomy must include provision of meaningful choices and maintenance of personal identity. Writing largely about nursing homes, Bart Collopy, Philip Boyle, and Bruce Jennings also argued for a view of autonomy that takes into account "the moral ecology" of LTC settings. A large ethnographic and anthropological literature offers insights into the complexity of this moral ecology, that is, the settings and arrangements of care (Henderson and Vesperi).

With its focus on intimate, repetitive tasks and assistance with bodily functions that adults usually handle independently and privately, LTC can profoundly affect the dignity of the consumers and alter their sense of personal identity and worth. Cognitively intact LTC consumers may retain a keen sense of privacy concerning their bodies, their possessions, and even information about themselves. Assembly-line approaches to dressing, toileting, and bathing may be perceived as demeaning. Questions arise about how much energy LTC providers should be obliged to expend protecting the dignity of consumers and helping them preserve their sense of identity. Even if consumers are cognitively incapacitated and completely helpless physically, many believe it is wrong to subject them to procedures that are inherently undignified.

DEPENDENCY OF LTC CONSUMERS. Functionally impaired people are, by definition, dependent to some degree. Some people receiving care, though they may have the ability to conceive, plan, and choose actions, are virtually helpless to initiate or carry out actions. This creates a paradox: The more physically dependent the LTC consumers, the more they must depend on the help of others to exercise autonomy. Although providers taking a rehabilitation stance may strive to have consumers do things for themselves, respect for the consumer's autonomy dictate that great care be taken in fulfilling requests. Striking the right balance between encouraging independence and providing help is an ethical issue for LTC providers.

GROUP-LIVING SETTINGS. When LTC is provided in a collective, residential setting, the needs and interests of residents can collide. Residents in group settings are always expected to modify their individual wishes and behaviors to adjust to collective situations, and such expectations are usually well understood by all who enter such a setting. But it is unclear what rules of conduct and mutual expectations should govern a nursing home, an entity that is neither a hospital nor a housing unit. To some degree, the facility's search for efficient routines defines permissible behavior and opportunities for nursing-home residents.

Typically, nursing homes accommodate, in multiple-occupancy rooms and close quarters, residents who are markedly varied in physical ability, cognitive ability, prognosis, age, social class, interests, and personal taste. Some now question, however, whether continuing to house residents in shared quarters is ethically justifiable. One reason why assisted living is attractive in the private market is the greater availability of singly-occupied quarters; as states begin covering assisted living services under Medicaid, they face a decision about whether to fund privacy as a minimum expectation or to encourage a two-class system of assisted living with publicly subsidized clientele living in boarding home situations. The advent of assisted living also challenges the very nature of congregate LTC and obfuscates the boundaries between home care and institutional care. If assisted living consumers are viewed as tenants of their own apartments, where they receive services as well, then laws pertaining to fair housing may prevent providers from moving them to a reputedly higher care setting such as a nursing home.

Nursing homes themselves are in considerable ferment about how to adapt to the current LTC world. A social movement, originally called the Nursing Home Pioneers, gained momentum in the 1990s. Dedicated to culture change in nursing homes, those identified with the Pioneers recommend a variety of remedies, including empowering the line staff, flattening nursing-home hierarchical structures, and refashioning the physical settings into smaller neighborhoods and households (Lustbader). Within this group are proponents of specific changes such as the Eden Alternative (Thomas), an approach to combat boredom, loneliness, and lack of meaning in nursing homes; and the Wellspring model, a version of continuous quality improvement directed at empowering nurse's aides (Stone et al.). Many of these developments are antithetical to more traditional approaches to nursing-home reform proposals such as establishing higher nursing-staff–to–resident ratios and vigorously enforcing quality of care standards.

FAMILY ROLES. LTC is inevitably a family affair. Family members provide most of the care given to people at home. Indeed, much paid home care is organized explicitly to give relief, assistance, or training to family members, who in turn are expected to do most of the work. Questions arise about what is right to expect of various family members, and even whether older persons should be forced to accept, against their will, help from a family member. One also wonders whether family anxiety for a relative's safety should lead to the placement of that relative in a nursing home. On the personal level, LTC evokes questions about the duties and rights of spouses, parents, adult children, and other relatives.

In practice, LTC providers, and especially case managers who coordinate and allocate care, sometimes view the whole family constellation as the client, especially if all the family members are elderly or if they live in the same household as the person getting care. But family members' interests are not always identical to those of the consumers, nor are their intentions always benign. For example, nursing-home staff often find that family members disagree with each other about the resident's care. They also sometimes note that the decisions of family members are motivated by an interest in minimizing the costs of care. Nursing-home personnel, who may themselves have a conflict of interest involving payment and money management, for example, when their recommendations entail more payment to the nursing home, often turn to the state's nursing-home ombudsperson to resolve such disputes. Home-care providers and state-designated case managers who purchase publicly subsidized home care also often disagree with family members about the type and amount of care needed and about whether a nursing-home admission is in the LTC consumer's best interest.

END-OF-LIFE ISSUES. Death typically occurs during a period of LTC, either at the end of decades of care or after a relatively short episode. For this reason, many of the issues about death that confront acute-care providers also arise in long-term contexts, including the use of cardiopulmonary resuscitation, starting or stopping a respirator, or starting or stopping tube placement for nutrition and fluid intake. Issues of active or passive euthanasia also arise, which in turn evoke basic questions about the extent of the obligation of the healthcare professional to preserve life on the one hand and to avert suffering on the other. It is a challenge to give proper, systematic attention to end-of-life issues in LTC, while also giving weight to the everyday ethical matters that shape the quality of LTC consumers' lives (Kane and Caplan, 1990).

RISKS, RISK AVERSION, AND LIABILITY. Functionally disabled people are frequently unable to protect themselves against outside dangers such as fending off an intruder or escaping from a fire. Increased risks are associated with the simplest activities—walking to the bathroom, getting out of bed, or boiling a pot of water. People with precarious physical health may be at increased risk of a fall or of a sudden health incident, such as a stroke or heart attack, that needs immediate attention. If the LTC consumer suffers memory loss, the risks to safety because of forgetfulness or bad judgment increase. At the same time, supervision and surveillance exact a high price in both dollars and personal freedom.

In every type of LTC, questions arise about when it is right to leave a vulnerable person unprotected and subject to risk. The corollary question, asked less often, is when is it right to force a functionally impaired person to accept protection and eliminate risks, even risks the person prefers to take. The extreme example of restricting people for their own protection is the use of physical restraints, which were formerly ubiquitous in nursing homes but have been curbed by regulatory changes following a highly publicized Institute of Medicine study, published in 1986, on the quality of LTC settings. Sedatives and psychoactive medications also have been used as a form of restraint and behavior control, presumably for safety reasons. On a less dramatic level, numerous organizational routines and professional practices and decisions designed to keep a consumer safe also restrict personal freedom and may conflict with consumer preferences. Although attorneys point out that LTC providers have rarely been sued successfully for injuries sustained by a consumer while the consumer was pursuing an expressed preference or choice, the fear of liability is pervasive in LTC industries (Kapp).

A concept variously called negotiated risk agreement, negotiated risk contracting, or managed risk agreement has gained prominence since the early 1990s as a mechanism for LTC consumers or their agents to take conscious risks and behave in a way that professionals fear endangers their health. Based on contractual principles, the notion is that the consumer who had been informed of risks related to certain behavior should be able to take those risks unless the well-being of others is clearly threatened. This is an emerging area of practice that has advocates and many detractors; it raises the potential for adjusting the power balance somewhat in favor of the consumer, but raises the specter of provider negligence masquerading as respect for autonomy. The effort to put negotiated risk agreements into place sharply reveals the flimsy information base for many of the risks that are guarded against in LTC (Kane and Levin; Kapp and Wilson).

PROFESSIONAL STANDARDS AND PARAPROFESSIONAL ROLES. It is a truism that ethical care must be competent care. The codes of ethics that govern health professionals generally require that health professionals act within the framework of correct and up-to-date scientific knowledge and that they comply with the standards of adequate professional practice. Such judgments are easier to make about specific medical and nursing procedures than about the more amorphous and less specialized services of LTC, even when professionals are delivering the services. Without clear criteria for an adequate assessment of LTC needs or a competent care plan for a person with particular characteristics, it is difficult to promulgate standards or hold any one individual accountable.

One might argue that standards for care be set high and held to rigidly, to ensure safety. The more particular educational and other standards (e.g., caseload size) are mandated, however, the higher the cost of services. Professionals may unwittingly deny services to some older persons by advocating standards that inflate prices. Because professional self-interest usually accompanies concern for consumers in advocacy for professional standards, this subject has ethical import. Also, the more rigid the standards, the less flexibility there is for consumers to work out plans that suit their individual preferences.

The mainstays of LTC are the nursing assistants, home-health aides, homemakers, chore workers, and personal-care attendants who do the bulk of the difficult, labor-intensive, sometimes unpleasant work. Little consensus has been reached about either the responsibilities of the paraprofessional LTC worker or the extent to which the worker should be expected to do independent problem solving. Historically, little attention has been paid to the rights of the paraprofessional worker, who is typically paid a poor wage and sometimes faces substandard working conditions in people's homes. The worker may also suffer verbal or physical abuse from consumers or their family members. The care providers are often members of ethnic or racial minority groups serving a largely white, middle-class clientele. With the movement toward consumer-directed care that began in the early 1990s, however, the rights and needs of workers have been raised as a major obstacle to such consumer control.

RESOURCE LIMITATION. Decisions about what ought to be done must take costs into account, particularly when governments pay or subsidize payment of the bills. For each element of LTC services and programs, one can ask whether it is worth the money, compared to other good uses for the resources. Limited resources result in fewer caregiving staff in residential facilities, poorly paid home-care attendants or limited hours of home care for each person, less space, less privacy, and less personal attention overall.

A scarce resource might be a single room in a nursing home or an extra half hour of attention at home. Without explicitly translating cost-consciousness into human terms—such as the numbers of baths or assisted trips to the toilet an LTC consumer is entitled to or the number of minutes an LTC consumer should have to wait after pushing a call button—authorities tacitly accept that the resources available are limited and that resource constraints will compromise the best care for functionally impaired persons.

INTERGENERATIONAL ISSUES. Finally, LTC forces consideration of what an ethical society should offer to older people. Older people—people over seventy-five—are by far the most numerous group needing LTC, but the lifetime costs of LTC may be greater for a younger person. Some LTC planners ask whether the claims on society for care of a younger person with a disability and an older one are different in kind, degree, or justification.

Although justifications are often made for caring for older people based on reciprocity across the generations, the elderly are given resources and encouraged to manage their own care less often than are younger persons with disabilities. Indeed, political action among younger persons with disabilities has led to changes for older people receiving community LTC. In the 1980s and early 1990s, several states restructured their LTC programs under Medicaid and state financing to include adults of all ages with disabilities. As a result, these administrators now need to determine how to allocate resources fairly among consumers of widely different ages and circumstances. Advocacy groups representing younger persons with disabilities argue for a model of LTC that gives more power to the LTC consumer or his or her agent (Litvak, Zukas, and Heumann). Such groups prefer a social rather than a medical model of care that would, as much as possible, relegate to the consumer the prerogative of selecting, training, supervising, and firing those who provide personal care. A personal-care assistant who accompanies the consumer as needed is perceived as liberating, whereas home care was seen as restricting. Authorities disagree about whether the personal-assistant model is desirable or feasible for the much larger group of elderly LTC consumers.

Policy Issues

As with acute care, LTC poses interrelated problems in access, quality, and cost. Access to care is uneven because of geographic variation in supply and price. Care is most available in the least-preferred nursing-home form, because that is the form that is publicly subsidized. Quality concerns are present for both nursing-home care and home care. Public and private costs are high. Reimbursement methods and levels for LTC often create perverse incentives. Flat-rate

systems discriminate against those who need the most care. At the same time, "case-mix-adjusted" systems, which increase payment for persons with greater disabilities, provide clear incentives against rehabilitation (Kane and Kane).

BENEFITS AND COVERAGE. The 1.9 million U.S. nursing-home residents represent about 5 percent of the country's elderly population. It is estimated, however, that an additional 10 percent of the elderly population have comparable functional impairments requiring LTC (Wiener, Illston, and Hanley). In contrast to many other industrialized countries, publicly funded LTC in the United States is available only to persons of low income, and, moreover, the vast bulk of public LTC expenditures are for nursing-home care. Despite expectations that LTC costs be met first by the consumers themselves, at least 50 percent of nursing-home costs in the United States are borne publicly (largely through Medicaid), because private resources are quickly exhausted. The public share of the costs also increases because some older people, to qualify for Medicaid, divest their resources in the years before they expect a nursing-home admission. The extent to which divestment increases public costs has been sharply debated. Publicly financed home-care benefits, though they became more widely available in the 1980s and 1990s, accounted for a relatively small outlay and were used by relatively few consumers. Further, almost all publicly funded home care has been capped at a rate less than the rate of public reimbursement for nursing-home care for the same consumer in the same state.

Nursing homes are perceived negatively. People do not want to live in them, send their family members to them, or expend their life savings and deplete their estates to pay for them. If the LTC-service setting were less aversive in terms of unappealing settings, rigid routines, and high costs, presumably some who now depend on volunteered family help would use paid LTC. This consideration dampens the enthusiasm of officials for expanding home-care benefits; they fear that home care, rather than substituting for nursing-home care, would be received by people formerly receiving uncompensated care from families.

Private LTC insurance is financially viable for only a fraction of the group at risk (Rivlin and Wiener). Both private insurers and public policymakers worry that if benefits were more desirable, they would be heavily used. After all, some LTC services (e.g., cooking, housekeeping, laundry) are intrinsically desirable even for people without LTC needs. Moreover, despite earlier beliefs, research has conclusively shown that at certain disability levels home care is more expensive than nursing-home care (Carcagno and Kemper). Economies of scale are achieved when brief, intermittent services and protective oversight are offered in centralized locations.

When community-based LTC is financed through Medicaid or state appropriations, case managers, usually social workers or nurses, typically perform initial assessments, authorize payments for home care, and monitor the quality of care and its continuing appropriateness. The case-management role promotes equity and efficiency in the use of benefits across a population but also creates a powerful agent, involved in the allocation of benefits, who may have no clear professional ethic, training, or authority. Home health agencies often complain that interposing a case manager between them and their clientele is wasteful and interferes with consumer choice; state officials argue that case managers who are separate from service delivery provide a disinterested advocate for the consumer. Juggling the roles of advocate and gatekeeper creates ethical tension for the case manager (Kane and Caplan, 1993). Case managers often have difficulty reconciling these roles but, at a minimum, should disclose to consumers the assumptions under which they work. In the early 1990s and before, informed-consent processes for case management were rudimentary.

Reimbursement issues are confounded by confusion about the extent to which LTC is a health program. In the United States, healthcare is considered a public responsibility (at least in part), whereas housing and social services are typically considered private responsibilities to be purchased with private income and with government subsidies for the poor. LTC includes social services and, when provided in nursing homes, housing. Policymakers have not determined whether they should extricate these components for financing purposes, or how to do so. Assisted living programs, such as those developed in Oregon in the early 1990s (Kane and Wilson), combine housing and board with service to functionally disabled, nursing-home-certifiable tenants in private apartments with kitchenettes, full baths, and doors that lock from the inside. Such programs may use outside home-care agencies to deliver the care, and in many states Medicaid reimburses the service component. This blurs the distinction between institutional care and home care. It also permits separating the financing of the room and lodging from that of the personal-care and nursing services, so the latter can be funded publicly and the former privately.

LTC costs and payment are also complicated by unclear boundaries between LTC and primary healthcare, acute hospital care, and post-acute care. Medicare, the universal health insurance program for persons over sixty-five, covers rehabilitation, skilled nursing-home care, and skilled home care in the immediate aftermath of an acute illness. These types of services, known as "post-acute" or "sub-acute" care,

fall in an ill-defined area between acute care and LTC. Efforts to save money in acute care and post-acute care—for example, through earlier hospital discharge or denial of Medicare claims for post-acute care—can result in higher LTC costs. Demonstration projects have paid a per capita rate to care providers who are then responsible for both acute care and LTC costs; the projects are meant to determine whether better or more efficient use can be made of the total dollars when acute care and LTC are integrated into a single program. The social health maintenance organization is one such model, and another is the Program of All-Inclusive Care for the Elderly, which was modeled on an innovative program in San Francisco's Chinatown that uses a day healthcare center as a key feature.

STANDARDS, REGULATION, AND QUALITY. The more professional standards are exacted for LTC services and the more providers are regulated, the more expensive LTC becomes. Because family members provide much LTC, some state policymakers suggest that professional-practice acts in most states are unduly restrictive in their requiring licensed nurses for many procedures routinely done by family caregivers. Others believe that vulnerable LTC consumers need protection by high standards for professional practice and managed professional supervision of nonprofessionals. This issue is salient because many LTC consumers would like to purchase cost-effective services. The break-even point, at which the price of community services exceeds that of home-based services, can be reached rather quickly and is influenced not only by the disability levels of the consumer but also by the price of the services. These, in turn, are influenced by regulations governing professional practices and agency licensure.

Regulation of care providers such as nursing homes and home-care agencies through state licensure, quality inspection, and federal certification programs also drives up costs, stifling innovation and consumer choice. Protection of vulnerable adults and avoidance of politically damaging incidents fuel these efforts. The supply of nursing homes is also regulated to stimulate community care and to save money (on the theory that a licensed bed will be used). This form of regulation has been criticized by those who believe that if market forces prevail, quality will improve.

Regulation of care settings, especially residential settings with great potential to affect quality of life, is hampered by disagreement about what should be included in the definition of quality and how various components of quality should be weighted. Although quality of life can be measured through direct interview with residents, including those with substantial cognitive disability (Kane et al.), the usual methods of accountability give greatest credence to low rates of negative health outcomes such as bedsores, infections, and weight loss. An Institute of Medicine committee charged to study the quality of LTC reported in 2001 that the field is characterized by profound disagreements about the very nature of quality; indeed, these very disagreements led to the inclusion of a minority report by committee members that placed higher emphasis on quality of life and consumer control as elements of quality (Wunderlich and Kohler).

FAMILY POLICY. Case managers make implicit and explicit decisions about the ability of family members to provide help before allocating publicly funded services to LTC consumers. LTC policymakers do not want to replace family care with public programs but want to protect families from undue burden. Respite programs have been developed specifically to provide episodic or emergency assistance to family caregivers. Various forms of compensation for family members have been suggested, ranging from tax credits to direct payment. In some states, LTC consumers have received cash payments, which they, in turn, can and often do use to pay relatives. Supporting these strategies, Nathan L. Linsk and his colleagues, in their 1992 book, *Wages for Caring,* noted the irony of paying strangers but not relatives. Direct payments to family caregivers are also seen as an income transfer to poor families. Opponents of family payment cite the cost implications. A midway position argues for family payments only when the caregiver has left the labor force to provide care—disqualifying most retirement-age spouses—and only for low-income families.

LTC LABOR FORCE. Paraprofessional workers in nursing homes and, more particularly, in home care, may receive minimum wages and no benefits. The cost implications of paying the workers an adequate wage are enormous. Although advocates of greater LTC benefits for senior citizens historically ignored the situation for workers, in the 1990s groups such as the Older Women's League formally recognized the condition of care workers as an issue. The very persons who perform the hands-on LTC tasks—typically, persons with low wages and nonexistent benefits—will become at risk for needing LTC themselves, without any personal financial reservoir from which to draw.

Conclusion

With the aging of the population and the chronicity of disease, long-term-care policies may be expected to continue to receive great attention. Many specific policies are in flux, and thematic and policy changes may be expected in response to current debates. The nagging questions about how a society can meet the ordinary needs of people with functional impairments competently, efficiently, and fairly—without compromising the autonomy and quality of life of the clientele—are likely to endure.

ROSALIE A. KANE (1995)
REVISED BY AUTHOR

SEE ALSO: *Abuse, Interpersonal: Elder Abuse; Aging and the Aged; Alternative Therapies; Autonomy; Care; Compassionate Love; Dementia; DNR; Grief and Bereavement; Healthcare Resources, Allocation of; Human Dignity; Informed Consent; Life, Quality of; Life Sustaining Treatment and Euthanasia; Medicaid; Medicare; Mentally Disabled and Mentally Ill Persons; Moral Status; Nursing, Profession of; Profit and Commercialism; Surrogate Decision-Making; and other Long-Term Care subentries*

BIBLIOGRAPHY

Agich, George J. 1993. *Autonomy and Long Term Care.* New York: Oxford University Press.

Carcagno, George J., and Kemper, Peter. 1988. "The Evaluation of the National Long Term Care Demonstration: 1. An Overview of the Channeling Demonstration and Its Evaluation." *Health Services Research* 23(1): 1–22.

Collopy, Bart; Boyle, Philip; and Jennings, Bruce. 1991. "New Directions in Nursing Home Ethics." *Hastings Center Report* 21(2): 1–15.

Henderson, J. Neil, and Vesperi, Maria D., eds. 1995. *The Culture of Long Term Care: Nursing Home Ethnography.* Westport, CT: Bergin and Garvey.

Institute of Medicine. Committee on Nursing Home Regulation. 1986. *Improving the Quality of Care in Nursing Homes.* Washington, D.C.: National Academy Press.

Kane, Rosalie A., and Caplan, Arthur L., eds. 1990. *Everyday Ethics: Resolving Dilemmas in Nursing Home Life.* New York: Springer.

Kane, Rosalie A., and Caplan, Arthur L., eds. 1993. *Ethical Conflicts in the Management of Home Care: The Case Manager's Dilemma.* New York: Springer.

Kane, Rosalie A., and Kane, Robert L. 1987. *Long-Term Care: Principles, Programs, and Policies.* New York: Springer.

Kane, Rosalie A.; Kling, Kristen C.; Bershadsky, Boris; et al. 2003. "Quality of Life Measures for Nursing Home Residents." *Journal of Gerontology: Medical Sciences* 58A(3): 240–248.

Kane, Rosalie A., and Levin, Carrie. 2001. "Who's Safe, Who's Sorry? The Duty to Protect the Safety of HCBS Consumers." In *Ethics in Community-Based Elder Care,* ed. Martha B. Holstein and Phyllis B. Mitzen. New York: Springer.

Kane, Rosalie A., and Wilson, Keren Brown. 1993. *Assisted Living in the United States: A New Paradigm for Residential Care for Frail Older Persons?* Washington, D.C.: American Association of Retired Persons.

Kapp, Marshall B. 1987. *Preventing Malpractice in Long-Term Care: Strategies for Risk Management.* New York: Springer.

Kapp, Marshall B., and Wilson, Keren Brown. 1995. "Assisted Living and Negotiated Risk: Reconciling Protection and Autonomy." *Journal of Ethics, Law, and Aging* 1(1): 5–13.

Linsk, Nathan L.; Keigher, Sharon M.; Simon-Rusinowitz, Lori; and England, Suzanne E. 1992. *Wages for Caring: A Survey of Attendant Service Programs for People of All Ages with Disabilities.* New York: Praeger.

Litvak, Simi; Zukas, Hale; and Heumann, Judith E. 1987. *Attending to America: Personal Assistance for Independent Living: A Survey of Attendant Service Programs for People of All Ages with Disabilities.* Berkeley, CA: World Institute on Disability.

Lustbader, Wendy. 2001. "The Pioneer Challenge: A Radical Change in the Culture of Nursing Homes." In *Linking Quality of Long-Term Care and Quality of Life,* ed. Linda S. Noelker and Zev Harel. New York: Springer.

Mollica, Robert L. 2002. *State Assisted Living Policy, 2002.* Portland, ME: National Academy for State Health Policy.

Rivlin, Alice M., and Wiener, Joshua M. 1988. *Caring for the Disabled Elderly: Who Will Pay?* Washington, D.C.: Brookings Institution.

Rosenbaum, Sara. 2000. *Olmstead v. L.C.: Implications for Older Persons with Mental and Physical Disabilities.* Washington, D.C.: AARP Public Policy Institute.

Rosenbaum, Sara; Teitelbaum, Joel; and Stewart, Alexandra. 2002. "*Olmstead v. L.C.:* Implication for Medicaid and Other Publicly Funded Health Services." *Health Matrix* 12(1): 93–138.

Stone, Robyn I.; Reinhard, Susan C.; Bowers, Barbara; et al. 2002. *Evaluation of the Wellspring Model for Improving Nursing Home Quality.* New York: Commonwealth Fund.

Thomas, William. 1999. *The Eden Alternative Handbook: The Art of Building Human Habitats.* Sherburne, NY: Summer Hill.

U.S. General Accounting Office. 1999. *Assisted Living: Quality-of-Care and Consumer Protection Issues in Four States.* Washington, D.C.: Government Printing Office.

Wiener, Joshua M.; Illston, Laurel H.; and Hanley, Raymond J. 1994. *Sharing the Burden.* Washington, D.C.: Brookings Institution.

Wunderlich, Gooloo S., and Kohler, Peter O., eds. 2001. *Improving the Quality of Long-Term Care.* Washington, D.C.: National Academy Press.

II. NURSING HOMES

The decision to enter a nursing home is the most wrenching outcome of long-term-care decision making. It changes almost every aspect of the life of an elder, who moves to new surroundings, may acquire a perfect stranger as a roommate, and must adhere to the nursing-home schedule. The either/or nature of the decision and the move to what has been described as a "total institution" (Lidz, Fischer, and Arnold) marks the decision about nursing-home admission as a "nodal" decision (Agich, 1993, 1995).

A nursing home is an institution in which persons, usually elderly (sixty-five years of age and older), live and receive nursing care and supervision. The provision of nursing care and supervision differentiates nursing homes from other senior residences; the lack of advanced medical and surgical services, and the fact that a nursing home is also a residence, differentiate it from a hospital. At any time, about 5 percent of those in the United States over sixty-five years of age are in nursing homes, many more than in acute-care hospitals. Over 40 percent of those over sixty-five will spend at least some time in a nursing home (Kemper and Murtaugh). Residents of nursing homes tend to be old, poor, and sick; younger patients, often with mental disorders, chronic conditions such as HIV-related disease, or post-traumatic conditions, account for a relatively small number. Nursing-home residents are disproportionately female and white.

Most nursing-home residents have trouble performing normal daily activities, such as bathing and dressing. They often have multiple long-term problems, such as confusion or walking difficulties; these changes frequently precipitate nursing home admission, when they overwhelm informal support systems. Nursing homes are increasingly used to provide further care after hospital discharge (Densen).

Ethical problems in nursing homes differ in several ways from those seen in other settings. Decision making often involves multiple related decisions made over time. There are multiple participants, and family members are often intimately involved. Many nursing-home residents are unable to make or communicate decisions, resulting in reliance on proxy decision makers. Institutional policies and practices act as powerful constraints on the autonomy of decision makers (Lidz et al.; Kane and Caplan, 1990).

Demographic changes in developed countries that have led to an increased need for nursing homes include an increase in the aging population in both absolute numbers and percentage of the population, nuclear rather than extended families, and more women in the work force. The emphasis on autonomy and the fear of lawsuits on the part of healthcare providers and institutions may be unique to the United States, but basic ethical conflicts between respecting personal autonomy and ensuring personal safety occur in nursing homes everywhere in the world.

Reimbursement

In the United States, nursing-home care is paid for almost entirely by Medicaid and "self-pay," with Medicare and long-term care insurance accounting for only a small percentage. Over two-thirds of those in nursing homes for more than six months are covered by Medicaid. Medicaid reimbursement is usually low, and nursing homes may react by raising the rates for other payers to subsidize the Medicaid population, maximizing the number of self-payers, or minimizing the amenities offered.

Asset management, in which assets are shielded or transferred while the elder becomes eligible for Medicaid, raises several questions. Is it ethically justified for relatively well-off elders to use programs meant for the poor? Alternatively, should those elders have to spend all their resources in the last few months or years of life? Several state programs have been developed in response to these questions, in which elders who purchase long-term care insurance are covered by Medicaid when their insurance runs out (Mahoney and Wetle).

Major questions regarding reimbursement remain. Who should bear the responsibility for the long-term care of elders? What are the ethically justified means of financing nursing-home care? What mix of long-term care settings should be offered as a matter of public policy? What incentives to improve care ought to be provided to those who care for nursing-home residents? In the United States, changes in healthcare policy in the future may affect reimbursement for long-term care, including nursing-home care.

The Admissions Process

A sustained effort by families to keep elders at home or in other community settings usually precedes nursing-home admission. Problems leading to admission may include increasing confusion, decreasing ability to care for oneself, and collapse of social supports.

Pertinent questions concerning nursing-home admission include "Who is making the decision?" and "Who ought to participate in making the decision?" The circumstances in which decisions are made exert powerful influence. Thus, a hospital may put pressure on the physician and family to have the patient discharged to a nursing home after acute problems are resolved. Involved parties may have conflicting interests and obligations. For example, family members may be involved as overburdened caregivers, concerned relatives, and proxy decision makers. These factors should be identified to prevent ethical conflict in the decision-making process.

Many conflicts arise between respecting the elder's autonomy and protecting his or her safety (Collopy). Participants may disagree about whether the elder's safety is actually threatened (elder: "I'm all right, I've just tripped once or twice"; versus family: "She falls all the time. I'm terrified she's going to break her hip"). This has been called the problem of "competing realities" in long-term care decision making (McCullough, et al.). Participants may also disagree about the relative safety of the nursing home. Healthcare professionals and family members may perceive the nursing home as a safer environment than it is. Confusion, falls, and increased dependency are common sequelae of nursing-home admissions. However, those admitted to nursing homes are often very frail, and it is usually not clear whether they would have fared better at home.

The nursing home itself challenges the elder's autonomy. Lack of privacy, regimented schedules, and uniform treatment of residents without regard for their wishes or interests are common. Autonomy is also constrained by other factors, including mental and physical disorders that limit the ability to make and carry out decisions, the elder's obligations to respect the legitimate interests of caregivers and family members, and the lack of a stable public policy establishing the obligations of society to elders and of elders and their families to society (Jecker, 1991, 1995). The ethical complexity of long-term-care decision making throws into question the relevance of the acute-care model of decision making, with its emphasis on patient autonomy (Agich, 1993, 1995; Hofland, 1990; McCullough et al.). A distinctive ethic may be required for long-term care, perhaps based on mediation and negotiation of opposing views (Collopy, Boyle, and Jennings; Moody).

Decision Making in Treatment

After admission to a nursing home, everyday issues such as phone access, roommate selection, and opportunity for spiritual growth must be addressed, requiring mediation among several concerns: respect for the elder's autonomy, the obligations of residents to each other, the institution's legitimate interests, and the family's role in decision making (Agich, 1993; Kane and Caplan, 1990, 1993). The task for nursing homes is to identify meaningful possibilities for the elder's exercise of everyday autonomy in the context of these legitimate constraints on autonomy.

Under the Patient Self-Determination Act (PSDA), implemented in 1991 in response to the case of Nancy Cruzan in Missouri, advance directives must be explained to the patient upon admission. The impact of the PSDA on the low rates of advance directives for nursing-home patients in the 1990s (Gamble, McDonald, and Lichstein) is not yet apparent. Issues requiring decision making that often arise in nursing homes include hospital transfers, artificial feeding, antibiotic use, amputation, and the use of restraints (Besdine; Volicer et al.).

Discussions of treatment choices should involve the resident, if he or she is able to participate, and family members or designated proxy decision makers, if the elder is unable to participate or desires their involvement. Although family members may not make the same choice the elder would make, many elders would still rather have family members make decisions for them (Menikoff, Sachs, and Siegler). Demented patients may be able to make some decisions about their healthcare. Decision-making capacity should be assessed by the physician relative to the particular decision that must be made. For example, a patient with moderate dementia might be able to decide not to have a leg amputated, and yet be unable to remember to take her medications without being reminded.

Competent patients or surrogate decision makers have the well-established right to refuse any treatment, though there is debate about whether they have the right to demand any treatment (Brett and McCullough). Trying a therapy for a time to evaluate its effectiveness may be a better choice than simply using or not using a treatment. However, institutions and caregivers, who have traditionally been reluctant to stop a treatment once begun, must be flexible if this approach is to succeed. Before such a trial of therapy, specific goals (such as expected improvements in status) should be agreed upon.

Conflict between family members and staff is often exacerbated by serious illness. For example, a family member who has not previously been involved in the patient's care may demand inappropriately aggressive care (Molloy et al.). When family members or staff members cannot reach a decision without significant disagreement, they may refer the matter to a nursing home ombudsman, an ethics committee or consultant, or, if there are issues of neglect or abuse, initiate a state inspection. Clerics may be helpful in addressing conflicts arising out of religious beliefs held by various participants. Legal proceedings are usually a last resort.

Many nursing-home residents with severe dementia who are not able to eat are kept alive with feeding tubes; many of these persons might not have wished to be kept alive under these circumstances. Legal decisions in U.S. courts in the 1980s and 1990s treated the provision of nutrition and hydration as medical decisions and recognized that artificial feeding is not always obligatory. However, withholding of nutrition poses special problems for some because of the special standing of "food and water" in human life. Many nursing-home policies require the use of artificial feeding if the resident's weight or oral intake falls below specified guidelines, even if this is against the patient's or family's wishes. This default position of artificial feeding is problematic in light of recent studies showing that feeding tube placement for administration of nutrition is associated with very low survival rates, and that it does not improve survival in patients with advanced dementia (Finucane, Christmas, and Travis; Mitchell and Tetroe; Rudberg et al.). Policies requiring artificial feeding may be questioned on both ethical and legal grounds. When nursing-home residents develop serious illness requiring treatment not available in the nursing home, transfer to the hospital becomes an issue. If a decision to limit medical intervention has been made, transfer may be unnecessary. Such decisions are best made well in advance of a crisis (Volicer et al.). When patients are transferred, advance directives written in the nursing home may not be sent to or considered valid by the hospital, and emergency services and other treatment unwanted by the elder or family may be given. Nursing-home administrators and physicians need to address this problem of the "portability" of advance directives.

Restraints

Restraints are commonly used in nursing homes to prevent falls and injuries to the patient and others, to prevent wandering, and for behavioral problems. Restraints can be physical (e.g., vests or wrist restraints) or chemical (e.g., drugs that alter behavior). Restraints may be used to protect the patient or for the convenience of the staff and can cause adverse physical and psychological outcomes, including death. Less use of restraints enhances the autonomy of nursing-home residents and several studies show either no change or a decrease in the risk of falls and injuries. However, restraint-free environments are often opposed due to inadequate staffing levels, fear of litigation, and the weight of traditional practice in the United States. The informed-consent process should address the benefits and risks of a restraint-free environment versus restraint use.

Research

Research in nursing homes (for example, into the treatment of urinary incontinence) may contribute to the quality of life of nursing-home residents. However, nursing-home research is complicated by problems of obtaining permission from nursing-home administrators to do such research, obtaining adequate informed consent or proxy consent in this vulnerable population, and ensuring privacy and confidentiality (High; Sachs and Cassel). Professionals should balance the protection of this vulnerable population with an accurate assessment of each elder's ability to give consent, and should allow those who are able to consent to participate. Proxy decision makers should consider what is known about an elder's preferences as well as the benefits, risks, and need for the research.

Staff Concerns

Nursing-home staff perform difficult, frustrating tasks, are usually poorly paid and poorly trained, and are often criticized by clients, family members, or better-paid staff members who do other jobs. Staff turnover is high in most nursing homes, affecting continuity of care and staff-elder relationships. Staff members are also often people of color, in contrast to nursing-home residents, which can lead to a mutual lack of understanding and, on occasion, to racist remarks and abuse from elderly residents or their families.

Staff members who provide regular personal care often develop strong emotional ties to residents; they are exposed daily to the outcomes of treatment choices and may disagree with patients, family members, or healthcare professionals about treatment choices. Information from staff members about the patient's wishes should be considered by those responsible for the patient's care.

Local, state, federal, and accrediting requirements and regulations pose ethical challenges to administrators in allocating the scarce resource of staff time. Complying with these regulations absorbs significant staff time and resources, diminishing the time and energy staff can devote to the care of residents. The worst institutions are unlikely to be caught, and the best are likely to spend substantial amounts of time on paperwork that does not clearly contribute to care. In addition, regulatory overemphasis on the safety of residents may restrict the autonomy of elders (Lidz et al.).

Death and Dying

A common cause of death in nursing homes is an infection or another acute illness superimposed on a chronic or progressive illness. Often, patients or family members, together with physicians and nursing home staff, have decided not to treat such illnesses aggressively. Many terminally ill patients in nursing homes are eligible for the Medicare hospice benefit. Hospice care may ensure that these patients receive improved treatment of pain and other symptoms; it may also make it easier for the family and staff to accept care focused on maintaining patient comfort rather than on treating disease. Hospice units have been developed in nursing homes; some have been designed specifically for the care of severely demented patients (Volicer et al.; Keay and Schonwetter).

Cardiopulmonary resuscitation (CPR) initiated in nursing homes or in seriously ill patients is rarely successful (Applebaum, King, and Finucane). Nursing homes may be justified in not offering CPR because of the very low probability of success. In any case, patients and family members should understand that CPR is only an attempt at resuscitation with little likelihood of success. "Do not resuscitate" (DNR) orders should not be equated with "do not treat" orders. Decisions about specific treatments should be discussed and well documented in advance.

When death is imminent, many nursing homes transfer the resident to a hospital or contact emergency medical services so that death can occur elsewhere. This may be contrary to the elder's and the family's wishes. Most emergency medical service protocols require cardiopulmonary resuscitation to be attempted, which may be traumatic to the staff and family.

Conclusion

The bioethics literature tends to typify ethical conflicts among people as involving a clash between beneficence and respect for an individual's autonomy. Nursing-home ethics is far more complex and subtle, both intellectually and practically; it includes the obligations of elders to family members, other residents, staff, and institutions; the management of scarce resources, especially in response to external constraints; the limits of caregiving obligations on the part of family members and nursing-home staff; and the anticipation and prevention of the ethical problems discussed in this article.

JILL A. RHYMES
LAURENCE B. MCCULLOUGH (1995)
REVISED BY AUTHORS

SEE ALSO: *Abuse, Interpersonal: Elder Abuse; Aging and the Aged; Alternative Therapies; Autonomy; Care; Compassionate Love; Dementia; DNR; Grief and Bereavement; Healing; Healthcare Resources, Allocation of; Human Dignity; Human Rights; Informed Consent; Life, Quality of; Life Sustaining Treatment and Euthanasia; Medicaid; Medicare; Mentally Disabled and Mentally Ill Persons; Moral Status; Nursing, Profession of; Palliative Care and Hospice; Profit and Commercialism; Surrogate Decision-Making;* and other *Long-Term Care* subentries

BIBLIOGRAPHY

Agich, George J. 1993. *Autonomy and Long Term Care.* New York: Oxford University Press.

Agich, George J. 1995. "Actual Autonomy and Long-Term Care Decision Making." In *Long-Term Care Decisions: Ethical and Conceptual Dimensions,* ed. Laurence B. McCullough and Nancy L. Wilson. Baltimore: Johns Hopkins University Press.

Applebaum, Gary E.; King, Joyce E.; and Finucane, Thomas E. 1990. "The Outcome of CPR Initiated in Nursing Homes." *Journal of the American Geriatrics Society* 38(3): 197–200.

Besdine, Richard W. 1983. "Decisions to Withhold Treatment from Nursing Home Residents." *Journal of the American Geriatrics Society* 31(10): 602–606.

Binstock, Robert H.; Post, Stephen G.; and Whitehouse, Peter J., eds. 1992. *Dementia and Aging: Ethics, Values, and Policy Choices.* Baltimore, MD: Johns Hopkins University Press.

Brett, Allen S., and McCullough, Laurence B. 1986. "When Patients Request Specific Interventions: Defining the Limits of the Physician's Obligation." *New England Journal of Medicine* 315(21): 1347–1351.

Collopy, Bart. 1995. "Safety and Independence: Rethinking Some Basic Concepts in Long-Term Care." In *Long-Term Care Decisions: Ethical and Conceptual Dimensions,* ed. Laurence B. McCullough and Nancy L. Wilson. Baltimore, MD: Johns Hopkins University Press.

Collopy, Bart; Boyle, Philip; and Jennings, Bruce. 1991. "New Directions in Nursing Home Ethics." *Hastings Center Report* 2(2): 1–15.

Densen, Paul M. 1991. *AHCPR Monograph: Tracing the Elderly Through the Health Care System: An Update.* Rockville, MD: U.S. Department of Health and Human Services, Public Health Service, Agency for Health Care Policy and Research.

Dunkle, Ruth E., and Wykle, May L. eds. 1988. *Decision Making in Long-Term Care: Factors in Planning.* New York: Springer.

Finucane, Thomas E.; Christmas, Colleen; and Travis, Kathy. 1999. "Tube Feeding in Patients with Advanced Dementia: A Review of the Evidence." *Journal of the American Medical Association* 282(14): 1365–1370.

Gamble, Elizabeth R.; McDonald, Penelope J.; and Lichstein, Peter R. 1991. "Knowledge, Attitudes, and Behavior of Elderly Persons Regarding Living Wills." *Archives of Internal Medicine* 151(2): 277–280.

High, Dallas M. 1992. "Research with Alzheimer's Disease Subjects: Informed Consent and Proxy Decision Making." *Journal of the American Geriatrics Society* 40(9): 950–957.

Hofland, Brian F. 1988. "Autonomy in Long Term Care: Background Issues and a Programmatic Response." *Gerontologist,* suppl. 28(June): 3–9.

Hofland, Brian F., ed. 1990. "Autonomy and Long-Term Care Practice" (Special issue). *Generations* 14 (suppl.): 1–96.

Jecker, Nancy S. 1995. "What Do Husbands and Wives Owe Each Other in Old Age?" In *Long-Term Care Decisions: Ethical and Conceptual Dimensions,* ed. Laurence B. McCullough and Nancy L. Wilson. Baltimore: Johns Hopkins University Press.

Jecker, Nancy S., ed. 1991. *Aging and Ethics: Philosophical Problems in Gerontology.* Clifton, NJ: Humana.

Kane, Rosalie A., and Caplan, Arthur L., eds. 1990. *Everyday Ethics: Resolving Dilemmas in Nursing Home Life.* New York: Springer.

Kane, Rosalie A., and Caplan, Arthur L., eds. 1993. *Ethical Conflicts in the Management of Home Care: The Case Manager's Dilemma.* New York: Springer.

Kane, Robert A., and Kane, Rosalie, eds. 1982. *Values and Long-Term Care: Factors in Planning.* Lexington, MA: Lexington.

Keay, T. J., and Schonwetter, R. S. 2000. "The Case for Hospice Care in Long-term Care Environments." *Clinical Geriatric Medicine* 16(2): 211–223.

Kemper, Peter, and Murtaugh, Christopher M. 1991. "Lifetime Use of Nursing Home Care." *New England Journal of Medicine* 324(9): 595–600.

Lidz, Charles W.; Fischer, Lynn; and Arnold, Robert M. 1992. *The Erosion of Autonomy in Long-Term Care.* New York: Oxford University Press.

Mahoney, Kevin J., and Wetle, Terrie. 1992. "Public-Private Partnerships: The Connecticut Model for Financing Long Term Care." *Journal of the American Geriatrics Society* 40(10): 1026–1030.

McCullough, Laurence B.; Wilson, Nancy L.; Rhymes, Jill A.; and Teasdale, Thomas A. 1995. "Managing the Conceptual and Ethical Dimensions of Long-Term Care Decision Making: A Preventive Ethics Approach." In *Long-Term Care Decisions: Ethical and Conceptual Dimensions,* ed. Laurence B. McCullough and Nancy L. Wilson. Baltimore, MD: Johns Hopkins University Press.

Menikoff, Jerry A.; Sachs, Greg A.; and Siegler, Mark. 1992. "Beyond Advance Directives—Health Care Surrogate Laws." *New England Journal of Medicine* 327(16): 1165–1169.

Mitchell, S. L., and Tetroe, J. M. 2000. "Survival after Percutaneous Endoscopic Gastrostomy Placement in Older Persons." *Journals of Gerontology* 55(12): 735–739.

Molloy, David W.; Clarnette, Roger M.; Braun, E. Ann; Eisemann, Martin R.; and Sneiderman, B. 1991. "Decision Making in the Incompetent Elderly: 'The Daughter from California Syndrome.'" *Journal of the American Geriatrics Society* 39(4): 396–399.

Moody, Harry R. 1992. *Ethics in an Aging Society.* Baltimore, MD: Johns Hopkins University Press.

Ouslander, Joseph G.; Osterweil, Dan; and Morley, John. 1991. *Medical Care in the Nursing Home.* New York: McGraw-Hill.

Rudberg, Mark A.; Egleston, B. L.; Grant, M. D.; and Brody, J. A. 2000. "Effectiveness of Feeding Tubes in Nursing Home Residents with Swallowing Disorders." *Journal of Parenteral and Enteral Nutrition* 24(2): 97–102.

Sachs, Greg A., and Cassel, Christine K. 1990. "Biomedical Research Involving Older Human Subjects." *Law, Medicine, and Health Care* 18(3): 234–243.

Volicer, Ladislav; Cantor, Michael D.; Derse, Arthur R.; et al., National Ethics Committee of the Veterans Health Administration. 2002. "Advance Care Planning by Proxy for Residents of Long-Term Care Facilities Who Lack Decision-Making Capacity." *Journal of American Geriatric Society* 50: 761–767.

Volicer, Ladislav; Rheaume, Yvette; Brown, June; et al. 1986. "Hospice Approach to the Treatment of Patients with Advanced Dementia of the Alzheimer Type." *Journal of the American Medical Association* 256(16): 2210–2213.

III. HOME CARE

Home care is an almost limitless array of preventive, therapeutic, restorative, and supportive services delivered to persons living in their own homes or the home of another in the community. In the long-term care context, home care comprises home-based services delivered to chronically ill or impaired persons. Although this care may, and increasingly does, involve high-technology medical services, the majority of care is directed at functional support (Koff). Home-care services can be divided into those services considered "skilled," such as skilled nursing, rehabilitation, speech therapy, occupational therapy, and physician home visits; and those considered "unskilled," such as personal assistance with activities of daily living (like bathing or dressing), household maintenance, monitoring, supervision, and instrumental assistance (for example, shopping or financial management).

Until the twentieth century, virtually all medical care was provided in the home. As modern medicine developed more effective and technically sophisticated interventions, medical care shifted to hospitals and physicians' offices. However, by World War I, the steadily growing numbers of persons with chronic illness reignited interest in formal home-care services. During the 1940s, limitations in the ability of hospitals to meet the increased demand for inpatient services contributed to the development of hospital-based home-care services. The 1965 amendments to the U.S. Social Security Act that created Medicaid and Medicare were intended, in part, to expand the supply of home care. Further amendments in 1967 made home care a mandatory benefit, and others in 1972 streamlined the terms of Medicare program participation for home-care agencies (Benjamin). By the mid-1980s, home care was described as the fastest-growing service under Medicare (Reilly et al.).

Growth in the home-care industry has been attributed to several factors, including the preference of patients for care at home rather than in institutions such as nursing homes, the availability of informal caregivers, the increased number of users, the intensity of utilization, and the increase in public reimbursement of services. As of 1987, home-care services were provided to about 7.7 million persons of all ages in the United States, but almost three-fourths of these persons were over the age of sixty-five (Wieland et al.). The elderly (over sixty-five) population in the United States is projected to increase by 40 percent by 2020, and the use of home care is expected to increase by 60 percent during that time (Rivlin and Wiener). Among the non-aged (under sixty-five) population, use of home-care services has been profoundly affected by the growth, in certain major cities, of the population of persons with acquired immunodeficiency syndrome (AIDS)—a 600 percent increase between 1984 and 1990 (Burbridge). The increasing use of formal home-care services—those paid for directly or by third-party reimbursement, such as Medicare, Medicaid, or private insurance—has triggered concerns regarding the cost, quality, and availability of home care. The home-care "industry" has experienced increased competition, oversight, and regulation as well as growth of the for-profit sector. There has also been a steady "medicalization" of home-care services, driven to a great degree by third-party reimbursement (Estes and Binney).

About 85 percent of home care is provided by informal caregivers, usually unpaid family members, friends, or acquaintances, and a majority of both formal and informal caregivers are women (Stone et al.). Care is provided in the most personal and intimate aspects of daily life to persons who may be vulnerable because of physical frailty and/or cognitive impairment. Several aspects of home care other than the location in which it is provided differentiate it from institutionally based long-term care. Because care is provided in the home of the client or of another individual, the client may have a stronger sense of autonomy and control, may be more comfortable, and may have the protection and security of others in the home. However, care at home raises concerns of quality assurance in unsupervised settings and the protection of the client from unscrupulous or abusive providers of formal and informal care.

Several concerns are shared in institutional and home-based long-term care. For example, problems arise in addressing autonomous decision making for persons with diminished cognitive function. There are also stresses involved in receiving intimate care from strangers. Many persons needing long-term care encounter serious limitations in the availability of services and in the funds to pay for them. Clear methods to ensure quality in both settings are lacking. And families experience stress whether care is provided at home or in institutions. There are, however, important differences. Autonomy is more strongly asserted by many home-care patients, but home-care patients may be more isolated and thus dependent on family caregivers

(Young et al.). The remainder of this article considers ethical issues that pertain to the individual receiving home care, to families, to paid workers, and to the system of care more generally.

The Home-Care Patient/Client

Chronically impaired patients, particularly elderly patients, may be at "ethical risk" of being excluded from decisions regarding their care, of having their preferences disregarded, and of having no voice in social policy decisions that affect them. This risk may result from several factors, including ageism, negative stereotypes regarding disability, misinformation, well-meaning but misguided paternalism, or reactions to spiraling healthcare costs driven in part by public spending for the old and disabled. The home setting itself may influence the nature and degree of ethical risk (Collopy et al.).

Home care may enhance the opportunity to make autonomous decisions, but it may also constrain and influence decision making. The traditional view of autonomy assumes that action is intentional, self-initiated, and not influenced by others; in reality, however, we live in a complex web of influences, including those of family members, loved ones, acquaintances, and professional caregivers. Nowhere is this web more evident than in care provided at home. Family, friends, and neighbors, as well as formal care providers, may all have an interest in the decision-making process regarding the nature and scheduling of care, the selection of workers to provide the services, and even whether or not the client can be maintained safely at home.

Safety and the assessment of risk are major considerations in the provision of home care and contribute to some of the most perplexing ethical dilemmas for providers of care. Most people of any age prefer living at home, no matter how humble or risky, to entering an institution. This preference, combined with an overestimation by some clients of their own abilities and an underestimation of the risk of living at home, frequently results in an insistence to be at home despite substantial safety concerns on the part of family and professionals.

Determination of risk is an inexact science, and it is not unusual for family and professionals to underestimate or disregard the comparable risks of institutional life. Caregivers feel strong obligation to act in the best interests of clients or loved ones by protecting them from harm, and these feelings are compounded by fear of liability should harm come to the client. While some commentators argue that fears of lawsuit have been exaggerated, they remain a powerful force in evaluating the safety of a home-based-care plan (Detzel and Kapp). An emerging model for addressing the question of risk involves "negotiating" what is an acceptable risk with the client and family by being clear about the nature of the risk and about their willingness to accept both the risk and the outcomes of negative events.

The level and nature of autonomy afforded the home-care client depends in part on the characteristics of the clients, such as their age or their cognitive or physical impairments. There are significant differences in the philosophy and organization of services for the elderly as compared to younger disabled persons (Simon-Rusinowitz and Hofland). Home healthcare for older persons tends to emphasize the avoidance of nursing home placement, to employ case management to coordinate services, and to use public regulation of providers to ensure quality of care (Eustis and Fisher). What is termed *personal assistance* in the support of the non-elderly disabled, however, evolved from the independent-living movement among working-age disabled persons who maintain that they are handicapped primarily by environmental barriers rather than by individual impairments or disabilities (DeJong et al.). Personal assistance encompasses a broader array of services than is usually found in medically oriented programs; it aims to maintain the client's well-being, personal appearance, comfort, safety, and interaction beyond the home. To the extent possible, these services to the disabled non-elderly are user-directed, with consumers supervising their personal care when possible. By comparison, for older clients, despite an emphasis on client autonomy, decisions such as scheduling services and selecting caregivers are made primarily by agency personnel without significant attention to consumer preferences (Hofland and David).

Clients may be motivated in several ways to control formal and informal caregivers. Clients are, after all, living in their own homes, and they are accustomed to having tasks accomplished in specific ways. They have habits and routines, and they may be supported by family members who share their preferences. Caregivers, for their part, are prompted to provide care and perform tasks not just by the wishes of the client but by their own values, preferences, work styles, and competing demands—and for formal caregivers, by the rules and regulations of their agencies and payors. Harry Moody argues that a model of decision making that focuses on accommodating and reciprocating autonomies is most appropriate in addressing these multiple interests. By this, he refers to a negotiation among competing needs and preferences. For example, a home-care client may not be able to refuse all formal care and remain at home and engage in behavior that is dangerous and disturbing to other persons in the building. He or she may, instead, negotiate staying at home with unwanted services.

Family Issues

Families are intimately involved in home care in several ways: They may be direct providers of informal services, may be involved in care decisions, or may live in the same home as the client and thus have their lives directly affected by formal care providers. While clients and their families might be expected to share values, preferences, and living styles, they often do not; sometimes, in fact, interests and values clash. For example, a family member may value safety and cleanliness more than the client does; the client may be more interested in preserving privacy and avoiding having a stranger "messing with my things." The relationship between formal and informal caregivers is poorly understood, raising concerns that the increased support of formal services may "erode" family caregiving (Hanley et al.). Ethical concerns arise when "needs assessment" for formal services includes consideration of the availability of family caregivers, as is required by law in some U.S. states. This raises the question of whether clients with family members who might provide services should be considered less eligible for home care than those with no such family members.

Conflicts may also arise about what can reasonably be expected from informal caregivers. Most families do not "dump" disabled family members into institutions but rather struggle to maintain elders at home for as long as possible. Surveys of family caregivers document a variety of stress-related illnesses, such as heart disease, stomach ulcers, and sleep disturbance, as well as alcohol or drug problems and marital difficulties (Brody). Because women are more likely to be caregivers, they carry a disproportionate share of the burden. Many women find themselves "sandwiched" between the care needs of an older parent or grandparent and the needs of a spouse, child, or grandchild. Because the extent of filial obligations is unclear, family caregivers may feel guilt and shame for not "doing enough," and persons needing care may feel either that they have been abandoned or that they are asking too much. Stephen Post argues that there are limits to familial obligations, and that social policy should do more to support the family in meeting its obligations.

Although we speak of the moral obligations of "the family," it is usually an individual family member, either explicitly or implicitly designated, who bears most of the burden of caregiving. These caregivers are usually women, most of whom have been providing care for more than five years; 35 percent of them are over the age of sixty-five, and 80 percent provide assistance every day of the week (Stone et al.). Women who provide home care to a parent, spouse, or other family member may do so at substantial personal cost, including personal health, lost professional and work opportunities, other personal interests, and other relationships. The interests of and burdens on caregivers should be considered when care plans are developed. If the care plan places heavy demands on an informal caregiver, it may justify constraints on client autonomy. Although "caregiver burden" is a well-recognized concept, Jaber Gubrium argues that we should hesitate to identify caregivers as "victims," noting that there are important factors that mitigate caregiver stress, including social supports, attitude toward caregiving prior to caregiving crises, personal well-being, a sense of mutuality between the caregiver and persons receiving care, and how prepared caregivers feel for the caregiving role (Archbold et al.; Zarit et al.).

Families differ in many ways that directly influence informal care and use of the formal system. While high levels of diversity exist within ethnic groups, differences among ethnic groups have been noted. Blacks and Native Americans have more widowed and divorced persons of both sexes than do whites, and they are somewhat more likely to live in extended family structures. There is also substantial home care provided by minority family members, attributable both to preference and to other factors, such as poverty, racial bias in the service system, and willingness to tend to young children in return for care (Brown; Cueller).

In healthcare, we tend to focus on the individual client; for most persons, however, there is a family context in which decisions are carried out. This context may constrain choices, but it also provides the individual with support and assistance that would otherwise be unavailable. Moreover, for clients whose capacity to make decisions is impaired, the family usually provides guidance in decision making (Nelson). This practice is supported in common law, and many states have enacted "family decision" laws that formalize this custom. The priority list is similar in most states: court-appointed guardians, spouse, adult children, parents, adult siblings, close friends, and extended family (Capron).

Although the family is usually viewed as a resource and source of support for the client, there are circumstances in which the family may perpetrate abuse and neglect. Protection of clients from abuse is difficult for several reasons. Abuse in the home may go undetected: The client may be unable or reluctant to report abuse due to extreme disability, fear of the caregiver, or shame. The client may be unwilling to act, preferring to stay in an abusive setting because alternatives are unknown, unavailable, or unattractive. Many states require that professional caregivers report suspected abuse of elderly persons via "elder abuse reporting laws," but responding to family failure in care is strategically difficult and ethically complex (Collopy et al.).

The Work Force

The paid work force for long-term home services consists of both skilled professionals and "unskilled" aides and personal assistants. Workers may enjoy the relationships that develop with patients and families, the opportunity to help others, and some flexibility in hours. However, workers may also face difficult working situations, travel to unsafe or dangerous neighborhoods, homes that are unclean and sometimes hazardous, and close contact with clients and/or family members who may be unpleasant, noncompliant, and even abusive. For unskilled workers such as aides and assistants, these difficulties are compounded by fluctuating schedules and hours, limited benefits, minimal training in necessary skills, and limited opportunities for promotion. The majority of home-care workers, both paid and informal, are women.

The quality of care and the reliability of workers are heavily influenced by the nature of the work, which may be monotonous and unpleasant, and by difficulties in attracting quality workers for minimum wage. In some cities, workers are drawn heavily from immigrant and/or minority populations, sometimes resulting in cultural conflicts and language difficulties between workers and clients. Clients may be uncomfortable having unfamiliar persons in their house, and workers may be treated with suspicion or hostility and confronted with racist comments. Work-force difficulties are increasingly exacerbated by the entry of women (who would otherwise provide informal care) into the paid labor force. Increased competition for workers from other service industries has reduced the availability of home-care workers in some areas. The affordability of some home-care services has been based, in part, on the low wages and benefits paid to unskilled workers, who are mostly women; this fact raises concerns regarding the exploitation of persons unable to find employment elsewhere.

The Healthcare System

Despite legislation intended to increase home-care services, restrictive eligibility requirements, perverse reimbursement incentives, and gaps in the continuum of care impede the home-care system. Not-for-profit agencies, such as the Visiting Nurse Association, face increasing competition for "attractive" clients, that is, those who are eligible for sufficient reimbursement. Hospitals, responding to reimbursement incentives, discharge patients who require heavier and more complex care. Third-party care "managers" regularly review clients' needs and have expanded paperwork and administrative reporting.

Case management, which has become an integral component of the home-care system, involves assessment of clients, determination of eligibility for public funding or insurance benefits, development of a care plan, and monitoring the quality of services (Quinn). While case management is viewed by many policymakers as fulfilling necessary gatekeeping and quality assurance functions, many home-care agencies view case management as yet another layer of bureaucracy and an additional expense in the system. Most case management agencies seek to empower clients by assisting them in implementing decisions. In their role as client advocates, case managers may find themselves in conflict with home-care agencies or family members who do not agree that the plan of care is safe, or who argue for more services than the agency can "afford" to provide under spending limits for individual clients or budget caps for groups of clients. The ethical conflicts case managers face as they balance the roles of gate keeping, quality assurance, and client advocacy are just beginning to be explored (Kane; Wetle).

Conclusion

Home care involves a complex and growing industry that is intricately intertwined with family caregiving. Most persons would prefer to remain at home, even when their need for assistance is substantial. Many persons would also prefer to give and receive care within a family context. However, the demand for home-care services can overwhelm the ability of family members to provide care in the face of other, competing family and work demands. Emerging changes in the healthcare system, including long-term-care insurance and public-healthcare reform, may encourage increased reliance on home care for persons with chronic conditions and illnesses. While additional resources for home care would be welcomed, we must be vigilant to the ethical concerns and values, not only of the home-care client but also of family caregivers and the paid work force, particularly women and disadvantaged persons. Efforts should also be made to develop formal services that are culturally appropriate and that meet the special needs of persons from diverse cultures and racial minorities.

TERRIE WETLE (1995)
BIBLIOGRAPHY REVISED

SEE ALSO: *Abuse, Interpersonal: Elder Abuse; Aging and the Aged; Alternative Therapies; Autonomy; Care; Chronic Illness and Chronic Care; Compassionate Love; Dementia;*

DNR; Family and Family Medicine; Grief and Bereavement; Healthcare Resources, Allocation of; Human Dignity; Informed Consent; Life, Quality of; Life Sustaining Treatment and Euthanasia; Medicaid; Medicare; Mentally Disabled and Mentally Ill Persons; Moral Status; Surrogate Decision-Making; and other *Long-Term Care* subentries

BIBLIOGRAPHY

Archbold, Patricia G.; Stewart, Barbara J.; Greenlick, Merwyn R.; and Harvath, Teresa. 1990. "Mutuality and Preparedness as Predictors of Caregiver Role Strain." *Research in Nursing and Health* 13(6): 375–384.

Arras, John D., and Porterfield, H. William., eds. 1995. *Bringing the Hospital Home: Ethical and Social Implications of High-Tech Home Care.* Baltimore, MD: Johns Hopkins University Press.

Benjamin, A. E. 1993. "An Historical Perspective on Home Care Policy." *Milbank Quarterly* 71(1): 129–166.

Brody, Elaine M. 1985. "Parent Care as a Normative Family Stress." *Gerontologist* 25(1): 19–29.

Brown, Diane Robinson. 1990. "The Black Elderly: Implications for the Family." In *Minority Aging: Essential Curricula Content for Selected Health and Allied Health Professions,* pp. 275–295, ed. Mary S. Harper. Rockville, MD: U.S. Department of Health and Human Services.

Burbridge, Lynn C. 1993. "The Labor Market for Home Care Workers: Demand, Supply, and Institutional Barriers." *Gerontologist* 33(1): 41–46.

Capron, Alexander Morgan. 1992. "Where Is the Sure Interpreter?" *Hastings Center Report* 22(4): 26–27.

Collopy, Bart; Dubler, Nancy; and Zuckerman, Connie. 1990. "The Ethics of Home Care: Autonomy and Accommodation." *Hastings Center Report* suppl. 20(2): 1–16.

Cuellar, Jose B. 1990. "Hispanic American Aging: Geriatric Education Curriculum Development for Selected Health Professionals." In *Minority Aging: Essential Curricula Content for Selected Health and Allied Health Professions,* pp. 365–413, ed. Mary S. Harper. Rockville, MD: U.S. Department of Health and Human Services.

DeJong, Gerben; Batavia, Andrew I.; and McKnew, Louise B. 1992. "The Independent Living Model of Personal Assistance in National Long-Term Care Policy." *Generations* 16(1): 89–95.

Detzel, Joyce, and Kapp, Marshall. 1992. "Developing Alternatives to Plenary Guardianship: Overcoming Fear of Legal Liability." *Gerontologist* 32(2): A131–A132.

Estes, Carroll L., and Binney, Elizabeth A. 1989. "The Biomedicalization of Aging: Dangers and Dilemmas." *Gerontologist* 29(5): 587–596.

Eustis, Nancy N., and Fischer, Lucy R. 1992. "Common Needs, Different Solutions? Younger and Older Homecare Clients." *Generations* 16(1): 17–22.

Gallagher, Elaine; Alcock, Denise; Diem, Elizabeth; Angus, Douglas; and Medves, Jennifer. 2002. "Ethical Dilemmas in Home Care Case Management." *Journal of Healthcare Management* 47(2): 85–96; discussion 96–97.

Gordon, Suzanne; Benner, Patricia; and Noddings, Nel., eds. 1996. *Caregiving: Readings in Knowledge, Practice, Ethics, and Politics (Studies in Health, Illness, and Caregiving).* Philadelphia: University of Pennsylvania Press.

Gubrium, Jaber F. 1990. *The Mosaic of Care: Frail Elderly and Their Families in the Real World.* New York: Springer.

Hanley, Raymond J.; Wiener, Joshua M.; and Harris, Katherine M. 1991. "Will Paid Home Care Erode Informal Support?" *Journal of Health Politics, Policy and Law* 16(3): 507–521.

Healy, T. C. 1998. "The Complexity of Everyday Ethics in Home Health Care: an Analysis of Social Workers' Decisions Regarding Frail Elders' Autonomy." *Social Work in Health Care* 27(4): 19–37.

Hofland, Brian F., and David, Debra. 1990. "Autonomy and Long-Term Care Practice: Introduction." *Generations* 14(suppl.): 3–9.

Holstein, Martha B., and Mitzen, Phyllis B., eds. 2002. *Ethics in Community-Based Elder Care.* New York: Springer.

Kadushin, G., and Egan, M. 2001. "Ethical Dilemmas in Home Health Care: A Social Work Perspective." *Health and Social Work* 26(3): 136–149.

Kane, Rosalie A. 1991. "Case Management in Long Term Care: It Can Be As Ethical and Efficacious As We Want It to Be." In *Ethics and Care Management: A Delicate Balance; Conference Proceedings 1989,* pp. 1–6. Philadelphia: Pennsylvania Care Management Institute.

Kapp, Marshall B., ed. 1994. *Patient Self-Determination in Long-Term Care: Implementing the Psda in Medical Decisions (Springer Series on Ethics, Law, and Aging).* New York: Springer.

Koff, Theodore H. 1988. *New Approaches to Health Care for an Aging Population.* San Francisco: Jossey-Bass.

Ladd, Rosalind Ekman; Pasquerella, Lynn; and Smith, Sheri. 2002. *Ethical Issues in Home Health Care.* Springfield, IL: Charles C Thomas Pub Ltd.

Marks, R. J. 2001. "Home Health Care, Ethics, and the Family." *Home Care Provider* 6(3): 76–77.

McCullough, Laurence B., and Wilson, Nancy L., eds. 1995. *Long-Term Care Decisions: Ethical and Conceptual Dimension.* Baltimore: Johns Hopkins University Press.

Moody, Harry R. 1988. "From Informed Consent to Negotiated Consent." *Gerontologist* suppl. 28(June): 64–70.

Nelson, James Lindemann. 1992. "Taking Families Seriously." *Hastings Center Report* 22(4): 6–12.

Olson, Ellen; Chichin, Eileen R.; and Libow, Leslie S., eds. 1995. *Controversies in Ethics in Long-Term Care (Springer Series on Ethics, Law, and Aging).* New York: Springer.

Parks, Jennifer A. 2003. *No Place Like Home: Feminist Ethics and Home Health Care (Medical Ethics Series).* Bloomington: Indiana University Press.

Perkel, R. L. 1997. "Safety in Home Care of the Frail Elderly: Dilemmas and Trade-offs. Would You Take This Patient

Home?" *Journal of Long Term Home Health Care* 16(4): 24–30.

Post, Stephen. 1988. "An Ethical Perspective on Caregiving in the Family." *Journal of Medical Humanities and Bioethics* 9(1): 6–16.

Quinn, Joan. 1993. *Successful Case Management in Long-Term Care.* New York: Springer.

Reilly, Thomas W.; Clauser, Steven B.; and Baugh, David K. 1990. "Trends in Medicaid Payments and Utilization." *Health Care Financing Review* 11(suppl.):15–33.

Rivlin, Alice M., and Wiener, Joshua M. 1988. *Caring for the Disabled Elderly: Who Will Pay?* Washington, D.C.: Brookings Institution.

Robbins, Dennis A. 1996. *Ethical and Legal Issues in Home Health and Long-Term Care: Challenges and Solutions.* New York: Aspen Publishers.

Semradek, Joyce; Tornquist, Elizabeth M.; and Gamroth, Lucia, eds. 1995. *Enhancing Autonomy in Long-Term Care: Concepts and Strategies.* New York: Springer.

Simon-Rusinowitz, Lori, and Hofland, Brian F. 1993. "Adopting a Disability Approach to Home Care Services for Older Adults." *Gerontologist* 33(2): 159–167.

Stone, Robyn; Cafferata, Gail L.; and Sangl, Judith. 1987. "Caregivers of the Frail Elderly: A National Profile." *Gerontologist* 27(5): 616–626.

Wetle, Terrie. 1992. "A Taxonomy of Ethical Issues in Case Management of the Frail Older Person." *Journal of Case Management* 1(3): 71–75.

Wieland, Darryl; Ferrell, Bruce A.; and Rubenstein, Laurence Z. 1991. "Geriatric Home Health Care: Conceptual and Demographic Considerations." *Clinics in Geriatric Medicine* 7(4): 645–664.

Young, Ann; Pignatello, Catherine H.; and Taylor, Marietta B. 1988. "Who's the Boss? Ethical Conflicts in Home Care." *Health Progress* 69(11): 59–62.

Zarit, Steven H.; Reever, Karen E.; and Bach-Peterson, Judy. 1980. "Relatives of the Impaired Elderly: Correlates of Feeling of Burden." *Gerontologist* 20(6): 649–655.

M

MALPRACTICE, MEDICAL

• • •

Medical malpractice is a legal system that permits victims of certain medical errors to sue for their injuries. It is a branch of tort law and, like tort law generally, is intended to achieve several policy objectives. (The discussion below focuses on medical errors committed by physicians, but the medical malpractice system may hold accountable other types of healthcare professionals as well as institutions such as hospitals and managed-care organizations.)

Objectives of the System

The first objective of the medical malpractice system is to compensate the victims (or in some cases their families) for the losses they sustained as a result of the malpractice. Although some of these losses, such as pain and suffering, are non-economic in nature, the malpractice system awards only money damages. The idea is to use money to restore the victim as much as possible to the condition the victim would have been in if the malpractice had not occurred. Along with pain and suffering, a successful plaintiff can recover the additional medical expenses necessitated by the malpractice episode, lost earnings (including both lost wages from having missed work and reduced earnings in the future as a result of diminished earnings capacity), and monetary compensation for other types of emotional deprivations, such as loss of enjoyment from being unable to engage in certain activities like sex or sports. It follows from these measures of damages that the same act of medical misfeasance—for example, the failure to correctly diagnose a treatable illness in a timely manner—can yield dramatically different damage awards for different victims. Someone who is old, for example, will have fewer years of work left than someone who is young, and therefore will receive less for diminished future earnings capacity.

A second objective of the malpractice system is to deter physicians from making medical errors that injure patients. The premise is that medical mistakes can be prevented by taking greater care, such as by spending more time with patients, employing more sophisticated diagnostic tools, and so forth. Taking greater care, however, consumes greater resources. The malpractice system gives physicians an incentive to invest these additional resources in order to avoid being liable for damages.

The third objective of the malpractice system is retributive justice—to punish wrongdoers and to enable victims to exact revenge. Along with sanctions imposed by criminal law, tort liability reduces the risk that victims will take the law, so to speak, into their own hands.

Functioning of the System

A plaintiff in a malpractice case must prove certain propositions in order to recover damages, including that the physician actually caused harm to the plaintiff and that the defendant was negligent, meaning that the defendant's behavior deviated from the applicable standard of care—that of a reasonable physician under the same circumstances. Typically, the plaintiff must prove through the testimony of expert physician witnesses how a reasonable physician would have behaved. At one time, before courts adopted more flexible approaches, only a physician from the same locality could testify about the standard of care, which made it difficult or impossible for plaintiffs in small towns to find suitable expert witnesses. The expert testimony, including testimony from opposing experts for the defendant, is supposed to describe how physicians *should* behave. In practice, however, experts may testify about how physicians *do* in fact behave, and judges and juries typically accept this evidence of professional custom as the standard of care. A notable exception is the case of *Helling v. Carey,* in which the Supreme Court of Washington State held that the entire profession of ophthalmology was failing to meet the standard of care by not routinely testing younger patients for glaucoma.

In theory, establishing whether or not someone is negligent involves a cost–benefit analysis; actors are negligent if the cost of preventing the injury is less than the risk of the injury, measured in terms of its probability and severity. In order to avoid being negligent, physicians therefore should expend enough resources to reduce patient risk to the point that any further expenditure on prevention would exceed the value of the risk being prevented, and therefore be inefficient. But because the value of a risk can be expected to vary from one patient to another, how is it to be calculated?

Here is where the doctrine of informed consent enters into malpractice law. In addition to promoting patient autonomy, informed consent assists patients and physicians in making accurate calculations about how much to spend to reduce the risk of error. By assigning a high cost to a particular injury, for example, risk-averse patients will demand greater risk-reduction expenditures. This raises a difficult question concerning how far the law will allow patient preferences to control the standard of care. Suppose a patient opts for a treatment approach that is contrary to mainstream medical practice. Does the patient's choice relieve the physician of malpractice liability? Traditionally, the law has recognized the need to permit physicians to deviate from customary practice in appropriate circumstances, such as when the mainstream approach has failed to provide a benefit to a specific patient; physicians who deviate from the mainstream approach are not negligent if, in addition to obtaining the patient's informed consent, they can prove through expert testimony that their approach would have been followed by a "respectable minority" of other physicians.

But why should a fully competent and informed patient not be permitted to agree to an alternative and complementary treatment that no other physician would employ? To what extent should malpractice law protect patients from their own folly? A related question is whether a patient ought to be permitted to waive the physician's malpractice accountability, in return, say, for a discount in the price of care. The law traditionally has frowned upon such releases from liability, fearing perhaps that patients who made such agreements must not be able to afford to pay for needed

services, and therefore they should not be deemed to be acting voluntarily. But from the physicians' perspective, this traditional view may no longer be feasible in the era of managed care, where patients may be covered by low-cost plans that do not pay for some services that the medical profession considers to be customary.

Physicians are covered by malpractice insurance, which pays the damage award, up to the policy limits, if plaintiffs are successful, and also covers the costs of the physicians' defense attorneys, who typically are hired and controlled by the insurance companies. Insurance covers only a portion of the physician's malpractice costs, however; physicians also incur uninsurable costs in the form of time lost from practice while defending cases, emotional costs, and possible loss of membership on hospital medical staffs and in managed-care networks. Malpractice insurance premiums are based principally on the physician's geographic location and area of medical specialty, rather than on the physician's past malpractice history ("experience rating"). Increasing premiums for physicians who are repeatedly and successfully sued for malpractice would seem to be an obvious means of helping to deter future misfeasance, but insurers contend that they cannot experience-rate physicians because the number of claims is too small.

Evaluation of the System

How well does the malpractice system perform its intended functions? According to the Harvard Malpractice Study, which examined hospital records in New York State from 1984, only about one out of eight patients whose records revealed that they had suffered a malpractice injury filed a claim, and only about half of these claims resulted in compensation. Other empirical data, however, have shown that the more severe the injury, the more likely the victims are to be compensated, and the greater the amount of recovery. Critics of the current system assert that the awards recovered are excessive, but others disagree. The system is clearly time consuming; claims take an average of twenty-five to thirty months to be resolved after they are filed with the insurer, which can create severe economic problems for victims who lack healthcare or disability insurance. In the United States, plaintiffs' lawyers take cases on a contingent fee basis, receiving an average of approximately 33 percent of the plaintiff's recovery if the case is successful. If the case is not successful, the attorney not only recovers nothing, but typically must pay out-of-pocket for court costs and expert fees. Attorneys therefore can be expected to refrain from taking cases that are marginal on their merits or that do not involve a substantial amount of damages. Because, as noted earlier, the amount of damages is contingent on such factors as the victim's age, some victims accordingly have difficulty finding lawyers to represent them. On the other hand, there are anecdotal reports that some plaintiff's attorneys file frivolous lawsuits in the hopes that the defendants will settle in order to avoid litigation costs. Unlike in Great Britain, where a plaintiff who loses a malpractice suit must pay the defendant's attorneys' fees and court costs, defendants in the United States must bear those costs themselves, and defense attorneys, unlike attorneys for plaintiffs, get paid regardless of whether they win or lose.

There is little empirical information on why so few malpractice victims assert claims. Clearly one reason is that they do not realize that they have been the victims of malpractice. Studies also have shown that patients who have positive interactions with physicians are less likely to file claims despite becoming aware of malpractice, and that patients are less likely to sue after physicians have apologized for mistakes. The latter practice is discouraged, however, by the fact that, in all but a handful of states, the physician's apology is admissible in a lawsuit as an admission of liability.

There are no good data on how well the malpractice system performs its deterrence or retributive functions. Some critics point out that medical errors persist despite the malpractice system and that the number of claims is growing. Others argue in effect that the system is overdeterring physicians by causing them to practice defensive medicine.

Malpractice insurance premiums comprise a substantial portion of the overhead of the practice of medicine. Premiums have tended to increase over time, due at least in part to significant increases in the number of suits filed (known as *frequency*) and the size of damage awards (known as *severity*). Premiums also reflect the cost of defending suits, including the costs of attorneys and expert witnesses. It is estimated that for every dollar of malpractice insurance premium, only 30 cents actually goes to victims.

Malpractice premiums also have gone through periods of rapid increase, especially around 1975, 1985, and beginning again in 2001, leading these periods to be characterized as *malpractice crises*. In addition to large premium increases, these crises are marked by insurance companies exiting certain markets, and anecdotal evidence suggests that some physicians switch from higher to lower risk specialties, move to geographic locations with lower premiums, or retire from practice prematurely. The malpractice crisis of 1985, for example, has been blamed for physicians leaving rural practices and abandoning obstetrics. The semicyclical nature of these crises, and their proximity to economic downturns, suggest that at least a partial explanation for why they occur can be found in the behavior of the malpractice insurance industry itself, which creates what are termed *insurance cycles*. These begin when insurance companies reduce premiums to attract more business. As claims frequency and severity continue to increase, the amount of premium funds becomes too small to pay claims, and a weak economy decreases the return on the insurance companies' investment portfolios, which they had counted upon to make up the shortfall. This leads to sudden, rapid increases in premiums, insurer insolvencies, and withdrawal of companies from less profitable markets. Eventually the market stabilizes, and insurers once more decrease premiums, beginning another cycle.

These crises have led to two main types of legislative responses. In reaction to the malpractice crisis of the mid-1970s, state legislators took steps to help ensure that healthcare providers had access to medical malpractice insurance. They provided for the creation of physician-owned mutual insurance associations, joint underwriting associations and similar entities called reinsurance exchanges, and state-run reserve funds, intended to augment the coverage provided by the market. The second major legislative response was that a number of state legislatures changed the rules governing the malpractice system to make it more difficult and less remunerative for victims to sue. These so-called reforms include *caps*, or statutory limits on the amount of damages or the amount of non-economic damages that a successful plaintiff can collect; reductions in the maximum length of time (set by statutes of limitation) that victims have in which to file suits; prerequisites to filing suits (such as first having the claim reviewed by a panel of physicians); and repeal of the collateral source rule, which allows plaintiffs to recover medical and other expenses from defendants even though these had been paid by third parties, such as health insurers. (The collateral source rule typically does not result in a windfall for successful plaintiffs, because insurers usually are "subrogated" to the plaintiffs' claims, meaning that the plaintiffs have to reimburse the insurers from the proceeds of their recovery. The effect of repealing the collateral source rule is that healthcare costs that once were shifted from health insurers to malpractice insurers must now be borne by the health insurers.) One of the broadest sets of reforms was enacted in California by the Medical Injury Compensation Reform Act (MICRA), which limits damages for pain and suffering to $250,000, places restrictions on attorney contingent fees, repeals the collateral source rule, allows health plans to require enrollees to submit malpractice claims to binding arbitration, and requires large damage awards to be paid in installments rather than in a lump sum.

Of all of the changes in the traditional malpractice system, only caps on damages and repeal of the collateral source rule appear to have reduced malpractice cost indicators, such as premiums. Many of the caps have been overturned by state courts as unconstitutional violations of equal protection laws or deprivations of the constitutional right to a jury trial. Courts have questioned, for example, why it should be more difficult or less remunerative for victims of medical malpractice to receive compensation than for persons who have suffered other types of injuries covered by tort law.

Another malpractice crisis is taking place in the early 2000s. Renewed calls are being made for state legislative action. One recurrent proposal is some form of "no-fault" system, whereby the current tort approach would be replaced with an administrative scheme similar to workers' compensation. Victims no longer would have to prove that a physician was negligent in order to recover damages; instead, an administrative body would promulgate a list of compensable events and a schedule of associated compensation amounts. Proponents argue that more victims would receive compensation, and do so more quickly and with lower administrative costs, than under the current system. Opponents point out that, in order to be affordable, no-fault proposals would have to reduce the maximum amount of damages that victims could recover, with some proposals eliminating compensation for pain and suffering altogether. Critics question the fairness of depriving those who are most seriously injured of the large recoveries they are entitled to under the current system.

So far, the no-fault program has been adopted only in a limited fashion, in Florida and Virginia. In both states, one set of malpractice claims—those that stem from birth-related injuries—has been withdrawn from the traditional tort system, and victims are compensated under an administrative system similar to workers' compensation. Neither state program provides compensation for pain and suffering. Florida provides no award for lost future earnings. Nevertheless, some studies suggest that if attorneys' fees are subtracted and if the portion of the no-fault award that is placed in reserve for future expenses is included, the Florida program provides the same amount of compensation to victims as comparable cases do under the tort system. It remains to be seen, however, whether a no-fault program extending to a wider set of malpractice claims would be economically feasible without more significantly reducing the size of recoveries.

One legislative development that has affected the medical malpractice system is the National Practitioner Data Bank. Mandated by federal law, the data bank receives reports of all payments made by insurers in response to malpractice claims, including settlements, as well as adverse actions by state medical boards, hospitals, and managed-care plans. Hospitals are required to check the database in the course of making privileging and credentialing decisions, and state medical boards are permitted to access the data bank when considering applications for medical licenses. The purpose of the data bank is to prevent physicians (and other healthcare professionals) who have had their licenses or hospital medical staff privileges revoked, suspended, or limited, or who have been involved in a number of malpractice actions, from concealing these facts when they seek licensure, hospital privileges, or membership in a managed-care physician network. One result is that physicians may be reluctant to settle malpractice cases, preferring instead to go to trial and hope to be vindicated, in which case no report will be filed with the data bank. This in turn may place physicians in conflict with their malpractice insurers, who may prefer settlement as a means of keeping down their litigation costs.

TROYEN A. BRENNAN (1995)
REVISED BY MAXWELL MEHLMAN

SEE ALSO: *Competence; Expert Testimony; Harm; Hospital, Contemporary Ethical Problems; Impaired Professionals; Law and Bioethics; Mistakes, Medical; Professional-Patient Relationship: Ethical Issues; Whistleblowing in Healthcare*

BIBLIOGRAPHY

Bovbjerg, Randall R., and Sloan, Frank A. 1998. "No-Fault for Medical Injury: Theory and Evidence." *University of Cincinnati Law Review* 67: 53–123.

Bovbjerg, Randall R.; Tancredi, Laurence R.; and Gaylin, Daniel S. 1991. "Obstetrics and Malpractice: Evidence on the Performance of a Selective No-Fault System." *Journal of the American Medical Association* 265(21): 2836–2843.

Harvard Medical Practice Study. 1990. *Patients, Doctors, and Lawyers: Medical Injury, Malpractice Litigation, and Patient Compensation in New York.* Cambridge, MA: President and Fellows of Harvard College.

Helling v. Carey. 83 Wash.2d 514, 519 P.2d 981, 67 A.L.R. 3d 175 Wash (1974).

Studdert, David M., and Brennan, Troyen A. 2001. "Toward a Workable Model of 'No-Fault' Compensation for Medical Injury in the United States." *American Journal of Law and Medicine* 27(2,3): 225–252.

U. S. Congress. General Accounting Office. 1987. *Medical Malpractice: Characteristics of Claims Closed in 1984.* Washington, D.C.: U. S. Government Printing Office.

U. S. Congress. Office of Technology Assessment. 1993. *Impact of Legal Reforms on Medical Malpractice Costs.* Washington, D.C.: U. S. Government Printing Office.

U. S. Congress. Office of Technology Assessment. 1994. *Defensive Medicine and Medical Malpractice.* Washington, D.C.: U. S. Government Printing Office.

Weiler, Paul; Newhouse, Joseph P.; and Hiatt, Howard H. 1992. "Proposal for Medical Liability Reform." *Journal of the American Medical Association* 267(17): 2355–2358.

Whitman, Amy B.; Park, Deric M.; and Hardin, Steven B. 1996. "How Do Patients Want Physicians to Handle Mistakes? A Survey of Internal Medicine Patients in an Academic Setting." *Archives of Internal Medicine* 156(22): 2565–2569.

MANAGED CARE

• • •

With the growth of employer-based medical insurance following World War II, fee-for-service indemnity insurance became the prevailing mode of financing healthcare delivery. Even prior to the rise of indemnity insurance, care was provided—for those who could afford it—in exchange for a fee or as part of a barter arrangement. Thus, a physician's order for care and the resultant delivery of care essentially commanded a payment from a payer source (for example, from a health insurance company, a self-insured employer, the government, or an individual patient) to a provider. For those who were insured and who could afford paying their co-pays and deductibles, there were few, if any, financial constraints on the delivery of healthcare in the fee-for-service era. Both healthcare costs and provider wealth soared under fee-for-service insurance; and there is compelling evidence of over-utilization of services, variable quality of services, and an increasing percentage of uninsured Americans in this period. If three cardinal measures of a well-functioning health system are quality, cost control, and access, fee-for-service financing was an across-the-board failure.

In this era, a mentality of entitlement arose among both physicians and insured patients. The insured patient was entitled to any care deemed beneficial by their physician; and the physician (by virtue of professional prestige and the resulting presumption that practice would be ethically balanced by the duties to both benefit and do no unnecessary harm to patients) was entitled to order any treatment he or she deemed to be consistent with that ethic. While physicians have, at the beginning of the twenty-first century, lost the political and economic power to practice in such an unfettered way, insured patients carry the mentality of entitlement forward, and Americans generally exhibit little understanding of the cost problems in healthcare. This is not to blame the general public as patients or consumers, but instead to assert the need for a more educated citizenry, as part of a next effort to seek a solution to the healthcare crisis of balancing quality, cost, and access.

The Rise of Managed Care

Between the end of World War II and the early 1980s, there were a few health maintenance organization (HMO)-precursor and healthcare cooperative arrangements in the United States in which individuals pooled their resources to assure themselves and their families access to medical care. In these arrangements, physicians usually settled for salaries for managing the care of their enrolled patients and population within a budget. The 1973 HMO Act created economic incentives for the creation of *federally qualified* HMOs. In essence, the act allowed for competition on cost and quality between HMO and fee-for-service arrangements. In the early 1980s, a major shift in the financing of healthcare began occurring in the United States. As a result, the financing and delivery of healthcare came to be integrated in a new way known as *managed care*. This shift also represented a significant change in the balance of power between the providers (physicians, hospitals, and delivery systems) and the financiers of healthcare private and public insurers.

In 1983, with the imposition of Medicare diagnosis-related groups (DRGs) the federal government took a major step to institute financial constraints on healthcare delivery. DRGs, which then applied only to hospitals, required hospitals to manage the care of a patient with a particular diagnosis for a set dollar or reimbursement amount. Hospitals, of course, began facing new economic threats under this arrangement. A critical unmanaged element in the healthcare delivery equation remained the physicians' accustomed approaches to ordering patient care. A hospital's failure to manage care within the Medicare reimbursement amount meant incurring a financial loss that needed to be recovered elsewhere. It also meant that surplus funds that used to be available through overpayments by Medicare could no longer be *cost-shifted* and used to support education, medical research, and charity care. Initially, this led to raising the costs for services to the privately insured, which translated into higher insurance premiums for employers and individuals. When employers or individuals could no longer afford premiums, the number of uninsured rose.

For physicians, as it had for hospitals, managed care arrangements represented a decisive change in the relationship between dollars and decisions to order healthcare services for patients. Physicians had historically been the directors of care, unconstrained by the payers in fee-for-service arrangements. Now the payers had achieved sufficient power to financially constrain physicians' ways of practicing medicine. Cost ceilings were created for the provision of specific services; physician utilization patterns became targets of payer scrutiny and additional financial controls; physicians were required to enter into risk-sharing arrangements in exchange for access to patients in insured networks; financial incentives like bonuses and withholds were instituted to control physicians' utilization of services; and physicians were encouraged to follow practice guidelines developed from a population perspective and focused on cost-effectiveness to manage patient care. In many ways medical practice had been absorbed into the insurance side of healthcare. Thus arose managed care: a way of integrating the financing and delivery of healthcare so that the former drives, rather than is driven by, the latter. Managed care includes various organizational arrangements, approaches, tools, and strategies. It is not a single definable practice. Common threads are fiscal incentives concerning healthcare service delivery.

At the same time that the economic struggle was going in progress who would control the price tag and reap the profits of healthcare, important efforts were underway to raise the quality of healthcare by encouraging a transition to medicine as an evidence-based practice, not simply an individually-practiced art. One way to manage healthcare dollars is to restrict payment to what we know works, that is, to pay only for healthcare that has been proven to generate valued patient outcomes. Managed care reasonably declared itself to be focused on payment for medically necessary, cost-effective care.

The Managed Care Backlash

Managed care ran into significant public opposition in the imposition of policies such as twenty-four hour hospital stays for new mothers and the refusal to pay for unproven interventions for patients with life-limiting diagnoses. (Interestingly, though it is managed care organizations that have been assailed for excluding coverage for experimental treatments, this exclusion is a carry-over from fee-for-service days. Traditionally fee-for-service insurers also refused to cover unproven interventions.) What was rational to a managed care mind was fundamentally irrational or uncaring to the public's mind. Disconnected from the growing cost crisis in healthcare, the public was deeply at odds with the ethic inherent in the workings of managed care. This sentiment should have led the managed care industry to assess the ethical difference and adjust its coverage and pricing accordingly, or engage the American citizenry in a deeper discussion of these important issues in the interest of managing healthcare costs. A few managed care organizations chose to acknowledge the difference between their ethic as the manager of healthcare for a population within a

defined budget and the ethic of their individual constituents and to work toward a resolution. Many if not most others ignored the fundamental tensions between individual and population good and the even larger tensions associated with for-profit healthcare payers displacing providers in the healthcare driver's seat. To date none of the significant health system stakeholders has prioritized an effective, rational public conversation around the polarizing goals of improving access, improving quality, controlling spiraling healthcare inflation, and enhancing patient and physician autonomy.

Managed care grew out of a serious need and effort to reduce healthcare spending. There were also serious concerns about quality in healthcare that were being pursued in tandem with and as part of the move toward managed care. If fee-for-service encouraged a culture of over-utilization, it also promoted harm through over-treatment; unbridled access to specialists undermined primary care and the coordination of care; and patients were subject to care recommendations that reflected the experience of the individual physician rather than systematic empirical information about patient outcomes. If the quality improvement movement rather than the struggle over wealth between providers and payers had led the managed care evolution, and communication with the public had been deliberate, things might have gone very differently.

And yet, who could take seriously discussions on such issues instigated by huge for-profit healthcare organizations that have come to dominate the healthcare marketplace? The public was never a real player in considering the big issues and has yet to be educated to understand the deeper questions that face the American healthcare system. The next evolution of our system will see a new group—or groups—in control. The options are: providers (who do not organize well); healthcare financing companies (the payers that have amassed incredible economic and political power along with potentially insurmountable public relations crises); medical manufacturing industries (the pharmaceutical and technology companies that are currently able to pass largely unregulated costs onto payers); group purchasers of insurance (employers, unions, and government that increasingly search for ways to cap their own financial risk and empower individual decision making and choice); individual purchasers of insurance (who have no market clout whatsoever and poor options for affordable insurance); patients (who are divided up into a myriad of insurance arrangements in ways that undermine their ability to organize and who feel entitled to all beneficial care); and the uninsured (40 million residents of the United States and growing).

The public backlash has been too significant to ignore: The public is now called upon to spend more for healthcare, while still facing threats to their felt entitlement to all beneficial care. Managed care organizations are assailed for failing to control costs, even as legislatures, courts and the court of public opinion prohibit them from implementing many of the tools that constrain costs. For-profit healthcare conglomerates now dominate the health system as a whole, and are among the only good bets on the stock market in 2003. Clearly, there is money there, but patients are not happy, providers are not happy, purchasers are not happy, and costs continue to rise exponentially.

In principle, managed care offers the major purchasers of healthcare (employers, unions, and government) competitively priced insurance, institutes quality-control measures to determine and encourage cost-effective care, and provides enrollees (the insured) fair access to quality healthcare from credentialed providers within a finite budget. If one assumes that effective cost control will promote a lower percentage of uninsured, managed care has the potential to serve the goals of quality, cost control, and access in a manner far superior to fee-for-service.

Yet between the principle of managed care and its implementation have fallen the shadows of public discontent and the ongoing struggle among stakeholders for economic ascendancy. The assumption has been that the market-guided evolution of managed care would issue in cost-contained, accessible, high quality healthcare for a larger share of Americans. That assumption has not been true at the beginning of the twenty-first century.

Many analysts believe that managed care is here to stay, although in forms rather markedly different from the classic HMO model of the 1980s. It is now best thought of as multiple arrangements that use selected elements of a managed care toolkit, the defining elements of which include definitions of medical necessity, practice guidelines, risk-sharing arrangements, financial incentives, and coverage policies.

Ethical Issues Raised by Managed Care Arrangements, Strategies, and Tools

From an ethical perspective, the most serious concern with managed care is that it threatens the fiduciary or trust relationship between physician and patient. Many have argued that the special *covenantal* relationship between the physician and patient necessitates a nearly absolute freedom from financial constraints on the part of the physician. While the physician–patient relationship has never been free from financial conflicts of interest, it has been argued that conflicts that induce under-treatment rather than overtreatment more seriously threaten the fiduciary quality of the relationship. In either case, however, the fiduciary character of the relationship appears sorely threatened. Despite this, the public seems to fear the withholding of necessary care more than overtreatment, and sees the physician's integrity to be more easily undermined by risk-sharing arrangements with insurers than by a more traditional for-profit practice arrangement. Ultimately, those who pursue the fiduciary profession of medicine are the last, best strongholds of the values we all hold concerning this vital human relationship. Both forms of financial conflict threaten the fiduciary role, and it falls to the moral character of the physician and other clinicians to hold the line against the compromising of that role.

Perhaps the truth is that it is easier to summon the moral courage and fortitude this requires under fee-for-service than under managed care. After all, if risk-sharing and financial incentives/disincentives and other threats are too onerous and direct, physicians will be hard-pressed to avoid the influence of the dollar on their decisions to order services. It seems clear that in the interest of maintaining the fiduciary quality of this professional role, some managed care *tools* for constraining physician utilization are themselves unethical and must be regulated.

It also seems clear that in addition to the responsibilities physicians have to their individual patients, physicians have obligations to the population of patients they serve—not only the patients in the same enrolled population, but all of the patients they might be called upon to serve (including patients requiring pro bono services due to being uninsured). The ethical tension in this role is unavoidable: Physicians must, at the same time that they seek to provide for their patients' needs, assume a resource management attitude. Physicians do not have the option of arguing that they should be able to practice without concern for cost. Somehow, in their everyday practice, they must manage this tension with an ethic of proportionality: The most serious of patient needs must be met with an appropriate outpouring of human and financial resources, while lesser needs are addressed proportionately.

This raises another issue as well: Some patients and groups of patients are much more expensive to treat than others. In short, there is a financial disincentive that automatically attaches to treating the neediest patients, unless risk-adjustment enters into the picture to protect providers. The very fact that an epidemic of service line closures is affecting the most vulnerable and costly patients (e.g., behavioral healthcare) suggests that very different solutions to the provision of certain healthcare services are needed where the market-based effort to control healthcare costs has collapsed.

The fact that resources are to be managed to deliver quality care to individuals based on their medical needs and to fairly distribute healthcare resources throughout a covered population represents a series of ethical quandaries. Managed care tools designed to manage the extreme ethical tension created by this dual goal include definitions of medical necessity, practice guidelines, and coverage policies. In managed care arrangements, evidence gathered about what works (i.e., improves the level of health from a population perspective) is captured in practice guidelines and coverage policies, that are then applied to coverage determinations for individuals.

One of the reasons medicine has always been considered an art is that it requires a depth of attention to the patient as a physical body and also as a person. While there may be algorithms to assist in determining care options when diagnoses are clear, when they are not clear, or the patient is outside clear diagnostic parameters, population-based formulas may well be off the mark. If medicine is both science and art, and contributes to healing and/or comforting through both intellectual and personal power, then clinical autonomy remains an essential feature of the practice of medicine that must somehow be blended with the power of population-based practice guidelines and coverage policies.

Further, one of the great fears must be for patients with conditions for which there are little or no practice guidelines and for which medical research has yet to find good options—and may even have few incentives to seek options. Vulnerable populations have been historically neglected in research. Mental and physical rehabilitation, crucial to quality of life, in some cases lack good evidentiary bases. Coverage for such interventions should not be denied when they may well represent a best chance for a functional life.

This leads to the issue of managed care's assumption that coverage be determined by a standard or set of criteria of medical necessity. What constitutes medically necessary care? Care that *may* restore function? That is *known* to restore function? Care that will *enhance* function beyond the normal range? Here again, the managed care disconnect from public sensibilities has been extreme. For the public, if something stands a chance of improving function or extending life, however small that chance, it is medically necessary care. For managed care organizations, there must be evidence that an intervention will improve function, as expressed in coverage policies and practice guidelines.

An Ethical Framework for Managed Care

The cornerstone of the traditional clinical ethics framework was, of course, patient autonomy or self-determination. The additional principles were beneficence, nonmaleficence, and justice. Can this framework be exported from clinical settings to organizational situations in which financing constrains patient care decisions and arrangements, or is a new ethical framework needed?

A novel framework seems to be required. One *could* say that the justice principle of the clinical ethics framework could be extended to guide the resource management responsibilities of managed care arrangements for their covered populations. But the principle of justice of the clinical ethics framework was always more individually than communally focused. It concerned the primacy of individual claims to benefits and individual rights not to be unfairly burdened for the sake of others, not communally beneficial distributions. Because managed care arrangements manage healthcare access and serve *both* populations and individuals, they have duties of *stewardship* and of protection of the fiduciary quality of clinical relationships. Because the personal good of healthcare is now available to individual patients through complex insurance businesses, *advocacy* supporting patient *autonomy* in clinical decisions and rights as an insured member of an enrolled population becomes an additional ethical imperative. Neither the patient-population tension nor the dependent relationship of care to coverage can be eliminated. The ethical tensions inherent in managed care must be named in a new healthcare organizational ethical framework, just as the tensions in clinical care were named in its ethical framework. If stewardship, autonomy, and advocacy should be included in the new framework, so must be principles of *truth telling* (both about clinical options and coverage), and *confidentiality*. Additional ethical principles, carryovers from the clinical ethics framework, are *beneficence* and *nonmaleficence*. Each of these principles must be interpreted for the financing and delivery arrangement that currently dominates the U.S. healthcare system: namely one in which financing constrains delivery.

Because managed care arrangements and tools provide the context for clinical relationships, a broader ethical framework for the analysis of ethically problematic situations is required. In addition, guidelines for the protection of essential features of clinical relationships are required. In the absence of these ethical principles and guidelines, there is no disciplined way to identify and remove unjustifiable threats to individual patients, or for that matter, to the population.

The ethical responsibilities of managed care organizations arguably extend to the broader community and society. They control distribution of healthcare resources, and as explained above, have compromised the capacity of provider organizations to cost-shift to support education, research, and charity care commitments. Society has yet to come to terms with the obligations of managed care organizations to support community needs such as these. This issue is even more problematic when one draws the distinction between nonprofit and for-profit health systems. Due to their tax-exempt status, the former are required to provide community benefit. Due to the fact that they pay taxes, the latter have no parallel requirement; they may operate like any business, supporting community interests as they deem conducive to their own interests, despite that they exert substantial control over the healthcare resources available to their community. It is essential to determine, from an ethical perspective, the stewardship responsibilities that exist for these organizations to support the health of the broader community.

KAREN G. GERVAIS

SEE ALSO: *Healthcare Resources, Allocation of; Health Insurance; Health Policy in the United States; Justice; Professional-Patient Relationship; Profit and Commercialism*

BIBLIOGRAPHY

Dudley, R. A. and Luft, Harold S. 2001. "Managed Care in Transition." *New England Journal of Medicine* 344: 1087–1092.

Eddy, David. 1996. *Clinical Decision Making: From Theory to Practice.* Boston: Jones and Bartlett Publishers.

Gervais, Karen G.; Priester, Reinhard; Vawter, Dorothy E.; et al. 1999. *Ethical Challenges in Managed Care: A Casebook.* Washington, D.C.: Georgetown University Press.

Journal of Health Politics, Policy and Law 24(5). 1999.

Journal of Health Politics, Policy and Law 24(6). 1999.

Randel, Lauren; Pearson, Steven; Sabin, James; et al. 2001. "How Managed Care Can Be Ethical." *Health Affairs* 20(4): 43–56.

Robinson, James C. 2001. "The End of Managed Care" *Journal of American Medical Association* 285: 2622–2628.

MATERNAL–FETAL RELATIONSHIP

• • •

I. Medical Aspects

II. Ethical Issues

III. Legal and Regulatory Issues

I. MEDICAL ASPECTS

During the last decades of the twentieth century, perinatal medicine made tremendous advances in scientific knowledge and in the successful application of this knowledge toward improving pregnancy outcomes. These advances have also brought a dramatic change in medicine's conceptualization of the fetus. No longer is the fetus defined predominantly as a part of the pregnant woman, but rather as a distinct entity that can be the independent focus of diagnostic tests and individual therapies: "A second patient with many rights and privileges comparable to those previously achieved only after birth." It is the widely shared view of obstetricians that the fetus is a patient to whom they owe ethical duties. The purpose of this entry is to delineate the medical advances that have brought about this change in fetal identity and to discuss the impact of these changes on pregnant women and the obstetrical decision-making process.

Pregnancy and Maternal Health

Maternal morality in pregnancy fell dramatically in the United States from more than one in 200 in 1935 to 7.7 per 100,000 in 1999. Most of this reduction was accomplished earlier in this century through improved surgical techniques and increased access to safe blood products, antibiotics, intravenous fluids, and improved prenatal care.

Despite these improvements, pregnancy still poses the risk of serious illness and, in rare cases, death. It has been calculated that the risk of mortality in pregnant women is 179 times that of the risk of death among women using the safest method of birth control. The major causes of maternal death are hypertensive disorders of pregnancy, pulmonary embolism, uterine hemorrhage, and sepsis. The risks of pregnancy are proportional to the age of the pregnant woman and to her underlying state of health. Women with medical illness may note worsening of their disease during pregnancy, sometimes with serious long-term consequences. But even women who begin a pregnancy in excellent health may find themselves suddenly confronting the morbidity and mortality risks associated with cesarean section (nearly 25% of all U.S. deliveries in 2000), postpartum hemorrhage (4–8% of all deliveries), or pre-eclampsia (a pregnancy-related condition that can lead to seizures, strokes or death in the pregnant woman) (5% of all pregnancies).

Pregnant women may experience preterm labor (U.S. incidence was 11.9% in 2001), the development of premature contractions that if not stopped can result in delivery of the fetus before adequate development has occurred. Preterm delivery poses significant risk of disability and death for the fetus. While preterm labor itself does not pose a health risk to the pregnant woman, many of the treatments recommended for its treatment have significant maternal side effects. The three drugs commonly used to treat (attempt to stop) preterm labor have serious side effects ranging from nausea, vomiting, dizziness, flushing, tremor, and jitteriness to life-threatening risks of pulmonary edema (fluid in the lungs), alterations in blood chemistries (hypokalemia, hyperglycemia), heart rate abnormalities (tachycardia, arrhythmias), hypotension, respiratory depression, and cardiac arrest.

For all women, pregnancy is a complex physiologic process; almost every organ system undergoes adaptation to support the maternal-fetal unit. It is important to appreciate the range of symptoms experienced by many pregnant women due to these physiologic changes. These include nausea, vomiting, fatigue, syncope (fainting), round ligament pelvic pain, backache, heartburn, hemorrhoids, constipation, urinary frequency, carpal tunnel syndrome (numbness and tingling of the hands), pedal edema, and sciatica (hip and leg nerve pain). Thus, while pregnancy is described as a normal physiologic process, it is not without common discomforts and the potential for serious illness. Most pregnant women willingly assume these sacrifices for their developing fetus.

Pregnancy and Fetal Therapies

Perinatal technologies have benefited the fetus by increasing the understanding of normal fetal development as well as improving prenatal diagnostic capabilities and therapeutic interventions. The fetus can be visualized with ultrasound, its well-being assessed with fetal heart-rate monitoring, and its diseases diagnosed with chorionic villus sampling, amniocentesis, and fetal blood sampling. Increases in diagnostic capabilities have been accompanied by the development of techniques to treat the fetus directly in utero. Our increasing ability to act on behalf of the fetus has made its claims to our care more compelling.

Prenatal technologies designed to benefit the fetus range from the simple to the complex, with differing risks and benefits for both the pregnant woman and her fetus. The most commonly used technology with the intention of improving fetal outcome is electronic fetal monitoring (EFM). EFM was introduced in the United States in the early 1970s with the promise that it would enable early detection of fetal hypoxia in labor and alert the physician to perform an immediate delivery, preventing the serious consequences of oxygen deprivation, including brain damage and stillbirth. Its use rapidly expanded from high-risk pregnancies to all pregnancies; in 1996, it was estimated that three-fourths of all U.S. pregnancies were monitored. Unfortunately, the wide acceptance of this technology occurred before adequate studies had been done to assess its efficacy and safety. There have been numerous randomized and controlled trials of EFM that have been unable to demonstrate a decrease in intrapartum fetal death or better newborn health in low-risk

pregnancies. However, the use of EFM was shown to double the C-section (cesarean section) rate for the indication of fetal distress, thus exposing more women to the increased morbidity and mortality risks of C-section without the promised fetal benefit.

Other technologies include internal monitoring, used almost exclusively in high-risk situations, and telemetry monitoring, which uses radio waves and is non-invasive. Internal monitoring can cause fetal injury and infection to both the mother and baby.

A C-section entails a greater risk of maternal morbidity and mortality than does a vaginal delivery. The mortality rate associated with C-section is between two and four times that associated with a vaginal delivery. Maternal morbidity is also more frequent and usually more severe with a C-section. The common causes of morbidity associated with C-sections are infection, injury to the urinary tract, risk of placenta accreta (where the placenta attaches to the incision in a subsequent pregnancy) and hemorrhage with the possible risk of transfusion. Even an uncomplicated C-section requires a much longer recovery period for the mother at a time when she is experiencing increased physical and emotional demands.

The simplest fetal therapies are medications given to a pregnant woman for the benefit of her fetus. A well-accepted treatment of a woman who develops mild diabetes during pregnancy is to give her insulin until delivery. This practice benefits the fetus by preventing its excessive growth and associated birth trauma and by avoiding the potential neonatal difficulties of an infant of a diabetic mother. While insulin is not essential for the pregnant woman's health, it may be beneficial by reducing her risk of C-section delivery and the potential harms of a mildly elevated glucose to her own organ systems. Digoxin is a medication administered to pregnant women for the benefit of a fetus with cardiac arrhythmia. Unlike insulin, digoxin offers no benefit to the health of the pregnant woman. The risks to the pregnant woman of ingesting insulin or digoxin are minimal if administered appropriately. In summary, these pharmacologic fetal therapies confer benefit upon the fetus and are minimally invasive; one offers some benefit for the pregnant woman; the other solely benefits the fetus.

An accepted but more invasive therapy of sole benefit to the fetus is a fetal blood transfusion for isoimmunization from Rh disease (a condition in which the immune system of the pregnant woman destroys the blood cells of the fetus resulting in fetal death if severe and untreated). The most common technique is cordocentesis, in which a needle is placed through the maternal abdominal and uterine wall into the umbilical blood vessel for the purpose of transfusing blood into the fetus. This technique is not without its risks for both the fetus and the pregnant woman. This procedure poses a 2 percent chance of fetal death. It also increases the risk of fetal bradycardia (a dangerous lowering of the heart rate), a condition that mandates an emergency C-section for the safety of the fetus. All the maternal risks of C-section delineated above are increased in an emergency C-section, with the addition of the increased risk of death from general anesthesia. Cordocentesis is an example of an accepted fetal therapy that is potentially beneficial for the fetus and invasive for the pregnant woman, with significant risks to her in complicated cases.

The most invasive fetal therapy is in utero fetal surgery. While these procedures are still uncommon, some successes have occurred. One example is the surgical removal of a lung mass in the fetus. The rationale for the surgery is that without prenatal removal, the fetal lungs will be unable to grow sufficiently to support survival after birth. Intrautrine shunt therapy for hydrocephalus (abnormal amounts of brain fluid causing brain damage and enlargement of the head) is an experimental surgical procedure. Another, more controversial surgery involves fetal surgery to fuse the spinal hole caused by myelomeningocele (spina bifida). Because spina bifida is not a life-threatening disease, some ethicists and physicians have called the procedure into question. In 2003 the National Institute of Child Health and Human Development began a study of prenatal and postnamtal closure of myelomeningocele to determine the long-term benefits.

In all maternal-fetal surgeries, the pregnant woman must undergo a major abdominal operation and take medications to prevent the preterm labor that might be caused by the surgery. The surgery entails the usual risks associated with a C-section but at a higher rate because of the type of uterine incision, the thickness of the uterine wall, and the need for general anesthesia. Because of the type of uterine incision necessary for this fetal surgery, the woman must have a C-section in this pregnancy, even if her fetus is stillborn, as well as in all future pregnancies.

Neonatal Advances and Obstetrical Decision Making

Simultaneous advances in neonatology have had a significant impact on obstetrical knowledge and care. The gestational age at which survival is possible in the modern intensive care nursery has been pushed back continuously over the past few decades to the age of twenty-four to twenty-five weeks (fifteen to sixteen weeks premature). Many fetuses/babies who in the past would have been considered nonviable now survive and develop normally. However, the cost of this success is measured in hundreds of thousands of dollars per premature infant and in the potential for severe lifelong impairments.

This improved neonatal survival has had two significant influences on the perspective of obstetrical providers. Most have seen or participated in the care of very premature babies; thus fetuses in utero from twenty-four weeks on possess a very concrete human image for those who care for them. In addition, the possibility of survival beginning at twenty-four gestational weeks creates an argument for aggressive obstetrical management at earlier and earlier stages of pregnancy. The lower the gestational age at birth and the lower the birth weight, the lower the chance of survival and the higher the risk of severe physical and mental impairment. Between twenty-four to twenty-eight weeks the likelihood of survival increases from 20 percent to 90 percent, with a 20 percent incidence of severe neonatal impairment in the survivors. Complicating this situation is the inaccuracy of techniques to estimate gestational age and fetal weight. The inability to predict with certainty before birth either the survival or the likelihood of impairment creates legitimate divergent perspectives on what to do in individual pregnancies and ensures difficult decision making for obstetricians and pregnant women.

Formerly, a woman who developed preterm labor at twenty-five weeks would have been allowed to deliver vaginally and comforted regarding the certain death of her baby. Today, that pregnant woman will be faced with the option and probable recommendation that the fetus be monitored in labor and delivered by C-section if needed for fetal benefit. A C-section at this gestational age is riskier for her than one at term and because the type of uterine incision required commits her to C-section delivery of future pregnancies. The chance of the infant's survival is between 30 and 50 percent depending on its weight (which is difficult to predict prior to delivery). If the infant does survive, there will be a significant chance of neurologic or physical impairment. Some women will choose to take any risk for a slim possibility of fetal benefit, and accept aggressive obstetrical management. Other women decide that the risk of C-section in this and future pregnancies combined with the potential suffering for their premature infant is not worth the slight chance of being able to take home a normal or mildly impaired child. They choose to let "nature take its course," and hope that their next pregnancy will be free of complications. For the obstetrician faced with this clinical dilemma, the uncertainty of prognosis (this fetus might do well), the availability of technologic intervention (C-section), the desire to do something, and the legal fear of doing nothing may prompt him or her to advocate intervention as the baby's only hope. This is a persuasive argument for most pregnant women, especially if alternatives are not presented as legitimate.

The beneficial effects of fetal therapies and neonatal advances are impressive when successful: Babies previously at high risk of stillbirth, birth trauma, hypoxia, and neonatal death now have a greater chance of being born safely and having a near normal development. However, some babies who would have died now survive but with significant handicaps and at a significant cost to the physical, emotional, and financial well-being of the mother, her child, and her family. Some therapies are recommended with hope of fetal benefit but without good scientific evidence and with known maternal risks of death and morbidity. Pregnant women must be able to choose the best medical option based upon accurate scientific knowledge and an honest appraisal of the uncertainties involved in medical science.

Pregnancy and Fetal Development

Increased understanding of fetal development has allowed identification of environmental factors that can promote or impair the development of a healthy fetus. The placenta was once felt to operate as a barrier allowing only those substances beneficial to the fetus to pass. Now it is known that the placenta is an efficient transporter of many substances to the fetus, regardless of their toxicity, including both therapeutic and recreational drugs. Media coverage has focused on the rising incidence of crack cocaine use by pregnant women. It has been estimated that 11 percent of pregnant women use an illegal drug during their pregnancies and that 75 percent of these women use cocaine. While there are methodologic shortcomings in the studies of cocaine's effect on pregnancy, many serious sequelae of using this drug have been suggested, including an increased spontaneous abortion rate; suspected cardiac, genitourinary, facial, and limb abnormalities (though these may be alcohol-related); growth retardation; and in utero strokes. Obstetrical complications include preterm delivery, abruption (placental separation), and fetal distress. Newborns who have been exposed to cocaine in utero experience withdrawal symptoms, making them more irritable and less able to bond with caregivers. Many believe that cocaine-exposed babies will be more likely to experience learning disabilities, though some research has shown that there is no difference in learning scores between cocaine-exposed children and other children at age 4.

Alcohol is a well-known danger to the developing fetus. Fetal alcohol syndrome has been identified in the offspring of women who consumed excessive alcohol during their pregnancy; it is defined by a triad of symptoms: gross physical retardation; central nervous system dysfunction, including mental retardation; and characteristic facial abnormalities. Fetal alcohol effects are more common; they include cardiac, genitourinary, skeletal, and muscular anomalies; hypoxia; irritability; and hyperactivity. While excessive alcohol use during pregnancy has clearly been documented to cause significant fetal harm, no minimum safe level of consumption has been established. Many experts have recommended total abstinence from alcohol during pregnancy as the only way to avoid all possible harm.

Smoking has significant effects on pregnancy outcome. Approximately 30 percent of U.S. women of childbearing age smoke. Cigarette smoking results in reductions in birthweight, length, and head circumference. It has been estimated that between 20 and 40 percent of all low birthweight births in the United States can be attributed directly to smoking. Smoking has also been associated with higher rates of spontaneous abortion, preterm birth, perinatal mortality, and deficits in later physical, intellectual, and emotional development. A comparison of the known perinatal dangers of alcohol, smoking, and cocaine consumption illustrates that the legal substances a pregnant women may ingest are no less medically harmful than the illegal ones.

Public policy aimed at improving perinatal outcomes by reducing the use of fetotoxic substances by pregnant women must be grounded in medical knowledge. Recreational drug use by most pregnant women is an addiction; they do not consume the drug to harm the fetus but to satisfy an acute physical or psychological need. To address the problem of addiction, comprehensive and supportive programs designed to enlist the individual in her own recovery are necessary. There have been documented successes in programs that emphasize early identification of women at risk for substance abuse and that utilize comprehensive education, prenatal care, psychological intervention, and social services. However, there are very few substance abuse programs available to pregnant women. In one notable case of criminal prosecution of a woman for drug use during her pregnancy, the accused woman had sought drug treatment during her pregnancy without success.

Punitive approaches to addictive disease are generally ineffective. They have the potential to drive the addicted individual away from the very care that could be beneficial. Because the developing fetus is so vulnerable to uterine exposure to toxins, it is critical that pregnant women not be deterred from care. Prenatal care alone, in the presence of continuing drug use, can improve perinatal outcome for the drug-exposed fetus.

Obstetrical Decision Making

While a pregnant woman and her fetus may be conceptualized as two independent patients, they are in fact intimately interdependent, and actions taken to benefit one may pose a risk to the other. A pregnant woman may suffer from a serious illness that requires a treatment that will itself pose risk to her fetus; premature delivery to improve maternal health and chemotherapy for maternal cancer are two examples. Alternatively, treatment for the benefit of the fetus (C-section delivery, treatment of preterm labor, fetal surgery) may pose a risk to the pregnant woman. In addition, a medical treatment for presumed fetal benefit may interfere with the nonmedical needs of the pregnant woman.

These situations have been described by many as maternal-fetal conflict when they more accurately might be described as maternal-physician conflict. When an obstetrician agrees with the pregnant woman's choice and underlying values, no conflict ensues, even in the presence of potential fetal risk. The disagreement that does occur often is based on differing views of what is beneficial for the pregnant woman and her fetus and what are acceptable maternal risks to achieve obstetrical goals.

Obstetricians have a predominant focus on the current pregnancy. Appropriately, they emphasize the medical health of their patient and the fetus, give expert advice to improve pregnancy outcome, and urge women to follow this advice as a priority in their lives. However, medical recommendations are at times influenced by the fear of malpractice, research interests, a reluctance to give up, and a provider's own personal values.

A pregnant woman's values may differ from those of her providers and she may place a different value on the physician's medically based goals. Like other adults, a pregnant woman must and does make decisions about her prenatal activity within the broader context of her life. Her obligation to her fetus is sometimes weighed against her obligations to her other children, her parents, her partner, or others with whom she has a special relationship. Her decision may be influenced by religious or other strongly held personal beliefs.

Some have argued that pregnant women should be forced to undergo certain treatments if the benefit to the fetus would be substantial and the risk to the woman would be minimal or low. Medical uncertainty and medical practice make this a difficult policy to administer rationally or fairly. As delineated above, perinatal medicine is limited by diagnostic and prognostic uncertainty. This is best illustrated by a legal case in which a judge ordered a woman to undergo a forced C-section. In seeking the court order, the obstetrician testified that without delivery by C-section, the fetus had a 99 percent chance of dying and the pregnant woman had a 50 percent chance of mortality. However, the pregnant woman fled the court's jurisdiction and had an uneventful vaginal delivery. The ability to predict fetal distress in labor is frequently inaccurate. Because of this uncertainty, a policy of enforcing obstetrical recommendations would allow obstetricians to make the wrong decisions sometimes but would never allow a pregnant woman to be wrong or right about decisions that profoundly affect her life.

The problem of precisely defining fetal risk is matched by the complex task of delineating what constitutes an acceptable risk of harm for the mother. Risks, no matter how small in the medical context, may take on a different meaning within the context of an individual's life. The small risk of maternal death from a C-section may be very significant to a single woman who is the sole supporter of her children. Bed rest for the prevention of preterm labor may mean the loss of work and health insurance for her whole family. A Jehovah's Witness who is forced to receive blood may believe she is condemned to eternal damnation and may undergo significant stress or rejection within her religious community.

If obstetricians are given the authority to force pregnant women to follow their recommendations, this force may be used in a very arbitrary way. Not only is there variation in obstetrical diagnostic and prognostic accuracy, there are obstetrical debates about the appropriate management of various conditions. The medical justifications in the reported cases of requests for court-ordered C-sections have included breech presentation, prior C-section, and rupture of membranes for twenty-four hours without signs of febrile morbidity. Many obstetricians would disagree with each of these indications for C-section. Furthermore, the women who have been subjected to court orders have been shown to be more likely subjects of other forms of discrimination. In one study of forced C-sections, 81 percent of the women belonged to a minority group and 24 percent did not use English as their first language, and all requests for the court orders involved women who received care at a teaching hospital or who were receiving public assistance.

If the use of force by doctors against pregnant women were to be legitimized, it would have negative implications for their therapeutic relationship. The relationship would become less cooperative and supportive and more adversarial; compromise in situations of disagreement would become less and less possible. Under these circumstances of care, some women might lie about their behaviors or symptoms, fearing that their obstetrician would use this information to force upon them unacceptable treatment. Others might avoid prenatal care completely. The adversarial climate created by the use of force would decrease the effectiveness of obstetricians in improving maternal and fetal health.

Conclusion

Perinatal advances have dramatically improved the perinatal survival and well-being of fetuses/babies, fulfilling the obstetrical goals of prenatal providers and the personal goals of pregnant women. Increased understanding of the developing fetus and improved technologies have given the fetus an enhanced human identity and status as a direct patient of the obstetrician. The new therapeutic options with their maternal risks have created difficult ethical decisions for the pregnant woman and her obstetrician. A discussion regarding the legitimate use of force against pregnant women for fetal benefit has begun. The resolution of this debate must take into account the implications of the uncertainty inherent in medicine, the maternal risks associated with fetal therapies, the inevitable influence of an obstetrician's personal values upon his or her medical recommendations, the harmful influence of force in any therapeutic relationship, and the ethical and constitutional rights of all parties, including pregnant women.

NANCY MILLIKEN (1995)
REVISED

SEE ALSO: *Abortion; Alcohol and Other Drugs in a Public Health Context; Alcoholism; Care; Compassionate Love; Embryo and Fetus; Feminism; Fetal Research; Genetic Screening and Testing: Public Health Context; Infants; Mental Health, Meaning of Mental Health; Mental Illness; Professional-Patient Relationship; Women, Historical and Cross-Cultural Perspectives;* and other *Maternal-Fetal Relationship* subentries

BIBLIOGRAPHY

Bruner, Joseph P.; Tulipan, Noel; Paschall, Ray L., et al. 1999. "Fetal Surgery for Myelomeningocele and the Incidence of Shunt-Dependent Hydrocephalus." *Journal of the American Medical Association* 282(19): 1819–1825.

Chasnoff, Ira J.; Burns, William J.; Schnoll, Sidney H.; and Burns, Kayreen A. 1985. "Cocaine Use in Pregnancy." *New England Journal of Medicine* 313(11): 666–669.

Chasnoff, Ira J.; Landress, Harvey J.; and Barrett, Mark E. 1990. "The Prevalence of Illicit Drug or Alcohol Use During Pregnancy and Discrepancies in Mandatory Reporting in Pinellas County, Florida." *New England Journal of Medicine* 322(17): 1202–1206.

Chervenak, Frank A., and McCullough, Laurence B. 1985. "Perinatal Ethics: A Practical Method of Analysis of Obligations to Mother and Fetus." *Obstetrics and Gynecology* 66(3): 442–446.

Council on Scientific Affairs. 1989. *Fetal Effects of Maternal Alcohol Abuse.* Chicago: American Medical Association.

Creasy, Robert K., and Resnick, Robert, eds. 1989. *Maternal Fetal Medicine: Principles and Practice,* 2nd edition. Philadelphia: Saunders.

Freeman, Roger. 1990. "Intrapartum Fetal Monitoring: A Disappointing Story." *New England Journal of Medicine* 322(9): 624–626.

Gabbe, Steven G.; Niebyl, Jennifer R.; and Simpson, Joe Leigh. 1986. *Obstetrics: Normal and Problem Pregnancies.* New York: Churchill Livingstone.

Hurt, Hallam; Malmud, Elsa; Betancourt, Laura; et al. 1997. "Children with In Utero Cocaine Exposure Do Not Differ from Control Subjects on Intelligence Testing." *Archives of Pediatrics and Adolescent Medicine* 151: 1237–1241.

Kolder, Veronika E. B.; Gallagher, Janet; and Parsons, Michael T. 1987. "Court-Ordered Obstetrical Interventions." *New England Journal of Medicine* 316(19): 1192–1196.

Lyerly, Anne D.; Gates, Elena A.; Cefalo, Robert C.; and Sugarman, Jeremy S. 2001. "Toward the Ethical Evaluation and Use of Maternal-Fetal Surgery." *Obstetrics and Gynecology* 98: 689–697.

Nelson, Lawrence J., and Milliken, Nancy. 1988. "Compelled Medical Treatment of Pregnant Women: Life, Liberty, and Law in Conflict." *Journal of the American Medical Association* 259(7): 1060–1066.

Pritchard, Jack A.; MacDonald, Paul C.; and Gant, Norman F. 1985. *Williams Obstetrics,* 17th edition. Norwalk, CT: Appleton-Century-Crofts.

Rhoden, Nancy K. 1987. "Informed Consent in Obstetrics: Some Special Problems." *Western New England Law Review* 9(1): 67–88.

Robertson, Patricia A. 1992. "Neonatal Morbidity According to Gestational Age and Birth Weight from Five Tertiary Care Centers in the United States, 1983 Through 1986." *American Journal of Obstetrics and Gynecology* 166(6) (pt. 1): 1629–1641.

Schulman, Joseph, ed. 1986. "Fetal Therapy." *Clinical Obstetrics & Gynecology,* special issue, 29(3): 481–614.

U.S. Congress. Committee on Governmental Affairs. 1989. *Missing Links: Coordinating Federal and Drug Policy for Women, Infants, and Children: Hearings.* Washington, D.C.: Author.

II. ETHICAL ISSUES

Only since the 1960s has it been recognized that the fetus in utero can be harmed by a range of maternal behaviors. Now that it is known that drinking, smoking, and using drugs during pregnancy can harm the unborn child, the question of what moral obligations a pregnant woman has to the fetus she carries has become a significant issue in biomedical ethics. When conflicts arise between what a pregnant woman wants to do or believes is right to do, on the one hand, and what may be best for the fetus, on the other, how and on what basis should those conflicts be resolved? And who should be involved in resolving them?

This article attempts to provide a conceptual framework for thinking about maternal–fetal conflicts. Whether one believes that women have moral obligations to their fetuses in utero depends largely on one's view of the moral status of the fetus—possibly the central issue in the abortion debate. The debate over whether (and at what developmental stage) fetuses can be harmed is a heated one. Pro-lifers think that fetuses can be harmed, and base their opposition to abortion on the ground that being killed is the ultimate harm. They also oppose behavior on the part of pregnant women that is likely to have less severe effects on the fetus. By contrast, many pro-choicers deny that fetuses (or at least early gestation fetuses) can be harmed. However, even if the pro-choice view of the fetus is the correct one, it does not follow that pregnant women are free to drink, smoke, or use drugs during pregnancy, if they are planning to have the baby. For if the pregnant woman does not abort but goes to term, her behavior during pregnancy can have lasting, destructive effects on the born child. Concern for the born child is a common ground that unites all people, regardless of their stance on abortion. This distinction between the fetus per se and the fetus-who-will-be-born differentiates maternal–fetal conflicts from the issue of abortion. Yet these conflicts are not entirely unrelated to the problem of abortion, because both issues concern justifications for restricting or controlling women's behavior during pregnancy.

The Moral Status of the Unborn

One of the thorniest issues in bioethics is the moral status of the fetus. (Here, the term *fetus* is used to refer to the unborn during all stages of pregnancy.) One view is that fetuses are merely potential children who do not have full-fledged moral rights, or perhaps any rights at all. According to this view, attempts to limit reproductive choices or coerce behavior during pregnancy violate very basic moral rights to bodily self-determination.

A different view is that fetuses are *pre-born children*, with all the rights of born children. Someone who regards the fetus in this way will think that a pregnant woman has the same moral obligations to protect her fetus from harm as she has to protect her born children. In keeping with this view of the fetus, some states have adopted *fetal rights* legislation, for example, making behavior during pregnancy that puts the fetus at risk of damage or death a form of child abuse.

Those who differentiate morally between fetuses and children tend vigorously to oppose fetal rights legislation, often seeing it as part of a larger political agenda to make abortion illegal. Even apart from the abortion question,

many people are concerned that any attempts to control women's behavior during pregnancy violate their rights to privacy and self-determination. At the extreme, the position taken by some feminists and civil libertarians is that whatever a woman does during her pregnancy is her own business. They have opposed even noncoercive measures, such as a bill requiring the posting of signs warning pregnant women of the dangers of alcohol consumption (Sack).

However, if a woman decides not to abort, but to carry to term, then her behavior during pregnancy may have an adverse effect not only on the fetus but also on the child who is born. Whatever one's position on the moral standing of fetuses, born children clearly have moral status and rights.

The right not to be injured is one of the most basic moral and legal rights. To extend this right to prenatal injury requires only the recognition that a person can be injured by events that occurred before his or her birth—indeed, even before conception. Here is an example of preconception injury: In the 1940s, diethylstilbestrol (DES) was sometimes prescribed to prevent miscarriage. Not only was the drug ineffective, it sometimes resulted in damaged reproductive systems in the female children of women who used it. When these girls grew up, their reproductive abnormalities sometimes led to miscarriages and premature births. Prematurity can cause cerebral palsy. Thus, a child might be born with cerebral palsy due to a premature birth ultimately caused by her grandmother's ingestion of DES years before her own conception (*Enright by Enright v. Eli Lilly & Co.*, 568 N.Y.S.2d [Ct.App. 1991]). The legal right to recover for injuries negligently inflicted during pregnancy has been widely recognized in the United States since the landmark case of *Bonbrest v. Kotz* (65 F. Supp. 138 [D.D.C. 1946]). Courts have been much more reluctant to accept a right to recover for preconception injuries, primarily out of a concern to confine liability within manageable limits. The important point for bioethics is that recognition of a moral right to be free from injuries inflicted before birth is not based on recognition of the fetus as having the moral status of a person. The concern is not primarily for the fetus but for the surviving child. At the same time, attempts to protect children from prenatal injury can be accomplished only through the body of the pregnant woman. As a result, some women have been subjected to forced cesareans (Annas, 1982; Rhoden, 1986, 1987; Nelson and Milliken). With the development of new fetal therapies and surgery, women could be asked, or even required, to undergo possibly painful and risky procedures for the sake of the not-yet-born child (Robertson). Thus, if the focus is exclusively on the prevention of harm to the future child, there is a risk of forgetting that the pregnant woman is a person in her own right, not merely a "fetal container" (Annas, 1986). The moral question, then, is how to balance the interests and rights of the pregnant woman against those of her not-yet-born child.

Most women who are expecting a child voluntarily adapt at least some of their behavior to protect their babies. But what if the woman is an alcoholic or a crack addict? What if, for religious or other reasons, she refuses a cesarean section her doctor thinks is necessary to prevent serious damage to her nearly born baby? Such cases "pit a woman's right to privacy and bodily integrity ... against the possibility of a lifetime of devastating disability to a being who is within days or even hours of independent existence" (Rhoden, 1987, p. 118). How should such conflicts be resolved? What moral obligations do women have to prevent harm to the children they intend to bear?

Conceptualizing Maternal-Fetal Conflict

People have moral obligations to other people, both those existing today and those who will exist in the future. The mere fact that people do not now exist is no reason to discount the interests they will have when they come into existence. If people today do nothing about the national debt, if they allow the ozone layer to be depleted, if they pollute the air and water, then actual (as opposed to possible or potential) individuals, living in the future, will be harmed by what is done, or is not done, today. There is a responsibility to these actual, though future, people not to destroy the world they will live in. That they do not now exist does not obviate present obligations to them. Similarly, women have moral obligations to their future children, that is, the ones they will bring into the world.

In the United States, as in most societies, the primary responsibility for protecting the interests of children belongs to their parents. Although parents have a great deal of discretion in deciding how to care for and raise their children, they do not have absolute freedom. In industrialized nations, at least, it is widely accepted that parents are not only morally but also legally obligated not to inflict injury on their children, to feed and clothe them, to provide them with necessary medical care. It would seem, then, that pregnant women who intend to complete their pregnancies have comparable moral obligations to avoid harming their not-yet-born children. However, preventing prenatal harm is not the only morally relevant consideration. The woman's own interests count, too. How are conflicts between the interests of the future child and the interests of the pregnant woman to be resolved?

Some object to the very notion of *maternal–fetal conflict*. They regard this as being misleadingly adversarial, pitting pregnant women against the children they will bear, when in most cases their interests are inseparably intertwined. A less adversarial framework stresses that what is good for pregnant women, such as better prenatal care, is also good for fetuses. While this is undeniable, some women want to do things, such as smoking or using drugs or alcohol, that risk harming their unborn children. Admittedly, behavior that endangers the fetus often endangers the health of the pregnant woman, but this does not necessarily make their interests identical. What if the woman is willing to risk her own health for the enjoyment the tobacco or alcohol or cocaine brings? She may decide—perhaps irrationally, perhaps not—that use of the substance is in her own interest, all things considered. That does not mean it is in the interest of her as-yet-unborn baby. It is wishful thinking to pretend that the possible harmful effect on the pregnant woman prevents the possibility of conflict.

Others object to characterizing the conflict as one between mother and fetus. In the so-called obstetrical cases (e.g., forced cesareans), the conflict may not be between mother and fetus. Rather, it is between mother and doctor, who disagree about what is best for both mother and child. In one case, doctors sought a court order because the fetus's umbilical cord was wrapped around its neck, a clear indication for an emergency cesarean. The woman, who had nine children, refused surgery out of concern for her own health, a belief in "natural childbirth," and an intuition that the delivery would turn out fine, despite the doctors' dire predictions. She delivered vaginally, and the child was fine (Rhoden, 1986).

Attempts to prevent prenatal harm often impose risks or burdens on pregnant women, particularly when an intervention, such as a cesarean section or blood transfusion, is deemed necessary to protect the unborn child. The moral question then becomes how much risk, burden, or sacrifice a woman must undergo for the sake of her future child.

Moral Obligations to the Not-Yet-Born

It is important to distinguish the question of moral obligation and responsibility from legal obligation. Only the most extreme legal moralist would advocate compelling people to do whatever they morally ought to do. Claims that women have moral obligations to their future children should not be construed as advocating legal coercion. Thinking about moral obligations to future children in the context of general parental obligations to children prevents sentimentalizing pregnancy and the imposing of especially stringent obligations on pregnant women, or thinking that pregnant women are morally required to subordinate all their interests to their fetuses. After all, parents are not morally required to avoid any and all risks to their children's health. The obligation is, rather, to avoid unreasonable risks of substantial harm.

With a few notable exceptions (King; Robertson; Shaw), most commentators have argued that a pregnant woman should not be forced to undergo medical treatment even when this is judged necessary to preserve the life or health or her fetus (Annas, 1982; Gallagher; Johnsen; Nelson and Milliken; Rhoden, 1986, 1987). Cesarean sections are major surgery and, while generally very safe, are associated with higher rates of maternal mortality, morbidity, and increased pain than occur with vaginal delivery. Requiring a woman to undergo a cesarean requires her to risk her own life and health for the sake of her not-yet-born child. This is contrary to our legal tradition, which forbids the forced use of the body of one person to save another. In one widely cited case, *Shimp v. McFall* (10 Pa. D. & C.3d 90 [1978]), a court refused to order David Shimp to donate bone marrow to his cousin, Robert McFall, who was dying of aplastic anemia. The court emphasized that there is no legal duty to rescue others. It would seem to follow that compelling a pregnant woman to undergo medical treatment for the sake of the fetus, when this is not required of other potential rescuers, violates equal protection.

There are compelling arguments against the government's using coercive and punitive measures to regulate women's actions in order to promote healthy births. Most people do not want to live in a society in which they can be compelled to undergo surgery or to sacrifice body parts, even if it would be morally incumbent on them to do so. Placing limits on what can be demanded of citizens, especially where bodily integrity is involved, is essential to a free society. This helps to justify the conviction that people are not legally obligated to donate parts of their bodies, even if others need them for life itself.

The situation is different when we consider people's moral obligations. While an absolute ban on forced donation seems the correct legal response, a balancing approach seems more appropriate from a moral perspective. Whether one has a moral obligation to donate a body part, or undergo invasive surgery, depends on the degree of risk and sacrifice incurred, balanced against the need of the endangered individual. Perhaps people are morally required to donate replenishable body parts, such as blood, to others who need it. Blood donation takes only an hour, has no lasting effects, and causes only slight discomfort to most donors. Where a special relationship exists between the potential donor and the needy person, there may be a moral obligation to incur greater risks and sacrifices. Parents may be thought to have a moral obligation to donate blood and bone marrow, and perhaps even nonreplenishable body parts, such as kidneys, to their children, because of their duty to protect and care for

their children, and because parents are supposed to love their children. Certainly a parent who refused to give a kidney to a dying child, saying, "It's my body, and I do not feel like donating," would be rightly regarded as morally deficient.

What are the implications for women whose doctors advise a cesarean section for fetal indications? Most women, faced with the possibility of a stillbirth or having a baby born with cerebral palsy, readily consent to the treatment their doctors recommend. Occasionally, however, a woman rejects a physician's recommendation. The moral justifiability of her refusal depends largely on her reasons for refusing. Typically, women who refuse cesareans do so out of religious objections, concern for their own health, or belief that a vaginal birth is best for the baby, and they disagree with the doctors' assessment of the risk. These are not selfish or unimportant reasons. Refusing a cesarean for such reasons is not obviously immoral. By contrast, it would be immoral for a woman to refuse a cesarean, and risk having her nearly born child die or suffer permanent disability, for a trivial reason, such as wanting to avoid a scar in order to be able to wear a bikini. One can morally condemn such a refusal, even if one thinks that she should not be compelled to submit to a cesarean.

"Lifestyle cases," where the risk to the child comes from nonessential behavior, such as drinking alcohol, smoking tobacco, or using drugs, present a different situation. In lifestyle cases, the welfare of the future child appears paramount. If the woman forgoes these substances, the only harm done to her is loss of pleasure and choice—in fact, abstention is likely to benefit her physically—while the potential harm to the child is serious. On the other hand, when the risk to the fetus is slight, the obligation of the pregnant woman is less clear.

Consider, for example, drinking during pregnancy. Heavy drinking during pregnancy can cause fetal alcohol syndrome (FAS), which is typically marked by severe facial deformities and mental retardation. One study showed that even moderate drinking—defined as one to three drinks daily—during early pregnancy can result in a lowering of IQ by as much as five points (Streissguth et al.). Perhaps most important, there is no established "safe" level of alcohol consumption. While there is no evidence that a rare single drink during pregnancy does damage, there is no guarantee that it does not. The safest course is therefore total abstention. But is the safest course the morally obligatory one? We do not require this standard of parents regarding their already born children. Having a single drink occasionally in pregnancy is arguably morally permissible, primarily because the risk of causing harm is very low (perhaps nonexistent), but also because the nature of the harm (loss of a few IQ points) is not so serious as to justify moral condemnation.

For a child of normal intelligence, the loss of five IQ points is not devastating. (At the same time, five IQ points can mean the difference between a mildly and a severely retarded child.)

If the occasional drink should be considered a matter of individual discretion, binge drinking, which has a 35 percent chance of subjecting a baby to full-blown FAS, clearly qualifies as an unreasonable risk to the health of a baby. So does smoking crack cocaine. Whether women have a moral obligation not to drink heavily or smoke crack during pregnancy is profoundly complicated by the fact that these behaviors are often the product of addictions. They are less than fully voluntary—some would say they are not voluntary at all. If a woman cannot modify her behavior, then she cannot have a moral obligation to do so.

But is it true that someone who is addicted cannot modify his or her behavior? The distinction should be drawn between being able to stop doing something at will, and not being able to stop at all. Although it is difficult to get over addictions, many smokers, alcoholics, and drug users do manage to change their behaviors. We can recognize that it may be very difficult for some women to fulfill their moral obligations to the babies they intend to bear, and acknowledge that they will need help to do so, without denying that they have such obligations.

Should drug or alcohol treatment be imposed on addicted pregnant women? Perhaps—if it could be shown that coerced treatment works, and therefore protects babies from prenatal harm. However, discussion of the justifiability of coerced treatment seems premature when there are not enough treatment programs for pregnant addicts who want to get over their addictions. Many in-patient alcohol rehabilitation programs exclude pregnant women, largely due to a fear of liability. The situation is even worse for pregnant drug addicts (Chavkin); sudden withdrawal of drugs can be as damaging to the fetus as continued exposure. As a result, a few treatment programs are able or willing to treat pregnant addicts. Even in areas where there are such treatment programs, there are not nearly enough spaces for all who want help. The absence of treatment programs makes it virtually impossible for substance abusers to fulfill their moral obligations to the children they intend to bear, even with the best will in the world.

To summarize, all women who intend to bear children have moral obligations to protect those children from the serious risk of substantial harm. Heavy smoking, binge drinking, and use of drugs such as crack cocaine and heroin constitute such risks. However, the moral wrongness of engaging in such behaviors during pregnancy is affected by the woman's ability to stop. A woman who is not addicted to cocaine, but who goes on using it during her pregnancy (perhaps on the weekends, because she enjoys it), fully aware of the risks she imposes on her future child, acts very wrongly indeed, and is properly blamed. It would be inappropriate similarly to condemn the pregnant woman who wants what's best for her baby and tries to get help with her addiction, only to be turned away because of the dearth of drug programs. Such a woman is trying to do the right thing; blame properly belongs with society for failing to help her. Nevertheless, if her baby is born damaged due to her drug use, she will—and should—feel moral regret at the harm caused by her drug habit, even if she should not be blamed.

The Intention to Bear a Child

Some people object to making the future child, rather than the fetus, the locus of moral obligation, on the grounds that the existence of the future child depends entirely on the pregnant woman's decision. These critics find it unacceptable that a woman can avoid her obligations to her not-yet-born child by ensuring that it not be born (that is, by aborting it). Moreover, a woman may decide to abort, but later change her mind and continue the pregnancy. During the period when she thought she would have an abortion, she may have continued to smoke and drink. As long as she did not intend to bring a child into the world, there was no one for whose sake she should abstain; continuing to smoke or drink seems morally acceptable in this light. Yet if she changes her mind and continues the pregnancy, she may have harmed the child she bears. Is she now morally blameworthy for the harm she causes?

Two responses can be made. The first is to recognize that moral responsibility for outcomes can extend beyond harms knowingly risked, to harms unintentionally caused. The fact that a woman did not intend to continue a pregnancy at the time she engaged in heavy drinking or used drugs does not entirely absolve her from blame. Even though she does not intend to have a baby at the time of the risky behavior, the failure to consider the possibility that she might change her mind may be negligent, and thus blameworthy. The second response concerns the futility of crying over spilt milk. It says that there is nothing a woman can do about her past behavior, and that if she changes her mind and decides to carry the pregnancy to term, she should focus on what she can do to ensure her baby's health. For example, giving up smoking in the second or third trimester gives the not-yet-born child a better chance than continuing to smoke throughout the pregnancy. If, despite her efforts, the baby is born damaged (a fairly unlikely result), the woman does not completely escape responsibility, but her blameworthiness is mitigated by the fact that she acted rightly once she decided to continue the pregnancy.

Another objection to making "the child she intends to bear" rather than the fetus the object of the pregnant woman's moral obligation is that often women do not "intend" to bear children. Drug addicts, in particular, may regard pregnancy as something that "happens" to them, often as a result of bartering their bodies for drugs, rather than something they intend. Nor do they necessarily choose to give birth: They may not be able to afford an abortion, or it may not be available in a particular geographical area. For some women, abortion is not a morally or culturally acceptable option. Do restrictions on the choice of whether to bear a child affect the woman's moral obligations to the child she bears? It can be argued that these restrictions do not affect how the woman ought to act, but they may affect how much she is to be blamed if she acts wrongly.

Consider a woman who deliberately gets pregnant, intending to have a baby. If she goes on drinking and smoking and using recreational drugs, knowing of the possible effects on her baby's health and making no effort to stop, she acts very wrongly indeed. By contrast, consider a woman who has no responsibility for becoming pregnant (she was raped), in a jurisdiction that prohibits abortion. She is the victim of two grave injustices, first in being raped and second in being denied an abortion. Still, that would not justify behavior likely to inflict severe damage on the child she will perforce bear. Ideally, she should behave as if the pregnancy were chosen, since she is prevented from terminating the pregnancy. That is, she should stop smoking, drink moderately or not at all, and so on. However, her failure to do so is certainly less blameworthy than the failure of a woman who has chosen to conceive and bear a child. Most cases will fall somewhere in between the extremes of deliberate conception and forced childbirth. In general, the fewer options a woman has regarding pregnancy and childbirth, the less she deserves blame for failing to fulfill her obligations to her future child. However, women are not relieved of moral responsibility simply because they do not see pregnancy as a choice.

Conclusion

Deciding to have a baby carries with it certain moral responsibilities. Children have a moral right to be protected from harm, whether inflicted post- or prenatally. This right to be free from harm imposes obligations on those in a position to protect children, including their mothers during pregnancy. Yet a single-minded focus on the risk of harm to the future child ignores the impact on the pregnant woman.

She is not a "fetal container" but an individual in her own right, one whose interests must be considered in determining morally permissible options.

Another factor in determining the moral obligations of pregnant women to their future children is the degree of risk and the nature of the harm. Just as parents are not morally required to avoid any and all risks to their born children, neither are pregnant women morally obligated to curtail their own interests to avoid even the slightest risk of harm.

Distinct from the question of the obligations women have to their future children is the issue of their blameworthiness for failing to fulfill those obligations. In general, blameworthiness is mitigated by the inability to have done otherwise. Such factors as addiction and the degree of control over reproductive ability must be considered in assessing morally the conduct of pregnant women.

BONNIE STEINBOCK (1995)
BIBLIOGRAPHY REVISED

SEE ALSO: *Abortion; AIDS; Alcohol and Other Drugs in a Public Health Context; Autonomy; Beneficence; Care; Coercion; Embryo and Fetus; Feminism; Genetic Screening and Testing: Public Health Context; Life; Professional-Patient Relationship; Women, Historical and Cross-Cultural Perspectives;* and other *Maternal-Fetal* subentries

BIBLIOGRAPHY

Annas, George J. 1982. "Forced Cesareans: The Most Unkindest Cut of All." *Hastings Center Report* 12(3): 16–17, 45.

Annas, George J. 1986. "Pregnant Women as Fetal Containers." *Hastings Center Report* 16(6): 13–14.

Arch, R. R. 1996. "The Maternal-Fetal Rights Dilemma: Honoring a Woman's Choice of Medical Care During Pregnancy." *Journal of Contemporary Health Law and Policy* 12(2): 637–673.

Bays, Jan. 1990. "Substance Abuse and Child Abuse: Impact of Addiction on the Child." *Pediatric Clinics of North America* 37(4): 881–904.

Burns, D. L. 1997. "Positive Toxicology Screening in Newborns: Ethical Issues in the Decision to Legally Intervene." *Pediatric Nursing* 23(1): 73–75; discussion 76–78, 86.

Capron, Alexander M. 1998. "Punishing Mothers." *Hastings Center Report* 28(1): 31–33.

Chavkin, Wendy. 1990. "Drug Addiction and Pregnancy: Policy Crossroads." *American Journal of Public Health* 80(4): 483–487.

Chervenak, Frank A., and McCullough, Laurence B. 1991. "Justified Limits on Refusing Intervention." *Hastings Center Report* 21(2): 12–18.

Daniels, Cynthia R. 1996. *At Women's Expense: State Power and the Politics of Fetal Rights.* Cambridge, MA: Harvard University Press.

Dickenson, Donna, ed. 2002. *Ethical Issues in Maternal-Fetal Medicine.* New York: Cambridge University Press.

Ford, Norman M. 2002. *The Prenatal Person: Ethics from Conception to Birth.* Williston, VT: Blackwell Publishers.

Gallagher, Janet. 1987. "Prenatal Invasions & Interventions: What's Wrong with Fetal Rights." *Harvard Women's Law Journal* 10: 9–58.

Gross, Michael L. 1999. "After Feticide: Coping with Late-Term Abortion in Israel, Western Europe, and the United States." *Cambridge Quarterly of Healthcare Ethics* 8(4): 449–462.

Harris, L. H. 2000. "Rethinking Maternal-Fetal Conflict: Gender and Equality in Perinatal Ethics." *Obstetrics and Gynecology* 96(5) pt. 1: 786–791.

Honig, J. 2001. "Rethinking Maternal-Fetal Conflict: Gender and Equality in Perinatal Ethics." *Obstetrics and Gynecology* 97(2): 325.

Hornstra, Deborah. 1998. "A Realistic Approach to Maternal-Fetal Conflict." *Hastings Center Report* 28(5): 7–12.

Johnsen, Dawn. 1986. "The Creation of Fetal Rights: Conflicts with Women's Constitutional Rights to Liberty, Privacy, and Equal Protection." *Yale Law Journal* 95: 599–625.

King, Patricia A. 1979. "The Juridical Status of the Fetus: A Proposal for Legal Protection of the Unborn." *Michigan Law Review* 77: 1647–1687.

Little, Margaret Olivia. 1996. "Procreative Liberty, Biological Connections, and Motherhood." *Kennedy Institute of Ethics Journal* 6(4): 392–396.

Lombardi, Joseph L. 2000. "Voluntary Intercourse and Fetal Rights." *Journal of Social Philosophy* 31(3): 338–352.

"Maternal Rights and Fetal Wrongs: The Case against the Criminalization of 'Fetal Abuse.'" 1988. *Harvard Law Review* 101: 994–1012.

Markens, Susan; Browner, C.H.; and Press, Nancy. 1997. "Feeding the Fetus: On Interrogating the Notion of Maternal-Fetal Conflict." *Feminist Studies* 23(2): 351–372.

Mathieu, Deborah. 1991. *Preventing Prenatal Harm: Should the State Intervene?* Dordrecht, Netherlands: Kluwer.

Mayer, L. 2001. "Rethinking Maternal-Fetal Conflict: Gender and Equality in Perinatal Ethics." *Obstetrics and Gynecology* 97(3): 482–483.

Morgan, Lynn M. 1996. "Fetal Relationality in Feminist Philosophy: An Anthropological Critique." *Hypatia* 11(3): 47–70.

Morgan, Lynn Marie, and Michaels, Meredith W., eds. 1999. *Fetal Subjects, Feminist Positions.* Philadelphia: University of Pennsylvania Press.

Moss, Kary L. 1990. "Substance Abuse during Pregnancy." *Harvard Women's Law Journal* 13: 278–299.

Murray, Thomas H. 1987. "Moral Obligations to the Not-Yet Born: The Fetus as Patient." *Clinics in Perinatology* 14(2): 329–343.

Nelson, Lawrence J., and Milliken, Nancy. 1988. "Compelled Medical Treatment of Pregnant Women: Life, Liberty, and Law in Conflict." *Journal of the American Medical Association* 259(7): 1060–1066.

Rhoden, Nancy K. 1986. "The Judge in the Delivery Room: The Emergence of Court-Ordered Cesareans." *California Law Review* 74(6): 1951–2030.

Rhoden, Nancy K. 1987. "Cesareans and Samaritans." *Law, Medicine & Health Care* 15(3): 118–125.

Roberts, Melinda A. 1998. *Child versus Childmaker.* Totowa, NJ: Rowman & Littlefield.

Robertson, John A. 1982. "The Right to Procreate and In Utero Fetal Therapy." *Journal of Legal Medicine* 3(3): 333–366.

Roth, Rachel. 1999. *Making Women Pay: The Hidden Costs of Fetal Rights.* Ithaca, NY: Cornell University Press.

Sack, Kevin. 1991. "Unlikely Union in Albany: Feminists and Liquor Sellers." *New York Times,* April 5, p. B1.

Samuels, Suzanne Uttaro. 1995. *Fetal Rights, Women's Rights: Gender Equality in the Workplace.* Madison: University of Wisconsin Press.

Shaw, Margery W. 1984. "Conditional Prospective Rights of the Fetus." *Journal of Legal Medicine* 5(1): 63–116.

Steinbock, Bonnie. 1992. "Maternal-Fetal Conflict." In *Life before Birth: The Moral and Legal Status of Embryos and Fetuses,* pp. 127–163. New York: Oxford University Press.

Streissguth, Ann P.; Barr, Helen M.; Sampson, Paul D.; Darby, Betty L.; and Martin, Donald C. 1989. "I.Q. at Age Four in Relation to Maternal Alcohol Use and Smoking During Pregnancy." *Developmental Psychology* 25: 3–11.

Strong, Carson. 1997. *Ethics in Reproductive and Perinatal Medicine: A New Framework.* New Haven, CT: Yale University Press.

Wellman, Carl. 2002. "The Concept of Fetal Rights." *Law and Philosophy* 21(1): 65–93.

Yeast, John D. 1995. "Prematernal Duty and the Resolution of Conflict." *Bioethics Forum* 11(1): 3–8.

III. LEGAL AND REGULATORY ISSUES

The intimate relationship between a woman and a fetus developing within her body has long given rise to vital questions of morality, religion, science, medicine, law, and public policy. The abortion controversy in the United States is perhaps the most easily recognized context for this debate over the extent of a pregnant woman's right to autonomy. But over the course of recent decades, this issue has extended far beyond the abortion debate to encompass numerous legal and public policy issues concerning the maternal–fetal relationship when women continue pregnancy and give birth. Courts, legislatures, state prosecutors and doctors have sought to compel women to behave in ways deemed likely to promote the birth of healthy babies. Women have faced pregnancy-related restrictions and penalties, including civil suit, criminal prosecution, and court-ordered surgery, aimed at a wide range of conduct: driving an automobile, failing to follow a doctor's advice, drinking alcohol, taking prescription and illegal drugs, among others. This entry describes the status of such efforts and explores the implications for children's well-being and women's liberty.

Biological Aspects of the Maternal–Fetal Relationship

Beliefs about the independent moral and religious status of the fetus vary widely among Americans. The physical status of a fetus, however, is clear: A fetus cannot exist apart from a particular woman prior to *viability,* which occurs at approximately twenty-four to twenty-eight weeks's gestational age. That a fetus does not and cannot exist wholly apart from the pregnant woman makes the maternal–fetal relationship unique.

A fetus makes unparalleled physical and psychological demands on a woman, subjecting her body to tremendous physical adjustments and creating significant risks for even the healthiest woman. Concomitantly, with the fetus completely dependent upon and entirely within a particular woman's body, her actions, experiences, and physical health during and even prior to pregnancy substantially affect fetal development and the health of her child at birth. Throughout their reproductive lives, women inevitably confront innumerable decisions, large and small, that create varying probabilities of harm or benefit to fetal development.

The biological realities of the maternal–fetal relationship may not dictate any particular social response, but they highlight the need to scrutinize the impact on women of any law or policy aimed at fetuses. If not formulated with care, governmental policies adopted to promote healthy births can substantially and unnecessarily intrude upon women's fundamental liberties, limiting their ability to decide how to live their lives, and creating tension between women and their healthcare providers.

Law Versus Morality

In general, women have a strong interest in giving birth to healthy children and go to great lengths to increase the likelihood that they will do so. Widespread consensus exists that a woman who chooses to bear a child has a moral obligation to consider the effects her actions will have on her future child. Current public policy recognizes a role for the government in supporting women's ability to have the healthy pregnancies they desire. Existing programs seek to

help women overcome obstacles such as poverty and dangerous addictions by providing prenatal care, food, housing, and drug and alcohol treatment, though the adequacy and appropriate scope of such programs is hotly debated.

Far more controversial are the rare instances when governmental action coerces rather than supports, and seeks to compel women to change their behavior. Should the government use punitive measures to regulate women's actions in an effort to promote healthy births? Should the government thereby transform women's moral obligations into legally required standards of conduct?

In spite of the moral complexity of these issues, U.S. law is quite consistent in granting pregnant women the right to make virtually all decisions affecting their bodily integrity and the well-being of their fetuses during pregnancy. For the most part, U.S. law does not recognize, let alone privilege competing fetal rights. Women retain the freedom to make their own judgments and to balance their obligations to their future children against other responsibilities, such as to family, religion and work. This approach is consistent with women's constitutional rights to liberty, privacy, and equal protection, guaranteed by the U.S. Constitution as well as by state constitutions.

Over the course of the past several decades, this legal consensus has been tested in a variety of contexts. These *tests* arise out of conflicts between pregnant women and their doctors—conflicts that look to the law for resolution. (Oberman, 2000). Often termed *maternal–fetal* conflicts, these issues have generated a veritable cottage industry for scholars in legal, medical, ethical, religious and philosophical circles (Kolder et al.; Markens; Nelson; Reid; Roberts, 1997; Steinbock). Legal and academic debates over the clashing rights of mothers and fetuses have emerged in various contexts, including substance abuse by pregnant women, home births, mandatory HIV screening in prenatal care, and a pregnant woman's rights to utilize a living will (Balisy; Dyke; Hafner-Eaton et al.; Oberman, 1996). As before, the center of the maternal–fetal conflict debate is the question of when and whether it is appropriate for the law to dictate a pregnant woman's behavior in an effort to benefit her unborn fetus. The medical, ethical and legal literature on maternal–fetal conflict is rich in analysis of the competing rights of mother and fetus. Yet, for all their depth and diversity, the overwhelming majority of articles reach an identical conclusion: In all but the most extreme circumstances, it is impermissible to infringe upon the pregnant woman's autonomy rights (But see Finer; Parness; Robertson).

The remainder of this entry examines some forms of pregnancy-related restrictions aimed at women, including exclusionary employment policies, civil suits for prenatal injuries, criminal prosecution, loss of child custody, court-ordered surgery and HIV screening.

Civil Suits for Prenatal Injuries

Some commentators have suggested that women should be subjected to civil liability for breaching *prenatal duties* (Shaw), such as the "duty to bring the child into the world as healthy as is reasonably possible" (Robertson, p. 438). The only appellate court to adopt such a standard, which was in Michigan, ruled in *Grodin v. Grodin* (1980) that a child could sue his mother for prenatal injuries if she failed to comply with the standard of a *reasonable* pregnant woman.

More recently, courts have refused to impose such duties, claiming that they are inherently subjective and that they would carry with them a host of unacceptable policy ramifications. The only state supreme court to consider the issue, the Supreme Court of Illinois, ruled in 1988 that a child could not sue her mother for prenatal injuries allegedly caused when the woman was in an automobile accident while she was pregnant. In rejecting the girl's request to recognize a legal right to begin life with a sound mind and body, the Illinois court noted the serious ramifications that would result for women: "[M]other and child would be legal adversaries from the moment of conception until birth" (*Stallman v. Youngquist*, p. 359).

A 2002 decision of the Superior Court of Massachusetts cited *Stallman* and similar decisions when ruling in favor of a mother's motion for summary judgment in an action brought on her child's behalf (*Remy v. MacDonald*). The child, through her father and appointed guardian, alleged that her mother's negligence in operating a vehicle resulted in numerous medical complications. The Court ruled that holding a pregnant woman legally accountable to her unborn child, "would present a court with problematic and impossible tasks of determining when the duty arises and how the nature of the duty is to be defined." (*Remy*, p. 7–8). Moreover, the court stated that civil liability, "rather than discouraging conduct so difficult to define in terms of duty, may unwittingly have the opposite negative effect of women fearing civil liability so that they may not reveal critical facts about their condition to their physicians resulting in less than adequate prenatal care." (*Remy*, p. 9).

Criminal Prosecutions for Actions During Pregnancy

The most common form of adversarial governmental action against women for engaging in behavior viewed as harmful

to fetal development has been criminal prosecution. State prosecutors have relied on laws that clearly were not intended to create special restrictions on women's actions during pregnancy, including laws prohibiting child abuse, distributing drugs to a minor, and murder.

Several prosecutions have been based on women's otherwise lawful actions. One of the first occurred in 1986, when a California woman was prosecuted for allegedly causing her infant son to be born severely brain damaged, and ultimately to die, as a result of her own excessive loss of blood during delivery (*People v. Stewart*). The prosecution claimed that, by waiting a number of hours before obtaining medical care when she went into labor and began bleeding vaginally, the woman had violated a statute that required parents to provide their children with clothing, food, shelter, and medical care.

Other prosecutions have involved alcohol use during pregnancy. A Massachusetts woman who suffered serious injuries in a car accident, including a miscarriage, was prosecuted for involuntary manslaughter of the fetus because she allegedly caused the accident by driving while intoxicated (Loth). In another reported case, a pregnant woman in Wyoming who notified the police that her husband had physically assaulted her was arrested for child abuse when they detected she had been drinking. The charges ultimately were dismissed in all three of these cases.

By far the most common reason for prosecuting pregnant women involves the use of illicit drugs during pregnancy. Of course, a woman's pregnancy does not immunize her from prosecution under generally applicable laws prohibiting the use or possession of drugs. In many cases, however, women have been subjected to special prosecutions and more severe penalties for the express reason that they were pregnant at the time they used drugs.

Although some women charged in these cases have pled guilty in return for reduced sentences, those who have gone to trial have prevailed in the overwhelming majority of cases. This is largely due to the fact that courts find the statutes under which the women are charged were not intended to apply to prenatal behavior (Brody and McMillin). The first three high state courts that reviewed the legality of prosecution for prenatal drug use all found that the statutes had been misapplied. In 1992, the Supreme Court of Ohio dismissed an indictment for child endangerment against a woman who allegedly used cocaine while pregnant (*Ohio v. Gray*). Also in 1992, the Supreme Court of Florida reversed a woman's conviction under a statute prohibiting the distribution of a controlled substance to a minor and imposing a penalty of up to thirty years imprisonment. In holding that the statute was not intended to apply to prenatal behavior, the court rejected the "State's invitation to walk down a path that the law, public policy, reason and common sense forbid it to tread." (*Johnson v. State,* p. 1297). In 1997, the Supreme Court of Wisconsin held that the state could not initiate proceedings to remove a child from his or her mother's custody, due to the mother's use of illegal drugs, because the term *child* in the statute does not include a viable fetus (*Wisconsin v. Kruzicki*). The court reasoned that the statute would be rendered absurd if the word child included a viable fetus, because a fetus cannot be, as worded in the statute, "removed from his or her present custody" (*Wisconsin v. Kruzicki,* p. 736).

However, in another 1997 decision, the Supreme Court of South Carolina upheld the trial court's conviction of a mother for child abuse following the mother's use of crack cocaine during her pregnancy (*Whitner v. South Carolina*). The court concluded that the word child in the state's child abuse and endangerment statute includes viable fetuses. In reaching its conclusion, the court reviewed earlier South Carolina decisions recognizing a fetus's legal rights and decisions, and distinguished other states's decisions holding that maternal conduct before the birth of a child does not give rise to criminal prosecution. It concluded that those other states's decisions were distinguishable because those states had "entirely different bodies of case law from South Carolina." (*Whitner,* p. 782).

The *Whitner* court also concluded that a woman's constitutional right to privacy is not violated when she is prosecuted for using illegal drugs during a pregnancy. It stated that the state's interest in protecting the life and health of viable fetuses is compelling, and that no fundamental rights are implicated in such prosecutions. The court reasoned that the use of crack cocaine is illegal by anyone, not just by pregnant women, and the additional penalty on pregnant women "simply recognized that a third party (the viable fetus or newborn child) is harmed by the behavior" (*Whitner,* p. 786).

The issue of prosecuting pregnant women for drug use reached the U.S. Supreme Court, albeit indirectly, in the case of *Ferguson v. City of Charleston* (2001). The case involved a hospital that routinely tested pregnant women for drugs, without obtaining informed consent. The hospital then used the results of these drug screens in order to facilitate criminal prosecutions. The Court held that, as a state-operated facility, hospital staff members were actors subject to the Fourth Amendment's strictures. As such, the drug testing of pregnant women without their informed consent amounted to *searches,* and violated the women's constitutional rights.

Loss of Child Custody for Actions During Pregnancy

States have attempted to deprive women of custody of their children based solely on women's actions during pregnancy, rather than on the customary determination of the current ability of the woman and other family members to care for the child. While most cases involved a woman's use of illegal drugs during pregnancy, several courts have based custody decisions on activity that was lawful but seen as detrimental to fetal development. For example, in 1987 a Michigan woman temporarily lost custody of her infant and was charged with child abuse because while pregnant she had taken Valium without a prescription to relieve pain from injuries she suffered in a car accident (*In re J. Jeffrey*).

The first high state court to consider this issue, the Supreme Court of Connecticut, ruled in 1992 that state law did not allow the termination of parental rights based on a woman's use of cocaine during pregnancy. The court cited the legislature's determination that the threat of losing custody of their children would cause women to avoid prenatal care and substance abuse treatment, and "would lead to more, rather than fewer, babies being born either without adequate prenatal care or damaged by prenatal drug abuse...." (*In re Valerie D.,* p. 764). However, the Supreme Court of Ohio, in *In re Baby Boy Blackshear* (2000), affirmed a Court of Appeals decision, holding that it is appropriate to remove a child from his or her mother's custody when drug testing proves, after the child's birth, that the child has cocaine in his or her system due to the mother's consumption of such drug. The court reasoned that, for purposes of the state's child abuse statute, R.C. 2151.031, a child born with cocaine in his or her system is an *abused child.*

Although the use of illegal drugs during pregnancy may at first glance seem to be the strongest justification for punitive governmental action such as the imposition of enhanced criminal penalties or deprivation of child custody, these approaches have been widely repudiated. The government clearly has a strong interest in preventing pregnant women from using dangerous drugs. With remarkable consistency, experts agree that this interest is best pursued through programs that help women overcome drug and alcohol dependencies and obtain prenatal care. Entities such as the U.S. General Accounting Office (GAO) and the American Medical Association (AMA) have argued that fear of prosecution and loss of custody of their children will discourage women from seeking care and increase the number of unhealthy births. As the Florida Supreme Court noted, "Rather than face the possibility of prosecution, pregnant women who are substance abusers may simply avoid prenatal care or medical care for fear of being detected. Yet the newborns of these women are, as a group, the most fragile and sick, and most in need of hospital neonatal care" (*Johnson v. State*, p. 1295–1296).

Court-Ordered Cesarean Sections

Courts in at least eleven states have ordered women, against their wishes, to give birth by cesarean section rather than vaginal delivery (Kolder et al.). The severe bodily intrusion of this court-ordered surgery contrasts sharply with our legal system's general refusal to order invasive medical procedures or to force one person to assume any personal risk to save the life of another. Although judicial opinions are rare in these time-pressured cases, three published appellate court decisions illustrate both the motivations behind and the harm caused by such court orders.

In the first published appellate court decision, the Supreme Court of Georgia in 1981 declined to lift a court order authorizing the performance of a cesarean section against a woman's religious objections where the examining physician found a "ninety-nine percent certainty" that the child would not survive a vaginal delivery and a 50 percent chance the woman would die (*Jefferson v. Griffin Spalding County Hospital Authority*, p. 459). With no analysis of the constitutional and policy implications, the court granted *temporary custody* of the fetus to the state and gave it full authority to make all surgical decisions concerning the birth. In the end, a court-ordered cesarean section was not performed; despite the physician's predictions, the woman gave birth by vaginal delivery to a healthy baby without adverse effects.

More recent appellate court decisions have ruled that compelling a pregnant woman to undergo a cesarean section against her will violates the woman's fundamental constitutional rights. (*In re A.C.*; *Baby Boy Doe v. Mother Doe*). In the most widely cited case, in re A.C., a three-judge panel of the District of Columbia Court of Appeals ordered a woman who was twenty-six weeks pregnant and terminally ill with cancer to undergo the surgery. The woman did not consent to the cesarean and her husband, parents, and attending physicians all opposed it on the ground that the woman's health and comfort should be the first priority. The cesarean section was performed nonetheless. The fetus was not viable and did not survive. The woman died two days after the cesarean section.

Following her death, the full Court of Appeals reversed the panel's decision, ruling that "in virtually all cases the question of what is to be done is to be decided by the patient—the pregnant woman—on behalf of herself and the fetus" (*In re A.C.*, p. 1237). The court found that a court order compelling a woman to have a cesarean section violates

her rights to bodily integrity and to refuse medical treatment, which are protected under both common law and the U.S. Constitution. The court graphically described the violent bodily intrusion that would be required to enforce an order against a woman who resisted: "[She] would have to be fastened with restraints to the operating table, or perhaps involuntarily rendered unconscious by forcibly injecting her with an anesthetic, and then subjected to unwanted major surgery. Such actions would surely give one pause in a civilized society…" (*In re A.C.*, p. 1244, n. 8). Indeed, in another case a court-ordered cesarean section was performed by tying the woman to the operating table and forcibly removing her husband from the room (Kolder et al.).

An Illinois appellate court similarly ruled in 1994 that ordering a woman to give birth by cesarean section would violate her constitutional rights. Citing *In re A.C.*, the court held that "a woman's competent choice in refusing medical treatment as invasive as a cesarean section during her pregnancy must be honored, even in circumstances where the choice may be harmful to her fetus" (*Baby Boy Doe v. Mother Doe*, p. 330).

At least one federal court has disagreed with the state decisions holding that court-ordered cesarean sections violate women's constitutional rights. In *Pemberton v. Tallahassee Memorial Regional Medical Center, Inc.* (1999), a federal district court held that a court-ordered cesarean section did not violate the mother's substantive constitutional rights. Pemberton was advised by a number of doctors that a vaginal delivery would likely harm the newborn. However, Pemberton opposed having a cesarean section. She returned to the hospital following a full day of labor and requested an IV because she had become dehydrated. Pemberton was denied an IV, and then returned home against the wishes of doctors at the hospital. Following a hearing conducted at the hospital, Pemberton was returned to the hospital, against her will, where her child was delivered via cesarean section.

Pemberton sued, claiming that numerous substantive constitutional rights were violated by the court-order. However, the court stated, "Whatever the scope of Ms. Pemberton's personal constitutional rights in this situation, they clearly did not outweigh the interests of the State of Florida in preserving the life of the unborn child" (*Pemberton v. Tallahassee Memorial Regional Medical Center, Inc.*, p. 1251).

A number of medical and public-health organizations have opposed court orders overriding a pregnant woman's decision concerning medical treatment. The AMA is among the organizations that has endorsed respect for women's constitutional right to bodily integrity: "[D]ecisions that would result in health risks are properly made only by the individual who must bear the risk. Considerable uncertainty can surround medical evaluations of the risks and benefits of obstetrical interventions. Through a court-ordered intervention, a physician deprives a pregnant woman of her right to reject personal risk and replaces it with the physician's evaluation of the amount of risk that is properly acceptable" (AMA, p. 2665). The practice of seeking court orders not only violates women's right to evaluate the risks and uncertainties involved in their medical care, it is counterproductive to the goal of promoting healthy pregnancies and births because it causes women to distrust physicians. Citing a case in which a woman left the hospital to avoid a court-ordered cesarean section, the AMA expressed concern that "women may withhold information from the physician.... Or they may reject medical or prenatal care altogether..." (AMA, p. 2665–2666). Furthermore, AMA Policy H-420.969 states as follows, "Judicial intervention is inappropriate when a woman has made an informed refusal of a medical treatment designed to benefit her fetus." Paragraphs 2 and 3 of H-420.969 further provide, "The physician's duty is to provide appropriate information, such that the pregnant woman may make an informed and thoughtful decision, not to dictate the woman's decision. A physician should not be liable for honoring a pregnant woman's informed refusal of medical treatment designed to benefit the fetus."

Exclusionary Employment Policies

In an effort to reduce perceived liability risks, some employers have sought to restrict the access of pregnant, or even fertile, women to jobs that might expose them, and consequently, their fetuses, to potentially hazardous conditions. In a unanimous decision, the U.S. Supreme Court ruled that such policies violate federal anti-discrimination law. The policy at issue in the case prohibited fertile women from working with lead in the production of batteries. The Supreme Court acknowledged that holding such jobs "late in pregnancy often imposes risks on the unborn child," but found that "Congress made clear that the decision to become pregnant or to work while being either pregnant or capable of becoming pregnant was reserved for each individual woman to make for herself." (*International Union, United Auto Workers v. Johnson Controls, Inc.*, p. 205–206).

Mandatory HIV-Testing and Treatment of Pregnant Women

Approximately 4 million women give birth each year in the United States. Of these, approximately 7,600 women are HIV-infected, and run the risk of passing on the fatal virus to their fetuses. (Eden, p. 661).

In 1994, a study known as Protocol 076, administered by the Pediatric AIDS Clinical Trials Group (PACTG), demonstrated a two-thirds reduction in perinatal transmission of HIV by administering Zidovudine (AZT) to pregnant women and newborns, reducing rates from approximately 25 percent to 8.3 percent. (Connor). Later studies demonstrated that the perinatal transmission rate may be as low as 3 percent when mothers are treated with AZT. (Eden, p. 661).

Most states reacted to this news by enacting statutes delineating procedures for doctors to counsel and test pregnant mothers for HIV. Some called for the mandatory HIV testing of all pregnant women, but a broad coalition of physicians, policy-makers, lawyers and public health specialists warned that such a move would discourage *at-risk* women from seeking prenatal care. As a result, no state mandates HIV testing for pregnant women.

Interestingly, at least two states mandate HIV testing of all newborns. (See N.Y. Public Health Law § 2500-f, for New York; and C.G.S.A. § 19a-55, for Connecticut). Because a newborn will not test positive for HIV unless his or her mother is infected with the virus, the HIV testing of newborns is effectively a test of the mother, as well. The ostensible purpose of such laws would be to notify the new mother of her HIV status, so that she might avoid transmitting the virus to her newborn via breast-feeding, and so that the infant might begin antiviral medications.

As implemented, there are several problems with these laws, stemming largely from the lack of appropriate training and funding for those who implement them. First, many women who have been indirectly *tested* for HIV via the testing of their newborns never receive appropriate counseling. Years of work with HIV patients demonstrates that pre- and post-test counseling is vitally important in assuring that infected individuals will obtain the information and treatment necessary to protect themselves and others (McGovern). Second, no mechanisms exist for monitoring the medical privacy of mothers of newborns who test positive for HIV. In virtually all other contexts, the law recognizes this loss of privacy as a grave risk, and vigorously protects the confidentiality of an individual's HIV status (McGovern). Finally, as late as 2003, the efficacy of these laws has been hampered by slow response times, such that mothers do not learn of the HIV status for several weeks after giving birth (McGovern).

Mandatory testing policies, whether directed toward pregnant women or newborns, are predicated upon the belief that the benefits of testing and treating the children outweigh the risks to their mothers. This reasoning rests on somewhat shaky scientific knowledge, as the long-term side effects of AZT on both the mother and child are not clear. In

2003, however, it seems that AZT does not inhibit cognitive function, growth, cause cancer, or impair immune function (Culnane et al., p. 152). Nonetheless, this risk-benefit calculus treats pregnant women (or new mothers) differently from the rest of the population, according them fewer rights, simply by virtue of the fact that they have given birth. As in other contexts, this treatment suggests that pregnant women are uniquely incapable of making morally trustworthy healthcare decisions, and that the state is therefore entitled to intervene. If the knowledge of one's HIV status were indeed so vitally important, one would expect to see widespread calls for mandatory testing of the entire population. Well into the third decade of HIV-related policy making (in even the first years of the twenty-first century), there has been no real effort in that direction.

Racial Disparities

In addition to the concerns about gender discrimination raised by pregnancy-related restrictions and penalties, virtually all of these pregnancy-related legal interventions have a disproportionately negative impact upon women of color. A 1987 survey of court-ordered cesarean sections published in the *New England Journal of Medicine* found that 80 percent of the women against whom orders were sought were African American or Asian (Kolder et al.). A 1990 study, also published in the New England Journal of Medicine, found that African-American women were ten times more likely than white women to be reported to health authorities when they tested positive for illegal drug use during pregnancy (Chasnoff et al.). Another 1990 survey of forty-seven women prosecuted for behavior during pregnancy found that 80 percent of the prosecutions were against women of color (Paltrow). As Dorothy Roberts effectively demonstrates in her book, *Killing the Black Body: Race, Reproduction, and the Meaning of Liberty,* these policies not only are problematic in terms of law, ethics and policy, but also they reflect a sentiment that the women of color are somehow *public property.* In a sense, these fetal-protection policies may be viewed as the contemporary legacy of slavery.

Conclusion

Attempts to impose special pregnancy-related restrictions or penalties on women have been relatively rare and typically have been invalidated by courts and opposed by interested organizations and most commentators. The threat of criminal prosecution, loss of custody of children, and court-ordered medical interventions risk deterring those women who are most at risk of poor birth outcomes from seeking prenatal care and drug and alcohol treatment.

The government can, however, do a great deal to improve the health of children by helping women to have healthy pregnancies. For example, experts agree that the high rate of infant mortality in the United States can be drastically cut by providing prenatal care to the approximately one-third of American women who receive inadequate or no prenatal care. Drug treatment programs routinely turn away pregnant women, and the few that will treat women during pregnancy have long waiting lists. Government studies have shown that expending the funds necessary to provide these services would actually save taxpayers three to four times as much in reduced infant healthcare costs.

While creating legal conflicts between a woman and the fetus within her is ineffective and even counterproductive, laws and policies that respect women's rights can effectively promote the healthy pregnancies and births that are in the interests of all.

DAWN E. JOHNSEN (1995)
REVISED BY MICHELLE OBERMAN

SEE ALSO: *Beneficence; Coercion; Communitarianism and Bioethics; Conflict of Interest; Conscience, Rights of; Fetal Research; Genetic Testing and Screening: Reproductive Genetic Screening; Infanticide; Infants; Insanity and the Insanity Defense;* and other *Maternal-Fetal Relationship* subentries

BIBLIOGRAPHY

A.C., In re. 573 A.2d 1235 (D.C. 1990) (en banc), reversing 533 A.2d 611 (D.C. 1987).

Baby Boy Blackshear, In re. 90 Ohio St.3d 197, 736 N.E.2d 462 (2000).

Baby Boy Doe v. Mother Doe. 260 Ill. App. 3d 392, 632 N.E.2d 326 (Ill.App. 1994).

Balisy, Sam S. 1985. "Maternal Substance Abuse: The Need to Provide Legal Protection for the Fetus." *Southern California Law Reveiw* 60: 1209.

Brody, David C., and McMillin, Heidee. 2001. "Combating Fetal Substance Abuse and Governmental Foolhardiness through Collaborative Linkages, Therapeutic Jurisprudence and Common Sense: Helping Women Help Themselves." *Hastings Women's Law Journal* 12: 243.

Chasnoff, Ira J.; Landress, Harvey J.; and Barrett, Mark E. 1990. "The Prevalence of Illicit-Drug or Alcohol Use during Pregnancy and Discrepancies in Mandatory Reporting in Pinellas County, Florida." *New England Journal of Medicine* 322(17): 1202–1206.

Chenault v. Huie, 989 S.W.2d 474 (1999).

Connor, Edward M., et al. 1994. "Reduction of Maternal-Infant Transmission of Human Immunodeficiency Virus Type 1 with Zidovudine Treatment." *New England Journal of Medicine* 331: 1173.

Culnane, Mary, et al. 1999. "Lack of Long-Term Effects of in Utero Exposure to Zidovudine among Uninfected Children Born to HIV-Infected Women." *Journal of the American Medical Association* 281: 151.

Dyke, Molly C. 1990. "A Matter of Life and Death: Pregnancy Clauses in Living Will Statutes." *Boston University Law Review* 70: 867.

Eden, Dorian L. 2001. "Is it Constitutional and Will It Be Effective? An Analysis of Mandatory HIV Testing of Pregnant Women." *Health Matrix* 11: 659.

Ferguson v. City of Charleston, 532 U.S. 67, 121 S.Ct. 1281 (2001).

Finer, Joel Jay. 1991. "Toward Guidelines for Compelling Cesarean Surgery: Of Rights, Responsibility, and Decisional Authenticity." *Minnesota Law Review* 76: 239.

Grodin v. Grodin, 301 N.W.2d 869 (Mich. App. 1980).

Hafner-Eaton, et al. 1994. "Birth Choices, the Law, and Medicine: Balancing Individual Freedoms and Protection of the Public's Health." *Journal of Health Pol'y & L* 19: 813.

Harris, Pamala. 2001. "Compelled Medical Treatment of Women: The Balancing of Maternal and Fetal Rights." *Cleveland State Law Review* 49: 133.

International Union, United Auto Workers v. Johnson Controls, Inc. 499 U.S. 187, 111 S.Ct. 1196 (1991).

Jefferson v. Griffin Spalding County Hospital Authority. 274 S.E.2d 457 (1981) (per curiam).

J. Jeffrey, In re. No. 99851 (Mich. Ct. App. April 9, 1987).

Johnsen, Dawn. 1992. "Shared Interests: Promoting Healthy Births Without Sacrificing Women's Liberty." *Hastings Law Journal* 43: 569.

Johnson v. State. 602 So. 2d 1288 (Fla. 1992).

Kolder, Veronica E. B.; Gallagher, Janet; and Parsons, Michael T. 1987. "Court-Ordered Obstetrical Interventions." *New England Journal of Medicine* 316: 1192.

Loth, Renee. "DA Sees No Politics in Fetal Death Case." *Boston Globe,* September 16, 1989, p. 25.

Markens, Susan, et al. 1997. "Feeding the Fetus: On Interrogating the Notion of Maternal-Fetal Conflict." *Feminist Studies* 23: 351.

McGovern, Theresa M. 2001. "Is Privacy Now Possible?" *Social Research* 327.

Nelson, Lawrence J. 1992. "Legal Dimensions of Maternal-Fetal Conflict." *Clinical Obstetrics & Gynecology* 35: 738.

Oberman, Michelle. 1996. "Test Wars: Mandatory HIV Testing, Women, and Their Children." *University of Chicago Law School Roundtable* 3: 615.

Oberman, Michelle. 2000. "Mothers and Doctors' Orders: Unmasking the Doctor's Fiduciary Role in Maternal-Fetal Conflicts." *Northwestern University Law Review* 94: 451.

Ohio v. Gray. 584 N.E.2d 710 (Ohio 1992).

Paltrow, Lynn M. 1992. *Criminal Prosecutions against Pregnant Women: National Update and Overview.* New York: Reproductive Freedom Project, American Civil Liberties Union Foundation.

Parness, Jeffrey A. 1985. "Crimes against the Unborn: Protecting and Respecting the Potentiality of Human Life." *Harvard Journal on Legislation* 22: 97.

People v. Stewart, No. M508197 (Cal. Mun. Ct., Feb. 26, 1987).

Pemberton v. Tallahassee Memorial Regional Medical Center, Inc. 66 F.Supp.2d 1247 (N.D. Fl. 1999).

Plambeck, Cheryl M. 2002. "Legal and Bioethical Considerations of Physician-Pregnant Patient Confidentiality and Prenatal Drug Abuse." *Journal of Legal Medicine* 23: 1.

Reid, Matthew C., et al. 1997. "The Case of Medea: A View of Fetal-Maternal Conflict." *Journal of Medical Ethics* 23: 19.

Reitman, Deanna Rae. 2002. "The Collision Between the Rights of Women, the Rights of the Fetus and the Rights of the State: A Critical Analysis of the Criminal Prosecution of Drug-Addicted Pregnant Women." *St. John's Journal of Legal Comment* 16: 267.

Remy v. MacDonald. Massachusetts Superior Court LEXIS 105 (2002).

Rhoden, Nancy K. 1986. "The Judge in the Delivery Room: The Emergence of Court-Ordered Cesareans." *California Law Review* 74: 1951.

Roberts, Dorothy E. 1991. "Punishing Drug Addicts Who Have Babies: Women of Color, Equality and the Right of Privacy." *Harvard Law Review* 104: 1419.

Roberts, Dorothy E. 1997. *Killing the Black Body: Race, Reproduction, and the Meaning of Liberty.*

Robertson, John A. 1983. "Procreative Liberty and the Control of Conception, Pregnancy, and Childbirth." *Virginia Law Review* 69: 405.

Shaw, Margery W. 1984. "Conditional Prospective Rights of the Fetus." *Journal of Legal Medicine* 5: 63.

Stallman v. Youngquist. 531 N.E.2d 355 (Ill. 1988), reversing 152 Ill.App. 3d 683, 504 N.E.2d 920 (1st Dist. 1987).

Steinbock, Bonnie. 1994. "Maternal-Fetal Conflict and In Utero Fetal Therapy." *Albany Law Review* 57: 781.

U. S. General Accounting Office. 1990. *Drug-Exposed Infants: A Generation at Risk—Report to the Chairman, Committee on Finance, U.S. Senate.* Washington, D.C.: Author.

Valerie D., In re. 223 Conn. 492, 613 A.2d 748 (1992).

Whitner v. South Carolina. 328 S.C. 1, 492 S.E.2d 777 (1997).

Wisconsin v. Kruzicki. 209 Wis.2d 112, 561 N.W.2d 729 (1997).

"Wyoming Case Against Pregnant Woman is Dismissed." *Reproductive Rights Update* 2: 6.

INTERNET RESOURCE

American Medical Association. 2003. "Legal Interventions During Pregnancy." (Policy H–420.969). Available from <http://www.ama-assn.org>.

MEDICAID

• • •

Medicare and Medicaid were created in 1965, and together they revolutionized public health insurance in the United States. Before Medicaid, healthcare insurance for the poor was not perceived as a societal or governmental responsibility.

Initial Goals and Early Challenges

Medicare and Medicaid could not be more different in their underlying philosophies and structures. Medicare was designed to be a universal entitlement program like Social Security. It was established to provide basic hospital and physician-care insurance for all elderly Americans and is financed through a special trust fund. Its benefits are controlled by the federal government and do not vary by state.

In contrast, Medicaid was designed to be a means-tested program funded by general revenue from the federal government and the states. Within federal guidelines and options states determine who will be covered, what services will be paid for, how much providers will be paid, and how the program will be administered. It was not designed to provide social insurance to the full poverty population but to cover particular recipients of public aid, mainly those receiving Aid to Families with Dependent Children (AFDC) and Supplemental Security Income (SSI). Soon after its inception Medicare was thought to be a model for the next step toward universal health insurance, whereas Medicaid was seen as a stigmatized program for the poor.

The history of the two programs, however, has shown that Medicaid has been the more important and effective vehicle for increasing access to healthcare services. Medicare has remained largely constant and rigid in its covered population and its structure. By contrast, the Medicaid program has been the structure to which policymakers have turned to repeatedly over the years to make incremental additions to the population covered by health insurance.

Growth in the Medicaid Safety Net

Medicaid began small. In 1966, there were four million enrollees and the annual cost was $400 million. Those numbers increased as persons in need of long-term care were added to the program after 1972. Although the number of recipients grew slowly between 1975 and 1990 (22 million to 26 million), total government costs for Medicaid increased dramatically, rising from $12 billion to $72 billion. By 2002 the number of enrollees had reached 47 million, making Medicaid slightly larger than Medicare, and total costs had reached $257 billion. However, not everyone who is eligible for Medicaid enrolls. Seventy-two percent of eligible children and 51 percent of eligible nonelderly adults are estimated to be enrolled. In 1999 Medicaid covered 5 percent of nonelderly adults and 15 percent of those with incomes below 200 percent of the poverty level.

The Medicaid program has grown in several important ways. Although originally it was limited to those who received cash benefits under AFDC (poor women and children) and SSI (the permanently disabled), more than half the persons Medicaid covered in the early years of the twenty-first century did not receive cash benefits from other programs. Indeed, Medicaid at that time was the principal source of funding for a vast infrastructure that served the poor and disabled, including safety-net hospitals, community and migrant health centers, mental health clinics, and school-based health programs.

Long-term care was added to the mandated benefits in 1972. Without private insurance, middle-class Americans may become impoverished because of out-of-pocket nursing home costs and "spenddown" to qualify for Medicaid. Institutional coverage also is provided for inpatient mental health services and intermediate-care facilities for the mentally retarded. Medicaid is also the largest payer for medical services for persons with AIDS.

The largest and most important expansions of the scope of Medicaid have been in the areas of prenatal care for poor women and healthcare for children. In 1989 poor women began to receive coverage for prenatal care. In 1997 the State Children's Health Insurance Program (SCHIP) was enacted to cover low-income children who did not qualify for Medicaid under the previous criteria. Together Medicaid and SCHIP account for 16 percent of the nation's healthcare spending, nearly as much as Medicare's share (18%).

Impact on the Nation's Health

Medicaid has achieved significant advances in the healthcare of the poor and previously middle-class persons who require mental health services or long-term care. With Medicaid, poor persons use health services at the same rate as nonpoor persons with a similar health status. Medicaid also provides access to a broader service package that supplements physician care, such as dental care and prescription coverage.

Medicaid has proved to be a better vehicle for incremental reform than Medicare because it is more flexible and does not have the high level of national political visibility and volatility that Medicare has. Additions to the Medicaid program typically have had three effects; they have (1) increased access to care, (2) shifted at least part of the cost to the federal government, and (3) increased the uncompensated care burden on healthcare providers. Overall, the health of the poor has improved significantly in the post-Medicaid era, with substantial declines in infant mortality, maternal mortality, and death rates for major diseases for which medical intervention is effective.

Major Criticisms of the Program

Medicaid is not a "user-friendly" program. Many persons who are eligible for the program are not enrolled. Once a person is enrolled, eligibility status is evaluated periodically, as frequently as every month in some programs. When income eligibility standards are no longer met, Medicaid coverage is suspended. This results in poor continuity of care and personal hardship.

The state-based nature of the program has resulted in variations in coverage and benefits across the states. Federal requirements ensure relatively uniform coverage for children, pregnant women, the elderly, and the disabled across the states. Childless adults are not covered by Medicaid regardless of their income level. Adults who are parents are the group for whom Medicaid eligibility varies the most widely from state to state. Half the states set eligibility below 40 percent of the federal poverty line; those whose incomes put them at the poverty level ($15,020 for a family of three in 2002) make too much to qualify for Medicaid in all but eighteen states.

Throughout its history there have been repeated cycles of cutbacks and expansions in response to fiscal pressure in the states. From the 1970s until the mid-1980s cutbacks eroded Medicaid coverage of the poor and began to reverse the progress that had been made in closing gaps in access to care across income groups. Since the mid-1980s, however, the trend has been to expand Medicaid eligibility and services. This has not been due to the increased political leverage of the poor but has occurred because from both the federal and the state point of view the cost-sharing arrangement makes it attractive to add to the program. Only in the early 2000s did the nation begin to reenter a period of fiscal crisis at the state level. As a result of a general economic downturn, state revenues declined while Medicaid costs expanded to account for a very significant portion of state governmental budgets.

The prospects for the future of Medicaid are unclear. Some states want the authority to cap enrollment levels and create waiting lists so that even those who qualify with incomes at 40 percent of less of poverty may not be enrolled. About half the Medicaid enrollees in the country are in managed-care plans, but that has not stemmed the tide of rising costs.

Issues for the Future of Medicaid

Medicaid reform is charged with moral issues that frame the fundamental policy decisions. Can public health insurance be equitable when it is targeted only to the poor, or is the inevitable outcome a lesser program? Can an equitable package of minimum benefits be determined? Will the trend toward using Medicaid to expand access to health insurance incrementally be reversed by a weakening of federal requirements and the fiscal crisis of state governments that began at the turn of the twenty-first century? How should society share the costs that a decent healthcare safety net will incur?

DIANE ROWLAND
CATHERINE HOFFMAN (1995)
REVISED BY BRUCE JENNINGS

SEE ALSO: *Access to Healthcare; Healthcare Resources, Allocation of; Health Insurance; Health Policy in the United States; Medicare*

BIBLIOGRAPHY

Boben, Paul J. 2000. "Medicaid Reform in the 1990s." *Health Care Financing Review* 22(2): 1–5.

Brown, E. Richard. 1983. "Medicare and Medicaid: The Process, Value, and Limits of Health Care Reforms." *Journal of Public Health Policy* 4(3): 335–356.

Brown, Lawrence D., and Sparer, Michael S. 2003. "Poor Program's Progress: The Unanticipated Politics of Medicaid Policy." *Health Affairs* 22(1): 31–44.

Davis, Karen, and Schoen, Cathy. 1978. "Medicaid: Successes and Problems." In *Health and the War on Poverty: A Ten-Year Appraisal.* Washington, D.C.: Brookings Institution.

Hurley, Robert E., and Draper, Debra A. 2002. "Medicaid Confronts a Changing Managed Care Marketplace." *Health Care Financing Review* 24(1): 11–25.

Jost, Timothy Stoltzfus. 2003. "The Tenuous Nature of the Medicaid Entitlement." *Health Affairs* 22(1): 145–143.

Kaiser Commission on Medicaid and the Uninsured. 2001. "Medicaid Facts: Medicaid's Role for the Disabled Population under Sixty-five." Washington, D.C.: Kaiser Family Foundation.

Kaiser Commission on Medicaid and the Uninsured. 2001. "Medicaid Facts: Medicaid's Disabled Population and Managed Care." Washington, D.C.: Kaiser Family Foundation.

Klemm, J. 2000. "Medicaid Spending: A Brief History." *Health Care Financing Review* (fall): 105–112.

Mann, Cindy. 2003. "The Flexibility Factor: Finding the Right Balance." *Health Affairs* 22(1): 62–76.

Reilly, Thomas W.; Clauser, Steven B.; and Baugh, David K. 1990. "Trends in Medicaid Payments and Utilization, 1975–89." *Health Care Financing Review* Annual Supplement: 15–33.

Rowland, Diane; Lyons, Barbara; and Edwards, Jennifer. 1988. "Medicaid: Health Care for the Poor in the Reagan Era." *Annual Review of Public Health* 9: 427–450.

Rowland, Diane, and Tallon, James R., Jr. 2003. "Medicaid: Lessons from a Decade." *Health Affairs* 22(1): 138–144.

Smith, V. K. 2002. *Making Medicaid Better.* Washington, D.C.: National Governors' Association.

Sparer, Michael. 1996. *Medicaid and the Limits of Health Reform.* Philadelphia: Temple University Press.

Stevens, Rosemary, and Stevens, Robert. 1974. "The Federal Role: An Aphilosophical Explanation." In *Welfare Medicine in America: A Case Study of Medicaid,* New York: Free Press.

Stuart, Mary E., and Weinrich, Michael. 1998. "Beyond Managing Medicaid Costs: Restructuring Care." *Milbank Quarterly* 76(2): 251–280.

Vladeck, Bruce. 2003. "Where the Action Really Is: Medicaid and the Disabled." *Health Affairs* 22(1): 90–100.

Weil, Alan. 2003. "There's Something about Medicaid." *Health Affairs* 22(1): 13–30.

INTERNET RESOURCE

Centers for Medicare and Medicaid Services. 2003. "Medicaid: A Brief Summary." Available from <http://www.cms.hhs.gov/publications>.

MEDICAL CODES AND OATHS

• • •

I. History
II. Ethical Analysis

I. HISTORY

The following is a revision and update of the first-edition article "Codes of Medical Ethics: History" by Donald Konold. Portions of the first-edition article appear in the revised version.

In the ethics of healthcare, explicit statements of ethical standards have been formulated for physicians and members of the other health professions, for persons conducting medical experiments involving human subjects, for administrators, and for patients and other laypeople who make healthcare decisions. These have often been written by members of the relevant practitioner group, but they may also be written by members of religious, cultural, national, or international bodies. While codes of ethics have long been regarded as the classic expression of these directives, various principles and rules have also been stated in the form of prayers, oaths, creeds, institutional directives, and statements. Prayers state a very personal commitment of duty; oaths publicly pledge the oath taker to uphold specified responsibilities; and codes provide more comprehensive standards to guide the practicing health practitioner, patient, or other decision maker. Each form of ethical statement implies a moral imperative, either to be accepted by the individual personally or to be enforced by a practitioner organization, religious community, or governmental body.

While practitioner bodies have often assumed responsibility for writing their own codes of ethics for their members, governmental, religious, and cultural bodies have also claimed authority to articulate the moral norms of conduct in healthcare. Disputes over who has the authority to articulate codifications of ethical duties in the medical sphere reveal important controversies over who can legitimately claim moral authority in determining what these duties are. This article first examines prayers, oaths, and codes written by health providers or practitioner groups, and then examines those written outside the profession.

Documents Created by Practitioners

MEDICAL PRAYERS. Healthcare providers in all ages have composed prayers expressing gratitude for divine blessings and asking for divine inspiration in their practitioner conduct. Such prayers signify that the writer stands within a religious tradition and grounds medical duties in that religion's moral framework.

An ancient Greek poem that has the quality of a prayer or a hymn was found inscribed on a monument in a sanctuary of Asclepias, originally on the south slope of the Acropolis. According to the poem, the physician should be "like God: savior equally of slaves, of paupers, of rich men, of princes, and to all a brother, such help he would give" (Etziony, p. 21).

Likewise, ancient Jewish sources include texts extolling the physician's healing. An early Jewish prayer was written by the early-twelfth-century Spanish poet, philosopher, and physician Yehuda Halevi (Etziony). The most widely acclaimed Jewish example is the Daily Prayer of a Physician, once ascribed to the Jewish physician and philosopher Moses Maimonides (1135–1204) but now believed to be the work of the eighteenth-century German Jewish physician

Marcus Herz (Rosner). In the manner of most medical prayers, the Daily Prayer asks for courage, determination, and inspiration to enable the physician to develop skills, meet responsibilities, and heal patients. It commits the physician to place duty to patients above the physician's own concerns and places the physician's healing in clear subordination to divine authority.

Many examples of Christian prayers of physicians exist from ancient and medieval times. More modern prayers sometimes reflect more eclectic, nondenominational perspectives. The theology expressed in the prayers of these physicians, who, theologically, are laypeople, is sometimes not an authoritative reflection of the tradition in which they stand.

OATHS FOR PHYSICIANS. In the ancient world physicians often expressed their ethical commitments in the form of oaths, which were an integral part of the initiation ceremony for medical apprentices. Like many medical prayers, ancient oaths reflect the physician's belief that success in the healing profession required an alliance with the deity in the treatment of disease. The ancient oaths often beseech the deity to inspire physicians to fulfill their moral obligations, reward those who honor their sacred trust, and punish those who violate it.

One of the oldest of these oaths, a medical student's oath taken from the *Charaka Samhita* manuscript of ancient India, contains concepts that had pervaded Indian ethical thought for many centuries before their inclusion in the oath at about the beginning of the common era (Menon and Haberman). Pledging the medical student to live the life of an ascetic and a virtual slave of his preceptor in accordance with Indian custom for apprenticeships, the path requires personal sacrifice and commitment to duty from the student comparable to the physician's responsibilities to patients. By the terms of the oath, the student physician is to place the patient's needs above personal considerations, serving day and night with heart and soul; abstaining from drunkenness, crime, and adultery; and scrupulously observing practitioner secrecy.

In sharp contrast to the medical ethics of the Western world, the Indian oath obliges the physician to deny services to enemies of his ruler, evildoers, unattended women, and those on the point of death. Ancient Indian thought condemned aid to anyone who was immoral or was involved in any circumstance that might suggest illicit sexual contact; it also condemned interference with the process of dying. Despite these differences, the oath of the Indian student reveals significant parallels between the medical ethics of India and those of the Western world, which may suggest a diffusion of ideas, probably from India to the West.

The most enduring medical oath of Western civilization is the Oath of Hippocrates. Despite its renown, its origin is obscure. It is a part of the Hippocratic Collection, which was catalogued and edited by a group of Alexandrian librarians sometime after the fourth century C.E. Copies of these writings available to modern scholars, however, date from the tenth to the fifteenth centuries C.E. and do not preserve the original text with verbal accuracy. None of the manuscripts in this collection can be positively verified as genuine works of the great Greek physician, and clearly the documents are the products of many contributors, with the earliest predating the latest by at least a century.

Twentieth-century scholars, especially Ludwig Edelstein (1943), have suggested that the oath conforms closely to the teachings of Pythagoras (fourth century B.C.E.). He noted the similarities with the principal ethical beliefs of the Pythagoreans, which included reincarnation, avoidance of shedding of blood, prohibition on taking of life, and commitment to sexual purity and secrecy. Edelstein held that the oath was composed by a group of Pythagoreans who practiced the healing arts. More recent historians of medical ethics have argued over whether the dependency is as close as Edelstein maintained, suggesting that the influence of other philosophical/ethical traditions may also be present (Carrick). Nevertheless, some degree of affinity of Hippocratic with Pythagorean thought is generally conceded. The oath, in accord with Pythagorean ethics, proclaims a more strict morality for physicians than was established by Greek law, Platonic or Aristotelian ethics, or common Greek medical practice.

The Oath of Hippocrates consists of two parts, the first serving as a contractual agreement between pupil and teacher and the second constituting an ethical code. The opening sentences pledge the novice physician (invariably a male) to become an adopted member of his teacher's family, to help support his teacher and his teacher's children in case of need, and to instruct his teacher's children free of charge. The oath forbids sharing the precepts and medical knowledge with anyone who has not taken the oath. Since familial bonds between teacher and pupil implied careful selection of those admitted to the family group, the covenant enabled physicians to prevent unworthy persons from entering the profession and to keep tight control on knowledge transmission.

The ethical code contained in the Oath of Hippocrates places restrictions on the medical techniques of the physician and defines relations with the patient's family. One who takes the oath pledges, "I will apply dietetic measures for the benefit of the sick according to my ability and judgment; I will keep them from harm and injustice" (Edelstein, 1943, p. 3). He also agrees to refuse to dispense poisons or abortive remedies, and to leave surgery (including lithotomy or removal of a stone from the urinary bladder) to those trained in that art. He makes the commitment that "whatever houses I may visit, I will come for the benefit of the sick, remaining free of all intentional injustice" (Edelstein, 1943, p. 3). The taker of the oath swears to abstain from sexual relations with all those in the houses the physician enters. Regarding confidentiality, in an ambiguously qualified way, the physician promises not to disclose that "which on no account one must spread abroad." The oath ends with a plea for reward that is unusually self-serving for a code of ethics: that if the physician keeps the oath he be "honored with fame among all men for all time to come." If he transgresses it, "may the opposite of all this be my lot" (Edelstein, 1943, p. 3).

The oath's provisions contrast sharply with what is otherwise known about ancient Greek medical practice, which permitted physicians to abet suicide and infanticide and to perform surgery. They introduced an element of respect for slave as well as freeman and, even though the secrecy requirement is qualified, it is extended outside the practitioner relationship. These precepts, though they represent the thought of only a small group of medical practitioners, extended their influence beyond the importance of the Hippocratic school of medicine in the ancient world.

For centuries following the appearance of the Hippocratic oath, the practitioners of the medical art showed no inclination to accept it. Hellenistic physicians ignored its injunctions without compunction. It is sometimes held that the rise of Christianity, which had certain ethical positions similar to Hippocratic ethics, is responsible for the ascendancy of the Hippocratic oath (Edelstein, 1943; Carrick). There is, however, very little evidence of early Christian interest in the Hippocratic oath; increasingly there is emphasis on important ethical differences between the Hippocratic and Christian traditions (Veatch and Mason). Medical historian Owsei Temkin has identified considerable tension between Hippocratic and Christian medicine and their ethical commitments. One exception to this generalization is the fourth-century Christian figure Jerome, who explicitly mentions the Hippocratic oath, but in doing so he points out that the Christian physician's obligation is even more stringent.

Precisely what happened to bring the oath into prominence during the Middle Ages is uncertain. Perhaps the early post-Constantinian Christian culture found similarities between Christian and Hippocratic views, as has been suggested. A strong case can be made, however, that although there were significant differences between Greco-Roman and Christian medical ethics, lay physicians were simply not sufficiently schooled in Christian theology to perceive them.

One way or another, increased attention to the oath led to renewed interest in it. Modifications were introduced in order to bring it somewhat more into harmony with Christian ideological concepts and practices. This could be taken either as evidence to support the convergence hypothesis or to support the contrary claim that the oath had to be corrected significantly to bring it into harmony with Christian thought.

The earliest of these extant revisions, titled "From the Oath According to Hippocrates Insofar as a Christian May Swear It" (dating from the tenth or eleventh century), substitutes a statement of Christian adoration of God for the references to the Greek deities in the original oath and replaces its covenant with a statement of teaching responsibilities based on Christian brotherhood, pledging the physician to teach the medical art to whomever wants to learn it (Jones; Leake). The injunction against surgery does not appear in this version of the oath. No reason is known for its omission, but later Christian versions do contain it. The appeal for reward and honor for the physician should he follow the oath is abandoned, probably because it is inconsistent with Christian views of grace.

The Oath of Asaf, from the seventh-century *Sefer Asaf* manuscripts of the oldest Hebrew medical work, reveals Hippocratic influences in its injunctions against administering poisons or abortifacient drugs, performing surgery, committing adultery, and betraying practitioner confidences (Rosner and Muntner). Like the medieval Christian oaths, it is consistent with Talmudic ethics and instructs physicians to give special consideration to the poor and needy, a concern absent from the Hippocratic oath. A revision of the Oath of Hippocrates also appeared in medieval Muslim literature, where the only significant changes replaced references to Greek gods with statements in harmony with Islamic theology. The oath in its original form was also known to Christian and Muslim scholars; however, among the Christian church fathers, only rare mention is made of it. The texts that do refer to the oath reveal a perception of a difference between Hippocratic and Christian medicine.

Following the transition from medieval to modern Western civilization, the Oath of Hippocrates apparently continued to be a model for ethical pledges by physicians. Its legacy is ambiguous. On the one hand, it repudiates exploitation of the sick, often the most vulnerable. On the other hand, it locates all authority about what constitutes a benefit in the physician's "ability and judgment." In this way, the oath has sanctioned a medical paternalism throughout the ages that is in conflict with the modern assertion of the right of patients to determine for themselves the benefits they seek from medical care.

Western medical schools in the eighteenth and nineteenth centuries, seeking to impart high ethical ideals to their students, administered oaths to their graduates. It is unclear whether or how often the Hippocratic oath itself was used, but certainly the typical oaths, such as that of the great medical school of Montpellier, incorporated Hippocratic ideas (Etziony).

Our knowledge of professional medical ethics in the early modern period is very limited. Historians have not done enough specific research in European and American medical schools and professional societies to know what local religious, philosophical, and political influences helped shape medical education. Additional research is underway. The received tradition holds that Western medical schools, seeking to commit their students to the pursuit of high ethical ideas, continued a tradition begun in the Middle Ages of incorporating Hippocratic concepts in oaths for their graduates, especially the covenant's requirement for the physician to instruct his teacher's children and the ethical injunctions for secrecy and against administering harmful drugs. During the nineteenth century, some medical schools in the United States required their graduates to take the Hippocratic oath in its original form, and that continued to be a common practice in the twentieth century, even though many of the oath's provisions were archaic or offensive to some of the students. A study published in 1991 found that 60 of 141 U.S. medical schools administered the Hippocratic oath (Dickstein et al.).

A document patterned after the Oath of Hippocrates appeared in 1948, when the newly organized World Medical Association (WMA) adopted the Declaration of Geneva. In 1991 forty-seven U.S. medical schools used it (Dickstein et al.). (Of the remainder, fourteen schools used the Prayer of Maimonides or more recently written oaths.) The declaration attempts to make the original oath applicable to modern conditions of medical practice and diverse cultural, religious, and ethnic groups in the world community. In doing so, it raises serious questions of how any one single ethical text could be made appropriate for a wide range of religious and cultural groups that clearly have fundamental differences, not only about significant medical ethical controversies, but also about the very foundations and meanings of ethical propositions. The Declaration of Geneva is a secular oath that contains no reference to religious tenets or loyalties, thus appealing to secular physicians while perhaps offending those who continue to ground their ethics in some particular religious framework.

Although the claim is made that the Declaration of Geneva simply updates the Hippocratic oath, the reformulation clearly involves significant differences. The declaration commits the physician to make the patient's health his or her first consideration, a provision reminiscent of the Hippocratic oath's pledge to use dietetic measures for the benefit of the sick. But in addition to the secularization of the declaration by the removal of the religious references, the 1948 text deletes the pledge to refuse to reveal information to those who have not taken the oath. The loose Hippocratic pledge of confidentiality is replaced with an exceptionless pledge, one that conflicts with the increasingly recognized necessity of disclosing in order to protect third parties from serious threats of harm, as well as with the more paternalistic exceptions seen in many modern interpretations of the oath. The oath's surgical restriction is also omitted from the declaration, as is the injunction against sexual contact with those in the patient's household.

The physician of the declaration vows not to let considerations of religion, nationality, race, party politics, or social standing interfere with his duty to his patient. Obviously, those who conceived and adopted the declaration found united support for clearer condemnation of these prejudices than the original oath provided. In sharp contrast, however, the declaration's statement of the physician's responsibility regarding suicide, mercy killing, and abortion is obscured in generalities that conceal modern controversy on these matters among physicians and laypeople alike. The physician of the declaration pledges only to maintain respect for human life from the time of conception and not to use medical knowledge in ways that are contrary to the laws of humanity. While the Declaration of Geneva has found some acceptance among medical professional groups, it has not been endorsed by significant national professional associations, and it certainly conflicts with the ethical precepts of many secular and religious groups in both East and West.

PRACTITIONER CODES. Physicians of the modern world have not been content with the spiritual inspiration of prayers and the moral commitments of medical oaths. The large medical institutions of urban society have required complex relationships among medical personnel who demand detailed procedures to prevent embarrassing ethical controversy and disruption of services. Lengthy treatises on medical subjects, which had enlightened physicians on ethical matters since the earliest times, were not easy to cite by paragraph and line and frequently concealed ethical instruction in needless verbiage. Reducing these essays to lists of rules, proponents of practitioner control produced elaborate ethical codes.

A code is an ordered collection of injunctions and prohibitions, usually created by an authoritative body and adopted as a statement of ideals and rules for a group or organization. The modern idea of codes derives ultimately from the Renaissance ideal of rationalizing Roman law, putting the diverse parts into some order and stating briefly and clearly the essence of the rule. Sometimes individually authored documents, such as the work of Sun Szu-miao and Thomas Percival discussed below, have taken on the status of systematic codifications.

One of the earliest codes of medical ethics appeared in China, where the Oath of Hippocrates never made a significant impression. From the seventh century, an indigenous Chinese tradition in medical ethics developed in works by Sun Szu-miao. Generally regarded as Taoist, his writing stresses the importance of preserving life and the subordination of self-interest to compassion for the patient. It reflects the differentiation of an elite group of physicians referred to as "great physicians" and marks the emergence of a group claiming special medical authority. A Confucian response authored by Lu Chih (754–805) attacks this elitist trend, indicating medicine should be the responsibility of all persons. This tradition received clear expression in the Five Admonitions and Ten Maxims listed by Ch'en Shih-kung in a seventeenth-century treatise on surgery (Unschuld). Along with much guidance for social intercourse, Ch'en's precepts instruct physicians to give equal treatment to patients of all ranks, to keep expenses modest, and to treat the poor without charge, providing the same services regardless of the amount of payment. Above all, the physician is to know the principles of Confucianism. The key Confucian virtues are compassion and "applied humaneness," terms that do not enter Western medical ethics until the twentieth century.

These instructions continue to characterize Chinese medical ethics in modern times, but they have had little influence elsewhere. Although they bear some resemblance to ethical concepts in Western medicine, there are significant differences and little evidence of crossfertilization.

In the West, the Royal College of Physicians provides an interesting example of a professional code. In the first Statutes of the College in 1555, and in the revision of 1647, there is a section entitled, De statutis moralibus seu penalibus. This contains precepts requiring good behavior in the meetings of the college, regular attendance and, in addition, proper etiquette between several physicians called into consultation. They admonish physicians not to disparage or accuse one another in public, but only before the college. They also prohibit physicians from telling their patients and the public the names and composition of medicines, "lest the people be harmed by abuse of them" (Clark, p. 384).

A treatise published in 1803 by Thomas Percival, an eminent physician of Manchester, England, strongly influenced the development of codes of medical ethics (Leake; Baker et al., 1993; Baker, 1993). Originally prepared in 1794 to mediate a dispute among surgeons, physicians, and apothecaries in Manchester, and expanded in 1803 to include physicians in general practice, Medical Ethics; or, A Code of Institutes and Precepts Adapted to the Professional Conduct of Physicians and Surgeons expresses standards of morality and etiquette that were in sharp contrast to the quarrelsome conduct of British practitioners of that era. Percival's treatise places emphasis on the professional relationships of physicians to one another; to hospital.personnel, apothecaries, and others engaged in the care of the sick; and to the law.

In its advice to physicians to treat patients with the eighteenth-century virtues of "tenderness, steadiness, condescension, and authority," it conveys the attitudes of the English gentleman philanthropically bestowing benefits on patients who are expected to show proper gratitude. Percival's Medical Ethics stands in the Hippocratic tradition, but begins to acknowledge obligations of physicians to the society as well as to patients. Unlike the Hippocratic oath, Percival holds both surgery and medicine as acceptable practices.

As befits a volume having its origins in a local dispute among professions, a principal concern of Percival's Medical Ethics is with the etiquette of professional conduct. It offers elaborate procedures for consultation among physicians in difficult cases and for preservation of distinction of rank in relationships between junior and senior physicians on hospital faculties and in consultations. It cautions physicians to display respect for one another, to avoid criticizing the practice of their colleagues, to conceal professional differences from the public, and not to steal patients from one another. In justifying these procedures, Percival reasoned that criticism of the profession was usually unfounded and always degrading both to the doctors criticized and to the profession. In most of its provisions, Percival's Medical Ethics suggests a modified utilitarian philosophy, calling for individual physicians to conduct themselves in a manner that would enhance public respect for the entire medical profession.

Among the earliest American writings in physician-authored ethics were those by Columbia University physician Samuel Bard and revolutionary patriot Benjamin Rush; early codes were also prepared by the medical associations of the cities of Boston and Baltimore and the state of New York. When the American Medical Association (AMA) was organized in 1847, it adopted a code of ethics drawn from Percival's Medical Ethics as well as these other sources. The code of ethics made no mention of etiquette for hospital staff and barely referred to the relations of physicians with pharmacists and courts of law, but it expanded and elaborated the principles for physicians in private practice, even presuming to include a statement of obligations of patients and the public to physicians.

The medical profession in the United States faced a crisis in public confidence in 1847. Medical licensure laws in most states had been repealed with the result that uneducated practitioners and charlatans had begun to compete for patients with educated physicians. In addition, a vigorous debate raged between various schools of medical science over which was the correct or orthodox system. Proponents of the code of ethics hoped that the public would cooperate with allopathic physicians in establishing standards for medical practice that would reinstate public respect for the medical profession.

The code of ethics contained a variety of restrictions on open competition among physicians. It branded as quacks all medical practitioners who lacked orthodox training, claimed special ability, patented instruments or medicine, used secret remedies, or criticized other practitioners. In doing so, it also became a weapon in the internal dispute among physicians of different schools, particularly challenging the homeopaths. The requirement of orthodox training made outcasts of physicians who belonged to medical sects such as the homeopaths, the eclectics, the Thomsonians, and later the osteopaths and chiropractors. Since each sect claimed superior results from its form of treatment, practitioners with sectarian designations were guilty of claiming superior ability as well as handicapped by their incomplete education.

Charging that these offenses resulted from selfishness and efforts to discredit rivals, the code of ethics also demanded that reputable physicians avoid any appearance of soliciting the patient of another doctor. Although these provisions united the profession against heterodoxy and quackery, the prohibition on claims of special ability produced conflict between general practitioners and aspiring specialists. This ethical rule ceased to cause dissension only after the establishment of specialist organizations to certify the credentials of their members and after specialization won sufficient acceptance to permit physicians to restrict practice to their specialties.

The code of ethics provided orthodox physicians with one means of exposing those undeserving of confidence. It stated that physicians should not consult professionally with anyone who lacked a license to practice or was not in good professional standing. Since professional standing was determined by the local medical societies, this provision had the effect of substituting a collective professional judgment for that of individual physicians and patients, thus superseding the Hippocratic oath's focus on the individual physician's judgment. In those cases where the patient insisted on inviting a consultant who was not approved by the local medical organization, the attending physician would have to retire from the case in order to retain professional standing. While physicians argued that they could not fulfill their obligation to patients if they admitted a right for fraudulent practitioners to advise in any capacity, their ethics required that they withdraw, thus giving full charge of the case to the allegedly unqualified practitioner. Moreover, the majority of physicians found the consultation restriction a useful means for excluding many qualified physicians from association with the dominant organization. Thus the codes served a monopolistic function as instruments for restraint of trade. Before 1870, regular medical societies excluded from membership and forbade consultations with female physicians and Negro physicians and, throughout the latter half of the century, with physicians who adopted a sectarian designation, even if they were certified by licensing boards. Because of mounting criticism, the consultation restriction was eliminated from the code of ethics in 1903, but its spirit was revived by a 1924 resolution of the American Medical Association forbidding voluntary association of its members with cultists. In effect, the AMA code, so vociferously debated in the nineteenth century was double edged: It did state, in Percivalian terms, certain ideals of good practice, but at the same time, it was an instrument to create a monopoly.

Establishment of the World Medical Association in 1948 encouraged physicians to develop international standards of medical ethics. The new organization adopted an International Code of Medical Ethics (International Code) in 1949, which attempted to summarize the most important principles of medical ethics. Since 1900, certification laws had reduced the prevalence of unqualified medical practitioners, and scientific advances had increased the effectiveness of trained physicians. By mid-century, physicians were directing their attention more to the actual treatment of patients and less to the formality of relations between one doctor and another, or between doctor and patient. The International Code reflects these new concerns in a shift away from the detailed regulations of the preceding 150 years. In place of elaborate etiquette for consultations and other medical confrontations, it recommends only that physicians behave toward colleagues as they would have colleagues behave toward them, that they call specialists in difficult cases, and that they not entice each other's patients. It warns against the profit motive and prohibits unauthorized advertising, medical care plans that deprive the physician of professional independence, fee splitting or rebates with or without the patient's knowledge, and refusal to treat emergency cases. It also commits physicians to honor professional secrecy in an unqualified way, an obligation that continues after the death of the patient, according to an amendment to the code adopted in 1968.

The International Code only hints at the ethical problems of abortion and euthanasia by asserting the physician's responsibility to preserve life. It does, however, warn specifically against any action that would weaken the patient's resistance without therapeutic justification. Applicable to the dying patient and experimental subject alike, this standard requires the physician to consider the patient's well-being above all else. The International Code also recognizes the need for adequate testing of innovations by urging great caution in publishing discoveries and therapeutic methods not recognized by the profession.

Using the International Code of Ethics as an example, the American Medical Association reduced its elaborate code to ten one-sentence Principles of Medical Ethics in 1957 (Ten Principles). This was intended as an epitome rather than a reduction. ("Every basic principle has been preserved," according to the Council that submitted the draft.) It retained the essentially Hippocratic focus on benefit of the patient, but added that the responsibilities of the physician extend also to the society.

Most of these principles had been anticipated in the International Code, but there are a few noteworthy exceptions. Reflecting a continuing distrust of sectarian practitioners by regular physicians in the United States, the 1957 principles warn against professional association with unscientific practitioners. They also oblige physicians who are AMA members to expose the legal and ethical violations of other doctors. Instead of warning against premature publication of discoveries, the 1957 principles urge physicians to make their attainments available to patients and colleagues. Finally, while reaffirming the principle of confidentiality, the 1957 principles authorize physicians to violate this principle when required by law or to advance the welfare of the individual or the community. This provision suggests more discretionary authority for the physician than do the codes of most nations and the World Medical Association, which emphasize the inviolability of professional secrecy.

By the late 1970s, there was again dissatisfaction with the principles. A special committee was appointed to prepare a new draft that would clarify and update the language, eliminate reference to gender, and seek a "proper and reasonable balance between professional standards and contemporary legal standards in our changing society" (American Medical Association, 1989, p. viii). The report submitting the new version acknowledged the increasing recognition of laypeople's role in defining the moral terms of the patient–physician relation. Nevertheless, the new code was prepared and adopted by a group made up entirely of members of the association. The new principles affirm the virtues of compassion and respect for human dignity. It, for the first time, shifts to the use of the language of "rights," saying that "a physician shall respect the rights of patients, of colleagues, and of other health professionals" (p. ix). It generally removes the traditional Hippocratic paternalistic authorization for physicians to act for the benefit of the patient according to the physician's judgment. For example, it permits breaking confidentiality only "within the constraints of the law" (p. ix).

Scientific advances and changing social standards in recent decades have raised ethical questions in a number of areas that are not adequately covered by existing general codes. The Council on Ethical and Judicial Affairs of the American Medical Association regularly issues opinions that elaborate (and occasionally contradict) the principles adopted by the AMA's legislative body, the House of Delegates. In recent years, other medical organizations, such as the American College of Physicians, have prepared and issued codes of ethics for their members.

Codes from Outside the Profession

GOVERNMENTAL CODES. In the twentieth century, a number of national governments have incorporated ethical codes into legal statutes governing the medical profession, to be enforced by an official, publicly appointed medical board. The precepts in these codes sometimes accord with the broader principles of the Percival tradition, but many provisions deal with problems of recent origin and reflect a modern concern for both public and individual welfare.

Some of these codes deal with single subjects. For example, the Nuremberg Code, which is the product of international law, deals with medical research on human subjects. In the United States, the federal government's regulations on the same subject function as a code of conduct as does the Belmont Report, a set of ethical principles on research developed by the National Commission for the Protection of Human Subjects of Biomedical and Behavioral Research (1978).

Underlying the development of these codes is a fundamental issue of ethics: Is the professional group or the general public responsible for deciding what the ethical norms of the lay–professional relation should be? Even if the profession is deemed the proper authority for determining what constitutes ethical conduct, it is not clear exactly who should have the authority to speak for the profession and what the content of the codes should be. Some functions of the codes are clearly more for public relations and control of competition rather than for articulation of ethical norms. Many provisions that clearly are normative in content are still controversial. It is increasingly doubtful that the organized professional associations should have the authority to speak even for the profession as a whole (including the large numbers of physicians who are not members of the organizations) and that these groups should have any authority to speak on ethical matters that affect laypeople.

While modern medical ethics has often presumed that the profession should define its own code of conduct, this has not always been the case. Religious as well as governmental groups have sometimes claimed this prerogative. Increasingly, professional groups as well as laypeople are insisting that judgments about ethics are not the exclusive province of the professions and that the norms of lay–professional relations should be grounded in cultural, philosophical, or religious commitments.

A government-sponsored medical oath was adopted in the former Soviet Union, where its Presidium approved the Oath of Soviet Physicians in 1971. Modeled after an oath that had been used at the University of Moscow since 1961, the Soviet oath pledged the physician to conduct himself in accordance with communist principles and to order his responsibility to the Soviet government. This commitment to political creed and government was unique among medical oaths. The Soviet oath did not neglect other moral obligations, however; it instructed the physician to honor professional secrets, constantly improve knowledge and skill, always be available to calls for medical care or advice, and dedicate all knowledge and strength to professional activities. Like other recent oaths, the Soviet oath voiced virtually the same ideal of humanitarian duty to individual patients that appears in the earliest medical creeds, but it also pledged the physician to serve the interests of society.

Postcommunist Russia is undergoing a major reassessment of its healthcare policies, including its medical ethics (Tichtchenko and Yudin). In November of 1991, the Russian Supreme Soviet adopted the Declaration of Rights and Liberties of Citizens, which includes the principle of voluntary consent for participation in medical experiments and declares a right of every citizen to qualified medical care in the state healthcare system.

The Russian Medical Academy has developed a "Solemn Oath" (1993) to replace the Oath of the Soviet Physician. The new oath is a modernized revision of the Hippocratic oath. Approved by the Minister of Health in 1992, it is an official government document, not merely the product of a professional medical association.

NONGOVERNMENTAL GROUPS. Throughout history, codes, prayers, and oaths dealing with medical ethics have also been sponsored by private groups, religious bodies, and consumer groups that do not represent the medical profession.

For centuries, the Catholic church has articulated moral views about medical matters including abortion, euthanasia, and fertility control. These have appeared, at least since the medieval era, in systematic theological treatises, cases of conscience (collections analyzing morally perplexing cases), and in the theology manuals of the early modern era (Kelly; Griese). Formal codes of medical ethics, such as the Ethical and Religious Directives for Catholic Health Facilities prepared by the United States Catholic Conference (1975; Griese), are not only considered binding on Catholics but also affect non-Catholics who are associated with Catholic health facilities and others who find their reasoning persuasive.

The statements of the directives on secrecy, consent, organ transplantation, and terminal care closely resemble those of other codes. It prohibits abortion, except when justified by the principle of double effect, that is, when it is an unintended result of a procedure employed to protect the mother. It prohibits both male and female sterilization except in the treatment of a serious pathological condition, and it prohibits artificial insemination. Thus, the directives articulate the Vatican's "Instruction on Respect for Human Life" (Sacred Congregation for the Doctrine of the Faith).

The modern consumer movement has also influenced the ethics of medical practice. As hospitalization became a major consumer service, consumers increasingly demanded the right of patients to minimum standards of care and respect. In 1972, the American Hospital Association responded to consumer pressure and adopted "A Patient's Bill of Rights," which pertains primarily to hospitals but involves physicians with several responsibilities to patients ("Statement," 1973). A physician who subscribes to the bill of rights is obligated, with limited exceptions, to keep the hospitalized patient informed of diagnosis, treatment, and prognosis, to instruct the patient fully regarding possible consequences and alternatives before obtaining consent for medical procedures, to honor a patient's refusal to consent to treatment to the extent permitted by law, to protect the patient's right to confidentiality and privacy from physicians and staff not involved in his or her case, and to instruct the patient of his or her care requirements after discharge. These standards represent a significant departure from the traditional paternalism prevailing in the patient–physician relationship.

Still, the Patient's Bill of Rights was generated by a professionally dominated group. On some issues, such as informed consent, it actually incorporates traditional paternalistic exception clauses that might be rejected by those emphasizing the rights of patients. Other bills of rights have been developed such as those for nursing home patients, the mentally retarded, children, and other vulnerable groups. It is not clear how the statements of these documents are to be sanctioned, since no mechanisms of enforcement are specified.

Conclusion

The difficulties that confront professional leaders, patients, surrogates, and public policymakers who undertake the establishment of ethical standards on new issues reflect the conflicts in fundamental values inherent in diverse views of medical ethics. The traditional professional ethics of physicians places great emphasis on the virtue of benevolence and the physician's responsibilities to serve the patient. This tradition honors the individuality of the patient–physician relationship, professional secrecy, and the physician's duty to promote the patient's welfare. In these and other matters, ethical formulations by physicians have been paternalistic, making the physician the dominant party in determining which action will best further both the physician's and the patient's interests. Codes prepared by interests outside the medical profession (including those written by religious and governmental bodies) have advanced other philosophical tenets as foundations for medical ethics. Some of these codes have focused on justice or equity in allocating resources. This has resulted in mounting ethical confusion as physicians become subject to competing ethical authorities with conflicting standards.

Responsibility for the development of ethical guidelines relative to the physician–patient relationship may be shifting from the physician to the society as a whole. In those contingencies not anticipated by accepted guidelines, the responsibility for ethical criteria rests partly with the individual physician, partly with patients, and partly with society's general ethical standards. Future success in the use of codes to control medical practice may well depend on an accommodation of the ethical norms of physicians with those of the larger society.

ROBERT M. VEATCH (1995)

SEE ALSO: *Abortion; Advertising; Confidentiality; Death, Definition and Determination Of; Double Effect; Informed Consent; Judaism, Bioethics in; Life; Life Sustaining Treatments and Euthanasia; Medical Ethics, History of; Patients' Rights; Professional-Patient Relationship; Profession and Professional Ethics; Race and Racism; Research, Human: Historical Aspects;* and other *Medical Codes and Oaths* subentries

BIBLIOGRAPHY

[*The bibliography for this article and its companion article can be found following the companion article.*]

II. ETHICAL ANALYSIS

The following is a revision and update of the first-edition article "Codes of Medical Ethics: Ethical Analysis" by the same author.

Codes, oaths, and prayers of medical ethics have emerged over the centuries from disparate sources, representing disparate societies, time periods, organizations, and perspectives. It is not surprising that they differ significantly in style and content. This article will examine systemically the ethical content of this divergent collection of documents from the earliest to contemporary times. In the Appendix, the reader will find the texts of codes and additional bibliography of codes and commentaries on codes for ethics of the medical and other health professions.

Ethical analysis of the codes of medical ethics creates problems. Such codes are not fully developed, systemic theories of medical ethics. On the other hand, the codes, at least the modern ones, are normally the product of much discussion, debate, and review. These codes, along with the historical documents that have had lasting significance, can reasonably be expected to reflect the basic ethical views of the organizations that have endorsed them.

When one turns to the substance of the codes, especially the codes written by physicians, one can identify what might be called a central ethical obligation, a basic principle that provides the physician with a core moral stance for resolving ethical dilemmas. Striking features are the presence of contradictions among the codes and the controversial nature of these central ethics.

Hippocratic Oath

Modern Western medical ethics has reiterated the central ethic of the Hippocratic oath into the twentieth century. The core ethic of the Hippocratic oath is the physician's pledge to do what he or she thinks will benefit the patient. This is repeated twice in the oath, once as applied to matters of diet, and once when referring to visits to the homes of patients.

The principle that the physician's first obligation is to do what the individual physician thinks will benefit the sick person is picked up in the Declaration of Geneva, where the physician swears, "The health of my patient will be my first consideration," and in the International Code of Medical

Ethics of the World Medical Association (WMA), which proclaims, "A physician shall owe his patients complete loyalty and all the resources of his science." Likewise, the postcommunist Russian oath has the physician pledge, in Hippocratic fashion, to work always for the patient's good (Solemn Oath of a Physician of Russia).

THE HIPPOCRATIC OATH'S INDIVIDUALISM. The first characteristic of the Hippocratic ethic is that it is individualistic; it concentrates only on the benefit to the individual patient. In contrast, classical utilitarian ethics of the tradition of Jeremy Bentham (1748–1832), John Stuart Mill (1806–1873), and G. E. Moore (1873–1958) would consider such a narrow focus on consequences for the patient to be ethically unjustified, unless it would serve the greater good of the greater number in the long run. They would consider benefits to all persons and to society as a whole. There is no evidence that the Hippocratic authors or their twentieth-century counterparts had such an indirect utilitarianism in mind. Rather, they seem to hold that the physician has a special ethical obligation to benefit his or her patient, independent of the net consequences for others who are not patients. The real test comes in cases in which the physician believes that one course will produce the most good in total, but another course will most benefit the patient. A physician who feels required to choose the course most beneficial to the patient is faithfully following the oath and rejecting the utilitarian alternative.

The American Medical Association (AMA), in its 1957 Principles of Medical Ethics, did not accept the Hippocratic individualism. It instructs the AMA physician that "the principle objective of the medical profession is to render service to humanity." The tenth principle made this interpretation unambiguous:

> The honored ideals of the medical profession imply that the responsibilities of the physician extend not only to the individual, but also to society where these responsibilities deserve his interest and participation in activities which have the purpose of improving both the health and the well-being of the individual and the community.

This focus on the community continued in the major revision of 1980. The last principle of that version is, "A physician shall recognize a responsibility to participate in activities contributing to an improved community" (American Medical Association, 1989, p. ix).

Here the AMA is closer to the now-abandoned Soviet physicians' oath of 1971 than to the Oath of Hippocrates. The Soviet physician more boldly swore "to work conscientiously wherever the interests of society will require it" and "to conduct all my actions according to the principles of the Communistic morale, to always keep in mind the high calling of the Soviet physician, and the high responsibility I have to my people and to the Soviet government." By contrast, the postcommunist Russian oath reverts to the pure Hippocratic focus on the good of the individual patient, abandoning any reference to the interests of the community or state (Solemn Oath of a Physician of Russia). The Criteria for Medical Ethics of the Ministry of Health of the People's Republic of China (1989) are actually closer to the postcommunist Russian oath and its Hippocratic ancestors by focusing on the interests of the patient. It lacks any appeal to the duty of the physician to the community that is seen in the AMA and the Soviet oaths.

THE HIPPOCRATIC OATH'S PATERNALISM. The central ethic of the Hippocratic tradition is also paternalistic. The physician is to benefit his or her patient "according to my ability and judgement" (Edelstein, 1943, p. 3).

Addressing the meaning of the injunction to protect the patient from mischief and injustice, Edelstein concludes that the oath means that "the physician must protect his patient from the mischief and injustice which he may inflict upon himself if his diet is not properly chosen" (Edelstein, 1943, p. 24).

This paternalism is also seen in the provision of the Hippocratic oath that medical knowledge is to be kept secret and not disclosed to people outside the Hippocratic group. A similar provision is seen in a sixteenth-century Japanese medical code called the Seventeen Rules of Enjuin, which actually required that, if a successor trained in the School of Enjuin could not be found upon retirement or death, the medical books of the school had to be returned to the school.

Physicians, according to Percival (1740–1804) (who also shared in this Hippocratic paternalism), should study not only tenderness and steadiness but also "condescension and authority, as to inspire the minds of their patients with gratitude, respect, and confidence" (Leake, p. 71). The AMA principles of 1957 and the 1959 British Medical Association (BMA) codes held that medical confidences could be broken if, in the judgment of the physician, it was in the patient's interest for them to be broken.

THE HIPPOCRATIC OATH'S FOCUS ON CONSEQUENCES. Finally, one sees the controversy of the Hippocratic patient-benefiting ethic when it is contrasted with other theories that can be called nonconsequentialist, that is, ethical theories in which certain principles are taken to be simply inherently right-making or where certain claims are taken to be "inalienable rights." Holders of views in which there are certain characteristics of actions that make them inherently tend toward being right (other things being equal) or holders of the view that certain things, such as life, liberty, and the pursuit of happiness, are "inalienable rights" would have to reject the ethic of doing what one thinks will benefit the patient. At least they would reject patient benefit in cases where benefiting the patient will be at the expense of fulfilling prima facie duties or respecting basic rights of the patient.

There may be a paradox in the Hippocratic oath. The physician is to do what he or she thinks will benefit the patient but is not to give an abortive remedy or a deadly drug and is not to "use the knife, not even on sufferers from stone." What is the physician to do who believes that giving a deadly drug or an abortifacient remedy, or using the knife, will benefit the patient? Perhaps this apparent contradiction is resolved by the belief of the Pythagorean physician that such actions can never be beneficial to the patient. In that case, the oath simply spells out some rules that guide the physician in deciding what will be beneficial. More likely, however, these actions are seen as inherently wrong even if they might be of benefit. If so, then the Hippocratic ethic abandons its consequentialism, at least for these cases.

Codes Written by Groups Outside the Medical Profession

Many of the more recent codes written by governmental and religious groups have not shown these characteristics of individualism, paternalism, and consequentialism. The Nuremberg Code (1947), one of the first codes relevant to medical ethics emerging in international law, could have addressed the problem of abuse of human subjects in medical research by retreating to Hippocratic individualism, thus making all use of subjects for purposes of gaining knowledge immoral (because, by definition, doing something for the pursuit of general knowledge is not acting for the purpose of benefiting the patient). It did not. Instead it acknowledged the legitimacy of physician participation in efforts to benefit society by doing research on human subjects. It introduced protections for those subjects by abandoning the exclusive focus on consequences—on producing benefits and avoiding harms—and replacing it with an ethic that speaks in terms of duties and responsibilities, including the duty to ensure that the subjects give their informed consent.

Other codes coming from governmental and religious sources adopted the language of rights as a way of signaling their break with the professional medical ethical traditions that focus exclusively on consequences. This focus on rights is influenced heavily by the tradition of the liberal political philosophy of John Locke, Thomas Hobbes, Jean Jacques Rousseau, and the authors of the Bill of Rights of the United States Constitution. It is a moral tradition significantly different from that of the traditional, professionally written medical codes.

The focus on rights and duties includes an emphasis on the right to give informed and voluntary consent not only for research but for all clinical, medical treatments. Consent, grounded in the moral principle of autonomy and the legal notion of self-determination, is totally absent from the classical codes written by medical professional groups. The introduction of the perspective of rights and duties, and the underlying moral notion of respect for persons (including the principle of autonomy), signals a rejection of both traditional Hippocratic paternalism and consequentialism. It also provides a way of moving away from pure individualism, incorporating a more social ethic without lapsing into a social utilitarianism that would completely subordinate the individual to the aggregate social good.

The first healthcare association that used the language of rights was the International Council of Nurses' Code for Nurses (1973, reaffirmed 1989). Still using gender-specific language, it nevertheless signaled a revolution in the philosophical orientation of professional codes when it said, "Inherent in nursing is respect for life, dignity and rights of man." This use of "rights" language also appeared in the American Nurses' Association (ANA) code revision in 1976, when it proclaimed (with more gender-neutral language), "Each client has the moral right to determine what will be done with his/her person." By making self-determination of clients its first principle, the ANA announced it was the first organization of healthcare professionals to abandon Hippocratic paternalism and exclusive focus on consequences. However, ambivalence persists; after announcing that self-determination is its first principle, it says that "the nurse's primary commitment is to the health, welfare, and safety of the client" (American Nurses' Association, 1985, p. 6). At this juncture, the nursing profession seemed unable to decide whether to abandon Hippocratic paternalism in favor of respect for rights of self-determination or remain Hippocratic.

The AMA followed this pattern in its 1980 revision. It begins to use rights language saying, "A physician shall respect the rights of patients, of colleagues, and of other health professionals" (American Medical Association, 1989, p. ix). It commits the physician for the first time to deal honestly with patients, reversing the long-standing, more paternalistic approach in which physicians were expected to withhold information when they believed it might harm the patient. Yet, it still proclaims the Hippocratic notion that the AMA's ethical statements are developed "primarily for the benefit of the patient," and not, apparently, to protect the patient's rights.

Specific Ethical Injunctions

The strictures against abortion, euthanasia, and surgery in the Hippocratic oath are examples of specific injunctions that occur from time to time in the codes and oaths of medical and physician ethics. Code-by-code comparison of these injunctions reveals interesting differences. The conflict among the codes on the question of confidentiality is perhaps the most dramatic.

CONFIDENTIALITY. The Hippocratic injunction on breaking confidentiality is sometimes taken to forbid breaking medical confidences. The text is really much more ambiguous. It says, "Whatever I may see or hear in the course of treatment in regard to the life of men, which on no account one must speak abroad, I will keep to myself holding such things shameful to be spoken about." The individual physician, however, is left with the question of just which things he or she hears "on no account must be spoken abroad." Possibly physicians are to use the "patient-benefiting" criterion for deciding when breaking the confidence is appropriate. That was the explicit principle in the 1959 version of the BMA code, which said:

> The complications of modern life sometimes create difficulties for the doctor in the application of this principle of confidentiality, and on certain occasions it may be necessary to acquiesce in some modification. Always, however, the overriding consideration must be the adoption of a line of conduct that will benefit the patient, or protect his interests.

The World Medical Association's International Code of Medical Ethics (1949, amended 1968 and 1983) and the Declaration of Geneva (1948, amended 1968 and 1983) both close any such patient-benefiting loophole in the confidentiality principle. They simply require "absolute secrecy," much as did the ancient Jewish Oath of Asaph. No exception is considered even in a case where the physician has learned that the patient is about to commit mass murder. The Ethical and Religious Directives for Catholic Health Facilities (1975) is almost as blunt. It requires that

> professional secrecy must be carefully fulfilled not only as regards the information on the patient's charts and records but also as regards confidential matters learned in the exercise of professional duties.

In keeping with their more social commitment to the welfare of others as well as the patient, the now outdated 1957 American Medical Association Principles (1957, revised 1971), and the American Psychiatric Association's (1973), which were based on them, were quite explicit in providing three exceptions to the general principle of confidentiality:

> A physician may not reveal the confidences entrusted to him in the course of medical attendance, or the deficiencies he may observe in the character of his patients, unless he is required to do so by law or unless it becomes necessary in order to protect the welfare of the individual or of the society.

Confidences could be broken not only when the physician thought it would benefit the patient but also when he or she thought it would benefit society or when it was required by law, for example, informing the police of a bullet wound incurred in a crime. The ethical problem of such broad exceptions, of course, is not only the paternalism of the patient-benefiting exclusion but also the potential subordination of the patient's interests and rights to the interests of the society.

The BMA was confronted by a particularly difficult case in which the physician disclosed to the parents of a sixteen-year-old that she was taking birth-control pills. He defended the breaking of the confidence on the grounds that he thought it was for her benefit. Since this was explicitly permitted by the BMA code at the time, the General Medical Council acquitted him of the charge of unprofessional conduct. After that case, the BMA in 1971 amended its confidentiality principle and became the first to recognize the patient's right to confidence in cases where the patient and the physician disagreed. The new position stated that "if, in the opinion of the doctor, disclosure of confidential information to a third party seems to be in the best medical interest of the patient, it is the doctor's duty to make every effort to allow the information to be given to the third party, but where the patient refuses, that refusal must be respected."

However, in the years that followed, the BMA's position seems to have reverted to a modified version of the old policy permitting disclosures "if it is in the patient's own interest that information should be disclosed but it is either impossible, or medically undesirable in the patient's own interest, to seek his consent" (British Medical Association, 1988, p. 21). The BMA also has added a provision permitting disclosure for social purposes when it is necessary to safeguard the national interest or when the doctor has an "overriding duty to society."

ABORTION. On the controversial subject of abortion, groups authoring codes have followed the ethical stances of their subcultures. The Hippocratic oath follows the Pythagorean prohibition on abortion, even though abortion was not considered unethical in the broader Greek culture (Edelstein, 1943). In the Oath of Asaph, the early medieval Jewish medical initiate is instructed, "Do not prepare any potion that may cause a woman who has conceived in adultery to miscarry." The 1975 Ethical and Religious Directives for (U.S.) Catholic Health Facilities follow, consciously and precisely, a traditional, theological explanation of official church teaching, devoting seven of forty-three principles to the subject. Directly intended termination of pregnancy before viability is never permitted nor is the directly intended destruction of a viable fetus. Treatments not intended to terminate a pregnancy but which nonetheless have that effect are permitted, provided there is a proportionately serious pathological condition of the mother and the treatments cannot be safely postponed until after the fetus is viable.

When the cultural base of the group writing the code is very broad, the code is predictably less specific about the ethics of abortion. The Declaration of Geneva said, "I will maintain the utmost respect for human life from the time of conception," without directly prohibiting abortion. Its 1983 revision softened the position even further, changing "from the time of conception" to "from its beginning" (Declaration of Geneva, 1948, amended 1968 and 1983). The WMA's International Code in its draft, but not in its finally adopted form, stated, "Therapeutic abortion may only be performed if the conscience of the doctors and the national laws permit." The American Nurses' Association (ANA), which also represents individuals with a wide variety of viewpoints, similarly avoids direct comments. In its code, revised in 1968 and in effect prior to the 1976 revision, the ANA says that "the nurse's respect for the worth and dignity of the individual human being extends throughout the entire life cycle, from *birth* to death" (italics added). The implication may be that fetal life is not included. A 1966 statement approved by the ANA Board of Directors recognizes "the right of individuals and families to select and use such methods for family planning as are consistent with their own creeds and mores," again appealing to individual conscience. Is the combined implication a toleration of the nurse's participation in abortion?

EUTHANASIA. An explicit obligation to preserve life is strikingly absent from the codes of ethics, both professional and public. In light of a widely held view that the duty, or one of the duties, of the physician is to preserve life, one would expect to find this duty emphasized. The only explicit, well-known reference is the weak formulation in the International Code (1949, amended 1968 and 1983), which says that "a physician shall always bear in mind the obligation of preserving human life." This obligation to "bear in mind" rather than explicitly attempt to preserve life is a very soft injunction, especially when combined with the patient-benefiting principle the code emphasizes.

Proscribing active killing is much more common in the codes, as might be expected from the general ethical prohibition on active killing, even for mercy, in many cultures and subcultures. The Hippocratic oath's formula is, "I will neither give a deadly drug to anybody if asked for it, nor will I make a suggestion to this effect." Interpretation of this prohibition is controversial. Some take it to forbid any criminal, malevolent homicide. What seems more likely, however, is a prohibition against merciful killing or assisting in suicide. While suicide, especially in the face of medical suffering, was not uncommon in ancient society, it was forbidden by the Pythagorean cult. This fact is cited by Edelstein in his defense of the hypothesis that the Hippocratic oath is a Pythagorean document (1943). According to the *Caraka Samhita,* acts "causing another's death" were one of the few things the Indian medical student should not do at his teacher's behest. The oath of Asaph instructs the Jewish medical student to "take heed that you not kill any man with a root decoction."

In the professionally written codes or those of the Catholic church, however, the prohibition against assisting in an act of killing has never been extended to apply to cooperating in withdrawal from treatment. The distinction between active killing and withdrawal of certain treatments is clear in the Ethical and Religious Directives for Catholic Health Facilities, according to which "the directly intended termination of any patient's life, even at his own request, is always morally wrong," and "euthanasia ('mercy killing') in all its forms is forbidden." The directives go on, however, to say that while "failure to supply the ordinary means of preserving life is equivalent to euthanasia … neither the physician nor the patient is obliged to use extraordinary means." Nor is it considered euthanasia "to give a dying person sedatives or analgesics for the alleviation of pain, when such a measure is judged necessary, even though they may deprive the patient of the use of reason, or shorten his life."

The AMA states in its Judicial Council Opinions that "the physician should not intentionally cause death" (American Medical Association, 1989, p. 13). At the same time, it acknowledges the legitimacy of forgoing life-sustaining treatment in accord with the preferences of the patient or surrogate. The postcommunist Russian oath, following the original Hippocratic language, commits the Russian physician never to give a deadly drug.

The distinction between active killing and forgoing treatment is made clearer when rights language is used, as in A Patient's Bill of Rights (1973), written under the auspices of the American Hospital Association. That document proclaims that "the patient has the right to refuse treatment to the extent permitted by law," presumably even if the result will be the death of the patient. However, there is clearly no corresponding right to drugs that will actively hasten death.

TRUTH-TELLING. One conspicuous conflict between the patient-benefiting principle and the more deontological ethical theories is over the question of what one ought to tell a dying patient. Historically, many of the professional codes are simply silent, presumably expecting the patient-benefiting principle to apply. The Indian oath of the *Caraka Samhita* is explicit: "Even knowing that the patient's span of life has come to its close, it shall not be mentioned by thee there, where if so done, it would cause shock to the patient or to others." The 1847 version of the AMA code instructs: "A physician should not be forward to make gloomy prognostications … but he should not fail, on proper occasions, to give to the friends of the patient timely notice of danger, when it really occurs; and even to the patient himself, if absolutely necessary." The violation of confidentiality in communicating to family or friends before informing patients either is not noticed or is justified on patient-benefiting grounds. Using the patient-benefiting principle as a basis for withholding the truth is traditional in professional physician ethics. The 1847 code makes the grounding explicit: "It is, therefore, a sacred duty … to avoid all things [that] have a tendency to discourage the patient and to depress his spirits."

The latent paternalism that justifies withholding information from patients for their own good is retained even in the period after 1980 when the AMA principles themselves pledge unqualified honesty. In the AMA Council on Ethical and Judicial Affairs' interpretation, an exception can be made to the requirement of informed consent "when risk-disclosure poses such a serious psychological threat of detriment to the patient as to be medically contraindicated" (American Medical Association, 1989, p. 32).

Even the authors of "A Patient's Bill of Rights" seem to yield to the paternalistic patient-benefiting principle when it conflicts with the patient's right to know. The bill first states that "the patient has the right to obtain from his physician complete current information concerning his diagnosis, treatment, and prognosis in terms the patient can be reasonably expected to understand." But it then qualifies this by stating, "When it is not medically advisable to give such information to the patient, the information should be made available to the appropriate person in his behalf." The

potential conflicts of such an exception with the right to privacy or the right to receive information necessary for informed consent are not discussed. By contrast, U.S. courts and many codes generated outside the Hippocratic tradition insist that information be adequate for the patient to make a self-determining choice, even if that information is potentially upsetting.

JUSTICE IN DELIVERING HEALTHCARE. Many of the codes of physician and other medical ethics have some reference to the duty to deliver healthcare justly or equitably. The Hippocratic oath uses a term, *adiki'e,* often translated into English as "justice," but it really means "wrongdoing" more generally; it does not refer to equality of treatment or equitable distribution of benefits. The statement in the Hippocratic oath that physicians must abstain from sexual relations with males and females, free and slave, during a medical visit is as close as the text comes to a pledge of equal treatment.

The ancient Chinese medical ethical codes are much more far-reaching in emphasizing equal treatment of rich and poor. The commandments written by Chen Shi-Kung, a seventeenth-century physician, include the explicit commitment that "physicians should be ever ready to respond to any calls of patients, high or low, rich or poor."

Equality of access seems generally recognized as an ideal in many modern codes even if it is absent in the Hippocratic original. The twentieth-century Declaration of Geneva holds forth this ideal: "I will not permit considerations of religion, nationality, race, party politics, or social standing to intervene between my duty and my patient." The American Nurses' Association code declares, "The nurse provides services with respect for the dignity of man, unrestricted by considerations of nationality, race, creed, color, or status." The AMA recognizes that society must make decisions regarding the allocation of limited healthcare resources and urges that they be allocated on the basis of "fair, socially acceptable, and humane criteria." At the same time, it emphasizes that the physician's duty is "to do all that he can for the benefit of his individual patient" (American Medical Association, 1989, p. 3). The postcommunist Russian oath, by contrast, pledges never to deny medical assistance to anybody and to provide care with equal diligence to patients regardless of means or national or religious affiliation.

The Ethics of Professional Relations

In contrast with the lay or public codes or bills of rights, virtually all professional codes devote significant attention to relationships among professionals. The Hippocratic oath begins with a covenant by which the new physician pledges "to hold him who has taught me this art as equal to my parents and to live my life in partnership with him, and if he is in need of money to give him a share of mine, and to regard his offspring as equal to my brothers in male lineage and to take them this art—if they desire to learn it—without fee and covenant." It includes a pledge to keep secrets, much as any initiation ritual into a cult might.

The longest of the three sections of the AMA code of 1847 is devoted to "the duties of physicians to each other and to the profession at large." Since many of the codes emerged at a point historically when the profession was separating itself from others claiming to offer treatments and cures, there is often, even to modern times, strong language forbidding association with those not properly members of the group. The American Osteopathic Association, for instance, requires that a physician "shall practice in accordance with the body of systemized knowledge related to the healing arts and shall avoid professional association with individuals or organizations which do not practice or conduct organization affairs in accordance with such knowledge."

In terms of the sociology of the professions, it has been suggested that restraints on advertising, rules structuring referral of patients, instruction on the ways of handling an incompetent member of the profession, or exclusion of those not properly initiated into the profession have important functions in maintaining the professional monopoly. Apart from their role in protecting professional interests, however, it is also pertinent to analyze them as sets of ethical obligations.

Three different kinds of ethical arguments may underlie the detailed formulations of professional obligations to other professionals. First, such duties to one's colleagues may be defended on what could be called "universal" grounds. That would be the case if the ethical principles claimed as the foundation of such intraprofessional obligations are principles generally recognized by all persons. For instance, the AMA code of 1847 states detailed rules regarding professional consultation prohibiting "exclusion from fellowship" of duly licensed practitioners and requiring punctuality in visits of physicians when they hold consultations as well as secrecy and confidentiality so that the patient will not be aware of consultants' disagreements. These standards for consultation are defended on the grounds that "the good of the patient is the sole object in view." Although it is not generally argued, there is a presumption that rational patients should accept this principle. We have seen, however, that the principle of patient benefit is quite controversial when put up against competing ethical principles.

A second foundation for intraprofessional duties might be a special ethic for a special group, which nonmembers would not be expected to share or even understand. This would be the case, for example, if the profession is viewed as a kind of club or fraternity that invents its own norms and applies them only to its own members. The ethic of a profession is in part the ethic of fraternal loyalty, of special obligation to one's adopted brothers. The professional obligation may be seen deriving from the professional nexus rather than from some more universal source. It is a special ethic of a special cult.

The ethic of the AMA's 1847 code, like the ethic of the code written by Percival, is an ethic of dignity and honor among gentlemen: "There is no profession, from the members of which greater purity of character and a higher standard of moral excellence are required, than the medical." The discussion of duties of physicians to each other begins with the admonition that "every individual, entering the profession, as he becomes thereby entitled to all its privileges and immunities, incurs an obligation to exert his best abilities to maintain its dignity and honor, to exalt its standing, and to extend the bound of its usefulness." The text goes on to entreat the physician to avoid "all contumelious and sarcastic remarks relative to the faculty, as a body; and while by unwearied diligence, he resorts to every honorable means of enriching the science, he should entertain a due respect for his seniors, who have, by their labors, brought it to the elevated condition in which he finds it."

This gentlemanly ethic of honor and purity (the Hippocratic phrase is "purity and holiness") gives rise to special ethical burdens for the medical profession that the layperson cannot be expected to grasp. Professional "courtesy" (gratuitous services for practitioners, their wives, and their children) should probably be understood in these terms. "Courtesy" is an ethical expectation for members of the brotherhood.

A third possible foundation confounds the two. It could be that professional duties are defended as being in the public interest (or in some other manner consistent with a more universal ethic), but that only members of the profession can be expected to understand this to be so. Advertising, for instance, could be attacked, as it is in the AMA's 1847 code, as "derogatory to the dignity of the profession," but it is defended as necessary to separate the profession from "the ordinary practices of empirics." The authors might well hold that it is really in the public interest that the separation be made, but also concede that only members of the profession could see the necessity of that separation.

If there are special ethical obligations for members of the profession that in principle cannot be recognized from outside the professional group, it follows that there are likely to be conflicts between the profession's formulation of its ethical obligation and the broader public's formulation. The issue is not the existence of different ethical responsibilities attaching to different roles, but rather a disagreement between the profession and the broader public over what constitutes the proper behavior of the professional in his or her specific professional role. Even if a profession agrees that it has a special duty to preserve life or limit advertising, it is still an open question whether the public wants physicians always to act on that norm. If the professional group holds that there is a special professional source of norms, then conflict is predictable.

A specific example of such conflict involves the ethics of advertising. Many professional codes, in the manner of the 1847 AMA code, prohibit or restrict advertising by members of the profession. The 1957 Principles of Medical Ethics of the AMA claim that "this principle protects the public from the advertiser and salesman of medical care by establishing an easily discernible and generally recognized distinction between him and the ethical physician." While such prohibitions on advertising might be seen as the behavior of a cartel restraining price competition, it is also possible that physicians really believe that they are engaged in a service that must not be peddled as a commodity. Whether the medical profession sees such advertising as unethical or not, the public may see restraint on advertising as unethical. At stake are not only two different perceptions of ways to maximize benefits to potential patients, but also two sources of ethical norms—one from within the professional nexus and the other from the broader society. In this regard, an important transition occurred when the committee responsible for the 1980 revision of the AMA principles acknowledged that increasingly the public will be determining the norms for moral conduct in the lay–professional relationship.

Conclusion

The codes, oaths, prayers, and bills of rights derive from disparate contexts, representing differing professional groups, public agencies, and private, lay organizations such as churches and patients' groups. It is not surprising that radically different ethical conclusions are reached and that they are based on radically different fundamental ethical theories and methods of ethical reasoning.

One critical problem faced by health professionals as well as laypeople is what ethical directives should be decisive when an individual professes identification with more than one group. A health professional may also be a member of a religious or cultural group that has an ethical framework relevant to the moral problems faced by the individual. For example, if the ANA position can be interpreted as endorsing the nurse's tolerance of a woman's right to choose abortion, what is the Catholic nurse to do, or what is a nurse who works in a Catholic health facility to do if he or she believes in the right of the individual to select methods for family planning? These conflicts for individuals who are simultaneously members of more than one group, each of which has authored a code, arise for many ethical issues in healthcare. Moreover, individuals may reach conclusions of conscience that fail to conform to any codes of ethics whether written by healthcare professions or by religious, cultural, or governmental groups. An active understanding of the ethical differences among these codes is needed to begin developing a response.

ROBERT M. VEATCH (1995)

SEE ALSO: *Abortion; Autonomy; Beneficence; Confidentiality; Competence; Human Dignity; Medical Ethics, History of; Principalism; Profession and Professional Ethics; Virtue and Character;* and other *Medical Codes and Oaths* subentries

BIBLIOGRAPHY

Baker, Robert. 1993. "The History of Medical Ethics." In *Companion Encyclopedia of the History of Medicine,* pp. 852–887, ed. W. F. Bynum and Roy Porter. London: Routledge & Kegan Paul.

Baker, Robert; Porter, Dorothy; and Porter, Roy, eds. 1993. *The Codification of Medical Morality: Historical and Philosophical Studies of the Formalization of Western Medical Morality in the Eighteenth and Nineteenth Centuries.* Dordrecht, Netherlands: Kluwer Academic Publishers.

Carrick, Paul. 1985. *Medical Ethics in Antiquity: Philosophical Perspectives on Abortion and Euthanasia.* Dordrecht, Netherlands: D. Reidel.

Clark, George. 1964. *A History of the Royal College of Physicians of London.* Oxford: Clarendon Press.

Dickstein, Emil; Erlen, Jonathan; and Erlen, Judith. 1991. "Ethical Principles Contained in Currently Professed Medical Oaths." *Academic Medicine* 66(10): 622–624.

Edelstein, Ludwig. 1943. "The Hippocratic Oath: Text, Translation, and Interpretation." *Bulletin of the History of Medicine,* supp. 5(1): 1–64.

Edelstein, Ludwig. 1956. "The Professional Ethics of the Greek Physician." *Bulletin of the History of Medicine* 30(5): 391–419.

Etziony, M. B. 1973. *The Physician's Creed: An Anthology of Medical Prayers, Oaths, and Codes of Ethics Written by Medical Practitioners Through the Ages.* Springfield, IL: Charles C. Thomas.

Griese, Orville. 1987. "Origin and Development of a Catholic Hospital Code of Ethics, 1921–1971." In *Catholic Identity in Health Care: Principles and Practice,* pp. 1–19. Braintree, MA: Pope John Center.

Jakobovits, Immanuel. 1975. *Jewish Medical Ethics: A Comparative and Historical Study of the Jewish Religious Attitudes to Medicine and Its Practice,* new edition. New York: Bloch.

Jones, William H. S. 1924. *The Doctor's Oath: An Essay in the History of Medicine.* Cambridge: Cambridge University Press.

Kelly, David F. 1979. *The Emergence of Roman Catholic Medical Ethics in North America: An Historical-Methodological-Bibliographical Study.* New York: Edwin Mellen Press.

Leake, Chauncey D., ed. 1927. *Percival's Medical Ethics.* Baltimore: Williams and Wilkins.

Menon, I. A., and Haberman, H. F. 1970. "The Medical Students' Oath of Ancient India." *Medical History* 14(3): 295–299.

National Commission for the Protection of Human Subjects of Biomedical and Behavioral Research. 1978. *The Belmont Report: Ethical Principles and Guidelines for the Protection of Human Subjects of Research.* Washington, D.C.: U.S. Government Printing Office.

Rosner, Fred. 1967. "The Physician's Prayer Attributed to Moses Maimonides." *Bulletin of the History of Medicine* 41: 440–454.

Rosner, Fred, and Muntner, Sussman. 1965. "The Oath of Asaph." *Annals of Internal Medicine* 63(2): 317–320.

Sacred Congregation for the Doctrine of the Faith. 1987. "Instruction on Respect for Human Life in Its Origin and on the Dignity of Procreation." *Origins* 16(40): 698–711.

Temkin, Owsei. 1991. *Hippocrates in a World of Pagans and Christians.* Baltimore: Johns Hopkins University Press.

Tichtchenko, Pavel D., and Yudin, Boris G. 1992. "Toward a Bioethics in Post-Communist Russia." *Cambridge Quarterly of Healthcare Ethics* 1(4): 295–303.

Unschuld, Paul Ulrich. 1979. *Medical Ethics in Imperial China: A Study in Historical Anthropology.* Berkeley: University of California Press.

Veatch, Robert M., and Mason, Carol G. 1987. "Hippocratic vs. Judeo-Christian Medical Ethics: Principles in Conflict." *Journal of Religious Ethics* 15(1): 86–105.

MEDICAL EDUCATION

• • •

When this subject was addressed in the first edition of this encyclopedia, the paucity of systematic analyses of the ethical issues peculiar to medical education was underscored (Pellegrino, 1978). In recent years, this deficiency has gradually been redressed, so that today, a considerable body of literature is available. This entry is therefore a substantial revision of the first. The emphasis has shifted from underlying values to more specific, normative issues, particularly in clinical education.

Ethical issues arise in medical education because of the special societal role of medical schools, the necessary intermingling of patient care with education, and the conflicts that may arise because of the obligations among students, patients, faculty members, and society. Similar ethical issues are present in the education of nurses, dentists, and the allied health professions.

The Social Mandate of Medical Schools

Medical schools occupy a unique moral position in society. They are mandated to meet society's need for a continuous supply of competent practitioners who can care for the sick and promote the public's health. For this reason, medical schools are supported as loci for the advancement and transmission of medical knowledge and are granted authority to select who shall study medicine, what shall be studied, and what standards of performance shall be established.

To achieve these goals, medical schools require certain special privileges, for example, to dissect human bodies, to provide "hands on" practical experience for students in the care of sick people, and to conduct human experimentation. These practices would be criminal were they not socially mandated for a good purpose. When medical schools, students, and faculty avail themselves of these privileges, they enter an implicit covenant with society to use them for the purposes for which they are granted.

To fulfill this social covenant, medical schools and their faculties must perform a tripartite function with respect to medical knowledge: 1) they must preserve, validate, and expand it by research; 2) transmit it to the next generation by teaching; and 3) apply it by practice in the care of the sick. However, these three functions have different aims. The aim of research is truth that requires dedication to objectivity, freedom of inquiry, rigorous design, as well as peer review and publication. The aim of teaching is learning that requires dedication to student welfare, competent pedagogy, and opportunities for students to practice their skills. The aim of practice is the welfare of the patient that requires dedication to compassion, competence, and ethical concern for the vulnerability, dignity, and autonomy of the sick person.

In the past, these three functions were less often in conflict with each other than they are today. This conflict is the result of several factors in the evolution of medical education since the late nineteenth century. The first factor is the realization of the power of the physical and biological sciences to advance medical knowledge and their integration into medical education. Second is the incorporation of teaching hospitals into medical schools for the clinical education of medical students (Flexner). Third is the increasing reliance on practice income to support salaries of medical teachers. Previously, teachers had been self-supporting practitioners from the community, while only a few were university-funded full-time teachers. Today's "tenure track" clinical faculty member is expected to excel in research, to support himself or herself financially through practice and overhead cost recovery from grants, and to teach at the bedside. Each function has its own legitimacy, but taken together, these functions conflict with each other.

Ethical Obligations of Medical Schools

The ethical obligations of medical schools as societal entities are defined in terms of the constituencies they serve: society, faculty, student body, and patients (Pellegrino, 1976).

Medical schools have been granted a virtual monopoly over the number of students they admit and the number of training places in the various specialties in teaching hospitals. Medical schools are the sole portal into the practice of the profession and, as a result, medical schools incur a responsibility to match the kind and number of physicians they produce with the needs of society. This requires a socially responsive appraisal by medical schools of the way resources are used and curricula are designed, as well as how faculty rewards are distributed. Societal aims sometimes can, and do, conflict with a medical school's pursuit of esteem among its peers, which usually comes not through renown in teaching or the quality of practitioners it produces, but excellence in producing research and academic leaders.

Another important obligation of medical schools is to ensure that graduates are competent to enter postgraduate training and are free of obvious traits of character that would make them dangerous practitioners. Today, most of those admitted to medical school graduate and obtain licenses. Few fail, particularly in the clinical years. This places an obligation on medical schools to evaluate not only a student's knowledge and skill, but some facets of his or her character as well. Close supervision by clinical teachers is mandatory if dubious character traits are to be detected. Educators must balance fairness in their evaluations of students against their obligations to protect future patients from unsafe or dishonest practitioners.

Another societal responsibility of medical schools is to ensure equal opportunity for admission to all qualified students. Despite early progress, there is recent evidence of retrenchment in the support, financial and otherwise, available for minority student recruitment in the United States and in Great Britain (Hanft and White; Esmail and Everington). Subtle forms of discrimination probably still exist in the interview process where it is difficult to detect and prove (Connolly). Gender discrimination and sexism are no longer legally tolerable, but remain a persistent social problem (Hostler and Gressard). Academic administrators and faculty members are morally obliged to ensure equitable treatment of all applicants and must assume collective responsibility for inequities and injustice. In doing so, medical schools must thread their way carefully through an ethical maze of competing claims for preferential treatment and reverse discrimination.

Ethical obligations exist in the relationship between medical schools and faculty members. Faculties are owed freedom of inquiry in research and teaching, justice in hiring, tenure, promotion, compensation, and redress for injury or grievances. Faculty members in turn are morally responsible for the quality of their instruction, for fairness in the evaluation of students, and for properly apportioning their time and effort between teaching and personally remunerative activities such as clinical practice and consultation. Imbalance among these activities compromises the societal responsibilities of a medical faculty.

Faculty and administration are therefore obligated to detect inadequate teachers and to rehabilitate and reassign them or terminate their appointments when necessary. Tenure is among the most privileged benefits of academic life. The obligation to use it responsibly rests squarely on faculty members and administrators.

Incidents of scientific fraud, abuse of consulting and travel privileges, and conflicts of interest are cause for legitimate public concern. While the number is small, such abuses by faculty members invite external limitations and regulation of privileges that can interfere with the educational mission. The ethics of medical academia cannot be a private matter since the moral behavior of academics affects students, patients, the use of public funds, and the quality of fulfillment of the medical school's covenant with society.

Some Ethical Issues Peculiar to Clinical Education

The ethical issues outlined thus far are particular only in part to medical education. What is unique is the medical school's engagement in clinical education, i.e., in providing "hands on" experience for students in the actual care of patients. It is here that serious conflict may arise between patient care and student learning.

Physicians since Hippocrates have taught their students from actual cases. Usually, this was accomplished by preceptorship with a practicing physician or by case demonstrations to entire classes of students. In the mid-nineteenth century, it was a rare school that incorporated more intimate involvement in the care of patients in its teaching (Ludmerer). Toward the end of the same century, William Osler involved students more directly as clinical clerks at the Johns Hopkins Hospital, where they " … lived and worked … as part of its machinery, as an essential part of the work of the wards" (Osler, p. 389). This practice lagged in other schools until the reform of education in 1910 (Ludmerer). Since then, however, it has become standard pedagogic practice.

Today, clinical education centers on practical experience under supervision at every level, from medical school through postgraduate specialty training to lifelong continuing education. Until recently, the merits of this training have been so much taken for granted that the ethical conflicts inherent in the process have been neglected (Fry; Pilowski).

Clinical education by its nature unavoidably puts the aims of caring for patients into potential conflict with the aims of teaching and learning. The involvement of medical students, interns, and residents in patient care slows the process of care, increases its discomforts and fragmentation, and, at times, poses significant danger to the patient. With close supervision by experienced clinical teachers, these potential conflicts are tolerable. The clinical teacher therefore carries a double responsibility for balancing the quality of his or her pedagogy with the quality of patient care.

The moral status of medical students is ambiguous. They are physicians in utero, that is, in a developmental state of competence to provide care. When they enter medical school they are laypersons. When they graduate they are physicians, still in need of further training before they can become safe and competent practitioners. During this process, they take on progressive degrees of responsibility associated with the privilege of caring for patients, although their capacity to fulfill that responsibility is limited.

Patients come to university hospitals primarily to receive optimal treatment, not to be subjects of teaching. They may understand in a general way what being in a teaching hospital means. This in no way suggests, as some assume, that patients give implicit consent to become "teaching material." Patients in teaching hospitals preserve their moral right to know the relative degrees of competence of those caring for them. They have a right to give informed consent to any procedures and to know whether an untrained or partially trained person will perform that procedure. When unskilled students participate in procedures, patients are owed appropriate supervision by someone of significantly greater competence who can protect their safety.

Medical students, therefore, should disclose the fact that they are students to avoid the attributions of knowledge and trust patients still associate with anyone bearing the title "doctor" (Greer; Ganos; Brody; Liepman). They should be introduced as students by their supervisors before procedures like spinal taps and chest taps are performed. For their part, students as well as their supervisors must thoroughly acquaint themselves with the procedures in question and must observe a sufficient number performed by experienced clinicians. Students are under an obligation to refrain from conducting a procedure until these requirements are met and to resist the "see one, do one" philosophy of some clinical teachers. They must also receive instruction on how to obtain a morally and legally valid consent (Johnson et al.).

Students must also be sensitive enough to discontinue even the simplest procedures, such as a venipuncture, if their efforts cause discomfort (Williams and Fost). These injunctions are particularly important in highly personal and sensitive situations such as learning to do vaginal or rectal examinations (Bewley et al.; and Lawton et al.).

Medical students also face problems of personal ethical integrity with respect to abortion, treating patients with acquired immunodeficiency syndrome (AIDS), and attitudes toward the poor (Christakis and Feudtner; Dans; Crandall et al.; Currey et al.; Holleman). They may observe unethical or unacceptable behavior of teachers or colleagues (Morris). The extent of their responsibility and the real possibility of punitive treatment if students "blow the whistle" is a difficult, unresolved, but genuine ethical issue. Students may cheat on exams or see others do so (Rozance; Stimmel). By virtue of their presence at the bedside as members of the "team," they may be drawn prematurely into advising about the ethics of other colleagues. Helping students to deal with these moral dilemmas poses a new challenge to students and to their clinical teachers. This is a crucial part of the ethical maturation of the student (Drew; Andre; Wiesemann).

Two final examples of recently debated ethical dilemmas center on the moral status of dead human bodies and of animals of other species similar to humans. To what extent may recently dead human bodies be used to teach intubation, resuscitation, and tracheostomy? Who can, or should, give permission? May it be presumed? Is it necessary at all (Benfield et al.; Iserson)? Are the moral rights of other animal species to be considered so that they never or rarely should be used in teaching or research? Do computer models or tissue and cell preparations adequately replace animal experimentation?

Conclusion

Despite the sanction society gives to clinical education, there are important ethical obligations that limit this privilege. In no sense can learning by practice be a "right" of medical students or medical schools no matter how high the tuition or the degree of social utility. The privileges of clinical education cannot be bought at any price by the student, or granted even for good purpose by the medical school. Only a social mandate can legitimize the invasions of privacy a medical education entails.

The ethical issues of clinical education have just begun to receive the ethical scrutiny they deserve. Fundamental conceptual issues like the moral status of medical students, dead bodies, and animals are coupled with very practical issues regarding student–faculty and student–patient relationships. Clearer guidelines are needed to deal with the ethical issues characteristic of clinical education. We can expect the literature on this topic to expand in size, sophistication, and importance in the immediate future.

EDMUND D. PELLEGRINO (1995)

SEE ALSO: *Clinical Ethics; Competence; Conflict of Interest; Dentistry; Ethics; Family and Family Medicine; Informed Consent; Nursing Ethics; Profession and Professional Ethics; Race and Racism; Sexism; Virtue and Character; Whistleblowing*

BIBLIOGRAPHY

Andre, Judith. 1992. "Learning to See: Moral Growth during Medical Training." *Journal of Medical Ethics* 18(3): 148–152.

Benfield, D. Gary; Flaksman, Richard J.; Lin, Tsun-Asin; Kantaki, Anand D.; Kokomoor, Franklin W.; and Vallman, John H. 1991. "Teaching Intubation Skills Using Newly Deceased Infants." *Journal of the American Medical Association* 265(18): 2360–2363.

Bewley, Susan. 1992. "Teaching Vaginal Examination." *British Medical Journal* 305(6849): 369.

Brody, Howard. 1983. "Deception in the Teaching Hospital." In *Difficult Decisions in Medical Ethics: The Fourth Volume in a Series on Ethics and Humanism in Medicine*, pp. 81–86, ed. Doreen L. Ganos, Rachel E. Lipson, Gwynedd Warren, and Barbara J. Weil. New York: Alan R. Liss.

Christakis, Dmitri A., and Feudtner, Chris. 1993. "Ethics in a Short White Coat: The Ethical Dilemmas that Medical Students Confront." *Academic Physician* 68(4): 249–254.

Connolly, Paul H. 1979. "What Are the Medical Schools Up To? Abortions and Admissions." *Commonwealth* 105(17): 551–552.

Crandall, Sonia J.; Volk, Robert J.; and Loemker, Vicki. 1993. "Medical Students' Attitudes Toward Providing Care for the Underserved: Are We Training Socially Responsible Physicians?" *Journal of the American Medical Association* 269(19): 2519–2523.

Currey, Charles J.; Johnson, Michael; and Ogden, Barbara. 1990. "Willingness of Health-Professions Students to Treat Patients with AIDS." *Academic Medicine* 65(7): 472–474.

Dans, Peter E. 1992. "Medical Students and Abortion: Reconciling Personal Beliefs and Professional Roles at One Medical School." *Academic Medicine* 67(3): 207–211.

Drew, Barbara L. 1992. "What If the Whistle Blower Is a Student? The Advisory Role of the Instructor." In *Ethical Dilemmas in Contemporary Nursing Practice*, pp. 117–127, ed. Gladys B. White. Washington, D.C.: American Nurses Publishing.

Esmail, A., and Everington, S. 1993. "Racial Discrimination against Doctors from Ethnic Minorities." *British Medical Journal* 306(6879): 691–692.

Flexner, Abraham. 1910. *Medical Education in the United States and Canada: A Report to the Carnegie Foundation for the Advancement of Teaching.* Birmingham, AL: Classics of Medicine Library.

Fry, Sara T. 1991. "Is Health Care Delivery by Partially Trained Professionals Ever Justified?" *Journal of Clinical Ethics* 2(1): 42–44.

Ganos, Doreen L. 1983. "Introduction: Deception in the Teaching Hospital." In *Difficult Decisions in Medical Ethics: The Fourth Volume in a Series on Ethics and Humanism in Medicine*, pp. 77–78, ed. Doreen L. Ganos, Rachel E. Lipson, Gwynedd Warren, and Barbara J. Weil. New York: Alan R. Liss.

Greer, David S. 1987. "To Inform or Not to Inform Patients About Students." *Journal of Medical Education* 62(10): 861–862.

Hanft, Ruth S., and White, Catherine C. 1987. "Constraining the Supply of Physicians: Effects on Black Physicians." *Milbank Quarterly* 65 (suppl. 2): 249–269.

Holleman, Warren Lee. 1992. "Challenges Facing Student Clinicians." *Human Medicine* 8(30): 205–211.

Hostler, Sharon L., and Gressard, Risa P. 1993. "Perceptions of the Gender Fairness of the Medical School Environment." *Journal of the American Medical Women's Association* 48(2): 51–54.

Iserson, Kenneth V. 1993. "Postmortem Procedures in the Emergency Department: Using the Recently Dead to Practice and Teach." *Journal of Medical Ethics* 19(2): 92–98.

Johnson, Shirley M.; Kurtz, Margot E.; Tomlinson, Tom; and Fleck, Leonard. 1992. "Teaching the Process of Obtaining Informed Consent to Medical Students." *Academic Medicine* 67(9): 598–600.

Lawton, Frank G.; Redman, Charles W. E.; and Luesley, David M. 1990. "Patient Consent for Gynaecological Examination." *British Journal of Hospital Medicine* 44(5): 326, 329.

Liepman, Marcia K. 1983. "Deception in the Teaching Hospital: Where We Are and Where We've Been." In *Difficult Decisions in Medical Ethics: The Fourth Volume in a Series on Ethics and Humanism in Medicine*, pp. 87–94, ed. Doreen L. Ganos, Rachel E. Lipson, Gwynedd Warren, and Barbara J. Weil. New York: Alan R. Liss.

Ludmerer, Kenneth M. 1985. *Learning to Heal: The Development of American Medical Education.* New York: Basic Books.

Morris, Mark. 1992. "When Loyalties Are Divided Between Teachers and Patients." *Journal of Medical Ethics* 18(3): 153–155.

Osler, William. 1943. *Aequanimitas: With Other Addresses to Medical Students, Nurses, and Practitioners of Medicine,* 3rd edition. Philadelphia: Blakiston.

Pellegrino, Edmund D. 1976. "Medical Schools as Moral Agents." *Transactions of the American Clinical and Climatological Association* 88: 54–67.

Pellegrino, Edmund D. 1978. "Medical Education." In vol. 2 of *Encyclopedia of Bioethics,* pp. 863–870, ed. Warren T. Reich. New York: Macmillan.

Pilowski, I. 1973. "The Student, the Patient and His Illness: The Ethics of Clinical Teaching." *Medical Journal of Australia* 1(17): 858–859.

Rozance, Christine P. 1991. "Cheating in Medical Schools: Implications for Students and Patients." *Journal of the American Medical Association* 266(17): 2453, 2456.

Stimmel, Barry. 1990. "Cheating in Medical Schools: A Problem or an Annoyance?" *Rhode Island Medical Journal* 73(9): 413–416.

Wiesemann, Claudia. 1993. "Eine Ethik des Nichtwissens." *Ethik Med* 5: 3–12.

Williams, Charles T., and Fost, Norman. 1992. "Ethical Considerations Surrounding First Time Procedures: A Study and Analysis of Patient Attitudes Toward Spinal Taps by Students." *Kennedy Institute of Ethics Journal* 2(3): 217–231.

MEDICAL ETHICS, HISTORY OF AFRICA

• • •

I. Sub-Saharan Countries

II. South Africa

I. SUB-SAHARAN COUNTRIES

The geographic region of sub-Saharan Africa includes all the African countries immediately below the Sahara Desert, together with all the associated island states but excluding the Republic of South Africa. Although the latter is within the region, it is excluded from this text in view of the heavy influence that apartheid exerted on indigenous African cultures. All the countries considered are bound by the Tropic of Cancer on the north and the Tropic of Capricorn on the south. In addition to a multitude of indigenous languages, the majority of the countries are either Anglophone or Francophone; five are Lusophone (Portuguese-speaking).

Medical ethics in sub-Saharan Africa is extremely complicated and cannot be considered homogeneous in any sense. This is because the vast geographic area (almost 23 million square kilometers, or about nine million square miles) contains forty-three independent countries with innumerable sociocultural groupings. Many of the countries

are nation-states only superficially, since their borders enclose ethnic groups that have little in common with their fellow citizens, being more closely affiliated with groups in other countries. Quite apart from the matter of indigenous cultures, these countries were under the domination of European colonial powers that sought to impose their cultures upon local cultures. Some countries gained political independence only in the 1980s, and in some supposedly independent countries (Angola, Mozambique, Sudan) civil strife based on ethnic differences has raged throughout most of their independent period. The interaction between an externally introduced culture and a local one is more complicated in the field of medicine than in any other. The differences in urban-center development in East Africa and West Africa demonstrate the role that colonial power had in influencing cultural and ethical values (Larson).

Traditional and Scientific Methods

Some of the countries have had contact with scientifically based European medicine for less than 50 years, and others for little more than 100 years. The development of medical ethics in all the African countries has therefore tended to follow the existing European ethical values, principally those of France and Great Britain, the two dominant colonial powers. European medical professionals, faced with traditional African medical practice, took the position that all such medical practices and values, as well as their practitioners, were bad. Traditional African healers were considered no more than quacks and deceivers and therefore were either ignored or actively persecuted. Even the traditional midwives or "birth attendants," as they are now known, who from time immemorial have provided help to women at a most difficult time, were looked upon with disfavor. To a certain extent such attitudes were underwritten by the beliefs and practices of the colonizers' religion, Christianity. Since much of traditional healing relied on the intervention of gods and spirits, which Christians found abhorrent, the practice of traditional healing was strongly discouraged. Furthermore, European medical ethics required that European doctors not associate with practitioners whose training and beliefs differed from their own.

With the rise of black consciousness and the acceptance of the notion that blackness is not a sign of inferiority, African peoples have begun to reappropriate the medical knowledge gained over centuries by traditional medicine and medical practice. In some countries laws have been passed recognizing traditional medical practice as legal and effective. This process has been very slow. Many African medical schools still do not offer any instruction in traditional medicine, and where interest exists, it is only at a research level. Financial grants have been made for research into the methods and preparations of traditional medicine. In a few instances medical scientists are actively involved with traditional practitioners.

This new collaboration between traditional and imported medical practice is likely to be furthered by the indigenization of African churches and the improvement of the quality of their leadership. Previously, priests and ministers in the majority of churches had been inadequately trained, and they tended to assume a patronizing approach to their congregants. Now, a growing number can be considered well educated; some can even be viewed as theologians who are able to help formulate the churches' views on subjects of such crucial importance as the conflict between traditional and modern medical practice. Medical professionals in the majority of countries now feel relatively free to develop new ways of practice and to work with traditional birth attendants, herbalists, and other healers without fear of losing either the respect or the comradeship of colleagues in Europe.

Traditional and Western practices are seeing crossover training in the areas of psychiatry, childbirth, and grassroots education. Much of traditional medicine touches on the realm of psychiatry. Involvement of traditional practitioners in psychiatric treatment makes for a more humane treatment and much better integration of patients into society (Lambo). Among other efforts that may be cited is the involvement of the University of Ghana Medical School in training programs for traditional birth attendants. In many countries the medical schools (Makerere University in Uganda, University of Nairobi in Kenya, and University of Yaounde in Cameroon, for example) are striving to identify relevant practices within their own societies, such as use of peer groups to educate members of their societies on health-related issues. These medical schools are, therefore, embarking on programs that identify and preserve traditional practices considered valuable (Jelliffe and Bennett). In these programs, traditional practices considered harmless or beneficial are to be permitted, and those practices considered truly harmful are to be eliminated.

Standards for Medical Practice

Most English-speaking countries have general medical councils or boards responsible for registration, accreditation, and supervision of medical practice. In most of these countries the boards of control are generally quite distinct from the ministries of health (Kenya Government). Many of these medical councils or boards, however, have fashioned policies more responsive to western European norms and needs than to African ones. These boards have had little time to devote to the development of ethical guidelines relevant to social and cultural conditions peculiar to life within African countries. Some principles remain fundamental, however: Privacy of the patient is respected, and so is confidentiality, although here and there disclosure is required by the government for various reasons, including payment for medical service, granting of sick leave by employers, and mandatory registration of births and deaths.

Healthcare Service

There are very few scientifically trained medical personnel in Africa. The ratio of scientifically trained doctors to population ranges from 1:3,000 in such better-off cities as Dakar (Senegal), Accra (Ghana), and Nairobi (Kenya) to 1:200,000 in some poorer rural areas, such as most of the Northern Region of Nigeria and all of the immediate sub-Saharan countries including Mauritania, Mali, Burkina Faso, Niger, and Chad, which are sometimes referred to as the Sahel. There are countries within which there may not be a single specialist in any recognized field of medicine. This immediately raises the issue of what kind of medicine is most suitable in such conditions.

European medicine has developed and gained the reputation of being "one-on-one" medicine, and it also has concentrated more on curative than on preventive medicine. In Africa, on the other hand, the practice of one-on-one medicine, if it is accepted as the ideal, means excluding 80 to 90 percent or more of the population, who have no access to Western-oriented medical facilities. Such medical practice also places an inhuman load on the few medical practitioners and quickly reduces them to no more than purveyors of drugs and injections. Fendall sees this as the "quantity versus quality" dilemma, although not all agree with his view.

Doctors in Africa are now being asked to view their role in light of certain priorities—the first being promotive and preventive health services and the second being curative—in terms of individual patient treatment in offices or hospitals. In attempting to respond to the first priority, many have pointed out that not much can be done until medical practice is so arranged that the community is both the consumer and the provider of its own healthcare. This can be done only if delegation of healthcare to nonphysician personnel, such as traditional birth attendants and community leaders, is done on a basis of genuine need. The debate will continue, but almost all the new medical schools have agreed that doctors' training should be responsive to the needs of the community and to the organization and priorities set by ministries of health.

Many African countries depend on the use of paramedical personnel in the running of health services at the level of primary healthcare. Paramedics are often the only healthcare personnel available at this level. They include clinical officers, laboratory technologists, public-health technicians, environmental health officers, and various kinds of nurses. They are usually trained at medical training colleges, which are non-university, diploma-awarding institutions established in countries including Zambia, Kenya, and Tanzania. Apart from the nurses, who take an oath at graduation, paramedical personnel are not subject to any ethically binding oath. This cadre of personnel has on occasion been the source of breaches of confidentiality.

Pharmacies and pharmacists, too, have presented new dilemmas to medical practice in Africa. The regulation of the drug supply has been the prerogative of the ministries of health and their relevant licensing bodies. In keeping with the increased number of university-trained pharmacists, there is increased licensing of private pharmacies, especially in Zaire, Kenya, Cameroon, and Nigeria. Pharmacists regard themselves as trained "doctors" and dispense drugs without prescription, including drugs that have previously required doctors' prescriptions. Pharmacies also may dispense inactive drugs or drugs that have no relevance to the patient's illness (World Health Organization, 1992).

The Ethics of Educating and Remunerating Doctors

Medical education has had to contend with the issue of "excellence versus quantity" in the training of doctors. Most African medical schools have felt it necessary to enroll students of the highest possible scientific caliber and to train them to internationally accepted standards. (These students are chosen based on their national high school final examination results.) The result has been that very few doctors can be graduated in any given year; but much more important, in many countries the best and sometimes the only available scientific skills are channeled into medicine, depriving other socially important areas of potential contributors. This is an ethical issue of considerable importance. In the end, many of the doctors produced choose to become specialists who can practice medicine only where they find quite sophisticated support facilities and services. Frequently they serve existing hospital needs rather than those of preventive medicine. The frustration and wastefulness of this situation underscore one of the major ethical issues on the African medical scene.

Doctors' fees have been the subject of debate in many African countries. Poverty is a major socioeconomic problem in all the countries of sub-Saharan Africa. Civil wars, political instability, ethnic violence, drought, and famine have transformed millions of already poor individuals into refugees who have fled across borders. In the midst of extensive poverty, charging fees for care raises serious ethical questions. In most of these countries, physicians are employed by the government and are not supposed to charge fees for their services. However, government pay schedules have not kept up with the cost of living, and many government doctors engage in private practice to supplement their salaries. In the late 1980s, the Kenya Medical Association considered fee schedules that would charge standard amounts for various services, without waivers or reductions for the poor. Objections were raised, and the schedule was not adopted. In Ghana, attempts have been made to adjust doctors' salaries to costs of living. In general, the costs of physicians' services, drugs, and hospitalization amid such serious deprivation deserve serious ethical scrutiny.

Population, Family Planning, and Abortion

Population control as advocated in the Western world unfortunately has blurred the issues of family planning and led to a debate that should have been completely unnecessary. There are two basic concepts in family planning. The first is to regulate total family size to a level that can be comfortably maintained using the available resources. The second is to space the intervals between pregnancies in order to promote the health of both mothers and children (King). Many African countries rightly consider themselves underpopulated. Some, such as Gabon, Cameroon, and the Central African Republic, want much larger populations. All feel that they need development for the benefit of their people; but with very few exceptions, they refuse to admit that curbing population growth is relevant to the need for increased development.

Unfortunately, some doctors have failed to recognize the doctor's role in articulating relevant issues in family planning. Many doctors seem not to understand the medical importance of postponing pregnancies until a woman is biologically most prepared and of helping to stop reproduction when biological factors are no longer in a woman's favor. They also fail to recognize that spacing of births— which used to be practiced in Africa based either on sexual abstinence or on a geographic separation of husband and wife—is necessary to ensure the health of both mother and child. The excessive mortality in childbirth for women fourteen to forty-five years of age has not been fully appreciated by most of the medical profession in Africa (World Health Organization, 1975). Even where this situation is recognized, continued adherence to inappropriate laws and practices imposed from Europe often means that family-planning services are withheld from the majority of the population in need. The Catholic church, through its influence in the French-speaking countries, did much to prevent medical leadership in family planning. French laws passed in 1920 prohibiting contraception are still on the statute books of many French-speaking African countries, despite their repeal by France and Mali in 1972 (Wolf).

In the field of contraception, the major ethical question the doctor faces is, therefore, whether he or she should encourage free provision of contraceptives by nonmedical personnel, knowing that Europe and the United States, which are the sources of these supplies, require that they be dispensed almost exclusively by doctors. The doctor must weigh the possibility of breaking outdated laws against the results of withholding such supplies from populations that have no other source.

Other serious ethical questions are raised in providing contraception to women who are not married, according to the traditional norms prevailing in their locality, or who want to practice contraception without the knowledge of their regular partner. Yet so tenuous are some of the marital relationships, so difficult is it to get some husbands into a hospital or family-planning clinic, that insistence on consent by both parties might, in the end, do an injustice to the woman. Physicians must resolve this ethical dilemma within their own national frontiers.

African societies generally do not accept abortion because they value highly the continuity of lineage; the unborn child, for example, may be a reincarnation of an ancestor. However, it would be untrue to say that abortions were not known in Africa before the arrival of white colonizers. In many African cultures, pregnancies resulting from taboo relationships or from adultery are terminated generally by women and the men are kept in the dark.

The question of abortion is now debated seriously. Many of the abortion laws in Africa are based on those of England and France, which repealed them in 1967 and 1974, respectively. However, in the majority of former British and French possessions the old laws are still on the statute books. The increasing number of illegal abortions, with their consequent mortality, morbidity, and sterility, have still not prompted the collective conscience of medical practitioners to have the laws reviewed. Zambia did review its laws and amend them in 1973, but stipulations within the new law, particularly one that the approval of two medical practitioners is required, make it unlikely to serve the majority of those in need. The Africa Regional Conference on Abortion held in Accra, Ghana, in 1973 agreed to call for a review of the laws, but little has been done.

The doctors' dilemma regarding abortion is twofold. Despite the law, increasing numbers of women risk their lives by recourse to back-street abortionists. At the same time

there are so few doctors to respond to such a wide range of needs that to make abortion laws more liberal may mean increasing the load on doctors still further. Given these problems, it is difficult to understand the view of some doctors in African countries that education, information, and services for fertility regulation should be limited.

Healthcare and Research in the Era of AIDS

The acquired immunodeficiency syndrome (AIDS), first recognized in 1981, has had the most profound impact on healthcare in Africa. Major concerns in healthcare provision are related to confidentiality, informed consent, counseling, research, drug therapy, serotesting, and care of the sick.

When AIDS was first identified as a major public-health problem and a rapidly spreading epidemic in Africa, many African governments reacted with violent denials. This behavior, which was attributed in part to the claim that AIDS originated in Africa, received support from some physicians and ministries of health. The early rapid spread of AIDS in Africa was partly a result of the fact that it was not acknowledged as a major public-health problem and thus received only slow governmental response (Ndinya-Achola).

Confidentiality and counseling are two components in AIDS-control programs that have received, at best, lip service in Africa. Counseling is an extension of preventive educational campaigns. At population levels these campaigns use information, education, and communication as their basic tools, and public-health officials as their main promoters. Counseling deals directly with the individual. The personal interaction between counselor and patient enables individuals to better understand their personal risks, to make informed decisions, and to take appropriate action.

Under ideal conditions, counseling is provided on a one-to-one basis and each case is dealt with on its own merit. Counseling also involves providing facilities that respond to the physical and emotional needs of the affected individuals and their loved ones. In Africa, AIDS counselors began to be trained in 1988; the needs of the society far exceed the number of counselors available. Much of the counseling that is provided is done by individuals who have no training. In many instances it amounts to informing an individual that he or she is infected with the AIDS virus; the healthcare provider is faced with the ethical question of whether to withhold information about the illness because there are no facilities to cater to individual needs.

Even where conditions are adequate and counseling facilities are available, confidentiality is a major issue because some of the trained counselors are not ethically bound to keep confidentiality. In particular, confidentiality is lacking in Africa for individuals diagnosed with AIDS. Counselors, however, are not the only healthcare providers ignoring confidentiality. Information regarding AIDS diagnosis often is leaked by hospital laboratory and other care staff.

Biomedical Research

Care for those with AIDS and drug therapy are two additional areas of major ethical concern. In many African settings the diagnosis of AIDS results in patient neglect because of the stigma attached to the disease. AIDS is a stigmatized disease in Africa mainly because the earliest information linked it to homosexuality, which is regarded as antisocial behavior in many parts of Africa. After it was ascertained that AIDS was being transmitted primarily by heterosexual contact, the homosexual stigma of AIDS lessened; but then AIDS became further stigmatized because of the rapid spread among heterosexuals by means of multiple sex partners and increased promiscuity. AIDS educational programs also had the inappropriate but true message that death is the final outcome. For these reasons, AIDS has had a negative impact on social interactions. Many people fear to be associated with a person with AIDS. This fear is evident even among professionals. Nurses have been a little more ethical in their approach to care of AIDS patients than physicians, perhaps because the nurses' increased contact with the patients makes them more sympathetic to the patients' plight.

During the early years of the AIDS epidemic, researchers from all over the world quickly identified populations in Africa for epidemiological studies (Van de Perre et al.; Kreiss et al.; Piot et al.). Clinical studies on drugs and vaccines are also being done. This research brings to the fore ethical questions about biomedical research in African countries that predated the AIDS epidemic: Should Western scientists do studies on populations that may never benefit from the results? Can appropriate informed consent be obtained in cultures that have different values? These questions are much debated within Africa and abroad (IJsselmuiden and Faden). Standards of research have been improved: Some medical journals, such as *East African Medical Journal,* insist that proof of informed consent be provided before articles are accepted; granting agencies in Europe and the United States require local ethical review before funding is provided; and local review boards are becoming quite strict.

One of the important contributions of biomedical research in AIDS is the development of antiretroviral drugs for treating infection caused by human immunodeficiency virus (HIV), the causative agent of AIDS. Although the available drugs do not currently offer a cure, some of them have been shown to prolong life significantly. These drugs are far too expensive for African populations. The same research groups that solicited funds for epidemiologic studies should be persuaded to do the same in order to make anti-AIDS drugs affordable for African populations. The first ten years of the AIDS epidemic has had profound social, cultural, economic, and health impacts in sub-Saharan Africa. These effects, which include loss of social structure, orphaned children, reduced productivity, and severe depletion of healthcare budgets, no doubt will significantly increase over the next decade. Even if medical care or a vaccine were made available immediately, the already large number of infected individuals will continue to burden the society. Healthcare standards will be influenced by the AIDS epidemic for a long time. The decade of the 1990s is the right time for African healthcare services to review their programs and put in place relevant practices and resources without compromising their ethics in caring for people with AIDS. It would be heartening to see African countries taking a lead in the care of people with AIDS.

Conclusion

Significant improvements are continually being made in medical training and standards of healthcare throughout sub-Saharan Africa. These improvements, however, are still not matched by proportionate improvement in medical ethics. Many African medical schools' curricula do not include ethics. Where it is included, the subject is still accorded very little time (usually a one-hour lecture). In order to sensitize doctors and other healthcare personnel on issues related to medical ethics, African medical schools and medical training colleges should be encouraged to develop curricula on ethics. It may also be necessary to sensitize populations on the subject along the same lines that disease prevention has been brought to the community level through health education.

JECKONIAH O. NDINYA-ACHOLA (1995)
BIBLIOGRAPHY REVISED

BIBLIOGRAPHY

Aja, Egbeke. 1997. "Changing Moral Values in Africa: An Essay in Ethical Relativism." *Journal of Value Inquiry* 31(4): 531–543.

Bryant, John H. 1969. *Health and the Developing World.* Ithaca, NY: Cornell University Press.

Feachem, Richard G., and Jamison, Dean T., eds. 1995. *Disease and Mortality in Sub-Saharan Africa.* New York: Oxford University Press.

Fendall, N. R. E. 1972. *Auxiliaries in Health Care: Programs in Developing Countries.* Baltimore: Johns Hopkins University Press.

Grant, J. P. 1989. "The Bamako Initiative." In UNICEF: *The State of the World's Children.* Oxford: Oxford University Press.

IJsselmuiden, Carel B., and Faden, Ruth R. 1992. "Research and Informed Consent in Africa: Another Look." *New England Journal of Medicine* 326(12): 830–834.

Institute of Medical Ethics Working Party on the Ethical Implications of AIDS. 1992. "AIDS, Ethics, and Clinical Trials." *British Medical Journal* 305(6855): 699–701.

Jelliffe, D. B., and Bennett, F. J. 1960. "Indigenous Medical Systems and Child Health." *Journal of Paediatrics* 57(2): 248–261.

Kasenene, Peter. 1998. *Religious Ethics in Africa.* Rochester, MI: Fountain Books.

Kenya Government. 1977. The Medical Practitioners and Dentists Act, Cap 253. *Kenya Gazette.* Nairobi: Government Printer.

King, Maurice H. 1966. "Family Planning." In *Medical Care in Developing Countries,* ed. Maurice H. King. Nairobi: Oxford University Press.

Kopelman, Loretta M. 2002. "If HIV/AIDS is Punishment, Who Is Bad?" *Journal of Medicine and Philosophy* 27(2): 231–243.

Kopelman, Loretta M., and van Niekerk, Anton A. "AIDS and Africa. Introduction." *Journal of Medicine and Philosophy* 27(2): 139–142.

Kreiss, Joan K.; Koech, Davy; Plummer, Francis A.; et al. 1986. "AIDS Virus Infection in Nairobi Prostitutes: Spread of the Epidemic to East Africa." *New England Journal of Medicine* 314(7): 414–418.

Lambo, T. Adeoye. 1971. "The African Mind in Contemporary Conflict." *WHO Chronicle* 25: 343–353. Jacques Parisot Foundation Lecture.

Larson, A. 1989. "Social Context of Human Immunodeficiency Virus Transmission in Africa." *Review of Infectious Diseases* 11(5): 716–731.

Magesa, Lauenti. 1997. *African Religion: The Moral Traditions of Abundant Life.* Maryknoll, NY: Orbis Books.

Ndinya-Achola, Jeckoniah O. 1991. "A Review of Ethical Issues in AIDS Research." *East African Medical Journal* 68(9): 735–740.

Paris, Peter J. 1994. *The Spirituality of African Peoples: The Search for a Common Moral Discourse.* Minneapolis, MN: Fortress Press.

Piot, Peter; Kreiss, Joan K.; Ndinya-Achola, Jeckoniah O.; Ngugi, E. N.; Simonsen, J. N.; Cameron, D. W.; Taelman, H.; and Plummer, F. A. 1987. "Heterosexual Transmission of HIV." *AIDS* 1: 199–206.

Seidel, G. 1993. "The Competing Discourses of HIV/AIDS in Sub-Saharan Africa: Discourses of Rights and Empowerment vs. Discourses of Control and Exclusion." *Social Science and Medicine* 36(3): 175–194.

Synder, Francis G. 1974. "Health Policy and the Law in Senegal." *Social Science and Medicine* 8(1): 11–28.

Van de Perre, Phillipe; Clumeck, Nathan; Carael, Michel; et al. 1987. "Female Prostitutes: A Risk Group for Infection with Human T-Cell Lymphotropic Virus Type III." *Lancet* 2(8454): 524–527.

Wolf, Bernard. 1973. *Anti-contraception Laws in Sub-Saharan Africa: Sources and Ramifications.* Laws and Population Monograph Series, no. 15. Medford, MA: Fletcher School of Law and Diplomacy, Law and Publication Program.

World Health Organization. 1975. *World Health Statistics Annual, 1972,* vol. 1, *Vital Statistics and Causes of Death.* Geneva: Author.

World Health Organization. 1992. "Safe Drugs for Everyone." *World Health* March–April, pp. 4–6.

II. SOUTH AFRICA

The histories of medicine and of medical ethics in South Africa are intimately linked to political, social, and economic aspects of that country's development, dominant components of which include racial discrimination and social segregation. A brief review of some key political events will provide an illuminating backdrop to a description of the evolution of medical services and the ethics of medical practice in this controversial country, which typifies in microcosm many of the world's diverse human problems and arguably poses the most challenging contemporary opportunity to demonstrate human ability to resolve conflict peacefully.

Political Background

During the period of the Dutch settlers (1652–1820) the indigenous Khoi-Khoi (pastoral people) and the San (hunter-gatherers) were treated with the arrogance and paternalism that for subsequent centuries epitomized European domination over blacks and exploitation through enslavement and colonial/cultural imperialism. These attitudes, together with warfare and the introduction of new diseases (e.g., smallpox in 1713), led to the decimation and destruction of the organized cultures of these indigenous peoples (Burrows; Laidler and Gelfand).

British annexation of the Cape (1795) and the arrival of British immigrants in Algoa Bay were followed by ninety years of conflict that included devastating wars between rival black tribes, the freeing of slaves (1833), the "importation" of Indians to work in the cane fields of Natal (1860), the first Anglo-Boer War (1880), several wars against the Zulus, and the bitter second Anglo-Boer War (1899–1902), during which twenty-six thousand Afrikaner women and children died in British concentration camps.

The British Parliamentary Act of Union (1910), which gave whites the right to self-determination, and the subsequent failure of the British to exercise their veto powers to restrain the Union Parliament from enacting oppressive racial laws (Native Land Act of 1913, depriving blacks of their land, and the Native Administration Act of 1927, depriving them of their right to self-determination), set the scene for the growth of Afrikaner political and economic dominance. The rise to power of the Nationalist Party in 1948 was followed by proliferation of apartheid policies, relentlessly entrenched through legislation that oppressed and dehumanized the black people of South Africa.

Black opposition evolved from powerless peaceful protest into a politically powerful process of potentially peaceful progress. It was hampered, however, by a growing culture of individual and group violence, fueled by brutal elements within the state security forces and by internal sources of conflict that horrified the world (Schlemmer). Intensification of black resistance, more clearly articulated demands for human rights globally, and changing foreign policy agendas progressively isolated South Africa from its previous friends and from international markets. By the 1980s economic decline, rapid population growth, urbanization, destabilization in the neighboring states, and collapse of communism in eastern Europe and the Soviet retreat from regional conflicts constituted the matrix from which arose the Nationalist Party's acceptance of the need to seek, with the black opposition parties, a negotiated settlement as a step toward developing a democratic South Africa (Benatar, 1992).

Legislative changes since the "unbanning" of the black opposition movements in February 1990 have included repeal of the 1913 Native Land Act, the 1927 Native Administration Act, the 1950 Population Registration Act, and the 1950 Group Areas Act, which together formed a powerful core of statutory discriminatory policies. While the transition period abounds with ironies and ambiguities, optimism that peaceful and constructive pathways to progress could and would be found followed the December 1991 Convention for a Democratic South Africa (CODESA) Conference and the March 1992 referendum. It is against this background that the history of medicine and medical ethics in South Africa can now be briefly reviewed.

History of Medicine

The first manifestation of any formalized medical service was the erection of hospital tents following a smallpox epidemic introduced by a visiting fleet in 1713. Further episodes of smallpox (1751 and 1755) led to the construction of two rudimentary hospitals, one for poor Europeans and the other for slaves, the well-to-do being treated at home.

Medical practice developed in two directions: a private commercial venture predominantly for those who could afford to pay, and a public service for the poor, to which the mission medical service (introduced by the Missionary Society of London) made a major contribution in rural areas for well over a century. Concern for public health, stimulated by the 1918 influenza epidemic, generated decades of successful research on infections in close collaboration with the World Health Organization (WHO). Public health services of a high standard were developed through the creation of medical schools with public teaching hospitals open to all—on a segregated basis; ostensibly separate but equal.

The developing systems of medical practice and of medical education mirrored the diverse characteristics of South African society. Undisputedly high standards of medical education in the Western tradition, dedication of generations of practitioners to high standards of medical practice and patient care, considerable goodwill between doctors and patients of all races, extensive public-health facilities—including teaching centers of excellence and well-funded private medicine—reflect the successes. Privileged access to medical education; fragmentation and duplication of health services; lack of planning; wide disparities in health and in access to healthcare (predominantly on a racially discriminatory and unequal basis); focus on curative hospital-based medicine; paucity of preventive, promotive, and rehabilitative services; paternalistic attitudes to patients; and dismissive attitudes to African traditional medicine reflect the racist and oppressive aspects of a system doomed to failure through its institutionalized neglect of civil and social justice (Van Rensburg and Benatar).

Deficiencies in the healthcare system were clearly articulated in the 1940s, and the case for reform toward a unitary health service has been the subject of intense debate since the 1980s (Benatar, 1986, 1990b, 1991). Traditional African medicine continues to be practiced, particularly in rural areas. While black Africans have increasingly accepted Western medicine, they eclectically choose varying combinations of modern and traditional medical advice (Edwards).

Medical Ethics

The South African Medical and Dental Council (SAMDC), a statutory body, was established in 1929 with the primary purpose of protecting the public through maintenance of high professional (including ethical) standards of practice and with a view to serving the interests of the medical and dental professions—insofar as these interests are compatible with high standards. The wide range of powers vested in SAMDC included the power to institute inquiries into any complaint, charge, or allegation of improper or disgraceful conduct of its members and to exercise disciplinary power over them.

As in most other Western countries in the first sixty years of the twentieth century, discussions on medical ethics in South Africa largely took place within the framework of the authoritarian, paternalistic behavior expected of professionals supposedly adhering to the Hippocratic Oath and similar codes. The first South African text on medical ethics (Elliott) was limited to discussion of ethical codes, professional secrecy, advertising, the conduct of consultations, fees and financial matters, and upholding the "traditions" of medicine, with only brief reference to abortion and sterilization, and to the ethics of investigative medicine. This text, based on Guy Elliott's experience of deliberations on ethical matters by the Medical Association of South Africa (MASA) and the SAMDC, provides a succinct outline of accepted medical ethics in South Africa (and in many Western countries) in the first half of the twentieth century.

Issues of bioethics have usually been stimulated by the widespread application of technological advances in everyday medical practice, the social changes that challenge many traditional professional values, cost considerations, uncertainty regarding the effectiveness of innovative treatments, and increasing concern for individual autonomy and shared decision making in the United States and Europe.

The pace of social change, and of change in medicine and bioethics in South Africa (a middle-income country—per capita gross national product (GNP) less than one-tenth that in the United States and falling), has been much slower. Expenditure on health has increased only marginally and, despite their high profile, modern lifesaving medical treatments are available only on a limited scale. Public and even professional debates on ethical issues in medicine have been very limited in a repressive, authoritarian society lacking a patients' rights movement and unaccustomed to public discourse on civil and political liberties (Benatar, 1988).

As in the United States, theologians have played a pioneering role in reawakening interest in bioethics; several conferences were held in South Africa (in the 1960s and 1970s) under church or theological auspices. The first, stimulated by the historic heart transplant in Cape Town (December 1967), was on the ethics of tissue transplantation (Oosthuizen). Others followed on abortion (Oosthuizen et al., 1974), euthanasia (Oosthuizen et al., 1978), professional

secrecy (Oosthuizen et al., 1983), and clinical experimentation (Oosthuizen et al., 1985). These provoked little ongoing public or professional debate. In the 1980s some medical schools began developing modern bioethics education programs, but progress has been slow and the programs remain (1) in a fledgling state, (2) dependent on enthusiastic physicians who have heavy professional responsibilities and minimal formal training in philosophical ethics, and (3) without the financial and institutional support to develop formal programs with committed support from other disciplines (e.g., philosophy, law). One medical faculty has published the proceedings of four symposia on bioethics (Benatar, 1985, 1986, 1988, 1992). These have encompassed theological, philosophical, and sociological debates on death and dying; resource allocation; the doctor–patient relationship; abortion and in vitro fertilization; research on humans; principles of biomedical ethics; moral reasoning; withholding and withdrawing treatment; healthcare of detainees; hospital ethics; the right to healthcare and the structure of health services; ethical considerations in relation to acquired immunodeficiency syndrome (AIDS); and teaching medical ethics. These proceedings reflect progressive movement toward the views being popularized in bioethics debates in the United Kingdom and the United States. By retaining a degree of "cultural sensitivity" they endeavor to avoid the pitfalls both of "ethical imperialism" and of "ethical double standards."

A milestone event in the history of medical ethics in South Africa was the inadequate SAMDC and MASA responses to the unethical manner in which state-employed medical practitioners provided professional attention to prominent black activist Steve Biko prior to his death during detention without trial in 1977. Failure of SAMDC to exercise its duty to protect the public by acknowledging the unethical behavior of Biko's doctors and taking appropriate disciplinary action against them, and MASA's response to SAMDC's deficient protection of the public met with resounding criticism nationally and internationally (Nightingale et al.). The sequence of events through which the efforts of a small group of rank-and-file members of the profession led to a Supreme Court injunction against SAMDC, which resulted in a reversal of its previous decisions and the imposition of disciplinary action, is well documented. The National Medical and Dental Association (NAMDA), formed in 1982 as a result of discontent with MASA's actions following the death of Steve Biko, has received international acclaim for its outspoken advocacy against discriminatory practices. MASA, which came under considerable criticism for its inadequate reactions to the Biko affair, has, to its credit, taken some sincere steps in an attempt to rectify its previous shortcomings. Its statements are now clearly on public record, and the challenge ahead is to ensure their further implementation in practice. Greater attention to ethical responsibilities toward prisoners, detainees, and hunger strikers has been a gratifying response to the Biko case (Benatar, 1990a; Kalk and Veriava). The public confession of guilt by the district surgeon who bore major responsibility for Biko's medical care, emphasizes the need to maintain professional independence in the face of state security and other coercive pressures.

Professional institutional responses intended to stimulate higher standards of ethical practice include the MASA and the Medical Research Council (MRC) guidelines on professional ethics and the ethics of medical research, respectively (both currently under further revision), and the publication by the College of Medicine of South Africa of its Credo. The long-standing requirement by some universities that all proposals for human and animal experimentation need approval by institutional ethics committees is spreading to other universities, and such prior approval has now become a requirement for all funding applications to the South African Medical Research Council.

Conclusion

In a period characterized by national economic attrition, real per capita expenditure on health of less than one-twentieth of what is spent in the United States, burgeoning population growth, rapid erosion of financial support for academic medicine, and political liberation with rapidly escalating human expectations, development of the discipline of bioethics in South Africa has been initiated and sustained more as a hobby by a few enthusiasts than as an integral component of medical education and practice. The need to include formal teaching of bioethics and clinical ethics in professional schools, which has gained widespread acceptance in the developed world, remains to be achieved in South Africa, as in other developing countries. Who should teach, what should be taught, how teaching of this discipline can be made most effective, and the ways in which such teaching can enrich medical and social education and practice are, as in any new discipline, matters of ongoing debate. If South Africa can learn from the developments in other countries and, with international support, use these lessons to build a national bioethics program and a better healthcare system in South Africa, this could contribute toward restructuring a new South Africa that could play a vital role in helping to rehabilitate southern Africa.

SOLOMON R. BENATAR (1995)
BIBLIOGRAPHY REVISED

BIBLIOGRAPHY

Baldwin-Ragaven, Laurel. 1999. *Ambulances of the Wrong Colour: Health Professionals, Human Rights and Ethics in South Africa.* Capetown, South Africa: University of Capetown Press.

Benatar, Solomon R. 1986. "Medicine and Health Care in South Africa." *New England Journal of Medicine* 315(8): 527–532.

Benatar, Soloman R. 1988. "Ethics, Medicine and Health Care in South Africa." *Hastings Center Report,* suppl. 18(4): 3–8.

Benatar, Soloman R. 1990a. "Detention Without Trial, Hunger Strikes and Medical Ethics." *Law, Medicine and Health Care* 18(1–2): 140–145.

Benatar, Soloman R. 1990b. "A Unitary Health Service for South Africa." *South African Medical Journal* 77(9): 441–447.

Benatar, Soloman R. 1991. "Medicine and Health Care in South Africa—5 Years Later." *New England Journal of Medicine* 325(1): 30–36.

Benatar, Soloman R. 1992. "Transition Towards a New South Africa." *South African Medical Journal* 81(6): 295–298.

Benatar, Soloman R., ed. 1985, 1986, 1988, 1992. *Ethical and Moral Issues in Contemporary Medical Practice: Proceedings of an "In House" Conference Faculty of Medicine, University of Cape Town.* Cape Town: University of Cape Town.

Benatar, Soloman R., and Van Rensburg, Hendrick C. J. 1995. "Health Care Services in a New South Africa." *Hastings Center Report* 25(4): 16–26.

Burrows, Edmund H. 1958. *A History of Medicine in South Africa.* Cape Town: A. A. Balkema.

Edwards, Stephen D. 1986. "Traditional and Modern Medicine in South Africa: A Research Study." *Social Science and Medicine* 22(11): 1273–1276.

Elliott, Guy A. 1954. *Medical Ethics.* Johannesburg: Witwatersrand University Press.

Hattingh, J. 2000. "Biomedical Ethics in South Africa: Current Challenges and Institutional Responses." *Biomedical Ethics* 5(1): 38–41.

Jochelson, Karen. 2001. *The Colour of Disease: Syphilis and Racism in South Africa, 1880–1950 (St. Antony's).* New York: St. Martin's Press.

Kalk, W. John, and Veriava, Yusut. 1991. "Hospital Management of Voluntary Total Fasting Among Political Prisoners." *Lancet* 337(8742): 660–662.

Laidler, Percy W., and Gelfand, Michael. 1971. *South Africa: Its Medical History 1652–1898: A Medical and Social Study.* Cape Town: C. Struik.

Landman, Willem A., and Henley, Lesley D. 1999. "Equitable Rationing of Highly Specialised Health Care Services for Children: a Perspective from South Africa." *Journal of Medical Ethics* 25(3): 224–229.

Landman, Willem A., and Henley, Lesley D. 2000. "Rationing and Children's Constitutional Health-Care Rights." *South African Journal of Philosophy* 19(1): 41–50.

London, L., and McCarthy, G. 1998. "Teaching Medical Students on the Ethical Dimensions of Human Rights: Meeting the Challenge in South Africa." *Journal of Medical Ethics* 24(4): 257–262.

Nightingale, Elena O.; Hannibal, Kari; Geiger, Jack; et al. 1990. "Apartheid Medicine: Health and Human Rights in South Africa." *Journal of the American Medical Association* 264(16): 2097–2102.

Oosthuizen, Gerhardus C. 1972. *The Ethics of Tissue Transplantation.* Cape Town: Howard Timmins.

Oosthuizen, Gerhardus C.; Abbott, G.; and Notelovitz, Morris. 1974. *Great Debate: Abortion in the South African Context.* Cape Town: Howard Timmins.

Oosthuizen, Gerhardus C.; Shapiro, Hillel; and Strauss, Sybrand A. 1978. *Euthanasia.* Cape Town: Oxford University Press.

Oosthuizen, Gerhardus C.; Shapiro, Hillel; and Strauss, Sybrand A. 1983. *Professional Secrecy in South Africa: A Symposium.* Cape Town: Oxford University Press.

Oosthuizen, Gerhardus C.; Shapiro, Hillel; and Strauss, Sybrand A. 1985. *Attitudes to Clinical Experimentation in South Africa.* Johannesburg: Hodder and Stoughton.

Schlemmer, Lawrence. 1992. "Violence—What Is to Be Done?" *South Africa International* 23: 60–64.

Van Rensburg, Hendrick C. J., and Benatar, Solomon R. 1993. "The Legacy of Apartheid in Health and Health Care." *South African Journal of Sociology* 24(4): 99–111.

Villa-Vicencio, Charles, and De Gruchy, John W., eds., 1994. *Doing Ethics in Context: South African Perspectives (Theology and Praxis, Vol 2).* Maryknoll, NY: Orbis Books.

MEDICAL ETHICS, HISTORY OF THE AMERICAS

• • •

I. COLONIAL NORTH AMERICA AND NINETEENTH-CENTURY UNITED STATES

North American physicians fashioned their ethics as professionals from the dominant cultural ideals of their era, from norms hallowed through centuries of professional tradition, from rules and regulations of newly established medical institutions, and from laws and legal institutions operative in the communities in which they practiced.

Christian Practitioners

The soil of religious values grounded the quest for professional ethics. For the majority of British and French physicians who settled North America in the seventeenth and eighteenth centuries, Jesus was as real and significant as Asclepius, Hygeia, and Panaceia had been to the author of the Hippocratic Oath. An intimate causal connection existed between character and professional righteousness. The beliefs and rituals of Christian institutions formed character. The ethically acceptable physician displayed the characteristics of a Christian.

Cotton Mather, a Puritan cleric who wielded considerable power throughout New England during the early eighteenth century, was a major figure in the evolution of North American medical ethics. He believed that Christian physicians who abided by the secrecy clause of the Hippocratic Oath became special confessors who had extraordinary opportunities for offering "admonitions of piety" to their trusting and needful patients (Mather, 1966). Because sin was the ultimate cause of all diseases—spiritual, mental, and physical—Mather expected physicians to prescribe Christian beliefs as well as drugs (Mather, 1972). Though he acknowledged confusion about the variety of remedies proposed as cures for any single disease, he would not dishonor "skillful and faithful" physicians (Beall and Shryock).

Though many Bostonians objected, Mather advocated inoculation during smallpox epidemics. He believed that the ultimate success of smallpox inoculation depended on God's mercy, but the validity of inoculation required trial-and-error testing and statistical comparisons between those naturally infected and those artificially inoculated. If deaths were prevented or suffering mitigated, as had occurred in Africa and Turkey, then inoculation was a good practice for doctors in North America. Its goodness as praxis was determined by the scientific demonstrations of practical trials involving mathematical standards and utilitarian outcomes that would be the basis for the reform of medical therapeutics during the nineteenth and twentieth centuries.

Gentlemen Practitioners

North American physicians repeatedly urged students and colleagues to be both Christians and gentlemen in their interactions with each other and with patients. The principal characteristics of a gentleman included proper birth, sufficient wealth, unblemished character, adequate learning, and civic service. While the importance of birth and wealth faded in the more egalitarian atmosphere of the New World, that of character, learning, and civic virtue grew stronger. Was a physician good because he cured many sick patients, or because he was a Christian and a gentleman? Doctors who prepared the earliest biographical dictionaries of deceased physicians in the United States and Canada judged their worth by Christian and gentleman standards, not by curative or preventive statistics (Thacher). Hallmarks of professional goodness depended on allegiance to the dominant cultural ideals.

Educated Doctors

Those who promoted higher standards for judging physicians frequently decried the immoralities of uneducated practitioners. In 1765, two years after the British assumed rule of New France (Canada) and ten years before the battles of Lexington and Concord, John Morgan proclaimed that most North American practitioners were ignorant, unsteady, irresolute, idle, negligent, and merciless. After six years as an apprentice to John Redman in Philadelphia, four years as a military surgeon, three years of medical studies in London and Edinburgh, and the luster of a European "grand tour," it was easy for Morgan to feel superior.

Wanting to improve this deplorable situation, Morgan and others established the first colonial medical school at the College of Philadelphia (1765). Samuel Bard, another Edinburgh graduate, delivered the first commencement address at King's College Medical School in New York City in 1769. Bard's judgment, no less harsh than Morgan's, was a fusion of Christian ethics, gentlemanly values, and academic ideals: "As those who have neither emulation nor honesty, who neither have abilities, or will give themselves the trouble of acquiring them, I would recommend it to such, seriously to consider the sixth commandment, 'Thou Shalt Do No Murder'" (Bard, p. 6). Morgan, Bard, and others fervently advocated formal education to produce morally acceptable doctors.

Because of the influx of practitioners from the United States and Great Britain, and because of British restrictions on degree-granting institutions in the colonies, enduring medical schools were not established in Canada until the third decade of the nineteenth century. In 1830, when the medical school at McGill University was one year old, twenty regular medical schools functioned in the United States. Graduates of these schools usually championed academic norms as measures of professional goodness: collegiate studies before medical ones, a systematic formal education in a medical school, improving medical science by careful clinical observations, development of effective teacher-pupil relationships, and continuing studies after formal education. Physicians were professionally good if they were Christians, gentlemen, and scholars.

Legal Proprieties

North American physicians were not considered wholly ethical unless they were law-abiding citizens. Throughout Canada's early history, its doctors associated professional propriety with approval by licensing authorities, established as early as 1788 when the British Parliament passed a licensure act governing the Canadian settlements (Heagerty). Two Canadian groups assumed licensing responsibilities: the College of Physicians and Surgeons of Lower Canada in 1847 and the College of Physicians and Surgeons of Ontario in 1869. The voluntary medical societies organized in Canada before 1850 were not concerned with licensing.

The situation was quite different in the United States. Legislators granted exclusive licensing rights to medical societies in some states and to separate boards of physicians in other states. Such licensing bodies had been established in most states by 1832. During the subsequent forty years, however, existing states repealed or ignored their medical licensing laws, and new states adopted none. Since possession of a medical degree was sufficient for licensing in many states, there seemed to be little need for sustaining separate powers for societies or boards. No group enforced these laws uniformly or effectively. Nor had the laws prevented the growth and development of medical quackery and sectarianism.

Legislators believed that free Americans could be trusted to discover the good physician and to sue the bad one. Even if a physician in the United States could be judged a good professional without being licensed, as was the situation between 1835 and 1875, he did not want to be accused of malpractice, much less convicted in court.

During the first half of the nineteenth century, the American culture, unlike the Canadian, experienced an outburst of religious pluralism, the populist effects of expansion to the West, an economic atmosphere of laissez-faire, and widespread opposition to centralized regulation by governmental authorities. These conditions fostered the lack of interest in licensure laws and the willingness of legislators to charter schools for homeopaths, hydropaths, and other sectarian practitioners.

These social and cultural conditions caused many practitioners to believe that standards of professional propriety were disappearing in a sea of populist relativism. If models of personal morality, such as Christian or gentleman, were so varied and even conflicting (Could Jewish doctors be good?), and if standards of knowing were so pluralistic that legislators relinquished efforts to distinguish among them, what could be done by practitioners who still believed in the integrity and dignity of a medical profession?

Codes of Ethics

To cope with the pluralism and relativism of the modern era, physicians created codes of professional ethics. During the last decade of the eighteenth century, Thomas Percival, a general practitioner in Manchester, England, had developed a systematic view of medical ethics based on the premise that it was possible to comprehend a moral order suitable for all medical practitioners. Universal truths about good professional behavior could be learned and applied by all conscientious and respectable doctors. Percival delineated these truths within a fourfold categorization of physicians as persons, caregivers, livelihood competitors, and civil servants.

The following admonitions exemplify Percival's approach. Physicians should be Christian gentlemen: considerate, reasonable, self-critical, temperate, educated. Doctors ought to interrogate patients privately and have special regard for their feelings and prejudices. Practitioners should consult openly and respectfully with each other, searching for proper remedies and sharing responsibilities in the care of the sick. Doctors ought to honor the trust of their communities by providing medical services free to public institutions and by providing medical knowledge needed by courts and governing officials. Percival included these and numerous other exhortations in a book on medical ethics published in 1803.

This book, together with John Gregory's lectures on medical education and medical ethics published in 1772, became a handy guide for North American practitioners who wanted practical criteria for judging propriety but had little interest in theoretical formulations of moral philosophy that might bring them too close to the Catholic traditions of the medieval universities. Most of these doctors were Protestants, and many were stalwart Puritans who, like Cotton Mather, deliberately rejected the "new moral philosophy" of the seventeenth and eighteenth centuries. In their view, these modern philosophies contained too much ancient paganism and too little Christianity, and placed more reliance on observation and reason than on faith and ritual.

Despite such theoretical objections, American physicians became exemplars of the "new moral philosophy" as they created codes of professional ethics during the first half of the nineteenth century. In 1808 an association of Boston physicians adopted a code of medical ethics composed of nine sections that addressed consultations between physicians, interfering with another doctor's practice, arbitration of differences between doctors, discouraging the use of quack medicines, promoting professional respectability, fees and exemptions from fees, practicing for a sick or absent doctor, and seniority among practitioners. All of these precepts could be found in the second chapter of Percival's *Medical Ethics*. Titled "Boston Medical Police," this code became the model for codes adopted by at least thirteen medical societies in eleven states during the ensuing thirty-four years.

In 1823 the New York State Medical Society adopted a code that resurrected the broader scope of Percival's original view. The New York doctors presented ethical claims about the personal character of physicians, quackery, consultations, patient care, and public obligations. In 1832 an original code was adopted by the Medico-Chirurgical Society of Baltimore. Norms were offered about the obligations of physicians to each other, quackery, consultations, and fees. This code also included a separate section about duties of patients toward physicians, an approach that had been taken by Benjamin Rush in a lecture to students. Rush thought that citizens should employ only serious-minded, educated doctors. Patients should not burden doctors with too many details of their illnesses, and they should strictly follow their doctors' orders and pay their fees promptly.

These examples of distinctive codes from Boston, New York City, Baltimore, and Philadelphia demonstrate the extraordinary interest in codifying professional ethics among American doctors, an interest that culminated in the adoption of a national code in 1847 by the newly established American Medical Association (AMA).

The AMA doctors accepted Percival's fourfold pattern of categorizing professional ethics and many of the specific claims cherished by the British practitioner. They advocated excellence of moral character, though Christian norms were no longer identified as the exclusive grounds for this character, probably because Isaac Hays, a prominent Jewish physician in Philadelphia, was a member of the committee that drafted the code. Though the AMA doctors valued proper education, they insisted that loyalty to professional colleagues was more important than scientific attainments. Article IV explicitly forbade association or consultation with irregular practitioners, that is, physicians whose "practice is based on an exclusive dogma, to the rejection of the accumulated experience of the profession," an injunction directed primarily against homeopaths. Standards of patient care included careful attention to professional secrecy, a proper number of visits to the sick, absence of gloomy prognoses, and refusal to abandon patients who have incurable diseases.

Physicians also had excellent opportunities for influencing the personal character of patients. Section 7 of Article I of Chapter 1 of the code is quite specific: "The opportunity which a physician not unfrequently enjoys of promoting and strengthening the good resolutions of his patients, suffering under the consequences of vicious conduct, ought never to be neglected." Sustaining Cotton Mather's view of the sickroom as a stage for confession and redemption, the AMA doctors accepted professional roles as moral therapists. Since "moral" then included what would be called psychotherapy today, the AMA code also sanctioned the devotion of those physicians who had chosen careers as superintendents of institutions caring for the mentally ill.

The AMA doctors emphasized the ideal of shared obligations between physicians and patients, between the profession and the public. Copying Rush, the AMA committee codified the rights of American physicians in a long list of obligations of patients toward their physicians. In the last chapter of the code these duties of patients were expressed more generally as the obligations of the public to the profession, for example, in supporting medical schools and allowing them to acquire cadavers for anatomical dissection. In return, the profession acknowledged a relatively new dimension of professional ethics by its willingness to provide medical knowledge to the governing groups of their communities. This knowledge was needed, for example, in adjudicating civil and criminal proceedings as well as in deliberations about the proper kinds of laws and institutions needed for sanitation, quarantine, and other public health measures.

Worthington Hooker, a general practitioner who later became a professor at Yale, focused on the ideal of reciprocal obligations in *Physician and Patient* (1849), the only comprehensive view of professional ethics published in book form by a North American practitioner before 1900. Hooker's religious beliefs were almost as conservative as those of Cotton Mather, but Hooker believed that moral philosophizing was acceptable for a Christian apologist. He became a moral philosopher of medicine. Like other conscientious midcentury doctors, he knew that religious, educational, and legal institutions had failed to provide a fully acceptable set of moral standards for judging physicians. Hooker believed that doctors were obliged to discover acceptable standards of professional behavior, to publicly proclaim these standards in a format that would be comprehensible to both professionals and the public, and to determine whether such standards had been honored by individual doctors. A code of medical ethics adopted and enforced by a national organization could become the cultural and social instrument for shaping a uniform and universal moral order for American doctors. Hooker viewed his book as an extensive commentary on the AMA code.

Thus, Hooker and many others touted the advantages of the AMA code. Professional righteousness in the United States could be measured by the extent of adherence to this code. Professionally virtuous doctors maintained professional secrecy, made the proper number of visits to the sick, did not offer gloomy prognoses, cared for the incurably sick, requested consultations as needed, and abided by the numerous other precepts in this code that was adopted voluntarily by many societies. In 1855 the AMA decided that all state and local societies wishing to send delegates to its meetings had to adopt its code of ethics.

Not a few chided the AMA's officers about the absence of enforcement procedures. Some state and local societies reprimanded members for consulting with irregular practitioners and occasionally expelled members for criminal offenses, gross immorality, or the sale of secret medicines. The AMA established a judicial council in 1873, but there is no evidence that the council enforced the code regularly or extensively. Similar difficulties affected Canadian practitioners.

One year after its establishment in 1867, the Canadian Medical Association adopted a code of ethics that was almost identical with the AMA code. Minor changes had been made in wording. One clause in the article about obligations of the public to physicians had been omitted, and a new paragraph in Section 3 of Article I permitted beginning practitioners to announce the existence of their offices in the public press. Although some doctors lauded its rules and enforcement was attempted, this code was hardly the final word in matters of medical ethics for most Canadian practitioners.

The attitudes of Canadians contrasted sharply with the sentiments of many practitioners in the United States who believed that the AMA code was as important as the Bible and the Constitution. If the American government could create a bill of rights suitable for all citizens, then the American medical profession could prepare a bill of rights suitable for all reputable medical practitioners. The AMA code of 1847 was that document. In filling a moral vacuum caused by religious pluralism, unacceptable educational standards, loss of confidence in traditional remedies, and ineffective licensure laws, the AMA code became the set of sacred values voluntarily created and professed by respectable and honorable doctors. Sick patients could place their trust in practitioners who gave their allegiance to this code.

In 1880, when one editor doubted that the majority of Canadian medical practitioners had ever read the code adopted by the Canadian Medical Association ("Code of Medical Ethics," 1880a), journal editors in the United States were about to receive an onslaught of articles for and against the AMA code. The problem involved the prohibition against consultation with any practitioners other than those exhibiting allegiance to the code. In 1882 the New York State Medical Society revised its code of ethics so that its members could consult with legally qualified practitioners regardless of their scientific or sectarian status. Seventeen state societies condemned this action, and the AMA refused to admit the New York delegates to its annual meeting. In the following year, the AMA expected all delegates to sign a pledge to obey its original code of ethics. Articles for and against the code and supporting or opposing the renegade New York physicians appeared in nearly all state medical journals. The code-loving conservatives withdrew from the New York State Medical Society and started a new organization that became larger than the original society. Conservatism was the order of the day; the code of 1847 withstood revision until 1903.

Exemplifying a practical application of the moral philosophy taught as a senior year course in most American colleges of the nineteenth century, the AMA code and its predecessors had nurtured professional unity and social respectability during the heyday of Jacksonian egalitarianism in the United States. These codified norms sustained important traditions in Western medicine, reminded all practitioners of essential duties to their patients and colleagues, and encouraged doctors to participate in those public institutions designed for the health and welfare of all.

Science Versus Codes

Those members of the New York State Medical Society who revised their code of ethics in 1882 exemplified a new breed of medical practitioner emerging in North America during the last three decades of the nineteenth century. These individuals could not accept the AMA code's claim that intraprofessional loyalty was more important than scientific truth. When Francis Delafield announced in 1886 that he and his colleagues wanted an association in which there would be no medical politics and no medical ethics, he heralded a fundamental change in the approach of North American practitioners to the perennial challenge of fashioning an acceptable set of professional ethics. Delafield and his colleagues wanted to associate with those practitioners who were able "to contribute something real to the common stock of knowledge" in medical practice (Konold, p. 39). They could no longer tolerate those practitioners who rested secure with a fundamentalist allegiance to the code of one organization whose precepts were rooted in eighteenth-century British experiences. The iconoclastic doctors of the late nineteenth and early twentieth centuries advocated a professional morality that would judge physicians in terms of their skillful application of specialized scientific knowledge in caring for the sick and the healthy. This new moral

philosophy of medicine gradually became institutionalized in some medical schools and societies between 1870 and 1900.

The more progressive schools established teaching and research laboratories, and hundreds of North American practitioners journeyed to the laboratories and clinics of Europe for instruction in the basic sciences, especially microbiology and pathology, and in the clinical specialties, especially the surgical ones. Between 1864 and 1894, American physicians organized more than a dozen national societies for medical specialists (e.g., pediatrics, obstetrics, urology).

These groups did not adopt written codes of ethics. Instead they proclaimed—by word and deed—the values of a liberal premedical education and a thorough education in the medical sciences, allegiance to the experimental method as the proper approach to truths about health and disease, and a strong belief in research and continuing education.

These doctors espoused the rightness of their values as dogmatically as those who believed in the AMA code. Physicians and patients knew of numerous practitioners who did not accept the code but were reputable as persons and successful as healers. The same could not be said for doctors who ignored the bacteriological discoveries, the vaccines, the antiseptic principles, the improvements in diagnostic technology, the pharmacological therapeutics— all based on the methods of experimental science and clinical trials. Good doctors were those who competently and humanely applied this medical science.

These values led to numerous reforms in North American medical education, facilitated and sanctioned by the reestablishment of licensure policies in all of the United States by 1898. In 1902 the Medical Council of Canada became the central licensing agency for the provinces. These new licensure approaches not only sanctioned the reform measures adopted by the progressive American and Canadian medical schools but also upheld obedience to law as an important measure of professional virtuosity.

The physicians who supported these laws and schools recognized that the AMA code said nothing about the more technically proficient environments of the modern hospitals emerging after 1870. To provide competent surgical care, doctors needed instruments and assistants. By the late 1890s, scientific practitioners needed X-ray equipment and laboratory machines that could not be carried in black bags. Technically imprecise care was immoral to these doctors.

Technically adequate care, especially surgical care, required the services of trained nurses. As hospitals became cathedrals of applied science, doctors supported the training schools for nurses initiated by London's Florence Nightingale in 1860. At least fifteen of these schools existed in North America by 1880 (Rosenberg, p. 219). The ethical values espoused by these professional nurses encompassed certain cultural ideals about women, as well as specific norms about knowledge and obedience. Women were believed to be the moral standard-bearers of Victorian society. Those who chose to become nurses were special women who sacrificed much for the glory of God and the needs of the sick. Soldiers in the fight against disease, these nurses organized militaristic training schools that prepared women, attired in starched and pressed white uniforms, to assist physicians obediently in applying scientifically derived medical knowledge.

The AMA code had said nothing about nurses or women or blacks. Physicians and patients welcomed trained nurses who were social products of a new moral philosophy of medicine that assigned special values to some women. Overcoming objections by most males, other women became doctors. Nearly 400 women physicians practiced in 21 states by 1881 (Burns, 1988). Excluded from the AMA, black physicians adapted to the segregationist culture of their era by organizing the National Medical Association in 1895. The AMA codifiers made no revisions to accommodate these scientific, professional, and social changes.

The most significant change involved the transformation of the hospital into a powerful institution that incorporated the moral values of religious charity, scientific excellence, specialized patient care, and social justice. The number of hospitals in North America grew from about 300 in the 1870s to more than 4,000 by 1910. These hospitals became arenas for moral confrontations between medical practitioners and nonprofessional administrators and other laypersons. They fostered the emergence of new healthcare workers and professionals, including laboratory technicians, nurses, occupational and physical therapists, social workers, and hospital chaplains. Each group forged its particular ethical agenda. Hospitals also supported the rapidly expanding urge for specialty differentiation among physicians. At the turn of the twentieth century, hospitals became the interpersonal crucibles that sustained and transformed the legacies of North American medical ethics.

Conclusion

Before 1900, North American physicians were morally acceptable if they cherished dominant religious ideals, behaved as gentlepersons, learned the fundamentals of medical science, revered a code of professional ethics, and abided by the laws of their communities. Professional virtuousness was measured by the extent of allegiance to the cultural and professional traditions of the West, as those traditions had been adapted to North American conditions. During the last quarter of the nineteenth century, a small group of doctors began to challenge some of the value claims for professional

orthodoxy. They believed that favorable results in curing and preventing specific diseases in particular humans made possible by the technically proficient behaviors of skilled professionals applying scientifically derived knowledge were more important than the status-seeking rituals of AMA codifiers or the religious beliefs of the professionals. Yet, the conservative tendencies were so tenacious that the majority of practitioners, at the opening of the twentieth century, still believed in codification as the primary method for establishing professional ethics and still displayed loyalty to the values of one association's code even though major changes in the cultural, scientific, technological, and institutional legacies had changed the nature of the quest for professional ethics.

CHESTER R. BURNS (1995)

BIBLIOGRAPHY

Bard, Samuel. 1769. *A Discourse upon the Duties of a Physician with Some Sentiments on the Usefulness and Necessity of a Public Hospital: Delivered before the President and Governors of King's College, at the Commencement Held on the 16th of May, 1769, as Advice to Those Gentlemen Who Then Received the First Medical Degrees Conferred by That University.* New York: A. & J. Robertson.

Beall, Otho T., Jr., and Shryock, Richard H. 1954. *Cotton Mather: First Significant Figure in American Medicine.* Baltimore: Johns Hopkins University Press.

Blake, John B. 1952. "The Inoculation Controversy in Boston: 1721–1722." *New England Quarterly* 25: 489–506.

Burns, Chester R. 1969. "Malpractice Suits in American Medicine before the Civil War." *Bulletin of the History of Medicine* 43(1): 41–56.

Burns, Chester R. 1977a. "American Medical Ethics: Some Historical Roots." In *Philosophical Medical Ethics: Its Nature and Significance,* pp. 21–26, ed. Stuart F. Spicker and H. Tristram Engelhardt, Jr. Dordrecht, Netherlands: D. Reidel.

Burns, Chester R. 1977b. "Richard Clarke Cabot (1868–1939) and Reformation in American Medical Ethics." *Bulletin of the History of Medicine* 51(31): 353–368.

Burns, Chester R. 1977c. "Thomas Percival: Medical Ethics or Medical Jurisprudence?" In *Legacies in Ethics and Medicine,* pp. 284–299, ed. Chester R. Burns. New York: Science History Publications.

Burns, Chester R. 1988. "Fictional Doctors and the Evolution of Medical Ethics in the United States, 1875–1900." *Literature and Medicine* 7: 39–55.

"Code of Medical Ethics." 1880a. *Canada Lancet* 12:286. Editorial.

"Code of Medical Ethics: Of the Duties of Physicians to Their Patients, and of the Obligations of Patients to Their Physicians." 1880b. *Canada Lancet* 12: 257–264. Editorial.

Fiering, Norman. 1981. *Moral Philosophy at Seventeenth-Century Harvard: A Discipline in Transition.* Chapel Hill: University of North Carolina Press.

Gregory, John. 1772. *Lectures on the Duties and Qualifications of a Physician.* London: W. Strahan.

Grob, Gerald. 1973. *Mental Institutions in America: Social Policy to 1875.* New York: Free Press.

Hampton, Isabel, et al. 1893. *Nursing of the Sick.* New York: McGraw-Hill.

Heagerty, John Joseph. 1928. *Four Centuries of Medical History in Canada and a Sketch of the Medical History of Newfoundland.* 2 vols. Toronto: Macmillan.

Hooker, Worthington. 1972 (1849). *Physician and Patient; or, A Practical View of the Mutual Duties, Relations and Interests of the Medical Profession and the Community.* New York: Arno Press.

Kett, Joseph F. 1967. "American and Canadian Medical Institutions, 1800–1870." *Journal of the History of Medicine and Allied Sciences* 22(4): 343–356.

Konold, Donald E. 1962. *A History of American Medical Ethics, 1847–1912.* Madison: State Historical Society of Wisconsin for the University of Wisconsin.

Ludmerer, Kenneth. 1985. *Learning to Heal: The Development of American Medical Education.* New York: Basic Books.

Mather, Cotton. 1966 (1710). *Bonifacius: An Essay upon the Good,* ed. David Levin. Cambridge, MA: Harvard University Press.

Mather, Cotton. 1972 (1724). *The Angel of Bethesda: An Essay upon the Common Maladies of Mankind,* ed. Gordon W. Jones. Barre, MA: American Antiquarian Society.

Percival, Thomas. 1975 (1803). *Medical Ethics; or, A Code of Institutes and Precepts, Adapted to the Professional Conduct of Physicians and Surgeons.* Huntington, NY: Krieger.

Roland, Charles G. 1984. *Health, Disease and Medicine: Essays in Canadian History.* Toronto: Hannah Institute for the History of Medicine.

Rosenberg, Charles. 1987. *The Care of Strangers: The Rise of America's Hospital System.* New York: Basic Books.

Sloan, Douglas. 1971. *The Scottish Enlightenment and the American College Ideal.* New York: Teachers College Press, Columbia University.

Smith, Wilson. 1956. *Professors and Public Ethics: Studies of Northern Moral Philosophers before the Civil War.* Ithaca, NY: Cornell University Press.

Stevens, Rosemary. 1971. *American Medicine and the Public Interest.* New Haven, CT: Yale University Press.

Thacher, James. 1967 (1828). *American Medical Biography; or, Memoirs of Eminent Physicians Who Have Flourished in America....* New York: DaCapo. Reprint of 1828 edition and 1845 supplement by Stephen Williams.

II. THE UNITED STATES IN THE TWENTY-FIRST CENTURY

The field now called bioethics originated in the 1960s in the United States. It has its roots in the traditional medical ethics of Anglo-American medicine, in the cultural setting of American healthcare, and in certain social, religious, and moral perceptions that had emerged in the American ethos. This entry will first delineate the background for the development of bioethics and then relate the events, issues, and concepts that stimulated its growth during the latter half of the twentieth century (Jonsen, 1998).

The Culture of U.S. Healthcare

Bioethics, in the broad sense of the study of ethical problems encountered as humans interact with the biological within themselves and in their environment, comprehends much more than medicine and medical science. Nevertheless, the development of bioethics can best be understood against the background of the development of medicine in the United States from 1900. The twentieth century saw enormous growth in American medicine—in the amount of money devoted to medical care, the number of persons with access to care, the number of personnel and specialties, the complexity of institutional systems, and the extent of scientific technology. Three principal lines of development that contribute to the interest in ethical questions are the changing role of the hospital, the predominance of science and technology, and the development of specialization (Jonsen, 1998).

Beginning in the late nineteenth century, hospitals were founded at an increasing rate and eventually became the principal sources of medical care in the United States. As medical diagnosis and treatment increasingly involved elaborate techniques and devices, it was seen as more efficient and economical to centralize care in hospitals. Physicians could allocate their time more conveniently; nurses, technicians, and medical specialists could coordinate their work more effectively. Communities desired hospitals as a matter of pride; cities needed hospitals for indigent patients. The passage in 1946 of the Hill-Burton Act, which provided federal support for local hospital construction, and the tendency of the newly popular health insurance to reimburse hospital care rather than office or home care accelerated the evolution of the hospital in the United States (Rosenberg; Stevens, 1989).

With seminal discoveries in bacteriology, pathology, and physiology during the nineteenth century, scientific medicine came into its own. But it became an integral part of medical practice in the United States only after the extensive reorganization of medical schools in the decades around 1900—a period marked by the vigorous efforts of the American Medical Association to reform medical education and to improve the standards of medical practice. Medical school reform was greatly stimulated by the Flexner Report,

Medical Education in the United States and Canada, sponsored by the Carnegie Foundation for the Advancement of Teaching. Scientific investigation, increasingly supported by the federal government, especially during and after World War II, brought research physicians into medical education and patient care. Experimentation involving human subjects, both patients and health volunteers, became more widespread as the National Institutes of Health opened and sponsored clinical research centers in the 1950s. The twentieth century brought a "new" medicine, one profoundly shaped by the biological sciences. Diagnosis and treatment took on forms dictated by the scientific knowledge generated in the laboratory, tested in clinics, and assessed by statistical methods.

The fascination of scientific knowledge and techniques drew many physicians into narrower fields of concentration. The vastly increased body of knowledge became too much for individual physicians to master. Moreover, it became possible for physicians to build careers by performing procedures focused on limited aspects of patient care. Thus, scientific medicine fostered the growth of specialties. Specialty boards, organized to test and certify competence in the particular fields of medicine, were established in a variety of specialties and subspecialties, beginning in the United States with the Board of Ophthalmology in 1917 (Stevens, 1971). The social and economic status of physicians improved significantly during the first half of the twentieth century and American physicians gradually moved from middle- to upper-class status, which distinguished them in attitudes, lifestyle, and place of residence from many of their patients (Starr).

In general, the three developments described above set the scene for the ethical concerns that began to surface in the United States in the 1960s. The concentration of specialized medical care in hospitals encouraged an impersonal, organizational approach to medical care. While social, behavioral, environmental, and personal aspects of illness were not totally neglected, scientific medicine focused on the biological and physical aspects; complaints that physicians had lost the ability to care for "the whole patient" were increasingly heard. As scientific knowledge increased, teaching in the sciences tended to crowd other concerns from the basic medical curriculum. Specialization narrowed attention to particular organ systems and diseases, and patients were shuttled between a variety of specialists rather than cared for by the family doctor. Leading medical educators felt obliged to continually stress the more comprehensive view of medicine, but educational, economic, and professional pressures constantly obscured these calls. By the 1960s, physicians, formerly close and familiar to their patients, had become "strangers at the bedside." This alienation was an important impetus for the emergence of bioethics (Rothman, 1991).

Social and Cultural Trends

In addition to these directions within medicine, cultural and social movements involved the public in the ethics of medical care to an unprecedented extent. The mass media stimulated public interest in medicine. By emphasizing new discoveries, dramatic incidents, and "human interest" stories, the media underlined growing tensions between complex medical technology and its humane use. Growing urbanization and the consequent uneven distribution of population heightened existing obstacles to healthcare. A higher standard of living and increased educational achievement for many increased the sophistication of patients. Growing support of biomedical research by the federal government during the 1950s and 1960s thrust research into the realm of public policy. The ability of persons to purchase healthcare, dramatically improved by the introduction of employment-based insurance in the 1930s and augmented for the poor and the elderly by the passage of Medicare and Medicaid in 1965, gradually began to erode. Healthcare in the United States, while technically superb, became extremely costly and, because of its cost and organization, excluded large numbers of Americans from adequate care. This situation had evolved into a social and political crisis by the late 1980s. No resolution had been found as the twenty-first century opened.

The slow but incessant influence of consumerism, from the concern about adulteration of food in the early decades of the twentieth century to the militant demands for consumers' rights in the 1970s, began to influence the healthcare system. The patients'-rights movement in the 1970s was a segment of a larger movement for civil rights. The women's movement brought attention to the care of women patients and the distribution of women professionals in healthcare. These movements heightened sensitivity to the unmet healthcare needs of women and people of color. The issues of birth control and abortion divided the public on the role of health professionals in family and population policies. Medicine began to draw practitioners from a culturally broader population, and many new allied health professions and technical specialties were added to the healthcare team, enriching and intensifying debates over values among healthcare providers. The peace movements of the 1960s and 1970s and growing ecological movements drew attention to burgeoning international health problems arising from war, environmental hazards, and pollution (McCally and Cassel; Leaf). These concerns challenged the role of medicine in maintaining the overall health and well-being of

Earth's population. Physicians for Social Responsibility was founded in 1971, on the premise that the health risks of nuclear armaments fell within the social responsibilities of physicians. Although threats to the global biological environment emerged as major research and political concerns in the 1970s, the study of ethical issues in these areas remained rather separate from the study of ethical issues in medicine and health sciences (Geiger; Jonsen and Jameton; Cassel and Jameton).

These social and cultural trends, together with the direction of the biological and medical sciences, were the background for the bioethics movement that began in the 1960s. Bioethics as it is known today had its roots in general public concerns over issues of individual rights, social justice, and environmental quality that marked American culture in that era. Before examining the bioethics movement itself, it is advisable to examine the ideas, activities, and interests that were its precursors.

Traditional Medical Ethics

The effort to establish a unified medical profession during the nineteenth century and the accompanying internecine strife among physicians of various doctrinal allegiances profoundly influenced the nature and content of medical ethics at the opening of the twentieth century. Although strains of the Hippocratic, medieval, and Enlightenment tradition were invoked, the dominant themes stressed the respectability and collegiality of the profession and detailed the etiquette of professional relationships that promoted those themes. At the beginning of the twentieth century, this goal of a unified profession was within reach. The American Medical Association (AMA), through the strenuous efforts of its chief spokesman, Joseph McCormack, represented the profession as dedicated to orthodox scientific medicine, the advancement of medical education, the elimination of quackery, and the promotion of public health, particularly through support of pure food and drug legislation (Burrow, 1977; Jonsen, 2000; Baker et al.).

One crucial mandate of professional ethics—that ethical physicians did not consult with or refer patients to unorthodox practitioners—was firmly in place in the early twentieth century. Decades before the turn of the century and for several decades afterward, many ill-trained or untrained persons practiced "medicine." A vast number of substances and devices were promoted as cures for various or all disorders. A strong public voice favored freedom of choice of practitioner, claiming that the "scientific" practitioners and drugs offered nothing better than their untutored and untested competitors. Others, particularly the

more educated practitioners, set out to discredit quacks, nostrums, and patent medicines.

This concern stimulated the debate among physicians over cooperation between physicians and "irregular" practitioners. Many regular physicians refused to treat patients who had received prior treatment from irregulars; medical society codes of ethics barred irregular practitioners from society membership, hospital admitting privileges, and joint practice with regular practitioners (Gewitz). During the years before World War I, the AMA led a fight that finally persuaded state legislatures and Congress to pass legislation controlling the practice of medicine and the sale of drugs. Midwives were among the targets of the campaign against quackery, and despite better health outcomes by many midwives at the turn of the century, the campaign for "scientific" practice won public support and midwives have been largely displaced by obstetricians (Leavitt). During the era before World War I, medical ethics appeared to some as exclusively concerned with the criteria that restricted practice to "orthodox" physicians. While self-interested motives can be imputed to organized medicine, many repudiated the "freedom of choice" argument out of the sincere concern that medicine "at least do no harm" (Burrow, 1977). Still, as many commentators have noted, medical ethics, in this matter, served the ends of medical monopoly (Berlant).

A second important question about consultation and referral was vigorously debated: whether referring physicians were entitled to a fee or "kickback" for having sent a patient to a specialist or consultant. This practice was particularly common in surgery. Some surgeons solicited patients through general practitioners who, in turn, found it lucrative to refer patients who sometimes did not require surgery. The abuses of fee splitting scandalized the public and many professionals. The American College of Surgeons, founded in 1915, required its fellows to take an oath that explicitly repudiated fee splitting. Although branded by all professional organizations as unethical, this practice continued in a covert way for many years (Davis).

Perhaps the most agitated debate in traditional medical ethics during the first half of the twentieth century was over the integrity of the patient–physician relationship. Fee-for-service practice by solo practitioners who sought to develop their own followings of patients was the predominant model. However, some "contract practice," in which a physician undertook to provide unlimited service to a designated population for an agreed amount, had long existed. Plantations in the American South had used this method for the medical care of slaves. Fraternal organizations formed by immigrant populations had insured their members in this way, and in the West, the railroad and lumber industries contracted with physicians to care for their workers. Many in the organized profession, however, objected to contract practice, condemning it as "cut-rate medicine," as inferior to private practice in the quality of care and personal relationship, and as allowing a "third party" to dictate conditions of care, to the possible detriment of the patient. The same objections met the forms of group practice that evolved from contract practice in the first half of the twentieth century. Bitter battles raged over these issues; many medical societies excluded physicians who were involved in these "schemes." A series of antitrust decisions by the U.S. Supreme Court, beginning in the 1940s and continuing into the 1970s, gradually cleared the way for the development of a variety of corporate practice forms, such as health maintenance organizations, that a few decades before would have been considered unethical forms of medical practice.

Another ethical issue was closely related: the debate over payment for medical care. The traditional ethics had required physicians to charge their patients fairly and to provide free or discounted services to those who could not pay. The emergence of free public clinics and hospitals in the late nineteenth century threatened that ethic. Many physicians claimed that even patients who could pay sought free care, draining the physicians' practices and making it impossible for them to provide charitable services, because they needed a steady income from paying patients to be able to afford to provide such services. Thus, at the turn of the century, extensive public use of free clinics was debated as an ethical question. Some argued that it was conducive to continued pauperization; others claimed that forcing poor people to pay for needed medical care was immoral. Some practitioners opposed free clinics because they viewed them as unfair competition by medical schools, which they saw as using free clinics to obtain patients for medical education. At the same time, the organized profession realized that the costs of care were beyond many persons and that physicians' incomes were low. Initial support was given to proposals emanating from organized labor for government-supported compulsory health insurance. By 1916, a broad coalition of organized medicine, labor, and social reformers had almost achieved the passage of national health insurance. World War I intervened, and the coalition was weakened: National health insurance seemed a "Germanic" proposal to many (Germany had long had such a program) and "socialistic" to others. Organized medicine, from then on, firmly opposed almost all forms of government health insurance. Again, it was proclaimed that because this would interpose government between doctor and patient, such programs would be unethical. This opposition persisted down to the passage of Medicaid and Medicare in 1965 (Marmor; Fein).

The AMA revised its 1847 Code of Ethics in 1903, 1912, 1947, 1957, and 1980. The revisions, successively more succinct, reflected an increased sense of professionalism and ideals about the scientific excellence of the practitioner. At the same time, the professional ethics expressed in official codes and in the positions taken by organized medicine on social questions reflected an interest in maintaining the status quo of the profession and the practice of medicine as it had been evolving in the late nineteenth and early twentieth centuries. With few exceptions, such as increased tolerance for group practice, the 1957 revision of the AMA Code, which consists of a condensation into ten "principles of medical ethics," bears little evidence of the major social changes that had begun to affect medical care in the United States. In 1985 the AMA Judicial Council changed its name to the Council on Ethical and Judicial Affairs; it now issues regular statements on issues of current ethical import, such as euthanasia, the obligation to care for patients with AIDS, and financial conflict of interest. Many major medical organizations, such as the American College of Physicians and the American Academy of Pediatrics, have formed ethics committees with a similar purpose. Although commentaries and informal codes on the conduct of nurses can be found as far back as the inception of the profession by Florence Nightingale (1820–1910), the American Nurses' Association did not adopt an official code of ethics for nurses until 1950.

Thus, during the first half of the twentieth century, medical ethics consisted of professionally devised propositions to enhance the unity and monopoly of the profession. Professional self-interest sometimes hid behind ethical claims that were often to the detriment of the public. At the same time, the profession, in encouraging improved medical education and advocating public health and safety measures, lived up to its more noble traditions (Jonsen, 1990).

The Influence of Theological and Philosophical Ethics

The medical profession in the United States imbibed an ethic from the Judeo-Christian culture of the nation. The ethical physician was expected to be respectful of religion and to be a "good Christian gentleman" (Burns, 1977). The dominant Protestant culture offered some admonitions about health and medicine. For example, in the nineteenth century physicians of strong Protestant faith urged the enactment of strict laws against abortion (Mohr). Nevertheless, theological ethics was relatively silent on particular issues concerning medicine and health.

Roman Catholic moral theology, however, had a long tradition of concern with moral questions in medicine. Since the seventeenth century, principles of Scholastic philosophy and theology had been applied to such issues as abortion, sterilization, and the duties of physician and patient. Acute analyses had been made of the duty to sustain life and the circumstances under which the death of a patient could be permitted. This tradition was conveyed to students in the Catholic medical schools that were founded in the nineteenth century. Father Charles Coppens, S. J., lectured in the Medical Department of Creighton University at the turn of the century. His 1905 book, *Moral Principles and Medical Practice: The Basis of Medical Jurisprudence,* treated abortion, sexual behavior, and the duties of physicians in light of philosophical and theological principles. His work represented "the emergence of medical ethics as a medical school subject, especially at religiously affiliated schools" (Burns, 1980, p. 282). During the 1940s and 1950s, this tradition was carried on in the extensive writings of theologians Edwin Healy, Gerald Kelly, Charles McFadden, Francis Connell, and Patrick Finney. In 1949 the Catholic Hospital Association issued *Ethical and Religious Directives for Catholic Health Facilities* (revised in 1954 and 1971), which obliged all physicians and health professionals working in Catholic institutions to follow Catholic moral tenets with regard to a number of specific medical procedures (U.S. Catholic Conference).

Catholic reflection on medical moral issues continues in the *Linacre Quarterly,* published by the National Federation of Catholic Physicians' Guilds since 1932. Theologians Charles Curran, Richard McCormick, Kevin O'Rourke, Margaret Farley, and Lisa Sowle Cahill are now the principal voices of this tradition. The Catholic tradition, in its doctrine of natural law, has affirmed that moral questions can be analyzed from a philosophical viewpoint, without explicit reference to revealed theological truths. Thus, common ground can be found with those who do not share the Catholic faith. This somewhat nonsectarian approach has allowed Catholic analysis of problems to have a significant influence on the intellectual development of secular bioethics.

The Protestant denominations, while not producing a detailed analysis of medical-moral problems, had taken positions on such questions as suicide, euthanasia, abortion, and contraception. In 1950 Willard Sperry, dean of Harvard Divinity School, published lectures given at Massachusetts General Hospital and the University of Michigan Medical School under the title, *The Ethical Basis of Medical Practice.* He offered reflective, humane, literary, but unsystematic commentary on such problems as truth telling, prolongation of life, and euthanasia as the era of medical technology was opening. Four years later, Episcopal theologian Joseph Fletcher published the groundbreaking and prescient study *Morals and Medicine.* Fletcher's work was the first to emphasize the patient's rights as the center of an ethics of medicine and to argue "the ethical case for our human rights ... to use

contraceptives, to seek insemination anonymously from a donor, to be sterilized and to receive a merciful death from a medically competent euthanasist" (p. 25). He strongly asserted the patient's right to be told the truth about his or her diagnosis and prognosis. Fletcher's book is the pioneering work of the new medical ethics.

Sixteen years later, Methodist theologian Paul Ramsey produced the foundational work of bioethics, *Patient as Person.* Ramsey, professor of religion at Princeton University, took the unusual step of spending a year in intense dialogue with physicians, scientists, and students at Georgetown University and immersing himself in the clinical activities of the Georgetown University Hospital. *Patient as Person,* first delivered as the Beecher Lectures at Yale University in 1969, examined questions, such as organ transplantation, experimentation with human subjects, and the use of life-supporting technologies, that had not been on the agenda of previous commentators on the moral aspects of medicine. Although he spoke from a very different theological ground than did Fletcher, Ramsey also placed the freedom and rights of the patient at the center of his ethic but subsumed patients and physicians within the scope of a theologically defined covenant. Despite the theological tone and language of Ramsey's work, its cogent analyses of issues such as consent were widely influential (Ramsey, 1970b). At about the same time, James Gustafson of Yale Divinity School produced thoughtful essays on the implications of medical and scientific advances. Many Protestant theologians followed the paths laid down by these pioneers, among them Kenneth Vaux, William May, Harmon Smith, James Childress, and Stanley Hauerwas. In 1987 the Park Ridge Center for the Study of Health, Faith, and Ethics was founded under the auspices of the Lutheran Hospital Association to foster religious reflection on the issues of bioethics. The center has published a fine series of volumes describing the teachings about medicine and morality of major Christian denominations and other world religions (Marty; Vaux). The distinctive features of modern bioethics begin to appear in Fletcher and Ramsey: attention to the effects of new technologies, affirmation of the centrality of the patient as free and responsible agent, and the invocation of the concepts and method of moral analysis from the classical disciplines of theology and philosophy.

The Jewish faith has an ancient tradition of reflection upon questions of life, death, health, and medical care. Issues in medical ethics, such as allocation of scarce resources, risk–benefit evaluation, quality of life, abortion, contraception, and indications of death, are discussed in great detail in Talmudic literature. The doctoral thesis of Immanuel Jakobovits, published in 1959 as *Jewish Medical Ethics,* drew these teachings together and brought them into contact with modern scientific advances. In so doing, Jakobovits gave a distinct identity to a field of study that had not been previously singled out in Jewish scholarship. Talmudic scholars such as Moses Tendler, David Bleich, David Feldman, Elliot Dorf, Laurie Zoloth, and the physician Fred Rosner have continued this effort. The first course in Jewish medical ethics was taught by Rabbi Tendler at Yeshiva University in 1956, and the Institute for Jewish Medical Ethics was established in San Francisco in the early 1980s.

The influence of moral philosophy came rather late to the analysis of medical-moral questions. Although the first AMA Code of Ethics was strongly influenced by the English physician Thomas Percival (1740–1804), who was affected to some extent by the philosophers of the Scottish Enlightenment, American philosophers paid scant attention to these questions. In 1927 Chauncey D. Leake noted in his edition of *Percival's Medical Ethics* that all of the classic codes represented "medical etiquette" or the tenets of professional courtesy rather than medical ethics. "It is interesting," he wrote, "that writers on medical ethics have seldom availed themselves of the philosophical analyses of the principles of ethical theory made by recognized ethical scholars" (Percival, p. 3). In words that predict the bioethics movement of the 1960s, Leake called for a medical ethics that would bring the systems of moral philosophy to bear on the problems of medical practice. He undertook to do this in a dialogue with philosopher Patrick Romanell (Leake and Romanell). Three decades later, moral philosophers were important figures in the elaboration of ethics of healthcare.

Secular academic philosophy did not find it easy to approach the practical problems posed by evolving science and medicine. In the 1950s philosophical ethics was struggling with the diverse theoretical challenges of naturalism, relativism, utilitarianism, Marxism, linguistic analysis, and positivism; hardly any attention was paid to the analysis of actual moral problems. This began to change in the 1960s as students vociferously raised questions about the moral legitimacy of the war in Southeast Asian and racial discrimination with their professors of moral philosophy. Interest in practical philosophy slowly appeared within academic philosophy. The questions of life and death raised by new technologies began to intrigue some philosophers. In 1969 Nicholas Rescher wrote an early article on the allocation of "exotic medical lifesaving therapy," such as dialysis and transplantation. Medical ethics began to be taught as an undergraduate philosophy course for which textbooks were produced (Gorovitz et al., 1973; Gorovitz et al., 1976). Daniel Callahan, trained in the analytic philosophy tradition at Harvard University, realized the ethical dimensions of the new medicine and in 1979 founded, with psychiatrist Willard Gaylin,

the Institute of Society, Ethics, and the Life Sciences, later renamed the Hastings Center. Although slower to enter the field of practical ethics than the theologians, philosophers such as Baruch Brody, K. Danner Clauser, Tom Beauchamp, and Stephen Toulmin made significant contributions to the methods and substantive analysis of biomedical problems. Indeed, as Toulmin has claimed, "Medical ethics saved the life of philosophy," imparting an intellectual vitality and moral urgency to a field that had turned from the moral concerns of personal and social life to arid speculation.

Legal scholars were also prominent in the early years of bioethics. William Curran and Paul Freund of Harvard University and Jay Katz of Yale University contributed to the important symposium on experimentation with human subjects sponsored by the American Academy of Arts and Sciences in 1966; Katz subsequently published major work in this area (Freund; Katz, Capron, and Glass). John Noonan wrote perceptively on abortion and contraception. As the issues surrounding death and dying became prominent, particularly with the Karen Ann Quinlan case in 1975, lawyers became deeply involved, because law has always taken a serious interest in the determination of the causes of human death. Similarly, the evolution of the doctrine of informed consent has been strongly influenced by jurisprudence and judicial opinion. It is difficult to distinguish between the lawyer and the bioethicist in such figures as George Annas, John Robertson, Alexander Capron, and William Winslade. Indeed, one of these scholars, in a 1993 book, asserted, "American law, not philosophy or medicine, is primarily responsible for the agenda, development and current state of American bioethics" (Annas, p. 2).

Many physicians and scientists have become interested and adept in bioethics. As the field developed, however, the majority of its practitioners came from theology and philosophy; relatively few physicians have devoted themselves to scholarly productivity. Notable exceptions are Edmund Pellegrino, Mark Siegler, Howard Brody, Eric Cassell, and Christine Cassel. They bring to their contributions the sense and sensitivity of the practicing physician.

Although ethics was once taught in American colleges as the summit of the curriculum (often by the president of the college), as the twentieth century opened, ethics had retreated from that academic prominence to a refined and remote subspecialty of philosophy. Many believed that ethics was "caught" rather than taught. Medical ethics, it was said, was best conveyed to medical students by the example of prominent physicians, such as William Osler, as well as by the role models of the leading teachers in individual medical schools. Their lives and writings were common touchstones of discussion. Moreover, resolution of ethical issues tended to emphasize the need for the excellent overall character and reputation of the physician, that is, an ethics of virtue. This emphasis on the good intentions of the physician was congruent with the model of practice then supported by the AMA—the independent practitioner in contract with the individual patient.

Medical jurisprudence, the study of the relationship between medical practice and the law, had been taught in American medical schools with some regularity during the nineteenth century. No course on medical ethics as such is known to have been offered until the late 1920s, except in the Catholic medical schools. The curriculum of the first known course in a secular medical school, offered by Park White at Washington University School of Medicine, St. Louis, in 1924, included discussion of group practice, consultations, relations with other practitioners, quackery, eugenics, euthanasia, and birth control (Burns, 1980). In 1926 the AMA recommended that medical ethics be made part of the medical curriculum. By 1931 it was reported that 43 percent of the sixty-seven American medical schools offered a course in medical ethics, most of these courses in the required curriculum. Approximately the same level was maintained through the 1950s, although course time was stretched to cover other subjects, such as medical sociology and economics, and it is unclear what topics were covered as medical ethics. During this era, Richard Cabot, who was both professor of medicine and professor of social ethics at Harvard University, was a dominant figure. He stressed the importance of personal integrity and honesty in the physician, as had the earlier professional ethics, but he placed this within the evolving framework of scientific medicine: Integrity must be manifested in clinical competence, the primary ethical obligation of the practitioner (Burns, 1977).

As the century progressed and the social and psychological sciences spread in collegiate education, discussion of the art of character development became increasingly overlaid with psychological and psychiatric analysis of the physician's character. Indeed, in the 1940s and 1950s, the Freudian model of psychological dynamics and of the doctor–patient relationship became prominent in the analyses of the virtues of physicians (Binger). Meanwhile, the increasing midcentury confidence in the social sciences tended to displace ethics terminology with concepts of "professional development," "human engineering," and so forth, sometimes even denigrating the admonitions of traditional morality as no more than "taboos." Ethics was often seen as so colored by religion that its teaching was bound to be covert indoctrination. In the secular climate of that time, any formal acknowledgment of ethics was suspect: Even the National Endowment for the Humanities, which eventually became a strong supporter of bioethics, originally excluded ethics from the list of the humanities whose study it would

fund. Thus, ethics was rarely taught in higher education and even more rarely in medical education. This hiatus in the teaching of medical ethics during the 1950s may be seen as a prelude to the bioethics movement, in which neglected ethical questions forced their way back into the consciousness of the profession and the public alike.

The first national conference on the teaching of medical ethics was held in 1972 under the sponsorship of the Institute of Society, Ethics, and the Life Sciences and the Columbia University College of Physicians and Surgeons. By this time, out of 114 medical schools, only three required an ethics course and only thirty-three offered ethics as an elective (Veatch, Gaylin, and Morgan). The Society for Health and Human Values, formed in 1969, and its attendant Institute on Human Values in Medicine, encouraged medical ethics teaching. In the decade that followed, the number of schools providing organized teaching of ethics increased, and faculty members, often philosophers and theologians, were appointed. The content of the course shifted from the traditional topics, such as truth telling, confidentiality, care of the poor, care of the dying, and relations among practitioners, to the newer problems raised by technology and the social setting of modern medical care. In 1987 ninety-five American medical schools reported that they required a course in medical ethics, and the Association of American Medical Colleges strongly urged the inclusion of ethics in the curriculum (Bickel).

Nursing Ethics

Although medical students received little formal instruction in ethics, nursing schools developed a strong tradition of ethics teaching. Several major works on ethics were published by nurses at the turn of the century, notably *Nursing Ethics* by Isabel Hampton Robb (1901). Although her text is marked by a stern and self-sacrificing message to nurses, it includes sensitive discussion of many aspects of nurse–patient and nurse–physician relations. Textbooks on nursing ethics published in the first two decades of the century went through many editions before fading from popularity in the 1940s and 1950s. Notable among the authors were Charlotte Aikens and Thomas Verner Moore, whose books made extensive use of case studies. In 1931 religious educator Paul Limbert published a defense of nursing ethics courses: They were needed, he argued, to make ethical concerns explicit and to assist student nurses in interpreting their clinical experiences in such a way as to foster good professional character. As in the medical ethics of that era, the emphasis was on the character development of the nurse rather than on principle-centered or patient-centered ethics.

An important theme for nursing ethics has always been the impact of the feelings and character—the "humanness"—of the practitioner on the care and cure of the patient. As new technologies developed with increasing efficacy, practitioners felt the need to redefine the role of their personality in relationship to those technologies.

At the beginning of the twentieth century, nursing was predominantly a home-based practice; by the end of the century, it had become predominantly institution based. This redefinition of the nursing role provided a stimulus for some of the recurring issues in the nursing literature of the early part of the century. For instance, whether a nurse should do housework, such as washing diapers or tending the fire in the grate, was a significant issue until the 1950s. How the nurse should react to the errors of quacks and regular physicians continued to be a prominent issue. In all such cases, texts resolved the questions in terms of dedication to the welfare of patients. Indeed, nursing ethics took an early stand against permitting patients to be injured by other practitioners, including physicians, and nurses have taken an increasing role in institutional quality control.

Like physicians, nurses struggled with the problem of "irregular" practitioners. In the earliest part of the century, the "untrained nurse" was represented in the nursing ethics literature as ethically, as well as technically, incompetent. The emergence of the licensed practical nurse in the 1930s and the increasing number of nursing aides during the century challenged professional nursing, and the ethics of relationships with these occupations has been delicate. In the 1970s the American Nurses' Association took a stand that a bachelor's-level education was necessary for professional nursing, calling into question the standing of nurses trained in hospitals and community colleges. In the 1980s nursing was again challenged by a recommendation from the AMA, calling for the creation of a "registered care technician" to perform some of the technical functions of nurses. The ethics of the relationship of nurse to physician is still being debated in the nursing ethics literature. It is commonly asserted that power and gender relationships are central to the ethics of nursing. Original presentations of the ethics of nursing have appeared: The works of Mila Aroskar, Martin Benjamin, Joy Curtis, Anne Davis, Marsha Fowler, Sara T. Fry, Sally Gadow, Amy Haddad, Andrew Jameton, Christine Mitchell, James Myskens, and Michael Yeo are notable. Their work carries the themes of nursing ethics into the broader stream of bioethics. The bioethics movement has also touched the many other professions involved in the care of patients: dentists, occupational therapists, pharmacists, physical therapists, physician assistants, medical technicians, and social workers.

Ethical Issues in the Emerging Biomedical Technologies

In the years after World War II, the rapid advances of biomedical science were translated into clinical interventions that could save and sustain life in ways never before possible. These technological advances brought not only the benefits of improved health and prolonged life but also a range of puzzling moral questions (Jonsen, 1998). One of the first of these technologies to raise explicit ethical concerns was the 1961 invention by Belding Scribner at the University of Washington of a technique for chronic hemodialysis of persons with end-stage renal disease. Because the first artificial kidney center in Seattle, Washington had limited machines and trained personnel, it could serve only a tiny portion of the 15,000 or so persons in need of such lifesaving care. A committee consisting of seven lay members and two physician-advisers was chosen to select patients who would be admitted. Those who were not admitted would die. The committee employed social criteria, such as productive livelihood and respectable citizenship, for selecting candidates from among the many medically eligible patients. There was a strong public reaction and much severe criticism of using social values in life-and-death decisions (Fox and Swazey, 1974).

Philosophers and theologians noticed the issue and engaged in debate over it (Rescher; Childress; Ramsey, 1970b). The issue of rationing the scarce resource of dialysis was resolved in 1972 by an amendment to the Social Security Act providing payment for about 90 percent of the high cost of dialysis. This led to further discussion comparing the plight of other persons in high-cost disease categories, such as hemophilia, with that of kidney patients. In justice, the argument ran, various other groups ought to receive similar public aid. This early example of the ethical dilemmas posed by the new technology exemplified some of the themes that would become central to bioethics: the acceptance of lay opinion into decisions formerly reserved to physicians, the appearance of philosophical and theological analyses of the issue, the recognition of questions of fairness in application of medical resources, and the profound implications of life-and-death decisions. Indeed, the questions "Who should live? Who should die? Who should decide?" became the theme of bioethics.

The first heart transplantations were done in South Africa in 1968; similar operations were attempted shortly thereafter in the United States. Optimistic claims by medical innovators fostered public enthusiasm, which turned to disillusionment when, after three years, the very poor survival rate resulted in a virtual moratorium on heart transplants (Fox and Swazey, 1974). As heart and kidney transplantation became more effective, ethical issues surrounding organ donorship arose. To encourage cadaver donorship, the Uniform Anatomical Gift Act was proposed by the U.S. National Conference of Commissioners on Uniform Laws in 1968 and subsequently adopted by all states (Katz, Capron, and Glass). Because of high costs and the scarcity of organs, transplantation forcefully raised questions of whether the gains of new technology could justify the costs. At the same time, the determination of death, traditionally done by noting the cessation of cardiorespiratory functions, began to be questioned: These criteria seemed obsolete under conditions of artificial respiratory support and did not allow for removal of organs for transplantation. A vigorous debate ensued about the ethical and legal implications of shifting to clinical criteria that would focus on cessation of brain activity. In 1968 a committee at Harvard Medical School formulated a statement defining *brain death* as a criterion for declaring death (Harvard Medical School). Brain death criteria were accepted and legalized slowly, beginning in Kansas in 1970. Still, considerable confusion required further refinement of the concept, leading eventually to the recommendation of a Uniform Statute for the Determination of Death, which has now been adopted in most jurisdictions (U.S. President's Commission for the Study of Ethical Problems in Medicine, 1981).

During this same period, artificial implants to assist or replace the heart were being developed. Denton Cooley in Houston, Texas, unsuccessfully attempted to implant an artificial heart in 1969. In anticipation of the time when such a device might be ready for use in humans, the National Heart and Lung Institute in 1971 established a panel to study the possible ethical, social, economic, legal, medical, and psychiatric consequences of its development. This was the first effort by the federal government to explore the ethical implications of new medical technologies (National Heart and Lung Institute; Jonsen, 1973). The first actual implantation of an artificial heart—in Barney Clark, at Salt Lake City in 1982—aroused considerable debate about the appropriateness of this device (Shaw).

By the mid-1960s, issues of research ethics had begun to ferment among scientists (Ladimer and Newman). The Nuremberg trials in 1947 revealed the horrors of the Nazi concentration camps, where cruel and lethal medical experiments had been performed on prisoners. Several articles on the ethics of human experimentation had appeared in the American medical literature, but the ethical issues of biomedical experimentation with human beings were not widely discussed, perhaps because many believed that nothing so horrible could happen in the United States (Alexander; Annas and Grodin). During World War II, however, the intense efforts to improve the capabilities of military medicine occasionally spurred researchers to design experiments

in which persons were treated dangerously and without their consent. In the years after the war, biomedical research was fueled by large infusions of funds from the newly expanded National Institutes of Health, and research projects were sponsored in hospitals throughout the country. As the volume and intensity of research increased, questionable practices appeared and were tolerated as the price to be paid in the war against disease. Informed consent of research subjects was rarely obtained, and oversight by anyone other than the researcher was unusual. In 1962 a number of children were born with serious congenital defects due to their mothers' ingestion of thalidomide, an unapproved drug. This tragedy stimulated congressional hearings at which the ethics of human experimentation, then largely uncontrolled, was aired. Subsequently, amendments to the federal Food, Drug, and Cosmetic Act in 1964 required full and free consent of all subjects of drug trials.

In 1966 Henry Beecher, professor of anesthesia at Harvard University, brought problems in the ethics of experimentation to the attention of the medical community. He detailed twenty-two medical experiments carried on by respected investigators that he branded as unethical because of lack of consent or inappropriate assessment of risks in relation to benefits (Beecher; Rothman, 1991). In 1966 (with revisions in 1968) the U.S. Public Health Service formulated guidelines for protection of the rights and welfare of human subjects in all federally supported research. In 1971 these guidelines became regulations of the Department of Health, Education, and Welfare, requiring research institutions to set up medical and lay panels to review all federally funded experimentation to ensure that subjects are informed and freely consent to the research procedure, and to determine that the scientific benefits justify the risks of the research (Levine).

A number of scandals in research ethics brought public attention to the need for regulation. At Willowbrook State Hospital in New York, a series of studies on hepatitis were conducted from 1965 to 1971 that involved infecting mentally retarded children with hepatitis virus. At the Jewish Chronic Disease Hospital in Brooklyn in 1963, live cancer cells were injected into senile patients without their knowledge or consent. In 1971 a study begun in the 1930s at Tuskegee, Alabama, came to public attention: A number of rural black men suffering from syphilis had been left untreated in order to ascertain the "natural history" of the untreated disease (Jones). In response to these and several other scandals, the U.S. Congress established the National Commission for the Protection of Human Subjects of Biomedical and Behavioral Research (1974–1977) to make recommendations for federal policy on the broad problems of human subjects in research as well as the special problems posed by research with fetuses, children, prisoners, and other dependent or vulnerable persons. These recommendations were codified in federal regulations and are now widely enforced in research institutions. The field of bioethics was significantly advanced by the work of this commission. Several scholars in ethics sat on the commission, and many philosophers, theologians, lawyers, and sociologists were asked to contribute to its deliberations, thereby stimulating thought about the issues and making public careful analyses of the problems and principles. The commission's *Belmont Report* (1978), stating the principles of research with human subjects, first enunciated the triad of bioethical principles: autonomy, beneficence, and justice. Federal regulations codified the commission's recommendations, and for the next several decades clinical research, scrutinized for ethical probity by institutional review boards, proceeded without incident. In the late 1990s, however, several deaths and widespread evidence of inadequate review of research led to a revival of concern. The ethics of research returned to the agenda of bioethics.

It became increasingly common during the twentieth century for people to die in a hospital, often under conditions of dehumanizing technology. This reawakened age-old discussions of death, dying, and euthanasia, now in light of the new technical potential of modern medicine. Although there had been several unsuccessful attempts to make euthanasia legal in the early years of the century, death and dying had become a taboo subject in medicine. Elisabeth Kübler-Ross's sensitive interviews with dying patients, captured in her 1969 book, *On Death and Dying,* did much to awaken interest in the psychology of dying.

In 1976 the state of California passed novel legislation about termination of life support. The Natural Death Act authorized patients to sign a legal document directing physicians to remove or to withhold life-support devices under carefully defined circumstances. Many states have followed California by enacting legal forms of "advance directives" to guide physicians in following the wishes of their dying, incompetent patients. In 1976 a New Jersey Supreme Court decision allowed the parents of Karen Ann Quinlan—a young woman not quite dead by the Harvard brain death criteria, but who could be maintained indefinitely on a respirator with no hope of recovery—to have their daughter removed from the respirator (*In the Matter of Karen Ann Quinlan,* 1976). Subsequent judicial decisions in many states and one U.S. Supreme Court decision—*Cruzan v. Director, Missouri Department of Health* (1990)—have elucidated the conditions under which life support might be forgone. Many of these decisions have been influenced by the bioethical debates over active and passive euthanasia. In

the 1990s, the debate over legalization of active euthanasia was renewed, spurred by the public perpetration of euthanasia by the physician Jack Kervorkian and by the advocacy of the Hemlock Society, which promoted legislation that would authorize physicians to provide "aid in dying" at the request of terminal patients. In the 1990s several states held initiatives to legalize this practice but only in the state of Oregon did the voters approve. Since 1994 citizens of that state have been permitted to seek, under stringent conditions, the aid of a physician to end their life. This and other efforts to make euthanasia legal have prompted important judicial decisions, even in the U.S. Supreme Court (*Vacco v. Quill,* 1997; *Washington v. Glucksberg,* 1997; Hillyard and Dombrink). These questions about the nature of appropriate care for the terminally ill, as well as many other ethical questions, are made more urgent by the increase in the numbers of elderly people in the United States: Since the beginning of the twentieth century, the number of Americans over the age of sixty-five has tripled in proportion to the general population (Jecker).

In 1978 the U.S. Congress reestablished the National Commission for the Protection of Human Subjects of Biomedical and Behavioral Research as the U.S. President's Commission for the Study of Ethical Problems in Medicine and Biomedical and Behavioral Research. Among the new commission's mandates were studies of brain death, genetic screening, access to healthcare, and the use of life-sustaining technologies (U.S. President's Commission, 1981, 1983a, 1983b, 1983c). Like its predecessor, it called on scholars from many disciplines to contribute to its deliberations. Its reports make up a veritable canon of bioethics. Its recommendations on the definition of death have been enacted into law in all states as the Uniform Definition of Death Act.

The ascendancy of technological medicine inspired critical study of the nature of the healthcare professions and institutions. Popular and academic works investigated the conceptions of health employed in medicine and the efficacy of medical services offered (Illich). They explored the nature and authority of the health professions and raised questions about ethical responsibilities of health professionals whose attitudes are shaped by economic and social forces (Freidson). The proper role of health professionals has been questioned in many contexts, including the right of health professionals to strike and the extent to which they bear responsibility for patients' lives, for behavioral factors affecting health, and for social and political factors causing disease. The helplessness of individuals in the face of a massive medical establishment led to a patients' rights movement. As evidence of this concern, the American Hospital Association published *A Patient's Bill of Rights* in 1973, with the suggestion that it be adopted by all hospitals. Attempts to pass federal legislation in support of a Patient's Bill of Rights have been unsuccessful.

Reproduction and reproductive technology also fostered debate. During the first part of the century, birth control was an important issue in the feminist movement. Not until the late 1960s were restrictions on the use and teaching of birth control removed in most states. The feminist movement, especially through Margaret Sanger (1879–1966), also sponsored and encouraged research on new birth-control methods (Gordon). In the 1960s abortion became a center of debate. The discussion began with the American Law Institute's model statute permitting abortion for medical and psychological conditions as well as after rape and for fetal defect. The "responsibility for pregnancy" issue for the most part dropped from the debate as it became an issue of women's right to control their bodies, on one side, and the claim of the fetus's right to life, on the other, a claim largely, although not exclusively, urged by Catholics. The U.S. Supreme Court in *Roe v. Wade* (1973) chose a position protecting the mother's decision in the first trimester of the pregnancy, with increasing possibility for legal restrictions during the second and third trimesters. Abortion, because of its intriguing questions about personhood, stimulated considerable professional, philosophical, and theological reflection (Callahan, 1970; Grisez). That reflection has, in the 1990s and early 2000s, ceded to vigorous, even violent political activism. Whether the reflection or the activism will prevail in policy remains to be seen.

In the 1960s advances in genetics and reproductive technology caused much speculation about social consequences of such possible innovations as cloning, in vitro fertilization, and extrauterine gestation. The concern over cloning human beings, vigorously debated in the 1960s, when the question was still speculative, resumed in 1996, after the successful cloning of the sheep Dolly by two Scottish researchers (Ramsey, 1970a; MacKinnon). Interest in the potential and the dangers of genetic manipulation was heightened by the development of recombinant DNA technology in the mid-1970s. Amniocentesis (a test to diagnose certain fetal disorders during early pregnancy) and improvements in genetic history-taking made possible the development of genetic counseling as a profession in the late 1960s, with attendant ethical questions (Hilton et al.). Many questions considered speculative in the 1980s came close to realization by the early twenty-first century. The federally sponsored project to map the entire human genome has become a focus for the study of the ethical questions involved in genetic diagnosis, treatment, and social policy. Its Ethics, Legal, and Social Implications Project has sponsored a wide variety of scholarly and institutional activities in the ethics of genetics (Juengst and Watson; Cooke-Deegan).

Questions about the biological basis of personality, achievement, and social behavior continued to arise. In the early part of the twentieth century the eugenics movement fostered many state laws requiring or allowing sterilization of persons with mental retardation or illness. Debate over sterilization arose again around 1970, when protection of women and minority groups against pressure for sterilization became an issue. The role of genetics in behavior continued to be debated with the development of sociobiology and studies on IQ and heredity. There was disagreement over the goals of genetic counseling, as well as over whether genetic factors in behavior could or should be identified. Screening of populations for genetically determined conditions was much debated (U.S. President's Commission, 1983c; Holtzman).

Biology and behavior was also an issue in the treatment of mental disorders by surgical methods. Prefrontal lobotomy was widely used but much debated after its introduction in 1935. With improvements in surgical techniques in the 1960s, new types of brain surgery were attempted for treatment of violence and other indications. The use of psychosurgery on prisoners became a public issue (Valenstein). The National Commission for the Protection of Human Subjects issued a report on this practice that recommended only its strictly controlled experimental application. A related but quite different form of brain surgery involves the implantation of tissue from aborted fetuses into those suffering from certain neurological and endocrine disorders. This practice, initiated in the late 1980s, aroused great debate. Several advisory committees convened by the National Institutes of Health approved this form of research as acceptable public policy, yet the federal government refused for almost six years to fund studies (Vawter et al.). Although this precise form of therapy has yet to be proven efficacious, scientific interest in the therapeutic value of embryonic stem cells stirred up an ethical storm. On August 9, 2001, President George W. Bush told the nation that "Embryonic stem cell research is at the leading edge of a series of moral hazards." He announced that he would appoint a council to monitor stem cell research and investigate other bioethical questions. The President's Council on Bioethics was established on January 16, 2002, headed by a distinguished bioethicist, Dr. Leon Kass (U.S. President's Council, 2002; Green).

Although psychosurgery is the most physically invasive mode of treatment for behavioral problems, all levels of psychiatric treatment were subject to ethical inquiry. The warrant and nature of involuntary commitment to mental hospitals had been a source of contention for many years (Rothman, 1980). Commitment laws in many U.S. states were modified in the 1960s to increase protection of individuals from arbitrary commitment, although at the same time, the policy of deinstitutionalization thrust many mental patients into a world for which they were unprepared. The right of hospitalized mental patients to receive treatment was established in the United States initially by the Supreme Court decision in *Wyatt v. Stickney* (1972). The use of drugs in treating psychiatric disorders became an issue after chlorpromazine and related major tranquilizers became widely available in the 1950s, reducing the need for hospitalization. The conventional medical view of behavioral problems as disease came under attack from radical psychiatrists such as Thomas Szasz (1961). Goals and values in psychotherapy came to the fore in discussions about treating patients who manifested "antisocial" behavior. The growth of behaviorism and behavior modification seemed also to challenge traditional libertarian values. Rapid evolution of the neurosciences has resuscitated ancient ethical questions about free will and responsibility and raised new ones about the limits of enhancement of cognitive and affective life. Scholars in bioethics are only beginning to study these questions.

In 1981 a previously unknown disorder of the immune system appeared, at first in men known to engage in homosexual activities. This disorder, named acquired immunodeficiency syndrome (AIDS), was quickly traced to a blood-borne retroviral infection. The resulting disease was relatively slow to appear but was, given the therapeutic possibilities available, inevitably fatal. It spread in epidemic fashion among gay men and among those who shared needles while taking drugs intravenously. Fear of the disease and widespread homophobia led to discriminatory actions against those infected. Old ethical questions about restricting freedom of persons suspected of having a communicable disease were revived. Public health needs appeared to conflict with personal rights. The duty of healthcare professionals to treat infected persons was vigorously debated, as was the right of infected care providers to practice. Bioethics, by now adept at the discussion of practical ethics, made a major contribution to these debates (Bayer).

The problem of just allocation of healthcare had been noticed in the earliest days of bioethics. At that time, however, it was largely defined in terms of selection of patients for rare and expensive technologies, such as dialysis. In the early 1980s, it was recognized that some 35 million Americans were not covered by any healthcare insurance (U.S. President's Commission, 1983b; Dougherty; Churchill). Ethical questions about the justice of such a system were raised as health-policy experts began to note the rapid inflation in healthcare costs. Lack of access to care competed with cost containment in public debate and political maneuvering. These problems became central to the concerns of many bioethicists, who began to produce acute analyses of the issues of justice in the healthcare system and its financial base. These ethicists raised and examined the politically unpalatable issue of rationing of healthcare resources (Daniels; Callahan, 1988; Menzel; Morreim).

Academic Bioethics

As the 1970s opened, a number of scholars were beginning to attempt to analyze the issues discussed above within the perspectives and methodologies of the two disciplines traditionally concerned with ethics, philosophy and theology. As these scholars began to publish and communicate, a distinct field of study called bioethics came into being. The word *bioethics* was first applied to the ethics of population and environment (Potter), and soon became the rubric for a diverse collection of considerations about the ethical issues inherent in healthcare and the biological sciences (Callahan, 1973). The term, although considered unsatisfactory even by some of those who employed it, was canonized by the inauguration of the *Encyclopedia of Bioethics* project in 1972 and by the publication of the first edition, edited by Warren T. Reich, in 1978. The scholars in this new field now come from many disciplines, such as theology, philosophy, social sciences, and law. Bioethics concentrates on a specific set of issues, such as those mentioned above, and employs a range of analytic methodologies, explained in texts such as *Principles of Biomedical Ethics* (Beauchamp and Childress) for the more theoretical questions and in *Clinical Ethics* (Jonsen, Siegler, and Winslade) for the more practical questions. It has professors, students, texts, journals, learned societies, and research centers. At the beginning of the twenty-first century, more than a dozen graduate programs offer higher degrees to students trained in the topics and methods of the field.

Bioethicists show considerable interest in the theoretical definition of the field and its methodologies. Albert Jonsen and André Hellegers published an essay in the early days of the field's existence in which they saw it as a mélange of traditional professional ethics, philosophical ethics, and theological ethics (Jonsen and Hellegers). Robert Veatch, however, was the first to attempt a full exposition of the theoretical underpinnings of bioethics. His 1981 book, *A Theory of Medical Ethics,* set the field firmly on the ethical considerations relative to autonomy of the patient. H. Tristram Engelhardt Jr. followed in 1986 with *The Foundations of Bioethics,* an even more strongly stated thesis about autonomy as the basis of the discipline. Nevertheless, some have asserted that bioethics, while it had its origins in the strong affirmation of autonomy for patients, may have moved too far in this direction and thereby neglected other aspects of healthcare, such as benevolence, community, and social justice (Pellegrino; Daniels).

The study of bioethics, together with other fields in applied ethics, has inspired much debate about the methods appropriate to studying practical ethics in general. Many of these nascent methods have lent a richer, more detailed texture to ethical discussion than is permitted by principle- and theory-based ethics. The long-abandoned casuistry that employs rhetorical and analogical reasoning to examine cases is now being viewed with renewed and critical interest (Jonsen and Toulmin; Arras; Sugarman and Sulmasy). Mathematical decision analysis has been used to study values through systematically related cases (Smith and Wigton). Stories, real and fictional, are used as texts open to moral interpretation according to the methods of hermeneutics (Brody; Hunter), and phenomenology seeks to capture the ethical subtleties of clinical encounters (Zaner; Carson). Echoing the language of ethics from the nineteenth century, but with much greater attention to depth and detail, interest in virtue- and character-based ethics is vigorous (Drane; Shelp).

Although the early development of bioethics was dominated by male scholars, women such as Elizabeth Fee, Renée Fox, Loretta Kopelman, Karen Lebacqz, Ruth Macklin, Ruth Purtilo, and Judith Swazey have made significant contributions to theoretical and practical bioethics, and feminist ethics has begun to attract much attention. Feminist bioethics offers social criticism of the treatment of women as patients and physicians, discusses the interrelationship between gender and power, provides fresh analyses of issues of traditional concern to women (such as pregnancy, birth, and reproductive choices), and emphasizes important theoretical concepts—such as caring, community, and responsibility—neglected by male scholars (Holmes and Purdy; Sherwin).

Other authors note the ethnocentricity of U.S. bioethics; it has been charged with a failure to reflect the concerns of people of color, and new work is beginning to appear that increasingly reflects diverse viewpoints. Collections of narratives of the African-American experience with disease and healthcare have begun to appear (Secundy and Nixon; White). A Center for Bioethics was inaugurated at Tuskegee University at the time of President Bill Clinton's formal apology to African Americans for the Tuskegee syphilis experiments; this center will concentrate on ethnic issues in bioethics. Some authors have discussed the tensions between expressed philosophical ideals and systematic patterns of discrimination, such as abuses of birth control, sterilization,

and selection of subjects for research (Dula; Flack and Pellegrino). U.S. bioethics is becoming more international and less ethnocentric in its concerns: American bioethicists visit many nations, and bioethicists from around the world spend time in American programs, stimulating cross-cultural comparisons and analyses (Fox and Swazey, 1984; Harding; Sagoff). American scholars are active in the International Association for Bioethics.

The tendency of ethics researchers to study clinical questions cooperatively with clinicians has inspired empirical study of ethics in healthcare. This in turn has fostered cooperation between the social sciences and normative philosophical ethics. Termed the *contextual approach* by some authors, it has begun to call attention to significant social and cultural features of life that affect ethical expression and debate (Weisz; Thomasma). Some researchers have used in-depth ethnographic techniques, such as participant observation and interviews, to study the microcontext of clinical settings; others are employing epidemiological methods to ascertain frequency of behaviors, such as resuscitation. The empirical social sciences and philosophy are beginning to converse with each other on the common ground of bioethics (Guellemin and Holmstrom; Bosk).

In the 1970s, as faculty members were appointed to teach ethics in medical schools, it became common for the ethicist to accompany physicians on teaching rounds. This led to the participation of ethicists in consultations about cases that presented particularly difficult ethical decisions. This practice came to be called clinical ethics. In 1977 ethicist John Fletcher was appointed assistant for bioethics to the director, Clinical Center, National Institutes of Heath, with responsibility for ethics consultation. Because philosophy itself provides little guidance about how to assist in actual decision making, various methods were devised to apply principles to practice. Clinical ethics spread from university hospitals to community hospitals; many individuals, physicians and philosophers alike, now act as clinical ethics consultants. The *Journal of Clinical Ethics* was initiated in 1991. As might be expected, some dispute surrounds the idea and practice of ethics consultation, because it seems to imply that some persons are "ethical experts," a notion rather foreign to a morally pluralistic culture (Fletcher, Quist, and Jonsen). The American Society for Bioethics and the Humanities published criteria for clinical-ethics consultation.

As the field of bioethics was beginning to form and as yet lacked institutional support for regular teaching and discussion, conferences and symposia were an important source for developing literature, teaching, and publicity. Some of the more important early conferences were the Joseph P. Kennedy, Jr., Foundation's International Conference on Abortion, held in 1967 in Washington, D.C.; a New York Academy of Sciences' conference, New Dimensions in Legal and Ethical Concepts for Human Research (Ladimer and Newman); a U.S. National Academy of Sciences Institute of Medicine's conference, Health Care and Changing Values, held in 1973; a series of transdisciplinary symposia on philosophy and medicine, the first of which was held in Galveston, Texas, in 1974 (Engelhardt and Spicker); and the 1975 conference Experiments and Research with Humans: Values in Conflict, sponsored by the National Academy of Sciences. In the 1990s such conferences, on a wide variety of topics, were announced at a dizzying pace.

Several privately funded institutes are devoted primarily to the study of bioethics. The Institute of Religion, established in 1954 at the Texas Medical Center, Houston, began to devote attention to bioethical issues in the late 1960s. The Society for Health and Human Values evolved in 1969 from a smaller interdisciplinary group that had formed the Committee on Health and Human Values in 1963 with support from the ecumenical United Ministries in Higher Education. In 1998 the Society for Health and Human Values, the Society for Bioethics Consultation, and the American Association for Bioethics united to form the American Society for Bioethics and the Humanities, which by 2002 had enrolled 1,500 members, drawn from bioethics, medicine, nursing, law, religion, and the social sciences. The Hastings Center, originally called the Institute of Society, Ethics, and the Life Sciences and founded in 1969 by Daniel Callahan and Willard Gaylin, investigates social, legal, and ethical aspects of the health sciences. It conducts a program for visiting fellows and associates; publishes the most widely read of the ethics journals, *Hastings Center Report* and *IRB: A Review of Human Subjects Research;* organizes study groups on special topics; and conducts courses for health professionals and others. In 2002 the Hastings Center had 109 fellows and almost 12,000 members.

For several years in the 1970s, the Joseph P. Kennedy, Jr., Foundation funded the Interfaculty Program in Medical Ethics, which joined Harvard University's Medical School, School of Public Health, and Divinity School to train scholars in this new field. In 1971 André Hellegers founded the Joseph and Rose Kennedy Institute for the Study of Human Reproduction and Bioethics, now known as the Kennedy Institute of Ethics, at Georgetown University. This program, initially financed by the Kennedy Foundation, has supported research by permanent and visiting scholars, courses and workshops in bioethics, and cooperative and consulting programs with private and governmental institutions. The Kennedy Institute has specialized in the creation

of fundamental research tools in the field of bioethics. Starting in 1972, the institute sponsored Warren Reich's project for the preparation of the *Encyclopedia of Bioethics,* a landmark in U.S. bioethical studies. Its National Resource Center prepares the computer-based bibliography of bioethical literature called Bioethicsline, a part of the National Library of Medicine's Medlars network; Bioethicsline is also published in book form as *Bibliography of Bioethics* (Walters). The Kennedy Institute originated the important *Journal of Philosophy and Medicine,* which is now published independently, and currently produces the *Kennedy Institute of Ethics Journal.* In 1993 the American Association of Bioethics came into existence to promote the exchange of ideas among bioethics scholars, encourage the development of new scholars, and maintain contact with international societies in bioethics.

As bioethics flowered, many ethical issues were being debated as matters of public policy. Some bioethicists found themselves working as public employees to aid in policy formation, and others served as members of and consultants to advisory bodies such as the National Commission for the Protection of Human Subjects, the U.S. President's Commission for the Study of Ethical Problems in Medicine, the now defunct Ethics Advisory Board of the Department of Health and Human Services, and state bodies such as New York's Task Force on Life and the Law and New Jersey's Bioethics Commission. Ten of the eighty-two "special government employees" working with the 1993 Task Force on Reform of Health Care were persons identifiable as bioethicists. The National Bioethics Advisory Commission was established by an executive order of President Clinton in 1995, and during the next six years this commission produced a series of excellent reports on such issues as cloning of human beings, stem cell research, and research involving persons who have mental disabilities. Beyond these official bodies, several thousand physicians, nurses, clergy, and laypersons sit, often with bioethicists, on the hospital ethics committees that have, since the 1980s, become part of most medical centers in the United States. Grassroots bioethics activities, such as the Oregon Health Decisions Project, strive to involve laypersons in making decisions about the ethics of healthcare allocation policy. Bioethics has become, to some extent, a philosophy for the people.

The bioethics movement has demonstrated extraordinary vitality in the United States since the 1970s. Its work effected significant changes in the practices of healthcare. Its first historian, David Rothman, wrote, "The record since 1966, I believe, makes a convincing case for a fundamental transformation in the substance as well as the style of medical decision making" (Rothman, 1991, p. 251). That transformation consists largely in the flow of lay opinion and judgment into the formerly closed world of medical decision and policy, in both clinical and research settings.

By the 1990s, bioethics was firmly established as a field of study within academic settings. This gives it a prestige and institutional base that it had previously lacked, but that may also imperil its vitality and independence. Although initially seen by some as a fad, bioethics is linked with social and personal issues deeply rooted in the culture of the United States during the twentieth century. The impact of technology on human life, the distribution of increasingly scarce health resources in an otherwise affluent society, the role of government in the pursuit of health by individuals and populations, and the voice of the consumer-patient in decisions about medical care—all these issues are central to the concerns of bioethics. Inevitably, ethical issues in the life sciences also embrace the larger social problems of environment and population. It is likely that the diffuse field of bioethics will take shape as it increasingly finds its place in the education of future health professionals, as it becomes part of the attempt by schools and consumer organizations to increase personal responsibility for health and environment, and as it attends to the formulation of public policy about social life in the biosphere.

ALBERT R. JONSEN
ANDREW JAMETON (1995)
REVISED BY AUTHORS

BIBLIOGRAPHY

Aikens, Charlotte. 1916. *Studies in Ethics for Nurses.* Philadelphia: W. B. Saunders.

Alexander, Leo. 1949. "Medical Science under Dictatorship." *New England Journal of Medicine* 241(2): 39–47.

American Hospital Association. 1973. *A Patient's Bill of Rights.* Chicago: Author.

Annas, George J. 1993. *Standard of Care: The Law of American Bioethics.* New York: Oxford University Press.

Annas, George J., and Grodin, Michael A. 1992. *The Nazi Doctors and the Nuremberg Code: Human Rights in Human Experimentation.* New York: Oxford University Press.

Arras, John D. 1991. "Getting Down to Cases: The Revival of Casuistry in Bioethics." *Journal of Medicine and Philosophy* 16(1): 29–51.

Baker, Robert; Caplan, Arthur; Emanuel, Linda; et al. 1999. *The American Medical Ethics Revolution: How the AMA's Code of Ethics Changes Its Relationship to Practitioners, Patients, and the Public.* Baltimore: Johns Hopkins University Press.

Bayer, Ronald. 1989. *Private Acts and Social Consequences: AIDS and the Politics of Public Health.* New York: Free Press.

Beauchamp, Tom L., and Childress, James F. 2001. *Principles of Biomedical Ethics,* 5th edition. New York: Oxford University Press.

Beecher, Henry K. 1966. "Ethics and Clinical Research." *New England Journal of Medicine* 274(24): 1354–1360.

Berlant, Jeffrey L. 1975. *Profession and Monopoly: A Study of Medicine in the United States and Great Britain.* Berkeley: University of California Press.

Bickel, Janet. 1987. "Human Values Teaching Programs in the Clinical Education of Medical Students." *Journal of Medical Education* 62(5): 369–378.

Binger, Carl A. L. 1945. *The Doctor's Job.* New York: Norton.

Bosk, Charles L. 1979. *Forgive and Remember: Managing Medical Failure.* Chicago: University of Chicago Press.

Brody, Howard. 1987. *Stories of Sickness.* New Haven, CT: Yale University Press.

Burns, Chester R. 1977. "Richard Clark Cabot (1868–1939) and Reformation in American Medical Ethics." *Bulletin of the History of Medicine* 51(3): 353–368.

Burns, Chester R. 1980. "Medical Ethics and Jurisprudence." In *The Education of American Physicians: Historical Essays,* ed. Ronald L. Numbers. Berkeley: University of California Press.

Burrow, James G. 1963. *AMA: Voice of American Medicine.* Baltimore: Johns Hopkins University Press.

Burrow, James G. 1977. *Organized Medicine in the Progressive Era: The Move toward Monopoly.* Baltimore: Johns Hopkins University Press.

Callahan, Daniel. 1970. *Abortion: Law, Choice, and Morality.* New York: Macmillan.

Callahan, Daniel. 1973. "Bioethics as a Discipline." *Hastings Center Studies* 1(1): 66–73.

Callahan, Daniel. 1988. *Setting Limits: Medical Goals in an Aging Society.* New York: Simon and Schuster.

Carson, Ronald A. 1990. "Interpretive Bioethics: The Way of Discernment." *Theoretical Medicine* 11(1): 51–59.

Cassel, Christine K., and Jameton, Andrew. 1982. "Medical Responsibility and Thermonuclear War." *Annals of Internal Medicine* 97(3): 426–432.

Childress, James F. 1970. "Who Shall Live When Not All Can Live?" *Soundings* 53: 339–355.

Churchill, Larry R. 1987. *Rationing Health Care in America: Perceptions and Principles of Justice.* Notre Dame, IN: University of Notre Dame Press.

Cooke-Deegan, Robert. 1994. *The Gene Wars: Science, Politics, and the Human Genome.* New York: Norton.

Coppens, Charles. 1905. *Moral Principles and Medical Practice: The Basis of Medical Jurisprudence,* 4th rev. edition. New York: Benziger Brothers.

Daniels, Norman. 1985. *Just Health Care.* New York: Cambridge University Press.

Davis, Loyal Edward. 1960. *Fellowship of Surgeons: A History of the American College of Surgeons.* Springfield, IL: Charles Thomas.

Dougherty, Charles J. 1988. *American Health Care: Realities, Rights, and Reforms.* New York: Oxford University Press.

Drane, James F. 1988. *Becoming a Good Doctor: The Place of Virtue and Character in Medical Ethics.* Kansas City, MO: Sheed and Ward.

Dula, Annette. 1991. "Toward an African-American Perspective on Bioethics." *Journal of Health Care for the Poor and Underserved* 2(2): 259–269.

Engelhardt, H. Tristram, Jr. 1986. *The Foundations of Bioethics.* New York: Oxford University Press.

Engelhardt, H. Tristram, Jr., and Spicker, Stuart F., eds. 1975. *Evaluation and Explanation in the Biomedical Sciences: Proceedings of the First Trans-Disciplinary Symposium on Philosophy and Medicine, Held at Galveston, May 9–11, 1974.* Dordrecht, Netherlands: D. Reidel.

Fein, Rashi. 1986. *Medical Care, Medical Costs: The Search for a Health Insurance Policy.* Cambridge, MA: Harvard University Press.

Flack, Harley E., and Pellegrino, Edmund D., eds. 1992. *African-American Perspectives in Biomedical Ethics.* Washington, D.C.: Georgetown University Press.

Fletcher, John C.; Quist, Norman; and Jonsen, Albert R.; eds. 1989. *Ethics Consultation in Health Care.* Ann Arbor, MI: Health Administration Press.

Fletcher, Joseph F. 1954. *Morals and Medicine: The Moral Problems of: The Patient's Right to Know the Truth, Contraception, Artificial Insemination, Sterilization, Euthanasia.* Princeton, NJ: Princeton University Press.

Flexner, Abraham. 1910. *Medical Education in the United States and Canada.* New York: Carnegie Foundation for the Advancement of Teaching.

Fox, Renée C., and Swazey, Judith F. 1974. *The Courage to Fail: A Social View of Organ Transplants and Dialysis.* Chicago: University of Chicago Press.

Fox, Renée C., and Swazey, Judith F. 1984. "Medical Morality Is Not Bioethics: Medical Ethics in China and the United States." *Perspectives in Biology and Medicine* 27(3): 336–360.

Freidson, Eliott. 1970. *The Profession of Medicine: A Study of the Sociology of Applied Knowledge.* New York: Harper and Row.

Freund, Paul A., ed. 1970. *Experimentation with Human Subjects.* New York: George Braziller.

Geiger, H. Jack. 1971. "Hidden Professional Roles: The Physician as Reactionary, Reformer, Revolutionary." *Social Policy* 1(6): 24–33.

Gewitz, Norman, ed. 1988. *Other Healers: Unorthodox Medicine in America.* Baltimore: Johns Hopkins University Press.

Gilligan, Carol. 1982. *In a Different Voice: Psychological Theory and Women's Development.* Cambridge, MA: Harvard University Press.

Gordon, Linda W. 1976. *Woman's Body, Woman's Rights: A Social History of Birth Control in America.* New York: Grossman.

Gorovitz, Samuel; Jameton, Andrew L.; Macklin, Ruth; et al., eds. 1976. *Moral Problems in Medicine.* Englewood Cliffs, NJ: Prentice-Hall.

Gorovitz, Samuel; Macklin, Ruth; Jameton, Andrew; et al. 1973. *Teaching Medical Ethics: A Report on One Approach.* Cleveland, OH: Case Western Reserve University, Department of Philosophy and School of Medicine.

Green, Ronald. 2001. *The Human Embryo Debates: Bioethics in the Vortex of Controversy.* New York: Oxford University Press.

Grisez, Germain G. 1970. *Abortion: The Myths, the Realities, and the Arguments.* New York: Corpus.

Guellemin, Jeanne Harley, and Holmstrom, Lynda Lytle. 1986. *Mixed Blessings: Intensive Care for Newborns.* New York: Oxford University Press.

Gustafson, James. 1970. "Basic Ethical Issues in the Bio-Medical Field." *Soundings* 53: 430–455.

Harding, Sandra. 1987. "The Curious Coincidence of Feminine and African Moralities: Challenges for Feminist Theory." In *Women and Moral Theory,* ed. Eva Feder Kittay and Diana T. Meyers. Totowa, NJ: Rowman and Littlefield.

Harvard Medical School. Ad Hoc Committee of the Harvard Medical School to Examine the Definition of Brain Death. 1968. "A Definition of Irreversible Coma." *Journal of the American Medical Association* 205(6): 337–340.

Hillyard, Daniel, and Dombrink, John. 2001. *Dying Right: The Death with Dignity Movement.* London and New York: Routledge.

Hilton, Bruce; Callahan, Daniel; Harris, Maureen; et al., eds. 1973. *Ethical Issues in Human Genetics: Genetic Counseling and the Use of Genetic Knowledge.* New York: Plenum.

Holmes, Helen Bequaert, and Purdy, Laura Martha, eds. 1992. *Feminist Perspectives in Medical Ethics.* Bloomington: Indiana University Press.

Holtzman, Neil A. 1989. *Proceed with Caution: Predicting Genetic Risks in the Recombinant DNA Era.* Baltimore: Johns Hopkins University Press.

Hunter, Kathryn Montgomery. 1991. *Doctors' Stories: The Narrative Structure of Medical Knowledge.* Princeton, NJ: Princeton University Press.

Illich, Ivan. 1976. *Medical Nemesis: The Expropriation of Health.* New York: Pantheon.

Jakobovits, Immanuel. 1959. *Jewish Medical Ethics: A Comparative and Historical Study of the Jewish Religious Attitude to Medicine and Its Practice.* New York: Bloch.

Jecker, Nancy, ed. 1991. *Aging and Ethics: Philosophical Problems in Gerontology.* Clifton, NY: Humana.

Jones, James H. 1981. *Bad Blood: The Tuskegee Syphilis Experiment.* New York: Free Press.

Jonsen, Albert R. 1973. "The Totally Implantable Artificial Heart." *Hastings Center Report* 3(6): 1–4.

Jonsen, Albert R. 1990. *The New Medicine and the Old Ethics.* Cambridge, MA: Harvard University Press.

Jonsen, Albert R. 1998. *The Birth of Bioethics.* New York: Oxford University Press.

Jonsen, Albert R. 2000. *A Short History of Medical Ethics.* New York: Oxford University Press.

Jonsen, Albert R., and Hellegers, André E. 1974. "Conceptual Foundations for an Ethics of Medical Care." In *Ethics of Health Care: Papers of the Conference on Health Care and Changing Values, November 27–29, 1973,* ed. Laurence R. Tancredi. Washington, D.C.: National Academy of Sciences.

Jonsen, Albert R., and Jameton, Andrew. 1977. "Social and Political Responsibilities of Physicians." *Journal of Medicine and Philosophy* 2(4): 376–400.

Jonsen, Albert R.; Siegler, Mark, and Winslade, William J. 2001. *Clinical Ethics: A Practical Approach to Ethical Decisions in Clinical Medicine,* 5th edition. New York: Macmillan.

Jonsen, Albert R., and Toulmin, Stephen E. 1988. *The Abuse of Casuistry: A History of Moral Reasoning.* Berkeley: University of California Press.

Juengst, Eric, and Watson, James. 1991. "Human Genome Research and the Responsible Use of New Genetic Knowledge." *International Journal of Bioethics* 2: 99–102.

Karen Ann Quinlan, In the Matter of. 1976. Arlington, VA: University Publications of America.

Katz, Jay; Capron, Alexander M.; and Glass, Eleanor Swift, eds. 1972. *Experimentation with Human Beings: The Authority of the Investigator, Subject, Professions, and State in the Human Experimentation Process.* New York: Russell Sage Foundation.

Kübler-Ross, Elisabeth. 1969. *On Death and Dying.* New York: Macmillan.

Ladimer, Irving, and Newman, Roger W., eds. 1963. *Clinical Investigation in Medicine: Legal, Ethical, and Moral Aspects.* Boston: Law-Medicine Research Institute, Boston University.

Leaf, Alexander. 1989. "Potential Health Effects of Global Climatic and Environmental Changes." *New England Journal of Medicine* 321(23): 1577–1583.

Leake, Chauncey D., and Romanell, Patrick. 1950. *Can We Agree? A Scientist and a Philosopher Argue about Ethics.* Austin: University of Texas Press.

Leavitt, Judith W. 1986. *Brought to Bed: Childbearing in America, 1750–1950.* New York: Oxford University Press.

Levine, Robert. 1986. *Ethics and Regulation of Clinical Research,* 2nd edition. Baltimore: Urban and Schwarzenberg.

Limbert, Paul M. 1931. "Are Courses in the Ethics of Nursing Worthwhile?" *Trained Nurse and Hospital Review* 87(4): 472–476.

MacKinnon, Barbara, ed. 2000. *Human Cloning: Science, Ethics, and Public Policy.* Urbana and Chicago: University of Illinois Press.

Marmor, Theodore R. 1970. *The Politics of Medicare.* London: Routledge and Kegan Paul.

Marty, Martin E. 1983. *Health and Medicine in the Lutheran Tradition: Being Well.* New York: Crossroad.

McCally, Michael, and Cassel, Christine K. 1990. "Medical Responsibility and Global Environmental Change." *Annals of Internal Medicine* 113(6): 467–473.

Menzel, Paul T. 1990. *Strong Medicine: The Ethical Rationing of Health Care.* New York: Oxford University Press.

Mohr, James C. 1978. *Abortion in America: The Origins and Evolution of National Policy, 1800–1900.* New York: Oxford University Press.

Moore, Thomas Verner. 1935. *Principles of Ethics.* Philadelphia: J. B. Lippincott.

Morreim, Haavi. 1991. *Balancing Act: The New Medical Ethics of Medicine's New Economics.* Dordrecht, Netherlands, and Boston: Kluwer Academic.

National Academy of Sciences. 1975. *Experiments and Research with Humans: Values in Conflict.* Washington, D.C.: Author.

National Heart and Lung Institute. Artificial Heart Assessment Panel. 1973. *The Totally Implantable Artificial Heart: Economic, Ethical, Legal, Medical, Psychiatric, and Social Implications.* Bethesda: National Institutes of Health.

Pellegrino, Edmund D., and Thomasma, David C. 1988. *For the Patient's Good: The Restoration of Beneficence in Health Care.* New York: Oxford University Press.

Percival, Thomas. 1803 (reprint 1927). *Percival's Medical Ethics,* ed. Chauncey D. Leake. Baltimore: Williams and Wilkins.

Potter, Van Rensselaer. 1971. *Bioethics: Bridge to the Future.* Englewood Cliffs, NJ: Prentice-Hall.

Ramsey, Paul. 1970a. *Fabricated Man: The Ethics of Genetic Control.* New Haven, CT: Yale University Press.

Ramsey, Paul. 1970b. *Patient as Person: Explorations in Medical Ethics.* New Haven, CT: Yale University Press.

Reich, Warren T., ed. 1978. *The Encyclopedia of Bioethics.* New York: Free Press; 2nd edition, New York: Macmillan/Simon and Schuster, 1995.

Rescher, Nicholas. 1969. "The Allocation of Exotic Medical Lifesaving Therapy." *Ethics* 79(3): 173–186.

Robb, Isabel Hampton. 1901. *Nursing Ethics: For Hospital and Private Use.* Cleveland, OH: J. B. Savage.

Rosenberg, Charles E. 1987. *The Care of Strangers: The Rise of America's Hospital System.* New York: Basic.

Rothman, David J. 1980. *Conscience and Convenience: The Asylum and Its Alternatives in Progressive America.* Boston: Little, Brown.

Rothman, David J. 1991. *Strangers at the Bedside: A History of How Law and Bioethics Transformed Medical Decision Making.* New York: Basic.

Sagoff, Mark. 1991. "Zuckerman's Dilemma: A Plea for Environmental Ethics." *Hastings Center Report* 21(5): 32–40.

Secundy, Marian Gray, and Lois LaCavita Nixon, eds. 1992. *Trials, Tribulations, and Celebrations: African-American Perspectives on Health, Illness, Aging, and Loss.* Yarmouth, ME: Intercultural Press.

Shaw, Margery W., ed. 1984. *After Barney Clark: Reflections on the Utah Artificial Heart Program.* Austin: University of Texas Press.

Shelp, Earl E., ed. 1985. *Virtue and Medicine: Explorations in the Character of Medicine.* Dordrecht, Netherlands: D. Reidel.

Sherwin, Susan. 1992. *No Longer Patient: Feminist Ethics and Health Care.* Philadelphia: Temple University Press.

Smith, David G., and Wigton, Robert S. 1987. "Modeling Decisions to Use Tube Feeding in Seriously Ill Patients." *Archives of Internal Medicine* 147(7): 1242–1245.

Sperry, Willard. 1950. *The Ethical Basis of Medical Practice.* New York: P. B. Hoeber.

Starr, Paul. 1982. *The Social Transformation of American Medicine.* New York: Basic.

Stevens, Rosemary. 1971. *American Medicine and the Public.* New Haven, CT: Yale University Press.

Stevens, Rosemary. 1989. *In Sickness and in Wealth: American Hospitals in the Twentieth Century.* New York: Basic.

Sugarman, Jeremy, and Sulmasy, Daniel. 2001. *Methods in Medical Ethics.* Washington, D.C.: Georgetown University Press.

Szasz, Thomas S. 1961. *The Myth of Mental Illness: Foundations of a Theory of Personal Conduct.* New York: Harper and Row.

Thomasma, David C. 1984. "The Context as a Moral Rule in Medical Ethics." *Journal of Bioethics* 5(1): 63–79.

Toulmin, Stephen. 1982. "How Medicine Saved the Life of Ethics." *Perspectives in Biology and Medicine* 25(4): 736–750.

U.S. Catholic Conference. Department of Health Affairs. 1971. *Ethical and Religious Directives for Catholic Health Facilities.* Washington, D.C.: Author.

U.S. National Commission for the Protection of Human Subjects of Biomedical and Behavioral Research. 1978. *The Belmont Report: Ethical Principles and Guidelines for the Protection of Human Subjects of Research.* Washington, D.C.: U.S. Government Printing Office.

U.S. President's Commission for the Study of Ethical Problems in Medicine and Biomedical and Behavioral Research. 1981. *Defining Death: A Report on the Medical, Legal, and Ethical Issues in the Determination of Death.* Washington, D.C.: U.S. Government Printing Office.

U.S. President's Commission for the Study of Ethical Problems in Medicine and Biomedical and Behavioral Research. 1983a. *Deciding to Forego Life-Sustaining Treatment: A Report on the Ethical, Medical, and Legal Issues in Treatment Decisions.* Washington, D.C.: U.S. Government Printing Office.

U.S. President's Commission for the Study of Ethical Problems in Medicine and Biomedical and Behavioral Research. 1983b. *Screening and Counseling for Genetic Conditions: A Report on the Ethical, Social, and Legal Implications of Genetic Screening, Counseling, and Education Programs.* Washington, D.C.: U.S. Government Printing Office.

U.S. President's Commission for the Study of Ethical Problems in Medicine and Biomedical and Behavioral Research. 1983c. *Securing Access to Health Care: A Report on the Ethical Implications of Differences in the Availability of Health Services.* Washington, D.C.: U.S. Government Printing Office.

U.S. President's Council on Bioethics. 2002. *Human Cloning and Human Dignity: An Ethical Inquiry.* Washington, D.C.: U.S. Government Printing Office.

Valenstein, Elliot S. 1974. *Brain Control: Critical Examination of Brain Stimulation and Psychosurgery.* New York: Wiley.

Vaux, Kenneth L. 1984. *Health and Medicine in the Reformed Tradition: Promise, Providence, and Care.* New York: Crossroad.

Vawter, Dorothy E.; Kearney, Warren; Gervais, Karen G.; et al. 1990. *The Use of Human Fetal Tissue: Scientific, Ethical, and Policy Concerns.* Minneapolis: University of Minnesota, Center for Biomedical Ethics.

Veatch, Robert M. 1981. *A Theory of Medical Ethics.* New York: Basic.

Veatch, Robert M.; Gaylin, Willard; and Morgan, Councilman. 1973. *The Teaching of Medical Ethics: Proceedings of a Conference Sponsored by the Institute of Society, Ethics, and the Life Sciences and Columbia University College of Physicians and Surgeons, June 1–3, 1972.* Hastings-on-Hudson, NY: Institute of Society, Ethics, and the Life Sciences.

Walters, LeRoy, ed. 1975–. *Bibliography of Bioethics.* Washington, D.C.: Kennedy Institute of Ethics.

Weisz, George, ed. 1990. *Social Science Perspectives on Medical Ethics.* Philadelphia: University of Pennsylvania Press.

White, Evelyn C., ed. 1990. *The Black Women's Health Book: Speaking for Ourselves.* Seattle, WA: Seal Press.

Zaner, Richard M. 1988. *Ethics and the Clinical Encounter.* Englewood Cliffs, NJ: Prentice-Hall.

III. CANADA

Two aspects of Canadian society are particularly determinative of the Canadian approach to bioethics: (1) the country's universally accessible, publicly funded healthcare system, and (2) the role of law. While a multitude of bioethical issues have occupied Canadians since the 1960s, there have been three major areas of bioethical activity: clinical ethics, research ethics, and ethics in public policy. The history of bioethics in Canada can be divided into two time periods: from 1800 to the 1960s, and from the 1960s to the present. During the first period, medical ethics predominated, although theological ethics and the ethics of nursing were also important. Since 1960, the field of medical ethics has been incorporated into the broader field of bioethics.

Medical Ethics: 1800–1960

In 1867, the year of Canada's formation as a nation, the Canadian Medical Association (CMA), came into being. At its first annual meeting in 1868, the CMA adopted the Code of Ethics of the Canadian Medical Association, which was closely modeled on the American Medical Association's code of ethics. Since then there have been a number of revisions to the CMA Code of Ethics, most recently in 1996. This code outlines general responsibilities, responsibilities to the patient, responsibilities to society, responsibilities to the profession, and responsibilities to oneself.

The Canadian Nurses Association (CNA) was established in 1908. However, the association did not have a code of ethics until 1954, when it adopted the one that had been prepared the previous year by the International Council of Nurses. In 1980 the CNA moved to establish its own code, which was published as *CNA Code of Ethics: An Ethical Basis for Nursing in Canada.* This code has since been revised on a regular basis (1985, 1991, 1997, and 2002) and is now entitled *Code of Ethics for Registered Nurses.* The content is structured around three themes: (1) the nature of ethics in nursing, (2) nursing values defined, and (3) nursing values and responsibility statements.

The Roman Catholic Church has played an important role in healthcare in Canada since colonial times. The Catholic Hospital Association of the United States and Canada (CHAUSC), founded in 1915, adopted a code of ethics in 1921 that dealt primarily with surgical issues in obstetrics and gynecology. This document was updated in 1935, and in 1949 it was revised and published as *Ethical and Religious Directives for Catholic Hospitals.* In 1954 the Catholic Hospital Council of Canada (established in 1942) declared its independence from CHAUSC and renamed itself the Catholic Hospital Association of Canada. It adopted its own moral code in 1955. Now known as the Catholic Health Association of Canada, this organization updated and renamed its moral code, the *Health Ethics Guide,* in 1971, 1991, and again in 2000. This document addresses issues related to social services and organizational ethics. The core focus areas for the Catholic Health Association of Canada are ethics, spirituality, values development, and social justice.

Canadian contributions to the medical ethics literature were few and far between until the 1940s. The most renowned Canadian physician of this period, Sir William Osler (1849–1919), made few references to medical ethics in his many publications. He did, however, have a great deal to say about the practice of medicine and about physician behavior. The chief virtues of the individual physician are variously referred to in his writings as equanimity (*aequanimitas*), imperturbability, and detachment. His stated ideal for the medical profession was that of "noblesse oblige" (Osler).

Not until the 1940s did a significant number of Canadian publications in medical ethics begin to appear, most of them written by Catholic theologians (e.g., LaRochelle and Fink). Some Catholic schools of medicine (e.g., the University of Ottawa) and nursing (e.g., the University of Montreal) made faculty appointments in medical ethics; and the professors who took these posts contributed to the growing body of Catholic literature in this field (e.g., Paquin,).

However, comparable work by philosophers and health professionals was noticeable by its absence.

Bioethics: 1960s–2000s

Beginning in the mid-1960s, the field of medical ethics underwent a radical transformation, and by the end of the 1970s it displayed all the features of what has become known as bioethics. In Canada the major actors in the development of bioethics have been professional associations, public commissions, and academic institutions.

The major professional health associations expanded their ethics activities during this period. In the early 1980s the CMA remandated its Committee on Ethics to deal with the whole range of bioethical issues, rather than those affecting only physicians. In 1989 the CMA established a Department of Ethics and Legal Affairs. The Royal College of Physicians and Surgeons of Canada created a Biomedical Ethics Committee in 1977, and the College of Family Physicians of Canada followed suit in 1991. The Canadian Nurses Association established an ad hoc ethics committee that met regularly from 1985 to 1997 to revise its code of ethics. In the Spring of 1997 this committee was given permanent standing.

A favored way of dealing with contentious social issues in Canada is through public commissions, such as federal and provincial law reform commissions. The federal Law Reform Commission was established in 1971 to review the federal laws of Canada on a continuing basis, and to make recommendations for their improvement, modernization, and reform. Bioethical issues were dealt with in the Protection of Life Project, one of four commission projects. Between 1979 and 1992, a dozen or so study papers, working papers, and reports to Parliament were published on topics such as euthanasia and assisted suicide, experimentation on human subjects, and medically assisted procreation. In 1992 the commission was terminated by the government for budgetary reasons. Five years later, in 1997, the federal government created the Law Commission of Canada. This commission has not undertaken specific projects concerning bioethics, but it has supported work on the governance of research involving humans.

Academic institutions have experienced tremendous growth in the area of bioethics since the 1960s. Courses in this field have proliferated in philosophy and religious-studies departments, where they are often the most heavily subscribed offerings. Bioethics instruction is now offered in every Canadian medical school at the basic degree level and is rapidly expanding into residency training programs. Nursing, health administration, and dentistry programs have also formalized ethics teaching, and in many universities instruction in the ethical aspects of animal experimentation is required for biology, zoology and psychology students.

Research in bioethics has been fostered by the creation of centers, institutes, and professional associations for practitioners in this field. The Center for Bioethics of the Clinical Research Institute of Montreal, established in 1976, was the first such organization in Canada. It was followed three years later by the Westminster Institute for Ethics and Human Values, based in London, Ontario (now defunct). By 2002 there were at least nineteen research centers and groups in Canada, most of them university based. A national association, the Canadian Bioethics Society, was formed in 1988 through a fusion of two previously established associations.

The Institutional Matrix of Bioethics

The Canadian healthcare system and Canadian law have been two of the most important forces shaping the context within which bioethics has developed in Canada. The healthcare system has also been the source of some of the most difficult bioethical issues Canadians have faced since 1971, when the country's national health insurance program was fully set in place (Taylor). Although Canadian legislation and jurisprudence have largely guided and supported work in bioethics, there have also been points on which they have clashed.

THE CANADIAN HEALTHCARE SYSTEM. The Canadian healthcare system is in reality not a single system, but rather a network of ten provincial and three territorial healthcare systems. The coherence of this network derives from the Canada Health Act (1984) and a series of accords between the federal, provincial, and territorial governments. The federal government provides funds to the provinces and territories for healthcare; the latter governments, in return, agree to incorporate the essential features of the national health insurance program into their healthcare systems. This sharing of responsibility is currently being challenged, however.

The Canadian national health insurance system, as defined in the Hospital Insurance Act (1957) and reaffirmed in the Canada Health Act (1984), is founded on a values system to which the Canadian people fiercely adhere. The principal features of this program (comprehensiveness; universality; accessibility; portability; and public administration) derive from Canadians' commitment to the principle of equality. Equality before the healthcare system, as Robert Evans has phrased it, is as strong a principle in Canada as equality before the law (Evans). The basis of this principle is

that all Canadians should have access to a similar level of care, regardless of their ability to pay for it.

There have been challenges, however, to the Canadian healthcare system's principle of universal access to hospital and medical services. The practice of user fees and extra billing by doctors, which is prohibited by the Canada Health Act, represented one such challenge. Extra billing would allow doctors to bill patients for charges exceeding what the national health insurance plan paid doctors for a medical service. For a short time in the mid- to late 1980s extra billing occurred in seven provinces. In response to this violation of the Canada Health Act, the federal government stopped transfer payments to these provinces, thereby providing the provincial governments with the necessary incentive to enforce the principles of the Canada Health Act. Extra billing has not occurred since.

The way a country organizes its healthcare system as a whole is not just an issue of economics and administration. It is also an issue of public ethics and is deeply rooted in the conflict between powerful interest groups and the requirements of justice (as interpreted by a society's governing ethos. The Canadian ethos of universal access with equal terms and conditions for all is being challenged by new questions of fairness. For example, the current Canadian Medicare program pays for physician and hospital services, but not drugs (unless these are administered in a hospital). For many patients, good health depends upon access to expensive medications, and since these are not covered by the national health insurance system they are at risk of incurring significant debt or, worse, doing without their medications.

Another issue concerns waiting lists. Some individuals who do not want to wait to access needed health services and who have the resources to pay for these services argue that they should not be prohibited from purchasing what they are able to pay for. Some of these concerns are examined in the final report of the National Forum on Health, which focused on values, striking a balance, the determinants of health, and evidence-based decision making The forum paid particular attention to the need to balance resources within the health sector, and between the health sector and other sectors of the economy (National Forum on Health). The emphasis in these reports was on the core Canadian value of equal access to care irrespective of ability to pay. The National Forum on Health called on the federal government to expand public health insurance to home care and drugs.

In 2002 there was renewed debate about the future of the Canadian healthcare system with particular focus on two issues: (1) public administration (whether there should be a single- or multi-payer system), and (2) delivery of goods and services (whether this should be public, private not-for-profit, or private for-profit). Two reports looked at the sustainability of the universally accessible, publicly funded healthcare system with particular attention to the question of whether Canada should move to a two-tier system by allowing the use of private hospitals and private insurance. The first of these reports was issued by the Senate Standing Committee on Social Affairs, Science and Technology, which undertook a study on the state of the healthcare system in Canada. The report is widely known as the Kirby Report—in reference to Senator Michael Kirby, who chaired the Committee. It endorses an increased role for private healthcare corporations.

The second report, Building On Values: The Future of Health Care in Canada, is by the Commission on the Future of Health Care in Canada (widely known as the Romanow Report, after the commission chair, Roy Romanow). The report examines four strategies for continuing to ensure access to high quality of care regardless of ability to pay: (1) more public investment (paid for by raising taxes or diverting resources from other programs), (2) more user pay (through charging fees as an incentive to deter abuse), (3) an increase in private choice (either for-profit or non-profit), or (4) a complete reorganization of the healthcare delivery system. A commitment to health care as a social good and service, not an economic commodity only available to those who can pay, informs the analysis.

BIOETHICS AND LAW IN CANADA. In Canada, the Constitution Act (1867) was amended in 1982 through the introduction of the Canadian Charter of Rights and Freedoms. This charter obliges government actors not to violate rights considered fundamental. Such rights include life, liberty, and security of the person; freedom of conscience, thought, belief, and expression; and freedom from discrimination. Democratic support for legislation that violates the charter does not compel the courts to uphold the legislation, since the charter protects fundamental freedoms and legal rights against even democratically composed majorities. This is illustrated in the 1988 Morgentaler decision of the Supreme Court of Canada, in which a law passed by a democratically elected government was struck down by the Supreme Court of Canada because it violated the charter.

Another significant case is the 1991 Ontario Court of Appeal decision in *Malette v. Shulman.* A Jehovah's Witness woman was taken to the hospital unconscious and bleeding after a car accident. The physician attending her was informed that she was carrying a signed but undated card refusing blood products, but he nonetheless gave her a transfusion in order to prevent her death from heavy loss of blood. The patient, Georgette Malette, sued him for the civil wrong of battery (unauthorized touching) and was awarded a favorable judgment, which the Ontario Court of Appeal upheld. The trial judge observed that, while the transfusion may have saved her life, the principle of respect for autonomous persons prevailed over principles of beneficence and nonmaleficence. In other words, society may not share her priority of interests, but it must respect her autonomy.

From the mid-1970s through the mid-1980s, numerous symposia, workshops, and position papers reflecting the thinking of a cross-section of Canadians supported the conclusion that contraceptive sterilization, in some circumstances, would be truly beneficial for some mentally disabled persons, as it would allow them to enjoy sexual fulfillment without the risk of bearing and rearing children. There was controversy only regarding the process that would be used to select individuals eligible for sterilization. It was not clear what conditions had to be fulfilled to protect mentally disabled persons from being sterilized for someone else's benefit. However, a 1986 decision of the Supreme Court of Canada (*Eve v. Mrs. E.*) clarified the law and dramatically affected practice. The Court declared categorically that sterilization should never be authorized for nontherapeutic purposes. In the absence of the affected person's consent, the Court believed that it can never be safely determined that such sterilization is for the benefit of that person. This decision has proved to be difficult for clinicians, parents, those with institutional responsibility for the care of mentally disabled persons, and, perhaps, for the latter themselves, for their social lives and privacy in relations with members of the opposite sex may be restricted for fear of pregnancy. This decision also serves as a focus for continuing discussions about what should be done when what is judged by some to be ethically justifiable has been declared to be illegal or unconstitutional.

Key Issues

Although Canadians have been preoccupied with many bioethics issues, the following discussion is limited to those issues that have most intensively mobilized the thought and action of Canadians in the fields of clinical ethics, research ethics, and ethics in public policy.

CLINICAL ETHICS. Several court cases in Canada illustrate the interplay between clinical ethics and jurisprudence when decisions have to be made regarding cessation of medical treatment. An ethical and legal consensus has grown in Canada since the late 1980s in support of the view that physicians are justified in withholding or discontinuing treatments that do little more than prolong a patient's dying and suffering. However, there continues to be debate about physician-assisted suicide and euthanasia, as illustrated in the legal cases summarized below.

In 1992 the Superior Court of Quebec affirmed that the request of a competent patient to discontinue life-supporting treatment should be honored (*Nancy B. v. Hôtel-Dieu de Québec*). Nancy B., a twenty-five-year-old woman, was permanently dependent on a respirator due to Guillain-Barré syndrome. After two years, while lucid and without clinical depression, she asked that the respirator be stopped, knowing that this would lead to her death. The court held that discontinuing treatment would not constitute criminal negligence or homicide. In so ruling, it cited the Canadian Law Reform Commission's recommendation that ambiguous sections of the Criminal Code of Canada should be changed so that the criminal law of Canada could not be interpreted as obliging physicians either to treat patients against their informed and free refusal or to initiate or continue treatments that are therapeutically useless and not in patients' best interests (Law Reform Commission).

A year later, in 1993, Sue Rodriguez—a competent woman suffering from amyotrophic lateral sclerosis who wanted to commit assisted suicide—brought a challenge to the prohibition against assisted suicide found in the Criminal Code. The Supreme Court of Canada upheld the prohibition by a five-to-four margin based on their application of the Charter of Rights and Freedoms to the facts of the case. Despite this decision, Sue Rodriguez ultimately died as a result of physician-assisted suicide, and no one was prosecuted in connection with her death.

Also in 1993, Robert Latimer was charged with first-degree murder in the death of his twelve-year-old daughter, Tracy Latimer. Mr. Latimer had placed his severely handicapped daughter (a quadriplegic child with the intellectual capacity of a three-month-old) in the cab of his truck and, with the intent of alleviating her suffering, asphyxiated her with carbon monoxide. In 1994 Mr. Latimer was convicted of second-degree murder and given the mandatory sentence of life imprisonment without eligibility for parole for ten years. He successfully appealed his conviction to the Supreme Court of Canada, and a new trial was ordered. In 1997 Mr. Latimer was tried again on a charge of second-degree murder, was again convicted, but was now sentenced to two years less a day (instead of the mandatory sentence of at least ten years in prison). Mr. Latimer again appealed his conviction and the Crown appealed the sentence. The Court of Appeal dismissed Latimer's appeal, allowed the Crown's appeal, and imposed the mandatory minimum sentence.

Mr. Latimer then appealed to the Supreme Court, and in 2001 the Court upheld the conviction and the life sentence with no parole for ten years.

These cases show that the courts in Canada will respect the wishes of competent patients to refuse life-sustaining treatment, reject the wishes of competent patients to actively bring about their own death through physician assisted suicide, and not tolerate deliberate actions to bring about the death of another person even when the motive is to alleviate suffering.

RESEARCH ETHICS. Canadians have been intensively occupied with elaborating the conditions for ethically acceptable research involving humans. In August 1961, Walter Halushka volunteered to be a research subject in a project to test a new anesthetic drug. Halushka suffered a cardiac arrest during the experiment, and though successfully resuscitated, he was left with some brain damage and could no longer continue his university studies. The Court of Appeal found that the physician-researchers had failed to inform Halushka that the test was of a new drug, that they had little previous knowledge about this drug, that the drug was an anesthetic, and that there was risk involved in its use. The investigators also failed to tell the subject that the test would involve putting a catheter up a vein in his arm into his heart. The Court of Appeal clarified the requirements for consent in the research setting:

> There can be no exceptions to the ordinary requirements of disclosure in the case of research as there may well be in ordinary medical practice.... The subject of medical experimentation is entitled to a full and frank disclosure of all the facts, probabilities and opinions which a reasonable man might be expected to consider before giving his consent. (*Halushka v. the University of Sasktchewan et al.*)

Though patients are rarely harmed seriously in clinical research, serious harm, and even death, can and does occur. It is particularly tragic when a research-related death occurs that might have been avoided if consent negotiations had been adequate. On October 13, 1981, Julius Weiss, a sixty-two-year-old man, died in a Montreal hospital while participating in a research project being conducted to test the efficacy of a drug (indomethacin, administered by eyedrops) designed to reduce swelling in the eye after cataract surgery. This project also required that Weiss undergo a series of radiological examinations called fluorescein angiograms to gauge the effects of the indomethacin eyedrops. Weiss had a history of heart problems and went into convulsions following a drop in blood pressure after the first injection of fluorescein dye. His heart stopped, resuscitation attempts failed, and he died. Weiss's widow and children sued the two physicians involved in the clinical study and the hospital where the study was conducted. In his judgment on this case, rendered on February 23, 1989, Judge Louis De Blois of Quebec Superior Court found that the patient would not have agreed to be in this project had he known it carried even a small risk of cardiac arrest and death (see *Weiss v. Solomon*).

In Canada, unlike other countries, health research involving humans is governed primarily by guidelines, not legislation. The first such guidelines were promulgated by the Medical Research Council of Canada in 1978 and later revised in 1987. Some years later, in the wake of a number of research-related controversies, a Tri-Council Working Group involving all three federal research funding agencies—the Medical Research Council of Canada (MRC), the Natural Sciences and Engineering Research Council of Canada (NSERC), and the Social Sciences and Humanities Research Council of Canada (SSHRC)—was convened to develop a common set of ethics guidelines that would govern virtually all publicly funded research involving humans in Canada (an international first). In 1998 the Tri-Council Policy Statement on Research Involving Humans was adopted. These guidelines outline the expectations regarding ethics review and set out the rules for researchers and institutions that receive public funds for research.

ETHICS IN PUBLIC POLICY. Between the 1960s and the 1990s, the issue of abortion dominated the public-policy debate in bioethics. The debate was ignited in the late 1960s, when the federal government proposed changes to the Criminal Code that would relax restrictions on divorce, homosexual acts between consenting adults, the distribution of contraceptives, and abortion. The last issue was the most contentious and engendered widespread public discussion and lobbying of members of Parliament. The law in effect at the time prohibited termination of pregnancy under any circumstances, and criminal sanctions could be brought against the pregnant woman and anyone who would perform the abortion. In 1969 a new abortion law (section 251 of the Criminal Code) was adopted that retained the criminal sanctions against both the woman seeking an abortion and anyone who would perform the act, but legalized termination of pregnancy if the following conditions were met: (1) the abortion had to be performed by a qualified medical practitioner in an accredited or approved hospital; (2) it had to be approved by a therapeutic abortion committee of the hospital; and (3) the continuation of the pregnancy would, or would be likely to, endanger the life or health of the woman seeking the abortion.

Following this liberalization of the abortion law, there were many complaints of unequal access to abortion services, as well as accusations from antiabortion groups that the law was being applied too loosely. Since the federal government refused to revise the law, both proponents and opponents of abortion decided to challenge the law in the courts.

In 1970 Dr. Henry Morgentaler established an abortion clinic in Montreal, in clear opposition to the law. After his third jury acquittal, in 1976, on charges of performing an illegal abortion, the Quebec government allowed his clinic to operate, despite vigorous protests from antiabortion forces.

In 1983 Dr. Morgentaler set up an abortion clinic in Toronto and was promptly arrested and charged, along with two colleagues. A jury once again acquitted him. This decision was appealed, and in 1985 the Ontario Court of Appeal overturned the decision of the jury and ordered a new trial. Dr. Morgentaler appealed this ruling to the Supreme Court of Canada. On January 28, 1988, the Supreme Court, in a 5-to-2 decision, overturned the Court of Appeal decision and restored the original jury acquittal. The Court also declared the 1969 abortion law unconstitutional because it violated the Canadian charter of rights and freedoms.

The Supreme Court heard another abortion-related case in 1988, this one initiated by an opponent of abortion. In 1981, Joe Borowski, a former Manitoba politician and antiabortion activist, challenged the 1969 abortion law on behalf of the fetus. A Saskatchewan court heard the case in 1983, and in its judgment rejected Mr. Borowski's claim that the fetus is a person with legal rights. Mr. Borowski appealed this decision. In 1989 the Supreme Court declined to decide the case because the appeal was moot, due to the abortion law having been struck down.

Between 1988 and 1991, the federal government made several attempts to pass a new abortion law, but none were successful. A bill introduced in 1989 would have recriminalized abortion except when performed by a doctor "of the opinion that, if the abortion were not induced, the health or life of the female person would be likely to be threatened." (Bill C-43 An Act respecting abortion, 2nd Sess., 34th Parl., 1989; defeated in the Senate January 31, 1991). Health was defined as including physical, mental, and psychological well-being. The bill was approved by the House of Commons in May 1990 by a narrow margin (140–131), and it was then sent to the Senate, where it received detailed examination. In January 1991, a vote was taken, but the Senate was deadlocked. Under Canada's Senate rules, a tie is considered a defeat. As a result, Canada is in the unusual circumstance of having no criminal restrictions on abortion.

New reproductive technologies have also generated considerable public-policy activity in Canada and have been the subject of several public inquiries, including a federal Royal Commission, which received and commissioned many submissions focusing on the ethical aspects of reproductive technology. Feminist concerns (e.g., regarding commercialization in paid contractual pregnancies) have figured prominently in the Canadian discussion of these issues (Overall; Sherwin). In 1996, Bill C-47, the Human Reproductive and Genetic Technologies Act, was introduced in the House of Commons. This bill died on the Order Paper, however, when an election was called before the legislative process was complete. (Bills under consideration that have not received royal assent are on the Order Paper. When an election is called, all such bills are considered dead.) Years later, in May 2002, Bill C-56, the Assisted Human Reproduction Act, was introduced. Ironically, it too died on the Order Paper in September of the same year when Parliament was prorogued (to terminate or suspend a legislative session). Bill C-56 did not share the same fate as the earlier bill, however, in that it was reinstated as Bill C-13, which at the time of writing was continuing through the legislative process. Interestingly, much of the public debate around this bill has not been about assisted reproduction, but about whether the embryos that remain after infertility treatment can be used for human embryonic stem cell research.

The Future

Canada is a multicultural nation. For the most part, however, bioethics has been (and continues to be) monocultural, reflecting the values of the white, largely Anglo-Saxon, professional class that has dominated Canadian society, including its science and medicine. If bioethics is to be relevant to Canadian society in the future, it must develop a multicultural sensitivity and expand the range of issues it considers, the perspectives from which the issues are viewed, and even the backgrounds of individuals working in the field.

DAVID J. ROY
JOHN R. WILLIAMS (1995)
REVISED BY FRANÇOISE BAYLIS

BIBLIOGRAPHY

Baylis, Françoise; Downie, Jocelyn; Freedman, Benjamin; et al., eds. 1995. *Health Care Ethics in Canada.* Toronto: Harcourt Brace.

Boetzkes, Elisabeth, and Waluchow, Wilfrid, eds. 2000. *Readings in Health Care Ethics.* Peterborough, ON: Broadview Press.

Borowski v. Attorney General of Canada. 39 DLR. (4th) 731; 33 CCC (3d) 402; 2 WCB (2d) 96 (1987).

Canada Department of Justice. 1982. *Canadian Charter of Rights and Freedoms,* Part I of the *Constitution Act, 1982,* being Schedule B to the *Canada Act 1982* (U.K.), 1982, c. 11.

Evans, Robert G. 1988. "'We'll Take Care of It for You': Health Care in the Canadian Community." *Daedalus* 117(4):155–189.

Eve v. Mrs. E., In re. 31 DLR (4th) 1 (1986).

Halushka v. The University of Saskatchewan et al. 52 WWR 608; 53 DLR (2d) 436 (1965).

Hebert, Philip. 1996. *Doing Right: A Practical Guide to Ethics for Medical Trainees and Physicians.* Toronto: Oxford University Press.

LaRochelle, S. A., and Fink, C. T. 1940. "Précis de morale médicale pour infirmières, médecins et prêtres. Quebec: L'Action catholique," English translation by M. E. Poupore. In *Handbook of Medical Ethics for Nurses, Physicians, and Priests,* 4th edition. Montreal: Catholic Truth Society.

Law Reform Commission of Canada. 1983. *Euthanasia, Aiding Suicide and Cessation of Treatment.* (Report no. 20.) Ottawa: Minister of Supply and Services Canada.

Malette v. Shulman. 67 DLR (4th) 321; 72 O.R. (2d) 417; 20 ACWS (3d) 301 (1990).

Morgentaler, Smoling and Scott v. The Queen. 44 DLR (4th) 385; 37 CCC (3d) 449; 3 WCB (2d) 332 (1988).

Nancy B. v. Hôtel-Dieu de Québec. 86 DLR (4th) 385; 69 CCC (3d) 450; 31 ACWS (3d) 160 (1992).

Osler, Sir William. 1985. *The Collected Essays of Sir William Osler,* vol. 1: *The Philosophical Essays,* ed. John P. McGovern and Charles G. Roland. Birmingham, AL: Classics of Medicine Library.

Overall, Christine, ed. 1989. *The Future of Human Reproduction.* Toronto: Women's Press.

Paquin, Jules. 1954. *Morale et médecine.* Montreal: Comité des Hôpitaux du Québec.

R. v. Latimer. 1 SCR 3 (2001).

Rodriguez v. British Columbia (Attorney General). 3 SCR 519 (1993).

Roy, David J.; Williams, John R.; and Dickens, Bernard M. 1994. *Bioethics in Canada.* Scarborough, ON: Prentice Hall Canada.

Royal Commission on New Reproductive Technologies. 1993a. *Proceed with Care, Final Report.* Ottawa: Minister of Government Services Canada.

Royal Commission on New Reproductive Technologies. 1993b. *Research Studies of the Royal Commission on New Reproductive Technologies,* vol. 1: *New Reproductive Technologies: Ethical Aspects.* Ottawa: Minister of Government Services Canada.

Sherwin, Susan. 1991. "Abortion Through a Feminist Lens." *Canadian Philosophical Review* 30(3): 327–342.

Sherwin, Susan. 1992. *No Longer Patient: Feminist Ethics and Health Care.* Philadelphia: Temple University Press.

Singer, Peter, ed. 1995. *Bioethics at the Bedside.* Ottawa: Canadian Medical Association.

Sumner, L. Wayne. 1987. "Abortion." In *Health Care Ethics: An Introduction,* ed. Donald VanDeveer and Tom Regan. Philadelphia: Temple University Press.

Taylor, Malcolm G. 1987. *Health Insurance and Canadian Public Policy: The Seven Decisions That Created the Canadian Health Insurance System.* Montreal: McGill-Queen's University Press.

Weiss v. Solomon. 48 CCLT 280 (1989).

INTERNET RESOURCES

Canada Department of Justice. 1982.*Canadian Charter of Rights and Freedoms,* Part I of the *Constitution Act, 1982,* being Schedule B to the *Canada Act 1982* (U.K.), 1982, c. 11. Available from <http://laws.justice.gc.ca/en/charter>.

Canadian Bioethics Society. 2003. "Working Conditions for Bioethics in Canada." Available from <http://www.bioethics.ca/>.

Canadian Institutes of Health Research. 2003. "Ethics—Useful Links: Academic Bioethics and Health Law Centers/Institutes in Canada." Available from <http://www.cihr-irsc.gc.ca>.

Canadian Parliament. 2002. *Bill C-13, An Act Respecting Assisted Human Reproduction.* Available from <http://www.parl.gc.ca>.

Commission on the Future of Health Care in Canada. Roy Romanow, Commissioner. *Building on Values: The Future of Health Care in Canada,* final report, November 2002. Available from <www.hc-sc.gc.ca/english/pdf/care/romanow-e.pdf>.

Medical Research Council of Canada; National Sciences and Engineering Research Council of Canada; and Social Sciences and Humanities Research Council of Canada. 1998. "Tri-Council Policy Statement on Research Involving Humans." Available from <http://www.nserc.ca/programs/ethics/english/ethics-e.pdf>.

Standing Senate Committee on Social Affairs, Science and Technology. 2002. *The Health of Canadians—The Federal Role, Final Report,* vol. 6: *Recommendations for Reform.* Available from <http://www.parl.gc.ca>.

IV. LATIN AMERICA

This entry presents a historical panorama of biomedical ethics in Latin America, the name given to a linguistic and cultural community encompassing South America, Central America, Mexico, and part of the Caribbean. From political, economic, and social points of view, the Latin American nations are quite different, although at present they have underdevelopment in common.

Since bioethics as a discipline flourished first in the United States, it is useful to compare medical ethics in North America, with its predominantly Anglo and northern European culture, and in Latin America, pointing out the differences between the two traditions within the Western culture.

First, the Latin American tradition of medical ethics is described; next, the incipient bioethics movement in Latin America is considered; then the major bioethical problems of the region are noted; and finally, the challenge to Latin American bioethics is discussed.

The Latin American Tradition of Medical Ethics

When Spain and Portugal established colonies in the Americas, they brought with them the profound influence of the Roman Catholic Church, heir to that Western culture whose roots are Greek philosophy, Judaism, and Roman law. The Catholic tradition has in fact defined Latin American ethics and the Latin American ethos. First, Catholic moral theology built a system of medical ethics based on (1) natural-law theory as the basis of morality; (2) the principle of the sanctity of human life as a moral criterion; and (3) the commandment of love, or the virtue of charity, as the golden rule. Second, through their pastoral role and religious authority, priests reinforced the paternalistic medical ethos of the Hippocratic tradition. The paternalistic model of medical responsibility centered on the principle of beneficence (that benefit must be produced and harm avoided); the principle of autonomy is not taken into account. Beneficent paternalism has dominated the relationships between doctor and patient, and between medicine and society, in Latin America up to the present day.

As the cultures of northern and southern Europe evolved in the Americas, the differences between the two were accentuated. Modernity did not have the same secular, liberal, and pluralistic cast in Latin America as it did in North America. In Latin America, morality was not detached from metaphysics and religion; it did not establish a new basis in scientific and political rationalism, nor did it set itself up as critical and autonomous over against the natural and supernatural order of the medieval epoch.

Beginning in the eighteenth century, it is possible to contrast two ethics: the classical tradition of virtue, represented by the Mediterranean peoples (particularly the Italians and Spaniards), and the tradition in which principles are central, dominant in the English- and German-speaking countries (McIntyre). In Latin America, the political paternalism of the *ancien régime* and the medical paternalism of the Hippocratic tradition go together; the result is a paternalistic model on both the individual-clinical and the social policy levels.

The ethics and ethos of Latin American medicine are expressed in professional codes of ethics and in health policy and legislation. The forebear of all these normative institutions was the *protomédicato*. Originating in the Roman Empire, the *protomédicato* was a tribunal of royal physicians (*protomédicos*) that granted professional licenses and acted as a judicial and legislative body in health matters. In the thirteenth century, Castile was one of the first kingdoms to establish legal regulations for medical practice and public health; examples of this were found in the School of Salerno, and the laws of Frederick II in Sicily (Mainetti, 1989). The *protomédicato* was transplanted from Spain to the Americas, where it endured until the period of independence (early nineteenth century), at which point medical instruction, practice, and policy began to be modernized.

In the twentieth century, professional associations and medical colleges in various countries began to formulate their own codes of ethics, in accordance with the deontological tradition that regulates the relationships of doctors among themselves, with the public, and with the state. One of the first such codes was drawn up in 1918 by Luis Razetti, a leading Venezuelan physician who specialized in medical deontology, under the influence of the French—an influence that was at that time very perceptible in Latin American society in general and in the medical culture in particular. This same code was later adopted in Colombia (1919) and in Peru (1920); it provided a basic model for other Latin American codes, which are essentially traditional guides for professional courtesy or etiquette, the relationships of physicians among themselves, with the patient, and with the state (León).

The medical codes promulgated in many Latin American countries are influenced by a variety of factors, among them biomedical progress, malpractice legislation, and the political changes throughout the region after decades of military rule. Brazil's Federal Code of Medical Ethics (1988), for example, incorporates concern about new problems like AIDS, and reformulates the rule of medical confidentiality. The Medical College of Chile has been very active since 1984, demonstrating its sensitivity to—among other issues— the participation of Chilean physicians in torture during the years of authoritarian rule that ended in 1984 (Mainetti, 1990).

The state's responsibility for healthcare has constitutional status in Latin American countries (Pan American Health Organization, 1989). The right to healthcare is included among social and economic rights. The first nation to incorporate the right to healthcare in its constitution was Chile, in 1925, followed by Bolivia, Cuba, Guatemala, Guyana, Haiti, Honduras, Mexico, Nicaragua, Paraguay, Peru, Uruguay, and Venezuela. The responsibility of the state for health planning is legislated by many Latin American countries, which provide for universal access to essential medical services and a national healthcare system that is either free or based on co-payments, but with limited coverage. In Latin American government, health policy generally demonstrates a significant gap between principle and practice: between justice, which theoretically endorses the equal right to health care, and actual practice in societies that, owing to their social and economic development, are not able to guarantee that this and other rights will be respected.

Codes of ethics and health legislation are based on a moral view that is both dogmatic (codified and legalistic, in contrast with philosophic, analytic, and critical) and authoritarian (based on professional authority, which is partly religious and partly governmental, rather than civic or democratic). The Latin American tradition of medical ethics can be defined as naturalistic, paternalistic, dogmatic, and authoritarian. The new Latin American medical ethics, represented by bioethics, has developed in contrast with this older tradition.

The Bioethics Movement in Latin America

The bioethics revolution that has occurred in the industrialized nations has arisen both from the scientific and technological progress of biomedicine and from the liberal and pluralistic character of those nations. By contrast, in the developing Latin American countries bioethical interests correspond more to those of a low-technology society and a tradition of confessional morality (Mainetti, 1988). Bioethics, based on the principles of beneficence, autonomy, and justice, may be seen as civic morality to which the parties to an increasingly conflictual relationship—physician, patient, and society—appeal. Or bioethics may be seen as medical culture, expressed in the "introduction of the moral subject into medicine," the promotion of the rational, free agent in the therapeutic relationship. It is fair to say, however, that bioethics has barely arrived in Latin America in either guise.

Latin American bioethics evolved over a period of thirty years, in three decade-long stages, commencing in the 1970s: reception, assimilation, and re-creation. Public and academic interest in bioethical topics appeared in the 1980s with the proliferation of new medical technologies, such as those used in intensive care units, transplants, and assisted reproduction, and with the appearance of democratic governments in the region. On the one hand, legal intervention in medical cases increased, due perhaps to the distances created between the professional and the patient by specialization. Malpractice and a patient's rights movement in Latin America imitated the early history of U.S. bioethics. On the other hand, there was an academic rehabilitation of practical, moral, and political philosophy as they could be applied to medicine. This development was in keeping with the kind of ideological pluralism and consensus formation that has characterized bioethics as a discipline in the United States.

The academic and professional development of bioethics in Latin America has been a process of incorporating the U.S. model in stages. As the twentieth century neared its end, the institutionalization of the discipline as expressed in the creation of research centers, professorships at universities, ethics committees at hospitals, and national commissions on bioethics could not be said to be significant. Nor had the three main functions of bioethical studies been carried out. These are the educational function (deontology and legal medicine still stand for ethics at medical schools); the consultative function (clinical and healthcare ethics are not practiced in hospitals and other healthcare facilities); and the political function (groups of experts have not formed to advise public institutions on biomedical norms). Bioethics is also just beginning to capture the attention of the public and the media.

Among the groups active on the Latin American bioethics scene, several deserve mention: the Instituto de Humanidades Médicas y Centro de Bioética of the Fundación Mainetti (Institute for the Medical Humanities and Center for Bioethics of the Mainetti Foundation) in La Plata, Argentina, and the Instituto Colombiano de Estudios Bioéticos (Colombian Institute for Bioethical Studies) in Bogotá, Colombia. The former, established in 1972, combines the European and Anglo-American traditions of medical humanism, serving as a model and resource center for other countries in the region, particularly through its Escuela Latinoamericana de Bioética (Latin American School of Bioethics, ELABE), directed by Juan Carlos Tealdi. The latter, founded in 1985 by Fernando Sánchez Torres, former dean of the National University of Colombia, together with the ASCOFAME (Colombian Association of Medical Faculties) with its Center for Medical Ethics, directed by Alfonso Llano Escobar, S.J., and the Colombian School of Medicine and its Health Care Ethics Committee, also lead in the process of renovating medical ethics in the region.

Other academic and professional associations have emerged in Latin American countries in recent years for the purpose of developing programs of bioethical studies: the Department of Bioethics of the Catholic University of Uruguay; the Sindicato Médico of Uruguay, a very important professional organization that appointed a bioethics commission; the Department of Bioethics of the Chilean Catholic University; and the Chilean Medical College, mentioned above. These associations work actively on deontological questions, and the Brazilian Association of Medical Ethics Teachers emphasizes bioethical issues.

The bioethics enterprise also can be evaluated by the number of people interested in the discipline; by courses, conferences, and other scientific activities; and by the publication of books and articles. The classic 1973 Latin American text on medical ethics, by Augusto León, was followed by several bioethics texts (Mainetti, 1988; Varga; Vélez Correa). According to a 1990 report issued by the Pan American Health Organization, conditions in Latin America were expected to encourage the development of programs to integrate medical ethics into the health system. This integration could occur along a broad spectrum ranging from legislation and public policies to academic curricula, and should include the revision of the ethics codes of established medical associations. To this end, the Latin American School of Bioethics has been coordinating a regional program of hospital ethics committees since 1989 (Tealdi and Mainetti). The growth of interest in bioethics justified a Latin American bioethics association to unite isolated efforts, and thus to offer a concerted response to the needs of the region. Meeting in La Plata, Argentina, in December 1991, representatives from several Latin American nations founded the Federaciòn Latinoamericana de Instituciones Bioéticas (Latin American Federation of Bioethics Institutions, FELAIBE).

In 1990 the Pan American Health Organization (PAHO) commissioned James Drane of the United States to produce a decisive report that reviewed the development of bioethics in Latin America and proposed several steps for the further regional development of the discipline (Drane and Fuenzalida). That same year, PAHO published a special issue on bioethics, edited by Susan Scholle Connor and Hernàn Fuenzalida-Puelma, formally introducing bioethics in Latin America. This was the first collection in which early authors in the field addressed diverse topics and set out different perspectives on the discipline. Finally, PAHO, a pioneer among international health organizations, created the Regional Program on Bioethics (1994) with headquarters in Santiago de Chile, but whose activities are decentralized in order to serve all the member countries of PAHO. This program—a comprehensive policy in bioethics and its associate disciplines—entered a new stage under the outstanding scholar Fernando Lolas Stepke's leadership (Programa Regional de Bioética, 2000).

Bioethics has become a field of new challenges in Latin America. A seeming uniformity hides a rich, heterogeneous set of activities. Not only European and Christian influences but also indigenous intellectual traditions are very important in the development of Latin American bioethics. It does not have its own philosophy, as Anglo-American bioethics is perceived to have, but it does have its own literature or narrative. The particular historical setting, cultural ethos, and social reality of Latin America could infuse new life into the global bioethics community. In this sense, a symptom of the new times is the fact that the Second Congress of the International Association of Bioethics took place in Buenos Aires, Argentina, in 1994, and the Sixth Congress was held in Brasilia, Brazil, in 2002. A "new Brazilian bioethics" or "hard bioethics," inspired by Brazil's contradictory social reality, began to flourish at the turn of the twentieth century, and explores alternative perspectives to traditional bioethical currents (Garrafa).

Bioethics first arrived in Latin America as a foreigner, and later underwent a transcultural shaping. Transplanted to a new habitat, bioethics took on its own distinctive character and voices and has become a strong intellectual and political enterprise (Lolas Stepke, 1994; 1998).

In comparison to the North American style of bioethics, Latin American bioethics takes a more theoretical and philosophical approach. As a search for a *critical, radical* and *global* bioethics, Latin American bioethics represents a global, "post-bioethical" age (Drane, 1998; Spinsanti). Although Latin American bioethics is far from being a unified theoretical system or a single coherent perspective, it represents the *ethica spes* of the new millennium.

Major Topics in Latin American Bioethics

Latin American countries share a concern about a number of problems with implications for both law and policy. A common sociocultural and public-health situation defines the Latin American biomedical ethos. Ethnomedical ethics ought to be an essential topic, because the health and disease conceptions, practices, and values, as well as the needs, of the native (precolonial) Latin American peoples are not properly understood by academic medicine and the health policy of the dominant culture. These peoples still await the fulfillment of the World Health Organization's proclamation calling for the integration of their healing arts into modern medicine. Among the most pressing bioethical issues facing Latin America are the following.

REPRODUCTIVE ETHICS. Both the prevention of human reproduction (contraception, sterilization, and abortion) and assisted human reproduction (reproductive technologies) are central issues for Latin American population policy. This policy is clearly linked to health and to religious, secular, and geopolitical factors. Underdevelopment and overpopulation form a vicious circle that distances societies more and more from the goal of sustainable development. The Catholic Church does not tolerate what it calls "artificial" control of fertility and condemns abortion, which is legally prohibited in most Latin American countries. To date neither public debate nor legislative reform has occurred, although the widespread and frequent practice of clandestine abortion effectively expresses Latin American governments' laissez-faire policies. The ethical complexity of assisted reproduction provokes polemics about the status of the embryo without leading to a declared war between "Catholics" and "secularists, " but this area requires legal regulation.

THE ETHICS OF DEATH AND DYING. In Latin America, death is not as medicalized nor is the medical profession as tormented about it as is the case in the First World. The technological assault on dying, the new *danse macabre* in the intensive care unit, does not offer the same sort of spectacle in Latin America as it does in the United States. Nevertheless, the contemporary "art of dying" is a challenge in Latin America, too, even if living wills, do-not-resuscitate orders (DNRs), the ethical principles of critical care medicine, and the pro-euthanasia movement have yet to become major issues. Palliative medicine, the hospice movement, and campaigns for death with dignity are the modern Latin American versions of *ars moriendi*. At the beginning of life, pediatrics ethics committees are improving regulations regarding the treatment of premature and disabled newborns. At the end of life, legislation authorizing removal and transplantation of organs has advanced markedly in many Latin American countries (Fuenzalida-Puelma).

RESEARCH ETHICS. Biomedical research in Latin America lacks both a legislative framework and an effective set of controls. Much research also lacks scientific validity and, motivated more by monetary interest than by interest in knowledge, overlooks patient's rights such as consent and confidentiality. Developing countries must create the scientific and financial conditions for research itself; they must also attract projects that involve international cooperation while avoiding the risks such cooperation often brings with it, including economic and human exploitation. Oversight committees are needed so that international standards, with criteria appropriate to the cultural modalities of each community, may be applied. U.S. standards of consent, for instance, cannot be implemented easily in the social conditions of developing countries (Levine). Questions that must be considered in the future include research priorities, allocation of resources for research, and access to new, experimental drugs. This last issue, which has an especially high profile because of the global AIDS crisis, now involves not only the right of patients to protection from possible ill effects but also their right to have access to such drugs, which may prolong or save their lives.

HEALTHCARE ETHICS. Health status in Latin America must be seen within a larger picture of underdevelopment, poverty, hunger, and economic crisis aggravated by the foreign debt of the region. Two global short-term goals set by the World Health Organization have not yet been reached in Latin America: Infant mortality has not been brought below 5 percent, and life expectancy has not risen beyond sixty-five years. Healthcare expenditures in Latin America did not exceed 5 percent of the gross national product in the 1970s and 1980s, compared with 10 percent for the so-called developed countries.

Although there is a plethora of medical students and an oversupply of physicians, approximately 75 percent of the population of Latin America does not receive medical attention. This dramatizes the gap between the proclaimed right to healthcare and the conditions necessary to exercise it. Primary care—including family planning, maternal and child care, immunization, health counseling and education, campaigns against tuberculosis, and treatment of infectious diseases—should be the goal of health policy in all developing nations. Healthcare policy must be focused on health as an indicator of development, oriented to the basic needs of the majority of the population, and designed to promote medical care based on criteria of equity, integration, participation, and efficiency (Pan American Health Organization, 1989).

Between 80 and 90 percent of the resources allocated to healthcare in Latin America is spent on secondary and tertiary care. "Bioethics in the time of cholera," to paraphrase the novelist Gabriel García Márquez—medical ethics faced with plagues like cholera and AIDS—sums up the challenge to healthcare ethics in Latin America.

ENVIRONMENTAL ETHICS. The environmental problems of Latin America are in part peculiar to the region and in part similar to those in western Europe and the United States. Overpopulated cities like Mexico City, Caracas, and São Paulo are more polluted than their European counterparts, and the Latin American urban crisis ranges from street cleaning to disposing of radioactive wastes from nuclear power plants.

In agricultural areas, the indiscriminate use of biocides contaminates crops and reduces the fertility of the soil. The extinction of animal and plant species produces imbalances in the ecosystem. Of worldwide importance is the devastation of the Amazon rainforest, the largest jungle in the world. An ecological reserve with an influence on world climate, the area has been deforested by 10 percent. It faces the prospect of destruction within half a century, for reasons not unrelated to the sizable foreign debt owed by Brazil.

Governments and publics in Latin America are just beginning to become conscious of the importance of the environment to human and animal health; to national, regional, and world economies; to the preservation of nature and of life itself. Some countries have environmental protection legislation, projects to protect or preserve natural resources, and active ecology movements. Bioethics, however, has yet to raise its voice in civic and public arenas with regard to environmental ethics (that is, ecological rights), a new type of third-generation human rights, and policies of sustainable development (Pan American Health Organization, 1987).

The Challenge of Bioethics for Latin America

Because of its humanistic medical tradition and the social conditions of developing countries, Latin America can offer a distinctive bioethics perspective. There are two dimensions to this perspective. First, a discipline established along European lines of the general philosophy or theory of medicine, with three main branches (medical anthropology, epistemology, and axiology), may be better equipped to transform academic, scientific medicine into a new humanistic biomedical paradigm (Mainetti, 1988). Such an approach would guard against the accusations often lodged against bioethics in the United States and Europe: that the discourse of bioethics only appears to humanize medicine while obscuring the real dehumanization of the system. For example, the bioethical discourse on autonomy may hide the depersonalization of medical care and its risks of iatrogenesis, exploitation of the body, and alienation of health. In response to the development of biomedicine in a technological era, bioethics may be able to play a more critical role, one that is less complacent or optimistic about progress.

Second, the Latin American reality of "bioethics in the time of cholera" requires an orientation toward social ethics, with an accent on the common welfare, the good society, and justice rather than on individual rights and personal virtues (the modern and classical traditions of morality, respectively). A macroethics of health or public health may be proposed as an alternative to the Anglo-American tradition of micro or clinical ethics. Greater emphasis can be placed on the social importance of medicine; as far as medical ethics is concerned, the great need in the developing countries is fairness in the allocation of resources and the distribution of health services. Latin America has not lost hope that it might be the continent of justice.

Several decades after its birth, bioethics in the United States is moving toward new intellectual models. This movement shows up in the revisionist-foundationalist debate within the discipline; the application of ethics to other discourses, including the political arena; the rediscovery of ethics of virtue; the return to what is experiential; and the cross-cultural and international dialogue. The bioethics revolution in North America and Europe—summarized in a high-technology *bios* and individualized ethos—must be complemented in Latin America by a humanistic *bios* and a communitarian ethos.

A promising outlook is emerging as the bioethics traditions and problematics of the two Americas move closer to one another. Perhaps in the context of the new world order and the beginning of the twenty-first century, bioethics—the bridge toward the future of humanity—will also be a bridge of inter-American cooperation and integration.

JOSÉ ALBERTO MAINETTI (1995)
REVISED BY AUTHOR
TRANSLATED BY MARY M. SOLBERG

BIBLIOGRAPHY

Brazil. 1988. *Federal Code of Medical Ethics.*

Drane, James F. 1996. "Bioethical Perspectives from Ibero-America." *The Journal of Medicine and Philosophy* 21(6): 557–569.

Drane James F. 1998. "Universal Medical Ethics." *Quirón* 29(2): 53–64.

Drane, James F. 1999. "Commentary" (to José A. Mainetti's "Complejo Bioético: Pigmalión, Narciso y Knock"). *Acta psiquiátrica y psicológica de América latina* 45(2): 109–121.

Drane, James F., and Fuenzalida, Hernán. 1991. "Medical Ethics in Latin America: A New Interest and Commitment." *Kennedy Institute of Ethics Journal* 1(4): 325–338.

Escobar Triana, Jaime. 1996. "Humanistic and Social Education for Physicians: The Experience of the Colombian School of Medicine." *The Journal of Medicine and Philosophy* 21(6): 651–657.

Figueroa, Patricio R., and Fuenzalida, Hernán. 1996. "Bioethics in Ibero-America and the Caribbean." *The Journal of Medicine and Philosophy* 21(6): 611–627.

Fuenzalida-Puelma, Hernán. 1990. "Organ Transplantation: The Latin American Legislative Response." *Bulletin of the Pan American Health Organization* 24(4): 425–445.

Garrafa, Volnei. "A Bioethical Radiography of Brazil." *Acta Bioethica 2000* Año VI(1): 177–182.

León, Augusto. 1973. *Ética en medicina.* Barcelona: Científico-Médica.

Levine, Robert J. 1982. "Validity of Consent Procedures in Technologically Developing Countries." In *Human Experimentation and Medical Ethics,* ed. Zbigniew Bankowski and Norman Howard-Jones. Geneva: Council for International Organizations of Medical Sciences.

Lolas Stepke, Fernando. 1994. "El discurso bioético: Una anécdota personal." *Quirón* 25(4): 28–30.

Lolas Stepke, Fernando. 1998. *Bioética.* Santiago de Chile: Editorial Universitaria, S.A.

Lolas Stepke, Fernando. 2000a. "Bioethics and the Culture of Life: A Contribution to Peace." *Bioética Informa* VI(19): 8–11.

Lolas Stepke, Fernando. 2000b. *Bioética y Antropología Médica.* Santiago de Chile: Mediterraneo.

Macklin, Ruth, and Luna, Florencia. 1996. "Bioethics in Argentina: A Country Report." *Bioethics* 10(2): 140–153.

Mainetti, José Alberto. 1988. "Bioethical Problems in the Developing Word: A View from Latin America." *Unitas* 60 (June): 238–248.

Mainetti, José Alberto. 1989. *Ética médica: Introducción histórica.* La Plata, Argentina: Quirón.

Mainetti, José Alberto. 1990. "Bioethics: A New Health Philosophy." *Bulletin of the Pan American Health Organization* 24(4): 578–581.

Mainetti, José Alberto. 1996. "In Search of Bioethics: A Personal Postscript." *The Journal of Medicine and Philosophy* 21(6): 671–679.

McIntyre, Alistair C. 1984. *After Virtue: A Study in Moral Theory,* 2nd edition. Notre Dame, IN: University of Notre Dame Press.

Pan American Health Organization. 1987. *Informe anual del director.* Washington, D.C.: Guerra de Macedo, Carlyle (Director).

Pan American Health Organization. 1989. *El derecho a la salud en las Américas: Estudio constitucional comparado.* Washington, D.C.: Author.

Programa Regional de Bioética OPS/OMS. 2000. "Instituciones y Centros especializados en Bioética en América Latina y el Caribe." Santiago de Chile: Author.

Razzetti, Luis. 1963. *Deontología médica,* Volume 1: *Obras completas.* Caracas: Ministerio de Sanidad y Asistencia Social.

Scholle Connors, S.; Fuenzalida, Puelma; and Hernán, L. 1991. *Bioethics. Sigues and Perspectivas.* Scientific Publications No. 527 of the Panamerican Health Organization.

Spinsanti, Sandro. 1995. "José Alberto Mainetti: Simboli dell' antichitá classica in America Latina." In *La bioetica: Biografie per una disciplina.* Milano: Franco Angeli.

Tealdi, Juan Carlos, and Mainetti, José Alberto. 1990. "Hospital Ethics Committees." *Bulletin of the Pan American Health Organization* 24(4): 410–418.

Varga, Andrew C. 1988. *Bioética: Principales problemas,* tr. Alfonso Llano Escobar as *The Main Issues of Bioethics.* Bogotá: Ediciones Paulinas.

Velez, Correa, and Alfonso, Luis. 1989. *Etica médica: Interrogantes acera de la medicina, la vida y la muerte.* Medellín, Colombia: Corporación para Investigaciones Biológicas.

MEDICAL ETHICS, HISTORY OF AUSTRALIA AND NEW ZEALAND

• • •

Medical ethics in Australia and New Zealand (Australasia) evolved slowly until the early 1980s, when major advances in reproductive technologies prompted widespread public discussion of bioethical issues surrounding human conception.

Early History

In the early decades of the twentieth century, ethical debates centered on issues of professionalism in the delivery of medical services, such as the permissibility of advertising by individual practitioners and the setting of standard fees to avoid "undercutting" by competitors. The branches of the British Medical Association (BMA) that had been set up in the colonial Australian states were federated in 1912, when a unified code of professional ethics, dealing mainly with the regulation of advertising and etiquette toward patients, was introduced (Egan). After World War I, medical schools in Australasian universities began to include brief didactic instruction in the ethical obligations of physicians. There was also some public discussion of abortion, methods of birth control, and confidentiality in relation to patients with venereal disease.

A Labour government with a strong social welfare platform was elected in Australia in 1941. In the late 1940s this government attempted to introduce a national health service, which would have provided universal access to healthcare for the first time in Australia. However, a bitter debate developed with the BMA, the majority of whose members saw the government's plans as a threat to the autonomy of medical practitioners and as the first step toward the nationalization of medicine. After legal challenges, the plans for a national health program were defeated in 1949 (Gillespie). Under the free-market policies of subsequent Liberal governments, access to publicly funded healthcare was available only to recipients of old-age and invalid pensions. This situation persisted until 1975, when the Labour government introduced Medibank, Australia's first national healthcare program, which provided access to government-subsidized healthcare for all. While the incoming Liberal/National coalition government gradually dismantled this program during the late 1970s, it was reinstated as Medicare in 1983 by the newly elected Labour government, and has continued to operate into the twenty-first century.

Ethical issues in reproduction became a major concern in Australasia in the early 1980s, following pioneering research on *in vitro* fertilization (IVF) carried out by a joint research team led by Carl Wood and Ian Johnston at the Monash University Queen Victoria Medical Centre and the Royal Women's Hospital in Melbourne during the 1970s. In 1983 this research led to the world's first live IVF births from frozen embryos and donated eggs, and the embryo research carried out by Monash University scientists in order to improve IVF and other assisted reproduction techniques sparked worldwide interest. These developments in reproductive technology stimulated much public discussion in Australia, particularly among Roman Catholics, who constitute over a quarter of the population.

Euthanasia

Care for the terminally ill became another widely debated issue in Australia in the 1980s. Influenced by the growing public support for voluntary euthanasia, the state governments of South Australia and Victoria passed legislation (in 1983 and 1988, respectively) permitting patients to refuse medical treatment in certain circumstances, even where such treatment might prolong their lives. In 1995 the Northern Territory's single-chamber parliament passed the Rights of the Terminally Ill Act, making it the first jurisdiction in the world to legalize active voluntary euthanasia. This legislation permitted doctors to carry out voluntary euthanasia, under certain specified conditions, for terminally ill patients with unbearable suffering. The lives of several patients were lawfully ended under this act before it was overruled by the Euthanasia Laws Act, passed by the Australian federal parliament in 1997.

Ethics Centers

Australasia's first research center in bioethics, the Monash University Centre for Human Bioethics, was established by the philosophy professor Peter Singer, together with colleagues in medicine, science, and the law, in 1980. A number of smaller research centers for bioethics were set up in Australasia during the next two decades, including Melbourne's St. Vincent's Bioethics Centre, Adelaide's Southern Cross Bioethics Institute (both of which have a Christian perspective on bioethics), Sydney's John Plunkett Centre for Ethics in Health Care, the Ethics Unit at Melbourne's Murdoch Childrens Research Institute, and the University of Otago Bioethics Research Centre in Dunedin, New Zealand. Bioethics research is also pursued by several of the large groups of philosophers appointed to the Centre for Applied Philosophy and Public Ethics, which was established by Charles Sturt University in both Canberra and Melbourne in 2000. The interdisciplinary Australasian Bioethics Association was formed in 1990, and its inaugural conference was held in Melbourne in 1991.

With Helga Kuhse and others from the Monash Centre, Peter Singer has written extensively on ethical issues arising from the new reproductive technologies and on questions surrounding the care of terminally ill adults and infants. Other noteworthy Australasian writers in bioethics include the philosophers Max Charlesworth, Julian Savulescu, and Robert Young; the feminist academics Renate Klein and Robyn Rowland; the lawyers Michael Kirby and Loane Skene; and the theologian Norman Ford. In 1989 the Monash Centre introduced Australasia's first master's program in bioethics, and this institution also publishes Australia's only peer-reviewed bioethics journal, the *Monash Bioethics Review*.

Reproductive Technologies

In 1982 advances in infertility research in Victoria led the government of that state to appoint Louis Waller, a professor of law at Monash University and an Australian law reform commissioner, to chair a committee whose mandate was to consider the social, ethical, and legal issues arising from IVF. The three reports produced by this committee supported the use of IVF under certain regulations, prompting the Victoria Parliament, in 1984, to enact the Infertility (Medical Procedures) Act, the world's first legislation to deal specifically with these new reproductive technologies (see Charlesworth 1989). Among other provisions, this legislation allowed IVF to be carried out at approved hospitals, for married couples who have already sought infertility treatment for at least twelve months prior to attempting IVF.

At the federal level, the National Bioethics Consultative Committee (NBCC) was established in 1988 as an advisory committee on issues such as access to information about their origins for children conceived through IVF; artificial insemination by donor; surrogate motherhood; and embryo experimentation. In 1990 this committee issued a report that supported surrogacy arrangements and proposed draft legislation to regulate such arrangements. In light of the heated public controversy that ensued, however, the Australian government decided against implementing its recommendations nationally. Nevertheless, most Australian states have not outlawed IVF-assisted surrogacy in cases where the surrogate mother receives no fee, and in 1994 the Australian Capital Territory enacted legislation to regulate such surrogacy arrangements. In 1991 the NBCC was subsumed under the existing National Health and Medical Research Council (NH&MRC), which merged the functions of the NBCC and the Medical Research Ethics Committee to form the Australian Health Ethics Committee.

The groundbreaking work of Australian researchers with human embryonic stem cells and biotechnology became the focus of much public discussion at the beginning of the present century. The cloning of human beings was outlawed in 2002, following the recommendations of a federal parliamentary standing committee, but research will be permitted on stem cells that had been extracted from human embryos prior to early 2001.

Human Experimentation

Australasia's first recorded institutional ethics committee to review human experimentation was set up at the Royal Victorian Eye and Ear Hospital in Melbourne in 1957 (McNeill), and at the instigation of the NH&MRC (which allocates government funding for medical research), Australian universities began, in the 1980s, to form ethics committees to oversee medical and other research carried out at those institutions. Following wide community consultation and a 1996 federal government review of the relatively brief NH&MRC guidelines on human experimentation, the detailed and remarkably broad-ranging *National Statement on Ethical Conduct in Research Involving Humans* was issued by the NH&MRC in 1999 as a guide for all human research ethics committees in Australia. The basic principles in the *National Statement* are integrity, respect for persons, beneficence, and justice, which are developed in more detail through their application to a variety of different types of research.

In New Zealand, the Medical Research Council (set up in 1937 by the government to supervise medical research) decided in 1968 that all research must adhere to the World Medical Association's Declaration of Helsinki, which stressed nonmaleficence and the need for informed consent on the part of the experimental subjects. In 1987 unprecedented public outrage followed revelations of an experiment involving clandestine selective nontreatment of women with cervical cancer, which was carried out at the National Women's Hospital in Auckland from 1966 to 1981. The New Zealand government immediately set up an inquiry into the experiment, which resulted in an amendment to the Human Rights Commission Act of 1977, that added a statement of patients' rights to proper standards of care and adequate disclosures to enable genuinely informed consent. This amendment also provided for the appointment of a national health commissioner to encourage awareness of these rights by members of the medical profession (Campbell).

Patient's Rights

During the 1990s there was considerable discussion in Australia about patients' legal rights to treatment information, prompted by the Australian High Court decision in *Rogers v. Whitaker* (1992), which gave legal recognition to a patient-centered standard of disclosure of medical information. Following this decision, the NH&MRC issued a booklet containing guidelines on providing information to patients.

Influenced by the increasing recognition of patient's rights, Australasian medical schools have gradually woven the teaching of ethics into their curricula. For example, the University of New South Wales in Sydney and the University of Newcastle began teaching substantive courses in ethics to medical undergraduates in the 1970s, and the University of Adelaide's medical school introduced ethics into the undergraduate syllabus in the early 1980s. Following the recommendations of the National Inquiry into Medical Education—a committee of academics and health professionals set up by the federal minister for health, which heard submissions during 1987 and 1988—many other Australian medical schools have included clinical ethics as part of their undergraduate programs. These developments in bioethics education should help promote lively and informed discussions of medical ethics issues in Australasia as they arise in the future.

JUSTIN OAKLEY (1995)
REVISED BY AUTHOR

BIBLIOGRAPHY

Armit, H. W. 1924. "Medical Practice." *Medical Journal of Australia* (October 25): 413–421.

Campbell, Alastair A. 1989. "A Report from New Zealand: An 'Unfortunate Experiment.'" *Bioethics* 3(1): 59–66.

Charlesworth, Maxwell J. 1989. *Life, Death, Genes, and Ethics: Biotechnology and Bioethics.* Sydney: ABC Books.

Charlesworth, Maxwell J. 1993. *Bioethics in a Liberal Society.* Cambridge, Eng.: Cambridge University Press.

Coney, Sandra. 1988. *The Unfortunate Experiment.* Harmondsworth, Eng.: Penguin.

Egan, Bryan. 1988. "Nobler Than Missionaries: Australian Medical Culture c. 1880–c. 1930." Ph.D. diss., Monash University, Melbourne.

Ford, Norman. 1988. *When Did I Begin? Conception of the Human Individual in History, Philosophy, and Science.* Cambridge, Eng.: Cambridge University Press.

Gillespie, James A. 1991. *The Price of Health: Australian Governments and Medical Politics, 1910–1960.* Cambridge, Eng.: Cambridge University Press.

Kasimba, Pascal, and Singer, Peter. 1989. "Australian Commissions and Committees on Issues in Bioethics." *Journal of Medicine and Philosophy* 14: 403–424.

Kuhse, Helga, and Singer, Peter. 1985. *Should the Baby Live? The Problem of Handicapped Infants.* Oxford: Oxford University Press.

Kuhse, Helga, and Singer, Peter, eds. 1998. *A Companion to Bioethics.* Oxford: Blackwell.

McNeill, Paul M. 1993. *The Ethics and Politics of Human Experimentation.* Cambridge, Eng.: Cambridge University Press.

Rowland, Robyn. 1987. "Making Women Visible in the Embryo Experimentation Debate." *Bioethics* 1: 179–188.

Singer, Peter; Kuhse, Helga; Buckle, Stephen; et al., eds. 1990. *Embryo Experimentation.* Cambridge, Eng.: Cambridge University Press.

Singer, Peter, and Wells, Deane. 1984. *Making Babies: The New Science and Ethics of Conception.* Oxford: Oxford University Press.

MEDICAL ETHICS, HISTORY OF EUROPE

• • •

I. ANCIENT AND MEDIEVAL. A. GREECE AND ROME

Ancient Greece and Rome are often treated together by scholars who seek to describe in a limited space any aspect of those two civilizations. Greek history is typically divided into the Mycenaean period (2000–1200 B.C.E.), the "dark age" (1200–750 B.C.E.), the archaic period (750–500 B.C.E.), the classical age (500–323 B.C.E.), and the Hellenistic period (323–30 B.C.E.); and Roman history into three phases: monarchy (753–509 B.C.E.), Republic (509–31 B.C.E.), and

Empire (31 B.C.E.–476 C.E.). During the archaic period the Greeks engaged in considerable colonization in the Near East and throughout the Mediterranean basin, including southern Italy. The Hellenistic period, which was immediately preceded by Alexander the Great's conquest of much of the Near East, was marked by a fusion of Greek and various Near Eastern civilizations. Roman culture was influenced by the Greeks of southern Italy and, to a much greater degree, by the various Hellenized peoples whom the Romans conquered during the last two centuries of the Republic. The culture of the first three centuries of the Empire is appropriately labeled Greco-Roman. During the last two centuries of the Empire, a gradual division between the Latin West and the Greek East culminated in the emergence of the European Middle Ages in the former and the Byzantine era in the latter.

The Ancient Medical Profession

Although some herbal medicine and primitive surgery were employed by Greeks as early as the time represented in the Homeric epics (before 750 B.C.E.), the understanding and treatment of disease were predominantly magico-religious. It was not until the late sixth or early fifth century B.C.E. that Greek philosophy provided a rational/speculative theoretical framework for understanding health and disease, and hence for the emergence of what may be called a medical profession. The development of such a framework for the practice of medicine marks the origin of the expectation that physicians are above all products of a scientific training and orientation; that is, that they deal with disease and other physical ailments both empirically and rationally, not magically, mystically, or superstitiously (Amundsen and Ferngren, 1983). Desacralized medicine was an important aspect of Greek culture that spread throughout the Mediterranean world during the Hellenistic period and was adopted and adapted by the Romans during the late Republic.

There were no institutions that granted medical degrees or certification, nor was there a licensure requirement at any time or place. All who wished could call themselves physicians and practice medicine. Nevertheless, from the fifth century B.C.E. until the end of the period under consideration, the prevailing picture is of a population that typically distinguished between physicians (*iatroi* in Greek, *medici* in Latin) and those who practiced a magico-religious healing.

THE HIPPOCRATIC OATH. Professional standards enforceable by sanctions against physicians did not exist. Those who chose to call themselves physicians and undertake the practice of medicine were not required to swear any oath or to accept and abide by any formal or informal code of ethics.

Several medical oaths, however, are known from classical antiquity. The most famous is the Hippocratic Oath, though no scholar today believes it was written by the historically elusive "father of medicine." Even the date of the oath's composition is unknown; some scholars place it as early as the sixth century B.C.E. and others as late as the first century C.E. Apparently it did not evoke much attention before the Christian era; the first known reference to it was made by the physician Scribonius Largus in the first century C.E.

Some of the stipulations in the oath are not consonant either with ethical precepts prevalent elsewhere in the Hippocratic Corpus and other classical literature or with medical practice as revealed in the sources. Attempts have been made either to explain away these inconsistencies or to attribute the oath to an author or school whose views were, in other respects as well, discordant with those characteristic of classical society. Most influential has been Ludwig Edelstein's theory (1967) that the oath was a product of the Pythagorean school, whose tenets included belief in reincarnation, the practice of vegetarianism and sexual purity, and a condemnation of abortion, suicide, and the shedding of blood. Although his thesis has appealed to many scholars, few now accept it (Deichgräber; Kudlien, 1970; Lichtenthaeler; Nutton, 1993). Parallels for even the most esoteric injunctions in the oath can be found outside Pythagoreanism. Furthermore, the Greek text offers many variant readings, some of which can be translated in significantly different ways.

THE IDEAL PHYSICIAN. One constant emerges from the variegated history of ancient medical ethics. When a Greek spoke of *iatroi* or a Roman of *medici,* each was using a word charged with meaning. Unless modified by a pejorative adjective, both meant compassionate, objective, unselfish persons, dedicated to their responsibilities. By the fifth century B.C.E. *iatros* was thus employed in a simile and metaphor; the good ruler, legislator, or statesman was frequently referred to as the physician of the state, and philosophers often described themselves as physicians of the soul. Such usage was carried over to the Latin *medicus.* The popular ideal of the physician was a dedicated, unselfish, and compassionate preserver or restorer of health—and, sometimes, inflicter of health-giving pain—always committed to the good of the patient, regardless of how far short of this ideal many physicians undoubtedly fell.

Beginning in the fifth century B.C.E., a body of medical literature developed that describes the ethics of Greek physicians. These books dealt with eminently practical concerns suggested by medical practitioners for their own benefit, such as issues of the physician–patient relationship, and obligations to the arts, to humanity, and to life itself.

General Etiquette and Deportment

Greek physicians' formulation of a standard of general etiquette and deportment provided the basis for a social expectation that has remained since that time: physicians are guided by certain basic standards of deportment or professional etiquette in dealing with patients (Amundsen and Ferngren, 1983). The physician should look healthy and be of suitable weight, "for the common crowd considers those who are not of excellent bodily condition to be unable to take care of others" (*The Physician* 1; in the Hippocratic Corpus). This is of particular significance, especially for classical Greek culture, in which health was considered by many both a virtue and an indicator of virtue. Health, the highest good, was set above beauty, wealth, and inner nobility. Health was a goal in itself, for without health, nothing else had value.

Especially in dealings with their patients, physicians should be cheerful and serene, but neither harsh nor silly. They should be reserved, speak decisively and briefly, exercise self-control, and not be excitable. Ostentation was regarded with particular distaste. Further, "It is disgraceful in any art and especially in medicine, to make a parade of much trouble, display, and talk, and then to do no good" (*On Joints* 44; in the Hippocratic Corpus). Physicians were urged to refrain from holding lectures for the purpose of drawing a crowd. Conducting one's practice with much fuss, although it might appeal to the vulgar crowd, smacked of charlatanism. Charlatans avoided consultations; good physicians, recognizing their own limitations and respecting their colleagues' knowledge, turned to other competent physicians for advice. Since consultations could lead to disputes, "Physicians who meet in consultation must never quarrel or jeer at one another" (*Precepts* 8; in the Hippocratic Corpus).

The Physician-Patient Relationship

Physicians' relationships with their patients usually commenced with an examination followed by a prognosis. Then the physician was faced with two or three ethical decisions: (1) whether to take the case if it appeared to be dangerous or hopeless; (2) what to tell the patient; and (3) what treatment to pursue.

INFORMING THE PATIENT. When determining what to tell their patients, two considerations impinged upon physicians: (1) the effect of their statement on the patient, and (2) the effect of these cases on their own reputation. There was considerable reluctance to take hopeless or doubtful cases. Some physicians, if they considered their cases hopeless, merely informed the patients that they were going to die, and left them. A treatise in the Hippocratic Corpus, probably written in the second century B.C.E., advises physicians to "conceal most things from the patient while you are attending to him ... revealing nothing of the patient's future or present condition. For many patients through this cause have taken a turn for the worse" (*Decorum* 16). If the case was dangerous and the outcome uncertain but not hopeless, it was sometimes suggested that the patient's relatives or some other third party be informed, or that the patient should be told and advised to make a will. Sextus Empiricus, a physician and philosopher of the second century C.E., argued that "The physician who says something false regarding the cure of his patient, and promises to give him something but does not give it, is not lying though he says something false," since in saying it he has regard to the cure of the person he is treating (*Against the Logicians* 1, 43). The great diversity of advice and examples in both medical and other literature shows that opinions on this delicate question varied considerably then, just as they do now.

CHOICE OF TREATMENT. The question of what treatment to pursue posed an ethical problem for some ancient physicians. Therapeutics were placed in three categories: the mildest, dietetics; next, drug therapy; and the most drastic, cutting or cauterizing. Those who abided by the Hippocratic Oath swore not to "cut for stone," which some scholars interpret as a rejection of all operative surgery. Especially in the last century B.C.E. and the first century C.E., different medical sects vigorously debated whether drug therapy was unethical and whether milder therapeutics were preferable. But some, like Scribonius Largus, argued that it was even more unethical to refuse to employ drugs responsibly when their benefit to patients was so obvious (Hamilton).

THE PATIENT'S COOPERATION. The cooperation of patients was, of course, recognized as important (*Aphorisms;* in the Hippocratic Corpus), for if they did not obey their physicians' instructions, their condition might worsen or they might die, in which case their physicians would be blamed (*The Art; Decorum;* both in the Hippocratic Corpus). A brilliant prognosis, including a description of what course their illnesses had already taken, might so impress the patients that they would be inclined to obey their physicians (*Prognostics;* in the Hippocratic Corpus). Persuasion might be used; a passage in the *Laws* of Plato advances the idea that good physicians will reason with their patients and persuade them to follow the treatments prescribed (cf. *The Statesman*). Galen remarks on the importance of convincing patients that remarkable benefit will ensue if their physicians' orders are obeyed. But it is the patients' respect and admiration for their physicians that are most desirable. Since faith in one's physician could render treatment more efficacious, Galen, for example, maintained that patients should admire their physician like a god.

CONFIDENTIALITY. Should physicians treat as confidential any information they acquired in their contact with patients? In the Hippocratic Oath, the following injunction appears: "What I may see or hear in the course of the treatment or even outside of the treatment in regard to the life of men, which on no account one must spread abroad, I will keep to myself, holding such things shameful to be spoken about." Edelstein sees in this stipulation a clear indication of Pythagorean purity, an insistence on secrecy "not as a precaution but as a duty" (p. 37). Those things that one ought not spread abroad, whether encountered within or outside of practice, are categorized as "shameful to be spoken about," or in another translation, "holy secrets." Elsewhere in the Hippocratic Corpus the physician is advised to "say only what is necessary. For … gossip may cause criticism of his treatment" (*Decorum* 7). In another treatise in the Hippocratic Corpus, the physician is urged "not only to be silent but also of a great regularity of life, since thereby his reputation will be greatly enhanced" (*The Physician* 1). While the stipulation to refrain from speaking too much may be motivated by a sense of duty to keep inviolable especially those private things physicians encounter in practice, the other two quotations belong in the context of a self-interested regard for reputation rather than a concern for the supposed "rights" of patients.

SEXUAL PROPRIETY. A very practical stipulation in the Hippocratic Oath reads, "Whatever house I may visit, I will come for the benefit of the sick, remaining free of all intentional injustice, of all mischief, and in particular of sexual relations with both female and male persons, be they free or slaves." Edelstein stresses again the Pythagorean tone of this injunction, especially the emphasis on justice, and sees in the prohibition of sexual relations with members of the patient's household evidence of Pythagorean severity in sexual morality. Whether this advice was motivated by ideals of purity or by merely pragmatic concerns, physicians who used their close contact with patients or their households to satisfy their sexual passions would earn not only disrespect and contempt but also distrust. Having a reputation as a seducer of patients and their family members simply did nothing to enhance one's medical career (see also *The Physician*).

Duty to the Art, Society, and Life

LOVE OF HUMANITY. Sometimes ancient medical literature addresses very fundamental questions of motivations for practicing medicine, physicians' role in society, and the obligations incumbent upon them in that role. One statement in the Hippocratic Corpus—"Where there is love of humanity [*philanthropia*] there is also love of the art [*philotechnia*]" (*Precepts* 6)—has often been taken to demonstrate that for Greek physicians, love of humanity and love of the art were the foundational motivations for their practicing medicine. Sir William Osler saw in it the Greek physician's "love of humanity associated with the love of his craft—*philanthropia* and *philotechnia*—the joy of working joined in each one to a true love of his brother" (Edelstein, pp. 319f.). The precept in question, however, may not be so lofty. Vivian Nutton, for example, sees it as simply a pragmatic assertion that physicians' showing love for humanity will foster in their patients a love for the medical art (1993). In any event, it is evident that for many physicians, love of one's honor, glory, and reputation provided a greater motivation than *philanthropia* (Amundsen and Ferngren, 1982).

The statement quoted from the *Precepts* in the preceding paragraph occurs in the context of a discussion about fees that is introduced by the admonition "I urge you not to be too unkind." The noun *apanthropia*, the antonym of *philanthropia*, is here translated by the adjective "unkind." In the Hippocratic Corpus *philanthropia* generally is little more than kindness and compassion. Owsei Temkin, however, emphasizes that one must take care not to trivialize their philanthropy (1991), which one may easily do by contrasting it with the nearly religious flavor that philanthropy took on during subsequent eras. A profound change occurred in late Hellenistic and Roman thought, which, affected by the influence of humanitarian and cosmopolitan ideas on both philosophical and popular ethics, began to see *philanthropia* (Latin, *humanitas*) as humane and civilized feeling toward humanity in general; that is, the principle of the common humanity of all people as expressed by the Stoic philosopher Sarapion around 100 C.E. in a poem titled "On the Ethical Duties of the Physician": "Like a savior god, let [the physician] make himself the equal of slaves and of paupers, of the rich and of rulers of men, and to all let him minister like a brother; for we are all children of the same blood" (Oliver, p. 246).

This sentiment is strongly present in Galen (second century C.E.), for whom the best physician was also a philosopher, motivated by *philanthropia* (Brain). Galen, however, conceded that many physicians were motivated not by *philanthropia* but by the pursuit of money or love of glory (Temkin, 1973). Although a few sources, such as Scribonius Largus, held that to be truly a physician, one must be motivated by *philanthropia* (Hamilton), a majority of our sources concur with Plato that the motivation to practice any art, including medicine, has little or nothing to do with the integrity of the art itself: the practitioner must only be competent (*Republic*). Nevertheless, while few physicians or laymen may have regarded *philanthropia* as essential for the physician, most people probably regarded lack of kindness and compassion as distinctly undesirable for a physician. Ample evidence suggests that the "presence of compassion among doctors was taken for granted by authors of the first century" and that, even much earlier, physicians "could think of compassion as rooted in medical ethics" (Temkin, 1991, pp. 33, 34).

FEES. Ancient medical writers expressed much concern about fees. Physicians were acutely aware that the appearance of greed could have a detrimental effect on their reputations. Hence, in the Hippocratic Corpus physicians are urged to be more concerned with their reputation than with financial reward, sometimes to give their "services for nothing, calling to mind a previous kindness or [their] present reputation," and to avoid beginning a case by discussing fees, since it could adversely affect patients, particularly those whose condition was acute (*Precepts* 6). Physicians were admonished to consider their patients' economic situation in setting fees and to provide less expensive remedies for the poor than for the rich (*On Diet*). In spite of such sentiments, physicians do not appear to have engaged in much charitable activity from a sense of duty to humanity, to the community, or to the poor (Hands). Furthermore, the subject of medical fees in antiquity is complicated because some physicians objected to being considered "hirelings" and, especially during the Empire, some insisted that medicine was a liberal art, which entangled their remuneration with the complexities of Roman laws governing honoraria (Kudlien, 1976; Temkin, 1979).

EXPERIMENTATION. Ancient physicians strove to improve their proficiency and the efficacy of their art. The most extreme example of medical experimentation was vivisection of human subjects, a very controversial subject (Ferngren, 1982). Celsus states that Herophilus and Erasistratus in Ptolemaic Alexandria performed vivisections on condemned criminals supplied by the crown. Whether or not Celsus's statement is accurate is debated (Von Staden, 1989; Scarborough), but he presents the arguments for and against the value of vivisection, concluding that "to lay open the bodies of men while still alive is as cruel as it is superfluous … [since] actual practice will demonstrate [what can only be learned from the living] in the course of treating the

wounded in a somewhat slower yet much gentler way" (pr. 74f.). There is ample evidence for the vivisection of animals either to gain new knowledge or to test new theories (Galen, *On Anatomical Procedures*).

Some physicians recognized that without attempting new procedures and remedies, medical knowledge and techniques would not advance (Michler). The author of *On Joints* in the Hippocratic Corpus, after describing the failure of a novel attempt at reducing a dislocation, writes, "I relate this for a purpose: Those things which after a trial show themselves to have failed and which show why they failed, also provide good instruction" (*On Joints* 47). The author of the same treatise urges physicians to study incurable cases. Commenting on the Hippocratic maxim "Experiment is perilous" (which can also be translated "Experience is unreliable"), Galen cautions that "In the human body, to try out what has not been tested is not without peril in case a bad experiment leads to the destruction of the whole organism" (Temkin, 1991, p. 60). Further, he asserts that in several instances he had refrained from testing some remedies when he had others whose effects he knew better, and he points out that rash experimentation presents a danger to the life of the patient (Ferngren, 1985).

Some physicians may have been deterred from experimenting on patients by a fear of being brought to court. Complaints can be found in classical sources that only the physician can commit homicide with complete impunity, but there were some very limited means for seeking redress against the negligent or incompetent physician, at least in Athenian and Roman law (Amundsen, 1973; 1977). But most physicians were probably deterred from any compelling desire to experiment primarily by concern for their reputations rather than by fear of litigation. Classical literature provides numerous examples of the worry expressed by laymen that physicians experiment at their patients' risk (Ferngren, 1982; 1985).

SHARING NEW TECHNIQUES. When new knowledge and techniques were discovered or developed, physicians were faced with the question of whether they should share this information with their colleagues—their competitors—and with the public at large. The Hippocratic Oath appears to have been composed for an exclusive sect. In it physicians swear not to impart their knowledge to those outside their sect. Similar sentiments are expressed elsewhere in the Hippocratic Corpus: "Things … that are holy are revealed only to men who are holy. The profane may not learn them until they have been initiated into the mysteries of the science" (*The Law* 5).

Apart from a few such statements, a desire to share new techniques or knowledge with other physicians pervades the medical literature. Those who published their medical knowledge and experience obviously did not desire to keep them secret. Galen was motivated in part by the wish to help physicians after him. But many physicians undoubtedly guarded their special techniques with jealousy. Galen shows no surprise at a surgeon's intentionally concealing his operative procedures from view, but expresses disappointment that even some of his own pupils would not share their anatomical knowledge with others (*On Anatomical Procedures*). His "philanthropy is not only that of the physician, but more comprehensively that of a philosopher who subjectively delights in study and objectively labors for the good of mankind. He thinks of his work as belonging to posterity …" (Temkin, 1973, p. 50). Some physicians wrote to instruct other physicians and also to edify laymen. In their desire to share medical knowledge with contemporaries and with posterity, at least a few Greek and Roman physicians achieved the most enduring manifestation of their *philanthropia* and *philotechnia* (Temkin, 1949).

Respect for Life

How did physicians view their responsibility to nature and, more specifically, to life? Or, to put it differently, how might they have interpreted and applied the maxim frequently quoted in the Hippocratic Corpus, "to help or at least to do no harm" (*Epidemics* 1.11)? Did the Greek or Roman physician feel bound by any sense of "respect for life"?

ABORTION. The Hippocratic Oath enjoins that the physician "will not give a pessary to a woman to cause abortion" (Jones's translation [1924]; Edelstein's [1967] "I will not give to a woman an abortive remedy" appears broader in scope than the Greek). Here again we encounter a situation in the oath that runs counter to the realities of ancient medical practice. Many physicians did perform abortions, and various techniques are described in the medical literature (Carrick). Both Plato (*Republic*) and Aristotle (*Politics*) encouraged abortion as a means of population control and for eugenics. Objections to abortion were relatively rare before the beginning of the Christian era; in both Greek and Roman law, abortion was a criminal offense only if performed without the consent of the woman's husband (or father, if she was not married). By the first century C.E., some pagan physicians such as Scribonius Largus (Hamilton), influenced as much by an increasing humanitarianism as by the Hippocratic Oath per se, refused to perform abortions under any circumstances. The physician Soranus of Ephesus (late first/early second century C.E.) gives three reasons for which a woman seeks an abortion: to rid herself of the consequence of adultery, to maintain her beauty, and to preserve her health. Only for the last would he perform an

abortion (*Gynaecia*). Soranus was highly critical of physicians who so strictly adhered to the injunction in the oath that they refused to perform an abortion even to save the life of the mother. It appears, then, that some physicians would perform abortions on request, some refused to do so for any reason, and others assumed a position on therapeutic abortion consonant with that of Soranus. The decision to perform or not to perform an abortion ultimately rested on the convictions of the individual physician. The opposition to abortion of the author of the Hippocratic Oath and such physicians as Scribonius Largus and Soranus was based less upon an idea of the inherent value or sanctity of life than on an abhorrence of physicians' using their art in actively terminating even fetal life.

DEFECTIVE NEWBORNS. While some voices were raised against exposure of healthy newborns, the morality of killing weak, sickly, or deformed newborns appears not to have been questioned by either nonmedical or medical authors (Amundsen, 1987). Soranus, who condemned any but therapeutic abortion, not only raised no objection to rejecting a defective newborn; he also provided criteria to be used by midwives in determining which newborns were worth rearing (*Gynaecia*).

PROLONGING LIFE AND PASSIVE EUTHANASIA. *The Art,* a treatise in the Hippocratic Corpus, defines medicine as having three roles: doing away with the sufferings of the sick, lessening the violence of their diseases, and refusing to treat those overwhelmed by their diseases, realizing that in such cases medicine was powerless. The decision whether to take on a possibly incurable case was entirely the individual physician's. Some cases in the therapeutic treatises in the Hippocratic Corpus are introduced with the advice that certain procedures should be followed if the physician chooses to attempt treatment (Amundsen, 1978). Ancient medical literature is divided on the question of whether physicians should withdraw from cases once it becomes clear that they will not be able to help. Some urged that physicians ought not to withdraw, even if by so doing they might avoid blame. Others felt that they should withdraw if they had a respectable excuse, particularly if continuing treatment might hasten the patient's death. Physicians did, however, sometimes attend cases considered incurable. In the Hippocratic Corpus many diseases that then generally ended in death are described with no mention of prognosis and with no recommendation to the physician that such cases be undertaken or rejected. For most of them, medications to be employed are named. It was recognized that it was necessary to deal with incurable conditions in order to learn how to prevent curable states from advancing to incurability, particularly in the case of wounds (Michler). Opinions varied on the physician's responsibility to undertake treatment of hopeless or dangerous cases. In recent times it has become almost dogma to assert that the Hippocratic physician would not take on hopeless cases, but this is demonstrably false (Von Staden, 1990). Nevertheless, some laymen in antiquity held that, as Cicero wrote to his friend Atticus, "Hippocrates too forbids employing medicine in hopeless [cases]" (Temkin, 1991, p. 139).

Celsus, a medical compiler of the first century C.E., appears to represent the mainstream of medical thought: "For it is the part of a prudent man first not to touch a case he cannot save, and not to risk the appearance of having killed one whose lot is but to die; next when there is grave fear without, however, absolute despair, to point out to the patient's relatives that hope is surrounded by difficulty, for then if the art is overcome by the malady, he may not seem to have been ignorant or mistaken" (*De Medicina* 5.26.1.c). Available evidence suggests that physicians who prolonged or attempted to prolong the life of patients who could not ultimately recover their health were generally viewed as acting unethically (Amundsen, 1978).

ASSISTED SUICIDE OR ACTIVE EUTHANASIA. Would the ancient physician have thought it helping or harming to agree to assist those who for any reason wished to end their lives? To this question a majority of ancient physicians would probably have replied, "Helping, or at least not harming." The right of a free person to control his or her life as each saw fit—if not always in its living, at least in its termination—was a generally accepted view (Cooper). Suicide was, under most circumstances, outside the moral interest of the law; the exception was whether the suicide of one accused of a crime should be construed as an admission of guilt (Hooff). If a person who wished to commit suicide enlisted the aid of a second party, the latter was not legally culpable for rendering such assistance. Extralegal sources contain few objections to suicide in general, fewer still to the suicide of the hopelessly ill (Gourevitch; Hooff). Assisting in suicide was a relatively common practice for Greek and Roman physicians, and condemnations of the practice were infrequent.

One such condemnation appears in the Hippocratic Oath: "I will neither give a deadly drug to anybody, not even if asked for it, nor will I make a suggestion to this effect" (following Kudlien's translation, 1970, p. 118, n.47). This statement immediately precedes the prohibition of abortion. Both prohibitions have at least this much in common: They are inconsistent with the values expressed by the majority of sources and atypical of the realities of ancient medical practice as revealed in most medical and lay literature. Some physicians, however, may have preferred not to assist a suicide, for it could prove to be a messy business, at least from a legal point of view. Under Greek and Roman law, physicians could be charged with poisoning their patients. Indeed, physicians were sometimes charged with, or at least frequently suspected of, doing so (Kudlien, 1970; Nutton, 1985). Some physicians refused to aid anyone in committing suicide; perhaps they condemned assisting suicide under all circumstances for philosophical or religious reasons, or on the grounds that such action was inconsistent with the role of medicine (e.g., the first-century physicians Scribonius Largus [Hamilton, 1986] and Aretaeus [Amundsen, 1978]).

AT THE MOST, A LIMITED "RESPECT FOR LIFE." In light of the Hippocratic Oath and several later sources that also condemn abortion and active euthanasia, Temkin asserts that "Sufficient material has now been gathered to prove the existence of a tradition which, in its uncompromising form, did not sanction any limit to the respect for life, not even therapeutic abortion ..." (1976, p. 5). This tradition appears to have been entirely negative in its emphasis: The physician would not actively terminate life by abortion or euthanasia. But it laid no stress on the positive correlate that would require the physician actively to attempt to prolong life. This negative tradition did, indeed, become stronger with the rise of Christianity and its introduction of the principle of sanctity of life: Abortion, infanticide, suicide, and euthanasia became sins. In addition, philanthropy became a virtue—the highest virtue, in fact—and the love of humanity and Christian compassion became central to the Western ideal of medical practice.

DARREL W. AMUNDSEN (1995)

BIBLIOGRAPHY

Amundsen, Darrel W. 1973. "The Liability of the Physician in Roman Law." In *International Symposium on Society, Medicine and Law, Jerusalem, March 1972*, pp. 17–31, ed. Heinrich Karplus. New York: Elsevier Scientific Publishing.

Amundsen, Darrel W. 1977. "The Liability of the Physician in Classical Greek Legal Theory and Practice." *Journal of the History of Medicine and Allied Sciences* 32(2): 172–203.

Amundsen, Darrel W. 1978. "The Physician's Obligation to Prolong Life: A Medical Duty Without Classical Roots." *Hastings Center Report* 8(4): 23–30.

Amundsen, Darrel W. 1987. "Medicine and the Birth of Defective Children: Approaches of the Ancient World." In *Euthanasia and the Newborn: Conflicts Regarding Saving Lives*, pp. 3–22, ed. Richard C. McMillan, H. Tristram Engelhardt, Jr., and Stuart F. Spicker. Dordrecht, Netherlands: D. Reidel.

Amundsen, Darrel W., and Ferngren, Gary B. 1982. "Philanthropy in Medicine: Some Historical Perspectives." In *Beneficence and Health Care*, pp. 1–31, ed. Earl E. Shelp. Dordrecht, Netherlands: D. Reidel.

Amundsen, Darrel W., and Ferngren, Gary B. 1983. "Evolution of the Patient-Physician Relationship: Antiquity Through the Renaissance." In *The Clinical Encounter: The Moral Fabric of the Patient-Physician Relationship,* pp. 1–46, ed. Earl E. Shelp. Dordrecht, Netherlands: D. Reidel.

Brain, Peter. 1977. "History of Medicine: Galen on the Ideal of the Physician." *South African Medical Journal* 52(23): 936–938.

Carrick, Paul. 1985. *Medical Ethics in Antiquity: Philosophical Perspectives on Abortion and Euthanasia.* Dordrecht, Netherlands: D. Reidel.

Cooper, John M. 1989. "Greek Philosophers on Euthanasia and Suicide." In *Suicide and Euthanasia: Historical and Contemporary Themes,* pp. 9–38, ed. Baruch A. Brody. Dordrecht, Netherlands: Kluwer.

Deichgräber, Karl. 1955. *Der hippokratische Eid.* Stuttgart: Hippokrates-Verlag.

Edelstein, Ludwig. 1967. *Ancient Medicine: Selected Papers of Ludwig Edelstein,* ed. Owsei Temkin and C. Lilian Temkin. Baltimore, MD: Johns Hopkins University Press.

Ferngren, Gary B. 1982. "A Roman Declamation on Vivisection." *Transactions and Studies of the College of Physicians of Philadelphia* 4(4): 272–290.

Ferngren, Gary B. 1985. "Roman Lay Attitudes Toward Medical Experimentation." *Bulletin of the History of Medicine* 59(4): 495–505.

Ferngren, Gary B., and Amundsen, Darrel W. 1985. "Virtue and Health/Medicine in Pre-Christian Antiquity." In *Virtue and Medicine: Explorations in the Character of Medicine,* pp. 3–22, ed. Earl E. Shelp. Dordrecht, Netherlands: D. Reidel.

Gourevitch, Danielle. 1969. "Suicide among the Sick in Classical Antiquity." *Bulletin of the History of Medicine* 43(6): 501–518.

Hamilton, J. S. 1986. "Scribonius Largus on the Medical Profession." *Bulletin of the History of Medicine* 60(2): 209–216.

Hammond, Nicholas G. L., and Scullard, Howard Hayes, eds. 1970. *The Oxford Classical Dictionary,* 2nd edition. Oxford: Clarendon Press.

Hands, Arthur Robinson. 1968. *Charities and Social Aid in Greece and Rome.* Ithaca, NY: Cornell University Press.

Hooff, Anton J. L. van. 1990. *From Autothanasia to Suicide: Self-Killing in Classical Antiquity.* London: Routledge.

Jones, William Henry Samuel. 1924. *The Doctor's Oath: An Essay in the History of Medicine.* Cambridge, Eng.: Cambridge University Press.

Kudlien, Fridolf. 1970. "Medical Ethics and Popular Ethics in Greece and Rome." *Clio Medica* 5(2): 91–121.

Kudlien, Fridolf. 1976. "Medicine as a 'Liberal Art' and the Question of the Physician's Income." *Journal of the History of Medicine and Allied Sciences* 31(4): 448–459.

Lichtenthaeler, Charles. 1984. *Der Eid des Hippokrates: Ursprung und Bedeutung.* Cologne: Deutscher ÄrzteVerlag.

Michler, Markwart. 1968. "Medical Ethics in Hippocratic Bone Surgery." *Bulletin of the History of Medicine* 42(4): 297–311.

Nutton, Vivian. 1985. "Murders and Miracles: Lay Attitudes Towards Medicine in Classical Antiquity." In *Patients and Practitioners: Lay Perceptions of Medicine in Pre-Industrial Society,* pp. 23–53, ed. Roy Porter. Cambridge: Cambridge University Press.

Nutton, Vivian. 1993. "Beyond the Hippocratic Oath." In *Doctors and Ethics: The Earlier Historical Setting of Professional Ethics,* pp. 10–37, ed. Roger K. French, Andrew Wear, and Johanna Geyer-Kordesch. Amsterdam: Rodopi.

Oliver, James H. 1949. "Two Athenian Poets." *Hesperia* suppl. 8: 243–258.

Scarborough, John. 1976. "Celsus on Human Vivisection at Ptolemaic Alexandria." *Clio Medica* 11(1): 25–38.

Temkin, Owsei. 1949. "Changing Concepts of the Relation of Medicine to Society: In Early History." In *Social Medicine: Its Derivations and Objectives,* pp. 3–12, ed. Iago Galdston. New York: Commonwealth Fund.

Temkin, Owsei. 1973. *Galenism: The Rise and Decline of a Medical Philosophy.* Ithaca, NY: Cornell University Press.

Temkin, Owsei. 1976. "The Idea of Respect for Life in the History of Medicine." In *Respect for Life in Medicine, Philosophy, and the Law,* pp. 1–23, by Owsei Temkin, William K. Frankena, and Sanford H. Kadish. Baltimore: Johns Hopkins University Press.

Temkin, Owsei. 1979. "Medical Ethics and Honoraria in Late Antiquity." In *Healing and History: Essays for George Rosen,* pp. 6–26, ed. Charles E. Rosenberg. New York: Science History Publications.

Temkin, Owsei. 1991. *Hippocrates in a World of Pagans and Christians.* Baltimore: Johns Hopkins University Press.

Von Staden, Heinrich. 1989. *Herophilus: The Art of Medicine in Early Alexandria: Edition, Translation, and Essays.* Cambridge, Eng.: Cambridge University Press.

Von Staden, Heinrich. 1990. "Incurability and Hopelessness: The Hippocratic Corpus." In *La maladie et les maladies dans la collection Hippocratique. Actes du VIe colloque international Hippocratique,* pp. 75–112, ed. Paul Potter, Gilles Maloney, and Jacques Desautels. Quebec: Éditions du Sphinx.

I. ANCIENT AND MEDIEVAL. B. EARLY CHRISTIANITY

Christianity arose in Palestine during the first half of the first century C.E. among the followers of Jesus of Nazareth, called the Christ, who believed him to be the Messiah and the Son of God. Although the first followers were almost exclusively Jews, this new faith spread quickly through the Mediterranean basin and soon attracted many non-Jewish converts. For its first three centuries it remained a religion of a small but steadily growing minority. Officially declared a forbidden religion by the Roman imperial government, its adherents endured spasmodic persecutions that culminated in the Great Persecution (303–311). Emperor Constantine, a convert to Christianity, pronounced it a legal religion in 313; Emperor Theodosius I (379–395) declared it the official religion of the state and abolished the public practice of pagan religious rites.

This article covers the Christian religion from its origins to the fifth century. The sources for early Christianity are primarily literary: the New Testament, composed by followers of Jesus during the first century; and the patristic literature (the writings of early church leaders and theologians until the end of the fifth century). During this era, the beliefs and practices of the new faith were articulated and refined amid many controversies, particularly about the divinity of Christ and the nature of redemption. Gradually, a core of beliefs and a canon of literature predominated as orthodox and a church organization emerged that promoted these beliefs. By the late fifth century, orthodoxy had achieved its enduring form in doctrine and hierarchy, both of which differed in some respects between western Europe and the Byzantine culture of the East. At the same time, certain heterodox or heretical Christian groups existed peripherally. One of these, Arianism, became a powerful political and religious force.

Medical theories and practice in the varied milieu of Greek and Roman paganism were so religiously neutral that a discussion of classical medical ethics need pay relatively little attention to the subject of religion. Christianity, however, is fundamentally different in its most basic tenets and principles from the salient features of the religious pluralism in which it took root. Issues of health, sickness, healing, life, and death are so integral to Christian theology that two questions need to be addressed before anything meaningful can be said about early Christian medical ethics: (1) What was Christianity's theological understanding of illness? (2) Were the use and practice of medicine regarded as appropriate for Christians?

What was the theological understanding of illness? Patristic theology viewed physical health as a good but not an absolute good, and much less the supreme good. Physical health could even be an obstacle to the supreme good, which was spiritual health. The church fathers emphasized that the soul is infinitely more valuable than the body, and that care for the latter is not to conflict with care for the former. Yet the majority of the sources maintained that the body is to be reasonably cared for, since God has provided the means for its care. The church fathers saw health as a blessing from God, but since it was only a relative good, it could be an evil if given a higher priority than it deserved. Conversely, sickness could be a good thing. A survey of the writings of the church fathers reveals the firm conviction that Christians should rejoice in sickness as well as in health. Sickness can correct or restrain one from sin, refine, admonish, increase patience, reduce pride, cause one to be less self-reliant and more dependent upon God, and make one more mindful of eternity and one's own mortality, thus helping to wean one from the material to the spiritual, from the temporal to the eternal (Amundsen, 1982).

Sin lurked in the background of all conditions of suffering. Without sin there would be no suffering, because the fall of the first humans created by God, Adam and Eve, was the ultimate explanation for the miseries of the present. Sin, in this sense, was generic in the human race. When the church fathers identified personal sin as the cause of sickness, it was usually in the context of pastoral exhortations intended to comfort and correct rather than to foster guilt.

In the literature of the first several centuries of Christianity, three sources of disease or illness were identified: God, demons, and nature. They were not mutually exclusive. While there appears to have been a hesitancy to attribute disease directly to God, the more his sovereignty was stressed, the more he was viewed as either sending or permitting illness through demonic or natural instrumentality. The subject of disease causality in the early Christian literature is rife with confusion and interpretive problems, especially considering the perceived role of demons.

What was thought to cause disease in any given case greatly affected the choice of means of healing: spiritual/miraculous (e.g., prayer, the sacraments, exorcism, and, beginning in late antiquity, the cult of saints and relics); medical (drugs, dietetics, and surgery—typically administered by a physician); or magical (demonic or occult practices). The first two of these approaches were often combined, and sometimes magic was employed, although its use was consistently condemned in Christian literature. A Christian was to depend upon God. Sometimes the line of dependence was direct; at other times it included one or several intermediaries. The church itself (i.e., its clergy and sacraments) and the saints became variable parts of a chain of dependence to which a spiritual/miraculous healing model was essentially integral. A magical model offered an inherently incompatible, conflicting, and competing structure of dependence. A medical model was not necessarily either harmonious and compatible with the church's structure of dependence, or incompatible, conflicting, and competing with it.

Did the potential for tension between Christianity and medicine ever lead to a rejection of medicine? Some scholars have maintained that several church fathers were diametrically opposed to medicine in any form for Christians (e.g., Harnack; Frings; Schadewaldt). Most sources that have been thus interpreted have lately been shown not to be hostile to medicine per se (Amundsen, 1982; Temkin). Although more scholarly work remains to be done, it is unlikely that any patristic source will ultimately prove to have made a blanket condemnation of medicine. Nevertheless, some church fathers maintained that only those who lacked spirituality sufficient for them to be able to rely exclusively on divine healing should use medicine (e.g., Origen [ca. 184–ca. 253], *Contra Celsum*). Others practiced an asceticism that so glorified suffering and disease that they would not avail themselves of help from any source, although they did not deny the propriety of medicine for other Christians (Harvey; Amundsen, 1982).

Even if no patristic sources totally condemned medicine, the existence of those passages that have been thus interpreted, together with numerous cautionary statements about medicine made by other church fathers, demonstrates an uneasiness and a real potential for tension. Scholars like Adolf Harnack, Hermann-Josef Frings, Hans Schadewaldt, and Vivian Nutton, have advanced two possibly complementary theories to account for the supposedly unequivocal condemnation of medicine by some church fathers and the general uneasiness about Christians' using medicine expressed by others: (1) An early, conservative hostility against medicine was gradually ameliorated by a Hellenistic, liberalizing influence; (2) Christianity's supposed emphasis on, and ostensible promise of, miraculous physical healing was a constant, major obstacle to compatibility. Both views betray a misunderstanding of the nature of the inherent, and hence enduring, tensions and compatibilities between Christianity and medicine (Amundsen, 1982), and the second compounds the error by exaggerating the importance of miraculous healing in the propagation of the Gospel and in the Christian community, especially during the second and third centuries (Ferngren, 1992). Generally the patristic sources see medicine and physicians as God's gifts. Christianity inherited from Hellenistic Judaism an appreciation of Greek medicine that defined disease naturalistically while denying neither God's sovereignty nor his prerogative to intervene in mundane affairs. Nevertheless, the church fathers regarded as both sinful and foolish the use of physicians and medicine apart from faith in God and the failure to recognize that all healing, other than magical (demonic or occult), comes from God (Amundsen, 1982; Temkin).

The Ideal Physician of Early Christianity

The tension between Christianity and medicine was overshadowed by their compatibility in one important sense: Jesus Christ was described as the great physician, the true physician, both the physician and the medication (Pease; Arbesmann; Schipperges, 1965; Temkin). Early Christian authors thus adopted and adapted a long-established tradition in classical literature that employed, in simile or metaphor, the idea of physicians as dedicated, unselfish, and compassionate preservers or restorers of health and, sometimes, inflicters of health-giving pain, always committed to the good of their patients. It was not uncommon for the term *Hippocratic art* to be used metonymously for the medical art, and Christian authors occasionally mention Hippocrates as an ethical ideal for the medical practitioner. Indeed, Christ was himself spoken of as being, "as it were, a spiritual Hippocrates" (Pease, p. 75), and it is to Hippocrates as the type of physician that Jerome (ca. 345–ca. 419), compares the Christian healer (*In Ioanem Commentarii*; cf. *Epistle* 125).

Early Christians found the "Hippocratic ideal" of decorum very appealing. Jerome wrote to a priest that it

> is part of your duty to visit the sick, to be acquainted with people's households, with matrons, and with their children, and to be entrusted with the secrets of the great. Let it therefore be your duty to keep your tongue chaste as well as your eyes. Never discuss a woman's looks, nor let one house know what is going on in another. Hippocrates, before he will instruct his pupils, makes them take an oath and compels them to swear obedience to him. That oath exacts from them silence, and prescribes for them their language, gait, dress, and manners. How much greater an obligation is laid on us who have been entrusted with the healing of souls! (*Epistle* 52.15; see Temkin, p. 182)

In a collection of letters incorrectly attributed to Clement of Alexandria (ca. 150–ca. 220), there is a passage that reads, "We are to visit the sick ... without guile or covetousness or noise or talkativeness or pride or any behavior alien to piety.... [I]nstead of using elegant phrases, neatly arranged and ordered ... act frankly like men who have received the gift of healing from God, to God's glory" (*De virginitate* 1, 112). This advice, which sounds as if it had been written for physicians, was intended for exorcists dealing with the demon-possessed. Every detail enunciated here, save for reference to piety and to God, is mentioned in the classical literature on medical etiquette, but one need not assume that the anonymous author of this letter was intentionally adopting principles of medical etiquette. Rather, the guidelines for conduct in both instances seem to be little more than practical etiquette for clergy as well as for physicians.

Compassion or philanthropy was the one feature of the "Hippocratic ideal" that the church fathers regarded as especially Christian. Origen writes that he followed "the method of a philanthropic physician who seeks the sick so that he may bring relief to them and strengthen them"

(*Contra Celsum* 3.74). In demonstrating the superiority of Christianity to pagan philosophy, he says that "Plato and the other wise men of Greece, with their fine sayings, are like the physicians who confine their attention to the better classes and despise the common man while the disciples of Jesus carefully study to make provision for the great mass of men" (ibid., 7.60). It was in caring for common people, especially for the destitute and the poor, that physicians evinced a Christlike compassion. Augustine (354–430) regarded his friend, the physician Gennadius, as "a man of devout mind, kind and generous heart, and untiring compassion, as shown by his care of the poor" (*Epistle* 159). He frequently mentions physicians who, motivated by charity, asked no remuneration for their services but undertook the most desperate cases among the poor with no thought of receiving any recompense (e.g., *Sermon* 175).

Eusebius of Caesarea (ca. 265–ca. 339) writes that Christ, "like some excellent physician, in order to cure the [spiritually] sick, examines what is repulsive, handles sores, and reaps pain himself for the sufferings of others" (*Ecclesiastical History* 10.4.11). And Origen paraphrases a well-known Hippocratic aphorism that a physician "who sees terrible things and touches unpleasant wounds in order to heal the sick … does not wholly avoid the possibility that he may fall into the same plight" (*Contra Celsum* 4.15; see Temkin, pp. 141ff.). Physicians, according to Augustine, should always have their patients' cure at heart (*Sermon* 9), for the practice of medicine would be cruelty if physicians were only concerned about engaging in their art (*In Psalmos*). Gregory of Nyssa (ca. 335–394) began a letter to the physician Eustathius with the statement that, "Philanthropy is the way of life [*epitedeuma*, "one's business"] for all of you who practice the medical art" (although almost certainly written by Gregory of Nyssa, it is usually printed as *Epistle* 189 of his elder brother, Basil). While philanthropy was a highly desirable attribute for many pagan physicians, it is no exaggeration to say that Christianity made it an ethical obligation for Christian physicians (Temkin). Indeed, for some it became the chief motivating factor for the practice of medicine.

Hence it is not surprising that Christians adopted and adapted the so-called Hippocratic Oath at some time before the end of the period under consideration. Several manuscripts of an "Oath of Hippocrates insofar as a Christian may swear it" are extant (Jones, pp. 54f.). The Christian Oath omits the enigmatic prohibition of cutting for stone and makes more specific and definite the antiabortion statement. Where the pagan oath reads "Into whatsoever houses I enter, I shall do so to help the sick, keeping myself free from all intentional wrongdoing and harm," The Christian Oath has "Into whatsoever houses I enter, I will do so to help the sick, keeping myself free from all wrongdoing, both intentional and unintentional, tending to death or to injury." While one should not make too much of the addition of the promise to keep oneself free from even unintentional harm, it is reasonable to suggest that this concern, although not inconsistent with pagan medical ethics, is even more consonant with an early Christian ethics of respect for life that manifested itself not only in a condemnation of such practices as infanticide and suicide (including active euthanasia) but also in a philanthropy that was regarded as owed to the destitute and the ill.

Philanthropy

There is an enormous gap between pagan and Christian concepts of philanthropy. Christian philanthropy was an outgrowth of the Jewish insistence that love, mercy, and justice were attributes of God and were essential for true worship of God (e.g., Mic. 6: 6–8). Christian philanthropy was the expression of agape, an unlimited, freely given, sacrificial love that was not dependent on the worthiness of its object, since it was the manifestation of the very nature of God, who himself is agape (1 John 4:8). It was incumbent upon all Christians to extend care to the needy, especially to the sick. By late antiquity the care of the sick had become a highly organized activity under the supervision of the local bishop (Ferngren, 1988). Institutions that with some qualification may be called hospitals, were established and maintained beginning in the fourth century. The most famous of these was the *nosokomeia* or *ptocheion* of Basil, who was the bishop of Caesarea from 370 to 379 (Miller; Temkin). These institutions, as well as orphanages and homes for the care of the elderly and destitute, first arose after the legalization of Christianity, were distinctly Christian, and were a direct outgrowth of Christian philanthropy.

During various outbreaks of plague, Christians responded with spectacular daring in their attempts to succor the ill, both Christian and pagan. One particular group, on whom we have only scant information, were known as the *parabalani* ("reckless ones") because of the risks they faced by caring for plague victims (Philipsborn). Their zeal in the face of imminent danger was motivated in part by the belief that death thus incurred ranked with martyrdom (Eusebius, *Ecclesiastical History*). Christians were so well known for their care of the destitute that Julian the Apostate (r. 361–363), the only pagan emperor after the legalization of Christianity, complained that the "impious Galileans support not only their own poor but ours as well" (*Epistle 22*). Henry Sigerist did not overstate the case when he said that Christianity introduced "the most revolutionary and decisive change in the attitude of society toward the sick.... It became the duty of the Christian to attend to the sick and the poor of the community.... The social position of the sick man thus became fundamentally different from what it had been before. He assumed a preferential position which has been his ever since" (p. 69f.).

The Sanctity of Human Life

The Christian imperative to a practical philanthropy that extended to the poor and the sick was not solely a manifestation of Christian love but was ultimately articulated as a theology of respect for life, a principle of the sanctity of human life predicated on the concept of the *imago Dei,* the belief that every human being was formed in the image of God (Ferngren, 1987). By virtue of sharing the *imago Dei,* all human life was of value, and therefore was owed compassion and care. Specific condemnations of contraception, abortion, and infanticide, however, are not found in the New Testament. And when they first appear in Christian literature during the second century, they seem not to be predicated upon a developed concept of the *imago Dei* as the basis of human value. Rather, such condemnations appear in the context of broad and fervent denunciations of the most offensive sins to which Christians felt pagans were especially prone, such as gladiatorial shows and other exhibitions of extreme cruelty, and sexual immorality of an extravagantly imaginative variety.

The history of the treatment of contraception and abortion in the early church is rife with difficulties. First, the distinction between contraception and abortion, at least in the early stages of pregnancy, was blurred in both medical and popular perceptions (Noonan, 1966). The question of when human life begins was, and still is, hotly debated. Ancient embryology, although scientifically inaccurate, was more helpful than modern science in answering this question. Aristotle's theory of fetal succession of souls—nutritive, sensitive, rational—had a profound impact on patristic discussions of abortion. A fetus that is "fully formed" (a very imprecise concept) is "ensouled," that is, possesses a sensitive soul and is "animate" (an equally imprecise concept). One that is not "fully formed" is not "animate," in that it is not yet "ensouled" with a sensitive rather than a nutritive soul. The transition from a nutritive to a sensitive soul—that is, animation—is marked by "quickening," the first movement of the fetus, which ostensibly happens about the fortieth day with males and the ninetieth day with females.

Furthermore, Christian condemnations of contraception and abortion were based on two quite different principles. One is that contraception and abortion before

"ensoulment" are essentially sexual sins but not the destruction of human life. The other is that contraception and abortion at any stage are indeed the destruction of human life. Both, of course, regarded abortion after "ensoulment" as homicide (Noonan, 1970; Connery; Gorman; Dombrowski). Some recent revisionist historians advance the argument that the early Christian community did not condemn abortion at any stage of fetal development until two factors conduced to condemning it: the desire to rely not only on evangelism to increase the Christian community but also on internal growth, and the developing contempt for women within the church that relegated them to the role of childbearers (e.g., Hoffmann). Such special pleading has little to commend it.

The Christian condemnation of infanticide, including exposure, however, was unequivocal and inclusive, counting the active or passive killing of any newborn, whether healthy, sickly, defective, or even grossly deformed, as the murder of one made in the image of God (Amundsen, 1987). Active euthanasia, except as it was condemned in the "Hippocratic oath insofar as a Christian may swear it," is not discussed in the sources, but must have been regarded as murder, especially given the early Christian community's attitude toward suicide. Although suicide was not included in the broad spectrum of sins of pagans that aroused the moral indignation of early Christians, it was condemned by numerous church fathers, beginning with Justin Martyr, who in the second century replied to the hypothetical question why Christians do not just kill themselves and save pagans the trouble, "If we do so, we shall be opposing the will of God" (2 *Apology* 4). At about the same time the anonymous *Epistle to Diognetus* states that Christians do not kill themselves because God has assigned them for an important purpose to a post that they must not abandon. Clement of Alexandria flatly states that suicide is not permitted for Christians (*Stromateis*). The anonymous *Clementine Homilies,* which reached their present form in the mid-fourth century, but were based on an original composed in the late second or early third century, assign to suicides a severe future punishment (*Homily* 12). Lactantius (ca. 240–320) condemns suicides as worse than homicides, since they not only commit violence against nature but are impious as well. Nothing, in his opinion, can be more wicked than suicide (*Divine Institutes*; *Epitome* 39). John Chrysostom (ca. 349–407) writes that all Christians justly regard suicide with horror, "for if it is base to destroy others, much more is it to destroy one's self" (*Commentary on Galatians* 1:4). His contemporaries Ambrose and Jerome also categorically condemn suicide, the former flatly stating that "Scripture forbids a Christian to lay hands on himself" (*Concerning Virgins* 3.7.32), and the latter that Christ will not receive the soul of a suicide (*Letter* 39). Both Ambrose and Jerome make one exception to their condemnation of suicide: when it is committed to preserve one's chastity.

Augustine's rejection of this one exception led him to engage in a thorough analysis of suicide in books I and XIX of his *City of God*. His argument against the permissibility of suicide is fivefold. First, Scripture neither commands it nor expressly permits it, either as a means of attaining immortality or as a way to avoid or escape any evil. Second, the Sixth Commandment of the Mosaic law, "Thou shalt not kill," must be understood to forbid it. Third, since individuals have no right on their own authority to kill even a person who justly deserves to die, those who kill themselves are homicides. Fourth, the act of suicide allows no opportunity for repentance. And fifth, suicide violates the foundational Christian principle of patient endurance of all that the sovereign Creator permits to befall humanity (Amundsen, 1989).

While the church fathers firmly held that death was not to be sought, they proclaimed that Christians should not fear physical death, since it would furnish them entry into the ineffable delights of heaven. Hence numerous patristic sources marveled at Christians who were afraid of dying, and especially at those who desperately clung to any hope of sustaining their lives when afflicted with seemingly hopeless illness. They viewed such conduct as tantamount to blasphemy, or at least as a sad contradiction of Christian values (Amundsen, 1989).

It was bad enough to stake one's futile hope of a temporary reprieve on physicians; but to resort to magic was even more reprehensible (Amundsen and Ferngren). For example, in the late fourth or early fifth century, John Chrysostom praised a mother who chose to allow her sick child to die rather than use amulets, although her ostensibly Christian friends had urged her to do so and she herself was confident that it could save her daughter's life (*Homily 8 on Colossians*). About 150 years later, the physician Alexander of Tralles employed quite different reasoning when he argued that it was sinful not to apply any remedy that might possibly save a patient's life, even amulets and incantations (Temkin). Alexander's attitude is interesting for three reasons. First, it demonstrates that magical remedies had already obtruded themselves into medicine. Second, it graphically illustrates a conflict of priorities between the physician and the theologian. And third, it is a very early, perhaps the earliest, hint of a physician's expressing a moral, indeed a religious, obligation to prolong life, in this case based on the reasoning that the supposedly greater sin of not doing all in one's power to save a patient was justifiably avoided by the lesser sin of using magical remedies.

Christianity developed a theological basis for the sanctity of human life, condemning contraception, abortion, infanticide (even of the sickly and deformed), suicide, and (by implication) active euthanasia. Although it did not embrace any sense of obligation to attempt to prolong life (nor did it until several centuries more had elapsed), its theology of sanctity of life did conduce to the reasoning of Alexander of Tralles that is described above, an attitude that grew even stronger during the Middle Ages.

Conclusion

In early Christian literature a reasonably clear, if not exhaustive, picture emerges of ideal physicians who were "Hippocratic" in their decorum and motivated by Christian philanthropy, and who so cherished the sanctity of human life that they would neither perform abortions nor assist in suicide, yet regarded desperate attempts to forestall death as inconsistent with ultimate Christian values. Nevertheless, such a description tells us nothing directly about the ethics of early Christian physicians except insofar as individual physicians may have agreed with and attempted to conform to such an ideal.

The ideal physician had been posited in classical antiquity, and that ideal included compassion as a desirable characteristic. However, agape—Christian love, which was the basis of philanthropy—was so central a tenet of Christian theology that it was applied to the physician as not merely a desirable but as an essential characteristic. The philanthropic basis of medical practice and the principle of the sanctity of human life became the hallmarks of Western medical ethics until modern times.

DARREL W. AMUNDSEN (1995)

BIBLIOGRAPHY

Amundsen, Darrel W. 1982. "Medicine and Faith in Early Christianity." *Bulletin of the History of Medicine* 56(3): 326–350.

Amundsen, Darrel W. 1986. "The Early Christian Tradition." In *Caring and Curing: Health and Medicine in the Western Religious Traditions*, pp. 40–64, ed. Ronald L. Numbers and Darrel W. Amundsen. New York: Macmillan.

Amundsen, Darrel W. 1987. "Medicine and the Birth of Defective Children: Approaches of the Ancient World." In *Euthanasia and the Newborn: Conflicts Regarding Saving Lives*, pp. 3–22, ed. Richard C. McMillan, H. Tristram Engelhardt, Jr., and Stuart F. Spicker. Dordrecht, Netherlands: D. Reidel.

Amundsen, Darrel W. 1989. "Suicide and Early Christian Values." In *Suicide and Euthanasia: Historical and Contemporary*

Themes, pp. 77–153, ed. Baruch A. Brody. Dordrecht, Netherlands: Kluwer.

Amundsen, Darrel W., and Ferngren, Gary B. 1982. "Philanthropy in Medicine: Some Historical Perspectives." In *Beneficence and Health Care,* pp. 1–31, ed. Earl E. Shelp. Dordrecht, Netherlands: D. Reidel.

Arbesmann, Rudolph. 1954. "The Concept of 'Christus Medicus' in St. Augustine." *Traditio* 10: 1–28.

Connery, John R. 1977. *Abortion: The Development of the Roman Catholic Perspective.* Chicago: Loyola University Press.

D'Irsay, Stephen. 1927. "Patristic Medicine." *Annals of Medical History* 9(4): 364–378.

Dombrowski, Daniel A. 1988. "St. Augustine, Abortion, and *Libido Crudelis.*" *Journal of the History of Ideas* 49(1): 151–156.

Ferngren, Gary B. 1987. "The Imago Dei and the Sanctity of Life: The Origins of an Idea." In *Euthanasia and the Newborn: Conflicts Regarding Saving Lives,* pp. 23–45, ed. Richard C. McMillan, H. Tristram Engelhardt, Jr., and Stuart F. Spicker. Dordrecht, Netherlands: D. Reidel.

Ferngren, Gary B. 1988. "The Organisation of the Care of the Sick in Early Christianity." In *Actes: Proceedings of the XXX International Congress of the History of Medicine,* pp. 192–198. Leverkusen, Germany: Vicom KG.

Ferngren, Gary B. 1992. "Early Christianity as a Religion of Healing." *Bulletin of the History of Medicine* 66(1): 1–15.

Frings, Hermann Josef. 1959. "Medizin und Arzt bei den griechischen Kirchenvätern bis Chrysostomos." Ph.D. diss., University of Bonn.

Gorman, Michael. 1982. *Abortion and the Early Church: Christian, Jewish, and Pagan Attitudes in the Greco-Roman World.* Downers Grove, Ill.: Intervarsity.

Harnack, Adolf. 1892. *Die griechische Übersetzung des Apologeticus Tertullians Medizinisches aus der ältersten Kirchengeschichte. Texte und Untersuchungen zur Geschichte der altchristlichen Literatur,* 8(4). Leipzig: J. C. Heinrichs.

Harvey, Susan Ashbrook. 1985. "Physicians and Ascetics in John of Ephesus: An Expedient Alliance." In *Symposium on Byzantine Medicine,* pp. 87–93, ed. John Scarborough. Dumbarton Oaks Papers, no. 38. Washington, D.C.: Dumbarton Oaks Library and Collection.

Hoffmann, R. Joseph. 1990. "Faith and Foeticide." *Conscience: A Newsjournal of Prochoice Catholic Opinion* 11(6): 1, 3–6.

Jones, William Henry Samuel. 1924. *The Doctor's Oath: An Essay in the History of Medicine.* Cambridge: Cambridge University Press.

Miller, Timothy S. 1985. *The Birth of the Hospital in the Byzantine Empire.* Baltimore: Johns Hopkins University Press.

Noonan, John T., Jr. 1966. *Contraception: A History of Its Treatment by the Catholic Theologians and Canonists.* Cambridge, MA: Harvard University Press.

Noonan, John T., Jr. 1970. "An Almost Absolute Value in History." In *The Morality of Abortion: Legal and Historical Perspectives,* pp. 1–59, ed. John T. Noonan, Jr. Cambridge, MA: Harvard University Press.

Nutton, Vivian. 1985. "From Galen to Alexander, Aspects of Medicine and Medical Practice in Late Antiquity." In *Symposium on Byzantine Medicine,* pp. 1–14, ed. John Scarborough. Dumbarton Oaks Papers, no. 38. Washington, D.C.: Dumbarton Oaks Library and Collection.

Pease, Arthur Stanley. 1914. "Medical Allusions in the Works of St. Jerome." *Harvard Studies in Classical Philology* 25: 73–86.

Philipsborn, Alexandre. 1950. "La compagnie d'ambulanciers 'parabalani' d'Alexandrie." *Byzantion* 20: 185–190.

Quasten, Johannes. 1950–1986. *Patrology.* 4 vols. Westminster, MD: Newman Press. Should be consulted for references to available texts and English translations.

Rengstorf, Karl Heinrich. 1953. *Die Anfänge der Auseinandersetzung zwischen Christusglaube und Asklepiosfrömmigkeit.* Münster: Aschendorff.

Schadewaldt, Hans. 1965. "Die Apologie der Heilkunst bei den Kirchenvätern." *Veröffentlichungen der Internationalen Gesellschaft für Geschichte der Pharmazie* 26: 115–130.

Schipperges, Heinrich. 1965. "Zur Tradition des 'Christus Medicus' in frühen Christentum und in der älteren Heilkunde." *Arzt und Christ* 11: 12–20.

Schipperges, Heinrich. 1990. "Krankheit IV. Alte Kirche." In vol. 19 of *Theologische Realenzyklopädie,* pp. 686–689, ed. Frank Schumann and Michael Wolter. Berlin: Walter de Gruyter.

Sigerist, Henry E. 1943. *Civilization and Disease.* Ithaca, NY: Cornell University Press.

Temkin, Owsei. 1991. *Hippocrates in a World of Pagans and Christians.* Baltimore: Johns Hopkins University Press.

I. ANCIENT AND MEDIEVAL.
C. MEDIEVAL CHRISTIAN EUROPE

The Middle Ages are typically divided into early (500–1050) and high and late (1050–1545). This survey of the history of medical ethics in medieval Europe will first examine the sparse evidence from the early Middle Ages, and then deal thematically with significant developments during the high and late Middle Ages. The Middle Ages was a period of monumental changes. There was, however, one constant— the nearly complete identification of society with the Catholic church, which became the most thoroughly integrated involuntary religious system in human history. The Catholic church, of course, evolved throughout the Middle Ages. Nevertheless, the indirect influence of the church on most— perhaps all—aspects of life, as well as the effects of its efforts to define, direct, and regulate the details of secular and religious life, provide a backdrop for much of the discussion that follows.

The Early Middle Ages

We know of the existence of a variety of medical practitioners from the early Middle Ages. Here and there in the sources are physicians who had been trained in Alexandria or in Constantinople, Jewish or Islamic physicians, and public or civic physicians in some of the surviving Roman cities of Italy and southern France. But primarily there are those who seem to have been little more than craftsmen who had learned their techniques as apprentices. The sources, nevertheless, call all these varied types *medici,* and often contrast them with *incantatores* (enchanters, magicians, witch doctors). *Medici,* although sometimes depicted negatively in the predominantly religious literature of the early Middle Ages, are presented favorably as practitioners of an art not inherently inconsistent with the teachings of the church. The *incantatores,* however, are invariably condemned in the literature, including secular and canon law, as diabolical practitioners of illicit arts inherently opposed to the church (Flint, 1989, 1991). In this sense the physicians of the early Middle Ages—indeed, throughout the Middle Ages—were regarded by those who spoke for the church as providing a theologically neutral alternative to the spiritually pernicious ministrations of the nearly ubiquitous practitioners of those healing arts that the church condemned (Amundsen, 1986).

Not only are these physicians, of whose ethics we have little or no direct evidence, contrasted with the *incantatores*; they also are distinguished from monks or other clergy who practiced medicine as part of their religious calling. Surveys of medical history typically describe the early Middle Ages as a time when medicine was practiced predominantly by monks who treated the ills not only of their fellow monks but also of the laity of the surrounding community, as an act of Christian charity. The rule of Saint Benedict, founder of the Benedictine order (early sixth century), is often cited in this regard. Chapter 36 of the rule is addressed to those who tend ill monks. Since, however, this chapter says nothing about medical care of the laity, scholars have emphasized that the rule may not be used as evidence for a policy of monastic medical care of the ill by the Benedictines (e.g., Park). But the steward, who, according to chapter 36, is largely responsible for the logistics of the care of sick monks, is admonished elsewhere in the rule to "take the greatest care of the sick, of children, of guests, and of the poor, knowing without doubt that he will have to render an account for all these on the Day of Judgment" (chap. 31). The "children, guests, and poor" in this context certainly would not be monks, nor should the "sick" here be limited to them. Still, this is far from a concise articulation of a monastic obligation to succor the ill of the lay community at large.

In the mid-sixth century, Cassiodorus wrote a rule for the members of a monastery he had founded. The section governing monk-physicians begins with praise for their performing "the functions of blessed piety for those who flee to the shrines of holy men" (*Institutiones* 1.31), which suggests his expectation that the ill would come to the monastery for medical care. The availability and quality of medical care at monasteries varied enormously during those early centuries. Only from the ninth century on can we speak with any certainty about monasteries' playing a key role in providing medical care for the sick poor (Park). Various church councils during the early Middle Ages enjoined bishops to provide accommodations for the destitute. These, originally called *xenodochia,* but soon more commonly known as *hospitia* or *hospitalia,* were attached to cathedrals or other churches (Ullmann). These *hospitalia* were not hospitals in the modern sense of that term (Miller). Often they provided only food, shelter, and some amenities; only occasionally were they staffed with medical attendants, who would then not have been monks but other clergy who devoted part of their energies to practicing medicine.

Cassiodorus wrote two documents that describe the duties of physicians. One, already cited as evidence for monastic medical care of the laity, gives inspirational guidance to those of his monks who were also physicians (*Institutiones*). The other, which he wrote as an official in the service of King Theodoric, regulated the activities of the civic physicians of Ostrogothic Rome and of the royal household (*Variae*). While in both documents Cassiodorus lauds the medical art, there is little other similarity between them. He urges the secular physicians to place their confidence in their art, while the monk-physicians are to place their hope in the Lord and not in the medical art itself. Although Cassiodorus stresses that the secular physicians are to be dedicated to their learned art and mindful of the oath by which they were consecrated, swearing "to hate iniquity and to love purity," his major concern is nevertheless with correcting negative aspects of medical practice: professional jealousies, envy, an unwillingness to share techniques with colleagues, and bedside bickering. While this secular document places a minor emphasis on the calling, motivation, or qualities of the secular physicians, the monk-physicians are to be deeply compassionate, distressed with personal sorrow at the misfortunes of others, and grieved by their suffering and peril. Motivated by compassion, they will "perform the functions of blessed piety," and their reward will be received from the Lord. Similarly, Cassiodorus' contemporary, Benedict, had charged his monk-physicians, "Before all things and above all things care must be taken of the sick, so that they may be served in very deed as Christ himself" (*Rule,* chap. 36). Their reward would come from the Lord.

While Cassiodorus' guidance to the secular physicians has no distinctly Christian flavor, the peculiar qualities of the monk-physicians are those of the ideal physicians of earlier Christian thought and of a variety of clergy who were to devote their lives to the charitable care of the sick, especially the poor, during the high and late Middle Ages. The best-known example is the Knights Hospitallers of Saint John of Jerusalem (late eleventh to the mid-sixteenth century), an order founded to provide shelter and care for pilgrims. These Hospitallers vowed to "serve our lords, the sick" (Hume). This phrase not only is an inversion of the lord–vassal relationship but also conveys the same ideal as the injunction in the Rule of Saint Benedict that the monk-physicians should serve the sick as if the latter were "Christ himself." These highly spiritual ideals of monastic medicine merged with the secular tradition of medical ethics and etiquette in the medico-ethical literature of the seventh through the tenth century.

Numerous medical manuscripts survive from the early Middle Ages, including several that deal with medical ethics and etiquette (MacKinney). Unfortunately the authorship, intended audience, and purpose of these medico-ethical treatises remain uncertain. They may have been composed by monks or other clergy as purely literary efforts. They may have been used as part of clerical education in the liberal arts, of which medicine was typically a subdivision (Amundsen, 1979). It is most unlikely that they were intended for, or used in, the training of physicians. These treatises present a fusion of the classical tradition of medical etiquette with Christian principles of compassion and charity. The bulk of each treatise was apparently drawn from, and sometimes directly attributed to, Hippocratic writings on etiquette: The physician's aptitude and ideal character, conscientiousness and diligence in practice, bedside manner, confidentiality, sexual propriety, proper relations with colleagues, and the preservation of one's reputation, that is, decorum in the broadest sense of the word. There is nothing distinctly Christian about any of this. But intermingled with such commonsensical precepts are distinctly Christian emphases: The physician should serve the rich and the poor alike, looking for eternal rather than material rewards, making "the cases of others his own sorrow." MacKinney correctly observes that "the monastic spirit dominated ... medical handbooks of the period." They were "classical as well as pious, and secular as well as ascetic" (p. 5).

We know little about the ethics of early medieval physicians except for some monks and other clergy who practiced medicine as an act of Christian charity, without thought of remuneration. We do not even know by whom, for whom, and for what purposes treatises devoted to medical ethics and etiquette were composed. Anyone could claim to be a physician and practice medicine. There were no licensure requirements and no professional organizations.

Only rarely do we encounter evidence of legal efforts to regulate physicians' activities, for example, by the Visigoths (Amundsen, 1971). Nor did the church make any concerted effort, during these early centuries, to define the responsibilities and regulate the conduct of secular or monastic/clerical physicians, other than to wage vigorous warfare against the use of illicit means of healing that typically were employed not by *medici* but by *incantatores*. Much of the time, the lines blur between secular physicians and those practitioners of medicine who were monks or clergy but practiced medicine for financial gain; many physicians who appear to have been secular were in fact clergy. Nor do we have any evidence about the behavior of physicians during epidemics that affected the villages and countryside during the early Middle Ages. But all these matters were to change during the high and late Middle Ages.

The High and Late Middle Ages

MEDICAL AND SURGICAL PRACTICE BY THE CLERGY. At the beginning of the high Middle Ages most monasteries could provide medical care for their members without resorting to the services of secular physicians. Nunneries typically engaged secular physicians for serious illnesses, although nuns attended to the minor health needs of members of their communities. There were some nuns, however, who were as medically sophisticated as any monastic/clerical or secular physician. The outstanding example is Hildegard of Bingen (1098–1179). Well known to her contemporaries as a visionary and mystic, she was also famous for her scientific and medical writings. While the propriety of monks treating monks and nuns treating nuns appears not to have been questioned, the role of the clergy generally as physicians and surgeons was beginning to be subjected to close scrutiny.

In the early twelfth century, the Cistercian abbot Bernard of Clairvaux received a demand from another abbot to send back to his former monastery a monk who had fled to Clairvaux. This monk had left because his abbot "used him not as a monk but as a doctor," and compelled him "to serve not God but the world; that in order to curry favour with the princes of this world he was made to attend tyrants, robbers, and excommunicated persons" (Amundsen, 1986, p. 84), which had brought considerable financial reward to his monastery. The monk was troubled about the spiritual propriety of this. Bernard permitted him to remain. The Cistercians shortly thereafter forbade their monk-physicians to practice outside their monasteries or to treat the laity (Miller).

A general church council, Lateran II, in 1139 promulgated a regulation having the rubric "Monks and canons regular are not to study jurisprudence and medicine for the sake of temporal gain," which condemned the avarice that motivated some clergy to pursue such studies: "[T]he care of souls being neglected … they promise health in return for detestable money and thus make themselves physicians of human bodies" (Schroeder, pp. 201–202). This law also expresses concern that clergy who practiced medicine would see "inappropriate things." But the major focus was that if financial gain were the motive for the study and practice of medicine and secular law, such pursuits were not appropriate for those who had dedicated themselves to a religious life. We should note, first, that this stipulation did not apply to most clergy but only to monks and canons regular ("regular" means living under a "rule," which did not include most clergy) and, second—and worth noting—that it was never incorporated into canon law. A regional council at Tours in 1163 enacted a law much narrower than the one of Lateran II. It simply prohibited monks and other regular clergy from leaving their religious institutions to study medicine or secular law (Amundsen, 1978). This regulation, which did not forbid the practice of medicine by clergy, became part of canon law.

In 1219 Pope Honorius III issued a rescript, also included in canon law, that extended the prohibition of the study of medicine and secular law to virtually all clergy whose major responsibility was the performance of spiritual duties. Many clergy, however, were not affected by this stipulation, whose prohibitions were significantly lessened by subsequent enactments (Amundsen, 1978). By the end of the Middle Ages, canon law still had not prohibited the clergy from practicing medicine. Surgery, however, was a somewhat different matter, since it involved much greater risk to the patient and increased the danger that a clerical practitioner might be held responsible for a patient's death and hence excluded from exercising his clerical office. In 1215, Lateran IV forbade clergy in major (holy) orders (subdeacons, deacons, and priests) to practice the part of surgery that involved cautery and cutting, in which clergy in minor orders (porters, acolytes, exorcists, and lectors) could still engage (Amundsen, 1978).

Although the practice of medicine by the clergy was permitted, the church was obviously uneasy about their motivation and the possible effects that it might have on their spiritual obligations. Many of the clergy who continued to practice medicine and surgery, at least with the tacit blessing of the church, did so predominantly for charity. For example, some clergy composed medical treatises so that their fellow clerics could treat the poor gratis. Many clergy also wrote medical handbooks to help the poor help themselves. The outstanding example is Petrus Hispanus, "who

publicly taught, wrote on, and practised medicine during the early stages of a highly successful ecclesiastical career that culminated with his election as Pope John XXI in 1276" (Siraisi, p. 25). He is the probable author of the *Treasury for the Poor,* which describes herbs the poor could gather to treat themselves.

During the high Middle Ages rapid urbanization brought about widespread suffering and disease in the growing towns and cities. In the late eleventh century, Augustinian canons (who were regular clergy like monks, but unlike them in that they did not live apart from society) and various lay brotherhoods established charitable institutions that included facilities for the destitute ill (Miller). A variety of such institutions were founded by bishops, kings, feudal lords, wealthy merchants, guilds, and municipalities as endowed charitable institutions. Members of various orders, like the Knights Hospitallers of St. John of Jerusalem, sometimes staffed these hospitals. Nursing orders also arose, committed to caring for the destitute ill in such institutions. The Knights Hospitallers' phrase "to serve our lords, the sick," perfectly captures both the idealism and spiritual motivation of these orders and the very essence of their ethics. But such practitioners constituted only a small proportion of physicians and surgeons of the high and late Middle Ages. By the mid-fourteenth century, most monasteries were paying secular physicians to treat their ill monks (Park). The church's desire to decrease clerical involvement in medical practice, especially for financial gain, combined with rapidly changing social conditions that, beginning around 1050, significantly altered the practice of medicine and the nature of medical ethics.

LICENSURE, GUILDS, UNIVERSITIES, AND A RECIPROCITY OF OBLIGATIONS. Stimulated by a dynamic revival of a commercial economy, dormant since the collapse of Roman civilization, a gradual transformation of European society began around 1050, an urban revolution that created a starkly altered context for nearly all aspects of life. One of its most salient features was the corporate nature of late medieval urban society, as manifested in increasing institutional sophistication and formalized specialization of labor, regulated either internally by guilds or corporations or externally by secular or ecclesiastical authority. Both regulatory features changed the basis for the practice of most trades and professions, including medicine and surgery. No longer would the practice of medicine be a right that anyone could claim, a free enterprise constrained only by individual conscience and criminal law. The practice of medicine would now be a privilege granted, enforced, and protected by the state or the church, at the state's or church's initiative or at the request of guilds or corporations of physicians or surgeons.

The earliest datable law instituting medical licensure is from the Kingdom of Sicily. In 1140, Roger II issued a statute specifying that those who wished to practice medicine were to appear before his officers and judges and be examined by their court. Those who practiced in defiance of this statute were to be imprisoned and their property confiscated. "… this has been arranged so that subjects in our kingdom may not be experimented on by inexperienced physicians" (Powell, p. 130; Hartung). A considerable advance over this legislation was made by Roger's grandson, Emperor Frederick II, who in his capacity as king of Sicily, in 1231 promulgated the *Liber Augustalis*. Thereafter the examination for licensure was to be conducted by the masters of the medical school at Salerno, and the license to practice would be issued by the emperor or his representative. Before the examination, the aspirant was to study logic for three years and medicine (to include surgery) for five years, and to practice for one year under the direction of an experienced physician. These revisions are introduced by the following justification: "We see a special usefulness when we provide for the common safety of our [faithful subjects]. Therefore, since we are aware of the serious expense and irrecoverable loss that can occur because of the inexperience of physicians …" (Powell, p. 131). Physicians must visit their patients twice a day and, at the request of the patient, once during the night. Fees were to be determined in part by the distance involved. The physician was required to swear to abide by the regulations fixed by the government, treat the poor gratuitously, and inform the authorities of any apothecary who prepared drugs at less than the required strength. Physicians were forbidden to make any contracts with apothecaries or to own apothecary shops (Powell; Hartung).

On the Iberian Peninsula, the first medical licensure regulation, in 1289, imposed no requirement for a course of study in a medical school; forty years later a new law established a university medical degree as a prerequisite for practice (García-Ballester et al.). The law of 1329 and subsequent legislation provided very specific regulations governing physicians' conduct and responsibilities. These regulations, which benefited both the general public and the qualified and responsible physician, evince a reciprocity of obligations between the profession and the state. Elsewhere in Europe, by contrast, artisans, merchants, surgeons, physicians, and professors were organizing into guilds, gaining charters from municipal, royal, or ecclesiastical authorities, and guaranteeing standards of quality of goods or services in exchange for the privilege of holding a monopoly in their service or commodity.

One of the most striking features of late medieval urban life was its corporative aspect, particularly its guild organization. Perhaps originally formed simply as social organizations under the auspices of a patron saint, guilds had three major interests: (1) social, manifested in both internal and external charitable efforts, and social life within the guild (banquets, etc.); (2) political, especially guilds involved in the production of economically vital commodities; and (3) commercial, involving the protection of financial and vocational interests. In respect to the last, the guilds, by obtaining charters, secured the right to exercise a monopoly on their product or service in a particular geographical area. Such a monopoly entailed the right to make and enforce standards of quality in their products or services, to control hours and working conditions, to limit competition among members, to limit entry into the craft or profession, and to ensure the proper treatment of customers. Part of the monopoly was the right to train and license new members, thus eliminating competition from outside the guild. Although one of the major aims of such measures was economic, the guilds frequently claimed that such restrictions were necessary to maintain a high level of competence and ethics in the trade or profession. Distinct from the merchant and craft guilds, the medieval universities were essentially educational guilds. Beginning in the late twelfth century, some universities gained charters and thus became corporate bodies designed to further educational interests and to protect their members. The *collegium* of teachers who examined the candidates for a degree was, at some universities, vested with the authority to grant a license or, at others, to recommend to secular or ecclesiastical authorities that a license be awarded.

Conditions were so diverse that generalities are often misleading. But usually surgeons were organized in craft guilds; physicians, at least in cities having a university, were not members of a craft guild but were part of, affiliated with, or under the supervision of the medical faculty of the university. In university cities, medical licensure requirements were generally instituted earlier than in those without a university but, from the early fourteenth century on, many cities and towns required those who wished to practice medicine within their jurisdiction to have a degree and license from an acceptable university. Physicians practicing in such places often organized themselves into *collegia* or guilds, and in some instances obtained the authority to examine and license physicians who wanted to practice within the community, regardless of the degrees held by the applicants (Siraisi).

Practitioners brought to trial for practicing without a license often accused medical and surgical guilds and faculties of self-interest (Kibre; Cosman). However, restrictions on medical and surgical practice, whether imposed by authorities or requested by medical faculties or medical or surgical guilds, were justified in terms of the common good, especially the grave dangers to the people if charlatans and quacks were permitted to undertake medical or surgical care. For example, the medical faculty of the University of Paris initiated medical licensure provisions and, in seeking ecclesiastical and royal support to enforce these regulations, continually appealed to the "public interest." The same appeal was made in the medical faculty's attempts to establish a right to oversee the activities of surgeons, apothecaries, barbers, and herbalists, and to prosecute unlicensed practitioners in ecclesiastical or secular courts. The unlicensed practitioners often were women who were frequently "caught in the crossfire" (to use Green's phrase, 1989, p. 447) of the legal battles between licensed groups like physicians and surgeons (see also Park, for analysis; Kibre, for narrative examples). As in the early Middle Ages, there was also a concerted effort to exclude the illicit supernatural from healing procedures. Often suspected of being "witches and exorcisoresses of the devil," unlicensed women practitioners were in double jeopardy (Amundsen, 1986, pp. 93–94).

Although guilds were organized to serve their members' self-interest, guild ethics generally were beneficial to the public. In 1423, the physicians and surgeons of London petitioned the mayor and aldermen to authorize the creation of a joint *collegium* of the two crafts. George Unwin, a historian of English guilds, remarks that their petition illustrates "the best spirit of professionalism at this period of London history." He summarizes its contents as follows:

> Their rules were meant to ensure that all practitioners in both branches should be duly qualified, if possible, by a university training, and they sought to provide a hall where reading and disputation in philosophy and medicine could be regularly carried on. No physician was to receive upon himself any cure [i.e., case], "desperate or deadly," without showing it within two or three days to the Rector or one of the Surveyors in order that a professional consultation might be held, and no surgeon was to make any cutting or cauterization which might result in death or maiming without similar notice. Any sick man in need of professional help but too poor to pay for it, might have it by applying to the Rector. In other cases the physician was not to charge excessive fees, but to fix them in accordance with the power of the sick man, and "measurably after the deserving of his labour." A body composed of two physicians, two surgeons, and two apothecaries, was to search all shops for "false or sophisticated medicines," and to pour all quack remedies into the gutter. (p. 173)

The foundational principles of medieval medico-surgical guild ethics were that each guild member must: (1) be ready to help the other; (2) protect the well-being and honor of the guild; and (3) help the sick. The order of these principles is very important. The guilds were functional, inherently selfish organizations designed to promote and protect members' special interests. They were brotherhoods, companies of people united more often than not by a common economic activity. The well-being and honor of the craft depended upon the mutual cooperation of its members. If these conditions were met, then the third—the service rendered or the commodity produced—could be effectively delivered. All these, in late medieval urban life, hinged upon the freedom of the artisans, merchants, professors, physicians, or surgeons to perform their functions unmolested by those who would illicitly meddle in their affairs. Hence they sought an exclusive right to fill a particular role; in exchange, a guild would guarantee a level of expertise in the production of its commodity or in the rendering of its service, and would assume the responsibility to police and to supervise its own members, both in respect to their qualifications, that is, training (leading to licensure), and to their performance. Regulations governing the minutiae of conduct, both within the guild and in relationships with customers or the community, varied considerably from guild to guild and from city to city. But the obligation to ensure competence and quality seems to have been a constant feature.

The highest guarantee of competence to practice medicine, recognized throughout Europe in the late Middle Ages, was a degree granted by a university medical faculty. A university curriculum in medicine, a set body of literature, and the presence of instructors qualified to teach and to test demonstrate that a standard of competence existed. The reality of such a standard has important ethical implications. Luis García-Ballester goes so far as to assert that "Everything connected with the conduct of the physician—from strictly technical matters ... to the question of fees or the problems of etiquette ...—was derived from this strictly technical organizational scheme ... what later became known as medical ethics had this technical, intellectual origin. The specific morality of the practitioner derived, therefore, from his being a healer technically trained, and was essential for his status as an expert in medicine" (pp. 44–45).

An underlying and sometimes articulated principle of medical and surgical guilds was that the guild would ensure that the ill of the community, including the poor and the hopelessly ill, would not be abandoned at the whim of individual physicians or surgeons. This was based at least in part on the conviction, which was very strong in the late Middle Ages, that one had an *officium,* that is, an office or calling, that carried with it certain duties and obligations. In a work devoted to the responsibilities attached to kingship, Thomas Aquinas wrote, "Nor has [the king] the right to question whether or not he will so promote the peace of the community, any more than a physician has the right to question whether he will cure the sick committed to him. For no one ought to deliberate about the ends for which he must act, but only about the means to those ends" (*De regimine principum* 2). In late medieval urban (i.e., corporate) life, physicians and surgeons, by virtue of their privilege of engaging in a legitimate *officium* within the corporate structure of society, had responsibilities both to their *officium* itself, as represented by the guild, company, craft, or *collegium*, and to the community that granted them their privileges.

THE CHURCH'S EFFORTS TO DEFINE THE RESPONSI-BILITIES OF PHYSICIANS. In 1215, a general church council, Lateran IV, promulgated a decree that required annual confession by all Catholics, on pain of excommunication. This decree was widely publicized and strictly enforced. In response, lengthy treatises on moral theology and numerous manuals to aid priests in interrogating penitents during confession were written by moral theologians in an effort to subject the broadest spectrum of human activities to Christian moral principles, including a wide variety of occupations. The discussion that follows is a very condensed summary of the sections of ten primary sources from the early fourteenth through the early sixteenth century that provided priests with a range of questions and moral guidance to be addressed to physicians and surgeons during their mandatory annual confession (Amundsen, 1981). Where the word *physician* appears, it should be understood to include "surgeon."

Competence and diligence. Physicians who are not competent according to accepted standards within the profession sin by practicing medicine. Simply possessing a degree in medicine does not in itself guarantee competence. Competent physicians sin if they do not conscientiously exercise diligence. Rashness, which may result from incompetence or negligence, is a sin in medical practice, especially if patients are harmed. Hence physicians should be cautious and not administer medicines about whose effects they are in doubt; patients should be left in God's hands rather than be exposed to additional danger. Generally, physicians sin if they engage in any experimentation at the patient's risk, especially if they experiment on the poor whom they treat without charge. Physicians also sin if they are so cautious that they fail to give the appropriate medicines, and especially if they do so in order to prolong the illness and thereby increase their fees.

Fees and charity. Beginning with the assumption that it is licit to receive remuneration for what one is not bound to do gratuitously, but bypassing consideration of how the scholastic principle of "just price" for services could be applied to medical practice, the moral theologians discuss a wide variety of moral aspects of medical fees. The most basic principle is that physicians should ensure that they accept only a "reasonable" fee, as determined by the quality of care; the physician's labor, diligence, and conscientiousness; the custom of the place; and the patient's means. A patient who is rich must not be exploited by exorbitant rates. More problematic is the sick pauper. Is the physician obligated to give free medical care to the poor? This, as we shall see when discussing the medico-ethical literature of the high and late Middle Ages, was a source of great frustration for physicians. Thomas Aquinas, beginning with the premise that "no man is sufficient to bestow a work of mercy on all those who need it," suggests that kindness ought first to be shown to those with whom one is united in any way. As for others, if one "stands in such a need that it is not easy to see how he can be succored otherwise, then one is bound to bestow the work of mercy on him." Hence a lawyer is not always obligated to defend the destitute, "or else he would have to put aside all other business and occupy himself entirely in defending the poor. The same holds with physicians in respect to attending the sick" (*Summa theologiae* 2–2, 71, 1). The authors of the confessional literature generally follow Aquinas and specify that physicians must treat the poor gratuitously if the patient would die without treatment.

An obligation to care (especially for hopeless cases). With the advent of medical licensure requirements and medico-surgical guild monopolies, the physicians' option of refusing to treat or of deserting hopelessly ill patients became more circumscribed. Social and religious pressures also changed. Typically the moral theologians maintain that "Desperate cases that, according to the judgments of men, are held to be fatal, sometimes the diligent physician is able to cure, but rarely ... therefore, clear to the end the physician ought to do what he can to cure the patient" and should not entirely withdraw from the patient "as long as nature does not succumb." If a rich miser is unwilling to employ the services of a physician, the physician is obligated to treat him or her gratis, even to provide medicines without charge; otherwise the physician is killing such a person indirectly. If the rich miser recovers, the physician may sue for fees and expenses; if the miser dies, the heirs are obligated to pay (Amundsen, 1981).

Spiritual obligations of physicians to patients. While the theologians were quite concerned to protect the patient from physical harm and financial exploitation, they were even more determined to guard the well-being of the patient's soul. At Lateran IV in 1215, the following decree was enacted:

Since bodily infirmity is sometimes caused by sin, the Lord saying to the sick man whom he had healed: "Go and sin no more, lest some worse thing happen to thee" [John 5: 14], we declare in the present decree and strictly command that when physicians of the body are called to the bedside of the sick, before all else they admonish them to call for the physician of souls, so that after spiritual health has been restored to them, the application of bodily medicine may be of greater benefit, for the cause being removed the effect will pass away. We publish this decree for the reason that some, when they are sick and are advised by the physician in the course of the sickness to attend to the salvation of their soul, give up all hope and yield more easily to the danger of death. If any physician shall transgress this decree after it has been published by the bishops, let him be cut off from the church till he has made suitable satisfaction for his transgression. And since the soul is far more precious than the body, we forbid under penalty of anathema that a physician advise a patient to have recourse to sinful means for the recovery of bodily health. (Schroeder, p. 236)

The stipulation that physicians must advise and persuade patients, before all else, to call a priest concerns the curative effect of confession rather than the opportunity to confess before dying. The moral theologians' discussions of this stipulation vary enormously in length, detail, and sensitivity to the problems that it posed. Several maintain that this requirement applied only to cases of extremely dangerous or mortal illnesses. Some go so far as to provide lists of applicable diseases, symptoms, or injuries, especially those demanding immediate attention. This interpretation of the decree is surprising, since it flies in the face of the specific intent that patients be made aware that the requirement to call a confessor is not to be taken as an indication that their condition is hopeless. And some of the authors of the confessional literature interpret it strictly along such lines, making no exceptions. They wrestle with the question of whether a physician is obliged to withdraw from a case if the patient refuses to call a confessor, and reach a variety of answers ranging from a strict "yes" to an unequivocal "no," some of the latter maintaining that if the physician were required to abandon the stubborn patient, "the precept of the church [would] seem against the precept of God." At the end of the Middle Ages, there was no uniformity either of practice or of interpretation of this piece of canonical legislation.

In the context of discussions of the requirement that physicians have their patients summon a confessor, some moral theologians raise the question of whether physicians are obliged to inform terminally ill patients of their condition. There is some disagreement among the moral theologians who address this issue, particularly since physicians (and here Galen is cited) typically tell patients that they will recover, even if there is little hope, since predicting a fatal outcome will likely remove all hope of recovery and hasten death. Generally the authors of the confessional literature insist, however, that unless physicians are certain that their terminally ill patients have set both their spiritual and their temporal affairs in order, they must inform them of their imminent demise, since otherwise harm may ensue to patients' souls and estates.

The second requirement of the legislation in question is for physicians to refrain from advising sinful means for the recovery of health. Several of the moral theologians simply quote that stipulation without elaboration. Others condemn specific matters, such as advising fornication, masturbation, incantations, consumption of intoxicating beverages, breaking the church's fasts, and eating meat on forbidden days.

Abortion and euthanasia. The authors of the confessional literature almost entirely ignore the subject of abortion when discussing the responsibilities and sins of physicians. While all include thorough discussions of abortion under the rubric "homicide" or "abortion" or both, only two include it in their extensive considerations of medical ethics. Apparently the rest did not think that physicians or surgeons were confronted with requests for abortions. Women who sought abortions would probably not have turned to physicians or surgeons, the overwhelming majority of whom were men during the high and late Middle Ages, but to another woman, such as a midwife or an unlicensed female practitioner.

Abortion, regarded both as a sexual sin and, under some circumstances, as homicide, was an issue fraught with interpretive problems during the Middle Ages (Noonan; Connery). The opinion of Jerome and Augustine (fourth century) that abortion is not homicide unless the fetus is "formed," that is, vivified or ensouled, was incorporated into medieval canon law, which also included a conflicting decree that applied the penalty for homicide to the induced abortion of a fetus at any stage of development. Theologians, canon lawyers, and the authors of the confessional literature were split between these two positions. The stricter interpretation generally forbade abortion at all times and under all circumstances. The more liberal interpretation, which was influenced by Aristotelian embryology, did not classify induced abortion as a mortal sin within the first forty days of pregnancy in the case of a male fetus, and eighty (or, according to some, ninety) days in the case of a female, and permitted abortion during these periods under a variety of extenuating circumstances. The conflict between the interpretations of these two camps was not resolved until long after the Middle Ages. Both, however, clearly condemned abortion as reprehensible if performed simply to destroy the unwanted consequence of sexual intercourse.

What we call active euthanasia is a subject that the moral theologians thus far surveyed never raised when discussing the sins of physicians; it was probably regarded throughout the Middle Ages simply as homicide on the physician's part and suicide on the patient's, assuming willing involvement by the latter. Martin Azpilcueta, better known as Navarrus, a leading canon lawyer and moral theologian of the sixteenth century, wrote in 1568 that the physician sins who gives any medicine that he knows is harmful, "even if he administers it out of pity or in order to please the patient." Navarrus's statement seems clear and unambiguous: active euthanasia, whether motivated by pity or by the wish of the patient, is sinful. This must be one of the earliest articulations regarding active euthanasia in such precise terms. Navarrus gives as his authority the canon lawyer Panormitanus (early fifteenth century), who had simply given the opinion that those having custody or serving a sick person sin greatly if, motivated by "a sort of pity," they obey or indulge the "corrupted desire" of the ill. Before active euthanasia was seen as a separate moral category, the closest the authors of the confessional literature could have come to including relevant comments in their sections on physicians' sins would have been to have stated that it was a sin for physicians to kill or poison their patients intentionally.

The effects of the moral theologians' efforts. Medieval European society was, with the exception of a small number of Jews and heretics (e.g., Albigensians and Waldensians), exclusively Catholic. Guaranteed the allegiance of virtually the entire population of western Europe and the prestige of ecclesiastical institutions, the church could exercise jurisdiction over areas of life that now would be the concern of either secular authority or the individual conscience. The church promulgated laws and expected obedience. Ecclesiastical courts imposed penalties ranging from penance to imprisonment to excommunication. The extent to which the confessional influenced ethics and conduct cannot be gauged with certainty. The authors of the confessional literature strove both to educate the laity so that they might be able to identify previously unknown sins, both of commission and of omission, and to correct sinful practices. The best confession was one that led to a changed life, and a changed life should be one in as close conformity to the expectations and standards of the church as possible. The priest's authority "to loose and to bind," although ultimately of eternal consequence, applied also to this life in that it included the authority—indeed, the responsibility— to grant forgiveness and restoration only to those who

satisfied the requirements of the confessional, and to impose sanctions upon those who refused. The ultimate sanction, excommunication, when imposed upon those who exercised their vocation by license, would deprive them of their livelihood. Whether such steps were ever taken against physicians during the high and late Middle Ages remains unclear. Nevertheless, the morally educating (or possibly alienating) effects of this annual interrogation, which employed the detailed scrutiny available to every priest in his confessional manual, must have been profound.

PHYSICIANS' AND SURGEONS' ADVICE ON ETHICS AND ETIQUETTE. In the extensive medical and surgical literature that has survived from the high and late Middle Ages, one occasionally encounters comments made directly on matters of medical ethics or etiquette. Surgical manuals, for example, often begin with a discussion of the moral and educational qualifications of a practitioner, bedside manner, fees, and a variety of related matters. Medical and surgical literature also contains comments that indirectly reveal aspects of the ethical standards of the author, especially in the tractates written by physicians who attempted to understand and deal with the outbreaks of plague that struck Europe during the late Middle Ages.

Loren MacKinney perceived that, by the twelfth century, a change in spirit had occurred in medical literature from monastic to secular, a "shift of emphasis from ideals to practical considerations," a "despiritualization of the medical physician," particularly in the introduction of various "tricks of the trade" and a predominant concern with fees (pp. 23ff.). He credits this change to such factors as rapid urbanization, and he is probably right to a degree. But it is important to note the different walks of life from which the authors of the sources came. While the literature from the early Middle Ages was likely composed by monks, that of the high and late Middle Ages was written mainly by secular physicians. So it is not surprising that its tone is less otherworldly than that of the earlier treatises. The later literature was written with the clear intention of providing practitioners with two types of information: (1) the ideal physician's character, preparation, and practice; and (2) very practical and sometimes questionable advice on how best to survive in the profession. Both were at least moderately informed by the teachings of the medieval Catholic church.

The first category consists of the same range of commonsensical advice as appears in Hippocratic treatises and in the medico-ethical literature of the early Middle Ages. The second appeared especially in discussions of fees. As early as the tenth century, the physician is advised: "At the outset, accept at least half of the remuneration without hesitation, for he who wishes to buy [your services] is disposed to pay and to beg [for treatment]. Get it while he is suffering, for when the pain ceases, your services also cease" MacKinney, p. 24). Somewhat more enlightened is the suggestion by William of Saliceto (thirteenth century) that "a high salary, if demanded, imparts to the physician an air of authority, which strengthens the confidence of the patient in him ... so that the sick man imagines from this that he is more skillful than others and ought therefore to be successful in curing him" (Mirfeld, p. 132).

Some of the advice that follows, written by physicians or surgeons, may appear particularly crass. It is, however, important to realize that the medical literature of the time stressed, in Luis García-Ballester's words,

> the mutual confidence that should exist between doctor and patient. Without such confidence the efficacy of the curative action would be greatly undermined .... the physician's or surgeon's confidence in his patient was demonstrated by two conditions of equal significance: the first was that the patient should carry out what had been prescribed by the healer; the second that the patient should pay the remuneration agreed upon. The fee would be for the doctor the objective and tangible expression of his relationship with the patient and that of the patient with the doctor, while, at the same time, it would be a guarantee of continuity in treatment. (p. 51)

Henry de Mondeville (fourteenth century) laments that "The chief object of the patient, and the one idea which dominates all his actions, is to get cured, and when once he is cured, he forgets his own obligations and omits to pay; the object of the surgeon, on the other hand, is to obtain his money, and he should never be satisfied with a promise or a pledge, but he should either have the money in advance or take a bond for it" (Hammond, p. 159; Welborn, p. 356). Mondeville's attitude was probably the fruit of bitter experience. Official documents from the late Middle Ages record many cases of physicians suing patients in order to collect their fees. In most cases in which the treatment had been unsuccessful, the suit went in favor of the patient. Quite unreasonable demands by patients for extensive credit, the necessity that physicians sometimes demand securities before undertaking treatment, and lucrative contractual arrangements all contribute to the complex and ethically ambiguous way in which late medieval medical and surgical practitioners made a living (Rawcliffe, for late medieval England).

One area in which physicians seemed to act against their more mercenary interests was in providing advice that would keep potential patients from needing their services.

Mondeville wrestled with the problem presented by surgeons' advising their patients how to stay healthy, "because the treatment which stops the onset of a new disease is more useful to a patient than all other treatments. But this is, as one can see, useless and harmful to the surgeon because he thus stops the appearance of a disease whose treatment would be advantageous to himself" (Hammond, p. 155; Welborn, p. 355).

Neither Mondeville nor his contemporary, John Arderne, seem to have felt any embarrassment over pressing for as high a fee as possible. The former recommends that "The surgeon should pretend that he has no living nor capital except his profession, and that everything is as dear as possible, especially drugs and ointments; that the fee is nothing as compared with his services; and the wages of all other artisans, masons, for example, have doubled of late" (Hammond, p. 156). He considered it essential that the fee not be reduced too much. It would be better, then, to charge nothing.

In determining how much to charge, Mondeville recommends that the surgeon consider three things: "First, his own standing in the profession, then the [financial] condition of the patient, and, third, the seriousness of the illness" (Hammond, p. 156; Welborn, p. 356). It was the second of these that was probably the most trying. Mondeville advises the doctor not "to have too much faith in appearances. Rich people have a bad habit of appearing before him in old clothes, or if they do happen to be well dressed, they make up all sorts of excuses for demanding lower fees" (Welborn, p. 356). So strong, though, is the sense of obligation to succor the poor gratis, or at least to give the appearance of doing so, that physicians and surgeons probably were quite frequently faced with very difficult judgments.

The motivation of physicians and surgeons to extend charity to the poor was more than the advantages that might accrue to their reputation and to the honor of the profession; it was a product of enlightened self-interest, with eternal consequences, fully compatible with the theology of the time, as is succinctly expressed by Mondeville: "You, then, surgeons, if you operate conscientiously upon the rich for a sufficient fee and upon the poor for charity, you ought not to fear the ravages of fire, nor of rain nor of wind; you need not take holy orders or make pilgrimages nor undertake any work of that kind, because by your science you can save your souls alive, live without poverty, and die in your house" (Hammond, p. 156).

While some effect of the church's teaching is manifest in even Mondeville's fee policies, in other areas spiritual concerns are more evident. An anonymous twelfth-century Salernitan treatise advises: "When you reach [a patient's] house and before you see him, ask if he has seen his confessor. If he has not done so, have him either do it or promise to do it. For if he hears mention of this after you have examined him and have considered the signs of the disease, he will begin to despair of recovery, because he will think that you despair of it too" (De Renzi, vol. 2, p. 74). This work was composed some time before Lateran IV of 1215, and thus before physicians were required "before all else to advise and persuade" their patients to call a confessor. The anonymous author of this treatise does not appear unusually devout. Indeed, were one to attach an adjective to the work, "eminently practical" would describe it better than any other. The author, of course, was a member of a society in which the belief in the necessity of confession before death was deeply ingrained. While he may not have considered it especially his own spiritual duty to look after his patients' spiritual as well as physical health, he must have considered the alternative of advising patients to confess only when in dire straits to be potentially dangerous to them.

The advice on confession, as it appears in a treatise attributed to Arnald of Villanova (late thirteenth century), is significantly different in emphasis from that in the anonymous Salernitan piece: "[W]hen you come to a house, inquire before you go to the sick whether he has confessed, and if he has not, he should immediately or promise you that he will confess immediately, and this must not be neglected because many illnesses originate on account of sin and are cured by the Supreme Physician after having been purified from squalor by the tears of contrition, according to what is said in the Gospel: 'Go, and sin no more, lest something worse happens to you'" (Sigerist, p. 141). This version, written after Lateran IV, quoting the same Scripture as the canon law, demonstrates the direct influence of a constitution of canon law on a strictly secular piece of medical literature, as does even more strongly the following passage in an anonymous plague tractate composed in 1411: "If it is certain from the symptoms that it is actually pestilence that has afflicted the patient, the physician first must advise the patient to set himself right with God by making a will and by making a confession of his sins, as is set forth according to the Decretals; since a corporal illness comes not only from a fault of the body but also from a spiritual failing as the Lord declares in the gospel and the priests also tell us" (Amundsen, 1977, p. 416). About a century earlier, similar advice had been given by Mondeville: "Do not let the patient be concerned about any business except spiritual matters only, such as confession and his will and arranging similar affairs in accordance with the rules of the Catholic faith" (Amundsen, 1986, p. 90). Whether these writings composed after Lateran IV are simply examples of lip service to ecclesiastical authority or reflect genuine approval of the underlying principle

upon which the legislation was based must remain an open question.

An eleventh-century treatise advises that the physician should "never become involved knowingly with any who are about to die or who are incurable" (MacKinney, p. 23). Although from the earliest times such counsel was common, in the late Middle Ages it was becoming increasingly less so. The previously quoted anonymous Salernitan treatise from the twelfth century advises the physician, just before leaving, to "promise the patient that with the help of God you will cure him. As you go away, however, you should tell his servants that he is seriously ill, because if he recovers you will receive greater credit and praise, and if he dies, they will testify that even from the beginning you despaired of his health" (De Renzi, vol. 2, p. 75). Although this treatise may be described as eminently practical, it is not clear that this particular bit of advice is ethical.

A parallel passage in a treatise attributed to Arnald of Villanova (late thirteenth century) is nearly identical, with the significant difference that instead of promising the patient "that with the help of God you will cure him," which still leaves the matter in doubt and at least partially in God's hands, it advises more crassly that "you promise health to the patient who is hanging on your lips" (Sigerist, p. 142). This treatise appears to have been hastily thrown together from various sources, since elsewhere it flatly contradicts the advice that the physician should promise health to the patient. Later it suggests that the physician "must be … circumspect and cautious in answering questions, ambiguous in making a prognosis, just in making promises; and he should not promise health because in doing so he would assume a divine function and insult God. He should rather promise faithfulness and attentiveness …" (Sigerist, p. 141). For two such opposing pieces of advice to be found in the same treatise is unusual. Such conflicting opinions, however, are typical of medical ethics in the late Middle Ages. For example, Bernard de Gordon (thirteenth–fourteenth centuries) advised that if there was little likelihood of a patient's recovering, "One should try to escape from such cases, provided one can do so honorably" (Demaitre, p. 153). Nevertheless, he also expresses a concern to do everything possible to postpone the death of terminally ill patients.

William of Saliceto (thirteenth century) recommends that the physician should "comfort his patient, and on every occasion should promise him restoration to health, even if the physician himself shall regard the case as desperate." He justifies this on the grounds that this will greatly encourage the patient, increasing his chances of recovering. He further suggests that the physician "acquaint the friends of his patient with the truth, and discuss the case fully with them as he shall deem best, lest he incur scandal or loss of reputation from inability to offer a satisfactory statement of the case, and lest the friends of the patient regard him with distrust: nor will he then be held responsible for having caused the death of a patient who shall die; but he will be given credit for having cured the man who lives and is restored to health" (Mirfeld, p. 122). William's reason for giving a favorable prognosis to the critically ill patient is strictly for the latter's benefit. He recommends that the physician tell the patient's friends the truth for the physician's own protection, a far different piece of advice from that in the two treatises previously discussed, which recommend that the physician, regardless of the patient's actual condition, advise those close to him or her that the case is dangerous and that the patient is not faring well.

Mondeville wrote that the surgeon "ought to promise a cure to every sick person, but he should refuse as far as possible all dangerous cases, and he should never accept desperately sick ones" (Welborn, p. 350). Physicians and surgeons were sometimes charged with the deaths of patients in the late Middle Ages, and the fear of facing blame for a patient's death still motivated some to recommend, as Mondeville did, that dangerous cases not be taken on. Mondeville, incidentally, writes at some length about how to ensure that a patient's friends or relatives can be compelled to exonerate the surgeon if a case should end in the patient's death (Welborn). Nevertheless, advice not to take on dangerous cases occurs much less often in late medieval sources than in the medical literature of ancient Greece and Rome. Instead, physicians are advised to protect themselves either by telling the relatives or friends of the patient that the situation is critical, regardless of the patient's condition, or to tell the truth in cases that actually are critical.

PLAGUE AND MEDICAL ETHICS IN THE LATE MIDDLE AGES. The devastating plague epidemics that periodically swept through Europe, beginning in 1348 and continuing well beyond the Middle Ages, tried and tested the ethics of medieval physicians far beyond conditions encountered in ordinary practice. Contemporary sources almost uniformly express the conviction that plague was extremely contagious. Merely being in the vicinity of the sick, many supposed, doomed one to become infected and die. Numerous sources describe parents deserting their dying children, children their parents, wives fleeing from their sick husbands, and husbands from their wives. All who could, fled the cities and towns to take refuge in the countryside. Not only were the sick deserted by their families; physicians would not come near them, and even priests would not meet the final spiritual needs of the dying. Such accounts are plentiful. But they must be set against abundant accounts of responsible actions by family members, magistrates, physicians, and clergy.

Some physicians undoubtedly did flee. In 1382 Venice stipulated that physicians who fled during epidemics would lose their citizenship. Barcelona and Cologne took similar action during the sixteenth century. While it is impossible to determine the extent to which physicians actually did flee from plague-ridden communities, the percentage was probably relatively small. A study of nearly three hundred plague tractates written by physicians between 1348 and the early sixteenth century found not even one allusion to physicians who fled from areas afflicted with plague (Amundsen, 1977). Medieval physicians were not at all timid in castigating their colleagues in writing. Vitriolic criticism, particularly of fellow physicians' theories and medical techniques, is found throughout the medical literature. If the flight of physicians had been extensive, then one should encounter among the plague tractates such statements as "Although many other physicians fled, I remained."

Many physicians did advise people to flee from plague-infected areas as the best form of prevention. This advice, however, was typically followed by the concession that since flight "rarely is possible for most people, I advise that, while remaining, you. ..." Prevention is the primary concern of most of the plague tractates. Even if they are unanimous in urging flight, it does not follow that the physicians who wrote them intended by doing so to justify flight for themselves and their colleagues. The authors of the tractates appear simply to have assumed that their readers would be able to avail themselves of the services of physicians during plague epidemics.

Did physicians who fled, or who refused to visit and diagnose those perhaps afflicted with pestilence, or who abandoned patients actually suffering from plague, violate their responsibilities as conceived at that time? Contemporary sources make it abundantly clear that both the public at large and physicians themselves viewed those physicians who fled from plague as having acted disgracefully. In the mid-fourteenth century, Guy de Chauliac, at one time personal physician to the pope, wrote concerning his own activities during the Black Death, the earliest and most devastating of a long series of plague epidemics: "It was so contagious ... that even by looking at one another people caught it .... And I, to avoid infamy, dared not absent myself but with continual fear preserved myself as best I could" (Campbell, p. 3). Faced with both extreme peril to themselves and with the knowledge of the extremely high mortality rate of plague victims, physicians found themselves in an ethical quandary. Chauliac wrote, "It was useless and shameful for the doctors, the more so as they dared not visit the sick, for fear of being infected. And when they did visit them, they did hardly anything for them, and were paid nothing" (Campbell, p. 3).

One tractate maintains that physicians "must treat the ill," and another that "they must treat or visit the ill" (Amundsen, 1977, p. 414). The difference between these two is very important. While the first holds that physicians must treat plague victims, the second asserts that physicians must treat or visit the afflicted. Physicians who fled from a plague-infected area or hid in fear obviously failed even to attempt to diagnose the condition. But if the sick were indeed afflicted with the plague (since not all who became ill during a time of plague were necessarily afflicted with the plague), did physicians have an ethical obligation to attempt treatment?

A basic feature of medieval medical and surgical guild ethics was an obligation to be available to treat the ill or injured of the community and not to abandon hopeless cases. To the moral theologians who wrote the confessional literature, the duty to treat and to stay with the patient was unequivocal, although they were considering normal conditions rather than the exigencies of plague epidemics. Physicians were ambivalent about whether to take on hopeless cases; so were authors of the plague tractates. During outbreaks of plague, some physicians viewed the disease as treatable and others as at least potentially curable. Many physicians felt compelled to investigate the various strains of plague and to seek ways both to prevent and to treat them. Many of the plague tractates discuss treatment, distinguishing among different varieties of plague and stressing their faith in the efficacy of their curative methods. Some physicians, however, considered all forms of plague to be incurable. Of course physicians had to visit the ill to determine whether they were suffering from pestilence. If the condition was diagnosed as plague, some physicians then sought to determine whether the patient was possibly curable.

A plague tractate composed in 1411 advises: "If the patient is curable, the physician will undertake treatment in God's name. If he is incurable, the physician should leave him to die, in accord with the commentary on the second of the aphorisms [probably a medieval commentary on *Aphorisms* II in the Hippocratic Corpus]. Those who are going to die must be distinguished by prognostic signs and then you should flee from them. He labors in vain who attempts to treat such as these" (Amundsen, 1977, pp. 416–417). A plague tractate written in 1406 suggests that physicians not immediately inform patients if their condition is diagnosed as hopeless. Nevertheless, the physician "should refrain from administering anything to the patient that will cause him to die quickly, for then he would be a murderer" (Amundsen, 1977, p. 417, n. 64).

Various contemporary lay accounts from the time of the Black Death accuse some physicians of hiding in their houses and refusing to visit the sick for fear of infection. The authors of many plague tractates, while advising the general public to avoid contact with those afflicted with plague, do not direct such advice to their colleagues. They recommend varied and imaginative prophylactic techniques for use when visiting plague victims. The variety and abundance of such recommended precautions show the extent to which many physicians thought they were effective; moreover, there are numerous artistic representations of physicians who employed prophylactic measures while visiting plague victims. Many tractates deal exclusively with prophylaxis because their authors feel that treatment must be left to the discretion of the physician handling the case. Those that do include a discussion of treatment generally express great confidence in the curative methods prescribed. Many introduce new methods claimed effective by physicians who say they have employed them.

Some people did recover from the plague, from some strains of the disease more than from others; and although such cases of recovery were often in spite of the treatments to which the patients had been subjected, the attending physicians would have thought that their techniques had indeed been effective. The success rate in medieval medicine was, of course, much lower than in modern medicine; hence the expectations of both physicians and the public were not nearly as high as those of the present. The efforts of physicians to combat and cure various strains of plague, as well as their attempts to educate people in prevention and treatment by writing plague tractates, graphically demonstrate a high level of ethical and professional responsibility.

Summary and Conclusions

The medico-ethical treatises of the early Middle Ages blend Hippocratic etiquette with Christian morality, particularly emphasizing compassion and charity. The high and late medieval treatises, while loyal to the traditional concerns of the genre, suggest a new pragmatism born of the realities of medical practice by secular Catholic practitioners in a society starkly different from that of the monastic ethos of the early medieval medical literature. Although no mention of guilds or universities appears in this later literature, its tone and emphasis demonstrate that its authors regarded the practice of the art of medicine as a privilege that required training and skill, and carried consequent responsibilities. While there is no direct articulation of physicians' obligations to their immediate community in this literature, the obligation to the Christian community at large—an obligation to extend medical charity to the poor and destitute—is implicit and sometimes explicit.

Treating dangerous and even desperate cases is not discouraged in the later literature nearly as often as it had been before. Warnings against it are so infrequent, compared with advice on what to tell critically ill patients and their relatives or friends, that one may conclude there was a growing tendency to take on dangerous or even hopeless cases. But were physicians who in the late Middle Ages declined to treat patients for whom they foresaw little or no hope of recovery, still acting within the strictures of accepted ethics? This was a time during which popular attitudes toward physicians' responsibilities to the terminally ill were changing. Physicians who refused to treat patients were accused of deserting them because they thought they would not be paid for their services, while physicians who continued to treat such patients were suspected of greed for ministering to patients they know would not recover.

We see these two extremes illustrated by two sermons preached in fourteenth-century England. Lanfranc of Milan exclaimed, "O wretched physician, who for the money that you may not hope to get, desert the human body travailing in peril of death; and allow him, whom, according to the law of God, you should love and have most concern for, of all creatures under heaven, to be in jeopardy of life and limb, when you can and know how to apply a suitable remedy" (Owst, p. 351). John Bromyard, by contrast, asserted, "All craftsmen would at once refuse a job for which unsuitable materials were provided. If a carpenter were offered wages for the building of a house with planks that were too short or otherwise unsuitable, he would at once say: 'I will not take the wage or have anything to do with it, because the timber is of no use.' Similarly the physician who can see no hope of saving his patient" (Owst, p. 351).

Bromyard's sentiments were deeply rooted in tradition, but attitudes were changing. This change is very significant for the history of medical ethics. It seems to have been the product of two complementary and possibly related catalysts. The first is that the practice of medicine and surgery had been changed from a right to a privilege. A specific authority, whether royal, ecclesiastical, or municipal, granted to a select few the privilege of practicing in a specified, limited region. The authorities who granted what was essentially a monopoly also were ostensibly responsible for protecting that monopoly, and the privilege of holding a monopoly carried certain responsibilities, among them to service the sick of the community indiscriminately.

The second source of the growing tendency to take on dangerous or hopeless cases is the increasing theological insistence that physicians should do all they could to cure until the end, or nearly the end, and the church's support for their right to receive fees under such circumstances. One sees in the confessional literature the seeds of what was later to blossom into a medical duty to prolong life. The view is strongly articulated that physicians are religiously obligated

to extend care to a rich miser even if he or she both resists treatment and refuses to pay. Some moral theologians also maintain that even if patients refuse to call a confessor, physicians must not desert them, since help must be given to those who are in danger, regardless of how stubborn they are. While this is still far from an imperative to prolong life, it is a significant change from earlier medical attitudes and practice.

This fundamental change in perceived responsibilities of physicians to their patients is illustrated by the acts of a late-twelfth-century and a mid-eighteenth-century pope, both of whom address the request of physicians to enter the priesthood. Clement III, in the late twelfth century, ruled that the physician in question should search his memory to ensure that he had never, even inadvertently, harmed a patient by any treatment that he had administered. In the mid-eighteenth century, Benedict XIV's ruling centered on the problem that physicians can never be entirely positive that they have consistently used every available means for patients who died under their care (Amundsen and Ferngren). The concern in the twelfth century was with harm perhaps inflicted actively on patients: "Did you ever harm patients by the treatment you gave them?" But by the eighteenth century, attention focused on harm that may have resulted from oversight: "Did you ever harm patients by failing to give them the treatment you should have given?" These two papal rulings highlight a fundamental change both in physicians' sense of responsibility to their patients and in social and religious expectations, a change that occurred primarily in the late Middle Ages.

We look nearly in vain in the medico-ethical literature of the late Middle Ages for statements on two topics of medical ethics: abortion and euthanasia. We cannot conclude from this that both theologians and physicians considered abortion and euthanasia ethical for physicians to perform. Indeed, the presumption is quite the opposite. Theologians and physicians alike took it for granted that both were sinful, so much so that their sinfulness need not be mentioned explicitly. Rather, it would seem that abortion was a procedure for which women would turn to someone other than a male physician or surgeon. Facilitating the death of a patient was undoubtedly so repugnant to medieval moral principles that to mention it as unethical for a physician to do would have been gratuitous, at least in a general treatise on medical ethics.

When the contents of the late medieval medico-ethical treatises are supplemented by guild ethics and the moral pronouncements of the theologians, as well as by the evidence of physicians' conscientious response to the outbreaks of plague, the picture that emerges is of relatively high ethical standards. Although "Hippocratic ideals" persisted throughout the Middle Ages and provided the basis for medical etiquette, the role and responsibilities of physicians and surgeons were variously affected by Christian morality. This is particularly evident in concern for the gratuitous treatment of the poor, both by individual physicians and by professional associations. The discipline of moral theology provided distinct criteria for medical ethics from a late-medieval Catholic perspective. Secular law and medico-surgical organizations, including university faculties, established regulations and standards of competence for medical licensure, and guilds and university faculties set precise codes of conduct. Essentially, the creation of medical licensure, medical faculties, and professional organizations helped to formulate medical professionalism and ethics in a sense that is still very much present today.

DARREL W. AMUNDSEN (1995)

BIBLIOGRAPHY

Amundsen, Darrel W. 1971. "Visigothic Medical Legislation." *Bulletin of the History of Medicine* 45(6): 553–569.

Amundsen, Darrel W. 1977. "Medical Deontology and Pestilential Disease in the Late Middle Ages." *Journal of the History of Medicine and Allied Sciences* 32(4): 403–421.

Amundsen, Darrel W. 1978. "Medieval Canon Law on Medical and Surgical Practice by the Clergy." *Bulletin of the History of Medicine* 52(1): 22–44.

Amundsen, Darrel W. 1979. "Medicine and Surgery as Art or Craft: The Role of Schematic Literature in the Separation of Medicine and Surgery in the Late Middle Ages." *Transactions and Studies of the College of Physicians of Philadelphia*, n.s. 1(1): 43–57.

Amundsen, Darrel W. 1981. "Casuistry and Professional Obligations: The Regulation of Physicians by the Court of Conscience in the Late Middle Ages." *Transactions and Studies of the College of Physicians of Philadelphia* 3(1): 22–39, and 3(2): 93–112.

Amundsen, Darrel W. 1986. "The Medieval Catholic Tradition." In *Caring and Curing: Health and Medicine in the Western Religious Traditions*, pp. 65–107, ed. Ronald L. Numbers and Darrel W. Amundsen. New York: Macmillan.

Amundsen, Darrel W., and Ferngren, Gary B. 1983. "Evolution of the Patient-Physician Relationship: Antiquity Through the Renaissance." In *The Clinical Encounter: The Moral Fabric of the Patient-Physician Relationship*, pp. 1–46, ed. Earl E. Shelp. Dordrecht, Netherlands: D. Reidel.

Campbell, Anna Montgomery. 1931. *The Black Death and Men of Learning*. New York: Columbia University Press.

Connery, John R. 1977. *Abortion: The Development of the Roman Catholic Perspective*. Chicago: Loyola University Press.

Cosman, Madeleine Pelner. 1973. "Medieval Medical Malpractice: The Dicta and the Dockets." *Bulletin of the New York Academy of Medicine* 49(1): 22–47.

Demaitre, Luke E. 1980. *Doctor Bernard de Gordon: Professor and Practitioner*. Toronto: Pontifical Institute of Medieval Studies.

De Renzi, Salvatore, ed. 1852–1857. *Collectio salernitana.* 5 vols. Naples: Filiatre-Sebezio.

Flint, Valerie J. 1989. "The Early 'Medicus,' the Saint—and the Enchanter." *Social History of Medicine* 2(2): 127–145.

Flint, Valerie J. 1991. *The Rise of Magic in Early Medieval Europe.* Princeton, N.J.: Princeton University Press.

García-Ballester, Luis. 1993. "Medical Ethics in Transition in the Latin Medicine of the Thirteenth and Fourteenth Centuries: New Prospects on the Physician-Patient Relationship and the Doctor's Fee." In *Doctors and Ethics: The Earlier Historical Setting of Professional Ethics,* pp. 38–71, ed. Andrew Wear, Johanna Geyer-Kordesch, and Roger K. French. Amsterdam: Rodopi.

García-Ballester, Luis; McVaugh, Michael R.; and Rubio-Vela, Agustín. 1989. *Medical Licensing and Learning in Fourteenth-Century Valencia.* Transactions of the American Philosophical Society, vol. 79, pt. 6. Philadelphia: American Philosophical Society.

Green, Monica. 1989. "Women's Medical Practice and Health Care in Medieval Europe." *Signs* 14(2): 434–473.

Hammond, E. A. 1960. "Incomes of Medieval English Doctors." *Journal of the History of Medicine and Allied Sciences* 15: 154–169.

Hartung, Edward F. 1934. "Medical Regulations of Frederick the Second of Hohenstaufen." *Medical Life* 41: 587–601.

Hume, Edgar E. 1940. *The Medical Work of the Knights Hospitallers of Saint John of Jerusalem.* Baltimore: Johns Hopkins University Press.

Kibre, Pearl. 1953. "The Faculty of Medicine at Paris, Charlatanism and Unlicensed Medical Practices in the Later Middle Ages." *Bulletin of the History of Medicine* 27(1): 1–20.

MacKinney, Loren C. 1952. "Medical Ethics and Etiquette in the Early Middle Ages: The Persistence of Hippocratic Ideals." *Bulletin of the History of Medicine* 26(1): 1–31.

Miller, Timothy S. 1978. "The Knights of Saint John and the Hospitals of the Latin West." *Speculum* 53(4): 709–733.

Mirfeld, John. 1936. *Johannes de Mirfeld of St. Bartholemew's, Smithfield: His Life and Works,* ed. Percival Horton-Smith Hartley and Harold Richard Aldridge. Cambridge, Eng.: Cambridge University Press.

Noonan, John T., Jr. 1970. "An Almost Absolute Value in History." In *The Morality of Abortion: Legal and Historical Perspectives,* pp. 1–59, ed. John T. Noonan, Jr. Cambridge, MA: Harvard University Press.

Owst, Gerald R. 1966. *Literature and Pulpit in Medieval England: A Neglected Chapter in the History of English Letters and of the English People.* Oxford: Basil Blackwell.

Park, Katharine. 1992. "Medicine and Society in Medieval Europe, 500–1500." In *Medicine in Society: Historical Essays,* pp. 59–90, ed. Andrew Wear. Cambridge, Eng.: Cambridge University Press.

Powell, James M., trans. 1971. *The Liber Augustalis or Constitutions of Melfi, Promulgated by the Emperor Frederick II for the Kingdom of Sicily in 1231.* Syracuse, NY: Syracuse University Press.

Rawcliffe, Carole. 1988. "The Profits of Practice: The Wealth and Status of Medical Men in Later Medieval England." *Social History of Medicine* 1(1): 61–78.

Schroeder, Henry Joseph, ed. 1937. *Disciplinary Decrees of the General Councils.* St. Louis, MO: Herder.

Sigerist, Henry Ernest. 1946. "Bedside Manners in the Middle Ages: The Treatise De Cautelis Medicorum Attributed to Arnald of Villanova." *Quarterly Bulletin of the Northwestern University Medical School* 20: 136–143.

Siraisi, Nancy G. 1990. *Medieval and Early Renaissance Medicine: An Introduction to Knowledge and Practice.* Chicago: University of Chicago Press.

Ullmann, Walter. 1971. "Public Welfare and Social Legislation in the Early Medieval Councils." In *Councils and Assemblies: Papers Read at the Eighth Summer Meeting and the Ninth Winter Meeting of the Ecclesiastical History Society,* pp. 1–39, ed. G. J. Cuming and Derek Baker. Studies in Church History, vol. 7. Cambridge, Eng.: Cambridge University Press.

Unwin, George. 1963. *The Guilds and Companies of London.* 4th ed. London: Frank Cass.

Welborn, Mary Catherine. 1938. "The Long Tradition: A Study in Fourteenth-Century Medical Deontology." In *Medieval and Historiographical Essays in Honor of James Westfall Thompson,* pp. 344–357, ed. James Lea Cate and Eugene N. Anderson. Chicago: University of Chicago Press.

II. RENAISSANCE AND ENLIGHTENMENT

Medicine in early modern Europe (from the later fifteenth century to the end of the eighteenth century) is best characterized by its diversity of practitioners, practices, and conceptual foundations. Even by the end of the eighteenth century, few places in Europe had effective regulations to restrict medical practice to people with certain kinds of certification, or to regulate their practices. University-educated practitioners differed sharply with one another about the true conceptual foundations of good and effective medical practice, while among the merely literate, or even the illiterate, practitioners, views about the constitution of good medicine varied even more.

Many medical changes occurred during the period: The number of university-educated physicians rose considerably, as did the number of other formally trained (usually apprenticed) practitioners. With the proliferation of schooling, the educational level of many ordinary practitioners rose. And while the beginning of the period was marked by the proliferation of various philosophical and medical systems, by the end of the eighteenth century most of those systems had been set aside by the educated elite in favor of varieties of a more unified "science."

Throughout the period, no formal systems of medical ethics existed per se. Yet medical practitioners took varying degrees of interest in ethical issues, issues that commonly focused on the personal character of the practitioner. The discussion of the period that follows is therefore divided into two parts: a description of the general structures of the period and the organization of medical practice; and the debates among the literate, and especially among the learned, over the foundations of good medical practice and behavior.

Social Structures of Medical Practice

European society underwent a major transformation from the fifteenth to the eighteenth century. Throughout the period, Europe remained an overwhelmingly rural region, and at times the population grew rapidly. And, because of demographic, economic, political, and intellectual changes, city life came to typify refinement. As a result, most of the great changes in medical practices and mores took place in the cities, although most of the people needing care continued to live in the countryside.

The vast majority of the people in Europe—nine in ten, or more, depending on when and where—lived in a rural environment: in small towns or villages, in hamlets, or on rural manors; a few even resided in the forests and fields. In the fifteenth century, many rural laboring people lived relatively well, since after the fourteenth-century plague (the Black Death), there was land enough for most. But during the sixteenth century, the European population increased rapidly (perhaps about 1 percent per year); it generally leveled off during the seventeenth and early eighteenth centuries; and late in the eighteenth century again began to increase rapidly. While at first, people could generally grow enough food for themselves and their landlords and a little extra, with the increasing population of the sixteenth century, the number of rural itinerant laborers and destitute began to rise rapidly (Flinn).

Ordinarily, rural people bartered with neighbors and used money only occasionally, relying on mental accounts of who owed what to whom. At local markets, though, they might purchase a few goods manufactured locally or imported from afar, and sell their own goods or labor. When they needed medical care, most ill people and those caring for them relied on practices long used: self-help; recipes for home remedies (or "kitchen physic") passed down through kin or neighbors; and other traditional practices that could be gathered from local people, which might include ritual and invocation (or what the educated sometimes called "superstitious" practices). Beyond the resources of neighbors and kin, the sick often had available to them the services of people with special knowledge or powers: clergymen, herb wives, sorcerers or witches, and people who healed by special powers of touch. In return for medical help, payment might be in coin, but probably more commonly added a debt to the mental balance of favors, or earned the practitioner goods or services such as chickens or eggs, pasturing an animal on the patient's land, or the patient's help in doing certain chores.

In a few regions, however—mainly from northern Italy along the Mediterranean coast to southern Spain, in the Low Countries and northern France, a thin strip along the south edge of the Baltic, and in southeastern England—urban life was more common. In the fifteenth and early sixteenth centuries, people in towns and cities raised animals for slaughter, and sometimes kept a plot of ground nearby on which they grew food. But by the later sixteenth century, many towns were becoming too large and too densely settled for such practices. Much of the increasing population was drawn from the countryside into the cities or, later, pushed to the overseas colonies. Many people spent a part of their lives in a city working as laborers or servants, returning to their towns or villages after accumulating enough money to establish a family. Others migrated to the towns and cities permanently, causing a huge expansion of wealthy, middling, and poor neighborhoods. The largest city in Europe, Naples, soon had rivals in Paris and London. Just how brutal were the conditions of urban life has been vigorously debated; what is clear is that urban mortality and morbidity rates in the age before plumbing and sewerage were very high indeed.

The cities wrought important economic changes, especially a greater use of money. The demand for food among the urban populations also transformed nearby regions into centers of market agriculture where individuals or landlords produced cash crops. In some areas, such as southeastern England and the Netherlands, this agricultural revolution brought into being a free yeomanry; in other regions, such as Prussia and Russia, it brought about a reenserfment of the peasantry by great landlords. Whatever the local consequences, throughout Europe people increasingly grew used to buying and selling labor and goods, and to handling money; even rural laborers often had a few copper pennies at their disposal.

With the increasing importance of money as a means of exchanging value, more and more people supplemented their incomes by engaging in medical practice for money, or relied upon it entirely for their living. Many, undoubtedly most, such people offered their services to ordinary people, doing so in their neighborhoods or traveling to offer their services among strangers. If itinerant, they found their customers wherever gatherings occurred: markets, crossroads, taverns, inns, alehouses, coffeehouses, and even street fights. They might also gather a crowd by saying something interesting from a platform or from horseback, or by presenting an entertainment from a table, wagon, or stage: These people soon acquired the name of *quacksalver* or *quack* (a term of obscure origin), or *mountebank* (probably from climbing on benches).

With the spread of the printing press and the growth of literacy in the later sixteenth century, medical advertising could be used to heighten the practitioner's reputation or to attract more people to the shows. Medical advertising could also publicize the practice of someone who did not travel but practiced out of a shop, inn, or house. By the later seventeenth century, as the postal systems of many regions of Europe developed, advertisements could be sent to agents for posting throughout a region, and medical customers could order remedies through the mail. The medical practitioners who relied on such methods for their incomes might offer special services (like cutting for cataracts or bladder stones, or setting bones), or sell special remedies (what became known by the eighteenth century as "patent remedies") (Cook; Porter, 1989; Porter and Porter).

In the cities and a few large towns, craft guilds of medical practitioners came into being or expanded from their late medieval roots. Guilds had municipal charters allowing their members the rights and privileges of citizenship, and the group the right to act as a corporation: to stand as one person before the local courts, to own property, to pass internal rules regulating their members and organizing them by rank, and often to restrict certain practices to their own members. Throughout early modern Europe, guilds of barber-surgeons and surgeons, or groups of barber-surgeons and surgeons in other guilds, could be found. In general, guilds of barber-surgeons and surgeons restricted the use of instruments on the body to their members.

The barber-surgeons undertook barbering and minor operations, such as opening a vein to let blood, and were ordinarily among the lower-ranking members of the guild (Pelling). The surgeons, far fewer in number and generally among the higher-ranking liverymen, undertook major operations, such as amputating limbs, setting bones, repairing hernias and fistulas, extracting teeth, and tending to wounds, sores, and ulcers. Among the armies and navies of Europe, surgeons performed most of the general medical tasks, and the kinds of operations that could be successfully performed gradually increased. Consequently, the status and income of surgeons grew during the period, and they began to be increasingly trusted by monarchs to develop certain kinds of medical policies for their kingdoms or principalities (Temkin; Gelfand).

Another kind of medical craftsmen were the apothecaries, or pharmacists. Originally wholesale importers of spices, by the early modern period many sold medicines from retail shops; some of the medicines they sold could be dangerous unless used under careful supervision. Many cities therefore had guilds of apothecaries, who were subject to rigorous municipal regulations. In the Scandinavian and Germanic lands, cities often restricted the selling of medicines to a very few official apothecaries, sometimes to just one. As their numbers increased, so did the tendency of apothecaries to give medical advice. It was from the surgeon-apothecaries that the general practitioners eventually arose (Loudon).

One other kind of medical corporation proliferated in the early modern period: that of the university-educated physicians, usually called a "college" (*collegium*) of physicians. Ordinarily, colleges of physicians had formal standing from a municipal or royal charter that gave members of the group sole right to practice "physic"—the giving of medical advice—in their city and the surrounding area. Regular members had to possess a university degree in medicine (by the sixteenth century, ordinarily Medicinae Doctor). The colleges of physicians ordinarily were not authorized to grant degrees (an important exception to this rule was the Faculty of Medicine in Paris, which had its roots in the medieval university; the professors of medicine of the university were elected from the Faculty). Independent colleges of medicine first came into being in several northern Italian cities, and by the early sixteenth century had spread to Spain, France, and England. By the seventeenth century, physicians in northern European cities like Amsterdam had established their own colleges. These colleges not only governed the physicians of a city but also, sometimes, took on other regulatory powers, such as inspecting the apothecaries' shops, examining apprentices in surgery and pharmacy, and even looking into the behavior of all local medical practitioners.

In the view of the learned physicians, a medical hierarchy should exist: the physicians at the top, governing the practices of the apothecaries and surgeons, and most other practitioners being outlawed. While this ideal could seldom be thoroughly enforced, physicians often worked to obtain its legal foundations from municipal or national governments. As an important part of their argument, they fostered the idea that physicians ought to be trusted more than other practitioners because of their learning, which not only gave them knowledge but also inculcated good character. Physicians spoke often of defending the "dignity" of their profession, and concerned themselves with cultivating the outward manners that would best exhibit their inward virtues.

A final medical institution must be mentioned, that of the city physician and, eventually, the physician or surgeon officer of state. In the later Middle Ages, on the Continent, some large cities began to revive the ancient tradition of employing a physician to see to the needs of the municipality. In return for an annual salary, the city physician treated poor citizens, advised on medical regulations (including plague orders), and often served in one or more of the municipal hospitals for the sick poor (if the city had any) (Russell). By the later sixteenth century, city physicians had become important officers of local government in many places. Moreover, as unified territorial states came into being in the seventeenth century, and sovereigns tried to impose more uniform codes of law and government, they, too, began to use medical advisers to help them govern. Given contemporary international competition, princes deeply felt the need to try to increase the general wealth and power of their countries. Part of their domestic policy therefore was concerned with bettering the health of the public and increasing the population. To do so, sovereign rulers frequently tried to co-opt existing medical corporations or to establish new ones.

In central Europe, by the later eighteenth century, medical advice had become important enough to government that the phrase "medical police" (meaning medical policy promoted and enforced through government agents) had become a common topic in discussions about the structure of state institutions (Rosen; Hannaway; Jordanova; Fischer-Homberger). But associating themselves with magistrates and government might give physicians and surgeons more authority among those who supported the government; it also might make them more subject to criticism during periods of public unease. The revolutionaries in France, for example, demolished most formal medical institutions during the mid-1790s.

With a rising population, increased urbanization, the spread of the market economy, greater literacy and formal education, and the development of nations, the significance of medical help outside networks of kin and neighbors increased. These changes had many implications for those who practiced medicine. With regard to the gender of the practitioner, for example, women seem to have dominated the practice of traditional medicine, while it was predominantly men who flourished in the commercial medical market (although not to the total exclusion of women). When it came to medical guilds, outside of Italy, memberships were generally limited to men or to the widows of members. Since virtually all European universities excluded women from receiving degrees, nearly all medical doctors were men. In the eyes of the governments, if not always in the eyes of the public, a group who recognized themselves as professional men sat at the top of the medical hierarchy: the physicians, and gradually the surgeons. They obtained many new mechanisms of medical regulation from the state (for example, the French crown established a new College of

Surgery in Paris in 1750, and a Royal Society of Medicine in 1776), and increasingly tried to regulate all other practitioners. They could not always succeed in imposing medical order on society, but their professional ideals were influential.

Debates about Medical Practice and Practitioners

Because the increasingly literate and monied public of the towns and cities had a host of medical practitioners from whom to choose, the medical professionals could not impose their ideals on others. While noble and wealthy patients often consulted physicians, they often also consulted surgeons, apothecaries, "quacks," and traditional healers. Without a single, inclusive medical profession and firm regulation to govern practitioners or establish uniform requirements for their training, patients could pick and choose the kind of medicine they preferred, as long as they could pay for it or obtain it through charity. Consequently, medical practitioners cajoled and persuaded their paying patients to do what they considered right (Jewson; Porter, 1985). (Those they helped through charity could take what was offered or go without.) As a result, the various medical groups, even the physicians, had few clear ethical codes on how to treat patients that were distinct from general sentiments. Notions of virtue and good behavior existed everywhere; concepts of "medical ethics" per se were few (Waddington).

The humanist movement of the Renaissance brought to light a plethora of ancient philosophies of nature, each with its own ethical foundations. Renewed Aristotelianism, Platonism, Stoicism, Epicureanism, Hermeticism, and Hippocratism: Among the learned, each had its medical adherents. When modern natural philosophers began to take precedence over the old, physicians of a Baconian, Cartesian, or Newtonian stripe often adopted moral notions consistent with their philosophical system. For instance, with a renewed interest in Hippocratism came a renewed interest in the Hippocratic Oath (Smith); with the spreading of Cartesianism came a hard-hearted attitude toward the use of living automata (animals) in bloody experiments (Guerrini). But none of these philosophical positions was solely medical, and so none of the ethical implications were strictly medical. The physician took no more and no less interest in the ethical implications of the natural philosophy he adopted than did any other learned person.

Moreover, it is possible to discern some of the general public's ideas of ethical medicine. One can see such general notions at work in the plague. During the first outbreaks (from the mid-fourteenth century), the best advice on avoiding the pestilence that a practitioner could give or take was to "flee fast and far." But as magistrates worked to prevent or ameliorate epidemics, in part by working with city physicians, a sense that the legally privileged physicians ought to help in times of crisis grew up alongside older notions of charity and self-sacrifice (Amundsen). By the seventeenth century, colleges of physicians suffered public embarrassment when many of their members (even those who held no public office) left town during an epidemic. In the London plague of 1665, for instance, many of the physicians' rivals, especially the chemical physicians, gained the respect of the public by staying and treating victims of the plague, showing by this disinterested public service that they ought to take precedence over the cowardly physicians. For whatever reason, the public was beginning to expect higher standards of behavior from medical practitioners than from all but a few others.

Another place where public notions of ethics in medicine can be found is in the general sense that physicians should not be overly commercial. Journals of literate sentiment, like *The Spectator* or *Gentleman's Magazine* (both of London), made fun of medical commercialism. For their part, physicians generally tried to avoid becoming personally involved in public medical disputes, frowned on advertising their practices or medicines as beneath the dignity of their calling, considered fee splitting and the taking of part of a fee in advance as "quackish," and even began to accept "honoraria" instead of fees. They also continued to treat without charge some of the poor who sought their help and, when they took up hospital posts (where they saw the sick poor inmates), received no fees for their once-a-week (or so) visits. Such general notions of good and charitable behavior, ordinarily shared between patient and practitioner, underlay the more detailed treatment of medical etiquette in the statutes of the various medical corporations.

The topics of more specific debate about moral medical behavior in the early modern period included what constituted the best medical learning; what kind of person made a good practitioner; what kinds of people ought to be prohibited from practice; and what medical practices should be encouraged and which discouraged. Debates about each of these topics could hardly be separated from the others, however, since they all surrounded what might be called the early modern equivalent of "virtue" ethics.

The two most numerous kinds of documents regarding early modern medical practice illustrate how interconnected were ideas about good practice and good character. One kind is the internal regulations of medical guilds and colleges of physicians. The statutes of the London College of Physicians, Society of Apothecaries, and Surgeons' Company, for instance, governed the behavior of the members closely but had almost nothing to say about medical practice per se. (One of the few explicit prohibitions in the College statutes is against making prognoses from the inspection of urine alone; the practices of "urine-casters" came in for much scathing comment from physicians in the early seventeenth century.) In drafting the statutes of the College of Physicians, the officers devoted much attention to whether and in what kinds of cases members might consult nonmembers, how members should behave during consultations, what the order of precedence would be during meetings and on ceremonial occasions, how they should write prescriptions, and so on, all trying to maintain the dignity, gravity, and exclusivity of the group. The same is true of the College of Physicians in Amsterdam, and colleges elsewhere in Europe; and it is equally true for guilds. One sees the same concern with character in the record of whom the London College of Physicians tried for medical misbehavior: They rarely distinguished between illicit practice and malpractice, insisting that in their examinations for membership, applicants had to show that they were the right sort of people in character as well as in knowledge, anyone else being de facto and de jure incapable of practice.

The second major class of historical documentation discussing the foundations of good or ill medical practice is the antiquackery tracts that proliferated during the early modern period. In them, physicians and others discussed practitioners' behavior far more than their medical practices. In England, perhaps the best-known early piece of antiquackery literature is by John Cotta, who passionately condemned the multitude of nonphysicians: empirics, women practitioners, fugitives, jugglers, quacksalvers, practicing surgeons and apothecaries, practicers of spells, witches, wizards, the servants of physicians, "the methodian learned deceiver or hereticke Physition," beneficed practitioners, astrologers, urine-casters, and itinerants (Cotta).

Cotta not only condemned the ignorance and bad practices of such people, he condemned above all their undisciplined characters. He explained how even good remedies cause harm when recommended by those who do not possess the learning, and hence the virtue, of physicians (Cotta, pp. 2–8). As one of his contemporaries noted, because learning and character were so closely associated, ignorance in medical practitioners could be recognized by bad behavior: "loquaciousness," "haste" in judging diseases and promising cures before the cause had been ascertained, "forwardness" in condemning and slandering proper physicians, and "boastfulness" about their own skills (Dunk, pp. 20–21). These behaviors exhibited by empirics were not tests of their knowledge but demonstrations of their indiscipline: outward signs of an inward character. Character had so foundational a role in medical practice because, as Cotta explained, "the dignitie and worth of Physicks skill consisteth *not (as is imagined commonly) in the excellence and*

preheminence of remedies, but in their wise and prudent use" (1612, p. 7; emphasis added). Wisdom and prudence could be built only on the coupling of solid learning with good character. Similar works on how the good physician alone could exhibit proper medical behavior can be noted throughout early modern Europe: Gabriele de Zerbi's *De cautelis medicorum* (1495); Laurent Joubert's *Erreurs populaires* (1578); Govanni Condronchi's *De Christiana ac tuta medendi ratione* (A Christian and Careful Manner of Healing, 1591); Rodericus à Castro's *Medicus-politicus* (The Responsible Physician, 1614); Paolo Zacchia's *Questiones medicolegales* (1621); and Friedrich Hoffman's *Medicus politicus* (1738).

In countering the links made by physicians between learning and virtue, other practitioners discussed their own notions of the sources of good character, frequently arguing that it came not from academic discipline but from an inner light. Since all knowledge ultimately stemmed from God and God's creation, they argued, their direct apprehension of things through experience and a properly prepared intuition made them the possessors of a more immediate wisdom than that of the pagan- and Islamic-influenced university physicians (as they often put it). Such arguments had been put forward forcefully by the influential chemical physician Paracelsus in the early sixteenth century; by the seventeenth century, these views had spread widely among medical chemistry's advocates (Debus; Webster).

Not only chemists but also many nonphysicians took the same view about godly practice. For instance, the Swiss Protestant surgeon Gulielmus Hildanus Fabricius wrote:

Though godlinesse be needfull for all sorts of men, yet it is most requisite in such as practise Physick, for God Almighty doth often abate the power of the Medicines, when he which administers them, is an ungodly and blasphemous man: and contrariwise, doth give wonderfull power to things despicable and vile, when they are administered by good and godly Physitians. (Fabricius, pp. 53–54)

Given the deep and bloody struggles over religion in the early modern period, comments about character and godliness divided people. Fabricius's ideas about the personal godliness of the practitioner affecting the efficacy of his medicines is quite different from the learned physician Cotta's view that even good medicines used by the unlearned could cause harm. Different kinds of medical practitioners had very different views about the inner qualities necessary for good practice, and how those qualities could be acquired. For a good Anglican like Cotta, or for his professional colleagues in all orthodox churches, sentiments about intuition and inner light such as Fabricius's smacked of dangerous religious "enthusiasm" (the sense of being inspired directly by God); for practitioners like Fabricius, linking virtue with higher education could only reinforce the position of the "dogmatists" (those who privileged reason over intuition and experience).

By the later seventeenth century, however, many physicians, too, had come to accept the importance of learning from experience, although they continued to believe that it had to be coupled with a disciplined and knowledgeable mind rather than based on intuitions. The scientific revolution had introduced notions that associated virtue with knowledge as much as (or even more than) dignity, and associated knowledge with experience (or, in English, "experiment") rather than learned debate (Shapin and Schaffer). The "virtuosi" of Europe launched detailed investigations into things, finding the best evidences of God not in human testimony and argument but in creation itself. Consequently, by the eighteenth century, many physicians, as well as surgeons, apothecaries, and empirics, placed great weight on furthering curative and preventive medicine through scientific trials.

The foundation for experiments such as James Lind's work on scurvy, or William Withering's on digitalis, or Lady Wortley Montague's on smallpox inoculation and Edward Jenner's on vaccination, or Antoine Mesmer's on "animal magnetism," had been "folk" custom. Ignoring what they considered the superstitious explanations of what happened, and concentrating instead on the material causes and consequences of various practices, such medical investigators throughout Europe explored new medicaments and treatments. In this enterprise, surgeons and apothecaries, and even unlicensed ordinary practitioners, could make contributions equal to those of physicians. Debates among medical practitioners still implied notions of who might be the best sort of person; but as the nineteenth century loomed, medical debates focused increasingly on what might be the best treatment rather than who might be the best treater.

Conclusion

Throughout Europe in the early modern period, one finds implicit and explicit notions about what constituted a good medical practitioner. Given prevailing public ideas about morality being linked first to character and only second to behavior, the question of *who* ought to practice *what* dominated medical debates. Oral codes and written rules governing medical etiquette proliferated, while people devoted relatively little attention to what we might consider medical ethics per se in the rules of good practice. Without a united and powerful profession, no group of medical practitioners could hope to universalize their own rules, although they often tried. Instead, they had to abide by the ordinary notions of virtue and morality held by their peers and the public. Notions of public and private virtue could be vigorously contested and undoubtedly affected the behavior of practitioners, but they were seldom strictly medical.

HAROLD J. COOK (1995)

BIBLIOGRAPHY

Amundsen, Darrel W. 1977. "Medical Deontology and Pestilential Disease in the Late Middle Ages." *Journal of the History of Medicine and Allied Sciences* 32(4): 403–421.

Cook, Harold J. 1986. *The Decline of the Old Medical Regime in Stuart London.* Ithaca, NY: Cornell University Press.

Cotta, John. 1612. *A Short Discoverie of the Unobserved Dangers of Severall Sorts of Ignorant and Unconsiderate Practisers of Physicke in England.* London: William Jones and Richard Boyle.

Debus, Allen G. 1977. *The Chemical Philosophy: Paracelsian Science and Medicine in the Sixteenth and Seventeenth Centuries.* New York: Science History Publications.

Dunk, Eleazar. 1606. *The Copy of a Letter Written by E. D. Doctour of Physicke to a Gentleman, by Whom It Was Published.* London: M. Bradwood.

Fabricius, Hildanus Gulielmus. 1640. *Lithotomia vesicae: That Is, an Accurate Description of the Stone in the Bladder.* London: John Norton.

Fischer-Homberger, Esther. 1983. *Medizin vor Gericht: Gerichtsmedizin von der Renaissance bis zur Aufklärung.* Bern, Switzerland: Hans Huber.

Flinn, Michael W. 1981. *The European Demographic System, 1500–1820.* Baltimore: Johns Hopkins University Press.

Gelfand, Tobi. 1980. *Professionalizing Modern Medicine: Paris Surgeons and Medical Science and Institutions in the Eighteenth Century.* Westport, CT: Greenwood Press.

Guerrini, Anita. 1989. "The Ethics of Animal Experimentation in Seventeenth-Century England." *Journal of the History of Ideas* 50: 391–406.

Hannaway, Caroline. 1981. "From Private Hygiene to Public Health: A Transformation in Western Medicine in the Eighteenth and Nineteenth Centuries." In *Public Health: Proceedings of the Fifth International Symposium on the Comparative History of Medicine—East and West,* pp. 108–128, ed. Teizo Ogawa. Tokyo: Saikon.

Jewson, Norman D. 1974. "Medical Knowledge and the Patronage System in Eighteenth Century England." *Sociology* 8: 369–385.

Jordanova, Ludmilla J. 1981. "Policing Public Health in France 1780–1815." In *Public Health: Proceedings of the Fifth International Symposium on the Comparative History of Medicine—East and West,* pp. 12–32, ed. Teizo Ogawa. Tokyo: Saikon.

Loudon, Irvine. 1986. *Medical Care and the General Practitioner, 1750–1850.* Oxford: Oxford University Press.

Pelling, Margaret. 1986. "Appearance and Reality: Barber-Surgeons, the Body and Disease." In *London 1500–1700: The Making of the Metropolis,* pp. 82–112, ed. Augustus L. Beier and Roger Finlay. London: Longman.

Porter, Dorothy, and Porter, Roy. 1989. *Patient's Progress: Doctors and Doctoring in Eighteenth-Century England.* Stanford, CA: Stanford University Press.

Porter, Roy. 1989. *Health for Sale: Quackery in England 1650–1850.* Manchester, U.K.: Manchester University Press.

Porter, Roy, ed. 1985. *Patients and Practitioners: Lay Perceptions of Medicine in Pre-Industrial Society.* Cambridge: Cambridge University Press.

Rosen, George. 1974. *From Medical Police to Social Medicine: Essays on the History of Health Care.* New York: Science History Publications.

Russell, Andrew W., ed. 1981. *The Town and State Physician in Europe from the Middle Ages to the Enlightenment.* Wolfenbüttel: Herzog August Bibliothek.

Shapin, Steven, and Schaffer, Simon. 1985. *Leviathan and the Air-Pump: Hobbes, Boyle, and the Experimental Life.* Princeton, NJ: Princeton University Press.

Smith, Wesley D. 1979. *The Hippocratic Tradition.* Ithaca, NY: Cornell University Press.

Temkin, Owsei. 1951. "The Role of Surgery in the Rise of Modern Medical Thought." *Bulletin of the History of Medicine* 25(3): 248–259.

Waddington, Ivan. 1975. "The Development of Medical Ethics: A Sociological Analysis." *Medical History* 19(1): 36–51.

Webster, Charles. 1982. *From Paracelsus to Newton: Magic and the Making of Modern Science.* Cambridge: Cambridge University Press.

III. NINETEENTH CENTURY. A. EUROPE

In the course of the nineteenth century, medical ethics was profoundly transformed in European countries. Social, political, economic, professional, and scientific developments influenced the relationship of physicians to their patients, to their colleagues, and to the state. Focusing on continental Europe, this article first briefly characterizes medical ethics in the eighteenth century and then discusses its transformation after 1800, in connection with the evolution of the medical profession, public health and social medicine, and medical science. Most examples are drawn from Germany and France, where debates on ethical issues in medicine became particularly intense. The codification of medical morality was based on different models in these two countries. While in the German states (and to some extent also in Spain) medical ethics was clearly influenced by the early Anglo-American professional codes, in France national traditions of codes of honor in nineteenth-century bourgeois society appear to have shaped doctors' rules of conduct.

The Gentleman Doctor

Medical ethics in the eighteenth century was determined by the personal integrity and gentlemanly manners of the physician. His moral decisions were generally based, not on written rules of conduct of a college of physicians, nor directly on the Hippocratic code, but mainly on his medical knowledge, reasoning, and an internal code of honor. Enlightenment natural law theory, as developed by Samuel Pufendorf and Christian Thomasius, may have contributed to this approach. It encouraged a morality based upon rational reflection and individual conscience, rather than upon religious and ecclesiastical precepts (Geyer-Kordesch, 1993b). Eighteenth-century doctors usually treated only a small number of wealthy patients, leaving the majority of the population to the care of barber-surgeons (trained by apprenticeship), midwives, and diverse lay healers. Physicians, like their patients, felt bound to the traditional Platonic and Christian virtues of wisdom, moderation, courage, justice, and faith, hope, charity, as well as to bourgeois Enlightenment virtues like order, cleanliness, and industry (von Engelhardt, 1985).

In the German-speaking world of the eighteenth century, particularly in Prussia, modern professional ethics began to take shape within the academic discipline of medical jurisprudence. Physicians who were called on to give expert testimony on legal cases (e.g., consummation of marriage, paternity, infanticide, murder, poisoning, assault) were exhorted to build their statements truthfully on empirical findings, to admit uncertainty in medical evidence, and to behave with dignity (Geyer-Kordesch, 1993a, 1993b). At some universities, such as Halle and Göttingen, graduating physicians had to take vows of faithfulness to and respect for the academic institutions, careful and rational treatment of poor as well as rich patients, and medical confidentiality (Helm). Ethical demands like these helped physicians distinguish their conduct from that of quacks.

Social and Professional Change

The industrial revolution, urbanization, and pauperization shaped new forms of medical care during the late eighteenth and the first half of the nineteenth century. The migration of working people to the industrial regions led to an expansion of hospital medicine. Towns created publicly funded posts for physicians to treat the registered poor (i.e., those who were officially entitled to financial support from the municipal poor-relief fund). Accordingly, doctors were now confronted with a much broader range of patients, especially from the lower classes. At the same time, medical education began to require the acquisition of practical skills in surgery and obstetrics. Surgery was integrated as an academic discipline, and eventually the occupation of barber-surgeons was abolished.

Doctors became involved in public health through campaigns of smallpox vaccination, which was made compulsory in several European states as early as the first third of the nineteenth century, for example, in Bavaria (1807), Sweden (1816), and Württemberg (1818). Other states (e.g., France and Prussia) tried to support their national vaccination programs with a combination of encouragement (bonus paid to parents per vaccinated child, cash prizes and medals for vaccinators), constraint (refusal of welfare benefits to parents of unvaccinated children), and education (La Berge).

In France a public-health movement coalesced in the 1820s, in which "hygienists" of various professional backgrounds (physicians, pharmacist-chemists, engineers, veterinarians, and administrators) made efforts to solve common health problems by undertaking scientific investigations into their causes. Pioneering studies in occupational and industrial hygiene were carried out by the leaders of this movement, the physicians Alexandre Parent-Duchâtelet and Louis-René Villermé. Differential mortality studies by Villermé and the statistician Louis-François Benoiston de Châtauneuf further demonstrated a strong correlation between standard of living, and health and longevity. Following the model of the Paris health council (founded in 1802), conseils de salubrité were soon formed in other French cities and departments to advise prefects and mayors in regulating public health. Some hygienists, especially Villermé, saw themselves as moral reformers who would enable workers through better material and environmental conditions to emulate the values of the middle class (La Berge).

As the connection between bad living conditions and disease became more and more obvious—particularly after the onset of cholera epidemics in Europe beginning in the 1830s, and through the experience of the typhus epidemic in parts of Silesia in 1848—liberal physicians such as Rudolf Virchow argued for the social character of medicine and recognition of the doctor as an "advocate for the poor" (Ackerknecht).

In this period of social and professional change, physicians' concern about medical competition and secure incomes deepened. The breakdown of the so-called patronage system, in which a doctor's services were remunerated by the patient with a voluntary lump sum at the end of the year, raised debates about new models of payment that could maintain the dignity and independence of the physician and defuse competition. The concept that all practitioners should become medical officials (employees of the state)—an idea originating from reform proposals of the French Revolution—was discussed in France and Germany, and was temporarily implemented in the German duchy of Nassau (Brand). An 1823 proposal to found societies of physicians that would collect and redistribute fees, suggested by the Bonn clinician Christian Friedrich Nasse in a monograph *Von der Stellung der Ärzte im Staate* (On the Position of Physicians in the State), was apparently not realized (Nasse). Instead, Russia, Prussia, Hanover, and Bavaria instituted a policy of limiting the number of licensed physicians during the first decades of the nineteenth century. Some medical ordinances, for instance, those of Baden (1807) and of the canton of Zurich (1821), made licensing as a physician contingent on a number of ethical obligations, such as helping patients at any time irrespective of their social status, being discreet, and continuing one's medical education (Anner; Brand).

Duties and Rights

Increasingly, doctors wrote about the duties entailed by their profession, often using the expression *deontology* (science of duty), a title that is still sometimes found in European literature about medical ethics. In 1831 the Spanish physician Félix Janer published a book *Elementos de moral médica,* which dealt with the "dignity and importance" of the medical profession and examined the doctor's relations to the patient, within the profession and to other healers, and to the state and law. Being strongly influenced by the *Lectures on the Duties and Qualifications of a Physician* (1772) of the Edinburgh professor of medicine John Gregory, Janer adopted the Scotsman's demand that medical men show temperance, sobriety, firmness of character, humanity, and candor. Interestingly, he also extended these moral requirements to surgeons. These developments in Spain occurred in the context of arising competition and disputes over competence between traditional university-trained physicians (*médicos puros*) and new *médicos colegiales,* who from 1827 on began to graduate from colleges for medicine and surgery. These institutions granted the title *médico-cirujano,* which gave access to hospital positions. Janer himself was involved in teaching these future "medico-surgeons," eventually becoming director of the Barcelona College. Not surprisingly therefore, he defended the unity of medicine and surgery and pleaded for harmonious relations between the two types of medical practitioners (Ortiz Gómez et al.).

Other important examples of literature on medical deontology from the first half of the nineteenth century are Christoph Wilhelm Hufeland's "*Die Verhältnisse des Arztes*" ("The Relationships of the Physician," the last chapter of his authoritative manual of medical practice, *Enchiridion medicum,* 1836; ten editions until 1857; English, 1842) and Maximilien Armand Simon's *Déontologie médicale* (1845; Spanish, 1852). Like Janer, both these authors dealt with the relationships and ethical duties of the doctor to colleagues, to patients, and to society. Simon added a part on the moral rights of physicians, including a right to political activity, especially in the reform of laws pertaining to public health. Here Simon differed from Hufeland, who wanted to keep physicians out of any involvement in politics, permitting them only to educate the public on rational behavior in matters of health and disease. Both Hufeland and Simon described altruism as the central moral principle of the medical profession. For Simon, Christian faith formed the undisputable basis of this altruism and of all specific duties of the physician.

Both physicians' renewed admonition to care equally for the rich and the poor reflects the larger social spectrum of patients, as compared to the eighteenth century. Simon welcomed the "now multiplied" number of hospitals and dispensaries for the sick poor, yet warned his colleagues, as did Hufeland, not to abuse this group of patients for harmful scientific experiments. On the question of euthanasia, both physicians stressed that the sufferings of the dying should be alleviated, if necessary by a liberal use of opium, but that any life-shortening measures were strictly forbidden, even if the patient demanded them. Hufeland feared dire consequences for society if the physician once transgressed the line by judging the necessity of a human being's existence; Simon advanced the religious argument that man is not the master of his life. These statements were in keeping with those of the Göttingen professor of medicine Carl Friedrich Heinrich Marx, who had discussed the topic in detail in his inaugural lecture De euthanasia medica (1826). They expressed a general point of view within the medical profession that remained undisputed until the end of the nineteenth century.

Contemporary problems involving competition among doctors are reflected in Hufeland's strong plea for cooperative conduct—"Disparaging a colleague means disparaging the art and oneself!" (p. 906)—and in his discussion of proper behavior during joint consultations, a topic treated in 1798 by the Hanoverian court physician Johann Stieglitz in a monograph Über das Zusammenseyn der Ärzte am Krankenbett (On the Meeting of Doctors at the Bedside). In cases of malpractice, however, Hufeland exhorted his profession to set greater store by the "saving" of the patient than by consideration for the colleague. Difficulties with the transition of medical practice from a gentlemanly calling to a modern, economically oriented profession are evident in Simon's energetic defense against the reproach that doctors were guided by commercial interests.

Codification and Control

For physicians in the states of the North German Confederation, and soon for those of the whole German Empire, the trade ordinance of 1869 became an important step in that transition. It defined medical practice as a trade that anyone could exercise (Kurierfreiheit), yet granted legal protection of the title Arzt (physician). It abolished the doctor's duty to help any patient in case of "urgent danger," which had been included in the Prussian penal code in 1851 and was regarded by many physicians as a coercion to provide treatment. The trade ordinance intensified the resolve of academic, state-certified physicians to distinguish themselves from lay healers by establishing professional societies.

In 1873, two years after the foundation of the German Empire, an association of German societies of physicians (Deutscher Ärztevereinsbund) was formed. Its main activities consisted of representing professional and economic interests. Many societies of physicians had codes of appropriate conduct, some of which were modeled directly on the code of ethics of the American Medical Association (AMA) of 1847, and thus basically on Thomas Percival's Medical Ethics of 1803. The disciplinary powers of those societies were limited to their own members, however.

In contrast to this, the so-called chambers of physicians (Ärztekammern), founded in German states beginning in the mid-1860s, formed state-controlled medical courts of honor, which were given authority to punish professional misconduct by all physicians in the respective district (except army doctors and medical officials, who were under the direct control of the state). Once created, the medical courts of honor seem to have been very active. It has been estimated that they engaged in more than 3,000 proceedings between 1904 and 1909 in Prussia, which at this time had about 15,000 physicians who were not employed by the state or the army. Most proceedings dealt with charges of misconduct in medical competition, such as unlawful advertising, underbidding other doctors, disparaging colleagues in the presence of laypeople, and unauthorized use of specialist titles (Huerkamp).

This German path toward well-organized intraprofessional self-control, authorized by the state, contrasted with developments in France. Here, the formation of medical professional organizations was hindered by postrevolutionary legislation that followed the principle of liberal individualism. The Le Chapelier law of 1791 prohibited members of the same occupation from forming organizations that would promote their common interests, and in 1810 associations of more than twenty people formed without approval of the government were forbidden. Physicians were subject to legal responsibility for malpractice: Harm to a patient was a tort, as defined by the civil code of 1803, and was also punishable as a criminal offense under some articles of the penal code of 1810 (Ramsey).

The "medical marketplace" of early-nineteenth-century France, however, led to proposals for additional disciplinary provisions. Legislation in 1803 had established the first uniform licensing system for medical practitioners in the whole of France, distinguishing "doctors of medicine" and "doctors of surgery," *officiers de santé* (health officers), and certified midwives. While the doctors were required to have studied at least four years at a medical school, health officers could qualify after three years' study but also by serving six years under a doctor or five years in a hospital. Unlike doctors, the *officiers*, destined to provide constant medical care for the rural population, were permitted to work only within the *département* that had given them license to practice. On the one hand, these legal requirements drew a sharp line between regular, licensed practitioners and irregular healers, such as itinerant quacks, sedentary empirics (vendors of special remedies), and folk healers, who could now be prosecuted for illegal medical practice. On the other hand, the institution of health officers, who represented a class of less-well-trained physicians, created fears of a lapse in standards and professional decline among doctors. Moreover, economic need caused many regular practitioners to collaborate with unqualified empirics, to promote their own proprietary medicines, or to offer special cures. In these circumstances, medical reform commissions from 1812 onward repeatedly suggested the establishment of "chambers of discipline" or "medical councils," whose jurisdiction would include both illegal practice and professional misconduct. None of these proposals was put into action, however, partly because they were linked to the controversial question of reforming the institution of health officers, and partly because many doctors did not wish any further intervention by the state. In 1892 legislation abolished the title of *officier de santé*, as well as that of "doctor of surgery" (Ramsey).

Beginning in the 1850s, the number of physicians relative to the population grew steadily in France, leading to still fiercer competition and precarious incomes. In addition, legislation between 1874 and 1905 imposed new duties on French doctors, such as treating poor patients in return for a moderate state remuneration, testifying as experts in courts, and surveying the standards of public health (e.g., quality of water supply, housing conditions). In the 1880s, in response to these developments, doctors began to form medical unions (*syndicats*) to promote their professional interests. Initially illegal but tolerated, the *syndicats* were legally recognized in 1892. The ultimate aim of their most radical members was to create an obligatory *Ordre des Médecins*, analogous to the *Ordre des Avocats* for lawyers (founded in 1810). Such an order did not emerge; Both the government and a majority within the medical profession opposed it. But in an attempt to set ethical standards for doctors, to regulate intraprofessional relationships, and to form a unified front toward the public, the medical syndicates adopted deontological statutes that were binding on their membership.

These syndical deontologies were modeled upon the male honor codes of bourgeois social and recreational societies (*cercles* or *sociétés à plaisance*), which flourished in mid-nineteenth-century France (Nye, 1993b). Like these societies, the syndicates regarded the personal honorability (*honnêteté*) of their members as essential and had a policy of solving internal conflicts *intra muros* (i.e., without recourse to the courts). Members were obliged to report cases of malpractice to the *syndicat*, which had the right to withdraw membership. In this context, the old idea of "chambers of discipline" was taken up again, for example, by the medical syndicate of the *arrondissement* of Avesnes, which prescribed the formation of such a "tribunal of honor" in its statutes of 1910 (Nye, 1993a). Generally, however, the disciplinary powers of French professional organizations remained relatively weak throughout the nineteenth century, compared to those of their counterparts in Germany, Britain, and the United States (Ramsey).

In 1900 the Paris medical syndicate organized an international congress on "professional medicine and medical deontology," at which key speakers proposed that the problems created by overcrowding and competition should be solved through "confraternity" and "the force of moral law." Many French treatises on medical deontology, published around the time of the congress, reflected the same demands. They furthermore insisted on medical confidentiality to protect not only the privacy of the patient but also the reputation of the profession. Accordingly, the medical syndicates in the 1890s resisted requirements of the public-health legislation to divulge the names of patients with contagious diseases, whereas doctors in the first half of the nineteenth century had done so freely during smallpox and cholera epidemics (Nye, 1993a).

Controversial Issues

In the second half of the nineteenth century, ethical issues arising from developments in preventive medicine, medical science, and hospital medicine became topics of intraprofessional as well as public debate in several European countries. Following the introduction of compulsory smallpox vaccination in the German Empire in 1874, the many newly established antivaccination societies agitated intensely until World War I. Refusal to have one's children vaccinated was based mainly on reasons of conscience resulting from individual weighing of benefits and risks. In part, the reasons also reflected a protest against the restriction of personal freedom in matters of health (Maehle, 1991). This aspect had surfaced as a problem already around 1800, when Johann Peter Frank, then director general of public health of Lombardy (Cisalpine Republic), proposed universal state-controlled health care in his *System einer vollständigen medicinischen Polizey* (Haun). Antivaccinationism was basically a medical lay movement. Societies against vaccination were guided by academics and few physicians, who were influenced by ideas of natural healing (through water cures, diet, exercise, sun, and fresh air) and social hygiene. The same was true for the organized antivivisection movement (Maehle, 1993), which emerged as a result of the increasing scientific use of animals associated with the rise of experimental physiology (Claude Bernard, Carl Ludwig), pathology (Virchow), and bacteriology (Louis Pasteur, Robert Koch). Antivivisectionist activities, imported from Britain in the 1860s, were particularly strong in Tuscany, Germany, Switzerland, and Sweden (Rupke). A general antiscientific and antimaterialistic attitude was often behind the overt argument that animal experiments were useless cruelties (Maehle, 1993).

The growing importance of hospital medicine, reflected in the large clinics of Vienna and Paris in the first half of the nineteenth century, combined with the progress in medical science, brought the ethical problems of human experimentation into the foreground. In 1880 the courts of Bergen, Norway, sentenced Gerhard Armauer Hansen, the discoverer of the leprosy bacillus, for inoculating a female hospital patient suffering from a particular type of leprosy with leprous material from another patient (with a different type of the disease) without prior information or consent (Vogelsang). Albert Neisser, professor of dermatology in Breslau, was fined in 1900; hoping to induce immunity against syphilis, he had injected syphilitic blood serum into eight uninformed female hospital patients (three children and five prostitutes) in 1892. These and other cases stimulated intensive public debate, which—like the vivisection controversy—often had antiscientific and anti-Semitic undercurrents. Prevented from careers in the German civil service, Jews were strongly represented in the so-called free professions, such as medicine or law. In medical university careers, doctors of Jewish origin tended to concentrate in the experimental disciplines (physiology, pharmacology, immunology) and the new specialty of dermatology and venereology, because they could hardly find entry to the prestigious "classic" professorships in internal medicine and surgery. Anti-Semites advanced propaganda arguments that animal

and human experimentation was an expression of "Jewish materialism" (Elkeles).

A concrete consequence of the debate on human experiments was a decree by the Prussian Ministry of Education in 1900 that required informed consent of the research subjects and prohibited scientific experimentation on minors and other persons who were not fully competent (Grodin).

New ethical challenges also emerged with the passage in the German Empire of the Health (1883), Accident (1884), and Retirement and Disability (1889) Insurance Acts; the scheme was soon copied by Austria (1888), Hungary (1891), Luxembourg (1901), and Switzerland (1911). The task of certifying sickness and disability placed physicians between the often conflicting interests of patients and insurance companies. Medical insurance tended to strengthen the patient's position; doctors began to complain that patients behaved as if they were their employers (Brand). On the other hand, insurance companies owned by factories could serve as a means for the social control of working-class patients (Frevert). For physicians the insurance scheme created hopes of economic improvement. In the long run, however, it heightened medical competition by drawing an increasing number of individuals into the profession.

Teaching Medical Ethics

Against this background, the proposal to include medical ethics in the curriculum for medical students was debated in Germany during the 1890s. At an 1898 conference on internal medicine at Wiesbaden, those who argued that an ethical attitude must be inculcated by the family, not at the university, and that ethics could not be subdivided according to the different professions, won the day. Yet the debate generated a spate of books that advocated the teaching of medical ethics. The Berlin medical historian Julius Pagel published a *Medicinische Deontologie* for prospective medical practitioners in 1897 (Pagel), the Wiesbaden physician Oswald Ziemssen, cousin of the renowned clinician Hugo von Ziemssen, a monograph *Die Ethik des Arztes als medicinischer Lehrgegenstand* (The doctor's ethics as a medical teaching subject) in 1899. Pagel gave a great deal of space to cooperative behavior among medical colleagues, demanded solidarity in cases of professional error, and advised doctors to act with self-confidence when seeing patients. Furthermore, the doctor should take care not to speak familiarly with members of the lower classes. Ziemssen built his book on codes of German societies of physicians and above all on Jukes de Styrap's *A Code of Medical Ethics* of 1878 (de Styrap). To some extent, he also drew on German philosophical traditions, arguing that the ethics of the physician were based on a combination of Immanuel Kant's categorical imperative, Arthur Schopenhauer's voice of feeling, and Johann Friedrich Herbart's practical judgment.

Contemporary philosophers, such as Friedrich Paulsen and Max Dessoir, also acknowledged the importance of teaching medical ethics with books and lectures. Paulsen pointed to the growing importance of medicine for modern society (von Engelhardt, 1989). Dessoir wanted the profession to compensate for a loss of ethical values in depersonalized doctor–patient relationships that resulted from specialization and the influence of medical science. Accordingly, he suggested a teaching program that would cover not only the "profession and character of the physician" and his "relationship to colleague and to the public" but also "vivisection and human experimentation" and "ethical principles in general" (p. 382).

Dessoir also served as an adviser to the Berlin neurologist Albert Moll, who provided the most significant contribution of this period with his 650-page *Ärztliche Ethik*. Moll argued that concern for medical ethics had concentrated on the physician's duties to colleagues and the profession (i.e., on medical etiquette), rather than on duties to the patient. He therefore put particular emphasis on ethical problems of medical practice, such as the doctor's refusing and breaking off treatment, euthanasia, deceiving the patient, advising extramarital sexual intercourse (e.g., in neurasthenia due to sexual abstinence, or in impotence), cosmetic surgery, and abortion. Moll devoted much attention to the issue of human experimentation, quoting numerous examples from the scientific literature. He oriented medical ethics to the well-being of the individual patient, not to the general welfare. Explicitly renouncing any basis in theological or philosophical systems of morality, he defined the doctor–patient relationship in legal terms, as a contract. This implied the physician's duty to fulfill the contract and the patient's obligation to respond by paying the fee. With this positivist approach, Moll reflected a general intellectual tendency of his time. In its comprehensiveness, his book provides a good overview of ethical issues in late-nineteenth-century European medicine.

Summary

In the nineteenth century there was a significant shift from reliance on largely implicit and nonsystematic notions concerning the gentleman doctor to written codes of professional etiquette and to a growing body of literature and theoretical perspectives concerning specific issues in medical ethics. In this century many of the concerns and methods now employed in medical ethics were first articulated.

ANDREAS-HOLGER MAEHLE (1995)

BIBLIOGRAPHY

Ackerknecht, Erwin Heinz. 1953. *Rudolf Virchow: Doctor, Statesman, Anthropologist.* Madison: University of Wisconsin Press.

Anner, Ernst. 1979. *Gelöbnisse der Medizinalpersonen im Kanton Zürich seit 1798.* Zurich: Juris.

Brand, Ulrich. 1977. *Ärztliche Ethik im 19. Jahrhundert: Der Wandel ethischer Inhalte im medizinischen Schrifttum—ein Beitrag zum Verständnis der Arzt-Patient-Beziehung.* Freiburg im Breisgau: H. F. Schulz Verlag.

Dessoir, Max. 1894. "Der Beruf des Arztes." *Westermanns Illustrierte Deutsche Monatshefte* 77: 375–382.

De Styrap, Jukes. 1878. *A Code of Medical Ethics.* London: Churchill.

Elkeles, Barbara. 1991. "Der moralische Diskurs über das medizinische Menschenexperiment zwischen 1835 und dem Ersten Weltkrieg." Hannover: Habilitationsschrift Medizinische Hochschule Hannover.

Frevert, Ute. 1984. *Krankheit als politisches Problem, 1770–1880: Soziale Unterschichten in Preußen zwischen medizinischer Polizei und staatlicher Sozialversicherung.* Göttingen: Vandenhoeck & Ruprecht.

Geyer-Kordesch, Johanna. 1993a. "Infanticide and Medico-legal Ethics in Eighteenth Century Prussia." In *Doctors and Ethics: The Earlier Historical Setting of Professional Ethics,* pp. 181–202, ed. Andrew Wear, Johanna Geyer-Kordesch, and Roger French. Amsterdam: Rodopi.

Geyer-Kordesch, Johanna. 1993b. "Natural Law and Medical Ethics in the Eighteenth Century." In *The Codification of Medical Morality: Historical and Philosophical Studies of the Formalization of Western Medical Morality in the Eighteenth and Nineteenth Centuries,* 1: 123–139, ed. Robert Baker, Dorothy Porter, and Roy Porter. Dordrecht, Netherlands: Kluwer.

Gregory, John. 1772. *Lectures on the Duties and Qualifications of a Physician.* corrected and enl. edition. London: W. Strahan.

Grodin, Michael A. 1992. "Historical Origins of the Nuremberg Code." In *The Nazi Doctors and the Nuremberg Code,* pp. 121–144, ed. George J. Annas and Michael A. Grodin. New York: Oxford University Press.

Haun, Irene. 1993. "Ethische Gesichtspunkte der Präventivmedizin in Johann Peter Franks (1745–1821) 'System einer vollständigen medicinischen Polizey.'" Göttingen: M.D. thesis, Georg-August-Universität.

Helm, Jürgen. 1992. "Tradition und Wandel der ärztlichen Selbstverpflichtung: Der Göttinger Promotionseid 1737–1889." Göttingen: M.D. thesis, Georg-August-Universität.

Huerkamp, Claudia. 1985. *Der Aufstieg der Ärzte im 19. Jahrhundert: Vom gelehrten Stand zum professionellen Experten: Das Beispiel Preussens.* Göttingen: Vandenhoeck & Ruprecht.

Hufeland, Christoph Wilhelm. 1836. *Enchiridion medicum, oder Anleitung zur medizinischen Praxis: Vermächtnis einer fünfzigjährigen Erfahrung,* 2nd enl. edition. Berlin: Jonas Verlagsbuchhandlung.

Janer, Félix. 1831. *Elementos de moral médica.* Barcelona: Verdaguer.

La Berge, Ann Elizabeth Fowler. 1992. *Mission and Method: The Early Nineteenth-Century French Public Health Movement.* Cambridge, Eng.: Cambridge University Press.

Maehle, Andreas-Holger. 1991. "Präventivmedizin als wissenschaftliches und gesellschaftliches Problem: Der Streit über das Reichsimpfgesetz von 1874." In *Medizin, Gesellschaft und Geschichte,* 9: 127–148, ed. Robert Jütte. Stuttgart: Franz Steiner Verlag.

Maehle, Andreas-Holger. 1993. "The Ethical Discourse on Animal Experimentation, 1650–1900." In *Doctors and Ethics: The Earlier Historical Setting of Professional Ethics,* ed. Andrew Wear, Johanna Geyer-Kordesch, and Roger French. Amsterdam: Rodopi.

Moll, Albert. 1902. *Ärztliche Ethik: Die Pflichten des Arztes in allen Beziehungen seiner Thätigkeit.* Stuttgart: F. Enke.

Nasse, Christian Friedrich. 1823. *Von der Stellung der Ärzte im Staate.* Leipzig: Cnobloch.

Nye, Robert A. 1993a. "Honor Codes and Medical Ethics in Modern France." Norman: Department of History, University of Oklahoma.

Nye, Robert A. 1993b. *Masculinity and Male Codes of Honor in Modern France.* New York: Oxford University Press.

Ortiz Gómez, Teresa; Valenzuela, José; and Rodríguez Ocaña, Esteban. 1991. "Ética y profesion en la medicina española del siglo XIX: Los 'Elementos de moral médica' (1831) de Félix Janer (1781–1865)." In *Actas del IX Congreso Nacional de Historia de la Medicina,* 1: 291–302, ed. Francesc Bujosa i Homar et al. Zaragoza: Secretariado de Publicaciones Prensas Universitarias de Zaragoza.

Pagel, Julius. 1897. *Medizinische Deontologie: Ein Kleiner Katechismus für angehende Praktiker.* Berlin: O. Coblentz.

Percival, Thomas. 1803. *Medical Ethics: A Code of Institutes and Precepts, Adapted to the Professional Conduct of Physicians and Surgeons.* Manchester: S. Russell.

Ramsey, Matthew. 1988. *Professional and Popular Medicine in France, 1770–1830: The Social World of Medical Practice.* Cambridge, Eng.: Cambridge University Press.

Rupke, Nicolaas A., ed. 1990. *Vivisection in Historical Perspective.* Rev. edition. London: Routledge.

Simon, Maximilien Isidore Armand. 1845. *Déontologie médicale; ou, des devoirs et des droits des médecins dans l'état actuel de la civilisation.* Paris: J. B. Bailliere.

Vogelsang, T. M. 1963. "A Serious Sentence Passed Against the Discoverer of the Leprosy Bacillus (Gerhard Armauer Hansen), in 1880." *Medical History* 7: 182–186.

Von Engelhardt, Dietrich. 1985. "Virtue and Medicine During the Enlightenment in Germany." In *Virtue and Medicine: Explorations in the Character of Medicine,* pp. 63–79, ed. Earl E. Shelp. Dordrecht, Netherlands: D. Reidel.

Von Engelhardt, Dietrich. 1989. "Entwicklung der ärztlichen Ethik im 19. Jahrhundert—medizinische Motivation und gesellschaftliche Legitimation." In *Medizinische Deutungsmacht im sozialen Wandel des 19. und 20. Jahrhunderts,* pp. 75–88, ed. Alfons Labisch and Reinhard Spree. Bonn: Psychiatrie-Verlag.

III. NINETEENTH CENTURY. B. GREAT BRITAIN

Questions of medical ethics acquired heightened significance in nineteenth-century Great Britain. The reform of the medical profession and the growing prominence of medicine within public policy brought ethical and medicolegal issues into sharper focus. For the first time, medical ethics assumed codified form.

The period from the early sixteenth century to the close of the eighteenth saw the founding of medical colleges and societies in Britain, among them the Royal College of Physicians. But such bodies played only a minor part in imposing ethical codes upon the profession as a whole—or even suggesting them. The Royal College of Physicians and the Royal College of Surgeons possessed jurisdiction over one city, London. There was no centralized medical regulation over most of the nation. With few exceptions, it was only in the nineteenth century that medical ethics were written down, the watershed being the publication in 1803 of Thomas Percival's *Medical Ethics; or, A Code of Institutes and Precepts Adapted to the Professional Conduct of Physicians and Surgeons.* Two circumstances provided impetus for codification, one intellectual, the other socioeconomic. Intellectually, the moral philosophy of the Scottish Enlightenment and the reawakening of religious conscience associated with Evangelicalism concentrated attention on man's (concern was almost wholly with males) duties to society. John Gregory, professor of medicine at Edinburgh, had published his *Observations on the Duties of a Physician* in 1770, and Rev. Thomas Gisborne, a friend of Percival, had included a section on obligations attending the calling of a physician in his *An Enquiry into the Duties of Men in the Higher and Middle Classes of Society in Great Britain, Resulting from their Respective Stations, Professions and Employments* (1794). Percival certainly drew on both in shaping his *Medical Ethics,* though it would be a mistake to assume that Percival was significantly concerned with academic philosophy. His handbook was first and foremost practical. It contained no discussion of any philosopher by name and did not refer to particular formal philosophical schools.

At the same time, the tremendous social transformations precipitated by the industrial revolution were posing exacting problems for medical practitioners. Newly emergent urban communities had severe medical needs but no deep-rooted traditions of professional service. In Britain's laissez-faire, free-market economy, doctors were tempted to adopt entrepreneurial attitudes, operating according to the law of "let the buyer beware." Moreover, new medical institutions were springing up, above all charity hospitals and dispensaries for the poor. Codes of practice governing the duties of doctors attached to these distinctive establishments needed to be formulated.

Thomas Percival (born in 1740) had studied medicine at Edinburgh. He became a senior and well-respected Manchester practitioner, and a leading light in the town's Literary and Philosophical Society. When a virulent intraprofessional feud flared up at the Manchester Infirmary in 1792—a sordid fracas concerning nepotistic appointments—he had been called in as a kind of peacemaker. His *Medical Ethics* arose from his musing on that unseemly rumpus. It was thus a work that spoke directly to the needs of its times. Percival set out some precepts, of a somewhat platitudinous nature, about the general duties and responsibilities of the physician to his patients, to society, and to his calling. Above all, he addressed himself in a direct manner to the tangible difficulties facing doctors in a commercial society.

High on Percival's list of priorities was the desire to secure harmony among practitioners and between the different grades of the profession. He addressed such questions as seniority and precedence, spelling out in detail the protocols of joint consultations. Though little interested in formal professional bodies, he was adamant that "medical men" should not compete against each other; instead they should cultivate, and be seen to cultivate, a comradely esprit de corps. Professional rivalries, naked jealousies, and controversies in public conducted through the medium of pamphlets would poison intraprofessional relations and ultimately work to the disadvantage of patients. Charging lower than normal fees, for instance, would deny a living to poorer brethren, and discourage the young from investing in a thorough medical education and training. A liberal profession could not be supported, Percival insisted, except as a "lucrative one."

Sentiments such as these give support to those, like Chauncey Leake and Ivan Waddington, who argue that Percival's *Medical Ethics* was misnamed, being in truth a work of "medical etiquette," primarily designed to bolster the collective status, dignity, and monopolistic power of the profession vis-à-vis the public. Percival certainly aimed to regulate "the official conduct and mutual intercourse of the faculty"; but it should not be forgotten that he added that this was to be accomplished "by precise and acknowledged principles of urbanity and rectitude"—that is, the unwritten but generally acknowledged code of gentlemanly behavior. In other words, he was concerned not with self-serving expediency but with humanitarianism, prudence, and honorable standards of virtuous conduct as understood by a gentleman.

Some American philosophers of medical ethics are inclined to see Percival as having written a work with strong foundations in academic ethical philosophies. It has, for example, been suggested that Percival and his successors may have drawn upon utilitarianism. There is little warrant for this reading in Percival himself. The great bulk of his text was concerned with resolving practical problems among medical men.

Percival upheld the ideal of the professional pyramid. Where wealth and density of population permitted a professional division of labor, the traditional hierarchical separation between physicians, surgeons, and apothecaries was to be maintained because it stimulated specialist skills. Yet physicians were not to lord it over the lesser "gentlemen of the faculty": in small communities, the humble apothecary was often the best expert on the circumstances of patients, and so his advice should be heeded.

Percival thus required courtesy among practitioners. A compassionate man, he insisted that the fears and feelings of the sick should be respected. Ever the realist, he acquiesced in the authority deriving from social status that the gentry were accustomed to wield. Wealthy patients would exercise the right to a second or third opinion: It was up to the doctors involved to manage such delicate circumstances with tact, preventing the dangers of "divide and rule." Likewise, though nostrums were an abomination, Percival judged that the astute physician would sometimes comply when a patient insisted on a worthless, but safe, favorite proprietary remedy.

With affluent patients, the one who paid the piper would evidently call the tune. But different rules must apply, Percival observed, when practitioners gave their services without charge. Charity patients in infirmaries could not expect to pick and choose among the physicians or to negotiate over treatments. Disobedient hospital patients must face dismissal. Likewise, it was permissible to experiment with new remedies or surgical procedures upon charity patients, so long as such innovations were attempted with due caution and humanity.

Prizing the close clinical relationship between practitioner and patient, Percival believed this depended primarily upon the character of the physician. The ideal practitioner was an academically educated, liberal gentleman who would combine "tenderness with steadiness," and "condescension with authority," displaying proper composure, dignity, tact, and courtesy. He must govern himself: be temperate, avoid intoxication, and take care to retire from practice before age eroded his powers and judgment. He must be civil to colleagues, benevolent toward patients. It was a paternalist ideal, entailing a gentlemanly noblesse oblige.

Percival's book became immensely influential in the United States, serving as the basis for the American Medical Association's (AMA) code of 1847. Though reprinted in 1849, it achieved less celebrity in Britain. This was not because it was superseded by any other more illustrious tome or rival ethical scheme. For subsequent works, like William Ogilvie Porter's *Medical Science and Ethicks: An Introductory Lecture* (1837) and Abraham Banks's *Medical Etiquette* (1839), largely echoed Percival's platitudes; and as late as 1878, Jukes de Styrap was still lifting phrases out of Percival in *A Code of Medical Ethics*. Rather, in contrast to that in the United States, the medical profession in nineteenth-century Britain seems to have felt little need for explicit ethical codifications.

The contrast is readily explained. In early-nineteenth-century America, no standard, universal, and accredited licensing procedures unambiguously demarcated orthodox practitioners from quacks and irregulars. Hence, when regulars banded together into state medical societies to enhance their prestige, the adoption of a code of ethics was of immense significance as a conspicuous shibboleth. In Britain, by contrast, licensing was already well entrenched; since 1815, the Apothecaries Act had stipulated nationwide minimum qualifications for practice as an apothecary or general practitioner. Thus, in Britain, regular doctors did not need written codes of ethics to prove their standing in relation to irregulars. In Britain regulars were already adequately defined in contrast with quacks.

Nor did regulars need codes of medical ethics to affirm their personal bona fides. British practitioners were confident that they were, first and foremost, *gentlemen*. Gentility came from birth and breeding, education, wealth, contacts, manners, mien, and so forth—or at least from the capacity to create a show of such attributes. (Needless to say, most medical practitioners were not, in the literal sense, the sons of gentlemen; rather, they aspired to genteel status.) Gentlemanly behavior depended heavily upon notions of personal honor rather than upon formal ethical or religious principles. A written ethical code might have seemed to impugn a gentleman's honor, rather as the British prided themselves politically upon not having a formal written constitution. It is thus no surprise that the British medical profession was indifferent to collections of medical ethics. Neither the Royal College of Physicians nor the Royal College of Surgeons drew up an ethical code for its members.

From professors of forensic medicine, students learned a little about the rules governing evidence to be given in court. The Manchester Medical Ethical Association was formed in 1847, aiming to bind its members to a slate of regulations outlawing the marketing of nostrums and the giving of testimonials for patent medicines. And the British Medical Association—the newly formed society of general practitioners and family doctors—set up its own medical ethics committee in 1853. Over the next fifteen years, however, it signally failed actually to draw up a corpus of medical ethics. Despite such token activities, no comprehensive manifesto of ethical principles was codified in Britain that was binding upon the profession as a whole.

Yet this is not to say that the profession was indifferent to ethics. As was vehemently argued in Thomas Beddoes's *A Letter to the Right Honourable Sir Joseph Banks ... on the Causes and Removal of the Prevailing Discontents, Imperfections, and Abuses, in Medicine* (1808) and in countless subsequent works, it was at bottom ethical commitments that distinguished honorable practice from quackery (although, Beddoes implied, all too often eminent regulars disgraced their vocation by unprincipled practices). And, of course, ethical dilemmas often arose that urgently needed resolution. A formal mechanism for upholding ethical standards was constituted in 1858 as a consequence of the establishment of the Medical Register, a public roll of all duly licensed practitioners. The body appointed to act as guardian of the register was the General Council of Medical Education and Registration of the United Kingdom, commonly known as the General Medical Council (GMC). The GMC was to admit properly qualified practitioners to the register, and to delete those whose conduct was professionally inadmissible—for example, those who had been convicted of a crime or who had been judged guilty of infamous professional conduct (such as adultery with a patient or vilification of colleagues). Sitting in camera, the GMC thus served as a sort of moral inquisition for the profession.

But what constituted "unprofessional conduct"? For most of the Victorian age, practitioners were held to less taxing standards than have generally been enforced in twentieth-century Britain. Considerable leeway was still permitted to engage in commercial and entrepreneurial activities. It was not unknown for eminent Victorian physicians to puff proprietary preparations with impunity, or to lend their names to extravagant publicity for spas, clinics, and balneological establishments. Such respectable medical organs as the *British Medical Journal* and *Lancet* published advertisements every week for nostrums, health foods, and medical institutions of doubtful probity (for example, so-called nursing homes that probably served as abortion clinics).

Nevertheless, the profession grew increasingly mindful of the fact that, in an age priding itself upon public probity, respectability, and heightened moral sensibilities, doctors had to be seen as above scandal. Trying situations easily occurred. For example, from the 1840s, thanks in part to the development of anesthetics, the scope for surgical intervention rapidly grew. Enterprising gynecologists and surgeons newly claimed to be able to treat a wide range of women's ailments, physical and psychosexual, through hysterectomy, ovariotomy, and similar operations upon the reproductive system. In the first flush of enthusiasm, some practitioners leapt in before the ethical implications had been adequately debated and resolved: Was proper informed consent being obtained for such operations? In the case of the removal of a womb, was it desirable to obtain the consent of the husband as well as of the patient? In the absence of diseased organs, was it permissible to perform operations for purely preventive or psychological reasons? Anxiety that the good name of the profession was being jeopardized by overenthusiastic intervention led to the expulsion, in the 1860s, of Isaac Baker Brown, a prominent advocate of clitoridectomy and similar surgery, from the Obstetrical Society (though he was disciplined not for the operations he performed but for the self-seeking manner in which he publicized them). Greater caution was subsequently exercised.

Whenever possible, the medical profession aimed to police its operations discreetly, retaining in its own hands the right to set moral standards. Thus, in ethically sensitive areas such as abortion, it was contended that termination of pregnancy was essentially a matter of clinical judgment in the individual case; in the last resort, only the personal physician was in a position to decide. Likewise, when legislation was proposed to control the sale of dangerous drugs, the profession was successful in safeguarding the right to supply narcotics on prescription.

In other medical spheres, however, ethical controversies arose that could not be kept within the circuit of professional discretion. This was because the Victorian age witnessed an unprecedented expansion of doctors' involvement in implementing state policy. For example, by 1900 new lunacy laws resulted in the compulsory confinement of nearly 100,000 mental patients. All had to be certified by due medical authorization. This created ethical predicaments for doctors that could not be resolved within Percival's notion of a tacit contract between physician and patient. Certain doctors, like the distinguished early Victorian psychiatrist John Conolly, warned of what a later generation was to call "psychiatric abuse": Some patients, Conolly feared, were being stripped of their rights and liberty not because they were sick but because they were nuisances or were merely eccentric.

It was in public health that the greatest ethical dilemmas arose. Before 1800, Great Britain had lacked the apparatus of medical police controls already in place on the Continent. This changed. The success of Jenner's variolation techniques (giving a dose of cowpox to create immunity against smallpox) led Parliament to make smallpox vaccination compulsory in 1853. Poor Law doctors—doctors appointed under the New Poor Law (1834) to tend to the parish poor, particularly those confined to workhouses— were to act as state agents in enforcing the legislation. Resistance and protests grew common during the next half-century, condemning compulsory vaccination as an iniquitous annulment of natural liberties and condemning doctors for serving as the lackeys of a coercive state.

A similar crisis arose in 1864 with the Contagious Diseases Acts. These sanctioned, under certain circumstances, medical inspection for signs of venereal disease of women detained by the police under suspicion of prostitution. Once again, opponents accused medical men of prostituting their art in the service of a corrupt state, and feminists argued that the acts were designed to provide disease-free vice for men. Around the same time, antivivisection agitators began accusing medical experimenters and scientists of inflicting cruelty upon dumb and defenseless experimental animals. The widening circle of medicine began to raise medical-ethical issues never dreamed of in the innocent days of Percival's *Medical Ethics*. Just before World War I these dilemmas came to a head when convicted suffragettes (militant feminists) went on a hunger strike, and prison doctors were instructed to administer forced feeding. Did their duty lie to society or to the prisoner (hardly a patient in the normal sense of the term, one who voluntarily seeks medical aid)?

In a characteristically British manner, professional bodies judged that the decision must be left to the doctor's scruples. The ingrained habits of individuality, specific to English liberal politics, and the cult of the gentleman that formed the unspoken code of male elites in all contemporary European societies meant that in professional eyes and, to a large degree, equally in the public mind the ethical dilemmas raised by medicine were best handled not by the law courts, jurists, academic philosophers, or Parliament but by the integrity of private practitioners following clinical judgment and their own consciences. These precepts, for better or worse, left a potent legacy to twentieth-century Britain. They certainly offered great latitude to the medical profession while placing heavy burdens upon its shoulders. Radical critics of the professions and their ideologies have contended, surely correctly, that the formulation of medical ethics enhanced the status and exalted the independence of the nineteenth-century doctors. How far this process helped to protect the public is more difficult to judge.

ROY PORTER (1995)

BIBLIOGRAPHY

Bartrip, Peter. 1994. "Secret Remedies, Medical Ethics and the Finances of the British Medical Journal." In vol. 2 of *The Codification of Medical Morality: Historical and Philosophical Studies of the Formalization of Medical Morality in the Eighteenth and Nineteenth Centuries,* ed. Robert Baker, Dorothy Porter, and Roy Porter. Dordrecht, Netherlands: Kluwer.

Beddoes, Thomas. 1808. *A Letter to the Right Honourable Sir Joseph Banks … on the Causes and Removal of the Prevailing Discontents, Imperfections, and Abuses in Medicine.* London: Richard Phillips.

Burns, Chester. 1974. "Reciprocity in the Development of Anglo-American Medical Ethics, 1765–1865." In vol. 1 of the *Proceedings of the XXIII International Congress of the History of Medicine,* pp. 813–819. London: Wellcome Institute for the History of Medicine.

Crawford, Catherine. 1987. "The Emergence of Forensic Medicine: Medical Evidence in Common Law Courts, 1730–1830." D. Phil. diss., Oxford University.

Crowther, M. Ann. 1994. "Forensic Medicine and Medical Ethics in Nineteenth-Century Britain." In vol. 2 of *The Codification of Medical Morality: Historical and Philosophical Studies of the Formalization of Medical Morality in the Eighteenth and Nineteenth Centuries,* ed. Robert Baker, Dorothy Porter, and Roy Porter. Dordrecht, Netherlands: Kluwer.

Gay, Peter. 1984. *Education of the Senses.* Vol. 1 of *The Bourgeois Experience, Victoria to Freud.* New York: Oxford University Press.

Gay, Peter. 1986. *The Tender Passion.* Vol. 2 of *The Bourgeois Experience, Victoria to Freud.* New York: Oxford University Press.

Leake, Chauncey D. 1971. "Percival's Medical Ethics: Promise and Problems." *California Medicine* 114(4): 68–70.

Moscucci, Ornella. 1990. *The Science of Woman: Gynaecology and Gender in England, 1800–1929.* Cambridge, Eng.: Cambridge University Press.

Pellegrino, Edmund. 1986. "Percival's Medical Ethics: The Moral Philosophy of an 18th-Century English Gentleman." *Archives of Internal Medicine* 146(114): 2265–2269.

Percival, Thomas. 1803. *Medical Ethics; or, A Code of Institutes and Precepts Adapted to the Professional Conduct of Physicians and Surgeons.* Manchester: J. Johnson and R. Bickerstaff.

Peterson, M. Jeanne. 1978. *The Medical Profession in Mid-Victorian London.* Berkeley: University of California Press.

Pickstone, John V. 1993. "Thomas Percival and the Production of Medical Ethics." In *Medical Ethics and Etiquette in the Eighteenth Century,* pp. 161–178. Vol. 1 of *The Codification of Medical Morality: Historical and Philosophical Studies of the Formalization of Western Medical Morality in the Eighteenth*

and Nineteenth Centuries, ed. Robert Baker, Dorothy Porter, and Roy Porter. Dordrecht, Netherlands: Kluwer.

Porter, Dorothy, and Porter, Roy. 1988a. "The Enforcement of Health: The British Debate." In *AIDS: The Burdens of History,* pp. 97–120, ed. Elizabeth Fee and Daniel M. Fox. Berkeley: University of California Press.

Porter, Dorothy, and Porter, Roy. 1988b. "The Politics of Prevention: Anti-Vaccinationism and Public Health in Nineteenth-Century England." *Medical History* 32(3): 231–252.

Porter, Roy. 1989. *Health for Sale: Quackery in England, 1650–1850.* Manchester, Eng.: Manchester University Press.

Smith, Russell. 1994. "Legal Precedent and Medical Ethics: Some Problems Encountered by the General Medical Council in Relying upon Precedent When Declaring Acceptable Standards of Professional Conduct." In vol. 2 of *The Codification of Medical Morality: Historical and Philosophical Studies of the Formalization of Medical Morality in the Eighteenth and Nineteenth Centuries,* ed. Robert Baker, Dorothy Porter, and Roy Porter. Dordrecht, Netherlands: Kluwer.

Waddington, Ivan. 1975. "The Development of Medical Ethics—A Sociological Analysis." *Medical History* 19(1): 36–51.

Waddington, Ivan. 1984. *The Medical Profession in the Industrial Revolution.* Dublin: Gill and Macmillan.

MEDICAL ETHICS, HISTORY OF EUROPE: CONTEMPORARY PERIOD

• • •

I. INTRODUCTION

Bioethics was flourishing in most of the countries of late-twentieth-century Europe. However, as a field of ethical reflection and an instrument of public policy, bioethics is hardly uniform across the continent. The development of medical science and technology, as in many countries throughout the world, has stimulated an interest in the attendant ethical issues. Yet the ways various countries have experienced that development differ, as have their ethical responses. Although influenced by social and political events, and by philosophical, literary, religious, and cultural ideas common to the European milieu, various countries and cultures have contributed in unique ways to the formulation of bioethical ideas. There is now a European Association of Bioethics, and in its deliberations, the commonalities of European bioethics can be found, as well as the distinct accents of the various national participants. This introduction will state some of the common themes; the articles that follow will emphasize national and regional distinctions.

Role of Medical Science and Technology

An important prerequisite to twentieth-century discussions and positions was the establishment in the nineteenth century of a natural scientific basis of medicine. Impressive progress in diagnosis and treatment, coupled with this development, led to new ethical problems. Concurrent with this process was an anthropological reduction—a loss of humanistic dimensions in the natural sciences and medicine leading to various attempts at balance and correction in the early twentieth century.

Philosophical Influences

Anthropological medicine and philosophical or existential psychiatry are important twentieth-century reactions to the one-sided natural scientific orientation of medicine. Various philosophical directions, associated with the names of Edmund Husserl, Martin Heidegger, Karl Jaspers, Jean-Paul Sartre, Maurice Merleau-Ponty, Gabriel Marcel, and José Xavier Zubiri, have influenced medicine. Theology has also made important contributions. An independent, intramedical discussion of methods and theory, beginning in the late nineteenth century, and the integration of psychology and sociology into medicine in the last few decades, have also affected contemporary European bioethics.

The situation of medical history in the medical faculties of the universities of Europe presents a different picture. The grand tradition of the presentation of history and theory, including the study of medical ethics, as part of the formal education required of medical students during the preclinical and clinical years was abandoned in the empirical, scientific nineteenth century. Only in Germany was it possible to establish a chair for medical history in almost every medical faculty.

These impulses and initiatives sought to bridge the separation between the natural sciences and humanities. The history of the patient was considered to be as important as the history of the illness. The ethical dimension was recognized anew in the understanding of disease, the concept of treatment, and the physician–patient relationship.

After 1900, discussions of the concept of cause led to a new appreciation of the anthropological dimensions of medicine. The concept of monocausality has been countered by that of multiconditionalism: Disease cannot be explained by one cause but by several causes. Constitution and disposition (i.e., the physical conditions of the individual) supplement the principle of exogenous infection; cause (*causa efficiens*) and aim (*causa finalis*) should not mutually exclude one another. Physical as well as mental illness can fulfill a purpose or meaning, can represent freedom in unfreedom, in the type of coping with these damages.

Literary Influence

The arts—in particular literary texts—also proffer important influences and models. Medical ethics has profited and will continue to profit from a unification with medical humanities. Novels and stories describe the attitudes and behavior of the patient as well as the physician in detail, drawing the reader into the context of the hospital as well as the wider social environment. Such literary depictions and interpretations, in providing examples, can play an important role in medical training. The scientific pleas for euthanasia at the beginning of the twentieth century find their supplementation or preparation in the literature of the nineteenth century. The texts of Guy de Maupassant, Henrik Ibsen, Theodor Storm, Anton Chekhov, and Hjalmar Söderberg describe conflicts in which the killing of a suffering and dying person is suggested; at the same time, there are warnings against active euthanasia. Normative opinions that equate health with the positive and illness with the negative are relativized or even reversed in the works of Marcel Proust, Thomas Mann, Robert Musil, Virginia Woolf, and many other writers. Health should also be understood as the ability to live with illnesses and disabilities, which may harbor opportunity and challenge. The patient has rights and duties, as does the physician; both can exhibit virtues. Their relationship manifests both asymmetry and symmetry such as differences in medical knowledge and experiences of pain and disease.

Political Influences

Ethical discussions of medical issues took place in all European countries even before World War II. Numerous essays and monographs were published on the ethics of the physician, ethics in research, and the ethics of patients, as well as the ethics of the family and of society. In 1901, the first

Congrès International de Médecine Professionelle et de Dèontologie Médicale took place in Paris. Many conventions on the subject of forensic medicine had already taken place. Bioethics in Europe is not uniform; different accents can be found in theory and practice. The differences are based on each country's respective artistic traditions as well as on the respective political and economic situations and legal regulations.

Undoubtedly, World War II and, after its end, the Nuremberg Code were turning points in bioethics. On the one hand, an increased tendency toward international uniformity in bioethics was reflected in such international declarations as, for example, Helsinki (1964) and Tokyo (1975), and in the introduction of ethics committees. On the other hand, the multitude of differing orientations retains its validity, even gaining a new weight through the presence of foreign labor and long-term migration in the European countries. Radical political changes in Eastern Europe and Germany through the collapse of communism made manifest the continuity of ethical opinions and social conditions that had been thought to be relics of the past; these hold new meaning for bioethics in the future.

Problems in bioethics must be solved on many levels, particularly in the Eastern European countries. At the center stands the task of finding a convincing ethical or humanistic solution for the vacuum of ideals left by the collapse of communism and the pressure of technical-scientific progress. Here, as is generally the case in the realization of ethical principles, the applicable legal regulations are of decisive importance. When moral principles are weak, laws can offer protection.

Medical Ethics and Bioethics

Because of the plurality of traditions that make up contemporary European bioethics, it is not possible to isolate a single path of development. The word *bioethics* itself denotes many things. Bioethics has been used to propose norms in the practices of modern biomedicine, norms of a religious-ethical nature, and norms of legal or philosophical ethics. Sometimes, under the new label *bioethics,* the method and arguments of already consolidated disciplines (moral theology, law, ethical guidelines for health professionals, moral philosophy) are easily recognizable, enriched only by the content of new problems.

In the different European cultural contexts, bioethics has had to confront a strong tradition of medical ethics that was developed and defended by physicians as their exclusive property. The proprietary claims of health professionals on medical ethics have produced ambivalent results. The independence of medical ethics has sometimes been able to protect the profession from the pressures that totalitarian ideology exerts on physicians to conform their behavior to the values imposed by the regime. Under the fascist and Nazi regimes (Italy and Germany) and in countries ruled by communism, medical ethics was denied an independent status in order to subordinate it to particular ideological visions (including racism, eugenics, the class struggle, and the dictatorship of the proletariat). In such situations, medical ethics' independence from the values that regulate the society created space for an ethics tied to philanthropic and universalistic ideals.

Nevertheless, the medical ethics elaborated by professional physicians can also obstruct the rise of formulations better adapted to the changing cultural situation. This is evident in many European countries by the many physicians who turn to traditional medical ethics, inspired by the ideals of Hippocratic medicine and strongly anchored in a paternalistic attitude toward the sick person, in order to oppose the medical models that are centered on the value of individual autonomy and the practice of informed consent.

The thrust toward bioethics is characterized, if compared with the strong tradition of an ethics developed by the medical profession itself, by the need for a civil ethics or an ethic of ordinary life elaborated in many voices. Bioethics is differentiated from medical ethics in being a consensual reformulation of rights and obligations in the context of medical practice and healthcare. This includes the professional obligations of physicians, but does not derive only from these. A further characteristic trait of bioethics in regard to civil or general ethics is the minimal ethical consensus, which obliges all citizens, in contrast to the maximal ethical consensus, which focuses on individual preferences.

A second issue that bioethics in Europe must face is its relationship with religious ethics. The weight of religious ethics relative to the moral problems posed by the corporality of man (sexuality, procreation, disease, health, death) and healthcare varies according to cultural context and type of religious communities in the society. In societies in which a single religion dominates, especially of the Catholic tradition (Ireland, Poland, Italy, Spain), religious ethics tends to superimpose itself onto bioethics, shaping it to its own norms. In countries in which a tradition of pluralism prevails, the two normative contexts—religious ethical and bioethical—are more clearly distinct.

Where religious ethics is seen as antithetical to secular ethics, a clear polarization can appear in the society; possible examples are Ireland, Poland, or Portugal, with their Catholic tradition. Justification of ethical judgment then consists of making reference exclusively to one set of values instead of another. This happens, for example, when clinical decisions are evaluated exclusively in terms of values considered to be absolute: sacredness of life versus quality of life, benefit of the medical act versus self-determination of the patient, and so on.

A third issue in the contemporary development of bioethics in Europe relates to the challenge of universalism. Developments in the ethics of medicine and biological sciences reveal two opposing challenges for bioethics: the need to be rooted in the particular, with respect to the cultures, traditions, and local communities of belonging, and the need to refer itself to universal values. Universalism is an intrinsic dimension of ethical rationalism. At the same time, universalism is necessary to ensure normative rules and moral obligations. The directives, for example, of "Good Clinical Practice for Trials on Medical Products in European Community" (1991) have had the aim of producing one practice of experimentation in this field. In Europe, in fact, the crowded national frontiers would easily create "enclaves" where biomedical practices prohibited beyond these frontiers would be legitimate. An international consensus has to be created to prevent a "tourism" in medical research.

The various bioethics developing in Europe face the challenge of particularism as much as that of universalism. The best forms of European bioethics are clearly those that are trying to respond to both these challenges.

Recommendations of the Council of Europe

The most relevant innovation for the history of bioethics in Europe is the approval of a "Convention for the Protection of Human Rights and Dignity of Human Being with regard to the Application of Biology and Medicine" by the Council of Europe. After almost five years of work and lively discussions, the steering Committee on bioethics of the Council of Europe (CDBI) presented a text which was approved by the Council of ministers in Oviedo (Spain), on April 4, 1997. The Convention is therefore known as the Oviedo Convention or "Convention on human rights and bio-medicine." Its main purpose is to reinforce the idea that, since Europe is becoming more and more integrated from a cultural point of view as well as economically and politically, it is necessary to find a common orientation also on the subject of bioethics.

Eighteen out of the forty countries of the Council of Europe have signed the Convention. The parliaments of the signatory States are now called upon to ratify this Convention, thus agreeing to bring national legislation into line

with the principles enunciated in the agreement. Indeed, unlike "Recommendations" of the Council of Europe and "Treaties," which are a mere expression of principles, the instrument of the Convention is particularly effective because it is binding on those states that ratify it, obliging them to apply its standards within their individual sets of laws. This means that the Convention is not an "exhortation," to the individual states, but has a normative value. As of September 2002, thirteen countries have also ratified the Convention they signed.

The choice made with the Convention was to focus on principles and rules that can help create a consistent set of laws, real European common rights in the bioethics area: the prevalence of human beings over science, respect for individual independence, protection of integrity and dignity, confidentiality of medical and genetic information, non-commercialization of the human body. In the Convention no position has been taken on widely debated topics, including medically assisted procreation, the cloning of embryos, or genetic engineering. The most controversial aspects of bioethics are expanded upon in additional protocols. Two of them have been drawn up so far: on the Prohibition of Cloning Human Beings (January 12, 1998) and on Transplantation of Organs and Tissues of Human Origin (January 24, 2002).

The essential elements of the Convention are: the primacy of the human being (article 2: "The interest and welfare of the human being shall prevail over the sole interest of society or science"); equitable access to healthcare (article 3: "Parties taking into account health needs and available resources, shall take appropriate measures with a view to providing, within their jurisdiction, equitable access to healthcare of appropriate quality"); the central role of information and consent (article 5: "An intervention in the health field may only be carried out after the person concerned has given free and informed consent to it. This person shall beforehand be given appropriate information as to the purpose and nature of the intervention as well as on its consequences and risks").

DIETRICH VON ENGELHARDT
SANDRO SPINSANTI (1995)
REVISED BY AUTHORS

II. SOUTHERN EUROPE

The term *southern European countries* includes all the occidental European countries in the Mediterranean area (Spain, France, Italy, Greece, Malta, and Cyprus), plus an Atlantic country closely related to them (Portugal). In addition to geographical and climatological affinities, these seven countries have for many centuries shared a common history centered on the Mediterranean Sea. Although they maintain local peculiarities and differences, the nations of southern Europe can be said to have a common identity.

This common identity is particularly evident in ethical issues (Gracia, 1993). Occidental ethics had its origin in the Mediterranean Greco-Latin culture, and since the days of the Greek philosophers, this ethics has centered on the concepts of virtue and vice. Only with the Enlightenment did a new ethical tradition, with right and duty as its main concepts, begin to take shape in central Europe. Since then the two approaches have widely been considered opposites, although they are in fact complementary. The ethics of virtue has persisted in those countries in which the Enlightenment had less influence, such as the Catholic or Orthodox southern European nations (Savignano), while the ethics of duty has prevailed in the Protestant central European and Anglo-Saxon countries (MacIntyre).

Today the occidental world harbors three palpably different ethical traditions, each with its own characteristics: the Anglo-Saxon, the central European, and the Mediterranean. Because modern bioethics is a product of the Anglo-American culture, Mediterranean countries have not attempted simply to import or "translate" bioethics but, rather, to re-create or remake the discipline according to their own cultural and ethical traditions (Gracia, 1990).

A "Latin Model" of Bioethics

If traditional Anglo-American philosophy is generally classified as empiricist, European philosophy has been more influenced by rationalism. Anglo-American ethics is generally more teleological and consequentialist, and European ethics more deontological. This explains why, for instance, the term *autonomy* has acquired a different meaning in the United States than in Europe. According to North American ethics, autonomy is the capacity to act intentionally, with understanding, and without controlling influences. On the other hand, European ethicists often interpret the principle of autonomy in a Kantian sense, as the capacity of human reason to impose absolute moral laws upon itself. The latter is a metaphysical assumption, while the former is only the lack of constraints. To European ethicists, acting autonomously means that the human reason is capable of freely establishing absolute and compulsory moral laws (freedom to). In the Anglo-American, on the contrary, freedom is understood only negatively, as the capacity to act without constraints (freedom from). The first is a maximal concept of autonomy, and the second a minimal one. These

two meanings are so disparate that an autonomous person, according to the European point of view, may not act autonomously from the Anglo-American perspective because of constraints such as ignorance or coercion. Moreover, it is also possible to deny the capacity of reason to impose on itself absolute moral laws, and to accept the concept of autonomous choice as the absence of external constraints.

The rational foundation of ethics is closely linked to the discussion of whether the principle of autonomy is relative or absolute. In Europe, the Anglo-American propensity to base ethical analysis on several theories, such as utilitarianism and contractualism, and on a few principles, such as autonomy and beneficence, is usually considered insufficient or less adequate. Europeans generally search for more universal or transcendental ethical foundations. The meaning of the concept of *transcendental* differs in central and southern Europe. Central European ethics often attempts to reach the transcendental dimension through an intersubjective procedure, such as the universalization of personal interests. According to many Mediterranean ethicists, the transcendental universality of ethical norms is reached in a more objective way, based on metaphysical concepts like *reality, human nature,* or *personhood* (Russo). The latter is, of course, the most classical position in occidental philosophy. It is no coincidence that this classical concept of metaphysics was born on the Mediterranean coast.

Modern northern European ethics, based on the concepts of right and duty, has been the matrix of ethical minimalism (or the ethics of duty), while the traditional Mediterranean ethics, based on virtue, has tended more toward ethical maximalism (or the ethics of happiness). While minimalistic ethics looks for the basic rights and duties of every human being and society, maximalistic ethics is concerned with life projects and ideals of perfection and happiness (in Greek, *eudaimonia*). During the sixteenth century, Mediterranean countries adopted anti-Protestant, and therefore antimodern, attitudes; they considered certain aspects of modernity to be fundamentally hostile to their cultural traditions: their medieval political, ethical, and religious ideals. These attitudes may explain why many Mediterranean nations belatedly and with difficulty adopted the doctrines of human rights and parliamentary democracy, the greatest achievements of the Anglo-American world. This may also explain the relative weakness of democratic practices in these countries in comparison with other areas. This antimodern stance enables one to understand the history of southern Europe since the nineteenth century, particularly the potency of antidemocratic movements and authoritarianism during the first half of the twentieth century. And while western European countries definitively adopted democracy and liberal systems following World War II, some of the Mediterranean countries maintained a markedly different identity.

All these elements help clarify why southern European countries have tried to elaborate a "Latin" model of bioethics (Leone). While the Anglo-American model is structured around the four classical principles of autonomy, nonmaleficence, beneficence, and justice, Salvino Leone, following Elio Sgreccia, bases the so-called Latin model on the four principles of the fundamental value of life; liberty and responsibility; totality (or therapeutic wholeness); and social subsidiarity (the idea that smaller units are always preferred to larger ones when it comes to addressing social problems) (Sgreccia; Palazzani). This search for distinctiveness also led Mediterranean ethicists to seek to establish their own terminology. The French expression *éthique biomédicale,* "meaning the desire to promote a new style of questioning in the field of biomedical sciences, both theoretical and educational" (Moulin, p. 280), has been adopted as an alternative term to the Anglo-American bioethics not only in French but also in other Mediterranean languages, such as Italian (Spinsanti, 1987) and Spanish. The reason for this terminological change is that for many authors, the word *bioethics* seems overly biologistic and suggests that ethical behavior is biologically determined. The alternative expression *biomedical ethics* was coined to avoid this danger. It situates the term *ethics* as the noun, with *biology* and *medicine* in secondary adjectival position. Of course, the term *bioethics* is also frequently used in Mediterranean countries, just as North American literature occasionally uses the expression *biomedical ethics* (Beauchamp and Childress).

The Ethics of Virtue and the Doctor-Patient Relationship

Mediterranean countries have created a realistic and personalist model of biomedical ethics, based on the classical Aristotelian-Scholastic philosophy and complemented with more modern European philosophical traditions such as phenomenology, axiology, and hermeneutics (Viafora, 1990). In this model, the idea of virtue acquires much more significance than in any other occidental tradition, a fact that has important consequences in the medical field. For example, trustworthiness is considered more crucial than the right to information (Dalla-Vorgia et al., 1992). Patients in southern European nations are generally less concerned with receiving detailed information or having their autonomy respected than with finding a doctor in whom they can place their full confidence (Gordon; Spinsanti, 1992; Fletcher; Loewy).

One virtue is particularly important in establishing a satisfactory doctor–patient relationship: friendship. The Spanish physician and humanist Pedro Laín Entralgo has written extensively on this topic, especially in his book *The Doctor–Patient Relationship* (Laín Entralgo, 1983 [1969]). This relationship must be based on what Laín Entralgo calls "medical friendship," composed of benevolence, beneficence, and confidence. His studies have had a substantial but not exclusive impact in Mediterranean and Latin American medicine; as a result, the idea of friendship as the cornerstone of the relationship between doctor and patient has gradually acquired importance in bioethics. The influence of his studies is also visible in North American bioethical literature (Siegler, 1979, 1981; Pellegrino and Thomasma; U.S. President's Commission; Cassell; Drane).

Friendship includes trust and confidence, which is why we talk about intimate friends; friendship is the ambit of trust. The three theological virtues (faith, hope, and love) are common between friends. The core of this relation is hope, understood as trust: we trust friends, we have faith in them, and we trust them because we love them. Friendship is more than ethics; it is almost a religion. Charity, or agape, is considered the most important virtue in the Judeo-Christian tradition. But, according to Laín Entralgo, agape can be considered perfect only when benevolence and beneficence, its main components, join friendship's trust and confidence (Laín Entralgo, 1985 [1972]). The result is, as Edmund Pellegrino and Warren T. Reich, two U.S. authors influenced by Laín Entralgo, have written, "com-passion," the act of putting oneself in the place of another in order to understand his or her experiences (Pellegrino, 1986, 1988, 1989; Reich, 1989, 1991). Compassion is not pity but, rather, the human relationship based on devotion, constancy, personal respect, and responsibility. As Reich says, it is the relation with the other, based on love, benevolence, comprehension, and friendship. Mediterranean bioethics has emphasized the study of the friendship aspect of the physician–patient relation, and the Spanish contribution has been important (Gracia, 1989).

Ethics and Law

The relationship between ethics and law is peculiar in the Mediterranean. In its origins, Roman law was substantially influenced by Stoicism, a school of thought that assimilated law and morality. Stoics considered nature the source of both law and morality; natural law could be known rationally, and thus formulated deontologically and axiomatically into a legal code. Because law expresses what is morally correct, ethics and law converged. Ethical goodness, the intention with which an act is performed, only added to the legal rightness of the act and to the virtue of the person involved.

Christian thinkers adopted this relationship between ethics and law without substantial changes, and it has been a latent presence both in canon law and in the moral theology of the Roman Catholic church. Thus, in Catholic nations such as those of southern Europe, law and morality are difficult to distinguish conceptually.

One of the problematic outgrowths of this tradition is legalism, the tendency to believe that every human act can be legally prefigured, that laws precede facts, making it possible to regulate beforehand every real or possible situation. Thus, in these countries court rulings are considered nothing more than the concrete application of statutory law. This law is prior to individual rulings, quite the opposite of the Anglo-Saxon common-law system. The traditions also diverge in that the Roman model is largely centralized and state-oriented and places less importance on social dynamics. The prevalence of state over society explains why Mediterranean countries have fostered more authoritarian and less democratic political practices than Anglo-Saxon ones.

Health Systems

That the state must, in southern European countries, take responsibility for what in other countries is considered the realm of private enterprise, illuminates another distinctive characteristic of Mediterranean bioethics: its overwhelming concern with healthcare justice. In fact, the health systems of these countries are mainly state-run. Justice plays the decisive role in European biomedical ethics that autonomy plays in North American bioethics (Thomasma).

France, Italy, Greece, Portugal, and Spain have similar national health insurance systems. Their common origins date back to the German Krankenkassen (patients' fund) system, designed by Otto von Bismarck in the final decades of the nineteenth century as a means of assuring medical assistance for workers. In distinction to the socialist European countries, where all the population was covered by an insurance system financed by public funds, Mediterranean countries, following the German model, began insuring only workers, and financing the system with the economic support of both workers and employers. Coverage was later extended by public funding, and today nearly the entire population of each country is protected. This process of generalization of the health insurance system took place during the zenith years of the welfare state, between the end of World War II and the economic crisis of 1973. In the mid-1970s, health insurance as well as the entire social security system, and perhaps the welfare state itself, experienced a crisis, mainly because of the costs explosion that made it impossible to satisfy the population's health expectations. To find solutions for this complex problem, most countries set up reform commissions aimed at proposing measures to make health insurance viable in the future.

In Spain, compulsory health insurance for all workers was enacted in 1942 and implemented in 1943. Over the next three decades, coverage was gradually extended. In 1986 it became a national health system very similar to those in Britain and Italy, covering the healthcare of most of the country's population (Gracia, 1987). This satisfied one of the people's greatest wishes but at the same time gave birth to a new problem, which became more and more acute as time went by: the scarcity of economic resources and the subsequent need to limit free health services. In order to analyze and evaluate the needs of the national health system, in 1990 the Spanish parliament set up a commission, known as the Comisión Abril Martorell. The commission's main report, published in July 1991, asserted the importance of the national health system in maintaining the level of health and well-being in Spain, and proposed certain amendments to increase efficiency without altering the basic system. One such modification would require every user of healthcare services to pay a percentage of the total cost, in an attempt to make everyone shoulder the burden of the constant increases in health expenses.

Patients' Rights

The way patients' rights were established marks another differentiating factor of Mediterranean countries. In the United States these rights, particularly the right to informed consent, took shape in the field of common law, while in Mediterranean countries their entry was directly through statutory laws and codes (Council of Europe, 1976; Gracia, 1989). In these countries, protecting patients' rights is a duty of the state more than the duty of individuals. In Spain, patients' rights were first established legally in Article 10 of the Health Law of 1986, and then socially.

In all Mediterranean countries the respect for patients' autonomy and their right to make decisions about their own bodies has grown remarkably in the last decades (Cattorini and Reichlin). This has produced profound changes in the role of healthcare professionals, as well as more litigation against physicians and other healthcare workers. The old juridical terms *professional incompetence* and *negligence* that referred to faulty medical procedures have come to be overshadowed by new complaints about health workers' lack of skill or their negligence in giving information, or about battery, for handling the patient's body without consent.

The patients' rights movement of the 1970s provoked wide-ranging legislative changes (Council of Europe, 1976).

For example, the large antipsychiatry movement in 1978, led in the Mediterranean area by Italy, prompted some countries to modify laws on the compulsory restraint of the mentally ill by passing new legislation more respectful of these patients' human rights and providing greater protection against possible abuse by family members or health professionals. In 1997, the Council of Europe introduced the "Convention on Human Rights and Medicine"; the fifth article of this document states that "an intervention in the health field may only be carried out after the person concerned has given free and informed consent to it. This person shall beforehand be given appropriate information as to the purpose and nature of the intervention as well as on its consequences and risks. The person concerned may freely withdraw consent at any time" (Council of Europe, 1997) The convention has been signed by all the Mediterranean countries, and has influenced national legislation about the rights of patients and informed consent.

Additional consequences of this new respect for patients' rights are the strict regulation of biomedical experimentation and the creation of institutional review boards to monitor every clinical trial and research project protocol, analyzing not only technical and methodological but also ethical aspects. On November 24, 1986, the Council of the European Community approved a directive on the protection of the animals used in research and other scientific projects (European Union). Every country of the European Community adopted its own legislation in the following years, and by the end of the twentieth century, research with animals was strictly controlled (Illera).

In an attempt to promote organ transplants while avoiding any kind of commerce and abuse in the donation process, all Mediterranean countries have introduced legislative criteria for brain death and have elaborated laws regulating transplants. The legal regulation of medical care to the dying has encountered greater obstacles, and has provoked heated debates over euthanasia (Gracia, 1987, 1988; Lefevre; Dracopolou and Doxiadis; Bompiani).

Issues related to the origin of life, especially abortion and new techniques for human reproduction, have been the subject of the most intense debates. Mediterranean countries have adopted conservative positions in these debates. In these nations the U.S. Supreme Court decision *Roe v. Wade* (1973), based on the right to privacy and restricting the right of states to legislate on abortion in terms of viability and trimesters, is not easily understood. In Mediterranean countries, abortion is held to be a public rather than a private issue and therefore a matter of justice and not of autonomy, since the life of a human being is believed to be at stake. Hence, in these countries, laws governing the interruption of pregnancy are based on exceptional circumstances or indications rather than on periods of time or terms of pregnancy. These laws allow abortion in three exceptional indications: great danger to the mother's health or life; important defects of the fetus; and rape. Only a few countries, such as Italy and Cyprus, have included a fourth indication: socioeconomic incapacity, valid during the first trimester of gestation. The Veil Act (1975) in France established that any pregnant woman can undergo an abortion during the first ten weeks of pregnancy if gestation is a source of anguish (*détresse*) for her, an indication that, in practice, is analogous to a law of terms (a period of time in which abortion is permitted without any indication). Since 1986 Greece has had a law of terms: Abortion is permitted in the first twelve weeks of pregnancy. After this period, gestation can be interrupted only with an ethical (nineteen weeks), eugenic (twenty-four weeks), or therapeutic indication (Glendon).

The problems presented by new techniques of human reproduction are so various and complex that every southern European country has established a specific commission for their study. The Comisión Palacios of Spain and the Commissione Santosuosso of Italy are examples. Both bodies have elaborated reports for legislative enactment, which has been achieved in both countries (Gracia, 1988; Fagot-Largeault; Mori; Walters; Bompiani). More important, these commissions highlighted the need for national committees on bioethics, which were firmly established in the Mediterranean area by the end of the century. This same process has taken place in Europe as a whole, where the Council of Europe in 1983 established the Ad Hoc Committee on Ethical and Legal Problems Related to Genetic Engineering, which a few years later became the Ad Hoc Committee of Experts on Bioethics and was later called the Steering Committee of Bioethics.

National Committees of Bioethics

National committees of bioethics have been set up because of the increasing complexity of biomedical research and to avoid dangerous research like that which made possible the construction of nuclear weapons during the 1940s and 1950s and the experiments carried out in Nazi concentration camps. The main aim of these committees is to help those involved in biomedical research by offering prudent criteria for conduct. On February 23, 1983, French President François Mitterrand created the first national bioethics commission in a European country, the Comité Consultatif National d'Éthique pour les Sciences de la Vie et de la Santé (CCNE). Its purpose is mainly to elaborate recommendations on ethical problems stemming from scientific research in biology, medicine, and other health professions (Isambert,

1989). It deals not with healthcare problems but with ethical questions raised by biomedical research. The CCNE is composed of thirty-six members plus a chairman who is appointed by the president of the republic. The departments of Education, Research, Industry, Health, Justice, Family, and Communication appoint sixteen members with proven competence and interest in ethical issues. Fifteen posts are filled by researchers and representatives of universities and the National Institutes of Health and Research. Five members, named by the president of the republic, are drawn from the "spiritual and philosophical" fields. Committee members are divided into working teams to prepare reports and recommendations. The documents so far produced have dealt with the use of fetal and embryonic tissues for diagnostic, therapeutic, or research purposes; techniques of artificial procreation; prenatal and perinatal diagnosis; the use of the abortion-causing drug RU-486; and the noncommercialization of the human body, among other topics. Every year, the committee organizes meetings of study and debate called the Journées Annuelles d'Éthique, in order to release the year's work to the public.

The French commission's work has stimulated bioethics studies in the Mediterranean area, much as the National and President's Commissions have done in the United States. Of the two possible methodologies identified by the Belgian philosopher of medicine Jean-François Malherbe—that of the lowest common denominator (the search for a formula everybody agrees with, even if it is ambiguous and makes room for very different interpretations) and that of the highest common denominator (requiring much more work, reflection, and dialogue)—the Comité Consultatif National opted for the second. This decision had an evident impact on the text of a report the committee issued, "Biomedical Research and Respect for the Human Being" (CCNE). French bioethics is coming to be, as Malherbe noted, "an active center of public morality in the life of people" (Malherbe, p. 227). The French ethics of the highest common denominator is similar to some of the most creative ideas from Jürgen Habermas and Karl O. Apels's "ethics of communication," which is based on the idea that in the context of a pluralistic society, ethics will flourish only if it takes into account the interests of every person actually or virtually involved in the conflict. The French committee has integrated German dialogic ethics with French personalism, widespread among French philosophers of the last century, and firmly established in certain Catholic (Maurice Nédoncelle), Protestant (Paul Ricoeur), and Jewish (Emmanuel Lévinas) phenomenological thinkers. According to Lucien Séve, these ideas have proved fundamental for the elaboration of a working procedure based on rational consensus and not on a merely strategic consensus.

The French committee has had great success, and hence this model has spread throughout Europe, including the Mediterranean countries. Malta instituted its Health Ethics Consultative Committee in 1989 (Le Bris). In March 1990 the Italian government approved the creation of the Comitato Nazionale per la Bioetica, directly responsible to the prime minister. The body is composed of forty members and, like the French group, is aimed at controlling research involving human beings. It has published documents on gene therapy, definition of human death, ethics of the use of seminal fluid for diagnostic purposes, biotechnological security, bioethical learning in the clinical setting, healthcare and terminally ill patients, organ donation, and ethics committees.

Portugal, following the French pattern, established the National Ethical Council for Life Sciences in June 1990 (Martinho da Silva). The body started functioning January 1, 1991, and in its three first years published three reports: on organ donation and transplantation (1991), on the use of human corpses in research and teaching (1991), and on new reproductive technologies (1993).

In 1984 Spain created a special committee known as the Comité Palacios to study problems related to new techniques of assisted reproduction (artificial insemination, in vitro fertilization, and so forth). In July 1992 the Department of Health published a legal order creating a health advisory committee whose main goal was assessing and informing the secretary of the department on scientific, ethical, professional, and social questions. This committee deals not only with problems of biomedical research but also with those raised by healthcare. This innovative feature distinguishes it from others in the region.

In southern Europe, institutional ethics committees were rare until the 1990s, in part due to the prevalence of socialized medicine and in part because Mediterraneans are not completely conscious of patients' rights. In Spain, for instance, such committees only became standard in hospitals late in the 1990s, following the General Health Law of 1986 that specifically mandates the protection of patients' rights.

Goals and Challenges for the Future

In the last decade of the twentieth century, new problems emerged; two of the most important were population ethics and ecology. Ecology is of increasing importance in all Mediterranean countries, and is beginning to be not only an ethical and intellectual issue but also a political force (Gafo; Poli and Timmerman). Latin European countries are neighbors of the underdeveloped nations situated on the southern Mediterranean coast, and they therefore understand very well that only a sustainable development can correct the unsustainable development of the First World and the underdevelopment of the Third World. Ecology in these countries will be not only an ethical compromise but also a political project, prompted by the left-wing parties. With the death of the Marxist ideology, ecology assumes the place once held by economic theory.

Due to the increasing importance of bioethics in the life of these countries, research and teaching are growing quickly. The teaching of bioethics has been introduced not only in schools directly related to healthcare, such as medicine, pharmacy, and biology, but also in theology, philosophy, and humanities (Comitato Nazionale per la Bioetica; Gracia, 1992). Literature is being published, and universities are supporting new research centers (Viafora, 1993). All of the research centers have been integrated into the European Association of Centers of Medical Ethics. Since 1990 the Milazzo Group has published *International Journal of Bioethics*.

DIEGO GRACIA
TERESA GRACIA (1995)
REVISED BY AUTHORS

BIBLIOGRAPHY

Beauchamp, Tom L., and Childress, James F. 1983. *Principles of Biomedical Ethics,* 2nd edition. New York: Oxford University Press.

Bompiani, Adriano. 1992. *Bioetica in Italia: Lineamenti e tendenze.* Bologna: Edizioni Dehoniane.

Bondolfi, Alberto. 1990. "Orientamenti e tendenze della bioetica nell'area linguistica tedesca." In *Vent'anni di bioetica: Idee, protagonisti, instituzioni,* ed. Corrado Viafora and Alberto Bondolfi. Padua: Fondazione Lanza/Gregoriana Libreria Editrice.

Brody, Baruch A. 1989. "The President's Commission: The Need to Be More Philosophical." *Journal of Medicine and Philosophy* 14(4): 369–383.

Cassell, Eric J. 1984. *The Place of the Humanities in Medicine.* Hastings-on-Hudson, NY: Hastings Center.

Cattorini, Paolo, and Massimo Reichlin. 1992. "The Physician, the Family, and the Truth." *Journal of Clinical Ethics* 3(3): 219–220.

Comitato Nazionale per la Bioetica. 1991. *Bioetica e formazione nel sistema sanitario.* Rome: Presidenza del Consiglio dei Ministri, Dipartimento per l'Informazione e l'Editoria.

Comité Consultatif National d'Eéthique pour les Sciences de la Vie et de la Santé (CCNE). 1988. *Recherche biomédicale et respect de la personne humaine.* Paris: Documentation Française.

Council of Europe. 1976. *Recommendation 779, on the Rights of the Sick and Dying.* Strasbourg: Author.

Council of Europe. 1997. *Convention for the Protection of Human Rights and Dignity of the Human Beings with Regard to the Application of Biology and Medicine: Convention on Human Rights and Biomedicine.* Strasbourg: Author.

Dalla-Vorgia, Panagiota; Katsouyanni, Klea; Garanis, Tina N.; Touloumi, Giota; Drogari, Potitsa; and Koutselinis, Antonios. 1992. "Attitudes of a Mediterranean Population to the Truth-Telling Issue." *Journal of Medical Ethics* 18(2): 67–74.

Dracopoulou, Souzy, and Doxiadis, Spyros. 1988. "In Greece, Lament for the Dead, Denial for the Dying." *Hastings Center Report* 18(Special supplement, August–September): 15–16.

Drane, James F. 1988. *Becoming a Good Doctor: The Place of Virtue and Character in Medical Ethics.* Kansas City, MO: Sheed & Ward.

European Union. 1986. "Council Directive 86/609/EEC of 24 November 1986 on the Approximation of Laws, Regulations and Administrative Provisions of the Member States Regarding the Protection of Animals Used for Experimental and Other Scientific Purposes. Official." *Official Journal* L 358(December 18, 1986): 1.

Fagot-Largeault, Anne. 1987. "In France, Debate and Indecision." *Hastings Center Report,* special suppl., 17(June): 10–12.

Fletcher, John C. 1992. "On Grinding Axes and Examining Practices." *Journal of Clinical Ethics* 3(3): 221–224.

Gafo, Javier, ed. 1991. "Ética y ecología." In *Dilemmas éticos de la medicina actual.* Madrid: Publicaciones de la Universidad Pontificia Comillas.

Glendon, Mary Ann. 1987. *Abortion and Divorce in Western Law.* Cambridge, MA: Harvard University Press.

Gordon, Deborah. 1990. "Embodying Illness, Embodying Cancer." *Culture, Medicine, and Psychiatry* 14(2, Special issue titled "Traversing Boundaries Between Inside/Outside, Individual/ Society, and European/North American Anthropology"): 275–297.

Gracia, Diego. 1987. "Spain: From the Decree to the Proposal." *Hastings Center Report,* special suppl., 17(June): 29–31.

Gracia, Diego. 1988. "Spain: New Problems, New Books." *Hastings Center Report,* special suppl., 18(August–September): 29–30.

Gracia, Diego. 1989. *Fundamentos de bioética.* Madrid: EUDEMA.

Gracia, Diego. 1990. "Orientamenti e tendenze della bioetica nell'area linguistica spagnola." In *Vent'anni di bioetica: Idee, protagonisti, instituzioni,* ed. Corrado Viafora and Alberto Bondolfi. Padua: Fondazione Lanza/Gregoriana Libreria Editrice.

Gracia, Diego. 1992. "Enseñanza postgraduada y formación continuada en ética médica," *Organización médica colegial* 21: 25–28.

Gracia, Diego. 1993. "The Intellectual Basis of Bioethics in Southern European Countries." *Bioethics* 7(2–3): 97–107.

Illera, Mariano. 1989. *Trabajar en experimentación animal.* Madrid: Fundación Universidad-Empresa.

Isambert, François-André. 1989. "Ethics Committees in France." *Journal of Medicine and Philosophy* 14(4): 445–456.

Laín Entralgo, Pedro. 1969. *Doctor and Patient,* tr. Frances Partridge. New York: McGraw–Hill.

Laín Entralgo, Pedro. 1964 (reprint 1983). *La relación médico–enfermo: Historia y teoría.* Madrid: Alianza.

Laín Entralgo, Pedro. 1972 (reprint 1985). *Sobre la amistad.* Madrid: Espasa-Calpe.

Le Bris, Sonia. 1992. *National Ethics Bodies.* Strasbourg: Council of Europe.

Lefevre, Charles. 1988. "In France, Terminal Stage Medicine Is Not Hopelessly Ill." *Hastings Center Report,* special suppl., 18(August–September): 19–20.

Leone, Salvino. 1990. "Il problema dei 'valori comuni' nelle deliberazioni dei comitati." In *I comitati di bioetica: Storia, analisi, proposte.* Rome: Edizioni Orizzonte Medico.

Loewy, Erich H. 1992. "Consent, Ethics, and Community." *Journal of Clinical Ethics* 3(3): 224–228.

MacIntyre, Alasdair. 1984. *After Virtue: A Study in Moral Theory,* 2nd edition. Notre Dame, IN: University of Notre Dame Press.

Malherbe, Jean-François. 1990. "Orientamenti e tendenze della bioetica nell'area linguistica francese." In *Vent'anni di bioetica: Idee, protagonisti, instituzioni,* ed. Corrado Viafora and Alberto Bondolfi. Padua: Fondazione Lanza/Gregoriana Libreria Editrice.

Martinho da Silva, Paula. 1990. "A bioética, o direito e um breve resumo sobre o quadro legislativo português." *Revista do Ministério público* 11(43): 163–167.

Mori, Maurizio. 1987. "Italy: Pluralism Takes Root." *Hastings Center Report 17,* special suppl., (June): 34–36.

Moulin, Anne Marie. 1988. "Medical Ethics in France: The Latest Great Political Debate." *Theoretical Medicine* 9(3): 271–285.

Palazzani, Laura. 1993. "Modello argomentativo. Per una valutazione bioetica nella prospettiva personalistica." In *Centri di bioetica in Italia,* ed. Corrado Viafora. Padua: Fondazione Lanza/Gregoriana Libreria Editrice.

Pellegrino, Edmund D. 1986. "Health Care: A Vocation to Justice and Love." In *The Professions in Ethical Context: Vocations to Love and Justice,* ed. Francis A. Eigo. Villanova, PA: Villanova University Press.

Pellegrino, Edmund D. 1988. "Every Sick Person Is My Brother or Sister." *Dolentium Hominum* 3(1): 65–70.

Pellegrino, Edmund D. 1989. "Agape and Ethics: Some Reflections on Medical Morals from a Catholic Perspective." In *Catholic Perspectives on Medical Morals: Foundational Issues,* ed. Edmund D. Pellegrino, John P. Langan, and John C. Harvey. Dordrecht, Netherlands: Kluwer.

Pellegrino, Edmund D., and Thomasma, David C. 1981. *A Philosophical Basis of Medical Practice: Toward a Philosophy and Ethic of the Healing Professions.* New York: Oxford University Press.

Poli, Corrado, and Timmerman, Peter, eds. 1991. *L'etica nelle politiche ambientali.* Padua: Fondazione Lanza/Gregoriana Libreria Editrice.

Reich, Warren Thomas. 1989. "Speaking of Suffering: A Moral Account of Compassion." *Soundings* 72: 83–108.

Reich, Warren Thomas. 1991. "The Case: Denny's Story, and Commentary: Caring as Extraordinary Means." *Second Opinion* 17: 41–56.

Russo, Giovanni. 1992. *Sessualità ed embriopoiesi nella genesi della bioetica in Italia.* Messina, Sicily: Istituto Teologico S. Tommaso.

Savignano, Armando. 1995. *Bioetica Mediterranea: Etica della virtù e della felicità.* Pisa: Edizioni ETS.

Séve, Lucien. 1988. *Recherche biomédicale et respect de la personne humaine.* Paris: Documentation Française.

Sgreccia, Elio. 1988. *Bioetica: Manuale per medici e biologi.* Milan: Vita e Pensiero.

Siegler, Mark. 1979. "The Nature and Limits of Clinical Medicine." In *Changing Values in Medicine,* ed. Eric J. Cassell and Mark Siegler. Frederick, MD: University Publications of America.

Siegler, Mark. 1981. "Searching for Moral Certainty in Medicine: A Proposal for a New Model of the Doctor–Patient Encounter." *Bulletin of the New York Academy of Medicine* 57(1): 56–69.

Spinsanti, Sandro. 1987. *Etica bio-medica.* Milan: Paoline.

Spinsanti, Sandro. 1992. "Obtaining Consent from the Family: A Horizon for Clinical Ethics." *Journal of Clinical Ethics* 3(3):188–192.

Symposium of the Council of Europe on Bioethics. 1990. *Europe and Bioethics: Proceedings of the 1st Symposium of the Council of Europe on Bioethics.* Strasbourg: Council of Europe.

Thomasma, David C. 1985. "The Philosophy of Medicine in Europe: Challenges for the Future." *Theoretical Medicine* 6(1): 115–123.

U.S. President's Commission for the Study of Ethical Problems in Medicine and Biomedical and Behavioral Research. 1982. *Making Health Care Decisions,* vol. 1. Washington, D.C.: U. S. Government Printing Office.

Viafora, Corrado. 1990. "Bioetica oggi: Un quadro storico e sistematico." In *Vent'anni di bioetica: Idee, protagonisti, instituzioni,* ed. Corrado Viafora and Alberto Bondolfi. Padua: Fondazione Lanza/Gregoriana Libreria Editrice.

Viafora, Corrado. 1993. *Centri di bioetica in Italia: Orientamenti a confronto.* Padua: Fondazione Lanza/Gregoriana Libreria Editrice.

Walters, LeRoy. 1987. "Ethics and New Reproductive Technologies: An International Review of Committee Statements." *Hastings Center Report,* special supplement, 17(June): 3–9.

III. THE BENELUX COUNTRIES

The Benelux countries—Belgium (population 10 million), the Netherlands (population 15 million), and Luxembourg (population 400,000)—with three languages (Dutch, spoken by 20 million; French, by 5 million; and German, by 500,000), and two Christian religions (Roman Catholicism and Protestantism)—have been leaders in European bioethics. Institutes for bioethics were founded in these countries in the early 1980s, the region's universities developed a full curriculum for medical ethics, and European bioethics associations of both organizations and individuals were founded in the Benelux nations.

Of the three possible approaches to medical ethics—the deontological, the forensic, and the philosophical–theological approach—the third one, particularly since the 1960s in Belgium and in the Netherlands, has produced a considerable amount of literature in both religious and lay ethics.

During the 1960s, early warning signals were issued by physicians and philosophers. Prominent among them was Jan H. van den Berg (1961; 1969), who warned against inevitable medical failures once patients become objects of medical science instead of persons and subjects of care.

The real boom in bioethics, however, did not come until the mid-1970s and 1980s, when bioethics gained institutional status. From then on, not only doctors and a few ethicists but also ordinary people, among them patients and politicians, became interested in bioethical issues. In 1974 a famous case of active euthanasia in the Netherlands, in which a physician terminated the life of her terminally ill mother at the latter's request, marked the beginning of a debate that would last several decades.

The institutionalization of bioethics is apparent in the existence of three centers for bioethics in Belgium (two in Brussels, one in Leuven) and six centers in the Netherlands (Amsterdam, Ede, Groningen, Maastricht, Nijmegen, Utrecht), as well as in a number of interfaculty working groups. In Luxembourg a national consultative ethics commission for the life sciences and health has existed since 1988 by government decree.

Belgium

In 1993 Belgium underwent a major constitutional change. Belgium became a federal state made up of three communities (French, Flemish, and German-speaking) and of various regions. Bioethics has been impacted because issues are always compounded by the institutional complexities of multiple governments, parliamentary assemblies, and powers. The Belgian approach to AIDS provides an example: preventive measures are taken by the communities, healthcare is provided by the federal state, and the hospital infrastructure is established by the regions (Binamé). Religiously speaking, the country was almost entirely Roman Catholic, though in matters of medical ethics—for example, contraception—a group of postwar Catholic doctors and moral theologians of the personalist tradition had taken a rather liberal stance. The Roman Catholic Church still plays an influential, albeit no longer a decisive role in Belgian bioethics in the twenty-first century. Academically, its bioethical message is carried by the universities of Leuven-Louvain, Namur and Antwerp.

However, during the last decades of the twentieth century strong lay trends entered bioethics. The universities of Brussels, Ghent, and Liège established centers or study groups for bioethics. In 1973 the Belgian Society for Ethics and Medical Ethics was founded. Since 1990, this association has had a Flemish-language section. Other important societies are: The Belgian Academy of Medicine and the National Foundation of Medical Research.

Medical ethics at universities was usually taught by faculty from either theology or philosophy departments. Rare exceptions where physicians taught medical ethics, such as Marcel Renaer at Leuven, proved the rule. In 1980 Leuven University created a chair of medical ethics that was held by Paul Schotsmans in 2002. The Leuven (Flemish-language) center and the Louvain (French-language) center, under the direction of Jean-François Malherbe and his successor Michel Dupuis, developed teaching programs for medical ethics at the graduate level and for members of ethics committees. The annual conventions on health law at Ghent University, started in the 1960s, bring together health lawyers and bioethicists from around the world.

LEGISLATION. The federal government took several initiatives in encouraging the development of bioethics. In 1987, the Ministry of Public Health organized a national convention in order to explore the key bioethical issues of the future. The congress was expected to generate significant policy recommendations. In fact, only a general proposal resulted: that vehicles for ongoing debate should be created and that medical practice ought to be protected against wild growth and carelessness in the new fields of biotechnology. In 1993 the National Consultative Bioethics Committee was created with thirty-five members. Its major task is twofold: to provide advice in the field of biomedical ethics, be it on request or on its own initiative; and to provide information to the public at large. Belgian legislation at the federal level covers the following bioethical areas: blood (1961, 1971) and issues of the contaminated blood (1994); organ transplants (1986); artificial insemination (1987); abortion (1990); human genetics (1992); euthanasia (2002); and patients' rights (2002). At the level of the French community, an agency for the prevention of AIDS was created in 1991.

ETHICS COMMITTEES. Strictly speaking, Belgium had no law on human experimentation as of 2002. In 1999 the Hospital Act (1964) was amended by an article that made the presence of an independent review board compulsory, thereby providing these boards with a legal basis. In fact, ever since the early 1980s, ethical guidance and control over biomedical experimentation emanated from the Order of

Physicians. Their National Council had already developed a set of ethical rules and guidelines in what was called a "code of deontology" by 1975, to be respected by all physicians. Then, in 1976, the National Foundation for Medical Research charged an ethics committee with as a prime task, the review of research at university centers. In the 1980s, several academic institutions insisted that medical research be done under proper ethical conditions. University hospitals and major centers quickly established institutional review boards (Delfosse). In 1984 the National Council ruled that research ethics committees had to give their approval before research could be initiated in any hospital. At the beginning of the new millennium, close to two hundred ethics committees were in place. Gradually many of these ethics committees have expanded their mandate: the original research ethics committees also became hospital ethics committees, thus covering clinical cases and healthcare policy. In principle these committees are advisory. It is fair to say that during the 1990s efforts were made to create greater consistency, if not uniformity, in the normative as well as the procedural working methods of ethics committees.

The Netherlands

Medical ethics in the Netherlands has, over the years, gained a solid basis and infrastructure. Most universities have medical faculties or working groups where medical ethics is taught. Research and training institutes provide medical ethics information for healthcare institutions and for policymakers, and, joined by professional organizations, they offer systematic ethical training for healthcare workers. In the world of healthcare, numerous ethics committees are in place, and at the public level, the media and politics play an important role. During the 1960s Christian traditions lost their grip on social life, leaving a gap that was gradually filled by, among other things, the new (medical) ethics. The debates in the Netherlands on contraception, on abortion, on euthanasia, as well as all other debates on bioethics, were characterized by lively public participation, including patients and their organizations, as well as the movements for autonomy and self-determination. Dutch society, known for its tradition of tolerance, has displayed an increasing moral permissiveness in problems of biomedical ethics (Moor). In the immediate post–World War II period, a number of theologians as well as physicians were active in the field. Many bioethicists, even into the twenty-first century, have a religious if not a theological background, although a profound change has occurred in their interaction with society. Having gone through secularization, many of them have acknowledged the *humanum* as a basic norm that carries common agreement in this pluralistic society.

INSTITUTIONALIZED BIOETHICS. Institutionalization of bioethics in the Netherlands is best illustrated in the area of ethics committees for both research and hospital ethics. The number of independent review boards (IRBs), which began to be established in the early 1970s, grew rapidly after 1984; hospital ethics committees (HECs) seem to have grown more slowly, mainly after the mid-1980s. IRBs needed several years of adjustment after the introduction of a European Directive for "Good Clinical Practice" (1993) (Berghmans et al., 1996). Finally, in 1999, the law on Medical Scientific Research was introduced. Since then, a tendency toward the legalization of ethical issues seems to have taken over (Dupuis).

A number of professional organizations (of physicians, nurses, and hospitals) have their own study services for ethics that help them to research and develop policies in healthcare. The six established centers for bioethics as well as medical schools run teaching programs, services to clinics and physicians, and research projects in bioethics.

Dutch society, particularly Dutch political society, has at its disposal five major advisory organs to assist in making healthcare decisions: the Health Council, the National Council for Public Health, the Sickness Fund Council, the Central Organism for Fees, and the College of Hospital Provisions. All these organizations may offer advice without being asked. The Netherlands Organization for Technology Assessment monitors the ethical aspects of applied medical technology.

Dutch universities played an important role in the development of medical ethics. In the 1970s the universities of Maastricht (Paul Sporken), Nijmegen (Theo Beemer, Maurice de Wachter), and Leiden (Heleen Dupuis) were leaders in curriculum development. During the 1980s several other teaching units were established throughout the country.

MAJOR TOPICS. During the 1960s discussion of bioethics in the Netherlands focused on contraception and abortion; since then, the new reproductive technologies have attracted increasing interest. Euthanasia has been a key issue since the 1970s, and scarce resources and distributive justice, since the 1980s. A few issues that otherwise might not have been considered of importance have become so due to their link with scarcity of resources; for example, reproductive technologies, organ transplantation, the issue of insurance in the context of clinical genetics, and access to healthcare, especially waiting lists. Pervading all of these major topics is the recognition that patients' autonomy is quasi-absolute. A patient's choice is often considered to constitute the value of medical service. This is particularly true for decisions at the beginning and the end of life.

DECISIONS CONCERNING THE END OF LIFE. Euthanasia remained, in principle and for many years, punishable under criminal law although it became legal under certain conditions, such as voluntary request, hopeless suffering, and a second opinion provided by a colleague physician. Furthermore, a lenient jurisprudence was favorable to the medical practice of euthanasia and assisted suicide during the decades after 1974. Despite the publication of well-documented national surveys (van der Maas et al.; van der Wal et al.), stating that only 2,300 cases of requested euthanasia and 400 cases of assisted suicide occurred, as well as 1,000 cases of active termination of the patient's life without request, some estimates still range between 2,000 and 20,000 cases of euthanasia per year. Another critical point of discussion was the low instance of notification by physicians to the forensic doctor about their practicing euthanasia. By 1995, 6 out of 10 cases of euthanasia still remained unreported. In 1998 five regional evaluation committees started evaluating all notified cases and would then report back to the Attorney General and Health Inspection. In January 2001 a law codified what already existed: carefully performed euthanasia and assisted suicide, followed by notification, would exclude physicians from being prosecuted. Dutch euthanasia practice and legislation is perceived as exemplary in several countries, including Belgium, although the legislation is strongly opposed by others (Keown). It is fair to describe the Dutch euthanasia development over the decades as a transition from a moral debate, carried out on a large public scale during the 1970s and early 1980s, to discussions during the 1990s about careful implementation of policies, procedures, and guidelines, bringing about a clearer perception of the real practice.

HEALTHCARE SYSTEM AND REALLOCATION ISSUES. The Dutch healthcare system is based on principles of egalitarianism and solidarity. The latter principle is characteristic of the financial organization of healthcare in the Netherlands. In the modern welfare state, the moral principle is not primarily to feel individually responsible for others in need but to be held communally responsible for helping those in need. In a sense society imposes the duty to contribute financially in order to succor the needy in society. Individuals agree with this principle out of well-understood self-interest (Government Committee). At the same time, in the actual system of healthcare distribution, regulatory and marketing strategies are not necessarily contradictory (Wachter). While the population does not like cuts in healthcare or increased premiums for healthcare insurance, there is general agreement that healthcare is for all, and that the cost of individual preferences of patients beyond the basic package should be paid by the individual. The list of items excluded from the basic package around the turn of the millennium included only dental care for adults. But critics also lobbied to privatize cosmetic surgery, nursing luxury, homeopathy, physiotherapy beyond nine sessions, and alternative medicine. The government has legislated on hospital provisions (1973), on fees (1980), and on budgeting in hospitals (1983), but some problems, for example the waiting lists, remain. During the 1990s, a reform system based on the following principles was introduced: (1) private initiative is possible, and government controls only quality of care, access, and cost; (2) hospitals may plan according to local needs; and (3) insurers are free to market care.

REPRODUCTIVE TECHNOLOGIES. During the 1980s the emphasis on reproductive technologies was prominent. In 1981 abortion was legalized, offering women in distress the possibility to be treated in officially licensed clinics. A conscience clause warrants the right of healthcare workers to refuse to participate. Meanwhile, artificial procreation had become the issue of the day. Commercial surrogacy remains prohibited; artificial insemination by donor is increasingly available in all kinds of relationships. Follow-up studies have shown that no serious problems have arisen in either the physical or the psychological development of children conceived through in vitro fertilization (IVF) (van Balen).

ORGAN TRANSPLANTATION. The Organ Donation Act (1998) was meant to increase donations, to provide for the just distribution of organs, and to fight commercialization. In fact, it appears that there are fewer donations every year. The main reason for this failure is the opting-in system, where only the individual can decide to donate. But then, only one-third of the adult population returned the request to the Central Organ Donor Registry.

CLINICAL GENETICS. Several commissions have studied issues of genetic counseling, registration, access, screening and testing, as well as therapy. During 1990 the government took a position on various issues. For instance, the government agreed with the intention of the private insurers to exempt applicants from the obligation to disclose data resulting from a previous genetic diagnosis. In the case of life insurance, for example, the exemption applies to a limit of 250,000 florins, meaning that for insurance below that amount the insurer will not ask for genetic information. The insurers have shown readiness to try this policy for five years, and have repeatedly renewed this agreement. They also will not ask for additional genetic investigation. Based on principles of privacy, confidentiality, and solidarity, this position finds broad support among ethicists. Also in the context of clinical genetics, the government asked in early 1993 that the research community end all embryo research of its own volition. Moreover, several governments intended to prohibit by law numerous types of embryo research, such as research on embryos older than fourteen days and the creation of embryos for the sole purpose of research. Although it had been suggested that the use of fertilized eggs as a source of stem cells in therapeutic research be accepted (Evers), the Embryos Act of 2002 prohibits, for a period of at the most five years, the creation of embryos—be it by IVF or by somatic cell nuclear transfer—for the sole purpose of research.

Luxembourg

The smallness of the territory of Luxembourg and the closeness of contacts intensify mutual knowledge and exchange of information. Within medical circles there is a remarkable amount of self-regulation under the guidance of the "collège médical," approved by the Minister of Health. In 1991 this body laid down an official compendium of laws,. the "Mèmorial." Doctors and hospitals are still accepted as decision makers in healthcare. Public debate on issues such as euthanasia has rather been scant (Gillen). Having no medical school of its own, Luxembourg sends its medical students to neighboring countries, where they study in Belgian, French, or German universities.

In 1988 the government established the National Consultative Committee on Ethics in the life sciences and health care. As an advisory group it is supposed to study problems in a pluralistic perspective and to suggest solutions. The commission is also expected to develop programs of public information in bioethics. Reports thus far have covered patenting genetically modified organisms, reproductive technologies, youth protection, genetic research, and anonymity.

Ethics committees in hospitals and research centers are being developed in the early twenty-first century.

MAURICE A. M. DE WACHTER (1995)
REVISED BY AUTHOR

BIBLIOGRAPHY

Balen, Frank van. 1998. "Development of IVF Children." *Developmental Review* 18: 30–46.

Berg, Jan H. van den. 1961. *Het menselijk lichaam: Een metabletish onderzoek,* 2 vols. Nijkerk, Netherlands: G. F. Callenbach.

Berg, Jan H. van den. 1969. *Medische macht en medische ethiek.* Nijkerk, Netherlands: G. F. Callenbach.

Berghmans, Ron L. P.; Meulen, Ruud H. J. ter; and Wachter, Maurice A.M. de. 1996. *Medisch-ethische toetsing van geneesmiddelenonderzoek in Nederland.* Maastricht: Institute for Bioethics.

Binamé, Georges. 1995. "Bioethics and the Belgian Parliament." In *Parliaments and Screening: Ethical and Social Problems Arising from the Testing and Screening for HIV and Genetic Disease,* ed. Wayland Kennet. Paris: John Libbey Eurotext.

Delfosse, Marie-Louise. 1990. "Les comités d'éthique en Belgique." In *Contrôler la science? La question des comités d'éthique,* ed. Madeleine Moulin. Brussels: De Boeck-Wesmael.

Dupuis, Heleen M. 2001. "Ethische aspecten van experimenten met mensen." In *Geneeskunde en ethiek in harmonie,* ed. Frits A. de Wolff. 's-Gravenhage, Offset Drukkerij BV.

Evers, Kathinka. "European Perspectives on Therapeutic Cloning." *New England Journal of Medicine* 346(20): 1579–1582.

Gillen, Ernest. 1996. "Second Round Table: Luxemburg." In *Euthanasia and Assisted Suicide in the Netherlands and Europe,* ed. Maurice A. M. de Wachter. Brussels: Official Publications European Communities.

Government Committee on Choices in Health Care. 1992. *Choices in Health Care.* Zoetermeer, Netherlands: Ministry of Welfare, Health, and Cultural Affairs.

Keown, John. 2002. *Euthanasia, Ethics and Public Policy. An Argument against Legislation.* Cambridge, Eng.: Cambridge University Press.

Maas, Paul J. van der; Delden, Johannes J. M. van; and Pijnenborg, Lucas. 1992. *Euthanasia and Other Medical Decisions Concerning the End of Life.* Amsterdam: Elsevier.

Moor, Ruud de. 1996. "Euthanasia and the Moral Permissive Society." In *Euthanasia and Assisted Suicide in the Netherlands and in Europe,* ed. Maurice A.M. de Wachter. Brussels: Official Publications European Communities.

Wachter, Maurice A. M. de. 1988. "Ethics and Health Policy in the Netherlands." In *Health Care Systems: Moral Conflicts in European and American Public Policy,* ed. Hans M. Sass and Robert U. Massey. Dordrecht, Netherlands: Kluwer.

Wachter, Maurice A. M. de; Wert, Guido M. W. R.; Meulen, Ruud H. J. ter, et al. 1992. "Bioethics in the Netherlands: 1989–1991." In *Regional Developments in Bioethics: 1989–1991,* ed. B. Andrew Lustig, Baruch A. Brody, H. Tristram Engelhardt, Jr., and Laurence B. McCullough. Dordrecht, Netherlands: Kluwer.

Wal, Gerard van der, and Maas, Paul J. van der. 1996. *Euthanasie en andere medische beslissingen rond het levenseinde. De praktijk der meldingprocedure.* The Hague: SDU.

IV. UNITED KINGDOM

This entry surveys the development of medical ethics in Britain in the twentieth and early twenty-first centuries and some substantive medical ethical issues arising in these periods. It describes the involvement of important organizations concerned with medical ethics, the development of academic courses in the subject, and the establishment of a largely charitably sponsored independent nongovernmental national bioethics committee and of national forums for teachers and students of bioethics. It suggests that a typically

British antitheoretical, commonsense, and situational approach to medical ethics is gradually modifying so as to include at least some theoretical issues in the teaching and study of medical ethics.

Medical Ethics at the Beginning of the Twentieth Century

Respect for the professions and for the churches—especially, in England, the established Anglican church—were well-entrenched characteristics of British society at the beginning of the twentieth century, and medical ethics conformed to these cultural realities. Thus the normative standards of medical ethics were left almost entirely to the profession itself to establish and maintain. It did so largely in conformity with Hippocratic medical tradition, the ethical norms of the British protestant churches (including prohibition of active euthanasia and of abortion except to save the life of the pregnant woman), and a reliance on selecting "gentlemen" of good and honorable character to join the profession. The Medical Act of 1858 had, at the instigation of the newly established British Medical Association, established the General Medical Council to protect the public by controlling admission to the medical register on the basis of explicit medical educational standards, including ethical standards, both to exclude "quacks" (unqualified practitioners claiming to be doctors) from practicing medicine and to ensure that only those orthodox practitioners who had attained the prescribed standards were admitted to the register of medical practitioners.

Moreover, qualified medical practitioners who fell below the prescribed standards were liable to disciplinary action, including removal from the register (and thus loss of their professional livelihood) if they were found guilty of "infamous conduct in a professional respect." Among the infamous activities that could result in removal were the carrying out of abortion or active euthanasia, and having a sexual relationship with a patient. Other matters of considerable ethical concern to the General Medical Council included abuse of alcohol and drugs, fee splitting, "covering" for medical practice carried out by unregistered persons, convictions in the courts that would bring dishonor on the medical profession, abuse of the financial opportunities afforded by medical practice, improper denigration of professional colleagues, advertising for the doctor's own financial advantage, and canvassing for patients. Thus, at the beginning of the twentieth century, British medical ethics was almost entirely the prerogative of the medical profession and was concerned with protection of patients and of the public health, and with maintenance of its own honor and dignity.

Social Justice and Healthcare: 1911, 1946, and Beyond

If concerns about more equitable distribution of healthcare were not part of the medical profession's medical ethics agenda at the beginning of the twentieth century, they undoubtedly were a concern for the reforming liberal government elected with a large parliamentary majority in 1906. By 1911 David Lloyd George, then chancellor of the exchequer and later prime minister, achieved passage of his National Insurance Act; this provided working people (not their families) with medical and unemployment insurance, which was funded by compulsory contributions from workers, employers, and government (Braithwaite; Fox). The medical profession, though not opposed to the principle of such general provision of healthcare, fought the government on grounds of inadequate fees and inadequate protection for patients' choice of doctor; more than 27,000 doctors threatened to withhold their services. By 1913, however, after compromising with the doctors, Lloyd George had won the day (Lloyd; Lawrence).

The extension of medical care to the general population remained a popular political objective in Britain, and a 1942 report by Sir William Beveridge led, via the 1946 National Health Service Act, to the Labour government's establishment of the National Health Service (NHS) in 1948. This offered preventive as well as curative medical care to every member of the British public; it was provided in response to need, free at the time of that need, and financed by taxes (Bruce; Klein; Webster). While the objectives and provisions of the NHS remain widely accepted, early expectations that widespread healthcare would produce a healthier nation with reduced requirements for healthcare have never been achieved. On the contrary, concerns about increasing, yet inadequate, health expenditure multiplied, especially from the 1970s (Maxwell); a government committee chaired by Sir Douglas Black produced a 1980 report showing vast inequalities of health status in the population correlating with economic and other social disadvantages. Conservative government policy in the 1980s was more concerned to reduce costs than to remedy such discrepancies, but the New Labour governments of the 1990s and early 2000s was explicitly committed to reducing health inequalities and committed considerable additional funding to the National Health Service for this purpose.

Voluntary Euthanasia: 1936 and Beyond

A quite different issue of healthcare ethics—voluntary euthanasia—has been of public concern in Britain for almost as long as the issue of justice in the provision of healthcare. Medical proposals for its legislation had appeared early in the twentieth century; and in 1936, following the creation of the Voluntary Euthanasia Society, the House of Lords debated and rejected a proposal to legalize voluntary euthanasia, which would have provided the legal right to request and be given medical assistance to die when suffering from incurable and fatal illness. Despite the admission by Lord Dawson, an eminent doctor, that euthanasia was carried out by many doctors (Dawson), he and another medical peer, Lord Horder, opposed the bill on the grounds that its proposals involved too many legal formalities and that, in any case, euthanasia was a matter best left to the discretion of doctors. (Many years later state archives were opened and revealed that Lord Dawson had deliberately accelerated the death of the dying King George VI, allegedly in order to enable the quality morning newspapers to report it first rather than risk the death being announced by a less-suitable evening newspaper.)

Euthanasia remains an intermittently burning public issue. Further proposals to legalize it were rejected by the British Parliament in 1969 and 1990; and in 1988 the British Medical Association (BMA) declared that, while allowing patients to die was properly a matter of medical discretion, active killing, even if requested by the patient in circumstances of severe and incurable suffering and disease, was always unacceptable and should remain illegal (BMA, 1988a). In 1992 a British doctor was convicted of attempted murder for administering undiluted potassium chloride to a long-standing patient of his who, in intractable pain, had repeatedly requested him to end her life (Brahams). His sentence of one year's imprisonment, however, was suspended, and the General Medical Council, while admonishing him, permitted him to continue practicing ("Decision on Dr. Cox," 1992). After the verdict a *British Medical Journal* editorial called for a royal commission to study active and passive euthanasia (the editorial's subtitle was "The Tide Seems to Be Running for Euthanasia" [Smith], and a *Lancet* editorial criticized the BMA's "unsympathetic public line" on euthanasia ["Final Autonomy," 1992]).

Nevertheless, the British debate about such cases and about the legalization of euthanasia in the Netherlands (e.g., Keown; Otlowski) did not result in any relaxation of British law. Two cases from 2002 clearly demonstrate the legal situation in the United Kingdom. On the one hand, refusal of life-prolonging treatment was undoubtedly a legal right: The High Court had admonished doctors for ignoring the instructions of a Ms. B. to cease treating her with artificial ventilation; after the doctors complied, she died. On the other hand, neither euthanasia nor assisting suicide was a legal right: On the same day that Ms. B. died, a Mrs. Pretty lost her case before the European Court of Human Rights to be helped to commit suicide (Boyd, 2002; JME, 2002). The

distinction between killing and assisting suicide (legally forbidden) and withdrawing life-sustaining treatment at a patient's instruction (legally required) had once again been reaffirmed.

Experimentation on Human Subjects: 1947 and Beyond

Medical ethics in Britain—as in all parts of the civilized world—was given a shocking impetus after World War II by the revelations at the Nuremberg trials of Nazi medical war crimes, and the 1947 Nuremberg Code on Human Experimentation was as readily accepted within Britain as elsewhere (see Doyal and Tobias). In the early 1960s, however, Maurice H. Pappworth, an English physician, claimed that many orthodox medical research investigations were unethical, and in a book first published in 1967 he enraged the British medical establishment by likening examples of British medical research to the research of the notorious Nazi doctors. Whether cause and effect or coincidence, in the same year the Royal College of Physicians (RCP) published a recommendation that all clinical research proposals should be subject to ethical review; this advice was widely circulated by the British government's Department of Health and Social Security. Over the next few years "ethical committees," or research ethics committees (RECs), were established in the majority of hospitals and other institutions conducting medical research.

Nonetheless, development and practice of these committees was recognized to be variable, and in 1984 the RCP published guidelines for RECs, updated in 1990 (RCP, 1990a), as well as reports titled *Research Involving Patients* (1990b) and *Research on Healthy Volunteers* (1986). In 1991 the Department of Health published the first of its own guidelines for RECs. In both sets of guidelines the advice is detailed; it is designed, in the words of the RCP document, "to maintain ethical standards of practice in research, to protect subjects of research from possible harm, to preserve their rights, and to provide reassurance to the public that this is being done. In achieving these objectives ethics committees should remember that research benefits society and that they should take care not to hinder it without good cause. Ethics committees also protect research workers from unjustified criticism." (RCP, 1990a, p. 3). While the RCP guidelines were widely accepted in Britain as the national standard for ethics committees, and while research on human subjects must be submitted to RECs, there was and remains considerable doubt about what proportion of British ethics committees actually implement them (Nicholson; Gilbert, Fulford, and Parker; Neuberger).

In a 1997 government technology assessment review, Richard Ashcroft and colleagues expressed concern about the need to take careful account of the cultural and religious backgrounds of research participants. Revised guidelines on research were issued by the Department of Health in 2001, and new European legislation in the form of a "Clinical Trials Directive" was expected to take effect across the entire European Union in 2004. When this is incorporated into U.K. law, it is likely to include a statutory role for RECs for the first time; human research will thus catch up with animal research, which has been legally regulated in the United Kingdom since 1876.

Abortion: 1938 and Beyond

Another major medico-moral issue of British concern has been abortion. Under the Offences Against the Person Act of 1861, procuring an abortion was a felony punishable by life imprisonment. In 1938 an English obstetrician-gynecologist, Alec Bourne, challenged the law by reporting himself to the police after carrying out a therapeutic abortion on a girl who had been the victim of multiple rape. He was found not guilty on the grounds that the patient's life, in the sense of her mental well-being, was at risk if the pregnancy continued; just as "child destruction" (as the act calls it) to preserve the life of the mother was legally permissible under the Infant Life Preservation Act of 1929, so abortion for the mother's well-being might be lawful (see Mason, McCall Smith, and Laurie). In the 1967 abortion act the law was liberalized to permit abortion in cases in which two doctors certify that the continuation of the pregnancy would be a greater risk to the life or health of the pregnant woman, or her existing children, than a termination; or that termination would prevent grave permanent injury to the physical or mental health of the pregnant woman; or that there is a substantial risk that the child would suffer serious physical or mental disability.

In practice many British doctors, accepting that during the first three months of any pregnancy the risk of continuing to normal birth is greater than the risk of therapeutic abortion, agree to abortion for any woman who after deliberation continues to request it. The upper limit of gestation at which abortion is permitted was reduced by the Human Fertilisation and Embryology Act of 1990 from twenty-eight weeks to twenty-four weeks. No upper limit applies in cases in which the mother's life is seriously threatened and in cases in which the child, if born, would probably be seriously disabled. Significant, though minority, opposition to abortion persists both within the medical profession and among the public. In Northern Ireland, a part of the United Kingdom, opposition to abortion among the Protestant as well as the Roman Catholic population is sufficiently widespread for the Abortion Act not to apply there.

"Official" British medical ethics, as represented in this context by the General Medical Council, the British Medical Association, and the Royal College of Obstetricians and Gynaecologists, accepts abortion when carried out according to the law while recognizing any doctor's or nurse's right of conscientious objection. Such practitioners are expected to inform their patients of their moral objections to abortion, to advise them that they may seek assistance elsewhere, and to give information about sources of such assistance if requested (BMA, 1988b).

Reproductive Technology: 1978 and Beyond

In July 1978 the pioneering work of Patrick Steptoe and Robert Edwards led to the birth of the world's first "test-tube baby"—and to a paradigm shift in bioethical thinking about human reproduction and genetics. From 1982, when the British government appointed a Committee of Inquiry into Human Fertilisation and Embryology (Warnock), until the passing of the Human Fertilisation and Embryology Act in 1990, the British public and the British medical profession were gripped by a vigorous debate about the moral issues associated with in vitro fertilization (Snowden, Mitchell, and Snowden; Council for Science and Society; Bock and O'Connor; Bromham, Dalton, and Jackson). As with abortion, the central moral issue was seen by many to be the moral status of the embryo/fetus, though other issues included possible adverse physical and psychological effects on children conceived artificially and also on the women involved with such techniques, especially in the case of surrogacy. Feminist concerns included the continuing debate about access by single heterosexual women and lesbian women to reproductive technology (Hanscombe and Forster; Chadwick).

The issues were resolved in an extensive government bill that, unusually, offered alternative clauses on the most contentious issue of all: research on, followed by destruction of, the human embryo. Members of Parliament (MPs) were given a free vote (i.e., without any party pressure to vote in one way rather than another) and asked to choose between allowing such research for up to fourteen days of embryo development, as recommended by the Warnock Committee majority report, or forbidding all such research on human embryos except when done therapeutically—that is, to facilitate transfer of the embryo into the uterus of a woman. (The latter is the position of the Roman Catholic church, though it is worth noting that the eminent Jesuit theologian John Mahoney had argued in 1984 that the early embryo is "unlikely to be possessed of a soul and personhood in its existence at the simple cell-multiplication stage prior to diversification" [p. 85]). After cliff-hanging public, professional, and parliamentary debate, the MPs accepted research for up to fourteen days of embryonic development and established the national Human Fertilisation and Embryology Authority to monitor and control all such activities.

Informed Consent: 1985 and Beyond

Of the many other medico-moral issues that have exercised both healthcare professionals and the public in Britain, two legal cases are particularly notable: the Sidaway case on informed consent to treatment and the Gillick case on treatment of minors without parental consent. In the Sidaway case, finally determined by the House of Lords in 1985, the plaintiff complained that her surgeon had been negligent in not warning her of the small risk of spinal nerve root damage, which had occurred. Their lordships decided by a majority to uphold the existing English legal doctrine according to which a doctor is not negligent if acting in a way supported by a body of reasonable medical opinion (the "Bolam test"). Nevertheless, by indicating what reasonable doctors could be expected to do in certain circumstances (for example, answer their patients' questions and warn them of any substantial risks!), the judges brought English law "edging toward" the American "reasonable patient standard" whereby the requirements of a reasonable person in the patient's situation would determine what information was required (Kennedy and Grubb)—though not all legal commentators agreed that even this modest degree of change was achieved in the case (Brazier).

In the Gillick case a mother asked the court to rule that doctors should not be allowed to give medication (birth-control pills) to her children under the age of sixteen without obtaining parental consent. Once again the case went to the House of Lords, which in 1986 rejected Mrs. Gillick's claim; it ruled that a doctor ought to try to persuade the minor to involve the parents in the consultation, but if the patient refused—provided the doctor had good reason to assess the minor as having sufficient maturity and understanding—treatment could be prescribed without involving the parents (Kennedy and Grubb).

In the early 2000s increased emphasis on the need for doctors to obtain informed and explicit consent from patients in relation to use of and retention of tissues after surgery or postmortem became more stringent in response to two NHS scandals. Thus the reports of two inquiries, one into defects in pediatric cardiac surgery at a Bristol hospital (Bristol) and the other into storage of pediatric pathology specimens at a Liverpool hospital (*Royal Liverpool*, 2001),

recommended (among a host of improvements) explicit informed-consent procedures for the retention of all tissues and organs (for research or teaching) removed for therapeutic or diagnostic purposes. These recommendation were put forth despite professional concerns that such explicit procedures would often cause unnecessary additional distress to recently bereaved families or to parents whose children were about to have surgery. The general trend in the early 2000s was to explicit and "fully informed" consent for all interventions (see, e.g., Doyal and Tobias), despite professional and philosophical concerns that such moves toward ever-greater "accountability" were excessively undermining trust in medical and other professionals, which though "old-fashioned" was nonetheless ultimately in the public interest (O'Neill 2002a, 2002b).

The Organization of Medical Ethics in Britain

At the beginning of the twentieth century, the final arbiter of medical ethics was the General Medical Council (GMC), a regulatory body largely composed of doctors. In the early twenty-first century, while the GMC's role remained pivotal, it was in the process of becoming a smaller organization with a larger representation of nondoctors and an organization far more open to influence from outside the ranks of the medical profession than ever before. In 2003 the GMC was reduced from 104 members to 35, of whom 19 were elected and 2 appointed by the medical profession, while 14 were nonmedical ("lay") (and thus comprising 40 % of the GMC in contrast to the previous 25 %). The lay members continue to be appointed by the Privy Council (a group of the United Kingdom's "great and good" appointed by the monarch and relatively independent of the government of the day, though many will have been appointed by virtue of their high office in current or previous governments). The GMC, as it notes itself on its web site, is "not here to protect the medical profession—their interests are protected by others. Our job is to protect patients."

The GMC licenses doctors to practice, and it can withdraw or put conditions on a doctor's license if a complaint is upheld. It is responsible for standards of medical education, including education in medical ethics, for quasi-judicial assessment of complaints against doctors, and for provision of advice on ethical standards and professional conduct. This advice used to come in a very slender volume, "the little blue book" (e.g., GMC, 1992), but more recently the GMC has provided a broader range of advisory booklets with more extensive "guidance on good practice," of which the core is covered in *Good Medical Practice* (GMC,

2001). This advice is sent to every registered medical practitioner and is also available to everyone on the GMC web site.

Although it has no official authority in matters of medical ethics, the British Medical Association, which is the doctors' professional association and trade union, provides considerable guidance on these issues to its members, to the government, and to the public. It has a multidisciplinary Medical Ethics Committee and an ever more impressive Medical Ethics Department of permanent staff. It provides individual advice and analysis to its members as requested, provides analysis and advice to government and official bodies, and publishes books relevant to medical ethics (e.g., BMA, 1993, 2001a, 2001b). (The BMA even experimented with what may have been one of the world's first computer programs offering doctors medico-moral advice [Sieghart and Dawson]).

Other professional influences on medical ethics are exerted during medical education by individual teachers, themselves influenced not only by the GMC and (often) the BMA but also by the Medical Research Council (a government run organization that funds and or carries out much of the UK's medical research program) and specialty organizations; the latter include the Royal Colleges of Physicians, Surgeons, Obstetricians and Gynaecologists, General Practitioners, Psychiatrists, and so on, all of which offer advice and guidance on medical ethics relevant to their specialties. So, too, do the medical malpractice organizations, such as the Medical Defence Union and the Medical Protection Society. In addition the employment contracts of most doctors in Britain exert some legally binding ethical pressure on their behavior. For example, general practitioners, though they are independent contractors, are required by their contracts with the NHS to provide emergency care in their vicinity whether or not those needing such care are registered with them; and they are also required by their contracts to accept "difficult to place patients" for a minimum of three months, when required by the NHS to do so. And surgeons in NHS hospitals, according to their contract of service, must, under normal circumstances, obtain written consent from their patients prior to operating. In addition there is a strong tradition in British medicine of consultation, especially with more experienced colleagues, about any difficult medical problem, including difficult medico-moral problems. A noteworthy if embryonic development at the end of the twentieth century was the creation of clinical ethics committees at some hospitals, set up to provide analysis and advice about particular ethical problems arising in clinical practice (not in research), to advise on ethical aspects of hospital policy matters, and to have at least some educational function (see, e.g., "Clinical Ethics Committees Supplement," 2001).

Nonmedical influences on British medical ethics include the range of forces typical of a modern Western democracy. The most important is undoubtedly the law, which, as noted above, has a major role in defining the arenas within which the medical profession may make its own choices about medico-moral issues. Nurses have undergone a metamorphosis from doctors' handmaidens to independent health professionals and have become increasingly influential in British healthcare ethics, especially through the activities and pronouncements of their disciplinary body, the (United Kingdom) Nursing and Midwifery Council or NMC (e.g., NMC), and of their professional association and trade union, the Royal College of Nursing or RCN (e.g., RCN 1991, 2001).

Many public pressure groups, patient groups, and special medical interest groups exist to try to influence the profession, the media, Parliament, and the public on such matters as healthcare ethics issues. Important examples include the Patients Association, the College of Health, the Consumers Association, MIND (which promotes the interests of the mentally ill), MENCAP (which promotes the interests of the mentally disabled or impaired), CERES (Consumers for Ethics in Research), GeneWatch (which is concerned with the ethics and risks of genetic engineering), and the local community-health councils and their successor organizations, the Patient Advocacy and Liaison Services (PALS), which protect patients' interests. Also important are several "right-to-life" activist groups such as the Pro-Life Alliance, LIFE, and The Society for the Protection of the Unborn Child, and "on the other side," the Voluntary Euthanasia Society and the Abortion Law Reform Association. And the media constantly, often daily, publish and broadcast on medical ethics issues.

From a plethora of possible examples, one media event is particularly worth noting: the prestigious BBC Radio Reith Lectures, given in 1980 by Ian Kennedy, then a lecturer in academic law (later to become a professor of medical law and ethics and a knight of the realm). Published in 1981 under the profession-provoking title *The Unmasking of Medicine,* the lectures brought into the arena of intelligent public discussion many of the standard themes of medical ethics, and argued forcefully that while doctors had special training and expertise in technical medical matters, they had no such training and expertise in moral matters. Even if they had had such training (which Kennedy advocated), they had no right to assume that moral decisions in medical practice were solely for doctors to make, in the way that technical decisions in medical practice might be. The resulting public and professional debate did much to achieve Kennedy's objective of bringing medical ethics "out of the hushed halls of Academe into the noisy market place of ideas" (Kennedy, 1981, p. xi).

The study and development of medical ethics in Britain has also been promoted by the Institute of Medical Ethics (IME). Originally named the Society for the Study of Medical Ethics, it was founded in the early 1960s by a Church of England priest, the Rev. (later Dean) Edward Shotter, who at the time had pastoral responsibility for medical students in London. Shotter soon recruited two other Protestant clerics, both from Scotland, who were to become influential in British medical ethics: Kenneth Boyd (Boyd, 1979, 1992; Boyd, Callaghan, and Shotter; Smith and Boyd; Gallagher and Boyd) and Alastair Campbell, founding editor of the IME's *Journal of Medical Ethics* from 1975 to 1980 and one of the earliest British contributors to the academic medical ethics literature (Campbell, 1972, 1978, 1984; Campbell and Higgs) and a Jesuit and psychologist Brendan Callaghan. Also recruited by Shotter was a secular Jewish doctor-philosopher, Raanan Gillon, who served as editor of the *Journal of Medical Ethics* from 1981 to 2001. Among the IME's activities have been the establishment of multidisciplinary ethics study groups within most of the British medical schools, various research projects, and the founding of two publications, the aforementioned *Journal of Medical Ethics* (1975) (by the end of the century the most highly cited journal in its field) and the *Bulletin of Medical Ethics* (1985; shortly afterward, the latter became independent of the IME, and it continues to be edited by its owner-editor, another Shotter medical recruit, Richard Nicholson).

Other organizations stimulating the early development of healthcare ethics in the United Kingdom were the medical ethics and or medical law centers at some of the universities. Pioneer centers in Britain included those at King's College, London; the University of Wales at Swansea; the University of Manchester; and the Universities of Birmingham, Hull, Oxford, St. Andrews, Leeds, and Warwick; the University of Wales at Cardiff; and the Universities of Glasgow and Bristol. Since the 1990s there has been considerable further expansion in the number of universities providing healthcare ethics, or law and ethics, teaching and research in the United Kingdom, and these have been joined by a few centers offering courses in medical humanities. In addition, the Society for Applied Philosophy is concerned with philosophical illumination of "areas of practical concern" that often include issues of healthcare ethics; it publishes the *Journal of Applied Philosophy*.

Of the various academic disciplines with an interest in medical ethics that has stimulated its development, and apart from law and theology as already mentioned, health economics has been particularly important in relation to resource allocation. Alan J. Williams (1985, 1996), Alan Maynard (1986; Maynard and Bloor), and Anthony J. Culyer (1992, 2001), from the Centre of Health Economics at York University, and Gavin Mooney and Alistair McGuire (1988) have been especially influential, particularly Williams, with his advocacy of the maximization of quality-adjusted life years (QALYS) as the centrally relevant criterion for health-service resource allocation.

Academic Courses, Degrees, and Chairs

The first British academic course in medical ethics seems to have been started by the ancient City of London guild, the Worshipful Society of Apothecaries (still a medical licensing body), when it instituted a diploma course in the philosophy of medicine in 1978, first taught by the Oxford philosopher Michael Lockwood. An annual one-week "intensive course in medical ethics for medical and nursing teachers" was started in 1983 at Imperial College, London, in cooperation with the IME, and in 1984 the Centre of Medical Law and Ethics at King's College, London, initiated a one-year postgraduate diploma in medical law and ethics, upgraded in 1987 to a master's degree. In 1985 the University of Wales introduced a highly popular part-time M.A. in healthcare ethics, and in 1987 the University of Manchester offered a multidisciplinary M.A. in healthcare ethics, administered by its Centre for Social Ethics and Policy. Since then various other British universities and colleges have developed a wide variety of courses in healthcare ethics.

British medical schools were slow to introduce the formal study of medical ethics; the Scots led the way at Edinburgh University and Glasgow University, with King's College Hospital in London being the vanguard in England under the leadership of the doctor-ethicist Roger Higgs. Full-time philosophers were appointed to teach the subject at medical schools at Liverpool and at the London Hospital; and St. Mary's Hospital Medical School London was the first to appoint a (part-time visiting) professor of medical ethics. Birmingham University Medical School appointed a veterinarian, David Morton, to the joint chair of biomedical science and ethics.

Although medical schools were stimulated into some activity by the report of an IME working group (Boyd, 1987) urging that they introduce the critical study of medical ethics, such teaching became widespread only after the GMC told medical schools that medical ethics and law should be part of the core medical curriculum and therefore compulsory for all medical students (GMC, 1993). In 1998 most of the teachers of medical ethics in U.K. medical schools, and others, published a consensus statement on the contents of a core curriculum in medical ethics and law in medical schools (Teachers of Medical Ethics).

By the early 2000s, however, although there were several professors of medical ethics holding personal chairs, and while many medical schools had at least one full-time teacher of medical ethics, the only established chair of medical ethics in a U.K. medical school had been established in 1996 at the University of Bristol Medical School, with Alastair Campbell holding the position until his retirement in 2003. While female let alone feminist influences cannot be said to characterise British medical schools, influential exceptions in the realm of medical ethics included Ruth Chadwick, Jenifer Jackson, Janet Radcliffe Richards, Donna Dickenson, Bobbie Farsides, Heather Draper, and Ann Sommerville, along with leading medical law and ethics specialists Margaret Brazier and Sheila Mclean.

Three National Groups Formed in the 1990s

At the beginning of the 1990s three national groups concerned with medical ethics were established. The first, the U.K. Forum for Health Care Ethics and Law, was designed to bring together the increasingly numerous and various academic and other organizations, teachers, and students in Britain concerned with healthcare ethics. The second was the Nuffield Council on Bioethics, a national independent and nongovernmental multidisciplinary committee established by the private philanthropic Nuffield Foundation, to review the ethical issues raised by medical research, starting with those involving genetic manipulation, The third was the Association for Healthcare and Medical Ethics Teachers, founded for medical ethics teachers in British medical and nursing schools.

The Nuffield Council on Bioethics has flourished, becoming as near to a national committee on bioethics as the United Kingdom seems likely to have. While it remains self-appointed and unofficial this enables it to be independent of government, and its funding seems secure now that the government's Medical Research Council and the Wellcome Trust have joined the Nuffield Foundation in supporting it. Helping to account for the high respect with which it is held are its independence and multidisciplinarity, as well as the high caliber of its reports and discussion documents, on subjects including ethical aspects of genetic screening, xeno-transplantation, stem cell therapy, health research in developing countries, the patenting of DNA, genetics, and human behavior (all available through the organization's web site). Also likely to be relevant to the development of medical ethics in the UK is the creation in 2002 of the Association for Medical Humanities.

Continental Influences

Three continental European influences on the British approach to medical ethics are also important to note. The Council of Europe has an international bioethics committee and has produced a Convention on Human Rights and Biomedicine, which is legally binding on signatory states (Council of Europe) and is in effect an extension of its European Convention on Human Rights. A protocol to the convention banning human reproductive cloning is in effect, and protocols on organ transplantation, medical research, and the embryo and genetics are being developed. The United Kingdom has not signed on to the convention, in part because it forbids a form of scientific research that is accepted in the United Kingdom: the production of human embryos for the purpose of research.

The European Union also has an international bioethics committee, but more importantly for U.K. bioethics it has distributed significant funding for bioethics research projects if these involve cooperation between member nations. This has resulted in several U.K.–led projects involving such areas as education in bioethics, ethical aspects of HIV/AIDS, stem cell research, virtue ethics and chronic illness, and neonatal research. The United Nations Educational, Scientific and Cultural Organization (UNESCO) also has an international bioethics committee and has produced a (nonbinding) Universal Declaration on the Human Genome and Human Rights, which was adopted by the United Nations. Academic bioethics in the United Kingdom is also influenced from continental Europe through participation in the European Association of Centres of Medical Ethics and the European Society for Philosophy of Medicine and Health Care.

Religious Influences on Medical Ethics

Religious organizations are influential in medical ethics in Britain, both at a personal level, affecting the decisions of patients, healthcare workers, and others concerning medico-moral issues, and as a result of institutional activities. Relevant institutions include the Church of England Board for Social Responsibility (see, e.g., Dunstan, 1987; Dunstan and Seller); the (Roman) Catholic Bishops' Joint Committee on Bioethical Issues (see, e.g., Catholic Bishops' Joint Committee); the (Roman Catholic) Linacre Centre (see, e.g., Linacre Centre); the (evangelical Protestant) Christian Medical Fellowship (which holds regular meetings and publishes the *Journal of the Christian Medical Fellowship*); and the Jewish Chief Rabbinate (one of whose members, Lord Immanuel Jakobovits, obtained the first doctorate devoted to Jewish medical ethics; see Jakobovits).

The National "Flavor" of Medical Ethics in Britain

While it is always risky to generalize, a pragmatic, situationist, commonsense, antitheoretical, and antiregulatory approach tends to characterize the British approach to medical ethics (as to do many other aspects of British life—though resistance to regulation may be being increasingly overridden). Despite this national reluctance to theorize, however, it is gradually being acknowledged that some theoretical underpinning is needed even for commonsense ethical decisions. In the context of medical ethics, a distinction is increasingly recognized between two medical ethical concepts ("Two Concepts," 1985). The first is traditional medical ethics, in the sense of promulgating and enforcing within the medical profession certain medico-moral norms—what Gordon R. Dunstan called "the obligations of a moral nature which govern the practice of medicine" (1981, pp. xxviii–xxxi). This sort of medical ethics has characterized medical education and practice since Hippocratic times. The second, more recent sort—philosophical or critical medical ethics—sets out to examine rigorously, and in the light of argument, justification, and counterargument, the issues of medical ethics, including the claims of traditional medical ethics.

Prompted from without as well as from within, the British medical profession has, since the mid-1970s, increasingly accepted the latter medical ethical concept as a proper part of medical thinking and education. Evidence for this includes the General Medical Council's greatly increased interest in medical ethics since it held a conference on medical ethics teaching in 1984; publication by the *British Medical Journal* in 1985–1986 of a series of twenty-six articles under the title "Philosophical Medical Ethics" (Gillon, 1985–1986); publication of *The Pond Report* on medical ethics teaching (Boyd, 1987), recommending such teaching in medical schools; the GMC's requirement that medical ethics and law should be part of the core medical curriculum (GMC, 1993); publication of the consensus proposals for the core curriculum (Teachers of Medical Ethics); the increasing teaching of critical or philosophical medical ethics in medical schools; and the increased attention paid to critical medical ethics by the British Medical Association.

But virtually all involved in the British medical ethics scene agree on one issue: the central importance of real cases, manifesting real medico-moral problems, in their real human context, for any adequate critical study, teaching, or understanding of the "humanized version of ethics" called for by the moral philosopher Jonathan Glover (1999).

RAANAN GILLON(1995)
REVISED BY AUTHOR

BIBLIOGRAPHY

Almond, Brenda, ed. 1990. *AIDS: A Moral Issue—The Ethical, Legal, and Social Aspects.* London: Macmillan.

Ashcroft, Richard; Chadwick, David; Clark, Stephen; et al. 1997. "Implications of Socio-cultural Contexts for the Ethics of Clinical Trials." *Health Technology Assessment* 1(9): 1–67.

Beveridge, Sir William. 1942. *Social Insurance and Allied Services.* Cmd. 6404. London: HMSO.

Black, Sir Douglas. 1980. *Inequalities in Health: Report of a Research Working Group* (The Black Report). London: Department of Health and Social Security. Also published as *Inequalities in Health: The Black Report,* by Sir Douglas Black, Jeremy Morris, Cyril Smith, and Peter Townsend. Harmondsworth, Eng.: Penguin, 1982.

Bock, Gregory, and O'Connor, Maeve, eds. 1986. *Human Embryo Research: Yes or No?* London: Tavistock.

Boyd, Kenneth. 1979. *The Ethics of Resource Allocation.* Edinburgh: Edinburgh University Press.

Boyd, Kenneth. 1992. "HIV Infection and AIDS: The Ethics of Medical Confidentiality: Report of an Institute of Medical Ethics Working Party." *Journal of Medical Ethics* 18(4): 173–179.

Boyd, Kenneth. 2002. "Mrs. Pretty and Ms. B." *Journal of Medical Ethics* 28(4): 211–212

Boyd, Kenneth, ed. 1987. *The Pond Report: The Teaching of Medical Ethics. Report of a Working Party of the Institute of Medical Ethics.* London: Institute of Medical Ethics.

Boyd, Kenneth, ed. 1990. "Assisted Death: Institute of Medical Ethics Working Party on the Ethics of Prolonging Life and Assisting Death." *Lancet* 336: 610–613.

Boyd, Kenneth; Callaghan, Brendan; and Shotter, Edward. 1986. *Life before Birth: Consensus in Medical Ethics.* London: SPCK.

Brahams, Diana. 1992. "Medicine and the Law: Euthanasia Doctor Convicted of Attempted Murder." *Lancet* 340: 782–783.

Braithwaite, William J. 1957. *Lloyd George's Ambulance Wagon: Papers Edited by Sir Henry N. Bunbury.* London: Methuen and Cox.

Brazier, Margaret. 1992. *Medicine, Patients, and the Law,* 2nd edition. Harmondsworth, Eng.: Penguin.

Brazier, Margaret, and Lobjoit, Mary, eds. 1991. *Protecting the Vulnerable: Autonomy and Consent in Health Care.* London: Routledge.

Bristol Royal Infirmary Inquiry. 2001. *Learning from Bristol: The Report of the Public Inquiry into Children's Heart Surgery at the Bristol Royal Infirmary, 1984–1995.* Cm. 5207. London: HMSO.

British Medical Association (BMA). 1988a. *The Euthanasia Report: Report of a Working Party to Review the British Medical Association's Guidance on Euthanasia.* London: Author.

British Medical Assoication (BMA). 1988b. *Philosophy and Practice of Medical Ethics.* London: Author.

British Medical Association (BMA). 1993. *Medical Ethics Today: Its Practice and Philosophy.* London: Author.

British Medical Association (BMA). 2001a. *Withholding and Withdrawing Life Prolonging Treatment: Guidance for Decision Making,* 2nd edition. London: Author.

British Medical Association (BMA). 2001b. *The Medical Profession and Human Rights: A Handbook for a Changing Agenda.* London: Author.

Bromham, David; Dalton, Maureen; and Jackson, Jennifer, eds. 1990. *Philosophical Ethics in Reproductive Medicine: Proceedings of an International Conference Held in 1988.* Manchester, Eng.: Manchester University Press.

Bruce, M. 1972. *The Coming of the Welfare State.* London: Batsford.

Campbell, Alastair. 1972. *Moral Dilemmas in Medicine.* Edinburgh: Churchill Livingstone.

Campbell, Alastair. 1978. *Medicine, Health, and Justice: The Problem of Priorities.* Edinburgh: Churchill Livingstone.

Campbell, Alastair. 1984. *Moderated Love: A Theology of Professional Care.* London: SPCK.

Campbell, Alastair, and Higgs, Roger. 1982. *In That Case: Medical Ethics in Everyday Practice.* London: Darton, Longman and Todd.

Catholic Bishops' Joint Committee on Bioethical Issues (U.K.). 1987. *On Human Infertility Services and Embryo Research: Response to the Department of Health and Social Security's Consultation.* Abingdon, Eng.: Author.

Chadwick, Ruth F. 1987. "Having Children" and "The Perfect Baby." In *Ethics, Reproduction, and Genetic Control,* ed. Ruth F. Chadwick. London: Routledge.

"Clinical Ethics Committees Supplement." 2001. *Journal of Medical Ethics,* suppl. 1, 27(2).

Clothier, Sir Cecil. 1988. *The Patient's Dilemma.* London: Nuffield Provincial Hospitals Trust.

Council for Science and Society. 1984. *Human Procreation: Ethical Aspects of the New Techniques.* Oxford: Oxford University Press.

Council of Europe. 1997. *Convention for the Protection of Human Rights and Dignity of the Human Being with regard to the Application of Biology and Medicine: Convention on Human Rights and Biomedicine.* Strasbourg, France: Author.

Culyer, Anthony J. 1992. "The Morality of Efficiency in Health Care: Some Uncomfortable Implications." *Health Economics* 1: 7–18.

Culyer, Anthony J. 2001. "Economics and Ethics in Health Care." *Journal of Medical Ethics* 27: 217–222.

Dawson, Lord. 1936. Speech to the House of Lords. *Parliamentary Debates,* House of Lords, 5th ser., vol. 103, cols. 488–489.

"Decision on Dr. Cox." 1992. *Lancet* 340: 1283.

Downie, Robin, and Calman, Kenneth. 1987. *Healthy Respect.* London: Faber; 2nd edition, Oxford: Oxford University Press, 1993.

Doyal, Len, and Gough, Ian. 1991. *A Theory of Human Need.* London: Macmillan.

Doyal, Len, and Tobias, Jeffrey, eds. 2001. *Informed Consent and Medical Research.* London: BMJ Books.

Dunstan, Gordon R. 1981. "Medical Ethics." In *Dictionary of Medical Ethics,* ed. Archibald S. Duncan, Gordon R. Dunstan, and Richard B. Welbourn. London: Darton, Longman and Todd.

Dunstan, Gordon R. 1987. "The Authority of a Moral Claim." *Journal of Medical Ethics* 13: 189–194.

Dunstan, Gordon R., and Seller, Mary, eds. 1983. *Consent in Medicine: Convergence and Divergence in Tradition.* Oxford: Oxford University Press.

Dunstan, Gordon R., and Shinebourne, Elliot, eds. 1989. *Doctors Decide: Ethical Conflicts in Medical Practice.* Oxford: Oxford University Press.

Evans, Don, ed. 1990. *Professional Studies in Health Care Ethics: Why Should We Care?* London: Macmillan.

Fairbairn, Gavin. 1991. "Complexity and Value of Lives: Some Philosophical Dangers for Mentally Handicapped People." *Journal of Applied Philosophy* 8: 211–217.

"The Final Autonomy" (editorial). 1992. *Lancet* 340: 757–758.

"Fourteen Papers from the General Medical Council's Symposium on Medical Ethics." 1985. *Journal of Medical Ethics* 11(1): 5–41.

Fox, Daniel M. 1986. *Health Policies, Health Politics: The British and American Experience, 1911–1965.* Princeton, NJ: Princeton University Press.

Fulford, K. William M. 1990. *Moral Theory and Medical Practice.* Cambridge, Eng.: Cambridge University Press.

Gallagher, Ursula, and Boyd, Kenneth. 1991. *Teaching and Learning Nursing Ethics.* London: Scutari.

General Medical Council (GMC). 1992. *Professional Conduct and Discipline: Fitness to Practise.* London: Author.

General Medical Council (GMC). 1993. *Tomorrow's Doctors.* London: Author.

General Medical Council (GMC). 2001. *Good Medical Practice,* 3rd edition. London: Author.

Gilbert, Claire; Fulford, K. William; and Parker, C. 1989. "Diversity in the Practice of District Ethics Committees." *British Medical Journal* 299: 1437–1439.

Gillon, Raanan. 1985–1986. "Philosophical Medical Ethics." A twenty-six-part series first published in *British Medical Journal* and subsequently published as *Philosophical Medical Ethics.* Chichester, Eng.: Wiley, 1986.

Gillon, Raanan, ed. 1994. *Principles of Health Care Ethics.* Chichester, Eng.: Wiley.

Glover, Jonathan. 1977. *Causing Death and Saving Lives.* Harmondsworth, Eng.: Penguin.

Glover, Jonathan. 1999. *Humanity: A Moral History of the Twentieth Century.* London: Jonathan Cape.

Hanscombe, Gillian E., and Forster, Jackie. 1982. *Rocking the Cradle: Lesbian Mothers—A Challenge in Family Living.* London: Sheba Feminist Publishers.

Harris, John. 1985. *The Value of Life: An Introduction to Medical Ethics.* London: Routledge and Kegan Paul.

Higgs, Roger. 1985. "On Telling Patients the Truth." In *Moral Dilemmas in Modern Medicine,* ed. Michael Lockwood. Oxford: Oxford University Press.

Hoffenberg, Sir Raymond. 1987. *Clinical Freedom.* London: Nuffield Provincial Hospitals Trust.

Holmes, Jeremy, and Lindley, Richard. 1989. *The Values of Psychotherapy.* Oxford: Oxford University Press.

Hope, Anthony; Sprigings, David; and Crisp, Roger. 1993. "Not Clinically Indicated: Patient's Interest or Resource Allocation?" *British Medical Journal* 306: 379–381.

Jackson, Jennifer. 1991. "Telling the Truth." *Journal of Medical Ethics* 17(1): 5–9.

Jakobovits, Immanuel. 1959. *Jewish Medical Ethics.* New York: Philosophical Library. Reprinted, New York: Bloch, 1975.

Jennett, Bryan. 1984. *High Technology Medicine: Benefits and Burdens.* London: Nuffield Provincial Hospitals Trust.

Kennedy, Ian. 1981. *The Unmasking of Medicine.* London: George Allen and Unwin.

Kennedy, Ian. 1991. *Treat Me Right: Essays in Medical Law and Ethics.* Oxford: Clarendon Press.

Kennedy, Ian, and Grubb, Andrew. 2000. *Medical Law: Texts and Materials,* 3rd edition. London: Butterworths.

Keown, John. 2002. *Euthanasia, Ethics, and Public Policy: An Argument against Legislation.* Cambridge, Eng.: Cambridge University Press.

Klein, Rudolf. 2000. *The New Politics of the NHS,* 5th edition. New York: Prentice Hall.

Lamb, David. 1985. *Death, Brain Death, and Ethics.* Beckenham, Eng.: Croom Helm.

Lawrence, Christopher. 1994. *Medicine in the Making of Modern Britain, 1700–1920.* London: Routledge.

Linacre Centre. 1982. *Euthanasia and Clinical Practice: Trends, Principles, and Alternatives—The Report of a Working Party.* London: Author.

Lloyd, Wyndham E. B. 1968. *A Hundred Years of Medicine,* 2nd edition. London: Duckworth.

Lockwood, Michael, ed. 1985. *Moral Dilemmas in Modern Medicine.* Oxford: Oxford University Press.

Mahoney, John. 1984. *Bioethics and Belief.* London: Sheed and Ward.

Mason, J. Kenneth; McCall Smith, R. Alexander; and Laurie, Graeme T. 2002. *Law and Medical Ethics,* 6th edition. London: Butterworths.

Maxwell, Robert. 1975. *Health Care: The Growing Dilemma.* New York: McKinsey.

Maynard, Alan. 1986. "National Health Service: Reflections on Enthoven." *Lancet* vol. 1.

Maynard, Alan, and Bloor, Karen. 1998. *Our Certain Fate: Rationing in Health Care.* London: Office of Health Economics.

Medical Research Council (U.K.). 1991. *The Ethical Conduct of AIDS Vaccine Trials; The Ethical Conduct of Research on Children; The Ethical Conduct of Research on the Mentally Handicapped.* London: Author.

Mooney, Gavin, and McGuire, Alistair, eds. 1988. *Medical Ethics and Health Care.* Oxford: Oxford University Press.

Neuberger, Julia. 1992. *Ethics and Health Care: The Role of Research Ethics Committees in the United Kingdom.* London: King's Fund Institute.

Nicholson, Richard, ed. 1986. *Medical Research with Children: Ethics, Law, and Practice. Report of an Institute of Medical Ethics Working Group on the Ethics of Clinical Research Investigations on Children.* Oxford: Oxford University Press.

Nursing and Midwifery Council (NMC). 2002. *Code of Professional Conduct.* London: Author.

O'Neill, Onora. 2002a. *Autonomy and Trust in Bioethics: The 2001 Gifford Lectures.* Cambridge, Eng.: Cambridge University Press.

O'Neill, Onora. 2002b. *A Question of Trust: The 2002 Reith Lectures.* Cambridge, Eng.: Cambridge University Press.

Otlowski, Margaret. 1997. *Voluntary Euthanasia and the Common Law.* Oxford: Oxford University Press.

Pappworth, Maurice H. 1967. *Human Guinea Pigs.* London: Routledge and Kegan Paul; 2nd edition, Harmondsworth, Eng.: Penguin, 1969.

Phillips, Melanie, and Dawson, John. 1985. *Doctors' Dilemmas: Medical Ethics and Contemporary Science.* Brighton, Eng.: Harvester Press.

Polkinghorne, John. 1989. *Review of the Guidance on the Research Use of Fetuses and Fetal Material* (The Polkinghorne Report). Cmd. 762. London: HMSO.

Rowson, Richard. 1990. *An Introduction to Ethics for Nurses.* London: Scutari.

Royal College of Nursing. 1991. "Issues in Nursing and Health." London: Author.

Royal College of Nursing, with British Medical Association and U.K. Resuscitation Council. 2001. *Decisions Relating to Cardiopulmonary Resuscitation.* London: Royal College of Nursing.

Royal College of Physicians (RCP). 1986. *Research on Healthy Volunteers.* London: Author.

Royal College of Physicians (RCP). 1990a. *Guidelines on the Practice of Ethics Committees in Medical Research Involving Human Subjects.* London: Author.

Royal College of Physicians (RCP). 1990b. *Research Involving Patients.* London: Author.

Royal Liverpool Children's Inquiry Report. 2001. London: HMSO.

Seedhouse, David. 2001. *Health: The Foundations for Achievement,* 2nd edition. Chichester, Eng.: Wiley.

Sieghart, Paul, and Dawson, John. 1987. "Computer-Aided Medical Ethics." *Journal of Medical Ethics* 13(4): 185–188.

Smith, Jane, and Boyd, Kenneth. 1991. *Lives in the Balance: The Ethics of Using Animals in Biomedical Research. Report of a Working Party of the Institute of Medical Ethics.* Oxford: Oxford University Press.

Smith, Richard. 1992. "Euthanasia: Time for a Royal Commission: The Tide Seems to Be Running for Euthanasia." *British Medical Journal* 305: 728–729.

Snowden, Robert; Mitchell, George; and Snowden, Elizabeth. 1983. *Artificial Reproduction: A Social Investigation.* London: George, Allen and Unwin.

"Special Clinical Ethics Symposium: The Case of Ms. B." 2002. *Journal of Medical Ethics* 28(4): 232–243.

Teachers of Medical Ethics and Law in U.K. Medical Schools. 1998. "Teaching Medical Ethics and Law within Medical Education: A Model for the U.K. Core Curriculum." *Journal of Medical Ethics* 24(3): 188–192.

"Two Concepts of Medical Ethics" (editorial). 1985. *Journal of Medical Ethics* 11(1): 3.

U.K. Department of Health. 1991. *Local Research Ethics Committees: Health Service Guidelines.* London: Author.

U.K. Department of Health. 2001. *The Research Governance Framework for Health and Social Care.* London: Author.

Warnock, Lady Mary. 1984. *Report of the Committee of Inquiry into Human Fertilisation and Embryology.* Cmd. 9314. London: HMSO.

Webster, Charles. 2002. *The National Health Service: A Political History,* 2nd edition. Oxford: Oxford University Press.

Williams, Alan J. 1985. "The Value of QALYs." *Health and Social Services Journal* 94: 3–5.

Williams, Alan J. 1996. "QALYs and Ethics: A Health Economist's Perspective." *Social Science and Medicine* 43: 1795–1804.

Wilson-Barnett, Jenifer. 1986. "Ethical Dilemmas in Nursing." *Journal of Medical Ethics* 12(3): 123–126, 135.

INTERNET RESOURCES

General Medical Council (GMC). 2003. "Protecting the Public." Available from <http://www.gmc-uk.org/about>.

Nuffield Council on Bioethics. 2003. Available from <http://www.nuffieldbioethics.org/home>.

Nursing and Midwifery Council (NMC). 2002. *Code of Professional Conduct.* Available from <www.nmc-uk.org>.

Royal Liverpool Children's Inquiry Report. 2001. Available from <www.rlcinquiry.org.uk>.

U.K. Department of Health. 2001. Research Governance Framework for Health and Social Care. Available from <http://www.doh.gov.uk/research/rd1/researchgovernance/socialcare.htm>.

U.K. Department of Health. 2003. "Research and Development." Available from <http://www.doh.gov.uk/research>.

V. REPUBLIC OF IRELAND

"Ireland" here refers to that part of the island of Ireland (twenty-six of the thirty-two counties) that achieved independence from British rule in 1921 and was declared a republic in 1949.

Ireland's moral traditions and its history in ethics are inextricably linked with centuries of religious history that are primarily rooted in the nineteenth-century Roman Catholic Church. After experiencing religious persecution under British rule, the government of the new Irish State reinforced the traditional religious ethos in its laws and institutions, particularly education and healthcare. The Irish Constitution of 1937 recognized the "special position" of the Holy Roman church as guardian of the faith of the great majority of Irish people. This constitutional recognition was deleted in 1972 when Ireland was preparing for membership in the European Economic Community; the deletion signaled recognition for a religiously pluralist state.

In what follows, bioethics in the Republic of Ireland is discussed in two time periods: 1922–1982 and 1983–forward. The period division marks a development of appeals to legal resolution to negotiate ethical diversity. Four areas of national development frame the discussion: reproductive ethics, research and ethics committees, obligations to prolong life, and establishment of the Irish Council for Bioethics.

Between 1922 and the early 1980s, a religious homogeneity of tradition and practice largely prevailed. While cultural changes are never abrupt, a change in Irish political and social conditions was initiated on January 1, 1973, when Ireland became a member of the European Economic Community (now known as the European Union). Ireland increasingly interacted with other countries whose philosophies of life were based on secular viewpoints. Moral questioning in the society, in politics, education, and healthcare practice became more sustained, open and tolerated.

Reproductive Ethics

In the early 1970s, women's groups actively protested a prevailing legal ban on contraceptives and the complete ban on elective abortion even in cases where women were victims of rape or incest. Women who could afford private healthcare could get contraceptives and abortion advice. Women who sought prenatal genetic testing generally could not be accommodated within the hospitals of the Republic of Ireland. The concern was that some test results might contribute to pro-abortion decisions. But private patients were often accommodated by referral outside the country. The justice of a two-tier health system came under moral and political scrutiny. A private citizen, Mrs. McGee, challenged the Irish government's long-standing prohibition of the sale and importation of contraceptives. Her efforts led to the Health (Family Planning) Act of 1979, in which the Irish state allowed restricted access to contraceptives. Outsiders may be incredulous at Ireland's preoccupation with reproductive ethics. However, this area of morality is central in Irish traditional religious teachings, which have consistently reaffirmed the primacy of women's procreative capacity and fetal life.

Until the 1980s, the topic of abortion was largely a closed moral and legal issue. Ireland had never rescinded the complete ban on abortion specified under the British Offences Against the Person Act of 1861. In practice, termination was permitted under the principle of double effect in exceptional cases, such as ectopic pregnancy. Yet Irish women did (and do) procure abortions. On average, six thousand Irish women a year go to England to have abortions under the provisions of the 1969 British abortion legislation. Irish women gradually became more politicized and organized public demonstrations, claiming their rights to control fertility. Serious polarization of views developed as other groups in society feared that elective abortion might be legalized in Ireland. A national campaign began to guarantee protection of embryonic life by means of constitutional amendment.

In 1983, the eighth amendment to the Irish Constitution gave "the unborn" the same rights to life as other citizens. Since then, this amendment has generated a complex series of political, legal, and moral challenges, leading to a Supreme Court judgment of 1992, *Attorney General v. X and Others,* which argues that abortions may lawfully be carried out in Ireland where continuance of the pregnancy constitutes a real and substantial risk to the life of the pregnant woman. A threat of suicide was specified as such a risk. Following the Supreme Court Judgment of 1992, it remains for the Irish government to provide legislation to specify the conditions under which it is lawful to have abortions in Ireland.

Moral concerns to protect fetal life also influenced the development of guidelines for in vitro fertilization (IVF) issued by the Institute of Obstetricians and Gynecologists. The guidelines specified that IVF should be offered to married couples who have been appropriately counseled and have given informed consent. Only sperm and ova from the consenting couple may be used, and all resulting fertilized ova should be placed in the potential mother's uterus. However, with the Government's establishment of a Commission on Assisted Human Reproduction in 2000, existing IVF guidelines and policies on all forms of assisted procreation began being researched and ethically assessed. Submissions from the public, service providers, and consumers were invited. The Commission consists of four working groups studying topics from the status of the embryo to gamete donation, anonymity or disclosure, access to assisted reproduction, and embryo research. The working groups draw on the expertise of fertility experts, lawyers, ethicists, geneticists, social theorists, and theologians. The debates on the Commission are evidence of the growing diversity of ethical and legal views on reproductive matters. The Commission's report is expected to form the basis for legal decisions on the status of the pre-implanted embryo, and implementation of policy recommendations or regulatory mechanisms for all forms of assisted reproduction and embryo research.

Research and Ethics Committees

For years, medical research and clinical trials in Ireland were assessed by Institutional Review Boards whose composition and procedures lacked any nationally agreed-upon guidelines. The ethical norms from the Declaration of Helsinki were applied. The death of a male participant in a nontherapeutic drug trial in Ireland resulted in the government's issuing of the Control of Clinical Trials and Drugs Act 1990. The principal features of this legislation are that, with certain exceptions, the minister for health must authorize all proposed clinical medical trials and members of the ethics committees examining protocols must be approved by the minister. Ethics committees have the responsibility for ensuring that participants in any trial give their informed consent personally or by proxy. The latter provisions allow for clinical trials with psychiatric patients who might not be considered competent to consent. To avoid a conflict of interest, investigators involved in any clinical trial are not allowed to give proxy consent.

Ethics committees in Irish public hospitals traditionally were given the job of adjudicating requests from doctors for female sterilizations. Women's groups and gynecologists are now rejecting this role for ethics committees, and criticize what is judged to be unwarranted religious influence on decisions of ethics committees in public hospitals. While doctors are increasingly trying to minimize intrusions into the privacy of the doctor–patient relationship, ethics committees are still established throughout the state for educational purposes and for consultation by patients, families, and healthcare practitioners.

Irish patients are now requiring more communication about diagnoses and prognoses, and also expect increased participation in medical decision making. The value of respect for patients and the importance of securing consent is a corollary of expectations for a role in decision making. In efforts to reinforce the values of respect for personal autonomy and informed consent, in 2001 the Irish government set up an inquiry into policies and practices surrounding post-mortems in the state since 1970, particularly with regard to the removal and retention of organs by hospitals. The stimulus for the inquiry came from parents of children who had died in hospital and whose organs had been removed and retained by hospitals for research without the consent of parents. The public, parents, hospital management, and scientific institutions recognize that the value of trust can be readily undermined if ethical guidelines are not in place to reassure relatives that consent will be sought for post-mortem tissue or organ procurement. While parents do not dispute the need for research, they argue that the issue is the informed consent of relatives and accountability of institutions in receipt of public money.

Since the 1980s, doctors in Ireland have experienced increasing lawsuits for alleged malpractice or negligence. Further analysis is required to determine the multiple causes for such an increase, but the Medical Defence Union, an indemnity insurer for doctors, continues to urge doctors to reflect on the quality of their relationships with patients and to work to improve levels of communication. The previously dominant model of strong paternalism characterizing the doctor–patient relationship and more general practices of healthcare institutions are under challenge due to changing educational experiences of doctors and nurses and a more questioning Irish population. Courses in ethics are taught in Irish medical schools, where almost 30 percent of students are now non-Irish. In their required university work, nurses are encouraged to reflect on reasons for their moral views and to consider the possible validity of diverse ethical positions. Religious orthodoxy is no longer taken for granted. Such courses are usually required of medical students and nurses, and vary in length from several weeks to a full year.

Obligations to Sustain Human Life

Public debate about moral obligations to prolong human life came to the fore in 1995. The family of a woman who was in a persistent vegetative state (PVS) for over twenty years appealed to the Irish courts to have a gastrostomy tube removed and to allow her to die naturally. The patient was made a ward of court because the healthcare institution responsible for her care had, many years earlier, differed ethically with the family concerning what life support measures were morally justified. In 1995, in *Re a Ward of Court,* the High Court and, on appeal, the Supreme Court judged that in the best interests of the woman, it would be legal to remove the feeding tube. Following the Supreme Court judgment, the Irish Medical Council and the Nursing Board issued statements for members, in effect disagreeing with the ethical basis of the Supreme Court decision and claiming that access to nutrition and hydration is one of the basic needs of human beings. The *Re a Ward of Court* case raised difficult questions about active and passive euthanasia, withholding and withdrawing life support systems. Who should be involved in life and death decisions is a concern with arguments to the effect that decisions about withholding life-support systems for the terminally ill are areas of medical decision making where patients and family members ought to have more voice. In trying to determine moral boundaries in the prolongation of life, the Roman Catholic tradition distinguishing obligatory and nonobligatory treatment (ordinary and extraordinary) may be justly recognized as a well-argued basis for granting patients considerable voice in their treatment decisions.

The Irish Council for Bioethics

In 2002, concerns about ethical questions in modern biotechnology and genetic engineering prompted the Irish government to establish the first Irish Council for Bioethics. Members are invited by virtue of their personal expertise and not as representatives of particular bodies or professions. The members range in specialty areas from genetics, molecular biology, nursing, fertility, theology, law, and ethics. The Council operates under the aegis of the Royal Irish Academy but is an independent body. The aims of the Council are to identify and interpret ethical questions raised by biological and medical research and to examine and report on a range of questions with a view to promoting public discussion and understanding. Where appropriate, the work will contribute to the formulation of new guidelines in areas such as genetically modified products, stem cell research, biological samples, Ethics Community and human genetic research.

As Ireland continues to be more actively integrated into the European Union, ethical pluralism is being acknowledged as a reality requiring open debate. The hope is that such efforts at public discussion will yield a stronger, because more consensual, public morality that will signal respect for the now undeniable differences of ethical viewpoints among Irish people. In the years ahead, the work currently under way should yield policy developments in assisted reproduction, research protocols, biotechnology, and debates about advance directives and obligations to prolong human life.

DOLORES DOOLEY (1995)
REVISED BY AUTHOR

BIBLIOGRAPHY

Clarke, Desmond M., ed. 1982. *Morality and the Law.* Cork: Mercier Press.

Control of Clinical Trials and Drugs Act. 1990. Annotated by Robert A. Pearce. London: Sweet and Maxwell.

Donnelly, Mary. 2002. *Consent: Bridging the Gap Between Doctor and Patient.* Cork: Cork University Press.

Dooley, Dolores. 1991. "Medical Ethics in Ireland: A Decade of Change." *Hastings Center Report* 21(1): 18–21.

Dooley, Dolores. 1999. "Reconciling Liberty and the Common Good: Genetic Screening in the Republic of Ireland." In *The Ethics of Genetic Screening,* ed. Ruth Chadwick et al. Dordrecht: Kluwer Publishers.

Edmondson, Ricca. 1992. "Moral Debate and Social Change." *Doctrine and Life* 42(5, special edition titled "Abortion, Law and Conscience"): 233–243.

Fogarty, Michael P.; Ryan, Liam; and Lee, Joseph. 1984. *Irish Values and Attitudes: The Irish Report of the European Value Systems Study.* Dublin: Dominican Publications.

Hannon, Patrick. 1989. "In Vitro Fertilisation." *Irish Theological Quarterly* 55(1): 7–17.

Hanafin, Patrick. 1997. *Last Rights: Death, Dying, and the Law in Ireland.* Cork: Cork University Press.

Hensey, Brendan. 1988. *The Health Services of Ireland,* 4th revised edition. Dublin: Institute of Public Administration.

Kearon, Kenneth, and O'Ferrall, Fergus. 2000. *Medical Ethics and the Future of Healthcare.* Dublin: Columba Press.

Madden, Deirdre. 2002. *Medicine, Ethics and the Law.* Dublin: Butterworth.

Medical Council of Ireland. 2003. *A Guide to Ethical Conduct and Behaviour and to Fitness to Practise,* 6th edition. Dublin: Irish Medical Council.

Murphy, Tim, and Twomey, Patrick, eds. 1998. *Ireland's Evolving Constitution.* Oxford: Hart Publishers.

O'Rourke, Kevin. 1989. "On Prolonging Life." *Doctrine and Life* 39(7): 352–366.

Ryan-Sheridan, Susan. 1994. *Women and the New Reproductive Technologies in Ireland.* Cork: Cork University Press.

Rynne, Andrew. 1982. *Abortion: The Irish Question.* Dublin: Ward River Press.

Sheikh, Asim. 2002. *Genetic Research and Human Biological Samples: Legal and Ethical Considerations.* Dublin: Health Research Board.

Smyth, Ailbhe, ed. 1992. *The Abortion Papers, Ireland.* Dublin: Attic Press.

Whyte, John H. 1980. *Church and State in Modern Ireland, 1923–1979,* 2nd edition. Dublin: Gill and Macmillan.

VI. GERMAN-SPEAKING COUNTRIES AND SWITZERLAND

Interest in bioethics in the German-speaking countries (Germany, Austria, and Switzerland) originated, as it did elsewhere, with medical-ethics questions related to both modern biotechnological potential and a growing ethical pluralism. These factors not only induced physicians to debate these issues, they were part of the reason for a "rehabilitation of practical philosophy" among a number of German academic philosophers and theologians that included a renewed interest in moral, social, and political problems.

In several respects, bioethics in Germany, Switzerland, and Austria differs from that in the United States or other European countries. First, as a major, collective, and socially visible effort, it developed relatively late—in the 1980s.

Some explanations for this are the lack of civil rights movements that would have endorsed issues of patients' rights; a widespread and deeply rooted medical paternalism; good, uniform access to medical care (and thus little need for allocation debates); a different philosophical tradition; and, in Germany, a severely disturbed moral self-assurance due to the relatively recent experiences of Nazi Germany's indescribable immoralities.

Second, there are many theological voices in German bioethics. In the German world, theology is given a legitimate academic presence within universities, where it enjoys the same juridical status as all other disciplines. It also possesses relative independence from religious institutions. Third, German law is solely statutory in nature and is not linked to case law, as it is in the American judicial system. Hence, going to court is a far less common way to trigger public discussion on difficult bioethics cases. In Switzerland, plebiscites (direct voting by the population on an issue) are an instrument of legislative decision making. In addition, legal authority resides partly with the Bund (federation) and partly with the 26 different cantons (states), which show remarkable legal differences in handling some bioethics problems.

Fourth, Germans place great importance on the study of the history of medicine and medical anthropology, the philosophical clarification of fundamental medical categories. Fifth, Germany labors under the historical weight of the Nazi regime's deadly medical experimentation, eugenics, and euthanasia—and of the concomitant moral degradation of many physicians. Thus, public mistrust of bioethics "experts" seems to be comparatively deep and widespread.

Not only does the Nazi specter affect the discussion of bioethics in Germany, but it is seen by many to have a direct connection to a number of issues discussed in contemporary bioethics. Concern is heightened by the fact that Nazi experimentation occurred despite the existence of guidelines for therapeutic and scientific research on human subjects that prohibited such treatment. These guidelines, thought to be the first of their kind, were originally published as a Circular of the Reich Minister of the Interior on February 28, 1931, and remained in force until 1945 (Sass, 1993). Several groups and movements have taken the position that preimplantation diagnosis, selective abortion, euthanasia, and gene therapy are not only immoral, but represent a continuation of Nazi ideology.

Philosophical Bioethics in Germany

The philosophical clarification of medicine's role, and of its fundamental categories (e.g., pathology, illness, healing) in Germany still has an influential intramedical tradition as medical anthropology (Weizsäcker). German medicine has long cultivated historical study, and the many institutes devoted to medical history increasingly view part of their work as preparatory to or incorporating moral reflection on medicine. Whereas medical ethics has traditionally focused primarily on aspects of the physician–patient relationship (e.g., truth-telling, confidentiality, humaneness), its spectrum has long since been broadened to cover all issues addressed by Anglo-American "bioethics." The latter, however, is opposed by many—be it merely as a label, as the writing of those who call themselves bioethicists, or as a discipline in general. Thus (in contrast to medical ethics), "bioethics" has frequently been understood as an ideological and uncritical defense of biotechnological progress or profit—or at least with a suspected (i.e., "analytical") style of philosophy.

German philosophers have thus been late to join the contemporary Anglo-American debate on any issue in applied ethics. Analytical philosophers had to leave the country under the Nazi regime—and continental philosophers of the period were rarely attracted by either utilitarianism or pragmatism, which are among the dominant theories in contemporary Anglo-Saxon ethics debates. Immanuel Kant (1724–1804), with his rejection of material ethical values and his predominant interest in a metaphysico-rational justification of ethics, has certainly been the major influence for those opposed to these theories.

At the beginning of the twenty-first century, this gap seems to have closed. Meanwhile, quite a number of philosophers consider bioethics a serious aspect of their own academic work. In 2003 the German book market still lacked a basic comprehensive textbook covering both in-depth theory and the whole spectrum of ethical problems in healthcare, which are covered by a number of influential Anglo-American examples. However, introductory anthologies (e.g., Wiesing; Düwell and Steigleder) and shorter monographs (e.g., Höffe; Schramme) have enriched the debate and provided educational material. Comparable to the Anglo-American context, bioethics has—not undisputedy—also become part of many public discussions and debates, with philosophers increasingly serving on ethics committees and presenting their views in newspapers and on talk shows. Simultaneously, this "expertise" (and its limits and dangers) has itself become subject of critical methodological reflection (Gesang; Ach and Runtenberg), again paralleling developments elsewhere.

Institutions and Teaching

Paralleling the belated onset of bioethical debates in German-speaking countries, the development of institutions focused

on the study of bioethics has also been comparatively slow. However, a number of chairs, institutes, and centers devoted to this field have been established, most of them university based. Many of them offer optional courses, but forthcoming revisons of federal regulations require medical ethics to be part of the medical curriculum. They are also involved, to various degrees, in consultation and research, with some publishing their own series on specific issues in bioethics and some drawing fellows and postgraduate students from different disciplines into collaboration and common discourse on ethical aspects of medicine, science, and the law. Since the 1980s, a pioneering role can be attributed to the *Institut für Geschichte der Medizin* (Institute for History of Medicine) at the University of Freiburg in Breisgau—now part of the *Zentrum für Ethik und Recht in der Medizin* (Center for Ethics and Law in Medicine); the *Zentrum für Ethik in den Wissenschaften* (Center for Ethics in the Sciences and Humanities) at the University of Tübingen; and the university-based *Zentrum für Medizinische Ethik Bochum* (Bochum Institute for Medical Ethics). Since the 1980s the *Forschungsinstitut für Philosophie* (Research Institute for Philosophy) in Hannover, founded with financing from—and under the auspices of—the Roman Catholic Church, has focused on issues at the intersection of religion and philosophy in the Catholic tradition of philosophical thought, offering a broad spectrum of activities in ethical research and education.

Among the more or less recently founded or reorganized bioethics institutions are the *Institut für Wissenschaft und Ethik* at the University of Bonn, the *Interdisziplinäres Zentrum für Ethik* at the University of Frankfurt/Oder; the *Ethikzentrum* at the University of Jena; the independent *Institut Mensch, Ethik und Wissenschaft* in Berlin (founded by various institutions that advocate for the rights of the disabled); and the *Institute für Ethik, Geschichte (und Theorie) der Medizin* at the Universities of Erlangen, Münster, and Göttingen. The institute in Göttingen is, moreover, linked to office of the interdisciplinary *Akademie für Ethik in der Medizin* (see below) as well as to the Information and Documentation Center for Medical Ethics (IDEM), which is part of Euroethics, a European database, and provides a database for German literature in the field. The institute in Bonn is in charge of the German Reference Center for Bioethics Literature (DRZE), which is a repository for both national and international literature.

In Switzerland, several institutes are active in the study and teaching of bioethics: most notably the *Institut für Sozialethik* and the *Arbeits- und Forschungsstelle für Ethik* (founded in 1989), both at the University of Zurich; the *Interdisziplinäres Institut für Ethik und Menschenrechte* at the University of Fribourg; the *Centre Lémanique d'Ethique* in Lausanne/GENF; as well as the *Institut für Angewandte*

Ethik und Medizinethik (IAEME; founded in 2000) and the unit of ethics in biosciences both at the University of Basel.

In Austria, the university-based centers in the field are the *Dokumentationsstelle für Ethik* in Vienna; the *Institut für Medizinische, Anthropologie, und Bioethik,* also in Vienna; and the *Koordinationsstelle für Grund- und Grenzfragen der Medizin* in Salzburg, In addition, the *Wissenschaftliche Landesakademie für Niederösterreich* (Scientific State's Academy for Lower Austria) has established an institute for the research, teaching, and study of bioethics. But, as in Germany and Switzerland, bioethics has become an expanding discipline, and is by no means restricted to established centers, but pursued by a growing number of academics in various disciplines and settings.

The first German-language journal for medical ethics, *Arzt und Christ (Physician and Christian)*, was founded in Austria in 1955. Since 1993 the journal has been called *Zeitschrift für medizinische Ethik (Journal of Medical Ethics)* and is published in Bonn, Germany.

Professional and Government-Appointed Bodies

Common to all German-speaking countries is the existence of a governing body regulating the contact of healthcare professionals and possibly administering sanctions against those who disobey to their rules. Characteristically, these institutions focus on determining professional ethics and they have widely recognized authority in judging new medical practices.

In Switzerland, the *Schweizerische Akademie der medizinischen Wissenschaften* (Swiss Academy of Medical Sciences) is a foundation comprised of all Swiss medical schools and physicians' associations. Its Central Ethics Commission prepares guidelines on specific issues of medical or research practice that are considered ethically problematic, such as policies for new reproductive technologies for withdrawing life-supporting treatment. In addition, the fourteen-member commission serves as a permanent ethics counseling body for physicians and the public.

Similarly, in Germany, the Federal Chamber of Physicians (*Bundesärztekammer,* membership in which is obligatory for German physicians) has established an Ethics Advisory Board to its Scientific Council to issue ethics guidelines for intraprofessional self-regulation and to serve as a counseling body. In areas of conduct that lack legal regulation, this type of binding professional self-legislation functions somewhat as a legal substitute for such regulations. Other important bodies are known as *Gesellschaften* or *Akademien* (societies of experts). They aim at promoting scientific debates and

research among their members and the public. The body for medical ethics in Germany is the *Akademie für Ethik in der Medizin* (Academy for Medical Ethics). Founded in 1986, it has in 2003 an interdisciplinary membership of approximately 450 members, most of whom are German. The *Akademie* receives a mix of public and private funding and provides a forum for research (working groups on specific topics), for expert and public debate, and for teaching medical ethics. Since 1989 it has published the second German language journal on medical ethics, *Ethik in der Medizin,* and in 1993 it established the first German bioethics literature database, IDEM. Another professional body (of both law and medicine) worth mentioning is the *Deutsche Gesellschaft für Medizinrecht* (German Society for Medical Law), which formulated recommendations on the treatment of severely disabled newborns (the Einbecker Recommendations). In Switzerland, the most important professional body is the *Schweizerische Gesellschaft für biomedizinische Ethik* (Swiss Society for Biomedical Ethics).

Finally, governments or parliaments in these countries have increasingly appointed working groups or expert commissions to issue advisory reports on a variety of bioethical and legal issues. The first to be published in Germany (by the *Bundesminister für Forschung und Technologie*) was the 1985 report of the Benda Commission on assisted fertilization, genome analysis, and gene therapy. In Switzerland, the *Expertenkommission Humangenetik und Reproduktionsmedizin* issued the Amstad Report, dealing with the same subjects, in 1988. These initial efforts were followed by number of similar working groups and expert commissions dealing with a variety of topics. They contributed to the increasing gain in public attention to problems in bioethic, although the ethical analyses contained in their reports are certainly less in-depth, and also less balanced, than, for example, the reports of the various President's Commissions in the United States. Participants with a background in philosophy served on these bodies only in rare instances.

The three German-speaking countries created national ethics councils later then almost any other European country. In 2001 each of them established such a body: in Germany the *Nationale Ethikrat* was established (in fruitful competition with the nonpermanent Commission for Law and Ethics of modern medicine); in Switzerland, which already had a national ethics commission for questions of nonhuman genetic technology, the Bundesrat appointed a *Nationale Ethikkommission im Bereich der Humanmedizin* (Swiss National Advisory Commission on Bioethical Ethics); and in Austria, the 18-member *Bioethik-Kommission* was established at the Federal Chancellery. All three bodies exercise an independent advisory function and are supposed to stimulate public debates in matters of bioethics.

They have already come up with a couple of published recommendations.

Ethics Committees for Human Experimentation

Local *Ethikkommissionen* (ethics committees), functioning almost exclusively as review boards for medical experiments on human subjects, exist in Austria, Germany, and Switzerland. Only in very few hospitals, committees have also been established to consider different ethics questions such as treatment decisions for individual patients or the development of institutional ethics guidelines. As in other Western countries, the institutionalization of review boards for medical research on humans occurred in response to the Nuremberg Trials of Nazi physicians, in accord with the 1964 Declaration of Helsinki and its subsequent revisions.

In Switzerland, the pioneering 1970 guidelines on research involving human subjects (revised in 1989 and 1997) issued by the Swiss Academy of Medical Sciences (*Schweizerische Akademie der Wissenschaften,* or SAMW) required the establishment of ethics committees at hospitals and research institutes to make certain that proposed projects were important, well designed, and of acceptable risk—and that subjects were insured and had given informed consent. The participation of nurses on these committees was required, leaving other details to institutional discretion. Since 1993 experimentation on human subjects is covered by federal law. The Federal Act on drugs and medical products (in force since 2000) requires all research on human subjects—be it publicly or privately funded—to get prior (ethical) approval by a research committee. The about 25 existing such cantonal committees are to have members of both sexes, among them nurses, lay persons, and at least three nonmedical members with experience in social, ethical, or juridical matters.

In Germany (see Toellner; Wiesing, 2002), the introduction of ethics committees was not generally recommended until 1979, when it was endorsed by both the German Federal Chamber of Physicians (*Bundesärztekammer*) for the chambers on state and federal levels and by the Federal Association of Medical Schools for the medical schools. In 1983 the Working group of Medical Ethics Committees (*Arbeitskreis Medizinischer Ethik-Kommissionen*) was founded. It is comprised of all ethics committees at the state physicians' chambers and the medical faculties. The workgroup meets annually to share experiences, promote standardization, and revise its procedural principles.

In 1985 the *Bundesärztekammer* turned the requests for ethics-committee review into an obligatory standard of professional practice. And finally, the German Drug Law

ACT (*Arzneimittelgesetz,*) of 1995—and under revision in 2003—is making it obligatory for any research on human subjects, their tissues or person-related data, to get approval from an ethics committee. For publicly funded research in 2003, there were 17 committees at the state chambers of physicians (*Landesärztekammern*), and 38 at the university-based departments of medicine. Most committees have between seven and nine members (plus substitutes) of a— legally required—interdisciplinary background. Local bodies possess some discretional freedom on how to interpret this requirement; only a minority of them include nurses or lay persons. Both public and professional trust and acceptance in those commissions' work seems to increase steadily, although a number of crucial issues are yet unsolved, for instance, regarding the missing evaluation and quality assessment procedures of the committees' work; or the lack of oversight, particularly of commercial or "free" (not institution-affiliated) committees. Other issues under debate are the coordination of different ethics committees in multicenter research, or possibilities to monitor ongoing research compliance to ethical standards.

In Austria, research ethics committees have been legally required since 1988 for the medical faculties and research hospitals. These prescriptions were revised in detail in 1993, and now require that the states issue legal regulations, according to which every ethics committee must include: (1) women; (2) at least one independent person and one physician with particular expertise in the research at stake; (3) at least one representative of the hospital's chaplain (or somebody else with ethical expertise related to patients, staff, and legal services; and (4) a pharmacist.

Specific Ethical Issues

EUTHANASIA. The *Guidelines on Assistance in Dying* of the Swiss Academy of Medical Sciences (issued in 1976, revised in 1981 and 1995) emphasize a patient's right to turn down any medical treatment. They further permit withholding treatment for irreversibly terminal patients, as well as for patients with a loss of consciousness considered irreversible. Dispensable "treatment" in such cases may explicitly include respiration and artificial nutrition. Decisions must include substituted judgments made with the help of the patient's next of kin, and they must consider the patient's best interests. As of 1995, living wills must be followed. Active voluntary euthanasia, however, is illegal under the Swiss Penal Code. Assistance in patient suicide, though not illegal, is not considered a proper activity for physicians. However, it is not explicitly and strictly said to be unacceptable under every circumstance. Assistance in suicide for competent terminally ill patients is provided by two Swiss societies, Exit and Dignitas, the latter being open also for non-Swiss patients. A highly controversial "suicide tourism" has thus developed, with 55 instances of assisted suicide by non-Swiss individuals in 2002.

The German Federal Chamber of Physicians modeled its 1979 guidelines on "assistance in dying" almost verbatim on the Swiss guidelines (Baumann). Remarkably, however, two points were left out: the explicit permission to withhold or withdraw respiration and artificial nutrition in the irreversibly dying patient, and the explicit permission to forgo treatment in patients with an irreversible loss of consciousness. Moreover, these early German guidelines consider living wills to be merely a nonbinding piece of evidence. In a 1993 update of these guidelines, this last point was explicitly reaffirmed. The 1999 revision of the guidelines, however, exhibit substantial changes. Advance directives (which have since become subject to separate guidelines) are granted a binding status, as long as they are precise and relevant. Furthermore, artificial nutrition, though part of the commonly indispensable basic support, can legitimately be withdrawn from an irreversibly terminal patient, as long as he or she is kept comfortable and neither hungry nor thirsty. Indispensibility of basic care and treatment, with the explicit inclusion of artificial nutrition, is, however, reconfirmed for patients with an irreversible loss of consciousness. Also reconfirmed is the impermissibility of active voluntary euthanasia.

The German Roman Catholic Conference of Bishops and the Protestant Church have repeatedly and strongly argued against active euthanasia, while emphasizing the need—and Christian obligation—to care in a humane and Christian way for the suffering and dying. A hospice movement that provides palliative care for the dying is seen by many as an appropriate way both to fulfill the obligation to care for the terminally ill and to eliminate the very reasons patients ask for voluntary euthanasia. In addition, any use of the term *euthanasia* in Germany conjures up vivid images of the use of the term by the Nazis as they carried out their goal of exterminating millions of fellow human beings who were deemed to be of "inferior" quality. The deeply emotional nature of this historical association explains current objections by many Germans to any discussion of euthanasia. The media and public culture are so aware of Nazi cruelties that lectures by Peter Singer and Helga Kuhse—Australian bioethicists who support both voluntary euthanasia and the permissibility of passive as well as active euthanasia (withholding treatment as well as directly killing) for severely disabled neonates on parental request—have been prohibited or protested in Germany and Austria (Schöne-Seifert). In the aftermath of this "Singer affair" (starting in 1989),

organizations of disabled people and other political and interest groups have vehemently argued that those in favor of euthanasia for severely disabled newborns are making an indirect judgment about the worth of a life and are in danger of creating a climate in which elimination of the unfit or discrimination toward the sick, feeble, and disabled will again be accepted. These objections have also been raised in debates about selective abortion, creating a rather widespread antibioethics climate in both Germany and Austria.

In Switzerland, withdrawing treatment for most severely disabled newborns is considered morally permissible and is narrowly specified as such in the Swiss guidelines. The German Society for Medical Law had issued rather similar recommendations (the so-called *Einbecker Empfehlungen* [Recommendations of Einbeck]) in 1986. At the time, the Society considered it morally permissible to let newborns die when they either suffer from most severe mental disabilities or can only be kept alive by permanent intensive care. After the Singer affair, these recommendations were revised (in 1992), and forgoing treatment is now restricted to newborns with irreversible medical problems that will lead to death within a short period of time.

Legalized active euthanasia at the request of terminally ill patients has been advocated by some German voices. For example, the *Deutsche Gesellschaft für Humanes Sterben* (German Society for Humanely Dying, or DGHS), founded in 1980, advocates for respect for the dying patient's autonomy. This lay organization, which does not enjoy much support in the medical or legal communities, also provides its members with forms for living wills, and in the past it has provided assistance in suicide (because suicide is not a criminal offense, assisting it is not illegal either). Physicians, however, are seen by law to stand under specific professional obligations (*Garantenpflichten*), which some courts—in contrast to the view dominant in the legal literature—have interpreted to include suicide intervention. Hence, there is an unresolved legal tension that makes jurisdiction on physicians' assistance (and consequent nonintervention) in suicide unpredictable. The credibility of DGHS was severely shaken in early 1993 when its founder and president, H. H. Atrott, was arrested for selling cyanide capsules—moreover at inflated prices.

In 1986, the *Alternativentwurf eines Gesetzes über Sterbehilfe* (Alternative Draft of a Law for Assistance in Dying) was published by a number of reputable experts in medicine and law (Baumann). Among its suggestions was one to waive prosecution of euthanasia (though illegal) when it is persistently requested, and if the euthanized patient was competent and suffering from terminal illness. However, the draft never succeeded, due to lack of sympathy for it from the Federal Chamber of Physicians and the German Legal Association.

Advance directives (see Meran et al.), be they in the form of living wills or of durable powers of attorney, have slowly started to play a role in medical decision making in all three German-speaking countries. Although the 1992 Care ACT (*Betreuungsgesetz*) in Germany in principle provides for both instruments, and although various forms for living wills are publicly available, the legal status of advance directives is disputed and considered uncertain. This situation discourages both its acceptance by the medical profession and wider use by patients. In 2003 a critically debated Supreme Court decision upheld a ruling that decisions to stop life-saving treatment cannot be validly made by a patient's advocate without confirmation of the courts. Critics consider this position both nonrealizable and contrary to a patient's right to self-determination. In the same decision, however, advance directives, at least for the terminal phase of disease, were acknowledged as expressions of a patient's autonomy in former days and as legally binding.

In Austria, the overall situation is very similar to that in Switzerland and Germany: Active euthanasia is illegal under the national Penal Code; withdrawing treatment is not, by either law or policies, regulated in any detail; and advance directives seem to be slowly gaining in use and impact.

ABORTION. With the 1990 reunification of the German nation, most laws and regulations of the former Federal Republic of Germany (West Germany) were applied to the citizens of the former German Democratic Republic (East Germany). However, there were very different models of legal abortion in the penal codes of the two Germanys, which resulted in a heated debate. In the West, a 1974 law permitted pregnant women to choose abortion until the end of the first trimester. Based on a charge of nonprotection of the rights of the unborn, the constitutionality of this law was challenged in 1975. The resulting interpretation of the constitution (*Grundgesetz*) by the Federal Constitutional Court (*Bundesverfassungsgericht*) held that human dignity (*Menschenwürde*)—a conceptually loose term that is used by both sides of the abortion debate to support their position—is constitutionally protected from the moment of conception. It enforced an *indication model,* permitting legal abortion until the end of the first trimester only if a physician certified that certain social or medical indications were present. Under this model, the physician was the ultimate moral agent and an acknowledged right to life of the unborn was to be balanced against medical or social hardship. Generous interpretation of these criteria often led to a de facto policy of abortion on demand in the first trimester, but

with different standards and variability in enforcement in the various states of the Federal Republic. In the German Democratic Republic, a *term model* for legal abortions operated since 1972, wherein abortion was allowed until the end of the first trimester and was cost-free.

In the new Germany, a heated public debate (though involving little philosophical analysis) took place on the underlying theological, moral, and political positions motivating the clashing views on abortion. In 1992 the federal parliament approved a compromise law under which abortion would be legal in the first trimester (and paid for by health insurance) as long as the woman had a consultation session prior to abortion. Mandatory counseling and education were intended as an additional step to strengthen fetal protection (a goal that was emphasized almost unanimously) and include informing a pregnant woman about existing supportive social, welfare, and employment programs, as well as kindergarten settings for the child, that might enable her to choose to continue her pregnancy.

However, conservative parliamentarians and the Roman Catholic Church petitioned the *Bundesverfassungsgericht* to declare the law unconstitutional. The German Supreme Court did just that in May 1993, stating that the counseling sessions did not go far enough in protecting fetal human life, as required by the (formerly West) German Constitution. The Court argued that the constitutional rights of a woman (to physical integrity, human dignity, right of personality) do not go so far as to allow her to claim a fundamentally protected legal right to kill an unborn child by means of abortion; that abortions at any point during a pregnancy are fundamentally wrong, and thus illegal; and that the state's duty to protect the unborn also includes maintaining and raising the public's consciousness of the unborn child's legal right of protection. However, the Court held that a future abortion law would be considered constitutional even if it abstained from prosecution of illegal first-trimester abortions that were performed at the pregnant woman's request, as long as she has undergone prior mandatory and explicit pro-life counseling. A new abortion law, which came into force in 1995, includes this requirement.

Both public and expert reactions to this legal reform are heavily split. Where some emphasize its being a socially integrative compromise, conservative critics deplore what they consider a violation of the embryo's human dignity, while others object to both the Supreme Court's and the legislation's blatant inconsistencies. For them, accrediting a full-blown right to life and dignity to the early embryo is incompatible with de facto permission of first trimester abortion on demand and the state's court-mandated provision of abortion facilities (Merkel). The required pro-life counseling is seen as a violation of women's right and competency to self-determination (Kuhlmann), and the pre-emption of prosecution for illegal abortions is considered to undermine the public's trust in the law.

In Switzerland (where women first began to acquire the political right to vote only in 1971), abortions had been permitted only for serious medical indications or in case of grave emergency (commonly interpreted to include rape and embryopathy). In the 1970s, opinion polls suggested that a majority of the Swiss people would opt for a liberalization of abortion law. However, a plebiscite in 1977 went narrowly against abortion on demand in the first trimester of pregnancy (with a majority of French-speaking and predominantly Protestant cantons [states] in favor of liberalization, and German-speaking and predominantly Catholic cantons against). A repetition of the plebiscite in June of 2002, however, saw 72 percent of the votes being in favor of first trimester abortions on demand, and they are now allowed, with only a prior comprehensive consultation with the physician who is going to perform the intervention.

In predominantly (85%) Roman Catholic Austria, first-trimester abortion on demand has nevertheless been legally permitted since 1975. Costs of medically indicated abortions are covered by insurance, while those resulting from abortions performed for nonmedical reasons must be paid for by the women themselves. A pro-life referendum initiated the year before the introduction of this law won only 18 percent of the vote, and none of the three major political parties supported the initiative.

NEW REPRODUCTIVE TECHNOLOGIES AND EMBRYO TESTING. A great deal of the public debate in German, Austrian, and Swiss bioethics continues to focus on reproductive issues. All three countries criminalize egg donation for reproductive purposes (and thus surrogate motherhood), the fertilization of more (3 eggs maximum) than are to be transferred (thereby theoretically preventing the existence of "spare" embryos), as well as any research on or manipulation of an embryo not in its own therapeutic intererest. Genetic manipulation on the germline cells (those from which gametes are derived) is prohibited.

In Germany, the Benda Report of 1985 recommended that a future reproduction law ban: (1) all forms of surrogate motherhood; (2) heterologous (with sperm other than a woman's spouse) in vitro fertilization (IVF) and assisted insemination by donor (AID), at least for single women; (3) research on embryos other than those that are purposefully left over from IVF; and (4) any genetic manipulation of germline cells. These measures were considered necessary to prevent violations of "human dignity." The first regulations, issued in 1985 by the Federal Chamber of Physicians, had the status of intraprofessional self-regulation. They were revised in 1988 and 1994, and now permit only homologous (using only the spouses' egg and sperm) IVF and GIFT (gamete-intra-fallopian-tube transfer), and only in married couples. Only somatic infertility is explicitly accepted as an indication for IVF, for example, and the restriction to homologity and marriage are justified by the well-being of the child-to-be. In accordance with the 1991 Embryo Protection Act, embryo donation and all forms of surrogate motherhood are prohibited (though, theoretically, unpaid-for donor sperm may be used in rare cases). However, no cases of AID have occurred since 1985, and issues of access to (heterologous) IVF—and its ramifications for family law—still await a long-planned reproductive medicine law.

In a second set of guidelines issued in 1985, the chamber prohibited the production of embryos for research and restricted embryo research to important questions of infertility treatment or embryo development—and to spare embryos less than 14 days old—after approval of the central commission. After heated public debates on the relevant meaning of human dignity and of reproductive autonomy, and on the permissibility of research even on spare embryos, the German Embryo Protection Act (*Embryonenschutzgesetz*) was introduced in 1991, setting unprecedented standards in terms of restrictivity. In summary, the law prohibits: (1) artificial insemination of an oocyte for any purpose other than a nonsurrogate pregnancy of the "possessing" woman, and (2) any kind of nontherapeutic manipulation or research on the embryo, even in case of spare embryos (whose occurrence is made unlikely by the first prohibition). In addition, (3) any single totipotent cell (an early embryonic cell from which a whole organism could still develop) is given the legal status of an embryo. Further restrictions rule out (4) reproductive egg donation and any form of surrogate motherhood, as well as (5) cloning or the creation of chimeras (organisms with a combination of human and animal genes). Violating these regulations can result in lengthy prison terms and monetary fines, but punishment applies only to third parties (i.e., physicians, researchers, and agencies), not to biological, gestational, or social mothers-to-be.

This law has been controversial, particularly in the light of the more recent options of "using" embryos for stem-cell research, which is clearly prohibited by this law. It has been praised by its proponents for its strict embryo protection, while critics claim it interferes with self-determination, responsible parenthood, and reproductive choice.

Preimplantation diagnosis (PID) is currently not practiced in Germany, but it is increasingly demanded by various people and groups. Initially, most legal experts considered PID implicitly prohibited by the Embryo Protection Act, though this view has been challenged by a growing number of experts. There is a broad consensus, however, that regulation of the issue is required before PID can be practiced. As can be witnessed in other countries, those strongly opposed to PID (and the involved selection of embryos) make several arguments. They consider the procedure to be: (1) a violation of the early embryo's dignity and right to life; (2) a form of, or at least an invitation to, unacceptable eugenics; and (3) discriminatory toward, or hurtful of, those disabled individuals who have been born with one of those diseases PID would select against. Those in favor of PID most commonly want it offered very restrictively to couples with a family history of severe hereditary disease. Not only do they question the plausibility of the above arguments, but they criticize what they consider an ethical double standard; that is, forbidding preimplantation diagnosis, while at the same time allowing elective abortion after prenatal diagnosis of the very same severe hereditary diseases (and even less severe ones) in significantly later stages of pregnancy.

Austria's Reproductive Medicine Act (*Fortpflanzungsmedizingesetz*) regulates both the use of new reproductive technologies and embryo protection. It was introduced in 1992 after long and heated debates, and it represents a political compromise between the Roman Catholic opposition to reproductive technologies on theological grounds and more liberal approaches that emphasize the benefits of new reproductive technologies to support individual reproductive freedom and choice. Both homologous and heterologous IVF or GIFT are permitted as infertility treatments for married couples or those in stable relationships, but embryo donation and all forms of surrogate motherhood are forbidden. Only freely donated sperm from living donors may be used, and, based on the concept of human dignity, a child conceived from donor sperm is permitted to know the identity of the biological father once he or she reaches maturity (records must be kept for thirty years). Issues of inheritance and other matters affecting IVF offspring are regulated elsewhere in the law. Preimplantation diagnostics, though not expressly mentioned, are considered forbidden and currently not practiced in Austria.

In Switzerland, the Swiss Academy for Medical Sciences (SAMW) issued guidelines on the use of new reproductive technologies in 1990. Homologous IVF in married or quasi-married couples, as well as IVF using anonymously donated sperm or eggs in married couples, are permitted as either infertility treatment or as a means to prevent transmission of a genetic disease. Embryo donation, all forms of surrogate motherhood, preimplantative sex selection, germline manipulation, and any research on embryos are all prohibited.

In 1992 the Swiss implemented Article 24, a constitutional amendment requiring federal regulation of embryo protection and of reproductive technologies according to the following restrictions: The manipulation of germline cells and embryos, the creation of chimeras, and the production of spare embryos are illegal; homologous and heterologous IVF are legal as an infertility treatment (allowing—like German and Austrian law, and in contrast to the SAMW guidelines—for later access to information about one's biological parent) or as a means to prevent transmission of a genetic disease; embryo donation and all forms of surrogate motherhood are illegal; but research on (the few available, see above) spare embryos is not explicitly ruled out. Since 2001 the federal Reproductive Medicine Act has been in force, prohibiting egg and embryo donation, the creation of surplus embryos, and the performance of PID. As in Austria and Germany, public opinion on these matters are heavily split.

EMBRYO RESEARCH AND CLONING. Since the late 1990s, embryo research is no longer an abstract ethical issue, but is being discussed with regard to stem-cell research with its promises of future therapeutic breakthroughs. In all three German-speaking countries, the creation of embryonic stem cells is prohibited by the above described laws. In 2001, both in Germany (by the *Deutsche Forschungsgemeinschaft*) and in Switzerland (by the Swiss National Fonds) the scientific communities questioned these prohibitions publicly and suggested that embryonic stem cells be imported from abroad, thus legally providing scientists with the tools to participate in the promising new research. Simultaneously, they and many others urged public debates and legal reforms that would allow Swiss and German scientists to use (deep-frozen) surplus embryos, the existence of which cannot completely be prevented even by the restrictive current laws.

In Switzerland, a research project on imported embryos began in 2001, while the issues were still subject to controversial public debates. In 2003 the country was awaiting a stem-cell research law, which will most probably permit the creation of stem cells from surplus embryos. The more general issues of embryo research will be handled in an additional future law regulating overall issues of research on human subjects.

In Germany, scientists have also started to work on imported stem-cell lines. Here, however, they waited for a clear legal basis, provided by a new stem-cell law implemented in the summer of 2002. While strictly prohibiting the destruction of early embryos, even for highly promising medical purposes, it nevertheless permits, under a number of restrictions, the importation of existing stem-cell lines. A majority of parliament members viewed this legislation as an acceptable compromise, whereas critics consider it to be another instance of ethical hypocrisy.

In Austria, no attempts have yet been made to legalize the importation of embryonic stem cells, and the whole matter of destructive embryo research is under debate.

Cloning, both for reproduction and for biomedical research, is one of the most recent bioethical issues dealt with in all three countries. Reproductive cloning by any method will certainly be ruled out by laws to come. Cloning for biomedical research purposes, on the other hand, has been rejected by a majority of experts and the public—though not unequivocally. Again, the moral status of (artificial) embryos, the moral claims of future patients, slippery-slope arguments, and the difficulties in handling the bioethical pluralism of modern societies will be prominent arguments in these discourses.

HUMAN GENETICS. The use of genetic testing techniques in Germany, Switzerland, and Austria is regulated quite strictly. Each of these countries has regulations regarding the use of genetic testing, the need for informed consent of the individuals involved, and the need to integrate genetic testing into a larger process of genetic counseling. The memory of eugenics experiments during the Third Reich inevitably generates negative emotions, especially in Germany, toward any medical intervention concerned with the prevention of hereditary disease. German reflection seems particularly concerned with the question of how far society and parents should go in accepting disabilities that can easily be discovered using prenatal diagnosis, while at the same time protecting the woman's right to decide whether or not to use prenatal diagnosis. Another major issue discussed in all three countries is the appropriate balance between people's autonomy (to know about a carrier status or genetic disease in themselves or their embryo, and to draw consequences they consider appropriate) and the protection of the same people from unwelcome or unbearable information, from unreasonable risk assessment, or from external sanctions upon their genetic status. There seems to be a strong public consensus for a ban on germline manipulation, whereas somatic gene therapy, although met with a much public suspicion, was applied for the first time in 1994 on somatic cells (cells other than those from eggs and sperm). The Federal Chamber of Physicians is currently at work on guidelines on somatic gene therapy.

The German Gene Technology Law of 1990 (revised in 1993) does not address questions of genetic testing or engineering in humans. Three commissions, one at the level of the federal parliament, and two composed of executives from state and federal governments have already issued recommendations for a law that would specifically regulate issues of genetic counseling and testing in embryos, neonates, carriers, high-risk persons, or at the workplace. For the time being, these issues are partly regulated intraprofessionally. Guidelines issued in 1991 by the German Federal Chamber of Physicians urge that genetic testing always be integrated with genetic counseling, that such counseling be provided by nonmedical personnel under medical supervision, and that consent be required for testing. The Commission of the German Society for Human Genetics also supports genetic testing only within nondirective genetic counseling. This commission also holds that screening for nonmedical information, such as the sex of the fetus, should be prohibited, and that information obtained by genetic testing is to be strictly confidential.

The Federation of Swiss Physicians asserted in 1991 that genetic analysis for occupational health or insurance issues must always be rejected, even if consent is given and the information is to be confidential. The Swiss Academy of Medical Sciences guidelines of 1993 assert that genetic testing must be part of a larger counseling relationship. The academy supports voluntary testing for (1) diagnosis of hereditary diseases, (2) carrier testing and genetic counseling for family or career planning, and (3) presymptomatic testing whenever medical intervention or changes in lifestyle may reduce or postpone disease. Counseling and education prior to testing are obligatory. Article 24 of the Swiss Constitution states that "the genetic endowment of a person cannot be analyzed, registered or revealed without that person's consent or a legal prescription." Probably still in 2003, a new federal act on human genetics will be enacted, regulating genetic testing in humans and providing safeguards against genetic discrimination.

In Austria a Gene Law was introduced in July 1994, regulating genetic counseling, diagnostics, and manipulation both inside and outside human beings. It prohibits any release of genetic information to third parties, notably insurance companies and employers.

ORGAN TRANSPLANTATION. Germany's long awaited Transplantation Act came into force in 1997. Basically, it confirms what had been the current policy regarding posthumous organ retrieval, namely the requirement of explicit prior consent by the donor, or substitute consent by his or her proxy. In addition, it restricts live donation, rules out any commercialization, and legally acknowledges the whole-brain definition of death (according to which a complete cessation of brain functioning indicates a person's death).

Various drafts for a transplantation law were debated over several years. The most likely legal regulation had once been a policy requiring that donation be requested of the deceased potential donor's proxy, consent of the patient being presumed if he or she had not objected to organ donation. Protests were raised against these suggestions, however, on the grounds that they disregard the right to self-determination and represent an uncritical protransplantation ideology. Among the protestors were a number of Protestant theologians, despite the fact that both the Protestant and the Catholic churches had officially praised organ donation.

The whole-brain definition of death was at the center of much debate and protest. German physicians officially adopted this definition in 1982, but this position has been a matter of intraprofessional policy, rather than legal statute. Rising concerns about the definition's underlying, allegedly reductionist concept of human life (spurred by recent cases involving attempted continuation of pregnancy in brain-dead women by maintaining them for weeks on life support, and by rumors that authorities of the former East Germany sold organs, sometimes prior to fulfillment of death criteria) had fueled public suspicion and professional objections, and had even raised the possibility of revision of the brain-death formula (Hoff and In der Schmitten).

In Austria, the 1982 *Krankenanstaltengesetz* presumes consent to organ procurement if the donor or his or her proxy do not oppose it—without, however, explicitly requiring that the proxy be informed about his or her right to oppose.

In Switzerland, the cantons (states) have different legal requirements for organ transplantation, with a majority having a presumed-consent policy. Efforts are being made to issue a federal transplantation law, which will likely be enacted in 2004.

Germany is a member of the Netherlands-based Eurotransplant Center, which computerizes the distribution of available organs, primarily according to tissue compatibility, among a network of European transplantation units. Organ information and distribution centers in Switzerland and Austria are more loosely affiliated with Eurotransplant.

RESOURCE ALLOCATION. Social-welfare systems in each of these countries provide almost universal coverage for health-related costs, as well as allowances for certain conditions (e.g., maternity, disability, old age, work-related injuries, dependent children). Overall health conditions, healthcare, and access to physicians are very good in each of these countries.

However, the steadily increasing costs of modern medical care have begun to endanger the unlimited approval of the underlying "solidarity principle" by which the rich and healthy pay for the care of the sick and needy. Moreover, various cost-containment policies that claim to increase cost-effectiveness without decreasing the quality of care have slowly increased public awareness of the underlying ethical questions of distributive justice and permissible rationing criteria. The debates on a decent maximum of generally accessible healthcare have only started. Again, public concern about a renaissance of Nazi spirit is raised by the prospect of rationing treatment, which might discriminate against the disabled and elderly.

ANIMAL EXPERIMENTATION. Strong concern exists throughout Europe for the ethical use and protection of animals in research. Swiss guidelines, inspired by animal-rights activists, have served as the basis for regulations in other countries. In the late 1970s, Switzerland became the first European country to include animal protection into its constitution, and in 1992 an amendment granted constitutional protection to the "dignity of creation." Germany's 1986 Animal Protection Act (*Tierschutzgesetz*) was revised in 1998 and contains detailed regulations concerning the type of experiments permissible, selection criteria for animals, supervision by qualified veterinarians, and standards for the treatment of animals in agriculture and as pets. Notice must be given to qualified animal-welfare commissioners. Animal-welfare committees exist in all states, with membership based on nomination by animal-welfare groups and academic training and professional experience. This legislation is supplemented by public education and information campaigns designed to bring about more humane treatment of animals in all spheres. The 1998 revision made it obligatory for any institution experimenting with vertebrates to appoint a qualified person to be officially responsible for animal protection. Experiments on dogs, cats, and apes require their being bred for research. Animal experiments for developing any kind of cosmetic product are prohibited.

In 2002 Germany finally—after more then ten years of debates, and through the addition of two words—incorporated animal welfare into its constitution. Article 20a of the German Constitution now reads "The state takes responsibility for protecting the natural foundations of life *and animals* in the interests of future generations." This amendment will not have any immediate effect, but it will influence the way in which future German legislation is drawn up and current laws are interpreted.

Austria passed its Animal Research Act (*Tierversuchsgesetz*) in 1989, which provides for criminal penalties if research is not reviewed or performed ethically or responsibly and according to current scientific standards. The law also calls for a reduction in the number of experiments performed and the number of animals affected. Attempts for a federal animal protection law unifying existing legislation in individual countries have so far been as unsuccessful as those for including animal welfare in the Austrian Constitution.

Conclusion

Despite a comparatively delayed academic and public interest in modern biothics in the three German-speaking countries, and despite some tendencies to avoid debates on certain issues regarding human life because of past atrocities, the field and its substantial and methodological problems have become widely acknowledged as important.

BETTINA SCHOENE-SEIFERT
HANS-MARTIN SASS
LAURA JANE BISHOP
ALBERTO BONDOLFI (1995)
REVISED BY BETTINA SCHOENE-SEIFERT

BIBLIOGRAPHY

Ach, Johann S., and Gaidt, Andreas, eds. 1993. *Herausforderung der Bioethik.* Stuttgart: Frommann-Holzboog.

Ach, Johann S., and Runtenberg, Christa. 2002. *Bioethik: Disziplin und Diskurs. Zur Selbstaufklärung angewandter Ethik.* Frankfurt: Campus Verlag.

Baumann, Jürgen; Bochnik, Hans-Joachim; Brauneck, Anne-Eva; et al. 1986. *Alternativentwurf eines Gesetzes über Sterbehilfe (AE-Sterbehilfe): Entwurf eines Arbeitskreises von Professoren des Strafrechts und der Medizin sowie ihrer Mitarbeiter.* Stuttgart: Thieme Verlag.

Bayertz, Kurt, ed. 1991. *Praktische Philosophie: Grundorientierungen angewandter Ethik.* Reinbek bei Hamburg: Rowohlt Verlag.

Beckmann, Jan P.; Brem, Gottfried; Eigler, Friedrich-Wilhelm; et al. 2000. *Xenotransplantation von Zellen, Geweben oder Organen. Wissenschaftliche Entwicklungen und ethisch-rechtliche Implikationen.* Berlin: Springer Verlag.

Bennett, Charles L.; Schwartz, Bernhard; and Marberger, Michael. 1993. "Health Care in Austria: Universal Access, National Health Insurance, and Private Health Care." *Journal of the American Medical Association* 269(21): 2789–2794.

Bernat, E. 1992. "Regulating the 'Artificial Family': An Austrian Compromise." *International Journal of Bioethics* 3(2): 103–108.

Braun, Kathrin. 2000. *Menschenwürde und Medizin. Zum philosophischen Diskurs der Bioethik.* Frankfurt: Campus Verlag.

Brudermüller, Gerd, and Seelmann, Kurt, eds. 2000. *Organtransplantation.* Würzburg: Königshausen und Neumann.

Bundesminister für Forschung und Technologie, Bonn. 1985. *In-Vitro-Fertilisation, Genomanalyse und Gentherapie: Bericht der gemeinsamen Arbeitsgruppe* (Benda Report). Munich: J. Schweitzer Verlag.

Christoph, Franz, and Illiger, Horst, eds. 1992. *Notwehr gegen die neue Euthanasiebedrohung.* Neumünster, Germany: Brücke-Neumünster.

Daele, W. van den, and Müller-Salmon, H. 1990. *Die Kontrolle der Forschung am Menschen durch Ethikkommissionen.* Stuttgart: Enke Verlag.

Damschen, Gregor, and Schönecker, Dieter, eds. 2003. *Der moralische Status menschlicher Embryonen.* Berlin: de Gruyter Verlag.

Doerner, Klaus. 1988. *Tödliches Mitleid: Zur Frage der Unerträglichkeit des Lebens, oder, die soziale Frage, Entstehung, Medizinisierung, NS-Endlösung heute, morgen.* Gütersloh, Germany: Verlag Jakob van Hoddis.

Düwell, Markus, and Mieth, Dietmar, eds. 1998. *Ethik in der Humangenetik: Die neueren Entwicklungen der genetischen Frühdiagnostik aus ethischer Perspektive.* Tübingen, Germany: Francke Verlag.

Düwell, Marcus, and Steigleder, Klaus, eds. 2003. *Bioethik: Eine Einführung.* Frankfurt: Suhrkamp Verlag.

Eser, Albin, and Koch, Hans-Georg. 1988. *Schwangerschaftsabbruch im internationalen Vergleich: Rechtliche Regelungen, soziale Rahmenbedingungen, empirische Grunddaten.* Band 1. *Europa.* Baden-Baden: Nomos Verlag.

Eser, Albin; Beck, Lutwin; Heinrich, Kurt; Honnefelder, Ludger; et al., eds. *Lexikon der Bioethik.* 3 vols. Gütersloh, Germany: Gütersloher Verlagshaus.

Expertenkommission Humangenetik und Reproduktionsmedizin. 1988. *Amstad Bericht.* Bern, Switzerland: Author.

Fischer, Johannes. 2002. *Medizin- und Bioethische Perspektiven.* Zürich: Theologischer Verlag.

Gesang, Bernward, ed. 2002. *Biomedizinische Ethik: Aufgaben, Methoden, Selbstverständnis.* Paderborn, Germany: Mentis Verlag.

Geyer, Christian, ed. 2001. *Biopolitik: Die Positionen.* Frankfurt: Suhrkamp Verlag.

Habermas, Jürgen. 2001. *Die Zukunft der menschlichen Natur. Auf dem Weg zu einer liberalen Eugenik?* Frankfurt: Suhrkamp Verlag.

Haker, Hille. 2002. *Ethik der genetischen Frühdiagnostik.* Paderborn, Germany: Mentis Verlag.

Hegselmann, Rainer, and Merkel, Reinhard, eds. 1991. *Zur Debatte über Euthanasie: Beiträge und Stellungnahmen.* Frankfurt: Suhrkamp Verlag.

Hoerster, Norbert. 1995. *Abtreibung im säkularen Staat: Argumente gegen den §218,* 2nd edition. Frankfurt: Suhrkamp Verlag.

Hoff, Johannes, and In der Schmitten, Jürgen, eds. 1995. *Wann ist der Mensch tot? Organverpflanzung und "Hirntod"-Kriterium.* Reinbek, Germany: Rowohlt.

Höffe, Otfried. 2002. *Medizin ohne Ethik?* Frankfurt: Suhrkamp Verlag.

Höffe, Otfried; Honnefelder, Ludger; Isensee, Joseph; and Kirchhof, Paul. 2002. *Gentechnik und Menschenwürde.* Cologne, Germany: Dumont Verlag.

Holderegger, Adrian, ed. 2000. *Das medizinisch assistierte Sterben. Zur Sterbehilfe aus medizinischer, ethischer juristischer und theologischer Sicht,* 2nd edition. Freiburg, Switzerland: Herder und Universitätsverlag.

Illhardt, Franz-Josef. 1985. *Medizinische Ethik: Ein Arbeitsbuch.* Berlin: Springer Verlag.

Keller, Rolf; Günther, Hans-Ludwig; and Kaiser, Peter. 1992. *Embryonenschutzgesetz: Kommentar.* Stuttgart: W. Kohlhammer.

Körtner, Ulrich H. J. 2001. *Unverfügbarkeit des Lebens? Grundfragen der Bioethik und der menschlichen Ethik.* Neukirchen, Germany: Neukirchener Verlag.

Kuhlmann, Andreas. 1996. *Abtreibung und Selbstbestimmung. Die Intervention der Medizin.* Frankfurt: S. Fischer Verlag.

Kuhlmann, Andreas. 2001. *Politik des Lebens, Politik des Sterbens. Biomedizin in der liberalen Demokratie.* Berlin: Alexander Fest Verlag.

Leist, Anton. 1990. *Eine Frage des Lebens: Ethik der Abtreibung und künstlichen Befruchtung.* Frankfurt: Campus Verlag.

Lorz, Albert. 1992. *Tierschutzgesetz mit Rechtsverordnungen und europäischen Übereinkommen: Kommentar,* 4th edition. Munich: C. H. Beck Verlag.

Meran, Johannes G.; Geissendörfer, Sylke E.; May, Arnd T.; and Simon, Alfred, eds. 2002. *Möglichkeiten einer standardisierten Patientenverfügung.* Münster, Germany: Lit Verlag.

McGregor, Alan. 1992. "Switzerland: Limits on Genetic Research and Artificial Insemination." *Lancet* 339(8805): 1345.

Meggle, Georg; Rippe, Klaus Peter; and Wessels, Ulla, eds. 1992. *Almanach der praktischen Ethik.* Opladen, Germany: Westdeutscher Verlag.

Merkel, Reinhard. 2002. *Forschungsobjekt Embryo. Verfassungsrechtliche und ethische Grundlagen der Forschung an menschlichen embryonalen Stammzellen.* Munich: dtv.

Nagel, Eckhard, and Fuchs, Christoph, eds. 1998. *Rationalisierung und Rationierung im Deutschen Gesundheitswesen.* Stuttgart: Thieme Verlag.

Patzig, Günther. 1993. *Angewandte Ethik.* Göttingen, Germany: Wallstein Verlag.

Rat der Evangelischen Kirche in Deutschland und Sekretariat der deutschen Bischofskonferenz. 1989. *Gott ist ein Freund des Lebens: Herausforderungen und Aufgaben beim Schutz des Lebens.* Gütersloh, Germany: Gütersloher Verlagshaus Gerd Mohn.

Sass, Hans-Martin. 1983. "Reichsrundschreiben 1931: Pre-Nuremberg Regulations Concerning New Therapy and Human Experimentation." *Journal of Medicine and Philosophy* 8(2): 99–111.

Sass, Hans-Martin, ed. 1988. *Ethik und öffentliches Gesundheitswesen: Ordnungsethische und ordnungspolitische Einflussfaktoren im öffentlichen Gesundheitswesen.* Berlin: Springer Verlag.

Sass, Hans-Martin, ed. 1991. *Genomanalyse und Gentherapie: Ethische Herausforderungen in der Humanmedizin.* Berlin: Springer Verlag.

Sass, Hans-Martin. 1992. "Bioethics in German-Speaking Western European Countries: Austria, Germany, and Switzerland." In *Bioethics Yearbook,* vol. 2: *Regional Development in Bioethics, 1989–1991,* ed. B. Andrew Lustig, Baruch A. Brody, H. Tristram Engelhardt, Jr., and Laurence B. McCullough. Dordrecht, the Netherlands: Kluwer Academic.

Sass, Hans-Martin. 1994. "Bioethics in German-Speaking Western European Countries: Austria, Germany, and Switzerland." In *Bioethics Yearbook,* vol. 4: *Regional Developments, 1992–1993,* ed. B. Andrew Lustig, Baruch A. Brody, and H. Tristram Engelhardt, Jr. Dordrecht, the Netherlands: Kluwer Academic.

Schöne-Seifert, Bettina. 1996. "Medizinethik." In *Angewandte Ethik. Die Bereichsethiken und ihre theoretische Fundierung. Ein Handbuch,* ed. Julian Nida-Rümelin. Stuttgart: Kröner Verlag.

Schöne-Seifert, Bettina, and Rippe, Klaus-Peter. 1991. "Silencing the Singer: Antibioethics in Germany." *Hastings Center Report* 21(6): 20–27.

Schramme, Thomas. 2002. *Bioethik.* Frankfurt: Campus.

Spaemann, Cordelia; Schmidt, Martin; and Spaemann, Robert, eds. 1997. *Töten oder sterben lassen? Worum es in der Euthanasiedebatte geht.* Freiburg, Germany: Herder Verlag.

Stauffacher, Werner, and Bircher, Johannes, eds. 2002. *Zukunft Schweiz.* Basel: Schweizer Ärzteverlag.

Thévoz, Jean-Marie. 1992. "Research and Hospital Ethics Committees in Switzerland." *HEC (Healthcare Ethics Committee) Forum* 4(1): 41–47.

Toellner, Richard, ed. 1990a. *Die Ethik-Kommission in der Medizin, Problemgeschichte, Aufgabenstellung, Arbeitsweise, Rechtsstellung und Organisationsformen Medizinischer Ethik-Kommissionen.* Stuttgart: Gustav Fischer Verlag.

Toellner, Richard, ed. 1990b. *Organtransplantation: Beiträge zu ethischen und juristichen Fragen.* Stuttgart: Gustav Fischer Verlag.

Weizsäcker, Viktor von. 1951. *Fälle und Probleme: Anthropologische Vorlesungen in der medizinischen Klinik,* 2nd edition. Stuttgart: F. Enke.

Wiesing, Urban, ed. 2000. *Ethik in der Medizin: Ein Reader.* Stuttgart: Reclam.

Wiesing, Urban, ed. 2002. *Die Ethik-Kommissionen—Neuere Entwicklungen und Richtlinien.* Köln: Deutscher Ärzteverlag.

Wikler, Daniel, and Barondess, Jeremiah. 1993. "Bioethics and Anti-Bioethics in Light of Nazi Medicine: What Must We Remember?" *Kennedy Institute of Ethics Journal* 3(1): 39–55.

Wolf, Jean-Claude. 1992. *Tierethik: Neue Perspektiven für Menschen und Tiere.* Freiburg, Switzerland: Paulusverlag.

INTERNET RESOURCES

Arbeitskreis Medizinischer Ethikkommissionen: State of the Are Informations. Available from <http://www.ak-med-ethik-komm.de>.

Nationaler Ethikrat. 2001. "Zum Import menschlicher embryonaler Stammzellen. Stellungnahme." Berlin. Available from <http://www.nationalerethikrat.de>.

Nationaler Ethikrat. 2003. "Genetische Diagnostik vor und während der Schwangerschaft. Stellungnahme." Berlin. Available from <http://www.nationalerethikrat.de>.

Schweizerische Akademie der Wissenschaften (SAMW). 1989. "Medizinisch-Ethische Richtlinien der Schweizerischen Akademie der Wissenschaften." Basel. Available form <http://www.SAMW>.

Tierschutzbericht. 2001. "der Deutschen Bundesregierung." Available from <http://www.verbraucherministerium.de>.

VII. NORDIC COUNTRIES

This entry provides a brief overview of the modern development of medical ethics in the Nordic countries: Denmark, Finland, Iceland, Norway, and Sweden. The focus is primarily on the period after the beginning of the 1960s. The entry begins by giving an account of the establishment of ethics review committees and other medical ethics bodies and organizations. Then changes in the educational and research situation are described, along with the establishment of special institutions for medical ethics. Finally, attention is given to some essential features of the debate on a few principal issues.

Codes, Ethics Bodies, and Organizations

The attempt formally to regulate physicians' duties toward their patients and colleagues began early in the history of medicine. Ethics codes in the Nordic countries can be traced to the early practice of physicians taking an oath of office and allegiance. For example, in seventeenth-century Sweden, when physicians still received doctoral degrees abroad, usually in Holland, permission to practice medicine required the taking of an examination given by the Swedish association of physicians, the Collegium Medicorum, which was founded in 1663. When passing the examination the physician had to take a special oath. The taking of an oath was an obligatory part of the examination of physicians in Sweden until the late nineteenth century and still is required in Denmark, Finland, and Iceland.

It was only after World War II, however, that the making of ethics codes in the Nordic countries came to encompass areas outside clinical practice and to include professional categories other than physicians. The current ethical guidelines for physicians' clinical work were adopted in their original forms by the Danish Medical Association in 1976, by the Finnish in 1956, by the Icelandic in 1918, by the Norwegian in 1961, and by the Swedish in 1951. During the 1950s and 1960s other health professional groups, such as nurses and physical therapists, began to develop their current ethical codes. The 1964 adoption of the Helsinki Declaration by the World Medical Association extended the codification to the explicit inclusion of ethics in research. To facilitate its implementation the Nordic countries created a system of ethics review committees.

Those committees are organized somewhat differently in the different countries. Denmark and Norway have regional committees, whereas Finland and Iceland have local hospital committees and Sweden has both regional and local committees. The Danish system, which was established in 1978, consists of seven regional committees and a central scientific-ethical committee. The committees in Norway are organized in a similar way. In 1985 regional committees were set up in each of Norway's five national service regions. To establish a coordinating and advisory body for those regional committees, the Norwegian Medical Research Council's Committee for Medical Research Ethics, which was formed in 1978, became the National Committee for Medical Research Ethics in 1990. In Finland the first ethics committee was set up at Helsinki University in 1972; since 1977 all medical faculties have had ethics committees. In Iceland the two national university hospitals have had ethics committees since 1976. In Sweden an advisory council was formed at the Karolinska Hospital in Stockholm in 1965. That council was superseded the next year by the first medical-faculty ethics committee, which was established at the Karolinska Institute. By 1967 similar committees were in place at all medical faculties in that country.

Since those committees were established, the call for assessment of the ethical implications of new technologies and other advances in medicine has increased. To respond to growing pressures on political decision makers an additional type of national ethics body was created. Its principal task is twofold: to provide expert knowledge to the government, the parliament, and the health-service authorities and to contribute generally to a continuous exchange of information and opinions on medical ethics issues among researchers, politicians, and the public. To that end the Danish Council of Ethics was established by the parliament in 1987; the National Research Ethics Committee, by the Finnish Parliament in 1991; the National Biotechnology Advisory Board, by the Norwegian government in 1991; and the National Council of Medical Ethics, by the Swedish government in 1985. Iceland still lacks a national body of this kind. (For further information about the origin, composition, and activities of these national bodies and of the review committees see Council of Europe; Solbakk.) In 1988 the Nordic Committee for Ethics in Biotechnology was created by the Nordic Council of Ministers. Like some of the national bodies, this committee deals with bioethical issues in the broad sense of the term. Besides issues in medicine, the Nordic Committee addresses ethical questions in, for example, stockbreeding and agriculture.

Several other bodies and organizations play an important role in the analysis and debate of issues in medical ethics. For example, ethics committees were set up within the medical associations of Denmark (1969), Finland (1975),

Norway (1962), and Sweden (1979), as well as within the National Finnish Board of Health (1988), the National Swedish Board of Health and Welfare (1984), and the Ministry of Health and Social Affairs in Norway (1988). In 1989 the Council of Ethics was established at the Office of the Director General of Health in Iceland. There are also a number of medical societies: the Delegation for Medical Ethics, established in 1969 within the Swedish Society of Medicine (earlier called the Swedish Society of Medical Sciences); the Society for Medical Law and Ethics, founded in Finland in 1980; the Danish Society for Medical Philosophy, Ethics, and Methodology, founded in 1988; and the Swedish Society for Medical Ethics, founded in 1989. In 1988 a section for medical ethics in the Nordic countries was established within the European Society for Philosophy of Medicine and Health Care.

Education and Research

Since the beginning of the 1970s medical ethics has been taught at medical faculties and nursing schools in all the Nordic countries. However, there are no uniform requirements regarding the scope and content of this teaching in any of the Nordic countries. At a meeting in Reykjavik, Iceland, in 1991, the medical associations of the Nordic countries agreed to work toward making medical ethics a compulsory subject at all medical faculties in those countries and creating teaching positions in the subject (Oldinger).

Textbooks have been written in most of the Nordic countries. For a long time *Medicinsk etik* (1971), a doctoral dissertation by Clarence Blomquist, a pioneer in Swedish medical ethics, was the only general introduction; it dealt with both metaethics and normative ethics and covered most of the principal issues in medical ethics at that time. Subsequently, a number of textbooks have appeared, including some broad general introductions (Fagerberg et al.; Andersen et al; Tranøy, 1991; Wretmark et al.), some more philosophically oriented works (Malmgren; Tännsjö, 1998), and some texts dealing not only with ethics but also with other philosophical issues in medicine (Bjarnason; Tranøy, 1978; Wulff et al).

The philosophical rather than the medical faculties have been responsible for most postgraduate education in medical ethics. Blomquist's *Medicinsk etik,* the first doctoral dissertation, was defended at the Department of Philosophy at Uppsala University in 1973. Since that time philosophy departments have produced dissertations on specific medical ethics issues such as suicide, paternalism, and abortion as well as on the nature and scope of philosophical medical ethics in general. Partly empirical doctoral dissertations that

focus primarily on issues in medical ethics have been written within the fields of sociology, nursing research, and medicine.

The establishment of two special institutions for medical ethics, one in Norway and the other in Sweden, as well as the foundation of a unit for the philosophy of medicine in a broader sense in Denmark, has improved the opportunities at medical faculties for both graduate and postgraduate education in medical ethics. The Center for Medical Ethics at the University of Oslo was founded in 1989. A chair in medical ethics was created at the University of Oslo Medical Faculty in 1992. Lund University in Sweden established the Department of Medical Ethics in 1991. The department came into existence through the creation of a chair in medical ethics at the Swedish Medical Research Council in 1990. In 1988 the University of Copenhagen established the Unit of Medical Philosophy and Clinical Theory at the Panum Institute.

Those institutions have strengthened the position of medical ethics as an independent research field at medical faculties. Research in medical ethics otherwise is carried on normally only in the form of time-limited projects and mainly outside medical faculties in philosophy departments and departments of theology. Some institutions focus on medical ethics as a principal area of research. For example, the Department of Health and Society at Linköping University in Sweden has had a chair for the philosophy of medicine since 1987. Two institutes have been established: one in Iceland in 1989, the Ethics Institute at the University of Iceland, and the other in Sweden in 1988, the Ersta Institute for Health Care Ethics in Stockholm. In Finland the Center for Bioethics was founded in 1991 at the University of Turku.

Principal Issues

ARTIFICIAL INSEMINATION AND IN VITRO FERTILIZATION. Among the Nordic countries only Norway and Sweden have laws that specifically regulate the use of noncoital reproductive technologies to achieve pregnancy. The use of human sperm, ova, zygotes, and early embryonic forms (blastemas) for research purposes also is restricted in the Nordic countries.

The ethical and legal debate in the Nordic countries over the use of noncoital reproductive technologies has focused mainly on artificial insemination by donor semen (AID), in vitro fertilization (IVF), and ovum donation. The closely related issues of artificial insemination by the husband's semen (AIH) and gestational surrogacy (surrogate motherhood) have attracted less attention. Except among certain religious minorities the use of AIH has generally been accepted.

To a large extent the 1987 Norwegian legislation on artificial insemination and IVF corresponds to the 1985 Swedish legislation. One point on which the Norwegian and Swedish laws differ is of particular ethical interest: the issue of whether it should be possible for a child to obtain information about the identity of his or her natural father. Sweden legislated in favor of the child's right to this information, and Norway legislated against it.

According to the Swedish legislation, (1) only women married or cohabiting with a man in circumstances of marital character should be allowed to receive insemination treatment; (2) insemination requires written consent by the husband or cohabitant, who will by virtue of that act be regarded as the legal father of a child born as a result of the treatment; (3) AID should be undertaken only in general hospitals under the supervision of a physician who specializes in obstetrics and gynecology, and the sperm donor should be chosen by the physician; (4) information about the sperm donor should be kept in a special hospital record for at least seventy years; (5) when a child conceived by donor insemination is mature enough, he or she has a right to obtain information about the identity of the natural father; and (6) when requested, the public welfare committee is obligated to assist the child in retrieving that information. (For literature on the debate and official reports preceding this law see Lindahl, 1985, 1988; U.S. Congress.)

The most controversial issue has been the right to obtain information about a child's father. The main point of departure for the Swedish legislation was the needs and interests of the child. In this respect the legislators decided to follow the general direction of modern legislation toward a gradual strengthening of children's judicial standing and the movement in society toward greater openness in family relations rather than the traditional patient-oriented perspective of clinical medical ethics. These two contrasting perspectives have dominated much of the debate.

PRENATAL DIAGNOSTICS AND ABORTION. The laws on abortion vary among the Nordic countries. In Denmark women have a legal right to abortion regardless of the reason before the twelfth week (law of 1973, in force the same year); in Norway, until the end of the twelfth week (law of 1975, in force from 1979); and in Sweden, before the end of the twelfth week or, after special consultation with a social worker, up to the end of the eighteenth week (law of 1974, in force from 1975). In Finland (law of 1970, in force the same year) and Iceland (law of 1975, in force the same year) abortion is permissible before the twelfth week, but only on certain indications (see below).

The situation in Sweden illustrates the way in which the legal status of the fetus and the understanding of its relationship to the mother changed during the twentieth century. Until the abortion act of 1974 a fetus was viewed as a separate individual, even during the first three months, and thus was legally protected. According to the earliest legislation, in the eighteenth century, abortion carried a penalty of death because it was equated with infanticide. As late as the 1920s the penalty for abortion was one year's to six years' imprisonment at hard labor. However, exceptions were made if abortion was necessary to preserve the health or life of the woman. This practice was ratified by law in 1938. From 1939 abortion was permissible up to the end of the twentieth week on any of the following three indications: medical (i.e., when, because of disease, physical defect, or weakness, childbirth would cause serious danger to the life or health of the woman), humanitarian (e.g., pregnancy after rape or incest or in minors), and eugenic (when there was reason to believe that the expected child would inherit mental disease, mental deficiency, or serious physical disease). After the twentieth week abortion was permissible only on medical grounds. Two additional indications were introduced before the abortion act of 1974: in 1946, sociomedical (i.e., when, considering the living conditions and other circumstances, it might be assumed that childbirth or care of the child would reduce the woman's physical or emotional strength seriously) and in 1963 teratogenetic (i.e., when there was reason to believe that the expected child, as a result of injury during the fetal stage, would suffer from a serious disease or defect). All these indications, somewhat differently formulated, are still used in Finland and Iceland.

In the debate surrounding the 1974 law on abortion the fetus often was no longer viewed as a separate individual but as a part of the woman's body. Abortion therefore became, according to this view, not a matter of weighing the value of one individual's life against the value of another's but a question of a woman's right to make decisions about her own body. The only legal limit to that right is the point in time at which the fetus has become viable, that is, able to survive outside the uterus. In Sweden the operation still may be performed at that time, but only if the woman suffers from a disease or physical defect and continued pregnancy therefore constitutes a serious threat to her life or health. Unless the operation cannot be postponed without danger to the woman, permission from the National Board of Health and Welfare is always required after the eighteenth week of pregnancy.

That exception has been questioned in an official Swedish investigation of the abortion law (Justitiedepartementet, 1989). The investigation points out that because abortion, according to the common medical definition, amounts to the expulsion of a nonviable fetus, this exception must mean that the operation is performed in such a way that the fetus is dead at delivery. The investigation found that unacceptable and required that instead efforts be made to save the life of both the woman and the fetus at that stage of pregnancy.

The investigation calls attention to the reevaluation of the legal status of the fetus that was undertaken after the abortion law was instituted. During the 1980s recurrent demands were made that an unborn child be protected from the risk of injury resulting from the mother's abuse of alcohol or narcotics. That request led to the conclusion that the woman and the prospective child no longer can be viewed as a single individual.

EUTHANASIA AND THE CONCEPT OF DEATH. Until the 1990s the dominant view on euthanasia in the medical profession in the Nordic countries was virtually that expressed in the mid-1800s by the Finnish physician Immanuel Ilmoni in his book on medical ethics *Om läkarens yrke och pligter* (1847). Ilmoni called euthanasia one of the most important special disciplines of the art of medicine. At the same time he made it clear that a physician may not in any circumstances deliberately contribute to shortening the patient's life even in cases in which the patient is "incurably ill, tormented beyond description, [and] fervently desires and demands death" (pp. 45–46).

In the late 1960s and during the 1970s, when the debate on euthanasia was most intensive in the Nordic countries, it would have been hard to imagine the medical profession supporting legislation that allowed physicians to comply with a terminally ill patient's wish to die. Among the earliest and most thorough contributions to the debate was Clarence Blomquist's book on euthanasia, *Livet, döden och läkaren* (1964). In that book Blomquist discusses the five principal definitions of euthanasia that were used in the debate: (1) the original meaning: medical care in the terminal phase of life, for example, the mitigation or relief of pain and discomfort of the dying; (2) causing death as a predicted but not intended side effect of treatment; (3) the acceleration of death; (4) passive euthanasia: discontinuing treatment or refraining from initiating treatment; and (5) active euthanasia: intentional killing in accordance with the patient's explicit or implicit wish to die or irrespective of the patient's will. Obviously, these different forms of euthanasia may overlap.

A fundamental issue in the debate has been where to draw the line between life and death. Brain-related criteria of death were introduced by law in Finland in 1971, in Norway in 1977, in Sweden in 1988, in Denmark in 1990, and in Iceland in 1991. The introduction of those criteria eliminated a minor but important part of the problem.

Throughout the 1970s even euthanasia as part of medical care in the terminal phase of life was disputed. The administration of painkillers was restricted to prevent terminally ill patients from becoming addicted to those drugs. In Sweden, for example, that restriction was not lifted until 1979. There was also concern that a more liberal administration of painkillers and tranquilizers might shorten a patient's life. Blomquist was among those who found this unintentional form of euthanasia, as well as the passive form, morally justifiable but did not support active euthanasia. Others, such as the Swedish professor of practical philosophy Ingemar Hedenius, advocated active euthanasia.

In 1992 Denmark became the first Nordic country to break with the traditional legal view on medical care in the terminal phase of life, passing a law according to which, unless there is particularly good authority for acting differently, a physician may not initiate or continue life-sustaining treatment of a terminally ill patient against wishes expressed in the patient's "living will." The law further provides that in the absence of a living will the physician may discontinue or refrain from initiating treatment that may prolong the life of a terminally ill patient. The physician also may administer painkillers, tranquilizers, and similar substances necessary for easing a terminally ill patient's suffering even when that may shorten the patient's life.

Three organizations for terminal care have been formed: in Sweden in 1973, the national organization Right to Our Death; in Norway in 1977, the national association My Living Will—the Right to a Death in Dignity; and in Finland in 1993, EXITUS. In 1985 a special organization for active euthanasia, EXIT, was founded in Sweden.

Concluding Remarks

Among other areas that have attracted special attention in the Nordic countries are ethical problems in medical research, for example, questions of integrity and the difficulty of meeting the requirements of informed consent in epidemiological and healthcare research. The frequent use of personal numbers in computerized official registers provides unique potential opportunities for population studies. At the same time it creates special ethical problems (Hermerén). Another field of increasing importance is the ethical consequences of technological and scientific developments in human genetics (for an overview see Berg and Tranøy 1989; Bischofberger et al.; Therkelsen et al; Nordisk Ministerråd, 1992, 1994). Finally, the ethical questions of health economics and setting priorities in healthcare have been debated. In 1987 in Norway a government-appointed commission produced a report on guidelines for priorities in public healthcare (Sosialdepartementet).

From the early 1960s to the end of the 1990s medical ethics underwent a sweeping transformation in the Nordic countries. From being viewed primarily as a concern only between the patient and the physician and only between colleagues, medical ethics has evolved into a field of systematic studies and extensive interdisciplinary and public debate. The scope has broadened from discussions of normative ethical issues to include metaethical analyses of the norms, values, and basic concepts of medicine. General awareness of the conflicts of interest and the incompatibility of the goals inherent in medical decision making and research has increased considerably, a development that benefits both patients and medical professionals.

B. I. B. LINDAHL (1995)
REVISED BY AUTHOR

BIBLIOGRAPHY

Airaksinen, Timo, and Vuorio, Manu J. 1988. "Medical Ethics in Finland: Some Recent Trends." *Theoretical Medicine* 9(3): 299–307.

Andersen, Daniel; Mabeck, Carl Erik; and Riis, Povl. 1983. *Medicinsk etik*. Arhus, Denmark: FADL.

Berg, Kare, and Tranøy, Knut Erik. 1989. "Ethics and Medical Genetics in Norway." In *Ethics and Human Genetics: A Cross-Cultural Perspective*, ed. Dorothy C. Wertz and John C. Fletcher. Berlin: Springer-Verlag.

Bischofberger, Erwin; Lindsten, Jan; and Rosenqvist, Urban. 1989. "Ethics and Medical Genetics in Sweden." In *Ethics and Human Genetics: A Cross-Cultural Perspective*, ed. Dorothy C. Wertz and John C. Fletcher. Berlin: Springer-Verlag.

Bjarnason, Ørn. 1991. *Sidfrædi og sidamá lækna*. Reykjavik: Idunn.

Blomquist, Clarence. 1964. *Livet, döden och läkaren: Om medicinsk dödshjälp*. Göteborg, Sweden: Zinderman Förlag.

Blomquist, Clarence. 1971. *Medicinsk etik*. Stockholm: Natur och Kultur.

Council of Europe. Ad Hoc Committee of Experts on Bioethics. 1992. *National Ethics Bodies*. Strasbourg, France: Council of Europe.

Fagerberg, Holsten; Bischofberger, Erwin; Jacobsson, Lars; and Lindmark, Gunilla. 1997. *Medicinsk etik och människosyn. Fjärde omarbetade upplagan*. Stockholm: Liber.

Finlands Läkarförbund. 1991. *Läkarens etik*. Helsinki: Author.

Giertz, Gustav. 1984. *Etik i läkarens vardag*. Stockholm: Svenska Läkaresällskapets Förlag.

Hermerén, Göran. 1988. "Ethical Problems in Register Based Medical Research." *Theoretical Medicine* 9(2): 105–116.

Hjelt, Otto E. A. 1891–1893. *Svenska och finska medicinalverkets historia, 1663–1812*. Helsinki: Helsingfors Central-Tryckeri.

Ilmoni, Immanuel. 1847. *Om läkarens yrke och pligter*. Helsinki: Simelii.

Justitiedepartementet. 1989. *Den gravida kvinnan och fostret— två individer. Om fosterdiagnostik. Om sena aborter*. Stockholm: Allmänna Förlaget.

Kjønstad, Asbjørn. 1987. *Helserett*. Oslo: TANO.

Lindahl, B. Ingemar B. 1985. "Philosophy of Medicine in Scandinavia." *Theoretical Medicine* 6(1): 65–84.

Lindahl, B. Ingemar B. 1988. "Medical Ethics in Sweden." *Theoretical Medicine* 9(3): 309–335.

Malmgren, Helge. 1990. *Medicinsk etik: En socialfilosofisk analys*. Stockholm: Almqvist och Wiksell.

Nordisk Ministerrad. Nordiskt Utskott för Etik inom Bioteknologi. 1992. *Risk, bioteknologi och etik*. Copenhagen: Author.

Nordisk Minsterrad. Noriskt Utskott för Etik inom Bioteknologi. 1994. *Bioetisk debatt i Norden 1993*. Copenhagen: Author.

Oldinger, Eva. 1991. "Undervisning i medicinsk etik bör vara obligatorisk vid alla medicinska fakulteter i Norden." *Nordisk medicin* 106(11): 308–309.

Solbakk, Jan Helge. 1991. "Ethics Review Committees [in Biomedical Research] in the Nordic Countries: History, Organization, and Assignments." *Health Care Ethics Committee Forum* 3(4): 215–220.

Sosialdepartementet. 1987. *Retningslinjer for prioriteringer innen norsk helsetjeneste*. Oslo: Universitetsforlaget.

Swedish Ministry of Health and Social Affairs. 1984. *The Concept of Death*. Stockholm: Swedish Committee on Defining Death.

Syse, Aslak. 1993. *Abortloven: Juss og verdier*. Oslo: Ad Notam Gyldendal.

Tännsjö, Torbjörn. 1991. *Välja barn: Om forsterdiagnostik och selektiv abort*. Stockholm: SESAM.

Tännsjö, Torbjörn. 1993. "Should We Change the Human Genome?" *Theoretical Medicine* 14(3): 231–247.

Tännsjö, Torbjörn. 1998. *Vårdetik. Tredje upplagan*. Stockholm: Thales.

Therkelsen, Aage J.; Bohlund, Lars; and Mortensen, Viggo. 1989. "Ethics and Medical Genetics in Denmark." In *Ethics and Human Genetics: A Cross-Cultural Perspective*, ed. Dorothy C. Wertz and John C. Fletcher. Berlin: Springer-Verlag.

Tranøy, Knut Erik. 1978. *Fra filosofi til fysiologi*. Bergen, Norway: Universitetsforlaget.

Tranøy, Knut Erik. 1988. "Medical Ethics in Norway: Modern Medicine—Traditional Morality." *Theoretical Medicine* 9(3): 337–350.

Tranøy, Knut Erik. 1991. *Medisinsk etikk i vår tid*. Søreidgrend, Norway: Sigma Forlag.

U.S. Congress, Office of Technology Assessment. 1988. *Infertility: Medical and Social Choices*. OTA–BA–358. Washington, D.C.: U.S. Government Printing Office.

Wretmark, Gerdt; Andersson Wretmark, Astrid; and Lundvigsson, Johnny. 1983. *Etik i vården—teori, praktik, forskning*. Lund, Sweden: Studentlitteratur.

Wulff, Henrik R.; Pedersen, Stig Andur; and Rosenberg, Raben. 1986. *Philosophy of Medicine: An Introduction.* Oxford: Blackwell Scientific Publications.

VIII. CENTRAL AND EASTERN EUROPE

This entry covers Poland, the Baltic states, Hungary, Romania, the Czech and Slovak republics, the former Yugoslavia, Bulgaria, Albania, and Cyprus. In these nations to the east and southeast of the Elbe River, the doctor–patient relationship and biomedicine itself have been characterized by the paternalism and dominance of a powerful elite within the medical establishment. Furthermore, a number of factors have profoundly influenced the status of healthcare as well as bioethics in this region. Among the most important are: (1) a relatively small percentage (around 5 percent) of the gross national product spent on healthcare, biomedical research, and environmental protection; (2) Prussian-like feudalistic attitudes (e.g., a rigid hierarchical system with a small and arrogant elite at the top and a large number of disempowered people below) preserved within universities and medical colleges. For physicians the idea of being the "captain of the ship" is still self-evident, and many believe that the behavior of older doctors provides the right ethical model for future ones.

In Hungary, Poland, Romania, the former Yugoslavia and Czechoslovakia, the Baltic republics, Bulgaria, and Albania, another determining factor that shaped medicine, healthcare, and bioethics was the form of Marxism that became the official ideology after the end of World War II. The hard ideology of Stalinist Marxism prevailed in Albania much longer than anywhere else in eastern and central Europe. These ideologies instructed morals and morality, so that only behaviors that brought people closer to communism were considered morally correct. Only infallible and omniscient party leaders knew exactly what these behaviors were.

Before World War II

In central and eastern Europe a feudal-capitalistic system existed prior to World War II. Agriculture was so dominant that in most of these countries the peasantry, unskilled agricultural toilers employed by owners of huge tracts of land, made up more than half of the population. These peasant workers were not able to rise from serfdom to free citizenry. This situation existed in large part because there had never been any genuine democracy in this region. The high degree of illiteracy, and the struggle for survival within the context of wars and ethnic strife, had a great impact on the people's health as well as on medical ethics.

A significant majority of people (normally peasants and poor urban dwellers) had no health insurance, and thus no access to professional care. Infant mortality, tuberculosis, and high overall death rates due to lack of treatment were very common. It was quite natural, for example, to view patients, usually those who were unable to pay, as teaching objects in university clinics and teaching hospitals. Healthcare was basically private, a profit-oriented endeavor that brought high earnings and social prestige to physicians—who carefully controlled their own numbers, especially the number of specialists. There existed a unified medical profession and a system of professional and ethical control. Within the profession certain basic norms concerning referrals, regulation of payments (neither overcharging nor undercharging), and advertisements were generally honored, and violators were punished.

Some dedicated individuals in these countries, usually physicians, kept the Hippocratic ethics alive by writing books and articles that, for generations, exerted a strong influence over the practice of doctors: for example, in Hungary, Jozsef Imre's *Orvosi Ethika* (Physicians' ethics), 1925; in Poland, Wladislav Bieganski's *Mysli i aforyzmy o etyce lekarskiej* (Thoughts and aphorisms on medical ethics), 1899. These authors concentrated almost as much on the duties of the patient as on those of the physician. In addition to the Hippocratic works as a source of ethical standards, Polish physicians relied heavily on Catholic moral theology in the development of bioethics, especially concerning such issues as abortion, birth control, genetics, and euthanasia.

After World War II

As a result of the Yalta agreement dividing Europe into spheres of interest, a large part of central and eastern Europe came under the dominance of the Soviet Union. The communist leaders launched a massive industrialization program in most countries of the region. This resulted in an unprecedented mobilization of people that contributed to significant changes in class structures (e.g., millions of peasants became industrial workers), disintegration of large family units, and increased migration to urban areas. All these changes occurred just after World War II.

These countries became monolithic states soon after the war. Moral pluralism existed only underground. Marxism shaped by Soviet communism or distorted forms of materialistic socialism provided the basis for the dominant philosophy and ethics. Moral rules were dictated by party leaders who claimed infallibility and ruled coercively, resulting in a monopolistic moral climate. Behind these rules there stood an irrefutable state power and an excessive bureaucratization of power, with extreme centralization of decision making.

Political theoreticians presented a future-oriented ethics in which every desirable human goal was placed in the future state of communism. At the same time they denied the right of existence to any autonomous professional ethics, believing that their form of Marxist ethics was adequate to answer all questions raised in any area of human endeavor. Ironically, the principal slogan in all these states was "The highest value in socialism is the human being."

However, as soon as a little freedom of speech was allowed beginning in the 1980s, it became obvious that the morals of socialism were in ruins, as was the socialist economy. Despite claims that the socialist healthcare system was of high quality, free, and accessible to everyone, it became evident that this was not so. Sociological surveys in these countries showed a very poor general state of health in the populations, high mortality rates, and severely reduced life expectancies. For example, in 1994 Hungary had one of the highest cardiovascular mortality rates in Europe for people below age sixty-five, and for all ages it placed fourth, after Romania, Bulgaria, and the former Soviet Union. This situation has not changed much into the twenty-first century. The percent of women in Hungary dying from cervical cancer is twice as high as the regional average; the suicide rate is the highest in Europe and about three times the regional average; the mortality rate from malignant neoplasm is also the highest in Europe, accounting for 21 percent of all deaths. Hungary and the former Czechoslovakia have the highest mortality rates for ischemic heart disease among countries in the region. There is a difference of almost five years in life expectancy between central/eastern and western Europe.

In addition, the crime, divorce, and suicide rates in the region rank among the highest in the world. Central and eastern European countries have placed a low priority on the prevention of accidents and illnesses and to occupational diseases. They have justified their notorious environmental pollution and destruction through the repeated use of slogans regarding the need to subdue nature for the sake of human progress.

The Soviet type of healthcare system was introduced in all these central and eastern European countries. Some of the features of the Soviet system, besides those already mentioned, included: little if any freedom for patients to choose their doctors; bribes and corruption, manifested mainly in the practice of patients' tipping physicians for services; injustices in distributing limited resources; prejudice against the elderly; mechanistic patient care; and a clash between heavy demand and very limited resources. There was also, incidentally, a predominance of women in the medical profession.

For decades the problems in Soviet-style healthcare could be hidden because fact-finding studies were regarded as "top secret" and revealing them was a serious political offense. Writers on the sociology or ethics of medicine were mostly either Communist party hacks or individuals afraid of writing the truth lest they lose their jobs. Consequently, it is little wonder that people in Western countries did not understand the decay and injustice that characterized the socialist healthcare systems of the region. Only after the political and economic collapse of these once-praised systems did they come under fierce criticism. The health laws of these countries seldom mentioned patient rights, and nothing at all was said about such principles as patient autonomy. In practice, physicians and healthcare institutions had no freedom in choosing patients, nor had patients any freedom in choosing doctors. Nevertheless, people could have access to healthcare that was theoretically free and officially had a high quality level. There is no doubt that many millions of people who, before World War II, might have died due to an inability to pay for medical care, could get essential treatments under the socialist system. This, in itself, was a great achievement.

Since state and party officials accepted no professional ethics beyond an exclusive Marxist version, teaching ethics meant teaching Marxist ethics. Its main features were the unrelenting struggle against the enemies of the working class and the constant urging of people to work and produce more. Ethics was taught in colleges and universities only by the departments (or institutes) of Marxism-Leninism. These institutes occasionally smuggled issues pertaining to medical ethics into medical universities, alongside the officially allowed themes of the Hippocratic Oath and the moral ills of private medical practice. Noticing the great interest of students in ethical issues in medicine, some teachers began to deal with euthanasia, transplantation, and confidentiality. But nowhere in these countries was the teaching of medical ethics/bioethics formally established or officially supported during the Marxist-Leninist era.

The pioneers who introduced a more contemporary medical ethics in health colleges and medical universities were quite often physicians. In Hungary, the first textbook on the subject was written by psychiatrist Janos Szilard in 1972; the second comprehensive textbook, written by Bela Blasszauer, a medical ethicist with a background in law and philosophy, appeared eighteen years later in 1990. In Poland, a popular collection of essays written by doctors was recommended for teaching medical ethics at medical universities (Kielanowski). These broadly based works on bioethics contained a number of previously undiscussed issues, including patient rights, informed consent, reproductive medicine, and refusal of treatment.

Since the end of the 1980s, and continuing into the twenty-first century, in Poland and Hungary more than six thousand hours are devoted to the six-year medical curriculum, and only thirty or less of these are assigned to the teaching of medical ethics. In certain medical schools there are no seminars, only lectures, depriving students of moral debates, discussions, and analysis of cases. In several countries seminar hours consist of surveying standard medical codes and existing health laws. Even in the early twenty-first century, a distinction was hardly ever made between laws and morals, laws and ethics. In Hungary, almost all the issues of bioethics were incorporated in the curriculum, especially such topics as informed consent, euthanasia, human experimentation, and patient rights.

Only a few countries at the turn of the twenty-first century, some years after the radical political changes throughout central and eastern Europe, encourage the teaching of bioethics, allowing bioethics to begin achieving a prominent place in the medical school curriculum. Whereas all Hungarian medical universities and health colleges teach thirty hours of bioethics, usually in the third year, in the Czech and Slovak republics bioethics is taught in ten medical schools; in Slovenia thirty hours of bioethics are given to medical students and fifteen hours to dental students. In Romania bioethics is on the medical school curriculum in Bucharest and Temesvar; in Estonia, one priority is to train bioethicists and to begin teaching in this area.

The war in the former Yugoslavia gave Croatia an impetus for developing medical ethics. Until the war, medical ethics was not taught as a separate subject in medical faculties but was a part of the history of medicine, social medicine, or forensic medicine. The same was true in Bulgaria and other Balkan countries. Since 1982, Croatia's capital Zagreb has been the seat of the Croatian Center for Medical Ethics and Quality of Life. In 1992, the medical faculty of Rijeka introduced medical ethics as an independent subject. It is the ambition of the Department of Social Studies at Rijeka to establish an international center of medical ethics for the neighboring countries.

Main Areas of Ethical Concern

Several issues are of universal and particular interest and are widely discussed in the media and are in the forefront of medical ethics education.

TIPPING. Sometimes referred to as *parasolventia,* gratuity, or even bribery, tipping was one of the most hotly debated medical ethics issues in many of these countries in the later years of the twentieth century (see, for example, Adam, 1986; Page; Szawarski, 1987; and Bologa). Outside of the

healthcare system, tipping has long been a common practice in many of these societies. Where there is a real or artificially created scarcity, and a tradition of some occupations with obligatory tips (e.g., waiters, barbers, concierges), the spreading of the practice to medicine may not be so surprising. The practice of slipping envelopes containing money into physicians' pockets for the treatment that was provided was not only unlawful but a violation of the basic idea of free healthcare, an idea that was supposed to make socialism superior to capitalism. In Hungary from the 1950s until the 1980s, the Communist party and the government waged a campaign against tipping. It was doomed to failure at the very beginning. So far every such attempt to eliminate or at least curb tipping has been absolutely ineffective.

Still, in the few articles on medical ethics or medical deontology that did appear in these countries, only the most courageous or the most trusted authors dared to write about tipping. Generally, they would have been prosecuted for damaging the reputation of the socialist healthcare system. Moreover, though it was (and is) a well-known phenomenon, it is very difficult to prove who took such money, how much, when, and why. In Hungary, the irony is that tipping is illegal, but nevertheless it is taxed. In Poland, since tipping makes healthcare unregulated and uncontrolled, the Code of Medical Ethics forbids accepting tips (Extraordinary Congress of Physicians). The Hungarian Code of Medical Ethics, on the other hand, only forbids accepting tips if they are given before treatment or given by colleagues working in the healthcare system (MOK).

In undergraduate medical education, ethics classes were devoted to this phenomenon. Ethics teachers were expected to educate future doctors to uphold socialist morality, which condemns taking money or any other form of bribe or gift from patients. Tipping has penetrated the whole system of medical care and hinders radical reforms in the system. Whether the cause is low professional salary, lack of public resources, the patient's feeling of gratitude, or simply a general moral decay, widespread tipping has morally eroded the system of healthcare. Some experts believe that the system would collapse without this extra income, which in some cases is many times greater than the state-paid salary. Other experts claim that no reform can be successful as long as the practice of tipping exists.

To a much smaller degree, health professionals other than physicians supplement their wages with occasional tips. A common feature of central and eastern European state healthcare systems is the very low salaries of doctors and other health workers. Still, some of these professions remain attractive because financial rewards can be hoped for as long as the system of gratuities persists. One can expect that debates will continue to probe the causes of this practice that has been causing major problems in the physician–patient relationship and also greatly distorts the relationship between physicians and nurses, as well as nurses and patients.

EUTHANASIA OF ADULTS AND INFANTS. Although discussion of euthanasia was long considered taboo in central and eastern Europe, it surfaced from time to time and aroused tremendous public interest. While laws in these countries forbid both active and passive euthanasia regardless of the status and prognosis of the patient (thus making no distinction between the active and the passive forms)—the latter is widely accepted and practiced. In Poland, euthanasia debates have been rare because the Auschwitz, Birkenau, Stuthof, Gross-Rosen, Treblinka, and Majdanek concentration camps were the sites of Nazi doctors' criminal practices and experiments. The memories of crimes against humanity and the moral teachings of the Catholic Church have made the Polish people very hostile to any argument favoring either form of euthanasia (Szawarski, 1987, 1988). In Romania, even under the communist dictatorship of Nicolae Ceausescu, there were scholars who openly advocated passive euthanasia: Erno Kiraly and Karoly Daniel introduced and endorsed the use of the living will in that country in the 1980s. In Romania it was not even possible to talk about bioethics until 1989; now there are hospital ethics committees for special care issues. In Czechoslovakia, physician Pavel Lukl advanced the idea of passive euthanasia in 1970. In Slovenia the practice of passive euthanasia is openly accepted, while active euthanasia, as everywhere else, is rejected (Straziscar and Milcinskij).

The Hungarian euthanasia debate dates back to the early 1920s, when a crusade to legalize active euthanasia, led by Karl Binding and Alfred Hoche (a German lawyer and physician, respectively), was rejected. In the 1970s the debate was renewed, and several articles and a book appeared (Boldizsar; Blasszauer, 1984; Czeizel, 1982). Those sympathetic to euthanasia were accused of deviating from the socialist norms and advocating discrimination among people on the basis of social worth (Horvath; Monory). The former Hungarian Health Act of 1972 states, without mentioning the word "euthanasia," that the physician's duty is to do the utmost until the very end for all patients, even those who suffer from incurable conditions. There is no mention of consulting the patient about his or her wishes. Nor is there discussion of what is to be done when legally mandated heroic efforts require respirators, dialysis machines, or other lifesaving devices that are in short supply.

In the case of seriously ill newborns, those who argued for the need to select infants to receive life-sustaining treatment were harshly condemned and even accused of behaving like the notorious Nazi doctor of Auschwitz, Josef Mengele (Mestyan). Because of Hungary's low birthrate, obstetricians were rewarded with promotions or premiums for infants who survived at least to the age of one. Therefore, up to the age of one the statistics are closely monitored, while beyond that age there is no incentive to provide high-quality healthcare. The decision to extend treatment to seriously ill infants belongs exclusively to physicians; in most cases the parents are not consulted. At the turn of the twenty-first century, however, some universities and county hospitals established infant-care ethics committees.

Only after the radical political changes of the late 1980s and early 1990s could such topics be discussed openly without accusations and reprisal. In Hungary a survey asked physicians, "Do you believe, in all circumstances, every possible effort should be made to sustain life?" Seventy-nine percent of responding physicians who worked in neonatal intensive-care units answered no (Schultz).

INFORMED CONSENT AND TRUTH-TELLING. Until the end of the twentieth century, in harmony with the existing paternalism, patients in central and eastern Europe usually received little, if any, information about their conditions. Physicians' unwillingness to discuss diagnosis, prognosis, and intended therapy with the patient was due to their training, their limited knowledge of contemporary bioethics, and their characteristically negative judgment regarding their patients' medical knowledge and ability to make rational medical decisions. Since the physician is the "captain of the ship," it was taken for granted that the patient's duty is to follow his or her orders. Hungarian sociologist Agnes Losonczi described the situation well when she stated that a sick person does not have as many rights as someone who seeks to have a washing machine repaired.

Generally, relatives of the patient were given medical information and left to decide whether to reveal that knowledge to the patient. Disclosure is still not common in cases of incurable disease; silence is believed to be justified by fear of patient suicide. This claim is simplistic and unsupported by fact, but despite arguments against deceiving patients, the dominant principle was expressed by prominent internist Imre Magyar: "One must never tell a hopeless prognosis, instead one must always give hope" (1978, p. 2). As long as a high court judge writes that an incurably ill patient must not be informed that a planned surgical intervention will bring only temporary relief, there is little hope that lawyers will fight for patients' autonomy (Toro). Silence still remains a practice in many places, despite the fact that after the collapse of communism, new laws in most countries require health professionals to honor the principle of informed consent.

Considering the prevalence of this practice of silence in central and eastern Europe, little can be said about the principle of informed consent. Although the law requires it, in reality the principle is not always honored. The Hungarian Health Act of 1997, for example, explicitly states that informed consent must be obtained before any medical intervention. Patients have seen some progress in regard to the right to access to medical documents, and many healthcare institutions provide documents to patients on request, without court intervention. The failure to obtain the consent of the patient drives most contemporary malpractice suits.

HUMAN EXPERIMENTATION, REPRODUCTIVE MEDICINE, AND GENETIC SCREENING.

Because high technology is still far from being widespread in central and eastern Europe, research is primarily related to pharmaceuticals. The Helsinki Declaration of 1975 is accepted everywhere as a guideline for ethical research using human subjects, and in some of these countries (e.g., Hungary and Romania) the guidelines have been incorporated into laws regulating biomedical research. Prisoners are excluded from any experimental or research protocol, and nontherapeutic research uses volunteers, usually students. The Polish Code of Medical Ethics (1991) makes no distinction between therapeutic and scientific research. In practice in central and eastern Europe, however, research ethical guidelines are often violated, and the region is infamous for its loose approach to honoring ethical principles.

In a few clinics and hospitals, artificial insemination, in vitro fertilization, and GIFT (gamate intra fallopian tube transfer) programs proceed under vague and inadequate legal and ethical norms.

Genetic screening is done in most central and eastern European countries, but in some of them (e.g., Hungary and Poland) it meets with opposition from the Catholic Church. In Cyprus, President Archbishop Makarios introduced compulsory screening for thalassemia, a hereditary blood disease. The screening has considerably decreased the occurrence of this disease.

CONFIDENTIALITY.

Throughout this region confidentiality is highly valued. Cases of its violation, however, hardly ever come before the courts because the laws in these countries allow many exceptions (the interest of the state, divorce cases, etc.). In practice, the violation of medical confidence is very common and goes hand in hand with the frequent violation of privacy. In the Marxist-Leninist era, the state had exclusive access to all patient records—patients were not even allowed to see them. In certain countries, like Hungary, the laws overregulated confidentiality; thus everything was viewed as a secret, which led to nothing being honored as a secret.

ABORTION.

In most of the former communist countries abortion was considered a hard-won right for women. Laws were lenient, allowing abortion for simple social reasons. In Hungary, for example, 4.5 million abortions were performed between 1956 and 1990. Some view this as a national tragedy, but the antiabortion movement has only been vocal since the Communist party's demise. Abortion was (and is) a major method of birth control: In the former Czechoslovakia there were ninety-four abortions for each 100 live births in 1988 (Albert).

In Romania, however, abortion was forbidden; as a result of illegal abortions, at least ten thousand women died from complications during the Ceausescu era. In Poland, a heated debate accompanies the attempt, strongly urged by the Catholic Church, to reverse liberal abortion laws. The 1991 Polish Code of Medical Ethics allows abortion under two special circumstances: if the mother's life and health are at risk, or if conception was the result of rape. In Lithuania, opposition to abortion is increasing, and the law that allows abortion on demand in the first trimester is considered by the antiabortion group in that country to be a crime against humanity. The debate is especially intense and interesting in the former East Germany, where abortion laws were far more liberal than in West Germany (Breese).

TRANSPLANTATION.

The policy of presumed consent for the donation of organs, tissues, or other biological material is universal in central and eastern Europe and provides an almost unlimited possibility for procurement of such materials for research, transplantation, and drug production. Lawmakers influenced by prominent members of the medical establishment were instrumental in enacting presumed-consent legislation that made organ procurement quite easy and opened the way to organ transplantation.

In these countries, transplantation has so far been largely limited to kidneys. In spite of the policy of presumed consent for donation, organs are as scarce as everywhere else and demand is high. The problem of organ procurement cannot be blamed on individuals' lack of willingness to donate their organs, but on the indifference of many health professionals. Their lack of motivation leaves many available kidneys unreported: In the early 1990s it was estimated that only 10 percent of potential donors in Hungary are made available to transplant centers. Age is one of the main criteria for transplant recipients, and in the 1980s and 1990s no "new" kidney was available for persons over the age of fifty. Heart and liver transplants have also taken place (e.g., in Hungary) and have received tremendous media coverage.

Consequently, the problem of obtaining organs has drawn great public interest and has become an important ethical issue for discussion. In these countries, where the medical establishments are strong and have significant political influence, the consent by the spouse or relatives of the dead person to use organs in most places is not necessary and their refusal is seldom honored.

MALPRACTICE. Charges of malpractice are very rare in central and eastern Europe, and successful lawsuits are even rarer. The most likely reason is not the superior professional skills of physicians working in these countries but the lack of patient rights, and the very powerful medical establishment that displays a high level of solidarity at critical times. The laws are worded in such a way that carelessness, negligence, or incompetence is difficult to prove as causally connected with the patient's state of health. Despite the fervent opposition of the medical profession, however, with the process of democratization and the planned reform of healthcare, and especially with the introduction of market conditions, malpractice is finding its way slowly into the patient–physician encounter. Insurance against malpractice had appeared in several of these countries by the beginning of the twenty-first century.

Western Help: Promising Changes

In central and eastern Europe the transition from a one-party system to political pluralism has opened the way to democracy with free elections, public control, and constitutional guarantees. These countries have begun to reform healthcare, allowing free choice of doctors; encouraging health insurance; providing mechanisms to finance health provision; overseeing the constant separation and reunification of healthcare and social services; allowing the extension of private practice; and encouraging reimbursement in accordance with the type of disease and number of patients.

The changes have brought a divergence of opinions on bioethical issues to the surface. Such world organizations as the World Health Organization (WHO), United Nations Educational, Scientific, and Cultural Organization (UNESCO), and the Council of Europe promise to bring help to the region. These organizations hold meetings, work out guidelines, keep data banks on bioethical activities, and encourage such endeavors. The Hastings Center in the United States has played a key role in helping to bring together the central and eastern European bioethicists and their western counterparts. It has provided books, journals, forums, and scholarships to a number of bioethicists in this region. The Centre for Philosophy and Health Care of

Swansea, Wales, joined the Hastings Center's Eastern European Program in the late 1980s. In the early 1990s it obtained support from the Nuffield Foundation, which has been quite generous in giving scholarships, libraries, and journals to many of these countries. The European Society for Philosophy of Medicine and Health Care, the European Association of Centers of Medical Ethics, the Jefferson Medical College of Philadelphia, the Inter-University Centre of Dubrovnik, the Center of Medical Ethics of Oslo, and the International Association of Bioethics have helped move bioethics out of the underground. Without such international help, bioethics in the region would be still back in Hippocratic times and would be poorer both intellectually and materially. In 1999 the Central and Eastern European Association of Bioethics was established with the participation of nineteen countries to promote dialogue among the former Soviet satellite countries and help each other to (re)humanize the healthcare systems.

BELA BLASSZAUER (1995)
REVISED BY AUTHOR

BIBLIOGRAPHY

Adam, Gyorgy. 1986. *Az orvosi halapenz Magyarorszagon.* Budapest: Magveto Kiado.

Adam, Gyorgy. 1989. "Gratuity for Doctors and Medical Ethics." *Journal of Medicine and Philosophy* 14(3): 315–322.

Albert, Alexa, et al. 1992. "Health Care in the Czech Republic: A System in Transition." *JAMA* 267(18): 2461.

Bieganski, Wladislav. 1899. *Mysli i aforyzmy o etyce lekarskiej.* Czestochowa, Poland: Logika Medycyny.

Blasszauer, Bela. 1984. *A jo halal.* Budapest: Gondolat Konyvkiado.

Blasszauer, Bela. 1990. *Orvosi egeszsegugyi etika.* Budapest: Tankonyvkiado.

Boldizsar, Ferenc. 1970. "Eutanazia—Igen? Nem?" *Valosag* 13(10): 34–41.

Bologa, Valeriu L. 1963. "Jegyzetek az orvosi etikarol." *Korunk* 22(6): 746–750.

Brahams, Diana. 1989. "Kidney for Sale by Live Donor." *Lancet* 1(8632): 285–286.

Breese, Wolfgang. 1990. "Twist in My Sobriety: Abortion in Germany." *Bulletin of Medical Ethics* 61(September): 13–16.

Czeizel, Endre. 1982. "A teratanazia." *Valosag* 25(6): 56–67.

Czeizel, Endre. 1988. *The Right to Be Born Healthy: The Ethical Problems of Human Genetics in Hungary.* Budapest: Kiado.

Daniel, Karoly. 1981. "Az eutanazia es a rakos betegseg utolso szakasza." *Korunk* 40(6): 16–24.

Doroszewski, J. 1988. "Medical Ethics in Poland." *Theoretical Medicine* 9(3): 351–370.

Extraordinary Congress of Physicians. 1991. *Polish Code of Medical Ethics: Resolution of the Extraordinary Congress of Physicians.* Bielsko-Biala: Polish General Medical Chamber.

Health Law and Act of its Execution: Egeszsegugyi torveny es vegrehajtasi rendelet. 1972. Budapest: Egeszsegugyi Miniszterium Kiadvanya.

Horvath, Tibor. 1973. "Eutanazia—az orvosetika es a bunteto–jog dilemmaja." *Magyar tudomany* 10: 644–652.

Imre, Jozsef. 1925. *Orvosi ethica.* Budapest: "Studium" Kiadasa.

Kielanowski, T., ed. 1985. *Etyka i deontologia lekarska* (Essays written by doctors and recommended for teaching of medical ethics at medical universities). Warsaw: PZWL.

Kiraly, Erno. 1982. "Eutanazia es buntetojog." *Korunk* 2: 123–127.

Kovacs, Jozsef. 1991. "Bribery and Medical Ethics in Hungary." *Bulletin of Medical Ethics* 66(March): 13–18.

Lang, Slobodan; Woolhandler, Steffie; Bantic, Zeljko; and Himmelstein, D. 1984. "Yugoslavia: Equity and Imported Ethical Dilemmas." *Hastings Center Report* 14(6): 26–27.

"London Kidney Exchange in Trouble." 1989. *Nature* 337(6026, February): 393.

Losonczi, Agnes. 1986. *A kiszolgaltatottsag anatomiaja az egeszegugyben.* Budapest: Magveto Kiado.

Lukl, Pavel. 1970. "Medizinisch–ethische Probleme der Reanimation." *Zeitschrift für innerliche Medizin* 25(21): 8–13.

Magyar, Imre. 1970. "Az orvos es a halal." *Orvosi hetilap* 111(51): 3011–3041.

Magyar, Imre. 1978. "Remenyt kell nyujtani." *Egeszsegugyi dolgozo* 2: 8.

Mestyan, Gyula. 1985. "Eletet—de milyet?" *Orvosi hetilap* 126(41): 2563–2565.

MOK. 1998. *Orvosetikai statutum.* Budapest: Hungarian Medical Association.

Monory, Bulcs. 1982. "Az eutanazia modern ertelmezese." *Magyar jog* 29(4): 307–312.

Page, Benjamin B. 1976. "A Letter from Czechoslovakia: Socialism, Health Care, and Medical Ethics." *Hastings Center Report* 6(5): 20–23.

Schultz, Karoly. 1993. "A Report from Hungary: Hungarian Pediatricians' Attitudes Regarding the Treatment and Non–Treatment of Defective Newborns. A Comparative Study." *Bioethics* 7(1): 41–56.

Straziscar, Stefan, and Janez Milcinskij. 1979. *Some Attitudes Toward Euthanasia in Slovenia.* Ghent, Belgium: World Congress of Health Law.

Szawarski, Zbigniew. 1987. "Poland: Biomedical Ethics in a Socialist State." *Hastings Center Report* 17(Special supplement, June): 27–29.

Szawarski, Zbigniew. 1988. "Treatment of Defective Newborns—a Survey of Pediatricians in Poland." *Journal of Medical Ethics* 14(1): 27–29.

Szawarski, Zbigniew. 1990. "Poland Moves Against Abortion." *Bulletin of Medical Ethics* 62 (October): 3–4.

Szilard, Janos. 1972. *Az orvosi etika kerdesei.* Budapest: Semmelweis Orvostudomanyi Egyetem.

Toro, Karoly. 1986. *Az orvosi jogviszony.* Budapest: Kozgazdasagi es Jogi Konyvkiado.

IX. RUSSIA

The history and state of medical ethics in Russia in the twentieth century has been defined by the influence of the communist regime. Communism, its evolution, and its deterioration, exercised and will exercise for a long time to come, a pervasive influence on the most diverse spheres of social life, including the area of medicine and health care.

Prerevolutionary Period

The ascendancy of the Bolsheviks in 1917 sharply interrupted the stormy development of Russian healthcare, whose beginnings coincided with the great reforms of 1861, which eliminated serfdom for a peasant population that comprised the overwhelming majority of the country. Prior to those reforms, peasants could turn only to the village folk doctor (practitioner of popular medicine) or, in certain cases, healers from among the Russian Orthodox monks. For the most part, the healthcare of serfs had been the responsibility of their owners.

One of the most important of the mid-nineteenth-century reforms was the creation of elected local self-governments: the *zemstvos,* which received some autonomy from the central authority. The organs of local self-government levied taxes that were used for general needs, including building and equipping hospitals, ambulances, homes for orphans and for the elderly, and other needs. *Zemstvos* also hired and paid doctors, doctors' assistants, nurses, and other medical personnel.

In 1864, 530 medical centers were opened in Russia. Each center served an average area of 4,860 square *versts* (one *versta* equals two-thirds of a mile) and a population of about 100,000 people. After fifty years, in 1914, there were 2,800 such centers, each of which served an area of 880 square *versts* and 27,000 people. Expenditures for *zemstvos* healthcare grew from 2.5 million rubles in 1870 to 57.7 million rubles in 1912. Before 1861, the country had 519 hospitals; by 1914, it had 1,715 (Solov'ev). The local doctor's ideals formed the ethos of Russian medicine. The ordinary *zemsky* (hired and paid by the *zemstvos*) physician had a modest social standing and a very modest income. He earned about as much as a factory worker. *Zemsky* physicians represented one of the largest groups within the Russian intelligentsia, along with *zemsky* teachers. Service to the people (i.e., the peasants) was a defining characteristic of the intelligentsia.

The ignorance and poverty of the peasants, whose work fed the whole country, evoked among the intelligentsia that considered itself dependent on the peasant class not only sympathy, but a guilt that moved them to active work on behalf of the peasants. Many of the intelligentsia, neglecting their own material well-being, saw as the highest meaning of their lives the unselfish service to the people. Thus was born the movement called the *narodniki,* that is, representatives of the intelligentsia who saw that their responsibility was to "go to the people," to work selflessly in the most far-away places in Russia. "Every comfort of life I have," wrote one of the most committed leaders of the *narodniki* movement, the philosopher and sociologist Petr Lavrov, "… is purchased with the blood, sufferings, and work of the millions.… I will discharge my responsibility for the cost in blood of my development, if I use my development to lessen evil now and in the future" (Solov'ev, p. 43).

Along with the more radically disposed social-democratic intelligentsia, the mass of *zemsky* physicians were very dissatisfied with the actual state of affairs, but they preferred the path of reform and the laborious work of education to the revolutionary path of violence. The first obstacles of the path of reform were the deep prejudices and lack of confidence of the peasants, their resistance to change from traditional lifestyles, including acceptance of medical aid or elementary hygienic recommendations.

The *zemstvos* system permitted physicians to achieve an unprecedented degree of professional autonomy; the government, however, constantly strove to curtail this autonomy. During these years, periodic meetings of local physicians were held to discuss current problems within the profession. In the *zemstvos,* physicians, together with representatives of the administration, participated in the formulation of local policies for healthcare. In 1883, the newly formed Society of Russian Doctors to the Memory of N. E. Pirogov assembled physicians of all specialties. The society, named in honor of the outstanding Russian surgeon Nikolai Pirogov (1810–1881), was the first independent organization of physicians. The Pirogov Society significantly influenced the formulation of ideas and policies about healthcare. It fought actively for improvements in the working conditions of peasants and factory workers, and mostly because of its efforts, in 1903 a law was adopted regarding the liability of owners for accidents in the workplace. The society strove to improve the health education of the people and battled for increases in budgets for medicine and healthcare. In 1910, the society blocked efforts of the authorities to unify the healthcare system and impose upon it strict government control. The society monitored physicians with regard to the norms of medical ethics, and fostered discussions about medical practice that touched on moral and ethical problems.

Medical ethics in Russia evolved, for the most part, in the light of European traditions, even though the specifics of Russian medicine left a noticeable mark. General practitioner and hygienist Matvei Mudrov (1776–1831), one of the first in Russia to concern himself with problems of medical ethics, believed that the Hippocratic Oath could be the foundation of a code of conduct for Russian physicians. Nikolai Pirogov, whose ideas attracted particular attention to the problem of medical mistakes, and Vjacheslav Manassein (1841–1901), general practitioner and organizer of state and local medicine as well as editor of the journal *Vrach* (Physician; 1880–1901), which devoted significant attention to discussions of medical ethics, developed their ideas along the same lines. Among the characteristics of Russian medical ethics of the prerevolutionary period, the marked paternalism connected with the long-standing tradition of subjugation of the personality to the state or to the peasant community stands out. Typical patients were illiterate and ignorant peasants who were considered unable to make reasonable decisions in their own best interests and, therefore, required direction from others.

The other significant characteristic was the peculiar understanding of social justice, which generated a feeling of eternal indebtedness to the most impoverished and unfortunate people in society. Not by accident, a physician of German origin, Fyodor Gaaz (1780–1853), who settled in Moscow and devoted himself to the medical care of prisoners in jails and their children, enjoyed great moral authority both during and after his life. Unselfish and self-sacrificing service was demanded of physicians who understood their duty, including the willingness to work at any time of the day or night, to venture into any weather at the first call to reach the bedside of a sick person as quickly as possible, and to spend as much time at his or her bedside as necessary. To appreciate this high idealism, one should bear in mind the vast expanses of Russia, which were (and are) far from being fully connected by roads.

These ideals were also reflected in the literary works of doctors who became famous writers: Anton Chekhov (1860–1904), Vikentii Veresa'ev (1867–1945), and Mikhail Bulgakov (1891–1940). Writers in Russia were traditionally leaders of public opinion and exerted great moral influence, so the works of Chekhov and Veresa'ev that were dedicated to *zemsky* physicians deeply influenced the education of the intelligentsia. In his *Physician's Notes* (first published in 1901), Veresa'ev sharply criticized violations of ethics in medical practice and research. For many years this book was at the center of significant discussions in Russian as well as western European literature. The ideal of the *zemsky* doctor was so deeply ingrained that it even survived the Bolshevik regime.

Communist Period

The communist regime came to power on the crest of a world war that was especially terrible and destructive for Russia. Immediately, the new government had to confront serious problems inherited from previous governments. Social collapse, hunger, and poor sanitary conditions caused huge epidemics of cholera, typhoid, and smallpox, so that the new government mounted a fierce fight against contagion (mass vaccinations, disinfections, isolation of infected, sanitary measures, and so on). Measures were taken to coordinate healthcare activities, resulting in extreme centralization. In July 1918, the Peoples' Commissariat for Health Care in the Russian Republic was founded.

This commissariat was the first national ministry for healthcare in the world, created a year before the British Ministry (Kazer). Under the leadership of the first Soviet People's Health Care Commissar, Nicholas Semashko (1874–1949), a doctor close to Lenin, all the departments of the government having anything to do with medical services were united under one ministry (Knaus). In subsequent years, however, organizations that were autonomous from this commissariat gradually appeared, though healthcare services for the railroads, the army, and other kinds of special services remained centralized. Healthcare services were supported financially by the state and were free to the people. These measures of the new authorities provoked severe criticism from members of the Pirogov Society who complained that the introduction by Soviet authorities of free healthcare would deprive physicians of their independence and initiative, both of which had been fought for during the earlier reforms. The regime, however, was not inclined to compromise with critics, especially with any type of organized opposition. The all-Russian Federation of Medical Workers (*Medsantrud*) was created in opposition to the Pirogov Society. The Pirogov Society was liquidated by 1922.

Medsantrud attempted to conserve the remains of democratic self-management of the ranks of medical workers, and this brought upon it the wrath of the authorities. For example, one of the principal organizers of Soviet healthcare, the People's Deputy Commissar for Health Care, Zinovii Solov'ev (1876–1928), wrote in 1923: "What is this 'public' and what in general can 'public' mean in the conditions of the Soviet government? Two different answers to these questions are not possible. Our public is to work on all aspects of Soviet life on the basis of the independent revolutionary class, the bearer of the proletarian dictatorship, the proletariat and its ally, the impoverished and the middle peasant class" (p. 54).

In this way the regime essentially redefined the social role of the physician. The physician was now considered a representative of the hostile bourgeois class, tolerated only as a specialist and permitted to work only under the strict control of the proletariat. In essence, however, that control was exercised by government and Party bureaucrats.

Meanwhile, the 1917 revolution and the ensuing civil war led to a serious decrease in the number of physicians in the country. In the first years after the revolution, about eight thousand physicians left Russia. Many doctors died from hunger and disease. Between November 1917 and August 1920, 46 percent of all physicians in Petrograd died (Knaus). In response, the authorities attempted the rapid training of new physicians. People were admitted into medical schools without even a secondary education and, at times, without even being able to read or write; final exams were eliminated. A system of "brigade education" was introduced whereby the knowledge of the group of students was evaluated on the basis of an oral exam of one of the students, on the grounds that the better prepared students would help the unprepared students in their training. There was, then, a rapid increase in the number of physicians, although, of course, at the cost of serious decline in professional standards.

Such reliance on collectivism was anything but accidental. Medicine, like everything else, was viewed from the class perspective. Individualistic bourgeois medicine was countered by collectivist proletarian medicine. The aim of the new medicine became the following: "The conservation of the life forces of the proletariat and the building of socialism in and of itself, of course, must be for us the main compass with respect to which a question regarding the tasks of our contemporary medical practice will be posed" (Solov'ev, p. 187). Consequently, the entire area of medical practice had to be reconsidered: "Characteristic of today's clinics is the fact that they were formed and exist today as the products of a discipline that is strictly individualistic. Contemporary capitalist society leaves its mark on medicine in the area of theory as well as particularly in the area of practice. The individualistic demand for care of a single person and not of a human collective creates corresponding methods of thought and practice" (p. 175). Key to the problem of shaping the approach and content of medical practice, according to Solov'ev, was the answer to the question of how "it is possible to strengthen the health of the human collective and restore [its] health once it has been destroyed" (p. 171).

These words affirmed the traditional approach of Russia regarding the importance of prevention in healthcare. This approach was implemented by making the work conditions and living conditions of people healthier, as well as by considering the social and ecological causes of many illnesses. At the same time, these comments by one of the leaders of Soviet medicine in its formative stages show clearly Bolshevism's negation of the self-worth of the individual, the reduction of human individuals to the role of cogs in a system of production, and the subjection of the individual to social expediency.

In the view of the Bolsheviks, considerations of class expediency defined the areas of morals and ethics. For example,

> The much celebrated theoretician of petty bourgeois morals, Immanuel Kant, advanced in his time a moral demand: "Never look on another person as a means to an end but always as an end in itself...." Can you imagine how far the proletariat would have advanced in its revolution if it had allowed itself to be guided by such a demand and not by the completely contrary demand of class interests.... The highest wisdom of the proletarian struggle consists not in that everyone claims his own rights, but in that everyone must selflessly, almost spontaneously, without phrases of superfluous gestures, without demanding anything for himself, pour all of his energy and enthusiasm into the common stream, and work for the goal, with the entire class, perhaps be the first to fall on the road. (Preobrazhenskii, 1923, pp. 72–73)

A systematic elaboration of medical ethics that could have corresponded to the ideological purposes of the new regime and the new system of healthcare was, with rare exceptions, not attempted. To the extent that the physician was considered as only an auxiliary, rather than as an independent professional, the idea of posing questions of specific medical ethics was deemed superfluous. Even though some problems had a distinctly moral-ethical content and as such were quite controversial (for example, abortion, confidentiality, and medical mistakes), they were not viewed as problems specific to medical ethics. In general, medical ethics or, as it was usually referred to, "physicians' ethics" was understood as the affirmation of a corporate morality opposed to the class interest of the proletariat. The viewpoint was rather widespread that Soviet people, regardless of their sex and profession, should be guided solely by the norms of communist morality, and that any specific norms of professional morality would only limit the scope of and adherence to the general norms.

With respect to medical education, systematic courses in medical ethics did not exist in prerevolutionary Russia nor were they created by the new regime. After the revolution, in fact, the initiation of new physicians by means of a professional oath, a revision of the Hippocratic oath, was eliminated, even though that practice had been obligatory since the beginning of the twentieth century. The social humanitarian preparation of medical students was limited to a course in Marxism-Leninism.

Against this background of ethical relativism and nihilism characteristic of the Bolshevik scorn for traditional moral values and principles, the earlier traditions of medical ethics could still be found. Among those who received medical education, many were inspired by the ideals of disinterested and self-sacrificing service that had characterized the ethos of *zemstvos* healthcare. The medical profession attracted intellectuals drawn to that sphere because it was not under the sway of particularly severe ideological control. The norms and values of medical ethics were transmitted under these conditions by means of informal communication and daily contact between professors and students and between experienced physicians and new colleagues.

STABILIZATION OF THE REGIME. From the end of the 1920s to the beginning of the 1930s, the communist regime consolidated itself; its radical revolutionary policies were gradually transformed into pragmatism. This pragmatism, of course, was specifically Soviet, oriented to the resolution of problems of building a communist state. All aspects of civil life began to be affected by organs of administrative and bureaucratic planning and management. Healthcare also fell under the planning system: The number of physicians in various specialties and the number of hospital beds, hospitals, and polyclinics in cities and villages, the direction and topics of medical research, the development of facilities in sanitoriums and health resorts—all were centrally planned.

Planning presupposes qualitative evaluations and measurements, and from this perspective Soviet medicine obtained impressive results. The number of doctors had long since passed one million (about 1.2 million in 1983), and a single doctor had about half as many patients as his or her counterpart in the United States. Many infectious diseases were practically eliminated, the frequency of infant mortality was significantly lowered, and the average life expectancy was increased. By these and certain other indicators the country approached the level of more developed countries or became equal to them. The results of the Soviet organization of healthcare attracted much attention outside the Soviet Union, particularly among Third World countries.

Policy in the area of healthcare, however, was always viewed as subordinate to policy in the economic sphere. Thus, when the Communist Party began to emphasize the industrialization of the country in 1929, the central task of the healthcare system was designated as the improvement of medical services to workers in the industrial centers, especially in the mining and metallurgic centers.

The system of healthcare that developed and remained relatively stable for many years was quite original in several respects. The physician became a civil servant, a kind of clerk, whose activities, regulated by numerous bureaucratic rules, consisted largely of writing reports that reflected his or her implementation of these rules. Any appearance of personal initiative was dangerous, especially because the physician's mistake could easily be interpreted as intentional, the act of a class enemy.

In relations with patients, the physician was a representative of state authority rather than an autonomous actor. Lack of autonomy, in its turn, made less urgent the problems of personal choice and responsibility. Low salaries of ordinary physicians as well as their low social prestige were among the reasons for the large number of female physicians in the country (about 80 percent). It was thought that physician's work was not so difficult, did not demand essential physical force, and therefore was well suited for women.

The social interaction of the physician and the patient was paradoxically characterized by two mutually exclusive elements. On the one hand, the long-reigning paternalism became even more entrenched, to the point where the individual regarded his or her health as a kind of state property—and therefore no one's—which could be squandered. On the other hand, health was viewed as the highest and ideal value, so high in fact that it was simply indecent to measure it by any sort of material equivalent, such as money. So, it was presupposed that self-sacrifice and unselfishness on the part of a physician was a kind of moral norm. The combination of these alternative, conflicting attitudes permitted the rather modest financing of medicine and healthcare, at a level that would ensure only the replacement of the labor force. Another characteristic of Soviet medicine was that patients were not permitted to choose their physicians.

Medical Deontology

In 1939, the famous surgeon and oncologist Nikolai Petrov (1876–1964) published an article, "Questions of Surgical Deontology," in the *Bulletin of Surgery*. In 1945, he published a small book by the same title. These publications were the first steps in the rehabilitation of medical ethics. Petrov justified the use of the term "medical deontology" by arguing that the concept of "physicians' ethics" had a narrower meaning. The latter, Petrov maintained, referred only to a corporate morality, reflecting the scientific and professional career interests of doctors (Petrov). This may have been a subterfuge designed to circumvent the ideological taboo on the problems of medical ethics. It is noteworthy

that such an attempt was made by a doctor who received his training and education before the 1917 revolution.

Wide discussion of the problems of deontology did not begin until the middle and at the end of the 1960s when writings on this topic by medical practitioners and philosophers began to appear. The 1969 First All-Union Conference on the Problems of Medical Deontology in Moscow played an important role in this development. In 1971, state authorities approved the text of a document called "The Oath of the Physician of the Soviet Union." The oath was required for all graduates of medical institutes who intended to enter into professional activities. The text of the oath demanded that physicians be governed by the norms of communist morals and spoke more of their responsibility to the people and to the Soviet government than to the patient.

At the same time, medical deontology was introduced into the curricula of the medical institutes. However, notwithstanding reports to the contrary in a number of Western sources, courses on deontology and medical ethics appeared only in the beginning of the 1990s. In most medical schools the subject of deontology appeared to be spread out in separate courses in medical specialties, and philosophers had not been drawn into its teaching.

After 1971, the stream of literature in the area of deontology increased sharply. The contents of these publications, however, were often one-dimensional, moralizing reflections: criticism of the anti-humanist Western medical system coupled with a confirmation of the indisputable moral superiority of Soviet free medicine and the disinterested Soviet doctor. Attention to concrete cases, mainly from the personal practices of the authors, was frequent. Authors, however, avoided discussion of truly difficult cases that presented moral or ethical conflicts. Apart from the fact that this literature signaled the presence of ethical problems in medicine, its real interest lay in its increasing references to the moral authority of prerevolutionary Russian medicine and its attempt to present Soviet medicine as a direct and uninterrupted continuation of the best traditions of the past.

Crisis and Breakdown of State Medicine

The government-supported awakening of interest in medical deontology coincided with the first signs of crisis in Soviet medicine. Starting in the 1970s, but primarily in the 1980s, the authorities and a small circle of specialists, and then finally the public at large, became aware of the high rates of infant mortality and the consequent reduction of life expectancy. The press began to write more often about failures in the medical field and about the callousness, greed, and low level of competence of physicians and other medical personnel. Notwithstanding the state's propaganda efforts, the people, who were losing confidence in physicians and in official medicine, turned more often to practitioners of alternative medicine.

These failures, as well as many others, revealed that the centrally planned and managed free medical system had used up all its own resources, among them the moral resource that had enabled the authorities to make do with "cheap" medicine for so long. It was clear that the communist modernization was accompanied by an erosion of traditional values, which was particularly noticeable as the medical profession became so large and more and more specialized. The turn to deontology was in some sense dictated by the efforts to mobilize the neglected moral factor in the face of growing medical crises. This attempt, to the extent that it appealed to values from the past, however glorious it might have been, could not succeed.

The attempt made during *perestroika* in 1987 to reform the system of healthcare without changing anything essential turned out to be unproductive. In 1991 the Russian parliament adopted a law providing for medical insurance for Russian citizens: This was an admission of the failure of state medicine. The stability during the last decades of the state system of healthcare was assured, even though the principles of free medicine and equal access to healthcare for all, in practice, deteriorated. The bribes that had to be given to physicians by patients and their families to some extent compensated for the pitiful financial circumstances surrounding healthcare. The availability of a special medical-care system for party members and other members of the *nomenklatura,* people given leading positions in various fields by the Communist party, made them less inclined to pursue radical reforms.

Previous stability itself made the process of thorough-going reform particularly painful for the people. The deeply rooted tradition of paternalism hindered the acceptance of personal responsibility for one's own health. In addition, social justice often was viewed as a pure leveling of differences. Finally, most people could not accept the idea that healthcare could be paid for, even though "free medicine" proved very inefficient.

Acute economic, ecological, sociopsychological problems during the period of reforms led to serious worsening of health of the population. For the first time since the beginning of the nineteenth century, mortality in Russia exceeded birth rate; morbidity, including infectious diseases, grew rapidly. These factors along with barely controlled commercialization of healthcare, limitation in access to medical services for most people, expense, and shortage of many crucial drugs generated on the part of many Russians a nostalgia about the free healthcare system of the past.

Specific Areas of Ethical Debate and Decisions

This section provides an overview of only those problems of medical ethics that have been treated in Russia in a rather original fashion.

ABORTION. Abortions in prerevolutionary Russia were considered criminal acts. In 1920, the Soviet government became the first in the world to legalize the artificial termination of a pregnancy at the request of the woman. Then, in 1936, in seeking means to improve the demographics, abortions were once again criminalized; in 1955, with some liberalization of the regime, they were again legalized to lessen the negative social consequences of widespread illegal abortions. The passage of legislation in 1993 permitted abortion at the request of the woman up to twelve weeks of pregnancy for any reason, and up to twenty-two weeks with consent of the woman for medical reasons. Abortion became a common means of birth control. The use of abortion for birth control may have resulted from a lack of contraceptive alternatives, as well as inadequate public knowledge and education about these matters.

Although abortions have been considered morally reprehensible, the attitude of people in concrete situations has been rather liberal. For many years the Russian Orthodox Church, the most influential confession in Russia, was prohibited from taking positions on any question of social significance. Even after the persecution of religion ceased, the church had not shown itself ready to express an opinion on most matters of biomedical ethics. One exception was the stance the church took on abortion. In 1990, the Patriarch of the Russian Orthodox Church confirmed the church's unequivocal censure of abortion; yet on a practical level priests tended to be more tolerant because of the hard economic situations of many women. In 1992, the Right to Life Society was formed to oppose abortions and was supported by the Russian Orthodox Church.

CONFIDENTIALITY. Controversial discussions occurred in the 1920s concerning the problem of physicians' secrets. The People's Commissar for Health Care, N. Semashko, announced "the abolition of physicians' secrets," which were understood as holdovers of bourgeois medicine. This position was based on the notion that an illness was not a disgrace but, rather, a misfortune. Full abolition of physicians' secrets would occur, it was thought, when that concept was accepted by the population. Until that time the necessity of maintaining physicians' secrets was linked to the fear that eliminating them would create an obstacle for people seeking doctors' advice and help.

Even though Semashko himself, no longer a people's commissar but a practitioner, spoke out in favor of physicians' secrets in 1945, his earlier viewpoint turned out to be more influential, for many healthcare workers did not understand the need for confidentiality. The requirement of confidentiality gained a legal basis only in 1970. Up to 1993, however, a patient who returned to work after illness was obliged to bring a sick-leave certificate from a physician. This certificate containing the patient's diagnosis was available to many people. New legislation changed this norm: A diagnosis would be filled in only with the consent of a patient; without consent only general reasons (disease, trauma, etc.) could be indicated.

DISCLOSURE TO PATIENTS. The subject of disclosure to patients has been marked by strong paternalistic tendencies. The overwhelming majority of those writing on the subject considered it unacceptable to inform a terminally ill patient of his or her diagnosis and prognosis. The practice of informing patients was not generally regulated, so concrete decisions were left to the discretion of the treating physician.

However, Russian laws on psychiatric treatment and on transplantation of human organs and tissues, which were adopted in 1992, contained norms of informed consent for patients and donors. Included in the legislation were norms governing the protection of the health of citizens, granting the patient the right to know his or her diagnosis and prognosis as well as the right to refuse this information.

The law also established specific rules regarding receipt and documentation of informed consent of patients undergoing biomedical experiments. The advent of *glasnost* (openness) in 1985 permitted public disclosure of the terrifying information about fatal biomedical experiments (such as testing of nuclear or chemical weapons, new drugs, etc.) carried out on soldiers of the Soviet Army and on prisoners under Joseph Stalin (1879–1953) and Lavrenti Pavlovich Beria (1899–1953) and even later. Some steps were undertaken for ethical control of biomedical experiments, but as of 1994 most researchers were not aware of internationally accepted norms of experimentation.

EUTHANASIA. As early as prerevolutionary times the well-known Russian jurist Anatoly Koni (1844–1927), opposing the dominant view, defended the admissibility of euthanasia

under certain exceptional circumstances: (1) conscious and insistent requests of the patient; (2) the impossibility of lessening the suffering with known methods; (3) agreement by a commission of doctors on the impossibility of saving the life; and (4) preliminary notice of the decision to the prosecutors. A law permitting mercy killing of a patient was adopted in the criminal code of 1922, but in subsequent legislation it vanished. It was practically inoperative and little is known about its utilization.

Sociological studies conducted among physicians in Moscow indicated that about 40 percent of them viewed euthanasia as permissible if the patient wishes it or in exceptional cases. However, many respondents did not seem to know what the word *euthanasia* meant (Bykova et al.). The public's attitude toward euthanasia appeared more tolerant: According to the findings of one public opinion poll, 55 percent of the respondents approved and 19 percent opposed the mercy killing by a physician of a terminally ill patient who wishes to die.

The majority of specialists in medical ethics, including physicians, jurists, and philosophers, have with rare exceptions adopted a sharply negative opinion of active euthanasia. The prohibition of active euthanasia, understood as acceding to a patient's request to hasten his or her death by medical means, was included in a law for "the protection of the health of citizens of the Russian Federation." Nonetheless, such forms of passive euthanasia as the refusal by the patient of treatment or the withdrawal of life-sustaining treatment from a hopeless patient were considered acceptable. The public's attitude toward euthanasia remained rather tolerant.

EUGENICS AND MEDICAL GENETICS. In the first decades of the twentieth century, Russia was among the world's leaders in the development of genetics. This interest in genetics generated a rather strong eugenics movement, which flowered in the 1920s. To some extent this interest may be explained by the consonance of eugenics with the central communist ideology of the creation of a "new man" who would be free of the "birthmarks" of capitalism. One of the leaders of Russian genetics, Nikolai Kol'tsov (1892–1940), following Francis Galton, spoke of eugenics as the religion of the future that still awaited its prophets. It was the powerful ruler of nature and the creator of life that would permit the creation of a perfect type of human being (Adams). In the 1920s, when ideological control was not yet particularly strong, the possibilities for forming a new human being were suggested by psychoanalysts as well as by those in other areas of scientific research.

The paths of communist ideology and eugenics diverged rather quickly, however. The principal criticism of eugenics was that the new human being should be formed by social, and not by biological, methods. Eugenic projects in Russia, because of such criticism, were interrupted long before they had achieved any practical realization. Inasmuch as Russian eugenics at that time was a form of medical genetics, the blow to eugenics also impeded research in human genetics. This setback was only the first of many caused in the Soviet Union by the reigning ideology associated with Trofim Lysenko, who taught the thesis of inheritance of acquired characteristics, which lasted until Khrushchev fell from power in 1964. Even afterward the development of medical genetics ran up against ideological obstacles, since many associated it with the eugenics that served as a basis for the murderous racism of the German Nazis. Since the beginning of *glasnost* and the end of ideological censorship, some far-reaching proposals with possible eugenic interventions in the Russian population have been published, among them, killing newborns with serious defects and forced sterilization of alcoholics and drug abusers. Genetecists, however, have been rather passive in relation to public discussions of these topics. Despite the growing public concern about the genetic effects of radiation and environmental pollution and despite rather intensive research in the field of medical genetics, Russia now has only limited capacity for genetic screening and counseling except in a few large cities. In 1994, the Russian human genome project started to study possible ethical implications of recent developments in human genetics.

REPRESSIVE PSYCHIATRY. The practice of using psychiatry as a weapon in the struggle against political dissidents began under the regime of Nikita Khrushchev. The first victim was Zhores Medvedev, who was punished for wanting to publish a book on the crushing of genetics in 1948. Medvedev was diagnosed by state psychiatrists as mentally deranged and was committed for treatment. The widespread use of psychiatry in this manner did not occur until later, during the regime of Leonid Brezhnev. Hundreds of victims, without any judicial proceedings and often without even being physically present, were sentenced for indeterminate lengths of time to special psychiatric hospitals under the jurisdiction not of the Ministry of Health but of the Ministry of Internal Affairs. "Treatment" ranged from "wall therapy"—merely keeping patients inside four walls—to forcible psychotropic injections. The practice came to be used even against ordinary citizens who had conflicts with local authorities. The Soviet psychiatrist Andrei Snezhnevsky (1904–1987) worked out the basis for this method of repression, using the concept of "creeping schizophrenia" with symptoms such as the "spreading of slander," "exaggerated religiosity," and "excessive appreciation for the West."

The center for expert studies and diagnoses of such afflictions was the V. Serbsky Institute for Forensic Psychiatry in Moscow.

Many cases of psychiatric repression became well known in the West. This caused the breach in 1983 in relations between the World Psychiatric Association (WPA) and the Soviet All-Union Society of Psychiatrists and Narcologists. The membership of the society in the association was renewed only in 1989. That same year, the Independent Psychiatric Association, founded in the Soviet Union in 1988 and actively involved in exposing psychiatric abuses, gained unconditional membership in the WPA.

A 1989 fact-finding mission of U.S. psychiatrists to Soviet psychiatric hospitals discovered that the malice of psychiatrists or of repressive state bodies was not the only cause of the abuse of psychiatry. Other factors included the poor training of medical personnel, the absence of adequate judicial mechanisms for the protection of the rights of patients, and the low level of ethical standards for hospital personnel. The aim of a 1992 law was the improvement of psychiatric treatment. According to this law, involuntary hospitalization in a psychiatric hospital was permissible only on the basis of a court's decision. The position of supervisor, to protect the rights of patients, was to be established in every psychiatric hospital. In 1993 the Russian Society of Psychiatrists—the most influential psychiatric association—adopted the Code of Professional Ethics of the Psychiatrist.

TRANSPLANTATION. The adoption in 1992 of a "law on the transplantation of human organs and tissues" provided an example of the direction of the reforms in Russian healthcare. Before adoption of this law, questions such as the determination of brain death, the rights of donors and recipients, and the permission for the removal of organs and tissues from cadavers were decided on by internal instructions of the Ministry of Health, instructions that were unknown to the population. On the one hand, this situation impeded the practice of organ and tissue transplants and, on the other hand, facilitated abuses, such as commercial use of human organs or the too-hasty declaration of brain death. The law on transplantation at last provided a legal basis for this area of medicine, and more important, became one of the first laws relating to healthcare using principles and practices accepted in the world community.

Perspectives for Russian Bioethics

Interest in the problems of bioethics grew as Russia emerged from isolation. Such interest evolved mainly through the efforts of a small group of enthusiasts. Neither the leadership of the healthcare system nor the government bureaucracy nor the public itself grasped the critical importance of problems in bioethics. Democratic reforms, to the extent that they will continue, will change this situation. As reforms develop, healthcare will become one of the most important priorities of social legislation and public interest. The reform of medicine and healthcare will make both physicians and patients much more independent and, consequently, responsible parties in social interactions.

Foundations of Legislation of Russian Federation on the Protection of the Health of Citizens, adopted in 1993, as well as other laws filled in many gaps in healthcare and legal regulations. The law opened the door for the creation of ethical committees (commissions) at federal (similar to France), regional, and local levels as well as in hospitals and biomedical research institutes to defend human rights in healthcare areas.

In 1992 the Russian National Committee on Bioethics (RNCB) was established under the aegis of the Russian Academy of Sciences. The main activities of the RNCB include the development of ethical guidelines for scientific research, proposal of legislation in healthcare and biomedicine, promotion of bioethical training and education, preparation of textbooks and methodical materials, stimulation of discussions on bioethical issues in the mass media, and encouragement of bioethics in Russian regions as well as in countries of the Commonwealth of Independent States. The RNCB prepared documents on such acute problems as mass vaccination and protection of human rights, ethical aspects of transplantation of organs, ethical regulation of new reproductive technologies, ethical control of biomedical experiments, and so forth.

"Free medicine" has not been a social priority, and whoever leads the government can find more critical need for expenditures than healthcare. But the failure of free medicine, however painful for the population, will provide the basis to hope for a better future. Already the harsh reality has caused people to realize that the government or the Ministry of Health is not alone responsible, nor will either pay for the people's health; people themselves must do so. People are also beginning to realize that medicine and healthcare are areas in which the fundamental rights and vital interests of people are realized (or not realized) and, consequently, this area requires moral and ethical consideration as well as legal regulation.

BORIS YUDIN (1995)

TRANSLATED BY RICHARD SCHNEIDER

BIBLIOGRAPHY

Adams, Mark B. 1990. "Eugenics in Russia, 1900–1940." In *The Wellborn Science: Eugenics in Germany, France, Brazil, and Russia,* ed. Mark B. Adams. New York: Oxford University Press.

Amnesty International. 1975. *Prisoners of Conscience in the USSR: Their Treatment and Conditions.* London: Author.

Bykova, Svetlana Y.; Yudin, Boris G.; and Yasnaya, Ljudmila V. 1994. "Is Euthanasia Permissible? Opinions of Physicians." *Chelovek* 2:87–92. In Russian.

Crawshaw, Ralph. 1974. "Medical Deontology in the Soviet Union." *Archives of Internal Medicine* 134(3): 592–594.

De George, Richard T. 1990. "Biomedical Ethics." In *Science and the Soviet Social Order,* ed. Loren R. Graham. Cambridge, MA: Harvard University Press.

Hyde, Gordon. 1974. *The Soviet Health Service: A Historical and Comparative Study.* London: Lawrence and Wishart.

Ivanyushkin, Aleksandr J. 1990. *Professional Ethics in Medicine.* Moscow: Medicine Publishers. In Russian.

Kazer, Michael Charles. 1976. *Health Care in the Soviet Union and Eastern Europe.* Boulder, CO: Westview Press.

Knaus, William A. 1981. *Inside Russian Medicine: An American Doctor's First-Hand Report.* New York: Everest House.

Kotel'nikov, Valentin Prokhorovich. 1987. *Ot Gippokrata do hashikh dnei.* Moscow: Znanie.

Malkov, Sergei M., and Ogyrtzov, Aleksandr P., eds. 1992. *Bioethics: Problems and Prospects.* Moscow: Institute of Philosophy of Russian Academy of Sciences. In Russian.

Petrov, Nikolai Nikolaevich. 1956. *Voprosy khirurgicheskoi deontologii.* Leningrad: Medgiz Publishers.

Petrovskii, Boris Vasil'evich. 1988. *Deontologiia v meditsine.* 2 vols. Moscow: Medicine Publishers.

Preobrazhenskii, Evgenii Alekseevich. 1923. *O morali i klassovykh normakh.* Moscow: Gos. izd-vo.

Ryan, Michael. 1979. "USSR Letter: Aspects of Ethics (2)." *British Medical Journal* 2(6191): 648–649.

Solov'ev, Zinovii Petrovich. 1970. *Voprosy sotsial'noi gigieny i zdravookhraheniia.* Moscow: Meditsina.

Tichtchenko, Pavel D., and Yudin, Boris G. 1992. "Toward a Bioethics in Post-Communist Russia." *Cambridge Quarterly of Healthcare Ethics* 1(4): 295–303.

"A Topical Interview Given by the Holy Patriarch Pimen." 1990. *Journal of the Moscow Patriarchate* 7: 12–21.

Veatch, Robert M. 1989. "Medical Ethics in the Soviet Union." *Hastings Center Report* 19(2): 11–14.

Veresa'ev, Vikentii Vikentevich. 1904. "Physician's Notes." In *The Confessions of a Physician,* tr. Simeon Linden. London: Grant Richards.

Yudin, Boris G. 1992. "Bioethics for the New Russia." *Hastings Center Report* 22(2): 5–6.

MEDICAL ETHICS, HISTORY OF THE NEAR AND MIDDLE EAST

• • •

I. Ancient Near East

II. Iran

III. Turkey

IV. Contemporary Arab World

V. Israel

I. ANCIENT NEAR EAST

In its conventional sense the term *ancient Near East* includes a diverse range of cultures. This article limits its coverage to Mesopotamia from the Sumerian period (beginning ca. 3100 B.C.E.) through the Babylonian period (ending with the Persian conquest in 539 B.C.E.), Egypt from about 3100 B.C.E. to its conquest by Alexander the Great (332 B.C.E.), and Israel from the Exodus (variously dated from 1446 B.C.E. to 1280 B.C.E.) to the destruction of Jerusalem by the Romans in 70 C.E.

In both Mesopotamia and Egypt thriving medical professions existed throughout the period under consideration. In Israel a distinct medical profession appears to have developed very late (second century B.C.E.). If anything that could be called medical literature was produced in Israel, it was at the very end of our period. By contrast a large body of medical literature, some of which has survived, existed in both Mesopotamia and Egypt.

Conceptual Observations

No writer in the ancient Near East appears to have addressed what we call medical ethics as an area of specific discussion. No one seems to have written even on that weak precursor of medical ethics known as medical etiquette. Nevertheless, medical ethics existed as much in the ancient Near East as in any other culture. The medical ethics of any society is generally congruous with that society's moral perceptions. As a subset of its ethical values, medical ethics will be as simple or as complex as any culture is monolithic or pluralistic. An ethical framework exists for the practice of medicine wherever those who treat disease, even in a magico-religious form, administer healing. In seeking to reconstruct the medical ethics of any society, one must understand the broad cultural framework within which healers function in order to appreciate the ethical considerations that directly or indirectly govern the practice of their art. This picture may be supplemented by the incidental illumination of relevant aspects of medical practice gleaned from medical and other literature, as well as by evidence of legal constraints upon the activities of practitioners of the healing arts.

J. V. Kinnier Wilson remarks that "Medically, as in other respects, Egypt, Mesopotamia, and Palestine were three quite different worlds. Each developed along independent lines of thought and was of its own kind" (p. 337). While this statement is essentially correct, Mesopotamia and Egypt are sufficiently similar when contrasted with Israel that they may be considered together, while Israel, because of its unique religious and moral outlook, merits separate treatment.

Mesopotamia and Egypt

THE UNDERSTANDING OF DISEASE AND THE ROLE OF PHYSICIANS. In Egypt and Mesopotamia all aspects of life were molded by religions that were naturalistic and polytheistic, based on the worship of cosmic forces, and steeped in magic. Health and physical wholeness were perceived as being present so long as life remained in harmony with the forces of deified nature, while illness reflected a dissonance between the individual and his or her total environment. It was imperative to identify the cause of sickness in order that the appropriate treatment might be given for the restoration of health. Edwin Yamauchi isolates four main sources of illness, which were not mutually exclusive: (1) a divine source which sent illness as a punishment for sin; (2) a demonic source which indwelt or tormented the individual; (3) a magical source sent from a sorcerer or practitioner of black magic; and (4) a natural source as discerned by experience. The modes of treatment would include: (1) prayer, sacrifice and repentance; (2) the exorcism of demons; (3) counter-magic; and (4) empirical applications of medicine, drugs, or surgery. Quite frequently different kinds of treatment were combined. (p. 99)

In both Mesopotamia and Egypt the treatment of disease attributed to divine, demonic, or magical sources fell within the purview of a class of healers different from those who treated disease attributed to natural causes. In Mesopotamia the latter class (the *azu* or *asû*) appears to have emerged much earlier than the former (the *āšipu*). According to Kinnier Wilson, "In Sumerian times—as it would seem—the *azu* was the only doctor who was prominent in society. It is only at a later period, in Babylonia, that one meets the *āšipu*, a specialist in incantations and a kind of medical 'diviner,' capable of reading the 'signs' of suffering or of divine punishment" (p. 349). The two professions were functionally and ideologically distinct, and only the *ašipu* was a priest. Similarly, in Egypt, the *seynu* (or *swnw*), like the Mesopotamian *asû*, was concerned with the treatment of physical conditions, whether sicknesses or injuries, for which a proximate, natural causality was evident; the *heri-ha'ab*, the equivalent of the Mesopotamian *ašipu*, was essentially a magician or exorcist (Kinnier Wilson). In a third category was the *wabw*, the priest of Sekhmet, lion-headed goddess of war, who both caused and cured epidemics. The *wabw* often combined features of both the *seynu* and the *heri-ha'ab*. Although each constituted a distinct profession, any two or even all three might be combined in the same practitioner.

MEDICAL ETHICS. The ethics of healers reflected an environment in which the understanding and explanation of reality were thoroughly religious: All aspects of life, including sickness and healing, received their meaning from religion (see Amundsen and Ferngren). The therapeutics employed by the *asû* and the *seynu* in dealing with acute diseases and injuries seem rational when compared with the predominantly magico-religious techniques of the *ašipu* and the *heri-ha'ab*. But the words of Owsei Temkin are cogent here:

> To be historically comprehensive, medicine cannot be defined as a science or the application of any science or sciences. Medicine is healing (and prevention) based on such knowledge as is deemed requisite. Such knowledge may be theological, magic, empirical, rationally speculative, or scientific. The fact that medicine in our days is largely based on science does not make other forms less medical—though it may convince us that they are less effective. (1977, p. 16)

Those ancient Near Eastern practitioners who seem to have been more rational than their magico-religious colleagues were not more ethical. Theirs were complementary, not competitive, professions. We do not have here a case of medical rationalism vying with superstition. Within their cultures neither approach was more or less rational than the other. Both perceived the causality of disease within an epistemological context in which spiritual, magical, and natural categories were not clearly distinguished. Hence, in this environment, the ethical obligations of healers must be appreciated in terms of their role as interpreters of sickness and healing within the broader cosmological realities and social values of their community. Within this general framework we can glean from the primary sources some specific, although fragmentary, aspects of medical ethics of the ancient Near East.

TO TREAT OR NOT TO TREAT. The Egyptian physician, as revealed by the medical papyri, made a prognosis before undertaking treatment. If the prognosis was favorable, the physician's comment was "an ailment that I shall treat"; if it was uncertain, "an ailment that I shall combat"; and if the prognosis was unfavorable, "an ailment not to be treated." The Edwin Smith Papyrus (a sixteenth-century B.C.E. copy of an earlier text that was probably written between 3000 and 2500 B.C.E.) contains the record of fifty-eight examinations, each followed by either treatment or a decision not to treat (Breasted). The author recommends treatment in forty-two cases and leaves sixteen untreated. In three of the hopeless cases (6, 8a, and 20), some alleviating treatment is indicated. In the Papyrus Ebers (Ebbell), which dates from roughly the same period, a small number of cases are regarded as untreatable (e.g., cols. 108–110), and in one hopeless case there is an attempt to relieve the patient. That specific alleviatory instructions are given only in a minority of hopeless cases does not necessarily indicate a lack of compassion. Incidental remarks in these papyri suggest that physicians carefully and gently treated their patients and showed kindness to the ill, injured, and maimed.

In Mesopotamia *ašipus* were prognosticators whose medical repertoire consisted mostly of incantations and charms, occasionally supplemented by ointments and purgatives. They did not hesitate to withdraw from cases that they regarded as hopeless. Their colleagues, the *asûs*, who administered medicines, performed some surgery, and seldom used incantations, seem only rarely to have refrained from treating hopeless cases, but continued with treatment to the end. This difference may be due in part to the fact that the *ašipu* treated primarily chronic illnesses, while the *asû* usually dealt with acute diseases and injuries (Ritter).

EUTHANASIA AND ABORTION. There is no direct evidence pro or contra regarding the ethics of euthanasia. It appears that in both Mesopotamia and Egypt those who committed suicide were regarded as having cut themselves off from the gods. A touching dialogue between a man contemplating suicide and his *ba* (soul), survives from Egypt, dating from the end of the third millennium B.C.E. (Pritchard). Although the man is not considering suicide owing to illness, the psychological struggle portrayed reveals a culture in which suicide was not accepted simply as a personal option without moral and religious compunctions, although the text suggests that it was not uncommon. Whether physicians assisted in suicide or viewed active euthanasia as opprobrious is unknown.

Prescriptions for induced abortion are found in the Egyptian medical papyri, but its legality remains unclear. In Mesopotamia, Middle Assyrian laws (fifteenth century B.C.E.?; Pritchard, 1969) stipulate that if a woman has an abortion by her own act, whether or not she survives the ordeal, she is to be impaled on a stake and left unburied. The purpose here (as in much other ancient law prohibiting abortion) is not to protect the fetus but to protect the husband's right to have the child he fathered. There is no mention of the involvement of physicians in abortion.

REGULATION OF THE MEDICAL PROFESSIONS AND LEGAL PROTECTION OF PATIENTS. The first recorded attempt to protect the patient from the incompetent physician is from Babylonia, in the Code of Hammurabi (ca. 1750 B.C.E.; Pritchard). There it is specified that if a physician performs a major operation with a bronze lancet on a member of the nobility that results in the patient's death, or an operation with a bronze lancet on his or her eye that results in its loss, the physician's hand will be cut off. If an operation with a bronze lancet results in the death of a commoner's slave, or if the operation causes the loss of the slave's eye, the physician is to pay half the slave's value in silver. No punitive regulations are extant governing medical procedures other than surgery. This is understandable, particularly in a culture permeated by magical beliefs. The unsuccessful use of incantations or sympathetic magic (the administration of medicinal herbs may be included in this category), in which the healing role of the practitioner is nearly passive because of the supernatural agents at play, stands in marked contrast to the active immediacy of the physician in surgery. The Code of Hammurabi also establishes fees for surgery. The amount is determined by the social status of the patient, indicating the intention of the legislator to peg medical fees to the patient's economic means.

Little is known about the regulation of healers in Egypt. Although there appears to have been no system of medical licensure, medical procedure became rigidly prescribed over the centuries. A Greek historian, Diodorus Siculus (first century B.C.E.), whose material on Egypt was derived from the sixth-century-B.C.E. Greek geographer Hecataeus, writes that Egyptian physicians gave treatment in accordance with ancient written procedures. If their patients died, the physicians were absolved from any charge. If they deviated from traditional methods in any way, they were subject to the death penalty, on the assumption that few physicians could be wiser than the physicians of old. In the *Politics,* Aristotle describes a slightly more flexible situation in Egypt, in which physicians could alter their prescriptions after four days; if they altered them earlier, they did so at their own risk.

Little evidence exists from the ancient Near East regarding experimentation with novel procedures. In a letter to the Assyrian king (seventh century B.C.E.?), a physician suggests that a particular prescription be tested on members of the domestic staff before being administered to a member of the royal family. While cesarean section is known to have been performed in Mesopotamia in the second millennium B.C.E. as a last resort to save the infants of dying women, the evidence suggests that the procedure was used only on slaves. These examples suggest the fear of risk involved in novel procedures. But there were other hindrances to therapeutic experimentation: the tendency of empirical physicians to rely on traditional procedures; the existence of a written tradition of medical knowledge and procedures in both Mesopotamia and Egypt; and the fact that medicine was often allied ideologically with religion. These factors are likely to have inhibited innovation that deviated from accepted practice even in late Egyptian medicine. Although evidence is lacking for Mesopotamian attitudes to novel procedures, they are not likely to have been more positive.

Ancient Israel

The basic difference between the worldview of the Hebrews (ca. 1300 B.C.E.—70 C.E.) and that of their ancient Near Eastern neighbors was one of religious outlook. Israel's religion was monotheistic, while that of its neighbors was polytheistic, focused on the worship of natural forces, particularly those associated with fertility. In the Hebrew Scriptures, the cosmos is perceived as being under Yahweh's direction. Although there is a personal force of evil (Satan), he is subordinate to Yahweh and poses no significant challenge to his authority. While polytheism imposed no absolute moral standards, the ethical beliefs of Israel were grounded in the character of Yahweh, who was regarded as the transcendent creator and sustainer of the world. Religion and ethics were inseparable, since both were derived from Yahweh, who was holy and required holiness of his people. Yahweh's absolute character gave authority to his revelation to Israel, and his holiness provided the ethical basis of Israel's laws. The law of Israel, the Torah, grew out of Yahweh's covenant with the Hebrews, which made them his special people. As a requirement of maintaining the covenant, Israel was to reflect the moral character of Yahweh in its national life.

THE HEBREW UNDERSTANDING OF DISEASE AND HEALING. In the Hebrew scriptures illness is viewed in its moral and spiritual dimensions rather than as a merely physical phenomenon. A close relationship between sin and illness was believed to exist at two levels: (1) Physical evil, including illness, entered the world as a consequence of sin; and (2) illness was sometimes visited upon both individuals and nations because of their sin. Hence disease and injury were a consequence of sin, but they were also within the realm of God's control. Yahweh says, "I kill and I make alive; I wound and I heal" (Deut. 32: 39). Disease, as a manifestation of God's wrath against sin, could be seen on both an individual (e.g., Num. 12: 9–12; 2 Kings 5: 25–27; 2 Chron. 21: 11–18) and a national level (e.g., 1 Sam. 5: 6–12). Yahweh promises health and prosperity to his covenant people if they are faithful to him, and disease and other suffering if they spurn his love (e.g., Exod. 15: 26; Lev. 26: 14–16; Deut. 28: 21–22, 27–28, 59–61; Ezek. 14: 21; Hos. 6: 1).

Passages often considered messianic offer the hope of healing, physical as well as spiritual (e.g., Isa. 53: 4–5; Mal. 4: 2). When the Messiah comes, "No one in Jerusalem will say 'I am sick'; the people who dwell there will be forgiven their iniquity" (Isa. 33: 24). The mental and physical anguish that accompanies the guilt of a person smitten and disciplined by Yahweh for sin is spoken of repeatedly in the Psalms (e.g., Ps. 38: 3, 5, 8), while to acknowledge and repent of sin is said to bring healing (Ps. 32: 3–5). Forgiveness and consequent healing were not viewed as the result of appeasing a hostile deity through ritual and offerings (see, e.g., Ps. 51: 16–17). Suffering in general, and sickness in particular, represented Yahweh's chastisement of his people, which was corrective rather than retributive. This theodicy, however, did not make suffering easier to endure for those who searched their hearts but could find no specific sin to be confessed (e.g., Ps. 88; Job, passim). The righteous sufferer must acknowledge God's inscrutable ways and ultimate goodness (e.g., Ps. 94: 12; Prov. 3: 11–12).

PHYSICIANS AND MEDICINE. The judgment upon King Ahaziah for consulting the god of Ekron concerning his illness (2 Kings 1: 2–4) resulted from the same kind of sin for which Asa, king of Judah, was condemned. Asa was seriously ill, "yet even in his disease he did not seek the Lord, but sought help from physicians. And Asa slept with his fathers" (2 Chron. 16: 12–13). Asa is not condemned for resorting to secular medicine as such but, rather, for consulting physicians who were probably Mesopotamian or, less likely, Egyptian. The procedures practiced by these physicians, even if empirical, would have been magico-religious. There is no evidence that priests functioned as physicians or surgeons in Israel. Their only involvement in matters pertaining to health was in the enforcement of a highly developed code of personal and social hygiene (Lev. 12, 13, 15, 21). Were there healers in Judah whom Asa could have consulted, whose practices would not have violated Jewish religious scruples? This question cannot be answered with certainty since there is no evidence in the Hebrew scriptures of the existence of a distinct medical profession.

The Hebrew word for healer or physician is the participle of the verb *rapha,* the original meaning of which appears to be "one who sews together" or "one who repairs." Its first participial occurrence is found in Gen. 50: 2, where Egyptian physicians are said to have embalmed Jacob. The verb itself is often used literally in the sense of healing from disease or injury (e.g., Gen. 20: 17; Num. 12: 13; 2 Kings 20: 5–8). When Jeremiah (ca. 645–ca. 575 B.C.E.) writes, "Is there no balm in Gilead? Is there no physician there?" (Jer. 8: 22), although he is speaking metaphorically, he attests the existence of both balm, as a therapeutic substance, and some kind of healers. The Israelites, of course, had knowledge of the rudimentary treatment of wounds and of herbs that could be used to treat various ailments traceable to natural causes. The Torah stipulates that if a person injures another in a quarrel and the injured party survives, the assailant is to be held financially liable "for the loss of his time, and shall have him thoroughly healed" (Exod. 21: 18–19). This passage implies that the expense both for medicines and for healers to dispense or apply them was to be borne by the guilty party. Several incidental references suggest the existence of binders of wounds (Isa. 3: 7), knowledge of the setting of fractures (Ezek. 30: 21), and the use of various therapeutic substances (Isa. 1: 6; Jer. 51: 8).

Although the Hebrew scriptures represent Yahweh as the only healer (e.g., Exod. 15: 26) and command Israelites to refrain from resorting to magical or pagan healing practices (see, e.g., Ezek. 13: 17–23), the use of natural or medicinal means is not discouraged, but is resorted to even in ostensibly miraculous healings (e.g., 2 Kings 20: 7). Medical knowledge may have been limited to folk remedies, however, and there probably were no systematized therapeutics, much less medical practitioners who were distinctively Hebrew. Not until the second century B.C.E. is there evidence of a Jewish medical profession. Contact with Greek civilization in the Hellenistic age provided Jews with something that neither Mesopotamia nor Egypt could contribute: a religiously neutral theoretical framework for a rational understanding of disease and healing that allowed the coexistence of both divine explanations of ultimate causality and natural processes of proximate causality within Yahweh's created order.

The earliest mention of a Jewish medical profession is in the Wisdom of Jesus Ben Sira (also known as Ecclesiasticus), composed in Palestine early in the second century B.C.E. Ben Sira urges his readers to honor the physician as a servant of God, who gives him his skill. Dependence upon God is essential for the patient, because it is God who heals. The physician, too, must depend upon God, "for also he supplicates God that he may make his diagnosis successful and his treatment to save your life" (38: 1–15, Noorda's translation [1979]). In spite of an occasional critic like Philo Judaeus (an Alexandrian Jew of the early first century C.E.), who scathingly condemned fellow Jews who trusted in medicine without reference to God and turned to him only as a last resort (Temkin, 1991), Hellenistic Jews accepted rational medicine based on the Greek model as fully compatible with their faith. Apart from the available medical resources, which were limited, healing could come only from Yahweh by confession of sin, supplication, and prayer (e.g., Job 33: 19–30).

MEDICAL ETHICS. Central to understanding Hebrew and Jewish medical ethics is the concept of the image of God (*imago Dei*). In the Genesis account of creation, Yahweh is depicted as having created man and woman in his image (Gen. 1: 26–27). Endowed with rationality, self-consciousness, and volition, the human personality in Hebrew thought was represented as mirroring Yahweh's image. Persons are spiritual beings, created to have communion with God, and responsible for their own moral actions. The concept of the *imago Dei* had implications for the protection of human life, which was believed to possess intrinsic value, and hence to be sacred. Even human beings with physical defects are said to bear God's image. Yahweh asks Moses, "Who has made man's mouth? Who makes him dumb, or deaf, or seeing, or blind? Is it not I, the Lord?" (Exod. 4: 11).

As a result of the Hebrew view of humanity as possessing intrinsic worth, the Torah exhibits a greater humaneness than other codes of the ancient Near East (e.g., the Code of Hammurabi). There are, for example, provisions that protect the rights of the blind and the deaf (e.g., Lev. 19: 14). The fetus was regarded as having been created by Yahweh and designed for a specific purpose (Ps. 139: 13–16; Jer. 1: 5; Isa. 49: 1). Yet abortion was not explicitly forbidden by either the Torah or later rabbinic Judaism. In fact, in the Talmud it was permitted in some circumstances. Whether the practice was acceptable in the pre-Christian era is disputed. The accidental destruction of the fetus was not a capital offense, but required monetary compensation (Exod. 21: 22–25). The newborn child, however, was regarded as fully human and deserving of the same protection as an adult. Infanticide, a common practice in the surrounding Canaanite culture, was expressly prohibited (Lev. 18: 21, 20: 2), and the exposure of newborn children was also condemned (see Exod. 1: 17–21; Ezek. 16: 5). Castration, sometimes practiced by Canaanites for religious purposes, was also forbidden, and eunuchs were excluded from Hebrew religious life (Deut. 23: 1).

The Hebrew scriptures provide no information regarding the behavior expected of Jewish physicians. Mesopotamian and Egyptian physicians had an enormously varied repertoire of religious and magical techniques of propitiation and manipulation, as well as of natural therapeutics, from which

to choose. They also had the freedom to be imaginative, active participants in processes in which the lines between what we call the natural and the supernatural were blurred. By contrast, Jewish physicians, working with and through natural means and processes, and eschewing any techniques involving magic or the demonic, were, along with their patients, to depend upon the Creator, from whom alone all true and licit healing came (Deut. 32: 39). Given the emphasis in the Hebrew scriptures on the compassionate nature of the God who heals, and the importance that Ben Sira assigns to the physician as an agent of God, it would be surprising if Jewish physicians were not encouraged to emulate the divine compassion in their treatment of the ill. This attitude would be especially compatible with the new emphasis on the meritorious nature of charity that is found in the Apocrypha (Jewish religious writings dating from third century B.C.E. to about 100 C.E. that were not included in the Hebrew scriptures). It is in the postexilic period (after 605–582 B.C.E.), too, that one begins to see a tradition of caring for the ill that makes the sick person no longer an object of stigmatization (e.g., Job 19, esp. 13–20; Ps. 42: 4–10), but a person deserving of special care, like widows and orphans (e.g., Sirach 7: 35; 2 Macc. 8: 28). This specific concern for the sick within the community of Israel is a theme that is extended and developed in the Talmud.

DARREL W. AMUNDSEN
GARY B. FERNGREN (1995)

BIBLIOGRAPHY

Amundsen, Darrel W., and Ferngren, Gary B. 1982. "Medicine and Religion: Pre-Christian Antiquity." In *Health/Medicine and the Faith Traditions: An Inquiry into Religion and Medicine*, pp. 53–92, ed. Martin E. Marty and Kenneth L. Vaux. Philadelphia: Fortress.

Biggs, Robert. 1969. "Medicine in Ancient Mesopotamia." *History of Science* 8: 94–105.

Breasted, James Henry, tr. 1930. *The Edwin Smith Surgical Papyrus: Published in Facsimile and Hieroglyphic Transliteration, with Translation and Commentary.* 2 vols. Chicago: University of Chicago Press.

Ebbell, Bendix, tr. 1937. *The Papyrus Ebers: The Greatest Egyptian Medical Document.* Copenhagen: Levin and Munksgaard.

Ferngren, Gary B. 1987. "The *Imago Dei* and the Sanctity of Life; The Origins of an Idea." In *Euthanasia and the Newborn: Conflicts Regarding Saving Lives*, pp. 23–45, ed. Richard C. McMillan, H. Tristram Engelhardt, Jr., and Stuart F. Spicker. Dordrecht, Netherlands: D. Reidel.

Ghalioungui, Paul. 1963. *Magic and Medical Science in Ancient Egypt.* London: Hodder and Stoughton.

Hogan, Larry P. 1992. *Healing in the Second Temple Period.* Göttingen: Vandenhoeck and Ruprecht.

Jacob, Irene, and Jacob, Walter, eds. 1993. *The Healing Past: Pharmaceuticals in the Biblical and Rabbinic World.* Leiden: E. J. Brill.

Kinnier Wilson, J. V. 1982. "Medicine in the Land and Times of the Old Testament." In *Studies in the Period of David and Solomon and Other Essays: Papers Read at the International Symposium for Biblical Studies, Tokyo, 5–7 December, 1979,* pp. 337–365, ed. Tomoo Ishida. Winona Lake, IN: Eisenbrauns.

Noorda, Sijbolt J. 1979. "Illness and Sin, Forgiving and Healing: The Connection of Medical Treatment and Religious Beliefs in Ben Sira 38, 1–15." In *Studies in Hellenistic Religions,* pp. 215–224, ed. Maarten Jozef Vermaseren. Leiden: E. J. Brill.

Oppenheim, A. Leo. 1962. "Mesopotamian Medicine." *Bulletin of the History of Medicine* 36(2): 97–108.

Preuss, Julius. 1978. *Julius Preuss' Biblical and Talmudic Medicine,* tr. Fred Rosner. New York: Hebrew Publishing.

Pritchard, James Bennett, ed. 1969. *Ancient Near Eastern Texts: Relating to the Old Testament,* 3rd edition. with suppl. Princeton, NJ: Princeton University Press.

Reiner, Erica. 1964. "Medicine in Ancient Mesopotamia." *Journal of the International College of Surgeons* 41(1): 544–550.

Ritter, Edith K. 1965. "Magical-Expert (=Āšipu) and Physician (=Asû): Notes on Two Complementary Professions in Babylonian Medicine." In *Studies in Honor of Benno Landsberger on His Seventy-fifth Birthday; April 21, 1965,* pp. 299–321. Chicago: University of Chicago Press.

Rosner, Fred. 1977. *Medicine in Bible and the Talmud: Selections from Classical Jewish Sources.* New York: Ktav.

Seybold, Klaus, and Mueller, Ulrich B. 1981. *Sickness and Healing,* pp. 16–96, tr. Douglas W. Stott. Nashville, TN: Abingdon.

Sigerist, Henry Ernest. 1951. "Ancient Egypt." In *Primitive and Archaic Medicine,* pp. 215–373, Vol. 1 of *A History of Medicine.* New York: Oxford University Press.

Sigerist, Henry Ernest. 1951. "Mesopotamia." In *Primitive and Archaic Medicine,* pp. 377–397, Vol. 1 of *A History of Medicine.* New York: Oxford University Press.

Temkin, Owsei. 1977. *The Double Face of Janus.* Baltimore: Johns Hopkins University Press.

Temkin, Owsei. 1991. "The Almighty God." In *Hippocrates in a World of Pagans and Christians,* pp. 86–93. Baltimore: Hopkins University Press.

Wilson, John A. 1962. "Medicine in Ancient Egypt." *Bulletin of the History of Medicine* 36(2): 114–123.

Yamauchi, Edwin. 1986. "Magic or Miracle? Diseases, Demons and Exorcisms." In *The Miracles of Jesus,* pp. 99–110, ed. David Wenham and Craig Blomberg, Vol. 6 of *Gospel Perspectives: Studies of History and Tradition in the Four Gospels,* ed. R.T. France and David Wenham. Sheffield, U.K.: JSOT.

II. IRAN

Iran, a vast country in Southwest Asia, was long called Persia by Europeans until, in 1935, its government requested that the common indigenous name, Iran, identifying the nation as the "land of the Aryan people," be used internationally. The extensive Iranian Plateau and surrounding lands have been the site of many powerful political regimes during its long history, beginning with the empire of Cyrus the Great, the first Achaemenid emperor, in 549 B.C.E.. Located along a highway for the movement of people and ideas from the prehistoric period on, its indigenous Aryan culture has been an important link between Hellenic, Indic, and Semitic intellectual and religious traditions. Within the limits of this article, the history of Persian medicine cannot be traced; only the ethics characteristic of that history will be treated.

Prehistoric Period

Little is known about the healing practices or beliefs of the earliest inhabitants of Iran. An epic poem, *Shāhnāmah* (Book of Kings), written in the tenth century C.E., relates ancient myths, legends, and stories that may reveal something of the ancient past. Surgery is mentioned in the tales of the superhuman exploits of the heros Rustam and Isfandyar. Rustam himself is said to have been delivered by an operation much like that now known as a cesarean section, while his mother was anesthetized with wine. Abortifacients were known. The Elamite civilization, centered around Susa in southern Iran from the third to the first millennium, had cultural contact (and often political enmity) with Babylon, and it is likely that the medicine of the Mesopotamian world was known by the Elamites (Sigerist). The Code of Hammurabi, ruler of Babylon (ca. 1750 B.C.E..), which contains strict injunctions and penalties regarding surgical practice and malpractice, is known primarily from a stela found at Susa in 1902.

The Aryan Period (Ninth-fourth Century B.C.E.)

The nomadic Aryan peoples migrated from Central Asia, north and east of the Caspian Sea, to the Iranian Plateau around the seventeenth century B.C.E. By the ninth century, they dominated the region, and in 549 B.C.E., Cyrus consolidated rule over its inhabitants and established the Achaemenid dynasty, the first Persian empire. He and his successors, Cambyses, Darius, and Xerxes, extended the boundaries of Persian rule from the Ionian Sea in the west to the Indus River in the south. During this period, Persian medicine was undoubtedly in contact with Greek medicine. A story related in ancient texts tells of an invitation from Persian King Artaxerxes to Hippocrates, on the advice of a Persian physician, to become physician to the Persian army during a plague; Hippocrates refused, saying, "I have no right to share the wealth of the Persians or to liberate from disease barbarians who are enemies of the Greeks" (Pseudepigrapha 3; see Temkin).

In the seventh century, the mysterious religious figure Zoroaster appeared in eastern Persia. Very little is known of his life, and the writings attributed to him are brief. However, by the first century B.C.E., a defined cosmogony and theology attributed to his influence had been collected in the vast literature called *Avesta,* of which his own *Gathas,* or hymns, are a small part. The doctrine is basically constructed around a cosmic duel between good and evil, of which light and darkness, life and death are the material symbols. The powerful spirit of good and light, Ahura Mazda, the wise and greatest god, battles Ahriman (or Angra Mainyu), spirit of evil and darkness, and the world is the battlefield. Humans participate in the battle through their free choices. As individuals, humans are to maintain purity of life through moral goodness, pursuit of truth and physical cleanliness, and avoidance of pollution by the dead and unclean substances. As members of society, humans are to assure justice between social classes.

The *Avesta* also contains the elements of a theory of health and disease. Diseases, created by Ahriman, come from dirt, stench, cold, heat, hunger, thirst, and anxiety, although magical causes are also recognized. Medicinal plants are the creation of Ahura Mazda. Rules of healthful living are prescribed; cupping and bleeding are recommended to reduce hot blood. The destruction of life is prohibited for theological reasons; it would contribute to the victory of Ahriman over Ahura Mazda. Thus, abortion is forbidden, and both men and women are punished as willful murderers. Special rules are laid down for the care of pregnant females (both human and animal). Surgery is recognized and strictly regulated; one ancient law requires that a surgeon have three successful cases before being licensed to practice.

Three kinds of healers are mentioned: healers with herbs, with knives, and with holy words (the latter, one text notes, being the most efficacious). There were also persons (*durustpat,* masters of health) trained to remove the causes of disease by purifying earth, air, water, and food. These physicians were often drawn from the noble and priestly classes. A modern Parsi (the contemporary Zoroastrians of India) scholar describes what he believes would have been the ideals of the Avestan physicians of ancient times:

> The first indispensable qualification of a physician was that he should have studied well the science of medicine. He should hear the case of his patient with calmness. He should be sweet-tongued, gentle, friendly, zealous of honour of his profession, averse to protracting illness out of greed and God fearing. An ideal healer heals for the sake of healing.... He should carefully watch the effect of

medicine that he prescribes … visit the invalid daily at a fixed hour, labour zealously to cure him, and combat the disease of the patient, as it were his own enemy (Elgood, 1951, p. 13).

Hellenistic Period (330 B.C.E.–224 C.E.)

In 330 B.C.E. Alexander of Macedon brought down the Achaemenid empire. For the next five centuries, the Greek culture that had long flourished on the Ionian frontier of the Persian empire dominated Persian ideas and institutions. Although the historical record is meager, it may be assumed that Greek medicine and Hippocratic ethics were included in this general influx of Hellenic culture. The Zoroastrian faith languished during that era, but it would not be unlikely that Avestan ideals that had permeated the culture survived.

Sassanid Period (224–632)

The Sassanid dynasty, after victories over Roman and Parthian armies in the mid-third century, ruled Persia for four centuries, restoring the traditions, law, and culture of ancient Iran and, above all, reforming and fostering the Zoroastrian faith. In the earliest years of the Sassanid era, an event of great importance for the history of medicine occurred. In the mid-250s, King Shāpūr I, son of the founder of the dynasty, defeated the Roman emperor Valerian and sacked the city of Antioch. The king invited many of the Antiochean scholars, including physicians, to a new city, Gondishapur, that he established in 260. His son enlarged the city and founded a university that in time became the center of scholarly work in Persia.

To Gondishapur in the late fifth century came a group of Persian Christians of a denomination called Nestorian. These Christians had originally dwelt in and around the Persian city of Nisibis, then moved to the Byzantine city of Edessa, where in 363 they established a school of theology. After certain of their theological beliefs were repudiated and their leader, the patriarch Nestorius, excommunicated by the Catholic church at the Council of Ephesus (431), the Persian Christians accepted an offer of asylum at Gondishapur from the Persian king Qubād. They brought with them not only works of theology but also an extraordinary library including Syriac translations of the Hippocratic corpus and of Galen.

Another scholarly migration entered Gondishapur in 529 when the Sassanid king Anūshīrvān the Just welcomed the Neoplatonists exiled from Athens, at the urging of his chief minister Buzurgmehr, who according to legend was himself a physician and philosopher. He is quoted as having said, "I read in medical books that the best physician is one who gives himself over to his profession.... I exerted myself in the treatment of patients, those whom I could not cure I tried to make their suffering more bearable.... From no one whom I treated did I demand any sort of fee or reward" (Elgood, 1951, p. 52).

The king also sent missions to India to procure the arts and sciences of Hindu culture, including the works of Ayurvedic medicine. By his order, a massive work on poisons was compiled, and many Greek and Indian books were translated into Pahlavi (ancient Persian). He convened what may have been the first medical convention, summoning the physicians of Gondishapur to debate the major medical questions of the day. During his long reign, Gondishapur became a leading center of scholarship; within its walls Greek, Jewish, Nestorian, Persian, and Hindu ideas were exchanged and enriched, and Islamic, Christian, and Zoroastrian ethical ideas mingled. The art of translation of the classic texts from Greek, Latin, and Syriac into Pahlavi and Arabic was fostered. The school of medicine existed for five centuries, creating from many sources the medical science generally known as Arabic or Islamic, and its great hospital, Bimaristan (House of the Sick), was the model for the Muslim hospitals of Baghdad, Damascus, and Cairo and the Christian hospitals of Jerusalem and Acre (Whipple).

Islamic Period (636–)

The victory of Arabian Muslim armies at al-Qādisiyah in 636 inaugurated the era of Islamic rule and culture in Iran. The distinctive ethic of Islam entered and eventually predominated in the rich mix of Persian life. Gondishapur continued to flourish under Arab rule and became more influential as its scholars, teachings, and books spread through rapidly expanding Islam, carrying Greek and Arabic medicine across Africa and, through Sicily and Spain, into Western Europe. The new Muslim rulers summoned scholars from Gondishapur to their capital at Baghdad, where they established a new center of medical science. Studies in biology, human anatomy, and pathology were encouraged. The caliphs in Baghdad, Damascus, and Cairo organized public-health administrations, staffs of public-health doctors, public hospitals, and a public examiner of physicians, responsible for their skills and their ethical standards.

Some of the greatest names of medical history were Persian: Ṭabarī, Rhazes (known as the Galen of Islam), Haly Abbas, Avicenna (Ibn Sīnā), all of whom flourished in the tenth and eleventh centuries. Their scientific work was renowned. (Avicenna's *Canon of Medicine* was used as a text in many European schools as late as the seventeenth century.) All of these distinguished physicians wrote treatises on the ethical qualities of physicians. The text of one of these, *Advice to a Physician,* by Haly Abbas, reflecting Hippocratic and Islamic sentiments, can be found in the Appendix of this encyclopedia. A book by the eleventh-century Iranian philosopher-physician Ibn-Hindū praises the nobility and criticizes physicians who use medicine only to win wealth and reputation, recalling the story that Hippocrates, when summoned by the Persian ruler, disdained to give his service only for gain (Mohaghegh). Another scholar of the next century, Niẓāmī 'Arūḍī, summarized the moral principles that should guide a physician:

> A physician should be of tender disposition and wise nature, excelling in acumen, this being a nimbleness of mind in forming correct views, that is, a rapid transition to the unknown from the known, and no physician can be of tender disposition if he fails to recognize the nobility of the human soul; nor of wise nature unless he is acquainted with logic, nor can he excel in acumen unless he be strengthened by God's aid, and he who is not acute in conjecture will not arrive at a correct understanding of any ailment (Elgood, 1951, p. 234).

Modern Period

For many centuries medicine in Iran was more or less as has been described. The foundation of Dār-ul-Funūn (the Polytechnic School) in Tehran in 1852 changed the situation. At first it was a military academy, but it soon began to develop into a university. The foundation of the Faculty of Medicine was laid by a number of excellent European and Iranian teachers. The school curriculum at first was a combination of Iranian and Western medicine, and the ethical point of view was influenced by Iranian tradition.

Iranian students had been sent to Europe for medical studies for several decades before the founding of the medical school at Dār-ul-Funūn. With the return of these physicians and scientists and the establishment of a modern hospital in Tehran in 1868, the curriculum of Dār-ul-Funūn and the practice of medicine were gradually westernized. Also, during the nineteenth century, a number of Western physicians resided in Iran, the most famous being a Frenchman, Charles Fourier, physician to Shah Nāṣir al-Dīn.

Since the period of Reza Shah (1923–1941), the program of the medical school of the modern University of Tehran has been based completely on modern medicine; medical ethics and the history of the medical tradition are both taught. Graduates of the Tehran medical school are asked to take an oath, an excerpt from which follows:

Now that I … have been found eligible to practice medicine, in the presence of you, the board of judgment of my thesis and others here present, I swear by God and the Holy Book of Koran and call to witness my conscience that in my profession I will always be abstemious, chaste, and honest and, as compared with the glory of the art of medicine, I will hold in contempt all else—silver, gold, status, and dignity. I promise to help the afflicted and needy patient and never divulge patients' secrets. I will never undertake dishonest work such as producing abortion and recommending a fatal drug. What I do, I will try always to be approved by God and be known for my uprightness.

In the Islamic Republic of Iran, founded in 1979, the interest in vivifying Islamic tradition and law touches medical ethics as well. Issues related to bioethics are sometimes treated in works dealing with Islamic religious law, the *shar'ia*. However, the premodern *shar'ia* contains little that can directly guide conscience and conduct in morally troublesome cases, such as the permissibility or prohibition of medical treatments. Muslim jurists have undertaken to provide new rulings, the most prominent of which states the rights of the patient in determining which modes of treatment are compatible with his or her religious and moral beliefs. These scholars are also grappling with the medical technology developed in the Western secular culture, technology that has altered conventional understandings of life and death and has posed perplexing questions for a new, religiously aware generation of Iranian physicians and their "believing" patients.

Some recent works in medical ethics, such as *Fiqh va ṭibb* (Islamic Jurisprudence and Medicine) and *Qānūn dar ṭibb* (Law in Medicine), reflect a change in the attitude of Muslim physicians, who have become increasingly aware of the role religion plays in the lives of Iranian men and women. Whereas in the early days of modernization and secularization, Iranian physicians, not unlike their counterparts in other Third World countries, "played God" in attempting to save and restore human health, the 1980s and 1990s are characterized by a growing concern about the religious and cultural values of the society. Thus, for instance, an important issue in Islamic law is the recommended segregation of females and males, which has implications for medical ethics. The ethical issue is whether it is permissible for a physician to treat a member of the opposite sex. While responses have varied among the Muslim jurists, there is a consensus that since a physician should never sexually abuse his or her patients, it is strongly recommended that a physician examine patients of the opposite sex only in the presence of a third person, as a safeguard. This applies to both male and female doctors. However, under special circumstances, when no doctor of the same sex as the patient is available and there is an urgency in treating the condition, the law permits male doctors to treat female patients and female doctors to treat male patients.

Advances in biomedical technology raise issues that challenge Islam to provide concrete and relevant solutions. A group of Muslim jurists and philosophers has begun to develop guidelines for dealing with ethical issues that confront the medical profession. Leaders in both secular and religious education have begun to prepare textbooks on medical ethics. Two of these works are especially significant: *Akhlāq-i pizishkī* (Medical Ethics), prepared and published under the supervision of the Ministry of Health in 1991, and a book with the same title, written by Manṣūr Ashrafī and published by the Medical Faculty of the Open University of Tabriz in 1988. The former includes chapters dealing with the juridical decisions by major Iranian religious leaders, including Ayatollah Khomeini, on issues related to what is known in the West as bioethics. The latter work is based more on the Western secular discussion of bioethical issues without any reference to Islamic or other religious views. Both are used as textbooks in the Iranian schools of medicine.

Major obstacles persist for those who work to solve the problems created when medical technology is brought into a culture steeped in religion. The most serious problem that confronts Muslims in general, and Iranians in particular, is denial of the ethical problems stemming from technicalization of the society and its adverse impact on interpersonal relationships. A striking example is acquired immunodeficiency syndrome (AIDS). To date, the Muslim ethical response to AIDS has characterized the disease as God's curse on those who engage in illicit sexual behavior. In this direct or indirect critique of the moral decadence of the West, important issues are overlooked, including the cause of the disease and its prevalence in the Muslim world, as well as guidelines for treatment of those affected.

Muslim jurists in Iran have not yet formulated relevant responses to some of the most complex ethical issues—those that arise because of human endeavors to improve health and extend life. The highly cherished religious value of compassion has been overshadowed by the language of condemnation for moral failure of humanity.

ABDULAZIZ SACHEDINA (1995)

BIBLIOGRAPHY

Ackerknecht, Erwin Heinz. 1968. *A Short History of Medicine,* 2nd. rev. edition, tr. Sula Wolff. New York: Hafner.

al-Akhavaynī al-Bukhārī, Abū Bakr Rabī ibn Ahmad. 1965. *Ḥidāyat al-muta 'allimīn fī al-ṭibb*, ed. Jalāl Matīnī. Dānishgāh Intishārāt no. 9. Meshed, Iran: Meshed University Press.

al-Ṭūsi, Naṣīr al-Dīn, Muḥammad ibn Muḥammad. 1964. [13th century]. *The Nasirean Ethics*, tr. and ed. G. M. Wickens. UNESCO Collection of Representative Works: Persian series. London: Allen & Unwin.

'Amilī, Ja'far Murtaḍa. 1989. *Akhlāq-i pizishkī dar Islām*. Tehran: Ministry of Health.

Aqili Alavī, M. H. 1870. (1770). *Khulāsat al-Ḥikmah*. Tehran.

Ashrafi, Mansur. 1988. *Akhlaq-i pizishki*. Tabriz: Open University.

Avicenna (Abū 'Alī al-Husayn ibn 'Abdullah ibn Sīnā). 1966. [11th century]. *The General Principles of Avicenna's "Canon of Medicine,"* ed. and tr. Mazhar H. Shah. Karachi, Pakistan: Naveed Clinic.

Browne, Edward Granville. 1921. *Arabian Medicine: Being the Fitzpatrick Lectures Delivered at the College of Physicians in November 1919 and November 1920*. Cambridge: Cambridge University Press.

Clendening, Logan, ed. 1942. *Source Book of Medical History, Compiled with Notes*. New York: Paul B. Hoeber.

Davis, Nathan Smith. 1903. *History of Medicine, with the Code of Medicine*. Chicago: Cleveland Press.

Elgood, Cyril Lloyd. 1951. *A Medical History of Persia and the Eastern Caliphate from the Earliest Times until the Year A.D. 1932*. Cambridge: Cambridge University Press.

Elgood, Cyril Lloyd. 1976. *Safavid Medical Practice; or, The Practice of Medicine, Surgery, and Gynaecology in Persia Between 1500 and 1750 A.D.* London: Luzac.

Eshraghī, R. 1969. *Akhlāq-i pizishkī*. Meshed, Iran: Meshed Medical School.

Haly Abbas ('Alī ibn al-'Abbās al-Majūsī al-Arrajānī) 1492. [10th century]. *Liber regalis disposito nominatus ex arabico*, tr. Stephen of Antioch, ed. Antonius Vitalis Pyrranensis. Venice: Bernardinus Ricius.

Iran. Ministry of Health. 1991. *Akhlāq-i pizishkī*. Tehran: Author.

Jurjānī, Isma'īl ibn al-Hasan. 1960. [11th century]. *Zakhī-rah-i-khwārazmshāhi*, 5 vols. Tehran: Tehran University Press.

Levey, Martin. 1967. *Medical Ethics of Medieval Islam: With Special Reference to al-Ruhavi's Practical Ethics of the Physician*. Philadelphia: American Philosophical Society.

Mohaghegh, Mehdi, tr. 1992. "Ibn Hindū: The Key to Science of Medicine and the Student's Guide to Study." *Medical Journal of the Islamic Republic of Iran*, suppl. 6: 29–37.

Mokhtar, Ahmed Mohammed. 1969. "*Rhases contre Galenum*: Die Galenkritik in den ersten zwanzig Büchern des Continens von Ibn ar-Razi." Ph.D. diss., University of Bonn. Text in Arabic and German.

Niẓāmī-'Arūḍī-i-Samarqandī, Aḥmad ibn 'Umar ibn 'Alī. 1936. [12th century]. *Chahār maqālā*. Tehran: Elmi Bookstore, tr. Edward Granville Browne under the title *Revised Translation of the 'Chahár Maqála' ("Four Discourses") of Nizámí-i 'Arú-di of Samarqand, Followed by an Abridged Translation of Mírzá Muḥammad's Notes to the Persian Text*. E. J. W. Gibb memorial series, 11(2). London: Cambridge University Press, 1921.

Plessner, Martin. 1974. "The Natural Sciences and Medicine." In *Legacy of Islam*, 2nd edition, ed. Joseph Schacht and C. E. Bosworth. Oxford: Clarendon Press.

Rahman, Fazlur. 1989. *Health and Medicine in the Islamic Tradition: Change and Identity*. New York: Crossroad.

Rhazes (Abū Bakr Muḥammad ibn Zakariyā al-Rāzī). 1955–1971. [9th century]. *Kitāb al-Hāwī fī al-tibb*. 25 vols., ed. Osmania Oriental Publications Bureau. Hyderabad-Deccan: Dāiratu'l-Ma'ārif-il-Osmania.

Said, Hakim Mohammed. 1975. "Traditional Greco-Arabic and Modern Western Medicine: Conflict or Symbiosis." *Hamdard: The Organ of the Institute of Health and Tibi Research* 18(1–6): 1–76, especially Appendix C, "Ethical Basis of Medicine," 71–76.

Said, Hakim Mohammed. 1976. *Al-Tibb al-Islami: A Brief Survey of the Development of Tibb (Medicine) During the Days of the Holy Prophet Mohammed (p.b.u.h.) and in the Islamic Age*. Karachi, Pakistan: Hamdard National Foundation. See especially "Muslim Medicine and Iran," pp. 80–82.

Siddiqi, Muhammad Zubair. 1959. *Studies in Arabic and Persian Medical Literature*. Calcutta: Calcutta University Press.

Sigerist, Henry Ernest. 1951. *Primitive and Archaic Medicine*. vol. 1 of *A History of Medicine*. New York: Oxford University Press.

Temkin, Owsei. 1991. *Hippocrates in a World of Pagans and Christians*, chap. 6. Baltimore: Johns Hopkins University Press.

Whipple, Allen O. 1936. "The Role of the Nestorians as the Connecting Link Between Greek and Arab Medicine." *Annals of Medical History* 8: 313–323.

Wilcocks, Charles. 1965. *Medical Advance, Public Health, and Social Evolution*. Commonwealth and International Library, Liberal Studies Division. Oxford: Pergamon Press.

III. TURKEY

The modern nation of Turkey is situated on the continents of Europe and Asia, with the majority of its landmass occupying the vast Anatolian peninsula of Asia Minor. Surrounded by three seas, the Mediterranean and the Aegean seas on the west and south, and the Black Sea on the north, its territory has been the home of many nations and civilizations. It was ruled by the Hittite and Phrygian kingdoms of the second and first millennia B.C.E., followed by the Persian, Hellenic, and Roman empires. In 330 C.E., the capital of the Roman Empire was moved to Byzantium, which was renamed Constantinople. In 1453, Mehmet II, the sultan of the Ottoman Turks, a people who during the previous century had invaded a great part of the deteriorating Byzantine Empire, captured Constantinople and established the

Ottoman Empire over Asia Minor (and, in the course of time, over much of the Islamic world, from the Crimea to Morocco and the Balkan peninsula). The Ottoman Empire lasted from 1299 to 1922, and in 1923 it became a republic under the leadership of Mustafa Kemal. Turkey's medicine and its ethics bear the marks of this long history.

The Turkic peoples, dwelling from time immemorial in Central Asia, migrated into China, India, the Caucasus, and Persia. The earliest Turkic religion was a shamanistic animism marked by totems and magic. Contact with the spirit world was mediated by male and female shamans, called *kam,* who healed the sick with magic and charms and music. Other healers, called *otaci,* are mentioned in various sources, and archeological findings related to *otaci* exist as early as the eighth century C.E. *Otaci* were described as wise people informed of the causes of illness, advising about healthy living and treating mainly with herbs, as well as by bone-setting, massage, acupuncture, moxa, branding, etc. *Otaci* joined in a guild of healers called *kutu.* They were, according to the sources, in frequent debate with exorcists, who taught that illness was caused by evil spirits and driven out by charms. This conflict was especially emphasized following the conversion of many of the Turkic peoples to Islam in the tenth century.

In Turkistan, where Turkic peoples were in contact with Chinese Buddhism, monks functioned as healers (*otaci bakshy* in Old Turkish). Although supernatural healing powers were often attributed to them, they practiced medicine without remuneration as a way of achieving Buddhahood. Monasteries were places of hospitality and healing. A medical literature in Uighur Turkish began to appear in the eighth century. During this period there was considerable mingling of Chinese, Indian, and Persian medical concepts. Although healers were no longer believed to have supernatural powers, the attitude of holding them in high esteem was part of the Islamic culture.

From the sixth to the thirteenth century, Turkish tribes formed kingdoms throughout Central Asia and the Near East. In the tenth century, many Turkic tribesmen who were employed in the armies of the Abbasid caliphs were converted to Islam (some tribes adopted Buddhism; others, Manichaeanism; and some followed Nestorian Christianity or Judaism). Following the rise and fall of several significant pre-Islamic and Islamic Turkic kingdoms, one tribe, the Seljuks, became the most powerful force in Anatolia. They extended their rule into Iraq, Iran, and Syria, and during the eleventh and twelfth centuries they created the first major Turkish state, which fostered a rich literary, artistic, and scientific civilization. In 1066, Nizamul Mulk, vizier of the Seljuk ruler Alp Arslan, founded the Nazamiye University in

Baghdad. The first state university known in history, it included a hospital. The Nureddin Hospital, founded by the Seljuk Atabeg Nurredin Zenagi in Damascus in 1154, educated many famous physicians, such as Ibn Abi Usaibia, Ibn al-Nafis, and Ibn al Qutt, and was the center of medicine at that period. The curriculum of the medical schools in the Seljuk period was demanding; after training and the presentation of their theses, the graduates were examined in the course of medical practice by the *muhtasib,* a high-ranking public official, and then swore an oath to practice medicine with competence and virtue.

During the reign of the Anatolian Seljuks, the nobility founded charity hospitals: In Kayseri, the Gevher Nesibe Hospital was established by Princess Gevher Nesibe in 1206, and the Divriği Hospital in 1228 by Princess Turan Melik; both are still standing. The hospital and medical school founded at Sivas in 1217 also remains; and the original charter, still extant, shows that the staff consisted of physicians, surgeons, ophthalmologists, nurses, and pharmacists. All persons in need, Muslim and non-Muslim, were accepted for treatment in these institutions. Although a rich medical terminology had existed in the Turkish languages in the eleventh century, medical literature in Arabic and Persian flourished during the Seljuk era and hundreds of Arabic and Persian works were written by Turks. Turkish cities—Ferghana, Tashkent, Samargand, Bokhara, Khwarizm, Balkh, Maraghah, Kashgar, Farab, and others—were the birthplace of many famous Islamic scientists, including Ibn Sina, Ibn Turk, Biruni, Farabi, and Harezm, and were also the important centers of Islamic culture.

Medical literature in the Turkish language began to flourish again in the fourteenth century. After the conquest of Constantinople, the Ottoman Empire continued to promote care for the needy sick and to further medical science and education. It was common for the large complexes built around mosques throughout the land to have a hospital attached for the sick poor, whether Muslim or not. Sultan Mehmet II opened a hospital in his new capital in 1470. A great hospital and a medical school were established within the complex of the Süleymaniye Mosque (1536). According to the founding documents, the professor of medicine was expected to be a faithful Muslim, virtuous, charitable, self-confident, courageous, gifted with intuition and keen senses, and educated in the subtleties of logic and medicine. He was required to teach students both medicine and the virtues and duties of the physician. Those who sought admission to medical school were to have graduated from the *medresse,* or university. (The Ottoman *medresse* not only provided necessary services of religion, science, and instruction; it also trained administrative and judicial personnel to meet the needs of the bureaucracy.) Medical school applicants were required to be persons of high moral character, and to be faithful Muslims. All received scholarships from charitable endowments. The professor as well as the students were supervised by a dean.

A chief court physician was the minister of health; he was responsible for public health, for the proper training of physicians and the administration of examinations, as well as for the safety of drug preparations. Physicians employed in the palace and hospitals outside were paid by the state, and their income increased in relation to their skill and rank. Still, there were more physicians practicing medicine in their special offices than employed by the state. Pharmacists, trained in an apprentice system, worked in hospitals and palace pharmacies. A school for surgeons and ophthalmologists existed in the sultan's palace.

Women were admitted to the practice of medicine during the Ottoman period, particularly for the care of women. The Topkapi Palace in Istanbul had a well-appointed infirmary for women in the harem, as well as an infirmary for royal pages. Renowned female physicians were summoned to care for women of the harem when necessary. Nurses were employed in the palace infirmaries as well as in hospitals outside the palace and were expected to be gentle, dedicated, and devoted to their patients. Midwives were respected and given official recognition after an apprenticeship. Women prepared and sold herbal extracts, and women inoculated against smallpox. Women were also influential in the founding of hospitals and the support of charitable works.

The ethics of Turkish medicine were formed by Islamic morality, Turkish mores, and the Hippocratic ideas inherited from Greek medicine. Many medical manuscripts from the thirteenth to the nineteenth centuries state these values in chapters generally titled "Advice for the Physician." Chief among the qualifications required of the Ottoman physician was good character, which included mercy, generosity, honesty, modesty, and an even temper. Physicians were expected to be clean and properly attired, and never to exaggerate. Such virtues were said to have a positive effect upon the sick person. Advice was also given about preserving confidentiality, charging fair prices, and serving the poor without charge. Physicians were warned not to make definitive statements about prognosis, since the course of disease is not predictable with certainty. Medicine made from unknown herbs, folk remedies, and experimental treatments were not to be used. Administering poisons and abortion, except for a therapeutic purpose, were strictly forbidden. In general, as the eminent fifteenth-century Ottoman surgeon Sabuncuoğlu noted, the conscience of the physician should prevail over his desires and passions.

Physicians and surgeons were held responsible for injuries that resulted from their ignorance, incompetence, or use of unorthodox methods. Islamic law required that patients give personal permission, in the presence of a judge and witnesses, before undergoing surgery. Many records of the religious courts bear testimony to this practice. Edicts were often issued to bar quacks from practice, and, in order to ensure that only qualified practitioners served the sick, examinations for medical licensure were frequently repeated and only the licenses of the successful renewed.

Although Turkish medicine had been in contact with European medicine since the sixteenth century (inoculation against smallpox was originally introduced into Europe from Turkey at the beginning of the eighteenth century) (Ünver), European medicine became influential with the founding, by Sultan Mahmud II, of a school of medicine in 1827 and a school of surgery in 1832; these schools were combined in 1836 and moved, three years later, to Galatasari, then a suburb of Constantinople. Although it was primarily a military school, civil students were admitted, too; all students were given scholarships by the state. European physicians joined the Ottoman instructors on the faculty, and from 1839 to 1870 the language of instruction was French. A vigorous flow into Turkey of faculty members from the European medical centers and a flow of students and specialists from Turkey to Europe marked nineteenth-century medical education. An Ottoman professor, Nahabed Roussignan, lectured on ethics in 1876–1877 at the University of Constantinople School of Medicine. The course was continued for many years by Professor Hovsep Nouridjan, who published his lectures as *Précis de déontologie medicale,* one of the earliest books on this subject printed in Europe. In 1933, the first department of medical history and ethics was founded by Süheyl Ünver in Istanbul University. Doctorates in medical ethics are now awarded, and as of 1994, ten of the twenty-eight Turkish medical schools had departments of ethics and such courses were given in all schools of medicine.

After establishment of the Turkish Republic in 1923, new laws and regulations were passed regarding healthcare, public health, and the duties of physicians. A successful fight was waged against epidemic diseases, and many municipal and state hospitals were founded all over Turkey. The Turkish Medical Association was founded in 1929, and the current version of the medical ethics code appeared in 1960; it comprises rules dealing with patient–physician and physician-physician relationships, confidentiality, advertising, human research, termination of pregnancy, malpractice, truth-telling, consultation, fees, and organization of practice. This code has juridical standing. Provincial medical associations have disciplinary authority over physicians who violate the code. Dentists and pharmacists have formed associations in recent years and also have codes of ethics. A National Congress on Medical Ethics was organized by the Medical Faculty of the University of Istanbul in 1977. It opened discussion of many topics, such as organ transplantation, determination of death, reproductive technologies, and military medicine. A second such congress was held in 1994.

A law on organ transplantation was passed in 1979. It specifies procedures for consent, donation, and determination of death, and prohibits advertising and commercialization of organs. Regulations dealing with the education and duties of those who provide family-planning services, including abortion and sterilization, appeared in 1983. Abortion, available on demand for any reason if there is no medical contraindication for the mother, is permitted up to the tenth week of gestation, and therapeutic abortion after that time; married women must have permission of their husband, and minors, of their parents. Married persons seeking sterilization must have consent of their spouse. Centers providing assisted reproduction must be licensed by the Ministry of Health. Embryos are not to be used for purposes other than reproduction and cannot be sold. A professional committee has been established for the oversight of assisted reproduction.

The Turkish Medical Association endorses the Nuremburg and Helsinki declarations. In 1993, a state regulation governing research with human subjects required review committees in research hospitals, and a Central Ethics Committee was established in the Ministry of Health. Local review committees sometimes function as ethics committees as well. In 1992, the Turkish Human Rights Association, the Turkish Medical Association, and the Torture Victims International Rehabilitation Council sponsored the Fifth International Conference on Torture and the Medical Profession in Istanbul. This conference issued a declaration against torture and specifically against any physician's involvement.

NIL SARI (1995)

BIBLIOGRAPHY

Esin, Emel. 1981. "'Otaci': Notes on Archaeology and Iconography Related to the Early History of Turkish Medical Science." In *Uluslararasi Türk-islam Bilim ve Teknoloji Tarihi Kongresi 14–18 Eylül 1981*, 5: 11–22. Istanbul: Istanbul Teknik Üniversitesi.

Kiyak, Yahya. 1987. *Lectures on Medical Ethics*. Istanbul: Marmara University.

Sari, Nil. 1988. "Educating the Ottoman Physician." *Tip Tarihi Araştirmalari. History of Medicine Studies* 2: 40–64.

Sari, Nil. 1989. "A View on the Dealers with Health in the Turkish Medical History." *Tip Tarihi Araştirmalari. History of Medicine Studies* 3: 11–33.

Ünver, A. Süheyl. 1958. *Turki nizam-i-tib ki tarikh*. Lahore: Avicanna Society.

IV. CONTEMPORARY ARAB WORLD

The Arab world comprises the twenty-one Arabic-speaking countries extending from the south of Iran westward to the coast of the Atlantic. Not all the people in these nations are descendants of the Semitic Arabs of the Arabian Peninsula, but the spread of Islam outward from Arabia in the seventh century led to widespread adoption of Arabic, the language of the Qur'an, Islam's scripture. Islam is the religion of 95 percent of the inhabitants of the Arab world. Of the world's nearly one billion Muslims, some 20 percent are Arab. Classical Arabic has been preserved through the constant standard in the Qur'an (the Islamic scripture that Muslims believe is God's very words received verbatim by Muhammad); colloquial dialects are used regionally but are easily understood by all.

Despite religion and language, the Arab world is not politically, socially, or economically homogeneous. Some countries are ruled by hereditary monarchies; others, by revolutionary military or quasi-military governments. Democracy is, on the whole, lacking, although it is the aspiration of the masses. Some countries are affluent (usually due to oil wealth), while others are poor; some are overpopulated and others sparsely populated. Currently the Arab world is categorized as belonging to the Third World. The average birth rate is 38.3 per 1,000, and the average infant mortality rate (first year of life) is about 68.2 per 1,000 (United Nations).

A characteristic of the region is the religious orientation of its people and the influence of religion on their lives. Islam recognizes both Judaism and Christianity as religions that come from God; all three religions hold generally the same prevailing moral values and thus have a unified ethical base. Society (of all religious backgrounds) tends to be conservative, sanctifying family integrity and family ties, upholding moralities prescribed by religion(s), averse to unchecked liberalism, and falling back on religion to categorize social trends and new lifestyles as acceptable or unacceptable.

Islam has a comprehensive framework of a legal system based on the Qur'an and tradition, covering all aspects of life, that serves as the source of legislation and the derivation of ethical rulings. And yet the great majority of the Arab world is not ruled by Islamic law, most of the governments being practically secular. One area has uniquely remained under the jurisdiction of Islamic law: that of family law. It is in this area that the bulk of medical ethics resides. Although many non-Muslims are physicians and patients in Arab countries, there is little dispute about medical ethics among them, since many common positions are shared by Islam, Christianity, and Judaism.

The medical profession is highly esteemed in the Arab world, and the physician is still called "the wise man," a centuries-old nomenclature. The physician is very highly regarded, and the doctor–patient relationship, based on trust and confidence, tends to be paternalistic.

Seeking medical help when one is sick is a religious duty. Muhammad said, "Your body has a right over you," and "Seek treatment, for God has created a cure for every illness; some already known and others yet to be known." The establishment of the medical profession is a religious duty of the community, which should designate some of its members to study medicine and should provide for the needs and requirements of medical education. A doctor should be appropriately qualified, for Muhammad said, "Whoever practices medicine without the appropriate knowledge is liable to pay compensation [if harm comes to the patient]."

It is not uncommon for medical practitioners who enjoy the confidence of their community to be consulted on nonmedical problems faced by families or individuals. People tend to accept that therapeutic ability is not absolute, and as long as the doctor has done his (or her) best, there is a willingness to accept and even forgive undesired outcomes. Insurance against professional liability is nonexistent, and the judicial system heeds this fact; unless it is a clear case of neglect or inexcusable ignorance, the physician is rarely held responsible for damages.

Medical education has deep historical roots in the major capitals (Baghdad, Cairo, and Damascus) since the era of Islamic civilization (eighth to sixteenth centuries). Modern schools have emerged since the nineteenth century, and many are as recent as the oil boom late in the twentieth century. With one or two exceptions, all Arab countries have one or more medical schools, Egypt, as many as thirteen.

English is the common language of education, with French or Arabic used in exceptional cases. Conversion to Arabic is under debate. Medical education and practice are open to both sexes and all religions without discrimination. Coeducation is the rule except in a few schools. There is no ban on examining the opposite sex. Dissection of the human body and postmortem examination are permitted; some schools, however, have to import cadavers from abroad to satisfy the need for teaching anatomy.

Medical Ethics

The Arab world has known medical ethics since the writings of Imhotep of Egypt (3000 B.C.E.) and the Code of Hammurabi of Babylon (about the same time). The Oath of Hippocrates (ca. 460–355 B.C.E.) later took over, and since the ninth century various Islamic adaptions of it, as well as treatises and books on medical ethics, have been contributed by Al-Rahawi, Ibn Rabban, Avicenna (Ibn Sīnā), and many others.

In modern times, medical ethics has been taught as part of the curriculum of various disciplines, but since the 1940s it has become a separate course in the majority of medical schools, whether as a part of forensic medicine, community medicine, history of medicine, or on its own.

Although Islam is the principal source of medical ethics, the increasing complexity of biomedical discoveries and technological achievements during the latter half of the twentieth century have made it difficult for religious scholars to comprehend the issues and formulate rules on ethical acceptability from an Islamic point of view. There has been need for a forum in which religious scholars join with biomedical scientists and specialists in relevant disciplines such as law and sociology, policymakers, economists, and civic leaders of both sexes, to discuss specific issues in order to develop an Islamic consensus. To continue this collaboration, institutions have come into being since the early 1980s: the Islamic Organization of Medical Sciences (IOMS, Kuwait), the Islamic Research Congress (Egypt), and the Fiqh Congress of Makka (Saudi Arabia). The rulings of these government-approved agencies have a high moral weight and almost fill the legal gap that results because legislation usually lags behind new developments. These agencies have significantly contributed to Islamic medical ethics, addressing a number of issues that will be surveyed briefly.

An important milestone was the formulation of the Islamic Code of Medical Ethics (IOMS, 1981), ratified by the First International Conference on Islamic Medicine (held in Kuwait, January 1981) and endorsed by many Arab and Islamic countries. This code comprises eleven chapters: Definition of Medical Profession; Characteristics of the Medical Practitioner; Relations Between Doctor and Doctor; Relations Between Doctor and Patient; Professional Confidentiality; Doctor's Duty in Wartime; Responsibility and Liability; Sanctity of Human Life; Doctor and Society; Doctor and Biotechnological Advances; and Medical Education. All topics were authenticated by sources in the Qur'an and Islamic law. The code also includes the latest version of the Islamic Medical Oath, which reads (roughly translated):

I swear by God: To regard God in practicing my profession; To respect human life in all stages, under all circumstances, and to do my best to rescue it from death, malady, pain and anxiety; To uphold people's dignity, cover their privacy, and keep their secrets; To be an instrument of God's mercy to near and far, virtuous and sinner, and friend and enemy; To pursue knowledge and to harness it for the benefit, not the harm, of humankind; to revere my teachers, teach my juniors, and cherish the fraternity with my colleagues; and to live my faith in private and in public ... and God is my witness to this oath.

Derivation of Islamic Medical Ethics

The totality of Islamic law, called the Shari'a, is drawn from the Qur'an, the verbal teachings of Muhammad, followed by analogy and consensus. The Shari'a is expressed in a code of moral behavior that states what is sinful and what is not, as well as a body of laws that states what is legal and what is not. These two systems need not coincide. (An example is a person who commits adultery in the privacy of a closed room. Such a person has committed a sin but not a legal crime, since Islamic law requires four witnesses in order to establish the legal charge of adultery. The fate of such a sinner is left entirely to God, who will punish or forgive upon the perpetrator's repentance and appeal for mercy.) When ruling on the admissibility (or inadmissibility) of an issue, jurists take into consideration a number of rules such as "Necessities overrule prohibitions," "Choose the lesser of two evils if both cannot be avoided," "Public interest outweighs individual interest," and, especially in matters not specified in the primary sources of Shari'a, "Wherever welfare goes, there goes the statute of God." Examples of applying some of these will follow later.

Sanctity of Human Life

Human life should never be violated except in situations explicitly specified in the penal code and observing the rigorous criteria it establishes. Commenting on the killing of Abel by his brother Cain (the two sons of Adam), the Qur'an states: "On that account We ordained for the Children of Israel that if anyone killed a soul, unless it be for murder or mischief in the land, it would be as if he killed the whole people. And if anyone saved a life, it would be as if he saved the life of the whole people" (5:32). This principle has been invoked when ruling on abortion and euthanasia.

Abortion

In general terms abortion is legally prohibited and punishable. However, some physicians perform abortions illicitly, mainly in the private sector. In some countries, if abortion is done to avoid tarnishing the family name (pregnancy of the unmarried is a great shame in the Arab world), this circumstance is considered a mitigating factor if the case ever goes to court. Tunisia has gone a step further and legalized abortion after the third child, thus allowing it to be considered a form of family planning.

Among the religious community, various views on abortion have been held over the centuries. The writings of early scholars differed according to their perception of the beginning of life, and their views continued to be followed by generations of their adherents. On the belief that life started when the mother felt the movements of the fetus inside her (quickening, usually at the end of four months), some thought that abortion before then entailed no aggression on life. Others maintained that the fetus attained its human form at the end of the seventh week, and aborting it at or beyond this date would be unlawful. The majority, however, espoused the views of the great jurist Al-Ghazālī (eleventh century C.E.), who believed that life started with the fusion of the male and female seeds, and that it proceeded through an occult phase to the palpable phase felt by the mother. This view of the beginning of life therefore outlaws abortion and makes it reprehensible at any stage of pregnancy.

Modern juridical opinion has put an end to the historical diversity of opinion and settled for Al-Ghazālī's, following a number of conferences in the 1970s and 1980s (see, e.g., Gindi, 1989b) at which religious scholars met with medical scholars and a full account of the process of conception and early development was illustrated by ultrasound and cinematographic recordings of the fetus in utero. Five criteria were collectively acknowledged as signifying the beginning of life: (1) it is a fairly clearly defined event; (2) it exhibits the phenomenon of growth; (3) such growth, unless interrupted, leads to the known subsequent stages of life; (4) it contains the genetic package characteristic both of humanity and of a unique individual; and (5) it is not preceded by any stage combining the first four criteria (Gindi, 1989a).

Abortion is permitted if the continuation of pregnancy poses a serious threat to the life of a sick mother (the choice of the lesser of the two evils if both cannot be avoided). In Shari'a the mother is the root and the fetus the offshoot, and it is lawful to sacrifice the latter if it is the only way to save the former.

Selective abortion for the sake of sex selection is doubly unlawful, being an aggression on life as well as discrimination against the female (almost invariably the unwanted sex). The Qur'an severely rebuked pre-Islamic Arabs (up to seventh century C.E.) for practicing female infanticide (16:59). Sex selection by means not entailing embryocide, to suit the wishes of individual families, has been debated. There is consensus that its admissibility would eventually lead to an upset of the sex ratio in favor of male preponderance, which could lead to grave social consequences.

Euthanasia, Suffering, and Care of the Elderly

Euthanasia and suicide are completely unacceptable in Islam. There are no euthanasia proponents, and therefore there is no debate. Suicide and complicity thereto are legal crimes, but the problem is of minute dimensions. The Prophet Muhammad told about a man who took his own life due to an illness that taxed his endurance, upon which God said, "My subject has himself forestalled Me; I have forbidden him Paradise" (narrated by Al-Bukhari). Resort to medical or surgical means for alleviation of pain is lawful, but the taking of life is a matter of God's sovereignty.

Patience in the face of unavoidable pain or adversity is an important value, and the Prophet teaches that through such patience a person's sins are washed away by God, like a tree shedding its leaves. The right to die is therefore not recognized because humans do not own life; they are only entrusted with it. The same applies to the "duty to die," recently proposed for human beings who, through age or infirmity, become consumers but not producers. Caring for a growing group of old and disabled can be very costly, as modern budget figures show, but under Islamic law society has to meet this need by rearranging expenditure priorities rather than allowing euthanasia. Care of the old is a principal value in Islam, especially with regard to one's parents: "Your Lord has decreed that you worship none but Him and that you be kind to your parents.... Whether one or both of them attain old age in your life, say not to them a word of contempt nor repel them, and lower to them the wing of humility out of compassion, and say: 'My Lord, bestow on them your mercy even as they cherished me in childhood'" (Qur'an 17:23, 24).

However, it is generally agreed that in his or her defense of life, the doctor is well advised to realize the limitation of medical efforts. It is the process of life that the doctor aims to maintain, not the process of dying. When treatment holds no promise, it ceases to be mandatory and withholding or discontinuing the artificial means is justified. No active intervention, however, shall be made to terminate life.

Death

Under ordinary circumstances the time-honored recognition of death based on cessation of heartbeat and respiration is workable, followed by a waiting period of two hours before the death certificate is issued. Nevertheless, advances in transplant surgery and the occasional need for a fresh heart for transplantation have called for a more sophisticated definition of death. Such a heart can usually be procured from a trauma victim whose brain—including brain stem—is dead and who therefore has been pronounced dead although artificial means are employed to maintain the functions of respiration and circulation.

The issue was discussed in a number of conferences bringing together high-ranking religious scholars and medical scientists (see, e.g., Gindi, 1989a). An old juridical rule, "The movement of the slain," was reviewed. Centuries ago it was ruled that if an aggressor stabbed a victim in the abdomen and the bowel extruded, this was considered a fatal injury; although the victim could still move, his or her prospects for life were practically nil. "The movement of the slain" was the descriptive term given to the death throes. If a second aggressor finished the victim off, the first aggressor would still be charged with murder for having dealt the fatal injury; and the second aggressor would be punished, but not for murder. Realizing that abdominal trauma with extrusion of the bowel is no longer considered a fatal injury by contemporary surgical standards, the scholars removed it from the category of "the movement of the slain." In its stead, the condition of brain death including the brain stem fulfills the description, since the victim has practically departed from life without the prospect of return and, in spite of the signs of life (circulation, respiration, etc.), is subject to the rulings governing the dead, including taking the heart for transplantation into a needy recipient, without the death of the patient being legally or morally attributed to the surgery. The disconnection of artificial life-support apparatus from such patients would be permissible.

Transplant Surgery

Transplant surgery is practiced in many Arab countries, and some have excellent units. The Qur'anic saying "And whoever saves a life, it is as though he has saved all the people" (5:32) is the basis of considering organ donation as an act of charity. It is a religious duty of the community to provide necessary donors, in analogy with the decree of Umar (the second caliph) that if a person dies due to lack of sustenance, the society should pay legal reparations as if they killed him. The human body is honored whether living or dead, but its surgical violation to procure a needed organ is ruled permissible by invoking the juridical rule of "choosing the lesser of the two evils," for the alternative would be the death of the prospective recipient. Bodily organs should not be offered for sale, but if purchase is the only source, then buying is permissible under the rule "Necessities overrule prohibitions."

In reality, however, apart from close relatives, most donors receive a price under the pressure of poverty. The need is felt for a governing authority to regulate the process, lest an exploitative market be created and patients with limited means be excluded. Donation should be purely and truly voluntary through consent of the living donor, bequeathed in a will or with the consent of the next of kin.

Transplantation of fetal suprarenal medulla to the brain to ameliorate certain diseases is lawful, although abortion performed specifically to obtain that tissue remains unlawful. The anencephalic fetus may be used as a donor, and its maintenance by artificial means for that purpose is acceptable, but removal of organs is permitted only after its natural death, without artificially terminating its life. Transplantation of sex glands to provide sex cells (ova or sperm) is unlawful because the prospective fetus would have been formed by elements not bound by a marriage contract. Sterile sex glands providing only hormones are devoid of that objection, but obviously their use is not medically feasible (Gindi, 1989c).

Hygiene and Preventive Healthcare

"Cleanliness is part of the faith," Muhammad said. Ritual ablutions are necessary before prayers several times daily, including a full bath (*tuhr*) after sexual intercourse, menstruation, and the puerperium. Muhammad forbade overindulgence in food and drink, and enjoined physical fitness. Circumcision of male children is required by Islam. Female circumcision, not an Islamic commandment, has been practiced in Sudan and Egypt since pre-Islamic times, and is now waning.

Preventive healthcare is well heeded. One of Muhammad's pertinent teachings is "If there is pestilence in a locality, do not enter it, and if you are already in it, do not go out." Alcohol is categorically forbidden by Islam (as are stupefying drugs, in order to protect mind and health). Nevertheless, the law in many Arab countries allows the sale and consumption of alcoholic beverages. Currently, there is widespread objection to the practice, and steps have even been taken to avoid alcohol in medicinal preparations. Extramarital sex is forbidden in Islam, although it certainly takes place in a clandestine manner. The virginity rate of girls at the time of marriage approaches 100 percent. The sexual revolution and its sequelae in the West since 1960 have not erupted in the Arab world, although the powerful influence of communications markets the Western model and at the same time evokes a strong reaction expressed in a revival of religious values.

Care of the environment is emphasized in Muhammad's teachings, but unfortunately poverty, overcrowding, and unbridled movement from rural to urban regions with limited and failing infrastructure have led to a gap between the real and the ideal in many Arab cities. Muhammad taught, "Faith has many branches, including the removal of dirt from the street," and "Beware of the triple curse of polluting water resources, shady spots, and trodden roads." On water conservation he instructed those expending much water while making the ritual ablution: "Economize, even if you are at a flowing river." Encouraging agriculture, he said, "Whoever farms land will be rewarded by God every time a person eats from its crop, even if a thief steals and eats from it." Another of his recommendations is "If the end of the world comes and you have a little shoot in your hand to plant, then plant it if you can."

Kindness to animals is a religious dictate. They should not be overburdened or worked to exhaustion or tortured, and they should not be killed except for food. Muhammad spoke of God's pleasure with a man who, encountering a thirsty dog unable to reach water in a well, filled his shoe with water and offered it to the dog, and—conversely—God's anger with a woman who imprisoned a cat. These concepts were borne in mind when discussing the ethics of animal experimentation. Although it is approved when necessary for medical research, due care and humaneness should be shown in keeping and handling the animals.

Contraception

Contraception is lawful provided both husband and wife agree. Contraceptive measures are easily available and in some countries are subsidized by the state to curb overpopulation. Family planning should not be directly or indirectly imposed; the method should not be harmful; it should not entail abortion. Governmental and voluntary agencies use propaganda and education to promote family limitation in overpopulated countries, whereas incentives for a larger family are given in the underpopulated, affluent countries. However, family limitation policies are often attacked by some religious elements for a variety of reasons (Hathout, 1989), including the accusation that they are "imperialistic" designs against poor countries (see Information Project for Africa). The use of the intrauterine contraceptive device has been controversial for fear that it acts by inducing abortion, but its use is widespread. The 1987 World Health Organization (WHO) announcement that its mechanism of action was contraceptive and not abortifacient was welcomed by religious authorities.

Breast-feeding is highly recommended in the Islamic tradition; the Qur'an says: "The mothers shall give suck to their offspring for two whole years, for those who desire to complete the term of lactation" (2:233). This would have been a potent measure for wider spacing of pregnancies at the level of the society at large, being associated with a high rate of ovulation suppression (of course it would not be a reliable prescription for contraception for the individual family). Unfortunately, the growing number of women joining the labor force does not work in its favor. Surgical sterilization (both male and female) is frowned upon except for pressing medical indications or at an advanced age (nearing menopause) for the highly parous woman.

Reproductive Interventions

The quest for fertility is legitimate, and treatment of infertility by medical or surgical means is lawful and available within the Shari'a. Artificial insemination is permitted only if the husband's semen is used; donor semen is forbidden (by religion and by law) because it is outside the marriage contract. Since legitimate marriage is the only approved venue for reproduction, in vitro fertilization technology is permitted only if it involves a married couple and is carried out during the span of their marriage. No alien "element" should be involved, be it donated sperm, donated ovum, donated embryo, or surrogate uterus. When the wife is widowed or divorced, she is no longer the wife of her husband, and she can no longer be impregnated by his semen that had been preserved in a semen bank, for the marriage contract has come to a conclusion. Surrogacy is outlawed, and contracts for surrogate pregnancy are null and void.

Alternative family structures, not based on legitimate marriage, have no place in Arab societies.

HASSAN HATHOUT (1995)

BIBLIOGRAPHY

Gindi, A. R. al-, ed. 1989a. *Human Life: Its Inception and Its End as Viewed by Islam,* tr. A. Asbahi. Kuwait: Islamic Organization of Medical Sciences and Kuwaiti Foundation for the Advancement of Science.

Gindi, A. R. al-, ed. 1989b. *Human Reproduction in Islam,* tr. A. Asbahi. Kuwait: Islamic Organization of Medical Sciences and Kuwaiti Foundation for the Advancement of Science.

Gindi, A. R. al-, ed. 1989c. *The Islamic Vision of Some Medical Practices,* tr. A. Asbahi. Kuwait: Islamic Organization of Medical Sciences and Kuwaiti Foundation for the Advancement of Science.

Hathout, Hassan. 1988. *Islamic Perspectives in Obstetrics and Gynecology,* pp. 95–100. Cairo: Alam al-Kutub.

Hathout, Hassan. 1989. "On Ethics and Human Values in Family Planning." In *Proceedings of 12th CIOMS Conference, on Ethics and Human Values in Family Planning,* ed. Z.

Bankowski, José Barzelatto, and Alexander Capron. Geneva: Council for International Organizations of Medical Sciences.

Information Project for Africa, Inc. 1990. Summary analysis of "National Security Study Memorandum 200—Implications of Worldwide Population Growth for U.S. Security and Overseas Interest. Dated Dec. 10, 1974—Classified. Declassified July 3, 1989. Released/U.S. National Archives, June 26, 1990." Washington, D.C.: Author.

Islamic Code of Medical Ethics: Kuwait Document. 1981. Kuwait: International Organization of Islamic Medicine.

United Nations. 1992. *Demographic Yearbook 1990.* New York: Author.

World Health Organization. 1987. *Mechanism of Action, Safety and Efficiency of Intrauterine Devices: A Report of a WHO Scientific Group.* WHO Technical Report Series no. 153. Geneva: Author.

V. ISRAEL

Medicine in Israel, like the country itself, is a blend of contrasts and contradictions, of compromises between tradition and modernity, between myth and reality. Israel, a tiny country made up of a dominant religion and culture (18 percent of the population are non-Jewish), is neither homogeneous nor monolithic. Over fifteen political parties are represented in the Knesset (parliament), and many Israelis are concerned about an ever-impending Kulturkampf between religious and secular factions.

Like all else in Israel, healthcare has been shaped by diverse inputs from a variety of lands of origin, and by the dialectic between the Mosaic and rabbinical tradition and modern Western secular humanism. Each of these major streams is itself heterogeneous. Lip service is paid to myths violated in practice, while traditions overtly denied and rebelled against often provide the spiritual sustenance in which rebels' values are rooted.

The ties that bind Jews to medicine are powerful and deeply rooted. Rabbinic leaders in the Middle Ages often practiced medicine for their livelihood, Maimonides being perhaps the best known in this tradition. In almost every society, Jews have been disproportionately represented in medicine. The most recent example is the 2.5 to 3 percent of Jewish immigrants to Israel from the former Soviet Union who are physicians, a ratio ten to fifteen times higher than that encountered in developed Western countries. The extraordinary value that Judaism places on human life explains in part the attraction of Jews to medicine. The Talmudic statement "He who saves a single life is regarded by the Scripture as if he saved an entire world" (Babylonian Talmud, Sanhedrin 37a) has led to the useful myth that life is of infinite value and to the "sanctity of life" concept that so permeates Jewish tradition.

The foundations of healthcare in modern Israel were laid by Zionist pioneers several decades before the creation of the State of Israel. These individuals were largely secularist, socialist ideologues with deep roots in the social justice ethos of Judaism and in the value placed on human life. Workers in 1912 created a "sick fund" for mutual assistance and healthcare insurance, similar in many ways to the *Krankenkasse* of Central Europe from which they had emigrated. But the principles underlying this Jewish institution were derived no less from the traditional principles of *gemilut hadisim* (loving charity or mutual aid) so clearly spelled out in the Torah, whose rituals the pioneers had often discarded or drastically modified. All were to be equal in the receipt of health care, and money was not to be collected from a person in time of need and distress. This nongovernmental Histadrut labor union sick fund continues to be the major healthcare provider in Israel today. It is both an insurer and a provider of healthcare, owning and operating hospitals and community clinics, and insuring about 80 percent of the population. Smaller sick funds, also funded by mandatory employee and employer contributions, cover the rest of the population.

During the last few years, as healthcare financing has become problematic worldwide—with citizens often placing a higher priority on such personal amenities as choice of physician and attractive waiting rooms than on the concept of equality—the egalitarian foundations of the healthcare system in Israel have been threatened. Gaps in the public sector are being met by a growing fee-for-service private sector. Nevertheless, Israel has managed to maintain both a respectably high level of healthcare and reasonably equal availability of this care, in spite of a relatively low national expenditure. Israel currently spends about 7.5 percent of its gross national product on health care, but since its GNP is considerably smaller than those of most Western European countries, the absolute per capita expenditure is modest.

Manifestations of the strong ethos for saving human life at all costs include the relatively high renal dialysis rates in Israel and the intense efforts made by the military medical corps to provide physician coverage virtually at the battle line, in order to enhance every possible chance to save soldiers' lives. Public appeals by private individuals regularly raise tens of thousands of dollars to send patients abroad for complex surgical procedures that are not performed in Israel.

Yet, simultaneously, there is much evidence that the myth of the infinite value of human life is often shattered in the face of economic realities. Open-heart surgery is rarely offered to those over eighty, and long waiting periods for critical surgical procedures are not uncommon because of limited resources. The distribution of physicians and facilities is not even, with development towns and Arab villages sometimes at a disadvantage compared with the major metropolitan areas. The continued public tolerance of preventable deaths due to smoking and traffic accidents also exposes the mythical nature of the commitment to human life "at all costs." Recently, however, there has been improvement in all these areas.

Consonant with the high priority given to life, the Jewish tradition, unlike Anglo-Saxon law, requires the physician to respond to a patient's call for help. This requirement to render assistance to someone in distress is not confined to the physician; it obligates any individual to come to the aid of a fellow human being. To refuse would fall under the prohibition "Neither shalt thou stand idly by the blood of thy fellow" (Lev. 19:16). A physician who does not respond to a sick patient's request is regarded as one who spills blood. This attitude is incorporated into Israeli secular law, under which a citizen's failure to render assistance at the scene of an accident is a criminal act. Just as the physician is obligated to render care, so is seeking of care by the patient mandatory. The reason for this obligation is that in Judaism, human beings do not possess full title to life or body. Humans are but the stewards of the divine possession they have been privileged to receive. The terms of that stewardship are not of human choice but are determined by the Almighty's commands. Jewish law forbids suicide and requires that all reasonable steps be taken to preserve life and health. When beneficence conflicts with autonomy, the former is given precedence by Jewish tradition, a view clearly in conflict with the modern Western consensus (Beauchamp and Childress).

While such a violation of autonomy for the patient's good is not enforceable in modern pluralistic societies, it is sanctioned in the Jewish tradition; and were Jewish courts fully empowered, they might force medical treatment on a patient if it were indisputably indicated. In modern Israel, in contrast with most Western countries, the courts have not always decided unequivocally for autonomy over beneficence. There has been at least one case where the Israeli Supreme Court permitted a surgical procedure against the expressed will of the subject in order to prevent danger to his life (*Kortam v. State of Israel* 40 [III] P.D. pp. 673–698).

Several medical ethical issues have attracted public attention in Israel over the years and provide interesting insights into the dynamics of Israeli society. For several decades, the issue of postmortem examinations and the laws regulating them were a major public and political issue (Glick). Judaism emphasizes respect for the human body in death as well as in life, and mandates early burial with integrity of the body preserved. Autopsies are permitted only if the information may contribute directly to the saving of a human life. With the creation of the first Israeli medical school, the rabbinate reached an agreement with the medical profession whereby autopsies would be permitted if three physicians attested that the cause of death was unknown. This exclusion of the deceased person's family from decision making and the subsequent frequent performance of post-mortem examinations, even over strenuous family objections, turned the issue into a source of festering conflict. Subsequently, with a change in the political constellation that gave more power to religious parties, the law was changed radically as part of a backlash against the previous "liberalism." Not only is family consent now required, but other provisions, such as veto power for any member of the family, have led from one extreme to another. In all likelihood, the last word has not yet been said on the subject.

In spite of the religious limitations on postmortem examinations, the use of organs from the dead for life-saving transplants is religiously acceptable and even mandated. For many years, the hesitation of the rabbinate to accept brain death as the end of human life created difficulties for heart and liver transplants. After careful study, Israel's Chief Rabbinate in 1986 officially permitted heart transplants when donors' total brain death can be assured. This view has not been accepted by all rabbinical authorities, but religious objections now play a relatively minimal role in the limitations on organ transplantation.

Another area of conflict, as in most Western countries, has been abortion policy. Many factors lead to a restrictive policy in Israel. The Jewish tradition accords major rights to the fetus. The demographic and geopolitical situation of the Jewish people, particularly after the Holocaust, would seem to favor a strongly pronatal and antiabortion approach. Yet the Israeli public is quite permissive sexually, and its youth is very much a part of Western society.

The Israeli compromise, meant to satisfy all parties, includes a law forbidding abortions except for a "valid" medical or social reason, as determined by a hospital committee. These indications are liberally interpreted. Abortions performed outside this framework are illegal, thus satisfying religious sentiments. But no physician has ever been prosecuted for such illegal activities, thereby soothing the libertarians. This precarious balancing characterizes many of Israel's solutions to such conflicts.

Israel has a national committee appointed by the minister of health that advises the minister on many of the more complex and controversial areas in medical ethics, such as in vitro fertilization, genetic engineering, and the like. The committee, called the Supreme Helsinki Committee, is an outgrowth of a committee originally charged with the regulation of research in human subjects according to the Helsinki Declaration. It includes physicians, nonmedical scientists, jurists, philosophers, and clergy. It prefers to work by consensus rather than by vote, and makes every effort to weave its way through the maze of potential legal, religious, and sociopolitical conflicts. In the area of reproduction, the problems are great, since—unlike most areas of law that are adjudicated by the secular courts—marriage, divorce, and family law are largely in the hands of rabbinical courts (Shapira, pp. 12–14). Permissive decisions in the area of new reproductive technologies, unacceptable under religious law, might label the offspring of such practices as bastards, with serious consequences for them in their attempts to marry.

Israeli medical schools now have courses in medical ethics. Most provide the largely secular students with philosophical as well as religious approaches. The Israel Society for Medical Ethics serves as a forum for discussion, for the issuing of position papers, and for raising the consciousness of healthcare professionals regarding medical ethics.

Some militant secular Israelis, chafing under the restrictions of Jewish tradition, have taken a number of bioethical issues to the courts in attempts to force rulings in favor of their position. Cases pressing the right to die have been brought before the courts without clear-cut resolution. Similar suits have been brought with respect to the restrictions placed on surrogate motherhood. These and other court decisions may bring about changes that legislators have been reluctant to press because of their hesitance to upset the "status quo"—which, in this case, refers to a freezing of the situation regarding the influence of the Jewish religion within Israel's public life prior to statehood.

In summary, Israel is a relatively young country that sees itself as part of the modern Western world, yet is the heir to an ancient and wise cultural tradition dating back thousands of years. Jewish tradition is characterized by a strong duty ethic, with emphases on both physician and patient responsibility; a high value on human life; and a strong sense of justice. Time will tell how successful Israeli society will be in distilling and blending the best of both these worlds.

SHIMON M. GLICK (1995)

BIBLIOGRAPHY

Babylonian Talmud, Sanhedrin 37a. 1969. London: Soncino Press.

Beauchamp, Tom L., and Childress, James F. 1983. *Principles of Biomedical Ethics,* 2nd edition. New York: Oxford University Press.

Glick, Shimon M. 1985. "Health Policy Making in Israel—Religion, Politics and Cultural Diversity." In *Health Policy, Ethics and Human Values: An International Dialogue,* pp. 71–74, ed. Z. Bankowski, John H. Bryant, and Robert Veatch.

Geneva: Council of International Organizations of Medical Science.

Jakobovits, Immanuel. 1959. *Jewish Medical Ethics: A Comparative and Historical Study of the Jewish Religious Attitude to Medicine and Its Practice.* New York: Bloch.

Kortam v. State of Israel. 40 (III) P.D., pp. 673–698. (In Hebrew.)

Shapira, Amos. 1987. "In Israel, Law, Religious Orthodoxy and the Reproductive Technologies." *Hastings Center Report* 17 (supp.): 12–14.

MEDICAL ETHICS, HISTORY OF SOUTH AND EAST ASIA

• • •

I. GENERAL SURVEY

The entries that follow deal with the complex and varied traditions of medical ethics and practice in east, south, and southeast Asia. In many respects these three areas have always represented very different cultural and geographical entities. The Indian subcontinent derived its cultural and linguistic influences from central and western Asia, but produced in Hinduism and Jainism its own religious, cultural, and intellectual forms, shaping attitudes toward disease and the ethics of medical practice. Concepts of human life and disease evolved quite independently in east Asia, where an agrarian society grew up isolated from other Asian peoples both by steep mountains and by what were for the early Chinese equally impenetrable oceans. Chinese society developed its own characteristic political and social practices—particularly its religion focused on the present world, and orientation toward its ancestors. Early Japanese attitudes toward nature differed from the Chinese, as the conceptions of an island people dependent on the seas for a living differed from those of plains-dwelling farmers. Nonetheless, significant interaction between China and Japan from about the seventh century C.E. infused Confucian ideas into early

Japanese foundations. Southeast Asia, today comprising Vietnam, Laos, Thailand, Malaysia, and Indonesia, and vividly characterized by Anthony Reid in *The Lands Beneath the Winds,* also evolved from independent social origins. As Reid writes: "Fundamental social and cultural traits distinguish Southeast Asia as a whole from either of its vast neighbors—China and India. Central among these are the concepts of spirit or 'soul-stuff' animating living things; the prominence of women in descent, ritual matters, marketing and agriculture; and the importance of debt as a determinant of social obligation" (Reid, 1988, p. 6).

Despite their very different cultural orientations, these societies are treated here as a group because they offered in traditional times a common contrast to Western medical practice and ethics, and have had throughout their histories a common influence from Buddhism. In more recent periods, the societies of east Asia have faced the common problem of reconciling the possibilities of Western medical technology with their own social goals. These common themes are explored here, by way of introduction to the more specialized articles that follow.

In traditional times, the societies of Asia never adopted the exclusively biological conception of disease that has become the norm in modern Western societies. In traditional Indian Ayurvedic medicine, as Desai Prakash argues, physicians classified the etiology of disease in three categories: external or invasive diseases caused by foreign bodies or possession states; internal diseases caused by disturbances of humors brought about by lapses in discretion; and a third category of disease brought about by the inexorable workings of karma. In ancient China, the metaphors were different but the origins of disease were understood to be equally complex, with health and illness deriving from the baneful or benevolent influence of departed ancestors, or the influence of demons. In Japan, the apprehension of human beings' relation to *kami,* (sacred world), and the southeast Asian conception of the relation of magic, religion, and health, allowed the possibility of social as well as strictly organic origins of disease.

These views of disease may reflect a general tendency in Asia to view the human order as more fully integrated with the natural and social orders than in the West. This contrasts with modern European conceptions of disease, which reflected a European, perhaps Promethean, notion that the human world could understand, analyze, and ultimately control the natural order. Asians' more complex vision of disease had important consequences for the relationship of the medical practitioner and his patient. Since disease could arise from a variety of sources, the Asian medical practitioner addressed a wider spectrum of issues in a patient's life than did his Western counterpart. Moreover, the Asian patient might be free to consult many more types of practitioners than the European counterpart. Hence varied traditions of medical practice existed side by side, with no single system of medicine having an exclusive legitimacy.

In part, this pluralism of Asian medical practice made it possible for Buddhist practitioners to spread throughout Asia, beginning in about the second century c.e. The notion of loving friendship, and its institutional expression in the establishment of charitable hospitals, dispensaries, and comfort stations on the way to famous shrines and temples, was one of the concepts Buddhist monks carried with them as they made their way across the trade routes of central Asia from India to China between the second and the seventh centuries c.e. Once in China, Buddhist monks found a social environment quite different from the one they had left, for although the Chinese intellectual world was open to Buddhist doctrines, Chinese society was not as open to monastic life with its implied rejection of family and ancestors. In China Mahayana or devotional Buddhism, which stressed the activities that the believer could perform while remaining within the realm of family and community, developed. Thus, in China, Buddhist healing practices not only were carried out within charitable institutions formally run by the Buddhist establishment but also came to merge with folk medicine and healing practices from other traditions.

By about the thirteenth century, the spread of Buddhism throughout Asia had provided a unity to traditional medical practice that had not existed previously. But this was at best a loose unity, in which Buddhist medical ideas came to coexist alongside traditional healing practices and institutions. When Western medicine came to Asia in more recent times, it experienced a similar fate. The importation of Western medicine to Asia was largely a product of colonial times; the earliest Western medical practitioners in Asia were often missionaries supported by European and American political or religious establishments. Twentieth-century Asian governments, consciously or unconsciously aware that Western medical technology could provide the same control over life and disease that Western military and social technology provided over political affairs, often vigorously pursued Western medical techniques. The Minister of Education of the government of Nationalist, or Guomindang, China declared in 1914 that he had "decided to abolish traditional Chinese medicine." Similarly, in 1874 the Meiji government in Japan decreed that all Japanese physicians had to have Western medical training.

Despite the vigorous efforts of Asian governments to promote Western medical education and practice, Western medicine has failed to supplant traditional medical practices in any of the countries under consideration, for several reasons. In part, the problem has been the absence of trained medical professionals: In China, for instance, despite the commitment of the government of the People's Republic to scientific medical practice, a realistic assessment of resources dictated that medical workers trained in traditional as well as modern Western techniques be employed. Possibly because of the paucity of trained personnel throughout Asia, Western medical practice has been and remains a largely urban and elite phenomenon. In part as well, traditional medical practices have proved their value as effective and inexpensive treatments for many of the maladies of modern life. As Pinit Ratanakul notes in the article on Southeast Asian countries, "This traditional method of healing may be especially suitable today for Southeast Asians, who, living in societies with increased urbanization and industrialization, need physical, psychological and spiritual care to enable them to cope with such change and the strains and stresses of modern life." Today, then, as in the past, different disciplines of medical treatment, each with its own ethical standards and requirements, exist side by side throughout much of Asia.

If modern Western medicine has not fully supplanted traditional medicine in Asia, the power and technology of modern medicine has in almost every country posed new ethical dilemmas. In some instances, as in the case of reproductive medicine, Western medicine has made accessible courses of action more radical than traditional medicine permitted. Abortion, though known and disapproved of in traditional Chinese and Indian medicine, has become much more common throughout Asia as population control has become an accepted political goal. Amniocentesis to determine the sex of a fetus has become a common practice in India, with female feticide often the consequence of the traditional religious imperative to produce a male heir. China's enthusiastic embrace of the Western market for blood products and the technology for obtaining them fostered the spread of AIDS in the 1990s in a population totally oblivious to the dangers of the technology and the disease.

In other areas of medicine, Western technology has fostered new and rather ominous practices in Asia. In China in the late 1980s, debate arose about the merits of sterilization of the mentally retarded and other types of genetic experimentation. Sadly, Asian practitioners of Western medicine have proved somewhat more willing to engage in experimentation on human subjects than have their Western counterparts, as well. Wartime experimentation during WW II by Japanese doctors in Manchuria has, of course, been condemned not only in the West but also in Japan. Unfortunately, such experimentation has also been carried out in contemporary Southeast Asia, though such action is increasingly condemned by Southeast Asian and Western governments. As a result of the new ethical dilemmas posed by Western medical technologies, medical ethics has become both a heated issue throughout contemporary Asia and the subject of frequent international conferences and journal articles.

R. KENT GUY (1995)
REVISED BY AUTHOR

BIBLIOGRAPHY

Reid, Anthony. 1988. *Southeast Asia in the Age of Commerce, 1450–1680: The Lands Below the Winds,* vol. 1. New Haven, CT: Yale University Press.

II. INDIA

In this article, India refers to the entire Asian subcontinent south of Afghanistan and the Himalayan range, including the modern nations of India, Pakistan, Bangladesh, and Nepal (often referred to as the "Indic" region) as well as the island nation Sri Lanka. In the third millennium B.C.E. there flourished a civilization in and around the Indus Valley known as the Harrapan city culture. Gradually, from the second millennium, the subcontinent was infiltrated by Indo-European tribes from Central Asia. These people formed the classical culture that survives to modern times with many transformations. In the eighth century, Muslim invasions began in the north, culminating in the powerful Mogul empire of the fourteenth and fifteenth centuries. Historic India is the home of two of the world's major religions, Hinduism and Buddhism, as well as of Jainism, and host to Islam, now the majority religion in Pakistan and Bangladesh, as well as to ancient Christian and Jewish communities in the south. From the interaction of Hinduism and Islam grew another religion in India, the Sikh faith. In the sixteenth century, India's cultural and religious influence extended into China and Tibet, as well as to the lands of Southeast Asia.

The origins of medicine in India stretch back to antiquity. The urban architecture of the earliest civilization, in the cities of the Indus Valley, demonstrates knowledge of sanitary techniques. One of the Vedas, the sacred lore of the early Indo-Europeans (ca. 1500–1000 B.C.E.), contains chants to ward off disease, and lists of herbal medicines. The ancient texts extolled by the *bhesaj,* persons skilled in the medicinal uses of herbs. Priest-physicians prescribed prayers and fasts, as well as herbal medicines. Out of this text, the *Atharvaveda,*

and other systems of philosophical speculations developed a system of medicine based upon a theory of bodily humors and a therapeutic regimen of herbs and plants. The term "Ayurveda," meaning knowledge of vitality and long life, designated this classical Indian medicine that is widely practiced in India today. Ayurvedic medicine developed in the fifth century B.C.E.; its earliest classical treatise, *Carakasamhita,* can be dated to the first century C.E. The oldest known Sanskrit medical manuscripts, discovered in a Buddhist monastery in China and dating from about 450 C.E., reveal a developed medical system, mentioning elixirs for long life (including garlic), eye lotions, enemas, aphrodisiacs, and ways of caring for sick children. The text mentions Indian physicians of renown, including the most famous, Sushruta (second century C.E.). After the adoption of Buddhism by King Ashoka (273–232 B.C.E.), Buddhist monks, who were not bound by the rigorous Hindu laws of purity and pollution, were free to mingle with common people and to invite them into their monasteries, thus bringing their medical skills to the needy and hospitality to the sick. They also seem to have brought Ayurvedic medicine to Tibet and China. Monks of the Jain tradition, which arose about the same time as the Buddhist tradition, also contributed to the development of the medical system. Early medical speculations and observations about the body, mind, and illness were consistent with tenets of all three major religions.

There appears to have been a flowering of medicine during the first millennium C.E. (Jolly; Winternitz). In the course of time, six classic texts of Ayurveda were recognized. Two of these, *Sushrutasamhita* and *Carakasamhita,* are named after the most famous physicians of the tradition, Sushruta and Caraka (first century C.E.); it is suggested that the word "caraka," which also means "one who moves about," refers to the itinerant Buddhist monks; Sushruta was a physician to a Buddhist king. The other four—*Ashtangahridaya,* attributed to the physician *Vagbhatta; Madhavanidana; Sarangadharasamhita;* and *Bhavaprakasha*—date from the eighth, ninth, thirteenth, and sixteenth centuries, respectively. The latter two reveal the influence of Arabic medicine, and the last mentions *phirangi roga,* the disease of the Franks (the Portuguese who came to India in 1498), probably syphilis. The use of opium as a therapeutic agent is prescribed in these later texts.

Assumptions of Ayurveda

Ayurveda is deeply rooted in the great religious and philosophical traditions of India, whose visions of human nature and the universe informed medicine and, in turn, were enriched by the concepts formed in medical practice (Dasgupta). Ayurvedic constructs of the self and the body, concerns central to the medical enterprise, grew in tandem with the faith traditions. Ayurvedic physiology and pathophysiology rest on a doctrine of humors (*doshas*) and bodily substances (*dhatus*). The principal humors are wind (*vata*), bile (*pitta*), and phlegm (*kapha*), representing movement, heat, and moisture in the body, respectively. The primary body substance, *dhatu,* is "organic sap" (*rasa*) derived from food, transformed in various ways as it moves through the body, stored in various reservoirs, and excreted as waste. Sap is first transformed into blood, then into flesh, fat, bone, marrow, and semen, the last being the purest product of the transformation.

Health is a state of balance of bodily humors and substances (*dhatusamya*); illness is disequilibrium. The body is affected by external factors, such as food and climate, as well as internal influences, such as anger and jealousy; social experiences, such as praise or scorn, also affect bodily states. Each of these may cause disease or restore health. This interactive universe of substances blurs the boundaries between inside and outside, and makes for a constant flux. The body is in dynamic relationship with the cosmos, whose elements of wind, fire, and water are reflected in the body; similarly, the body is seen as a reflection of the mythic cosmogony, in which the primordial person arises from chaos and is differentiated into multiple forms. Breath (*prana*) is the supreme force that unites bodily parts and becomes the definition of life (*jiva*): "People say of a dead person, that his limbs have become unstrung," say the *Upanishads* (ancient religious discourses). Ayurvedic medicine visualizes the sick person as in a state of fragmentation; his or her bodily components must be taken apart, cleansed, and put together again (Desai, 1989). Breath also becomes equated with the narcissistic and metaphysical components: *ahamkara* and *atman. Ahamkara,* "I-ness," literally the saying of the word "I," is the perishable self; and *atman,* cognate with the Greek *atmos,* is visualized as a self beyond death, without properties, pure consciousness, and transcendental. Although Hindu, Buddhist, and Jain traditions have differing notions of the self, they share common beliefs about the transience of the perishable body, often a source of pain, and the consubstantiality of the body with the universe.

The theory of *gunas* (literally "strands" or "qualities") is an aspect of *samkhya* and an important foundation of Hindu ethics. Inherent and substantial, *sattva* (goodness), *rajas* (vitality), and *tamas* (inertia) are found in all material substances in various combinations and determine the overall constitutional disposition of persons, foods, activities, bodily substances, and so forth. Physically *sattva* is cool and light; *rajas,* hot and active; and *tamas,* heavy and dull. Psychologically they are calmness, passion, and lethargy or stupidity, respectively. In character they are purity or virtue, happiness or sorrow, and darkness or evil, respectively. Contemplation, meditation, silence, devotion, and fasting promote goodness; love, battle, attachment, pleasure seeking, and emotionality enhance vitality; sloth, sleep, and idleness increase inertia. In the hierarchy of values, the *sattva* categories tend to reign supreme and become less material and closer to the idea of *sat* (truth or essence); in Ayurvedic discourses they are understood to be the same as the mind or the self. The ethical aim, therefore, is to transform physical and mental dispositions from inertia to activity to goodness. Such transformations are promoted by ingestion of foods and performance of activities that are conducive to the higher strand. Therapeutic aims are also to transform the self and the body to higher levels of functions: from imbalance to equipoise, from idleness to activity, from agitation or pleasure seeking to calmness and contemplation.

The Physician

An Ayurvedic physician, called a *vaidya,* is one of the quartet (the physician, the drugs, the attendant, and the patient) responsible for amelioration of diseases. Although esteemed for their powers to bring about health and disease-free states ("the cause of virtue"), physicians were regarded with mixed feelings in ancient India; anxiety concerning disease and death was displaced onto them. Physicians contracted impurity from their handling of body products, lesions, and corpses, and through their "democratic practice of mingling with the common people" (Chattopadhyaya). Religious texts enjoined people not to receive food from physicians and to avoid them at religious ceremonies. Taboos concerning touching caused palpation to fall into disuse as a diagnostic tool.

The Ayurvedic texts demand that a physician excel in theoretical knowledge, have extensive practical experience, be dextrous, and observe the rules of cleanliness. A physician began his education as an apprentice, teacher and pupil choosing each other. A good teacher was free from conceit, greed, and envy; the student was calm, friendly, and without physical defects. The physician must be compassionate, virtuous, of high lineage, devoted to learning, rational, and always ready to act. The *Carakasamhita* regards the profession as suitable to the upper castes: Brahmins (for the welfare of all living beings), Kshatriyas (for their own protection), and Vaishyas (for livelihood). The *Sushrutasamhita* also permits the Shudras, the lowest caste, to be physicians. Later the vaidyas became a caste, an occupational division, and the profession passed from father to son. In modern India, physicians, Ayurvedic or otherwise, may be from any caste.

Carakasamhita contains an extensive ethical treatise in the form of an initiation oath to be sworn by one entering the practice of medicine. Among its injunctions are these:

> Day and night, however you may be engaged, you shall strive for the relief of the patient with all your heart and soul. You shall not desert or injure your patient even for the sake of your life or your living.
>
> You shall be modest in your dress and appearance and speak words that are gentle, pure, righteous, pleasing, worthy, true, wholesome, and moderate.
>
> When entering a patient's house, you shall be accompanied by a man who is known to the patient and who has his permission to enter. Having entered, your speech, mind, intellect, and senses shall be entirely devoted to no other thought than that of being helpful to the patient, and of things concerning him only. The peculiar customs of the patient's household shall not be made public.
>
> Though possessed of knowledge, you should not boast very much about it. Most people are offended by the boastfulness of even those who are otherwise good and knowledgeable.
>
> There is no limit at all to which knowledge of Ayurveda can be acquired, so you should apply yourself to it with all diligence. The entire world is the teacher of the intelligent and the foe of the unintelligent. Hence, knowing this well, you should listen and act according to the words of instruction of even an unfriendly person when they are worthy and such as to bring fame and long life to you, and are capable of giving you strength and prosperity. (Menon and Haberman, 1970, pp. 295–296)

Sushrutasamhita describes procedures that include an ingenious method of making a new nose when the original has been cut off (a form of humiliation that was a common punishment for criminals and unfaithful wives). The text also contains directions for dissection of the cadaver. However, dissection for purposes of teaching and study was not normally practiced. The objection to dissection was based on the deep-seated Indian taboo on contact with dead matter of any kind. The doctrine of *ahimsa* (nonviolence), which was taught by Buddhism and Jainism, did not prevent dissection of a dead body, provided the body was not deliberately killed for that purpose; but *ahimsa* did act as a check on vivisection of any creature.

Care of animals such as cows, horses, elephants, and even birds formed an integral part of the prevailing religious beliefs. Mention is made in the literature of hospitals for sick and wounded birds. Although ancient Indian physicians were taught the care and treatment of animals, there were also veterinarians who cared only for animals.

Quacks and charlatans were unequivocally condemned. They were known by their loose tongues, superficial knowledge, pretense, and arrogance. When the patient worsened, they abandoned him. The fate of their patients was worse than death; one can survive a thunderbolt, says *Carakasamhita,* but not the medicine prescribed by quacks. A physician, on the other hand, was to hold his tongue, not enter into needless debates, and apply himself continuously to new learning. He was to avoid women who belong to others, not to enter the house of a patient without the presence of a person known to the family, to maintain confidentiality, and never to mention a patient's approaching death.

Modern Indian physicians, especially those trained in Western medicine under the British, took the Hippocratic oath. The Indian Medical Council promulgated its code of ethics in 1970. The code directs physicians to serve humanity without regard to religion or race, social or political affiliation. A physician must provide pro bono services, maintain confidentiality, and hold teachers in esteem with a sense of gratitude. An adulterous relationship with a patient or with a patient's family member is considered a breach of ethical principles (Medical Council of India).

The Origin of Life

The origin of life is a major concern of the authors of traditional medical texts. An embryo is formed through the union of the woman and the man when both have appropriate humoral dispositions and appropriate nourishment. The life principle is thought either to enter at the moment of conception or to be a latent property of the seeds; the latter is comparable to fire in the rays of the sun becoming manifest on passing through a lens, or the combining of male and female germinal substances. At other times the moment of quickening or the descent of the fetus in the womb is seen as a moment of independent life or viability. Defective germinal substances, "unnatural" coitus, failure of nourishment or inappropriate nourishment, and weakness or disturbance in humors explain the unexpected, such as multiple pregnancies and infertility. Initially the fetus is visualized as genderless and becomes male or female in the third to fourth month of pregnancy. Among the rites of passage, *samskaras,* there is one that is performed at this stage of pregnancy to promote the development of a male child.

Having a male child is a Hindu religious obligation, for the performance of funerary rites by a son secures passage to the land of the forefathers. In this rite of passage, the son symbolically reconstitutes the body of the dead father and reunites him with his lineage. Therefore, a man must have a son; if necessary, he must take another wife to beget a son, invite his younger brother or a Brahmin of good conduct to impregnate his wife (a custom called *niyoga*), choose another willing woman, or otherwise adopt, procure, or purchase a son. The epic *Mahābhārata* provides examples of *niyoga*—the birth of the father of Pandavas, the protagonists, and of the Kauravas, the antagonists of the epic—and of in vitro fertilization—the development of embryos in pots, as in the case of the Kauravas. The birth of the last liberated sage of the Jain tradition, Mahavira, provides an example of embryo transfer from one womb to another, as does the birth of an older sibling of Lord Krishna (Desai, 1988). In light of these traditions, modern forms of surrogacy or new technologies present few problems.

Contraception and abortion also have precedents in Indian tradition. The medical texts dwell upon ways of enhancing the possibilities of conception through manipulation of a number of variables; the same variables can be manipulated to retard the chances of conception. In practice, sexual congress outside the Hindu religious Law was not prohibited for men, but women were scorned if found lacking in virtue—especially widows, who were forbidden to remarry—and means had to be sought to prevent unwanted pregnancies. *Bhavaprakasha,* a sixteenth-century medical text, provides a list of oral contraceptives. Modern methods of contraception have been introduced in India, and a massive family-planning campaign includes male and female sterilization. Research work on antipregnancy vaccine and depot preparations (large doses suspended in oil so that they are slowly released over a long period of time) of hormones is ongoing.

Medical texts, especially the *Sushrutasamhita,* describe various forms of arrested fetal development, fetal death, stillbirth, and obstructed deliveries, and the treatments for them that consist of induction of labor and/or destruction of the fetus. The text cautions against hasty action and requires royal permission to induce abortion and extraction of the fetus in case of danger to maternal life. Although early religious texts consider abortion to be a sin, equal to the killing of a Brahmin, by the seventeenth century Ayurvedic physicians were advising the use of an herb, administered vaginally, for the induction of labor, "a useful remedy for pregnant women in poor health, widows, and women of liberal morals" (as quoted from Vaidya Jeevanamin Chandrashekar, p. 45).

In colonial India abortions were governed by English law; in 1972 the government of India legalized abortion, mainly to prevent illegal abortions and to give further impetus to family planning. Abortions in the first trimester, and under special conditions in the second trimester, are available on demand. More recently, RU-486, "the morning after" pill, has been introduced in India on an experimental basis.

Amniocentesis has become extremely popular in India. Overwhelming preference for boys, permissive abortion laws, and the crushing burden of dowries have led parents to seek to ascertain the sex of the fetus, so that a female can be aborted. A vigorous debate, both for and against using the new technology for sex selection, has ensued, one camp arguing in effect that feticide is better than infanticide and the other decrying the culture's age-old cruelties against women (Desai, 1991).

Disease, Death, and the Laws of Karma

Karma is the operative principle of Hindu ethics and has come to mean that every action has a consequence: "As you sow, so shall you reap." Karma has explanatory power for questions like "Why me?" and encourages action for future rewards. The cycle of birth, death, and rebirth, as well as that of health and disease, is governed by the laws of karma. The laws of karma also have dominated Buddhist and Jain ethics.

The ancient physicians classified the etiology of diseases into three categories. External or invasive diseases were caused by foreign bodies, war injuries, possession, or infestation. Internal diseases were disturbances of humors brought about by lapses in discretion, which included faulty diets, overexertion, sloth, sexual indulgence, and mental disturbances. The third category was reserved for the workings of karma, fruits of action from past deeds or previous lives. Some disease states were also seen as the workings of time, as in aging. The unseen hand of karma was invoked in all diseases, a schema that brought ordinary actions like dietary habits and seasonal observances under the umbrella of ethics. Mental illnesses also arose from these etiologies: possession by spirits, disturbances in humors, and lapses in discretion. Like other conditions that defy easy explanations, epidemics and natural disasters were thought to be caused by the collective misdeeds of a population or of a ruler. Physicians of the era of Caraka and Sushruta paid homage to the principle of karma but argued that passivity on part of a physician who assumed predetermination of disease or death made the whole medical enterprise meaningless. Human effort was always a factor in the workings of karma, and the human body was the object of physicians, who held alleviation of diseases and restoration of health as their primary objectives.

On the other hand, there were incurable diseases. It was prudent of physicians to be wary of heroic efforts to prevent the inevitable, which not only brought loss of income but social censure and ignominy as well. If the physician knew that a case was hopeless, he was to do no more than sustain the nutrition of a dying patient. Thus, prolonging life with artificial means is not always acceptable. Those who have led a full life must, like ripened fruits, fall from the tree; untimely death of the young is another matter. Yet, death is not the opposite of life; it is simply the other end, the opposite of birth. Those who are born must die.

Debates in the West on the issues of aging, the care of the terminally ill, and euthanasia have prompted a reexamination of medical ethics in the East. Not surprisingly the Hindu, the Jain, and the Buddhist views converge and have a place for a "willed death" or, more correctly, "hastened death" (Young; Desai, 1991; Bilimoria, 1992; Fujii, 1991). Shrinivas Tilak (1989), after examining Hindu and Buddhist texts, concluded that aging represents points in a life cycle, indicating both growth and maturity as well as eventual decline and loss; at the end point it is an indicator of ultimate dissolution of life. Hindu texts bemoan the inevitability of death, and the Buddhist texts point to pain and unhappiness as inherent in life. In the face of approaching or inevitable death or debilitating and painfully long suffering, traditional ethics provides "permission to leave" voluntarily. Also, the anxiety occasioned by the uncertain timing of death is to be mastered by death that is willed; choosing the moment of death is permitted to ascetics or otherwise superior and elevated souls. Each of the three traditions provides for taking a vow to gradually refrain from taking food and water (and medications, when relevant); thus one ultimately starves to death. The early discourses do not regard this as suicide, which is a death brought upon oneself in a state of desperation and imbalance, and therefore belongs to a different category. The three traditions, which uphold *ahimsa* as central to the view of sanctity of all life, find little difficulty with death that is hastened by starvation. A telling episode in the life of Mahatma Gandhi illustrates this debate (Parekh). A calf that had no hope of surviving and was suffering was put to death with Gandhi's consent. Gandhi rejected the view that killing was never justified and always represented violence. He said that there is violence when the intention is to cause pain; otherwise it is simply an act of killing. When confronted by his critics, especially the Jain merchants of Gujarat, with the problem of euthanasia, Gandhi gave the following response:

1. The disease from which the patient is suffering should be incurable.
2. All concerned have despaired of the life of the patient.
3. The case should be beyond all help or service.
4. It should be impossible for the patient in question to express his or her wish.
5. So long as even one of these conditions remains unfulfilled, the taking of life from the point of view of ahimsa cannot be justified.

Although Gandhi believed that he had arrived at his position independently, he was building on the position advanced by ancient medical authorities.

Other Systems of Medicine

Yoga philosophy and the related tantra have enriched the Indian medical system on the periphery. In classical yoga thought, the *Yogasutra* of Pantanjali, the aim is to bring the mind to focus by inhibiting its waywardness, through successive disciplines of body and thought and by regulation of body functions. Thus body and mind are yoked and come into correct conjunction. Later elaborations have included arduous physical practices and other forms of meditation. Modern relaxation techniques and biofeedback, popular in the West, owe their origin to the discipline of yoga.

Yogic thought visualizes the body in concentric layers, proceeding from the less important outside to the vital inside, from gross to subtle, from hard to soft, and from more material to less material. The body is penetrable and its boundaries permeable; only the innermost self, which must be realized through yoga, is an adamantine core of permanent joy and bliss.

Other forms of yoga, especially the kundalini yoga, advance a concept in which the spine is a vertical axis along which are chakras (wheels or lotuses), centers of energy and impulses. The lower chakras represent vegetative functions (e.g., genitoexcretory, digestive, circulatory, and respiratory); the higher ones, centers of thought and emotion. In this dualism, kundalini, the spiritual aspect of a person, lies dormant in the lowest chakra at the base of the spine; it must be awakened through yogic exercises and made to travel up the spine, activating other chakras on the way and finally uniting with the highest chakra, where the principle of consciousness resides. The regulation of breath is critically important in these exercises, for the breath is the source of energy and must travel through the chakras into the various nerves or channels (*nadis*). The left-handed form, tantra, is a fringe discipline emphasizing esoteric sexual practices. The feminine powers are invoked and sought for the purpose of incorporating them in the self of the practitioner. The way to accomplish this is literally to reverse the flow of sexual fluids from men to women. Ultimately the enriched semen will be forced up the spinal axis to repose in the head as a collection of the most vital and purified energy.

Another Indian medical system is the siddha tradition, practiced mainly in southern India. Based on the Ayurvedic principles, it favors the Greek pharmacopoeia, especially the metallic oxides. The use of astrology in diagnosis and treatment, including the wearing of precious and semiprecious stones, is quite common in India. There is also a rich tradition of folk medicine, including exorcists, bonesetters, snakebite curers, and those who use mantras for cure.

The Yunani or Arabic system of medicine was brought to India by the Muslim invaders. Accepted by the rulers, it began to displace the older Ayurvedic practice to the periphery but also interacted with it. Its humoral thinking, based on Galenic principles, was congenial to Ayurveda. The examination of the radial pulse became a central feature of Ayurvedic diagnosis, and whereas the Ayurvedic pathophysiology had until then been exclusively humoral, the liver and blood were now implicated in folk pathophysiology. Muslim rulers patronized the system and founded publicly funded hospitals and dispensaries. Hakims, the practitioners of Arabic medicine, enriched the Ayurvedic herbal apothecary with their metallic oxides. They often specialized in the treatment of male sexual dysfunctions. This system is especially patronized by the Muslim population of the subcontinent.

"Allopathy" is the term by which modern Western medicine is known in India. European missionaries, especially from Portugal and France, brought it in the fifteenth century, and the British introduced the system in the delivery of care of their own personnel, later founding hospitals and medical schools in the major Indian cities. Allopathy pushed Ayurveda and Yunani to the periphery of medical practice. Today in India all systems are patronized, allopathy more in the cosmopolitan areas and the indigenous systems more in the rural. Patients often move from one to the other, depending on their own explanatory system or the success or failure of one or the other. The indigenous systems are more often chosen for the treatment of chronic conditions, which by definition have failed to be cured by modern methods. Although antibiotics have changed the epidemiology of acute conditions, they are seen as heavy and harmful with many side effects, in contrast to the gentler herbal preparations. Preparations for internal use have to meet the test of culturally constructed theory of inputs and fluxes. The most significant impact of modern antibiotics has been on maternal and infant morbidity and mortality.

In the 1990s most hospitals are staffed by practitioners of allopathic medicine. There are over 100 allopathic medical schools, over 500,000 hospital beds, and over 300,000 licensed medical practitioners. About 100 Ayurvedic colleges exist, and over 250,000 practitioners, but they have only 20,000 hospital beds. Research in Ayurvedic and Yunani medicine has been organized under central institutes.

Surgery, for which ancient India was famous, has passed into the domain of modern Western medicine. With anesthesia, asepsis, and blood transfusion, modern surgical practice has totally excluded the traditional forms. Organ transplants are becoming common, since traditional beliefs about construction of the body from discrete parts allows for removal and replacement. However, extreme poverty has created a widespread and unregulated market in which poor people offer corneas and kidneys for sale to the wealthy.

A fragmented, either commercialized or bureaucratic system of care that is neither easily accessible nor affordable is the major ethical problem of India. Emigration of physicians and nurses to the West has not helped. Multinational drug cartels and fly-by-night Indian drug firms with little regulation in manufacture or prescription form a lethal combination with diagnoses made by divination or without examination. The cultivation of public health and prevention points a way out of the current problems.

PRAKASH N. DESAI (1995)
BIBLIOGRAPHY REVISED

BIBLIOGRAPHY

PRIMARY TEXTS

Arnold, David. 2000. *Science, Technology and Medicine in Colonial India (New Cambridge History of India. No 3 No 5)*. New York: Cambridge University Press.

Bhavaprakasha, 1981, tr. Gaurishankar Mayashankar Shastri. Ahmadabad, India: Sastu Sahitya Vardhak Karyalaya. In Gujarati.

Brihadāranyaka Upaniṣad, 1962, tr. F. Max Muller In *The Upanishads*, pt. 2. New York: Dover.

Carakasamhita, 1981–1985 (1884), tr. Priyavrat Sharma, 3 vols. Varanasi, India: Chaukhambha Orientalia.

Mahābhārata, 1973, tr. Johannes Adrianus Bernardus Van Buitenen, 3 vols. Chicago: University of Chicago Press.

Sushrutasamhita, 1980, tr. Vaidya Jadavji Trikamji Acharya and Narayana Ram Acharya. Varanasi, India: Chaukhambha Orientalia.

SECONDARY SOURCES

Barua, Archna. 1996. "A Note on—Euthanasia and the Contemporary Debate." *Indian Philosophical Quarterly* 23(3–4): 467–472.

Bilimoria, Purushottama. 1992. "The Jaina Ethic of Voluntary Death." *Bioethics* 6(4): 331–335.

Bilimoria, Purushottama. 1995. "Legal Rulings on Suicide in India and Implications for the Right to Die." *Asian Philosophy* 5(2): 159–180.

Chandrashekar, Sripati. 1974. *Abortion in a Crowded World: The Problem of Abortion with Special Reference to India.* London: George Allen and Unwin.

Chattopadhyaya, Debiprasad. 1977. *Science and Society in Ancient India.* Calcutta: Research India Publications.

Clooney, Francis X. 1995. "Back to the Basics: Reflections on Moral Discourse in a Contemporary Hindu Community." *Journal of Medicine and Philosophy* 20(4): 439–457.

Dasgupta, Surendranath. 1975 (1922). *A History of Indian Philosophy,* 5 vols. Delhi: Motilal Banarsidass.

Desai, Prakash. 1988. "Medical Ethics in India." *Journal of Medicine and Philosophy* 13(3): 231–255.

Desai, Prakash. 1989. *Health and Medicine in the Hindu Tradition: Continuity and Cohesion.* New York: Crossroads.

Desai, Prakash. 1991. "Hinduism and Bioethics in India: A Tradition in Transition." In *Theological Developments in Bioethics: 1988–1990.* vol. 1 of *Bioethics Yearbook,* pp. 41–60, ed. Baruch A. Brody, B. Andrew Lustig, H. Tristram Engelhardt, Jr., and Laurence B. McCullough. Dordrecht, Netherlands: Kluwer.

Dukle, P. D. 1997. "Medical ethics." *Journalof the Indian Medical Association* 95(3): 91.

Fujii, Masao. 1991. "Buddhism and Bioethics." In *Theological Developments in Bioethics: 1988–1990.* vol. 1 of *Bioethics Yearbook,* pp. 61–68, ed. Baruch A. Brody, B. Andrew Lustig, H. Tristram Engelhardt, Jr., and Laurence B. McCullough. Dordrecht, Netherlands: Kluwer.

Jaggi, O. P. 2001. *Medicine in India: Modern Period (History of Science, Philosophy and Culture in Indian Civilization, Vol. Ix: Part 1).* New York: Oxford University Press.

Jolly, Julius. 1977 (1901). *Indian Medicine,* tr. Chintamani Ganesh Kashikar. New Delhi: Munshiram Manoharlal.

Jonsen, Albert R. 2000. "Medical Ethics of India and China" In *A Short History of Medical Ethics,* pp. 27–42. Oxford University Press.

Medical Council of India. 1980. *Code of Medical Ethics,* suppl. to *Christian Medical Association of India Journal* (June).

Menon, A., and Haberman, Herbert Frederick. 1970. "Caraka Samhita." *Medical History* 14: 295–296.

Pandya, S. K. 1999. "Medical Ethics in India: Then and Now." *Acta Neurochirurgica Supplementum* 74: 35–46.

Parekh, Bhikhu C. 1989. *Colonialism, Tradition and Reform: An Analysis of Gandhi's Political Discourse.* New Delhi: Sage Publications.

Ravindran, G. D.; Kalam, T.; Lewin, S.; et al. 1997. "Teaching Medical Ethics in a Medical College in India." *National Medical Journal of India* 10(6): 288–289.

Tilak, Shrinivas. 1989. *Religion and Aging in the Indian Tradition.* Albany: State University of New York Press.

Winternitz, Moriz. 1967 (1913, 1920). *History of Indian Literature,* tr. Subhadra Jha, 3 vols. Delhi: Motilal Banarsidass.

Young, Katherine K. 1989. "Euthanasia: Traditional Hindu Views, and the Contemporary Debate." In *Hindu Ethics: Purity, Abortion, and Euthanasia,* pp. 71–130, ed. Harold G.

Coward, Julius J. Lipner, and Katherine K. Young. Albany: State University of New York Press.

Zysk, Kenneth G. 1998. *Asceticism and Healing in Ancient India: Medicine in the Buddhist Monastery.* New Delhi: Motila.

III: CHINA. A. PRE-REPUBLICAN CHINA

The following article has been retained from the first edition, with minor revisions by the original author.

The cultural history of China, as reflected in its literature, shows that for at least two thousand years the Confucian worldview, an ideology concerned with the structure of social life, dominated Chinese society until the collapse of the empire early in the twentieth century. Although less obvious, the philosophy of Taoism exerted a strong influence on Chinese society in the same period. A third major influence in ancient China, that of Buddhism, was introduced from India about the first century c.e. Buddhism exerted its greatest impact on social life and scholarship in China from about the sixth to the early ninth century. Subsequently some of its metaphysical concepts were integrated into Confucianism, its worldly assets were secularized, and its teachings continued mostly on the level of a folk religion. Medical ethics in China, as a consequence of the parallel existence of these three major ways of life, reflects some of the values of all of them.

This article will focus on the history of explicit medical ethics in prerepublican China. By "explicit medical ethics" is meant those norms allegedly present in interactions between medical practitioners and their clientele. The historian has no way of investigating whether norms, as they were expounded by various groups providing health care in China, actually formed the basis of these groups' actions; it is a well-documented fact that explicit ethics are usually far more rigid than the norms actually followed. One can only infer, then, the ethical norms proposed as an appropriate basis of the actual relationship between individual practitioner and patient in prerepublican China. Evidence of appeals to a code of ethics is extant only with respect to a few individuals. One cannot infer from the explicit ethics of a few practitioners the ethics of the whole group. Professional organizations of medical practitioners that might have attempted to enforce a single code of ethics were unknown in prerepublican China.

Historical sources allow for an understanding of the values regarding life and death contained in various ideologies propagated in China. These values, of course, have their immediate bearing on norms regarding the provision of healthcare and medical services. The historical sources further make possible an understanding of the relationship among various practitioner groups and between these groups and the general public. In addition, the historical material forces one to distinguish between traditional explicit medical ethics and modern explicit medical ethics. The former was characteristic of a period in history during which no group of independent practitioners achieved a place in the top ranks of the respective culture's social hierarchy; values dominant in society concerning life and death seem to have been quite stable during this epoch. One purpose of traditional explicit medical ethics, then, may be understood as an attempt by the medical group expounding it to demonstrate its continuous adherence and conformity to fixed, well-defined values.

Modern explicit medical ethics, in contradistinction, results from technologically based advances in Western medicine during recent decades. It represents an attempt to transform values into norms for new situations. The age-old values regarding life and death cannot simply be extended to the consequences of recent developments in healthcare. In contrast to the past, medical scientists in all modern societies work at the forefront of medical progress, and new norms, often representing differing values, have had to be created to cope with situations that formerly were inconceivable, for example, organ transplantation, allocation of scarce primary medical resources, and the maintenance of physiological functions in the terminal patient.

Although statements about medical practice and practitioners are found early in various branches of Chinese literature, the first lengthy and explicit statement on medical ethics of physicians, that of Sun Ssu-miao, appeared in the seventh century. The probable causes for the emergence of such statements at that time demand closer investigation. Medical practice, in whatever form it is carried out, represents a basic necessity for survival not only of the individual but also of the society. Although communities are known that severely restrict, or even totally deny, medical practice, on grounds of the religious beliefs they follow, one otherwise finds an active acceptance in all cultures known so far.

The utilization and the improvement of available primary medical resources (i.e., medical knowledge and skills, drugs and medical technology, medical equipment and facilities) may be viewed as an integral part of most cultures. The problematic variable is which segment of society utilizes and controls these primary medical resources. At the beginning of the Confucian era in China, about two thousand years ago, several groups already participated in the utilization and control of the primary medical resources then available. These resources included preventive and curative therapeutic strategies that derived from separately conceptualized understandings of health and illness. These included a metaphysical perspective concerning the origin of health and illness, which identified the influence of ancestors and demons as responsible for illness, and a naturalistic concept that focused on the relationship between humankind and its physical environment.

The ancestral paradigm is the earliest known conceptual response in China to the experience of illness and early death. It is documented in inscriptions on oracle bones dating back to the Shang dynasty (approximately from the eleventh century B.C.E. on). Even though this perspective lost its dominant position as an explanation of illness and for the design of strategies to prevent or cure illness by the middle of the first millennium B.C.E., it has survived in China until the present. Ancestral healing places living humans in a community with their ancestors, who, although dead, continue to exist. The ancestors guarantee the health of the living as long as the latter adhere to certain norms, and they send individual illness or social catastrophe when they notice a departure from these norms by an individual or society. Prayers and sacrifices by the living may cause the ancestors to withdraw their wrath and restore health or social harmony.

The ancestral paradigm was superseded during the period of the Warring States, in the middle of the first millennium B.C.E., by a belief in the power of demons (i.e., metaphysical entities not directly related to a living human being) to cause illness. Demons, it was assumed, will cause harm to a person regardless of that person's lifestyle; protection is achieved not by adherence to specific moral tenets but by alliances with the forces of stronger metaphysical entities, especially those of sun, moon, the stars, or thunder. Spells and talismans served to demonstrate these alliances and scare away demons in the lesser ranks of the supernatural hierarchy.

When in the early 1970s, a tomb sealed in 167 B.C.E. was unearthed near Changsha in the Chinese province of Hunan, the artifacts found included numerous texts related to healthcare and therapy. These manuscripts offer the earliest available evidence of the development, in ancient China, of a broad gamut of empirical therapeutic strategies, ranging from minor surgery and massage, dietary concerns and recommendations concerning sexual intercourse, to cauterization and, most prominently, elaborate pharmacotherapy. The resort to herbal, animal, and mineral drugs, as well as man-made substances, to cure and prevent illness remained the most important strategy in Chinese medicine until the twentieth century. Most of traditional Chinese medical literature consists of a long series of ever more comprehensive and sophisticated herbals discussing all possible facets of drug lore, and an even greater number of prescription collections, ranging from specialized treatises focusing on one problem to encyclopedic works. Inherent in the use of drugs against illness is an ontological notion that derives from demonologic beliefs. If they did not serve to cure symptoms such as pain or diarrhea, fever, and cough, drugs could kill intruders causing trouble in the organism. At about the time China was united in the second century B.C.E., a further approach to understanding health and illness found its way into medical literature: the ideology of systematic correspondence. Based on a dualistic paradigm of yin-yang and on a scheme of five phases, the entirety of observed phenomena in the human organism and its environment was seen as a system of interrelated, and hence corresponding, items and processes. A person remained healthy as long as he or she was able to live in accordance with the underlying laws of this system; departure resulted in illness. Healthcare on the basis of these ideas was not so much focused on the treatment of manifest diseases as on prevention and on intervention at the earliest signs of change from a perceived status of normalcy. This system of healthcare did not rely on drugs but on an application of needles meant to exert stimuli that serve to regulate imbalances. Nevertheless, the medicine of systematic correspondence also included strong ontological notions. On a more abstract level, if compared with pharmaceutics, the medicine of systematic correspondence harbored as one of its central notions an idea of "evil" entering the organism from the outside or being generated inside. This "evil" could be transmitted inside the body through a complicated system of conduits and network vessels, and had to be located in order to be purged or eliminated.

The theoretical framework and the terminology of the medicine of systematic correspondence closely paralleled the basic tenets and the language of the social theory of Confucianism. Health of the individual body was achieved by the same means as harmony of the social organism, that is, by adherence to specific moral rules. Deviance resulted in illness or social disorder. Just as no enemy was believed to be able to disturb society from within or to enter from outside as long as these rules were upheld, no illness could emerge in the body or be stimulated by an intrusion from the outside as long as an individual followed a specific lifestyle.

For this reason one may call the medicine of systematic correspondence *Confucian medicine*. Confucian medicine, into which the utilization of drugs was integrated in the twelfth century C.E., was successfully challenged as the officially sanctioned healing system only with the downfall of the imperial society early in the twentieth century.

At the beginning of the Confucian era in the second century B.C.E., medical practice appears to have been in the hands of a variety of practitioners following the principles of the different known medical sciences. In addition there were practitioners, such as a mother treating her child or a neighbor, who possessed and utilized primary medical resources regarded as empirically effective. One has to keep in mind, then, that there was no group with any degree of professionalism practicing medicine in China at that time. In other words, no group of medical practitioners can be said to have been close to having control over all primary medical resources that were available in China almost two thousand years ago.

While it may readily be assumed that the motivation for some people to practice medicine was to help a family member or friend, there is no way to investigate the motives and the actual ethical bases of those persons who chose medicine over any other occupation to earn a living or to exert a social impact. Chinese texts concerned with medical ethics, however, clearly indicate that the desire for control over secondary medical resources (i.e., material and nonmaterial rewards that accrue from medical practice, such as financial wealth or social influence) was a major determinant of the way in which medicine was practiced. At the beginning of the Confucian era, medical practitioners had little control over secondary medical resources. The evaluation of their practice depended on public opinion, that is, on the satisfaction of the laity.

During the following twenty centuries, various groups attempted to reach higher levels of professionalization, that is, to increase the proportion of their control over available primary and secondary medical resources at the expense of the public. One of the important means employed to achieve this end was the appeal to medical ethics (Unschuld, 1979).

Prior to the seventh century C.E., outside of the imperial court in China, no systematic attempt to teach practitioners in medical schools or similar institutions is known. In the first half of the seventh century, the establishment of medical teaching institutions both in the capital of the empire and in the most important provincial cities was decreed. This may be interpreted as an attempt by Confucian decision makers to preserve control over medical resources for the ruling class, the gentry-bureaucracy. The founding of these medical institutions reflects a basic tenet of Confucian ethics, the prevention of the accumulation by any one group in society of control over primary and secondary resources of any kind, which might result in a shift of power and possibly a social crisis or even change.

The underlying principle of many political decisions made in Confucian China was the suppression of emerging groups that had been able to gain control over specific resources. Medical resources were obviously recognized by

Confucian decision makers as potential sources of power if accumulated and controlled by specific groups. Several political measures were undertaken to prevent the emergence of socially accepted, influential groups of practitioners. One was to emphasize the unethical character of practicing medicine for a livelihood by pointing out the evil practices employed by those doing so. It was urged that every educated man should possess sufficient medical knowledge to be able to care for his relatives. Another means was to place all extrafamilial care in the hands of civil servant physicians who were representatives of the Confucian class. Thus, it is not surprising that the education of medical officers in the seventh century was designed to supplement the common basic Confucian education. This tendency was further strengthened during later centuries.

The first noteworthy text of medical ethics appeared during the period when the first medical schools began to produce graduates. The author, a noted physician named Sun Ssu-miao (581–682?), was heavily influenced by both Buddhist and Taoist thought. Despite the fact that he was also well versed in Confucian scholarship, he refused on several occasions to accept calls to serve at the court. Sun Ssu-miao may well be called an outstanding representative of free-practicing physicians outside the Confucian group. By "free-practicing physicians" we mean those practitioners who traveled or stayed at home and treated all kinds of patients, in contradistinction to those physicians who had acquired their knowledge solely to assist family members or friends in need, or to serve as civil servants on medical assignments. The fact that Sun Ssu-miao's explicit medical ethics appeared at the same time as the establishment of the medical schools might suggest that it was a well-timed presentation designed to expound to the public the medical ethics of the group he represented.

In his voluminous medical work Ch'ien-chin fang (The Thousand Golden Prescriptions), Sun Ssu-miao chose the heading "On the Absolute Sincerity of Great Physicians" for the chapter devoted to medical ethics. The selection of the term *ta-i* (great physician) implied on the one hand that Sun Ssu-miao did not intend to speak for all medical practitioners of his time, but only for those whom he regarded as "great." It is a common characteristic of medical professionalization in East and West that at some time or other a few individuals form an elitist group that attempts to distinguish itself from the mass of its colleagues through the demonstration of its exclusive possession of superior primary medical resources. It should also be noted that Sun Ssu-miao's choice of the term *ta-i* was meant to imply that his group had a status similar to that of the most highly regarded imperial court physicians, or *t'ai-i*. The Chinese characters for these

two terms are closely related in structure and meaning. Considering the low-ranking social position officially accorded to free-practicing physicians in Confucian China, the use of this title represented a bold demand for the social elevation of their elitist group of practitioners.

Sun Ssu-miao's treatise was meant to serve two purposes. First, by laying stress on the evaluation of treatment procedures rather than on the outcome of treatments, as was common at the time, he provided a measure of protection for the practitioner in instances where prognosis was unfavorable or outcome unsuccessful. The second purpose was to imply that his "great physicians" should be trusted more than was usually the case. As an introduction to his explicit medical ethics, Sun Ssu-miao provided his readers with a framework of the healing system he and other great physicians allegedly adhered to. It was based on the same theories and concepts that underlay the Confucian-supported medicine of systematic correspondence. Other writings of Sun Ssu-miao reveal, though, that he also favored demonic medicine, a healing system persistently repudiated by Confucians. In his explicit medical ethics, Sun Ssu-miao chose not to mention this aspect of his medical beliefs. He laid a great emphasis on thorough training for those who wish to practice medicine successfully and thus aspire to the title "great physician." Such tactics were important at that time, because the medical practitioners approved for governmental service were being institutionally trained in official medicine and were thus calling into question the background of free-practicing physicians.

It is characteristic of explicit medical ethics, as propounded by individuals who strive for a higher level of professionalism for their group, to incorporate the basic social values of the dominant groups in society. Therefore, Sun Ssu-miao's explicit ethics frequently stresses certain values central to Confucian and Buddhist thought, such as *jen* (humane benevolence) and *tz'u* (compassion). Furthermore, certain maxims are emphasized, for example, the obligation to maintain life and to treat human beings regardless of their status, origin, appearance, or the kind of disease they have.

Sun Ssu-miao seems to have grasped some important psychological aspects of the patient-physician relationship. He apparently realized that in order to gain the confidence of patients, and thus unlimited access to secondary medical resources, the physician must appear neutral and above normal human emotions, uncorrupted by even the most tempting worldly rewards.

One recognizes as well Sun Ssu-miao's sense of belonging to the larger group of medical practitioners when he points out the inappropriateness of abusing physician-colleagues in public. The detrimental effects of such short-sighted behavior, directed toward individual gain, have been recognized by the best minds of the East and West as impeding group professionalization. Thus, from the very beginning of explicit ethics in medicine, elements were incorporated that seem to have little to do with the actual performance of medical treatment and may be regarded as beneficial solely to the medical practitioners.

Finally, Sun Ssu-miao touched on the problem of remuneration. Greed seems to have been one of the gravest complaints raised by the public against practicing physicians. Many statements, promulgated by Confucian interests, expressed this view. If the public were to be convinced that at least the "great physicians" did not intend to cheat their patients, then another system of equitable remuneration had to be elaborated. Sun Ssu-miao referred to a saying of Lao-tzu (604–? B.C.E.), the founder of Taoism, to the effect that good deeds would certainly be rewarded by fellow humans and that evil practices would induce retaliation from the spirits. Thus Sun Ssu-miao approached both the Confucian ideal of virtue as its own reward in the continuation of one's name or fame in posterity and the Buddhist idea of reward or retaliation through supernatural forces, in either this or a later life (if not in another world).

The history of explicit medical ethics in China in the centuries following Sun Ssu-miao very much resembles a debate among three main groups. These were the free-practicing physicians (including Buddhists, Taoists, and others) in whose interest Sun Ssu-miao had spoken, the orthodox Confucians, and a group within Confucianism consisting of ordinary scholars (and at least part-time medical officials) who practiced medicine as a paid profession.

About 150 years after Sun Ssu-miao had published his ethics, Lu Chih (754–805), a well-known scholar from the top ranks of the Confucian bureaucratic hierarchy, made some statements on medical ethics that might be regarded as a direct answer to Sun Ssu-miao. He elaborated on the idea that medical knowledge, and the ability to practice medicine, must be regarded as open to everyone. The implication is that practitioners who specialized in medicine would become superfluous. Lu Chih also chastised those who practiced medicine for living in a manner characterized by greed and evil, and noted that they did so without suffering any kind of retaliation. This observation put Sun Ssu-miao's system of retribution in question. However, Lu Chih also pointed out that those who had practiced medicine without undue concern for material gain but, rather, as an obvious consequence of their concern for humanity had been rewarded one or two generations later, through the happiness and prosperity enjoyed by their children and grandchildren.

Lu Chih closed his remarks with an open critique of Taoist and magical practitioners, among whom Confucian historians counted Sun Ssu-miao. At the beginning of the thirteenth century a Confucian scholar-physician named Chang Kao published twelve short stories concerning medical ethics. While decrying the non-Confucian practitioners as "common physicians," Chang Kao recognized the need to allay the fears of orthodox Confucians, who were always suspicious of attempts to gain control over specialized resources.

In his stories, entitled "Retribution for Medical Services," Chang Kao conspicuously resorted to Buddhist concepts of reward and retaliation by forces of another world. These stories center on four major dimensions of medical ethics: greed vs. altruism; exploitation of sexual opportunities; conscientiousness in medical practice; and the problem of abortion.

The last is of special interest because other medical authors showed little concern over the practice of abortion. Relevant prescriptions are frequently provided in major collections. During the reign of the Mongol Yuan dynasty (1260–1367) an official decree prohibited unqualified women from performing abortions. Chang Kao's exceptional handling of this problem was certainly based on his adherence to Buddhist principles. The structure of his entire message seems highly psychological. In the first story, Chang Kao extolled the use of primary medical resources as an appropriate way to gain merit by giving assistance to others. In the second story, he recounted an example of very laudable behavior of a Confucian scholar-physician designed to reinforce confidence in that group. The third through the tenth stories portrayed the decay of morals and depicted examples of many "evil" practices (among them abortion) performed by physicians and others who openly practiced for money with the ulterior motive of cheating the patients. All of these characters received their proper punishment through the actions of gods, spirits, or demons. The last two stories again helped to create confidence in the group to which Chang Kao belonged.

About one century later Ko Ch'ien-sun (fl. 1348), a free-practicing physician, made an ethical statement that was somewhat different from others. In contrast to Confucian ethics, which stressed the study of literature, he emphasized the necessity of gathering clinical knowledge at the bedside as a prerequisite of the well-versed practitioner. Ko Ch'ien-sun departed even farther from official medicine in stating that the origin of his miraculously effective prescriptions rested with a supernatural being who had handed them to him and they were not, in fact, derived from concepts and theories of nature underlying Confucian medicine. Ko Ch'ien-sun is mentioned here as only one example of the vast heterogeneity often overlooked in Chinese traditional medicine.

Most interesting in Ko Ch'ien-sun's statements was the emphasis placed on the outcome of his own practice and the paucity of details concerning his treatment procedure. His reversion to outcome evaluation and other such evidence reminds one that ethical statements found in the literature cannot be taken as representative of the medical group as a whole. It must be assumed that they represent the views of a progressive minority, where "progressive" means an intention to increase professional control over the resources available in society.

In 1522, Yü Pien wrote an interesting modification of the orthodox Confucian claim that everyone ought to possess medical knowledge. Speaking for the group of practicing physicians, he stated that not everyone needed to have medical abilities but that those who called on "common physicians" for assistance could not be regarded as showing sufficient filial piety, and added that medical knowledge was imperative for those who wished to assist their relatives. This very cautious, almost paradoxical, statement may be interpreted as an attempt to legitimize free-practicing Confucian physicians and at the same time to discourage the public from resorting to practitioners outside the Confucian sphere of influence.

New dimensions were incorporated into medical ethics by Kung Hsin, who lived around 1580, and by his son Kung T'ing-hsien (fl. 1625), both of whom had been imperial court physicians. Kung Hsin explicitly rejected patient solicitation, a practice common in China in his time and later. Patient solicitation implies that a particular physician may be better than at least some of his peers. The awareness of differences in standards of performance necessarily leads to public distrust of the group as a whole and, therefore, constitutes an obstacle to further professionalism. Only where the notion predominates that all members of the practitioner group are alike in their standards of performance will there be confidence among potential clientele.

Kung T'ing-hsien, the son, wrote short treatises entitled "Ten Maxims for Physicians" and "Ten Maxims for Patients." In the first of these he underlined the mastery of Confucian knowledge as a prerequisite for medical practice, a point his father had not explicitly mentioned. In his ethical prescriptions for patients, Kung T'ing-hsien demanded that they resort only to "enlightened physicians," willingly take their medicines, start treatment early, avoid sexual intercourse, refrain from belief in heterodox medical resources (i.e., not Confucian-sanctioned), and not worry over medical expenditures. This last point was underscored with the familiar

rhetorical question "I ask you what is more valuable to you: your life or your property?"

Ch'en Shih-kung (fl. 1605) also belonged to the free-practicing group of Confucian physicians. He was the first known Chinese physician to suggest that such persons as prostitutes could be treated without risking defamation. Ch'en Shih-kung also offered his colleagues what may be the first investment counsel for physicians when he advised them to invest excess capital in real estate and not to spend money in unethical places like wine houses. His profound sense of belonging to a larger group led Ch'en Shih-kung to urge his peers not only to avoid open criticism of each other but also actively to display benevolent loyalty among themselves despite differences in training and opinion. Finally, he elaborated upon the prohibition of patient solicitation. He counseled that it was inappropriate for physicians to give extravagant presents or costly dinner invitations to other people. His remarks represent a most pragmatic view of medical ethics (Lee). The progress in professionalization that becomes evident through the claims made in explicit medical ethics reached its peak at the end of the era of imperial China. Hsü Yen-tso (fl. 1895), the last author to be cited in this regard, followed the trend when he offered advice to both physicians and patients. He held that in order for a practitioner to maintain a proper level of morality, he was obliged to treat anyone who requested help, regardless of social or financial status; to provide conscientious treatments; to show extreme sincerity; and to respond to any call as soon as possible. In a statement regarding the patient-physician relationship he reminded his colleagues that patients await the arrival of the practitioner as if he were a supernatural being, like the Buddha himself. From this perspective it is not surprising that he asked patients to place themselves entirely in the hands of the practitioners. He demanded that patients have no secrets; that they bind themselves permanently to the physician, not only temporarily in case of an emergency; and that they be isolated from their normal social environment during treatment. The last stricture was possibly meant to prevent discussion of the case and the treatment provided, and had the effect of precluding criticism or interference from outsiders. Thus, at the end of the era of Confucianism, control by a specialized group over medical resources had progressed to a stage incompatible with the original Confucian maxims.

PAUL U. UNSCHULD (1995)
BIBLIOGRAPHY REVISED

BIBLIOGRAPHY

Doring, Ole. 2002. *Advances in Chinese Medical Ethics: Chinese and International Perspectives*. London: RoutledgeCurzon.

Guo, Z. 1995. "Chinese Confucian Culture and the Medical Ethical Tradition." *Journal of Medical Ethics* 21(4): 239–246.

Harper, Donald. 1990. "The Conception of Illness in Early Chinese Medicine as Documented in Newly Discovered 3rd and 2nd Century B.C. Manuscripts (Part I)." *Sudhoffs Archiv* 74(2): 210–235.

Jonsen, Albert R. 2000. "Medical Ethics of India and China" In *A Short History of Medical Ethics,* pp. 27–42. New York: Oxford University Press.

Lee, T'ao. 1943. "Medical Ethics in Ancient China." *Bulletin of the History of Medicine* 13: 268–277.

Needham, Joseph. 1970a. "China and the Origin of Qualifying Examinations in Medicine." In *Clerks and Craftsmen in China and the West: Lectures and Addresses in the History of Science and Technology,* pp. 379–395. Cambridge, Eng.: Cambridge University Press.

Needham, Joseph. 1970b. "Medicine and Chinese Culture." In *Clerks and Craftsmen in China and the West: Lectures and Addresses in the History of Science and Technology,* pp. 263–293. Cambridge, Eng.: Cambridge University Press.

Nie, Jing Bao. 2000. "The Plurality of Chinese and American Medical Moralities: Toward an Interpretive Cross-Cultural Bioethics." *Kennedy Institute of Ethics Journal* 10(3): 239–260.

Qiu, Ren-Zong. 1988. "Medicine—The Art of Humaneness: On Ethics of Traditional Chinese Medicine." *Journal of Medicine and Philosophy* 13: 277–300.

Unschuld, Paul U. 1979. *Medical Ethics in Imperial China: A Study in Historical Anthropology.* Berkeley: University of California Press.

Unschuld, Paul U. 1985. *Medicine in China. A History of Ideas.* Berkeley: University of California Press.

Unschuld, Paul U. 1986. *Medicine in China. A History of Pharmaceutics.* Berkeley: University of California Press.

Tsai, D. F. 1999. "Ancient Chinese Medical Ethics and the Four Principles of Biomedical Ethics." *Journal of Medical Ethics* 25(4): 315–321.

Ware, James, ed. and tr. 1966. *Alchemy, Medicine, Religion in the China of A.D. 320: The Nei Pan of Ko Hung (Pao-pu tzu).* Cambridge, MA: MIT Press.

Yü, Ying-shih. 1964–1965. "Life and Immortality in the Mind of Han China." *Harvard Journal of Asiatic Studies* 25: 80–122.

Zhang, Daqing, and Cheng, Zhifan. 2000. "Medicine Is a Humane Art: The Basic Principles of Professional Ethics in Chinese Medicine." *Hastings Center Report* 30(4): S8–S12.

III. CHINA. B. CONTEMPORARY CHINA

Republican Period (1912–1949)

In January 1912, after decades of social upheaval and a failed struggle to achieve a constitutional government, the Qing dynasty, which had ruled China since 1644, collapsed and the Republic of China was inaugurated, with Sun Yat-sen (1866–1925) as its first president. Although the Republic was enmeshed in constant political and social turmoil, a strong movement of visionary intellectuals pressed for the modernization of Chinese life in all its aspects. While many reformers called for the wholesale abolition of Chinese culture and customs, others sought to blend Western political forms and scientific technology with what they saw as "the essence of Chinese culture." The Chinese attitude toward medicine during most of the twentieth century has been formed by these conflicts.

Western medicine had achieved recognition, principally among the elite but to some extent in the general population, during the latter decades of the nineteenth and first years of the twentieth centuries, largely due to the influence of Christian missionary physicians and nurses, and the hospitals they maintained. The effectiveness of the Northern Manchuria Plague Prevention Service, organized along Western lines to combat the 1910–1911 epidemic of pneumonic plague in Manchuria, heightened the prestige of Western medicine, particularly in its preventive and public-health aspects. (It was on the occasion of this epidemic that two practices abhorrent to Confucian morality, cremation and autopsy, were permitted by imperial edict.) This service was the first, and the prototype, public-health service in China (Wu). Peking Union Medical College, founded in 1915 with support from the Rockefeller Foundation, became the center of medical science and education in the Western mode. Although only a tiny segment of China's doctors practiced Western medicine, they attained positions of influence in government, education, and circles of intellectual reform. In 1914, Minister of Education Wang Daxie told a delegation of traditional physicians, "I have decided to abolish Chinese medicine" (Croizier, p. 69). In the next few decades, eighty-nine Western-style medical schools were established, and thousands of Western-trained students graduated. Although this development was frequently interrupted by wars and civil unrest, the values of modern medicine gradually took root in the Chinese soil, where they grew in uneasy association with traditional values.

The abolition of traditional medicine, however, much desired by reformers and government, was not a simple matter. Three times the Republican central government attempted to abandon traditional medicine and prohibit its practice, but each time it met with strong resistance. In 1913, the central government promulgated regulations that excluded the teaching of traditional medicine from the curriculum. In reaction, some intellectuals insisted that traditional medicine could be made more scientific and even integrated with Western medicine. They also noted that traditional doctors were likely to be the only sources of care for most people for many years to come. In 1929 Yu Yan, a physician and an official of the Ministry of Health, outlined administrative measures to curb and eventually abolish the practice of traditional medicine: traditional doctors were to be reeducated and were not allowed to organize schools or to advertise. Traditional doctors responded by organizing the first national association, the Institute for National Medicine (1931), with the goal of protecting and promoting traditional medicine. Even this group, however, affirmed that traditional medicine must be made more scientific, advocating research on the pharmacological basis of the thousands of drugs used in Chinese medicine.

Nevertheless, during the 1930s almost all Western-trained physicians refused to compromise and adamantly rejected traditional medicine. Westernizing authors, physicians and nonphysicians alike, argued that traditional medicine was unscientific, as different from Western medicine as astrology from astronomy, geomancy from geometry, alchemy from chemistry. Efforts to make traditional medicine more scientific or to ally the philosophical views of traditional medicine to the scientific principles of modern medicine were repudiated as nothing more than another example of the reactionary conservativism that had harnessed Chinese life for centuries. Such proposals were called "ignorant, nonsensical, blind, babbling." In the harsh words of one prominent physician, "Why should modern medicine accept this marriage proposal from such a lazy, stupid wife with bound feet wrapped in yards of smelly bandages?" (Croizier, p. 107). In 1933, the president of the Executive Department of the central government, Wang Jingwei, declared any discussion of yin yang or the five elements without anatomical dissection scientifically untenable, and the therapeutic efficacy of unanalyzed drugs doubtful. With his support, licensing authority over all physicians, Western or traditional, was located in the modernized Ministry of Health, thus holding traditional practitioners to standards they could hardly meet. Even so, attempts to abolish the practice of traditional medicine failed in the end. In 1949, 65 percent of all physicians practiced traditional medicine. The uneasy relationship between Western and traditional medicine would continue into the era of the People's Republic.

MEDICAL ETHICS. *Ethics of Medical Practice* (1933), by the Western-trained physician Song Guo-Bin (1893–1956), might be called the first modern book on Chinese medical ethics. The author sought to integrate Western medical ethics with traditional ethics drawn from Confucianism. Ethics is the *tao*—path or way and, by extension, principle or reality—of practicing medicine, and is constituted by the Confucian concepts of humaneness and righteousness. Song defined humaneness as the Western concept of fraternity, and righteousness as what is appropriately done in compliance with humaneness. Physicians should have a spirit of love for people and a zeal to do good. The principle of humaneness requires physicians to treat poor patients at no charge when necessary; the principle of righteousness requires physicians to be competent, not to do harm, not to take advantage of the patient's vulnerability for their own benefit, not to experiment uselessly, and not to practice favoritism. On the moral character of physicians, Song followed his predecessors, emphasizing the right ordering of one's thoughts and feelings and the right ordering of one's world: the physician who is not ordered in body and spirit can hardly order the body and spirit of his patient. The physician should have the virtues of diligence, devotion, warmheartedness, and dignity. The responsibility of the physician to the patient is to treat disease, promote health, and relieve suffering. Song was the first Chinese medical ethicist to argue systematically for the obligation of confidentiality, although he recognized that this obligation is not unconditional. The patient's consent to disclosure, possible harm to others, or the legitimate needs of criminal justice release the physician from confidentiality. Among colleagues, physicians should respect self and others, and should maintain a friendly feeling and a modest attitude. The obligation of the physician to the state and society is prevention of disease and death, applying remedial measures, research on the cause of death, and the support of public charities. Song rejected contraception and abortion as immoral. Although Song's volume was known principally within the academic world, it was acknowledged as the standard statement of ethics for modern Chinese medicine. In contrast to Song's ethical idealism, the life of the woman physician Yang Chongrui (1891–1956) represents ethics in practice. After graduating from Peking Union Medical College in 1917, she went to the countryside as one of the first Chinese physicians to bring modern medicine to the peasants, in accord with her personal maxim, "Sacrifice in order to benefit the people." She established the first school of midwifery in China and, at the end of her life, was chief of the Bureau of Maternal and Child Health. She is one of the heroines of Chinese medicine and is often cited as the ideal physician.

People's Republic Period (1949-)

On October 1, 1949, the People's Republic of China came into being, a "people's democratic dictatorship" based on Marxist principles as interpreted for China by Mao Zedong. This event marked a radical break with Chinese tradition, which, based on Confucianism, had long been in decline and was considered by the new rulers to be incompatible with progress in a revolutionary society. Medicine and healthcare were to be thoroughly modernized, first on the Soviet model and later in harmony with indigenous practices. Medical ethics was to be reformulated to serve politico-ideological work performed by healthcare providers.

The availability of healthcare to the whole Chinese population was a major goal of the People's Republic, and remarkable successes were achieved, given the resources available. From the beginning, Chairman Mao took a personal interest in policies that would improve personal and public health. Statistics for life expectancy for the population as a whole and for newborns in particular were greatly improved over those of other Third World countries, and approached the statistics of developed countries. Many endemic infectious diseases, such as cholera, smallpox, and plague, as well as many nutritional diseases, were brought under control.

HEALTHCARE IN RURAL AREAS. The first national conference on healthcare was held in August 1950. Policies that would govern healthcare were announced: they were designed to respond to the needs of workers, peasants, and soldiers; to emphasize prevention; to effect cooperation between Western and traditional medicine. Soon thereafter, the policy of mass movements was added, that is, highly organized and rapid campaigns to eradicate filth and pests and to instill habits of good health and exercise. For the first time in Chinese history, affordable and competent healthcare became available to millions of laboring people and peasants.

In June 1964, Mao Zedong issued "Instruction on Putting Stress on the Rural Areas in Health Care," in which he criticized the existing healthcare system for its elitist and urban orientation. Urban practitioners, even scientific researchers, were sent to the countryside to practice and to train the public-health workers known popularly as "barefoot doctors." The implementation of this instruction did much to promote healthcare in the rural areas; nevertheless, at the end of the twentieth century, much remains to be done and, indeed, some deterioration has occurred. At the same time, these policies were detrimental to medical education and to scientific advances in medicine and healthcare.

TRADITIONAL AND MODERN MEDICINE. In the early years of the People's Republic, Marxist thought clearly favored modern scientific medicine and labeled traditional medicine as reactionary. Western medicine, however, was viewed as capitalist and imperialist. A realistic assessment of the need for healthcare made it clear that all available resources, including traditional medicine, had to be engaged in the vast work of bringing care to the masses. Mao Zedong issued "An Instruction on the Work of Traditional Chinese Medicine" (1954) ordering the integration of traditional and Western medicine into a unified new medicine. In research, education, and care, efforts were made to bring these two forms of medicine together. In *united clinics,* both sorts of practice were encouraged, Western-trained physicians were required to study traditional techniques, and many large hospitals had sections for Western and for traditional treatment. A document of 1958 stated, "The objective is … a new type of doctor, versed in both Chinese and Western medicines, and one who has acquired communist consciousness under the leadership of the Party committees" (Croizier, p. 185). The ancient practice of acupuncture, for example, was applied to surgical anaesthesia. Reports of this experiment stimulated great interest in acupuncture throughout the world (Risse).

Official policy now favors the coexistence and competition between traditional Chinese medicine and modern or Western medicine, and the integration of these two into a new medicine (Qiu, 1982). Now the debate focuses on whether traditional medicine should be taught in its pure form, which would make it difficult to attract young people, or whether it should be modernized, leaving an uncertainty about what it would then offer. By 1987, the number of traditional physicians had declined to 279,000, while the number of modern physicians had risen to 1,132,000, 80 percent of all physicians. A 1986 survey showed that only 7 percent of respondents depended exclusively on traditional physicians.

HUMAN EXPERIMENTATION. Traditional medicine had no place for human experimentation in the modern sense; research came to China with Western medicine. In the 1950s, the government revealed that during the 1930s and 1940s, some foreign and Chinese physicians at Peking Union Medical College had used poor patients as experimental subjects without their informed consent. One such experiment, done by the American physician Richard Lyman in 1936, involved filming drug-induced seizures of healthy rickshaw drivers, who had been paid the equivalent of two U.S. dollars. This film was shown publicly with sensational effect during the "Ideological Transformation" of 1951–1952 and again during the Cultural Revolution. Since that revelation, many health officials and members of the public have been hostile to human experimentation. As a result, some insufficiently developed or inefficacious therapies became widely available without adequate human testing. In the 1950s, for example, during the movement known as "Learning from the Soviet Union," Vladimir Filatov's tissue therapy, in which human or animal tissues were inserted under the skin as a "biogen" for the cure of a great variety of diseases, was widely used with some fatal results. At the same time, some medical researchers used themselves as subjects for herbal medicines or new drugs and died of poisoning. After 1980, the method of clinical pharmacological trials was introduced into China, together with the principle of informed consent. Institutional review boards to provide oversight began to be set up at the request of foreign groups sponsoring research in China, although as of 1993 there is no universal governmental regulation of research.

MEDICAL ETHICS. During the early years of the People's Republic, Mao Zedong's writings were required reading for every Chinese. In the field of healthcare all medical personnel were required to read his essays "In Memory of Dr. Norman Bethune" and "Serve the People," in which Chairman Mao urged the people to cultivate their moral character in terms of the values of life and death. When one died for the people, he argued, it was a worthy death, weightier than Tai Mountain; otherwise, it was lighter than a feather of the wild goose, as Chinese ancient historian Sima Qian put it. Mao held up as an exemplar for healthcare workers the Canadian physician Norman Bethune (1888–1939), who dedicated himself to the care of Chinese soldiers and civilians during Japan's war against China (1937–1945), praising him as a virtuous person, selflessly committed to those in need, conscientious in his work, warmhearted toward all people, and continually improving his skills. The essay on Bethune was viewed as an incomparable formulation of medical ethics during the Maoist era. Contemporary Chinese bioethics can be dated from 1979, when a conference on the philosophy of medicine, sponsored by the Chinese Society for Dialectics of Nature and the China Association of Science and Technology, was held in Guangzhou. Philosophers, physicians, and health administrators who attended this conference focused on two issues in medical ethics: the concept of death and the justifiability of euthanasia, and the delivery of healthcare without discrimination. The latter problem arose because the Cultural Revolution's emphasis on serving workers, peasants, and soldiers led to discrimination in healthcare services against persons labeled *capitalists* and *bourgeois reactionaries,* and to deaths of well-known persons as the result of negligence (Cai).

Until the 1980s, the discussion of medical ethics was confined to academic circles, specialized journals, and conferences on philosophy of medicine. Two journals, *Medicine and Philosophy* and *Chinese Journal of Medical Ethics,* appeared in the early years of the decade. In 1986 and 1987, however, two legal cases, one on active euthanasia and the other on artificial insemination by donor (AID), drew the attention of lawyers, journalists, policymakers, legislators, and the general public. The first two National Conferences on Philosophy of Medicine and Medical Ethics, devoted to

social, ethical, and legal issues in euthanasia and in reproductive technology, were held in July and November 1988. The Chinese Society for Medical Ethics was established in 1988 and affiliated with the Chinese Medical Association. During the decade, most medical universities and colleges, as well as nursing schools, instituted required or elective courses on medical ethics. The curriculum includes study of the moral tradition, medicine in society, the patient-physician relationship, euthanasia, genetics, experimentation, reproduction, and health policy. Dozens of books on medical ethics were published, including Zhi-Zeng Du's *An Outline of Medical Ethics* (1985) and Ren-Zong Qiu's *Bioethics* (1987). Teachers of medical ethics, drawn from philosophy and medicine faculties, were trained in doctoral and master's programs and in special workshops.

DEATH AND EUTHANASIA. During the Cultural Revolution, the concept of brain death was criticized as "bourgeois, capitalist and reactionary," created by "Western doctors ... to unscrupulously open up a source for organ transplantation" (Jiang et al., p. 225). In fact, the problem of brain death arose not so much because or organ transplantation, which is not widespread in China, but because respiratory support was increasingly being employed for terminally ill persons. This was considered both futile for the individual and wasteful of health resources. At the 1988 conference on euthanasia, all participants, including physicians, ethicists, and lawyers, endorsed the concept of brain death, following guidelines widely accepted in Western countries, such as the Harvard criteria (Qiu, 1982). As of 1993, however, no administrative or legislative rules legalize the definition of death by brain criteria. As modern techniques for life support, such as ventilation, dialysis, and artificial nutrition, have become more common, particularly in urban hospitals, the problem of their appropriate ethical use has been noted. Academic discussion of euthanasia has centered on how it might be identified as a special modality of death differentiated from natural death, accidental death, suicide, murder, and manslaughter. Ancient Chinese physicians were aware of the limits of medicine and asserted that when disease attacks the vital organs, it is beyond cure. Passive euthanasia for the terminally ill, long a part of traditional Chinese medicine, has been extended without qualm to the irreversibly comatose, seriously defective newborns, and very-low-birth-weight infants. At the 1988 conference, ethicists argued for the justifiability of euthanasia on the basis of the principles of beneficence, respect for autonomy, and justice. In the resolution passed at the conference, participants endorsed the right of terminally ill persons to choose the way of dying and encouraged the use of living wills. These principles and practices, while borrowed from U.S. bioethics, are compatible with the Confucian concept of *humaneness*. Other deeply embedded Chinese attitudes influence thought on this subject. For example, euthanasia for the defective newborn is rendered more acceptable in view of Buddhist beliefs that such an infant must have failed in virtue in a previous life, while Confucian filial piety often causes reluctance to allow one's parents and the elderly to die (Qiu, 1980).

Active euthanasia, however, remains a subject of debate. In 1986, in Hanzhong, Shaanxi Province, two children of a comatose woman suffering from liver cirrhosis asked physicians to end her life by an overdose of morphine, without informing their siblings. The legal case brought against them evoked widespread media discussion. After their conviction on murder charges, they appealed to the Supreme Court, which in 1991 ruled that the defendants were not guilty since the harm to the decedent was minor in view of her inevitable death. Several surveys in 1986 and 1988 showed that the majority of respondents accept passive euthanasia, and even active euthanasia in certain circumstances.

REPRODUCTIVE TECHNOLOGY. Under the influence of the Confucian view of the importance of having a male successor to carry on the ancestors' lineage, infertile couples experience heavy psychological and moral pressure. In a traditional family, the woman is often blamed for the infertility of the couple and stigmatized or abused. Eagerness for offspring is stimulating the development of reproductive technology that replaces the traditional customs of "wife borrowing" and, among the wealthy, concubinage. At the 1988 conference on social, ethical, and legal issues in reproductive technology, artificial insemination by husband (AIH) and by donor (AID) were asserted to be widely practiced among the population. Sperm banks existed in eleven provinces, most of them without procedures to address ethical and legal issues. Except for a few centers in large cities, AID is undertaken without policies relating to the selection of donors and recipients, and the legal status of the child remains unresolved. The clash of traditional values and modern society was manifested in the first legal case involving reproductive technology, in which a Shanghai family refused to accept a baby boy conceived by donor sperm. In some clinics, prenatal sex selection has been practiced. The participants in the 1988 conference argued against it on the grounds that it could worsen the sex imbalance and cause negative social consequences. In the following year, the Ministry of Health prohibited the practice. In vitro fertilization (IVF) is limited to a few centers.

FAMILY PLANNING. In the early years of the People's Republic, China's enormous population and its prospect for

continuous growth were recognized as a serious threat to all the social and economic gains expected from the modernization. During the 1950s, limitations on childbirth were encouraged by mass propaganda and contraceptive education. In 1980 the government announced an official policy of "one couple, one child" (the census of 1982 showed China's population had surpassed 1 billion people). This policy has caused thorny ethical problems. Although there is widespread agreement that control of population growth and limitation of reproductive freedom are ethically justifiable in view of China's vast and growing population, argument continues over whether "one couple, one child" is the best policy and over the means employed to implement it. Not only does it conflict with the traditional value that associates more children with better fortune; it also imposes significant hardships on families in rural areas, where labor needs and the care of elderly parents require several children. A 1979 survey by the Chinese Society of Sociology found that a majority of peasants in the villages near cities want two or more children, whereas the majority of respondents in cities are satisfied with one child. The one-child policy is implemented by intensive contraceptive education, by economic incentives and penalties, by sterilization (sometimes compulsory), and by abortion (sometimes coerced). Although population-control programs are officially designed as programs of incentives, education, and persuasion, the line between persuasion and coercion is not always clear, and the efforts of zealous officials in some places have clearly crossed the line. Again, the policy is most burdensome on dwellers in rural areas, where contraceptive services are often inadequate and local officials, under pressure from above, may employ abusive means. In recent years, reports of compulsory sterilization and coerced abortion have convinced certain international agencies and foreign governments to withhold financial support for population-control efforts in China.

Traditionally abortion has not been seen as a serious ethical issue in China. Most Chinese would agree with the ancient sage, Xun Kuang (286–238 B.C.E.), who argued that human life begins at birth; abortion (and contraception) were rarely discussed in pretwentieth-century medical literature, even in treatises on gynecology. Today, however, repeated and late abortions do arouse concern among healthcare workers and ethicists. Unmarried women who become pregnant often seek a late abortion. Late abortion puts physicians in a dilemma, since it involves a conflict between obligation to the health of the patient, due to the dangers of late abortion, and obligation to the society to limit births. Finally, the socially imposed limits on reproduction and the desire for male offspring have encouraged some, especially in rural areas, to revive the ancient practice of female infanticide. This practice, long judged immoral by many commentators, such as the great philosopher Han Fei (third century B.C.E.), has always been abetted by the widespread and deep poverty of the peasants, for whom a girl child was a burden rather than a benefit. Condemned as criminal by the Law Protecting Women's Rights passed by the National People's Congress in 1992, this practice remains difficult to detect and to prosecute.

REFORM OF THE HEALTHCARE SYSTEM. Since the founding of the People's Republic in 1949, the healthcare system of China has consisted of four main components: workers' healthcare in state-owned factories or institutions; public medical service; free preventive immunization; and rural cooperative medical service. In all but the free preventive service, the costs of care are funded by the government, by employer/cooperative contributions, and by a small registration fee (typically less than the equivalent of ten cents per visit, although the fee can be graduated up to about one dollar if the patient wishes to see a professor in an academic hospital). The self- or privately employed must pay the full cost of their care. These programs have extended healthcare far more widely than ever before in China's history and have significantly improved the health of the population. Throughout most of China, patients have access to well-organized health services, provided by many levels of professionals at little cost.

Despite such progress, however, programs have faced major problems: the demand for treatment always exceeds the supply; ordinary people often receive less adequate care than officials; and almost all hospitals suffer large deficits, making renovation and replacement of equipment impossible. Since the implementation of a 1980 policy to dismantle the cooperative farms, the rural medical services have deteriorated and, in some poor rural areas, health care is not accessible to villagers. The government's most recent efforts to reform the healthcare system involve implementing the contract system that has proven successful in agriculture. In this way, hospitals can supplement their government budget by increasing fees for registration, tests, and drugs, after approval from the local Bureau for Prices. A portion of these increases will be paid by the patient and the remainder by the factories and institutions for which they work. Since 1988, economists, ethicists, health administrators, and officials of the Ministry of Health have argued over whether it is ethically justifiable to consider healthcare a market commodity.

PROFESSIONAL ETHICS CODE. In December 1988, the Ministry of Health promulgated an ethics code for medical personnel that consists of seven articles: (1) rescue the dying and heal the injured, carry out socialist humanitarianism, always keep the patient's interest in mind, treat disease and relieve suffering by every possible means; (2) respect the patient's person and rights, treat patients as equals without discrimination on the basis of nationality, sex, position, social status, and financial situation; (3) serve patients conscientiously and politely, deport oneself in a dignified manner, speak to patients in a refined manner, be amiable, care for patients with compassion, concern, and solicitude; (4) be honest in performing one's duties, conscientiously observe discipline and law, do not serve selfish interests with medicine; (5) maintain confidentiality for patients, saying nothing that would harm the patient or reveal the patient's secrets; (6) deal properly with the relationship between colleagues and coworkers, learning from each other and holding each other in respect; (7) be rigorous and dependable in work, vigorous in spirit and eager to make progress, endeavor to improve professional proficiency, continuously renew knowledge, and increase technical competence.

This is the first code of ethics promulgated in the People's Republic of China, although the Chinese Medical Association had published a very brief seven-article "Doctor's Creed" in 1937 (Wang). While the new code is quite similar to medical codes around the world, it should be noted that "respect for the patient's person and rights" does not directly translate into the Western concepts of autonomy and informed consent. While it is now much more common to inform patients fully and to allow them to choose the course of therapy, older paternalistic practices, such as refraining from telling patients their diagnosis and depending on families and even work units for decisions about a patient's care, still prevail. In China, "informed consent with the aid of family and community" might more accurately express the ethical standard.

COMPULSORY STERILIZATION OF THE MENTALLY RETARDED. A regulation for compulsory sterilization of the severely mentally retarded, promulgated in Gansu Province in 1988, specified that mentally retarded persons are to be sterilized when (1) retardation is caused by familial genetic factors, inbreeding, or other congenital factors; (2) the IQ is below 49; and (3) there is behavioral disability in language, memory, orientation, and thinking. Persons who meet these criteria are permitted to marry only after they have been sterilized. Women who meet the criteria and are pregnant must undergo abortion and be sterilized (Lei et al.). Other provinces, following Gansu's lead, drafted similar regulations on compulsory sterilization, while others were more cautious, incorporating sterilization into their comprehensive regulations on family planning. Proponents of such regulation argue that the proportion of mentally retarded persons in the population is too high, that the burden to support them is too heavy, and that the heavy burden has seriously impeded social development and will influence future generations.

At a 1992 national workshop on ethical and legal issues in limiting procreation, participants pointed out that genetic factors play only a minor role in the epidemiology of mental retardation and that data on the incidence, prevalence, and etiology of the mentally retarded population are of variable reliability and subject to widely differing interpretations. Conference participants argued that if the goal is to reduce the mentally retarded population, only those whose mental retardation is known to be caused by genetic factors should be selected for sterilization—a policy requiring an adequate number of medical geneticists to perform genetic tests and identify the causal factors of mental retardation. The effort to reduce the incidence of mental retardation should focus on improving perinatal care and maternal and child care, developing prenatal diagnosis and genetic counseling, preventing inbreeding, and implementing programs of community development. When sterilization is recommended, it should be in the best interest of the retarded person, as a contraceptive measure that reduces personal misfortune; proxy consent should be obtained. Also, it was argued that the relatively high proportion of mentally retarded persons is not a cause of economic underdevelopment, but an effect of it. From the legal perspective, compulsory sterilization infringes upon some civil rights laid down in the Constitution and other Chinese laws, such as the right to inviolability of the person and the right to guardianship for the incompetent. The considerations raised by the 1992 workshop were delivered to the government and apparently have impeded the expansion of compulsory laws. However, existing laws have not been repealed or revised, and there is no strong public protest against them.

CONTROLLING THE SPREAD OF SEXUALLY TRANSMITTED DISEASES. As a result of a major health campaign in the early years of the People's Republic, the incidence of sexually transmitted diseases in the Chinese population was drastically reduced through a combination of medical, educational, and social policies (sometimes quite harsh, particularly against prostitutes). After three decades of dormancy, sexually transmitted diseases (STD) began to rise in the 1980s: from 1980 to 1992, some 700,000 cases of STD were reported (the actual number is probably much higher), including about 1,000 persons who have tested positive for infection with human immunodeficiency virus (HIV). Countermeasures have been taken in recent years to check the epidemic of STD, and several laws, ranging from management and surveillance to prohibition of drug trafficking and prostitution, have been enacted. However, programs for controlling STD are inhibited by several factors. One is the revival of an ancient concept in which disease is seen as punishment for misbehavior instead of being caused by a particular microorganism. Sexually transmitted disease is sometimes called "Heaven's punishment for moral deterioration." The Chinese National Expert Committee on acquired immunodeficiency syndrome (AIDS) attempts to counter this view in "An Open Letter to Medical Care Workers," asserting, "The disease is not the punishment to an individual, but a common enemy to the whole of mankind.... Every medical-care worker ought to be full of love in the heart, and help our compatriots who are threatened by AIDS with our hands and knowledge" (National Expert Committee, p. 1). The second factor is discrimination against patients and infringement upon their individual rights. HIV-positive persons have been expelled from their jobs or schools; AIDS patients have been refused admission to hospitals. Many medical workers have expressed reluctance to care for AIDS patients. A Health Department requirement that doctors fill out an STD patient card and send it to the public health office drives patients away from care, sacrificing the opportunity for education and treatment. The third factor is the lack of legitimate and effective policy to change at-risk behavior such as drug use, prostitution, and unsafe sexual behavior. In 1992, some cities set up hot lines to provide counseling and to protect patients' rights to confidentiality and privacy.

Conclusion

Since the new policy of reform and openness initiated at the end of the 1970s, China has been undergoing yet another fundamental change. Marxism faces challenges from internal pressures and from Western ideas and economics. Confucianism is still deeply engraved in the Chinese mind, but Buddhism, Taoism, Islam, and Christianity are experiencing a revival. Tension and conflict are inevitable as diverse and often incompatible values come to the fore at this historical juncture. Many fields, including medicine, face new challenges, and in this environment the field of medical ethics is flourishing as never before in China. As in many other nations, scholars have delved into problems, published articles, initiated courses, and formed organizations devoted to bioethics.

The word *ethics* is now translated into Chinese as *lun li*, two characters signifying "hierarchical human relationships" and "principle" or "pattern." Combined, these two characters designate guidelines for interpersonal relationships. In

Chinese thought, ethics, or the guide for interpersonal relationships, blends with the laws that govern the universe. Thus, traditional Chinese philosophy, particularly Confucian, has a predilection for ethics, teaching how to be human within an orderly human community. In the last two centuries, Western influence in ideas and commodities has introduced an individualism not native to Chinese thought. Since the late nineteenth century, Chinese scholars have studied Western science and philosophy, with a particular interest in philosophical pragmatism. Marxist philosophy pays relatively little attention to ethics as such, since ethics is considered to be formulated by political ideology. Despite Western and Marxist influence, traditional Chinese ethics still weighs powerfully in the Chinese mind and in Chinese society.

The current interest in bioethics in China has been stimulated and influenced by American bioethics. Several leaders in Chinese bioethics are familiar with the American literature and participate in international bioethics activities. Also, since Western scientific medicine has long prevailed in China, Western ethical concerns are readily recognized, particularly as medical technologies are diffused. Thus, the principles of American bioethics—beneficence, nonmaleficence, autonomy, and justice—are frequently cited in Chinese discussions. However, these principles are not simply foreign imports: they correspond to significant Chinese values. Beneficence corresponds to the paramount Confucian virtue, ren, translated "benevolence" or "humaneness," which traditional Chinese medicine proposed as the primary virtue of the physician. It requires compassion and help for the sick, and the duty to avoid harm, as well as the obligation to care for the poor without charge (Qiu, 1988). Respect for autonomy, while not a traditional virtue in Chinese thought or medicine, which was strongly paternalistic, does correspond to the aspirations for personal freedom and social emancipation that marked the powerful current of modernization, sometimes known as the May 14th Movement, that began in the early twentieth century and continues to influence Chinese intellectuals (Spence, 1982). While not encouraged in the culture of the People's Republic, personal autonomy plays a real, if limited, part in modern thought about bioethical issues. Finally, justice in healthcare corresponds to the socialist ideal that a healthcare system accessible to all persons, regardless of social class or economic status, is best realized by a centrally controlled, nonentrepreneurial service system (Sidel and Sidel). This ideal prompted the vast extension of health services in the 1950s and inspires debates over contemporary plans to reorganize those services. Thus, while Chinese bioethics may occasionally speak in terms similar to Western bioethics, its spirit and ideas are properly Chinese: it is a blend of traditional, modern, and socialist Chinese thought, created in the unique conditions of an evolving great nation.

REN-ZONG QIU
ALBERT R. JONSEN (1995)
BIBLIOGRAPHY REVISED

BIBLIOGRAPHY

Andrews, Bridie J. 2003. *The Making of Modern Chinese Medicine.* New York: Cambridge University Press.

Becker, Carl. 1999. "Money Talks, Money Kills—The Economics of Transplantation in Japan and China." *Bioethics* 13(3–4): 236–243.

Bowers, John Z., and Purcell, Elizabeth, eds. 1974. *Medicine and Society in China.* New York: Josiah Macy, Jr., Foundation.

Cai, Gen-Fa. 1980. "A Preliminary Approach to the Problem of Medical Ethics." *Medicine and Philosophy* 2: 44–48.

Chen, C. C., and Bunge, Frederica M. 1989. *Medicine in Rural China: A Personal Account.* Berkeley: University of California Press.

Cong, Yali. 1998. "Ethical Challenges in Critical Care Medicine: A Chinese Perspective." *Journal of Medicine and Philosophy* 23(6): 581–600.

Crozier, Ralph C. 1968. *Traditional Chinese Medicine in Modern China: Science, Nationalism and Tensions of Cultural Change.* Cambridge, MA: Harvard University Press.

Dikotter, Frank. 1995. *Sex, Culture and Modernity in China: Medical Science and the Construction of Sexual Identities in the Early Republican Period.* Honolulu: University of Hawaii Press.

Dikotter, Frank. 1998. *Imperfect Conceptions.* New York: Columbia University Press.

Doring, Ole. 2002. *Advances in Chinese Medical Ethics: Chinese and International Perspectives.* London: RoutledgeCurzon.

Du, Zhi-Zheng. 1985. *An Outline of Medical Ethics.* Nanchang: Jiangxi People's Press.

Du, Zhi-Zheng. 2000. "On the Development of Teachers of Medical Ethics in China." *Hastings Center Report* 30(4): S37–S40.

Fox, Renée C., and Swazey, Judith P. 1982. "Critical Care at Tianjin's First Central Hospital and the Fourth Modernization." *Science* 217(4561): 700–705.

Fox, Renée C., and Swazey, Judith P. 1984. "Medical Morality Is Not Bioethics—Medical Ethics in China and the United States." *Perspectives in Biology and Medicine* 27(3): 336–360.

Henderson, Gail E., and Cohen, Myron S. 1984. *The Chinese Hospital: A Socialist Work Unit.* New Haven, CT: Yale University Press.

Holst, Erik. 1994. "Medical Ethics in China." *Lancet* 344(8934): 1427–1428.

Horn, Joshua S. 1969. "Away with All Pests …": *An English Surgeon in People's China.* London: Hamlyn.

Jiang, Yu. 1977. "Criticize the Bourgeois Medical View—Grab the Transplantation Organs from Brain Dead Patients." *Exchange of Medical Information* 4: 225–228.

Jonsen, Albert R. 2000. "Medical Ethics of India and China" In *A Short History of Medical Ethics,* pp. 27–42. New York: Oxford University Press.

Lei, Zhen-Hua; Guo, Ze-Zhong; He, Guan-Xin; Liu, Cai-Hong; and Liu, Yun-Hua. 1990. *Handbook for Family Planning.* Lanzhou: Lanzhou Xinhua Press.

Li, Benfu. 2000. "Ethics Teaching in Medical Schools." *Hastings Center Report* 30(4): S30–S32.

National Expert Committee on AIDS/HIV Prevention and Control (China). 1990. "Open Letter to Chinese Medical Personnel." *Health Newspaper,* Dec. 1, p. 1.

Nie, Jing Bao. 2000. "The Plurality of Chinese and American Medical Moralities: Toward an Interpretive Cross-Cultural Bioethics." *Kennedy Institute of Ethics Journal* 10(3): 239–260.

Pang, M. C. 1999. "Protective Truthfulness: the Chinese Way of Safeguarding Patients in Informed Treatment Decisions." *Journal of Medical Ethics* 25(3): 247–253.

Qiu, Ren-Zong. 1980. "Concept of Death and Euthanasia." *Medicine and Philosophy* 1: 77–79.

Qiu, Ren-Zong. 1982. "Philosophy of Medicine in China (1930–1980)." *Metamedicine* 3(1): 35–73.

Qiu, Ren-Zong. 1987. *Bioethics.* Shanghai: Shanghai Peoples Press.

Qiu, Ren-Zong. 1988. "Medicine—The Art of Humaneness: On Ethics of Traditional Chinese Medicine." *Journal of Medicine and Philosophy* 13(3): 277–299.

Qiu, Ren-Zong. 1991a. "The Fiduciary Relationship Between Professionals and Clients: A Chinese Perspective." In *Ethics, Trust and the Professions: Philosophical and Cultural Aspects,* pp. 247–259, ed. Edmund D. Pellegrino, Robert M. Veatch, and John Langan. Washington, D.C.: Georgetown University Press.

Qiu, Ren-Zong. 1991b. "Morality in Flux: Medical Dilemmas in the People's Republic of China." *Kennedy Institute of Ethics Journal* 1(1): 22–27.

Qiu, Ren-Zong. 1991. "Morality in Flux: Medical Ethics Dilemmas in the People's Republic of China." *Kennedy Institute of Ethics Journal* 1(1): 16–27.

Risse, Günter B., ed. 1973. *Modern China and Traditional Chinese Medicine: A Symposium Held at the University of Wisconsin, Madison.* Springfield, IL: Charles C. Thomas.

Scheid, Volker. 2002. *Chinese Medicine in Contemporary China: Plurality and Synthesis.* Durham, NC: Duke University Press.

Sidel, Victor W., and Sidel, Ruth. 1973. *Serve the People: Observations on Medicine in the People's Republic of China.* New York: Josiah Macy, Jr., Foundation.

Siven, Nathan. 1988. *Traditional Medicine in Contemporary China: A Partial Translation of Revised Outline of Chinese Medicine (1972): With an Introductory Study on Change in Present Day and Early Medicine.* Ann Arbor: Center for Chinese Studies, University of Michigan.

Song, Guo-Bin. 1933. *Ethics of Medical Practice.* Shanghai: Guoguang Bookstore.

Spence, Jonathan D. 1982. *The Gate of Heavenly Peace: The Chinese and Their Revolution, 1895–1980.* New York: Penguin.

Spence, Jonathan D. 1990. *The Search for Modern China.* New York: W.W. Norton.

Wang, J. 1944. "The New Document of Medical Ethics." *Chinese Medical Journal* 30: 39–40.

Wu Lien-Te. 1959. *Plague Fighter: The Autobiography of a Modern Chinese Physician.* Cambridge: W. Heffer & Sons.

Zhang, Daqing, and Cheng, Zhifan. 2000. "Medicine Is a Humane Art: The Basic Principles of Professional Ethics in Chinese Medicine." *Hastings Center Report* 30(4): S8–S12.

Zhou, Yimou, ed. 1983. *Chinese Physicians on Medical Morality.* Changsha: Hunan Press of Science and Technology.

IV. JAPAN. A. JAPAN THROUGH THE NINETEENTH CENTURY

The following is a revision of the first-edition articles on (1) the same subject by the same author, and (2) "Traditional Professional Ethics in Japanese Medicine" by Takemi Taro. Portions of the first-edition articles appear in the revised article.

The history of Japanese medical ethics must be seen in the context of the stratified development of Japanese culture. In each of the four layers discussed here, particular attention will be paid to medicine and ethics and the ways they were constituted with respect to changes in law, religion, custom, tradition, and social and political institutions.

Early Japan

The earliest layer of Japanese cultural stratification is the magico-religious universe of the ancient Japanese people, which persisted in subsequent periods (often submerged under later cultural layers and foreign traditions). From archaeological evidence, early mythic narratives, and poetry, we surmise that the ancient Japanese worldview was based on a mythic mode of apprehending the origin and nature of human beings, *kami* (usually translated as "deities"), the world, and the cosmos. This indigenous Japanese religion was later called Shintō or the "way of the *kami*." Early Shintō understood life to be essentially good and beautiful; evil was simply that which was unclean, ill omened, or inferior. Even the term *tsumi* (often translated as "sin") meant defilement or lack of beauty—for example, sickness, disaster, and error, all due to the influence of evil spirits and removable by ablution and lustration. The early Japanese believed that there were numerous *kami* and *mono* ("spirits," especially those of the fox, snake, badger, and other animals), which could possess humans and cause sickness. As a result, people depended on diviners, shamans, healers, and magicians to deal with physical and mental problems, to prevent disasters or sicknesses, and to avoid pollution. For example, early writings refer to medicinal fruits and plants as well as to common practices to avoid pollution, such as avoiding contact with sick people, menstruating women, and death. The early Japanese resorted to herbal infusions, hot-spring baths, frequent bathing, or gargling for prevention and healing. These practices are mentioned in the eighth-century *Kojiki*, a compilation of Japanese mythology, and even in fourth-century Chinese chronicles that describe Japan.

Socially, early Japan was organized by *uji* (a lineage group often translated as "clan"); the Yamato kingdom, an old designation for Japan, which emerged around the third or fourth century, was in effect a confederation of semiautonomous *uji*-groups under the nominal political authority of the chieftain of the leading *uji*, later known as the imperial household.

The Ritsuryo System

In the wake of the political changes on the Asian continent in the sixth and seventh centuries, Japan acquired a second cultural layer, with the heavy influx of Chinese civilization through Sinified Korea, including Confucianism, Taoism, and the Yin-Yang school, as well as law, medicine, philosophy, ethics, and various sciences and technologies and Buddhism. Stimulated by the unification of China, Japanese leaders made a serious attempt to unify Japanese culture and society. The Ritsuryo system—an important and early synthesis of religious, cultural, social, and political ideas—is the concrete embodiment of this second layer of Japanese culture. Its basic principles, especially the doctrine of the mutual interdependence of Shintō-, Confucian-, and Taoist-inspired imperial ideology and Buddhism, survived until the sixteenth century. Thanks to the emerging synthetic cultural matrix, the Japanese learned that it was possible to apprehend a universal structure governing the world of nature and the human body. Especially noteworthy was the popularization of an East Asian tradition of medicine much later called *kampō-i*, or "Chinese-style medicine." As early as 602, a prominent Korean Buddhist monk, Kwalluk, brought to Japan a series of books on diverse subjects, including astronomy, medicine, and magic. From that time on, with active support from the Yamato court, Chinese medicine was spread rapidly throughout Japan by émigré Korean and Chinese physicians, pharmacologists, and Buddhist priests, who utilized their medical knowledge for healing as a part of their religious activities. Many Japanese physicians were especially attracted by the medical theories of the Chinese scholar Sun Ssu-mo (581–682?).

In the main, Chinese medicine combined an emphasis on the prevention and healing of disease with a concern for *ethical behavior,* in the belief that the body is not an individual's own possession but a gift from one's parents, and that one's health depends on the harmonious interaction of the negative (*yin*) and the positive (*yang*) principles. Thus it was one's filial duty to maintain one's health by maintaining harmony with the environment, inasmuch as sickness was believed to arise from imbalance at the physiological, psychological, or cosmological level. Chinese medicine also encouraged acupuncture (*hari*), massage (*amma*), moxa treatments (*akyu* or moxibustion, the application of plants as counterirritants, set on key acupuncture points and burned slowly), and herbal medicine. Chinese medicine did not stress anatomical studies and surgery, largely because of the Confucian emphasis on the sacredness of the human body.

Significantly, Buddhist leaders in Japan affirmed that what one learned from the Chinese medical-ethical tradition was in complete harmony with the fundamental Buddhist principle of compassion. In keeping with this principle, when Prince Regent Shōtoku (573–621) built a temple in what is today Osaka, he provided an asylum, a hospital, and a dispensary on the temple grounds. Following his example, pious monarchs and aristocrats sponsored medical and philanthropic works. Buddhism introduced to Japan not only the savior deity Amida (Amitâbha), and the bodhisattva of great compassion, Kannon (Avalokitesvara), but also the Buddha of Healing, Yakushi-nyorai (Bhaisajya-guru). The Chinese-inspired Taihō Code, promulgated in 702, stipulated the establishment of a Ministry of Health, to be staffed by ten physicians, who were massage specialists, herbalists, and magicians. Judging from the records of the imperial storehouse, the Shōsō-in, built in the mid-eighth century in the capital city of Nara, the Yamato court imported a variety of continental herbal medicines. Another subdivision of the government, the Onmyō-ryo ("*Yin-Yang* bureau") was staffed by specialists in divination, astrology, and calendar making; its main task was to combine magico-religious features (e.g., geomancy, divination techniques, fortune-telling, and exorcism) and the semiscientific art of observing planetary movements.

During the seventh and eighth centuries the imperial government supported the officially sanctioned Buddhist schools but also strictly controlled the activities of their clerics by enforcing the Sōni-ryo ("law governing monks and nuns"). The government also made a serious effort to (1) discourage the popularity of the unauthorized Buddhist clerics—the rustic shamans, magicians, and healers who came under the nominal influence of Buddhism and wandered from village to village, offering divination, magic and healing; and (2) confine legitimate monks and nuns to monastic quarters, keeping them from exercising black magic and practicing medicine. On both accounts, the government failed miserably. The unauthorized clerics, called *ubasoku,* continued their preaching, philanthropic, magical, and healing activities among the lower strata of society, which were all too often ignored by official Buddhist schools. On the other hand, some of the officially sanctioned Buddhist monks, notably Genbō (d. 746) and Dōkyō (d. 772), were reputed to have miraculous healing and incantational powers, and they wielded great influence in court circles.

During the Heian period (781–1191), two new Buddhist schools, Tendai and Shingon, were introduced from China, bringing with them new forms of magic, incantations, and cosmological speculation, all of which greatly facilitated the blending of indigenous Japanese (Shintō), Chinese, and Buddhist traditions. Similar eclectic tendencies appeared in medicine and ethics, as exemplified by the thirty-volume medical work *Ishimpo,* compiled in 984 by Tanba Yasuyori. This work integrated native Japanese insights into the T'ang Chinese medical framework and coupled this with ethical exhortations. From the Heian period on, the term *kampō-i* ("Chinese-style medicine") was used in Japan to refer to this hybrid system comprising Buddhist, Confucian, *Yin-Yang,* and Japanese beliefs and practices, and covering a wide range of subjects: acupuncture, herbalism, moxibustion, massage, cures for the diseases of various internal organs, nutrition, dermatology, hygiene, pediatrics, obstetrics, and so forth. It was also during the Heian period that the government actively promoted its health service and the training of physicians.

For the most part, however, medical services were monopolized by the upper strata of society. The masses had no recourse except to traditional, indigenous folk or popular practices, for example, moxibustion and massage coupled with talismans and incantations. Ironically, the Heian period also witnessed, among both the elites and the masses, the popularity of native as well as Chinese forms of omen lore, demon lore, directional taboos, and exorcism. In this situation, even though learned Buddhist leaders expounded the lofty themes of the compassionate Buddha Amida, their teaching was easily transformed into a "*nembutsu* [recitation of Amida's holy name] magic" by the peasantry.

During the Kamakura period (1192–1333), the Japanese polity was split between the courtier-based Kyoto court and the samurai-based feudal regime (*bafuku* or shogunate) in Kamakura, not far from present-day Tokyo. Understandably, the Ritsuryō ideology declined, as did the Heian government-inspired health service. In its place a new class of professional physicians emerged who charged fees for their services. The thirteenth century witnessed an unusual

heightening of Buddhist spirituality, which added luster to outstanding medical and philanthropic activities by saintly Buddhist monks. One monk, named Ninshō, of the Ritsu school, is credited with having cared for 46,800 patients in his medical relief station in Kamakura, and with having established a leprosy sanatorium in Nara. Among the many dedicated priest-physicians of the Kamakura period, mention must be made of Kajiwara Shozen, the compiler of two important medical works—the *Tan-i-shō,* a fifty-volume work in Chinese, and the *Man-an-pō,* a sixty-volume Japanese work.

During the Muromachi period (1338–1578), a semblance of the feudal regime under the Ashikaga dynasty was maintained even as the social order steadily broke down. Toward the end of this period, three strongmen—Oda Nobunaga (d. 1582), Toyotomi Hideyoshi (d. 1598), and Tokugawa Ieyasu (d. 1616)—terminated the moribund Ritsuryō religious, cultural, social, and political synthesis. During the later Muromachi period, the various schools of Buddhism were unable to exert significant spiritual influence, the only exception being Zen, which inspired art, culture, and learning, and was instrumental in transmitting the syncretistic Neo-Confucianism of Sung Dynasty China (960–1279), as well as legal, philosophical, and medical classics of the Yüan (1276–1368) and Ming (1368–1644) dynasties. During the Muromachi period a number of Japanese physicians (both secular and clerical) studied in China, and able Chinese physicians migrated to Japan. Warfare among warrior families, especially the devastating Onin War of 1467–1477, promoted interest in surgery. Many prominent surgeons of this period were military men who combined medicine, Zen, and the martial arts.

The Muromachi period is also uniquely important in the history of Japanese medicine because of the coming of European medicine with the arrival of Portuguese traders and Roman Catholic missionaries. In the mid-sixteenth century, Jesuit missionaries established clinics, hospitals, dispensaries, and leprosy sanatoriums in Japan. One of the famous medical missionaries was Luis de Alameida, a successful surgeon-turned-Jesuit. For the most part, the European missionary-physicians admired the high quality of *kampō-ijutsu* (Chinese-style, mostly *internal* medicine) then available in Japan, and they contributed new knowledge and techniques in surgery, which were badly needed in the war-torn nation. After 1560, when the Society of Jesus terminated its medical activities, Japanese physicians who had been trained by European missionary-physicians carried on their work until the feudal regime decided to exterminate all traces of Catholic missionary influence from Japan in the mid-seventeenth century. Although the tradition of Namban (literally, "Southern Barbarian") medicine was short-lived, its scientific approach, coupled with an altruistic spirit and ethical imperative, left a significant imprint on the history of Japanese medicine and medical ethics.

The Tokugawa Era

In 1603, Tokugawa Ieyasu, one of the three strongmen mentioned above, inaugurated a shogunate that lasted until 1867, when the last Tokugawa shogun returned the prerogative of ruling the nation to the young Emperor Meiji. A different synthesis of religious, cultural, social, and political elements developed during the Tokugawa period. The Ritsuryō system discussed above tried to subsume two *universalistic* principles—*tao* ("the way"; *michi* in Japanese) of Confucianism and *dharma* ("the law"; *hō* in Japanese) of Buddhism—under the indigenous tradition represented by Shintō and the imperial system. The Tokugawa synthesis of religious, cultural, social, and political elements (the third layer of Japanese stratification) was based on universalistic Neo-Confucian principles of immutable natural laws and natural norms implicit in the human social and political order, grounded in the Will of Heaven (*t'ien*; *ten* in Japanese). Ironically, it was the Confucian thrust that stimulated the nativist *kokugaku* ("national learning") movement, which in turn fostered the resurgence of Shintō as the guiding principle for restoration of an imperial regime in 1868, inaugurating Japan's *modern period.*

From the perspective of medical history, the Tokugawa period was rich in variety, propelling the development of Chinese (classical Confucian and Neo-Confucian) and nativistic Japanese medicine, and the return of Western medical science. During the Tokugawa period, following the regime's policy in favor of Neo-Confucianism, Japanese medicine separated from its Buddhist underpinning and sought a new foundation in Neo-Confucian metaphysics, physics, psychology, and ethics. Under Neo-Confucian influence, *idō* (the "way or ethics of medicine") was summed up in the phrase *i wa jin nari* ("the practice of medicine is a benevolent art"). Significantly, the first systematic treatises on medical ethics written in Japan, the *Ibyo-ryogan* and the *Byoi-mando,* by Takenaka Tsuan, as well as the *Yojo-kun* ("Instruction on Hygiene"), by Kaibara Ekken (d. 1714), were published in the early Tokugawa period. About that time, among the physicians of *kampō-i* ("Chinese style medicine"), a group called *gosei-ha* ("school of later centuries") taught an intricate fusion of medicine and Neo-Confucian philosophy and became quite influential.

One of the most influential works on healthcare was the *Yojo-kun* ("how to live well"), by the samurai and physician Kaibara Ekken. A Neo-Confucianist scholar, Kaibara wrote widely on various subjects for the edification of people in all walks of life. His lifelong dedication to the cause of healthcare is summarized thus: "Medicine is the practice of humanitarianism. Its purpose should be to help others with benevolence and love. One must not think of one's own interests but should save and help the people who were created by Heaven and Earth." This represents the view that human beings are created by the union of Heaven and Earth, that is, the parents. Since medicine is an art that can make the difference between life and death, it is a profession of utmost importance. This means that physicians must be culturally and intellectually accomplished. Kaibara urged physicians to be conversant with the best medical books, to think logically and precisely, and to acquire important theories, practicing *lifelong education.* He proposed an ideal image of the physician, who excels in qualities of character and scholarship, in contrast to the *inferior physician,* who serves his own interests rather than saving others. At the end of his treatise Kaibara lists eight requirements for the physician: (1) to have a high goal in life; (2) to be cautious; (3) to acquire scholarship of broad knowledge; (4) to make the medical profession a full-time pursuit; (5) to be thirsty for new and ever greater knowledge; (6) to be humble; (7) to be clean at all times; and (8) to be magnanimous.

Meanwhile, in the latter part of the seventeenth century two interesting phenomena developed: (1) the emergence of "ancient studies" (*kogaku*) within the Japanese Confucian tradition, which encouraged *kampō-i* ("Chinese-style medicine") physicians to react against the Neo-Confucian orientation and to return to classical Chinese medicine; and (2) the emergence of the Japanese "national learning" school (*kokugaku*), inspired by Confucian *kogaku.*

Clearly, the *ancient studies* school was a reaction among Japanese Confucianists against the regime-sponsored Neo-Confucian orthodoxy that involved advocating a return to ancient Confucian sages. *Ancient studies* precipitated the rise of a school of medicine called *koihō-ha* ("school of ancient medicine") among Japanese *kampō-i* physicians, who advocated a return to ancient (i.e., Han dynasty, 206 B.C.E.—220 C.E.) Chinese medicine and, more specifically, tried to retrieve the medical work of a Han physician, Chan Chingchung. For example, Chan's book on fevers and their remedies, the *Shokan-ron,* became widely read in Japan.

Paradoxically, the philological-philosophical approaches of *kogaku* inspired some nativists to apply its scholarly method to the study of ancient Japanese classics, thus developing the school of "national learning" (*kokugaku*), which soon grew into an influential movement and eventually joined with other nativists in the anti-Tokugawa and pro-royalist movement. One of the leading theoreticians of this school, Motoori Norinaga (1730–1801), was a physician. We are told that in his youth he studied both Neo-Confucianism and the Neo-Confucian-inspired *gosei-ha* tradition of medicine, but gradually discarded Neo-Confucianism in favor of national learning and repudiated the *gosei-ha* medical orientation, turning to the *koihō-ha* tradition. Other "national learning" scholars, such as Ueda Akinari (1734–1809) and Hirata Atsutane (1776–1843), were also physicians. Hirata attached great importance to mental therapy and excelled in taking his patients' psychosomatic conditions into account.

Western medicine, briefly introduced by the Jesuits, returned to Japan under Dutch influence. In order to exterminate Catholic influence, the Tokugawa feudal regime had proclaimed the policy of national seclusion in 1639, terminating all contacts with Western powers. It had allowed only non-Catholic Holland to maintain a small trading post in Nagasaki. Through this minimal contact, Dutch medical supplies and surgical methods continued to influence the Japanese medical profession. As early as the mid-seventeenth century a Dutch physician, Casper Schambergen, spent nearly a year at Nagasaki, teaching Dutch medicine. His influence greatly enhanced cosmopolitan (Westernized) medicine, especially surgery, then called the *aranda-ryu geka* ("Dutch surgical school"). This school became popular through a translation of the *Tavel Anatomia* (*Kaitai-shinsho*) by Mayeno Ryotaku, Sugita Gempaku, Nakagawa Jun'an, and Katsuragawa Hoshu in 1774. In 1823–1828, Philip Franz von Siebold, a German physician and scientist attached to the Dutch trading post in Nagasaki, was permitted to operate a clinic and an academy that attracted a number of able Japanese medical students. He revisited Japan in 1859–1862. Those Japanese students who studied Dutch learning had been well grounded in Confucian learning, which to them was essential for moral cultivation, whereas Dutch (and later, other Western learning in general) was considered practical learning. Hence the famous motto "Eastern ethics and Western science."

The Meiji Synthesis and Modern Japan

The once powerful Tokugawa feudal regime was exhausted politically when the last Tokugawa shogun surrendered feudal power in 1867. It was succeeded by the Meiji-era synthesis of religious, cultural, social, and political ideas that survived until the end of World War II in 1945. Unlike the Tokugawa regime, which authenticated its policy and culture in terms of *universalistic* Neo-Confucian principles, the Meiji regime reverted to *particularistic* Shintø and imperial traditions reminiscent of the Ritsuryō synthesis of the

seventh century, notwithstanding the Meiji emperor's Charter Oath to the effect that "uncivilized customs of former times shall be abolished" and "knowledge shall be sought throughout the world." (Understandably, the basic contradictions of the Meiji synthesis have haunted modern Japan until our own time.)

In the modern period Japan welcomed Western knowledge and technology, which inspired, among other things, modern Westernized law, philosophy, ethics, and medicine. In medicine, the Japanese government officially adopted the German system of medical education in 1869. In 1873, there were slightly over five hundred Westernized physicians and twenty-three thousand traditional *kampō* doctors (or *kampō-i*). From 1876 on, the government required all physicians to study Westernized medicine, although *kampō* medicine, which never lost its official recognition, continued to flourish throughout the nineteenth century and into the twentieth. In retrospect it becomes evident that from early times to the modern period, through all the cultural layers, Japanese medicine and ethics—nurtured by Sino-Korean culture, Buddhism, and Western influences—never completely lost its ancient, indigenous orientations, including magico-religious beliefs and practices.

JOSEPH MITSUO KITAGAWA (1995)

BIBLIOGRAPHY

Bartholomew, James R. 1989. *The Formation of Science in Japan: Building a Research Tradition*. New Haven, CT: Yale University Press.

Ebisawa, Arimichi. 1944. *Kirishitan no shakai katsudo oyobi Namban igaku*. Tokyo: Fuzanbō.

Graf, Olaf. 1942. *Kaibara Ekken: Ein Beitrag zur japanischen Geistesgeschichte des 17. Jahrhunderts und zur chinesischen Sungphilosophie*. Leiden, Netherlands: E. J. Brill.

Hattori, Toshirō. 1955. *Heian jidai igakushi no kenkyu*. Tokyo: Yoshikawa Kobunkan.

Hattori, Toshirō. 1971. *Muromachi Azuchi Momoyama jidai igakushi no kenkyū*. Tokyo: Yoshikawa Kobunkan.

Ishida, Ichirō. 1983. *Kami to Nihon-bunka*. Tokyo: Perikansha.

Kaibara, Ekken. 1974. *Yojokun: Japanese Secret of Good Health*. Tokyo: Tokuma Shoten.

Lock, Margaret M. 1980. *East Asian Medicine in Urban Japan: Varieties of Medical Experience*. Berkeley: University of California Press.

Loewe, Michael; Blacker, Carmen; and Lama Chine Rama, Rinpoche, eds. 1981. *Oracles and Divination*. Boulder, CO: Shambala.

Philippi, Donald L., tr. 1959. *Norito: A New Translation of Ancient Japanese Ritual Prayers*. Tokyo: Kougakuin University. Reprinted under the title *Norito: A Translation of Ancient*

Japanese Ritual Prayers. Princeton, NJ: Princeton University Press, 1959.

Tucker, Mary Evelyn. 1989. *Moral and Spiritual Cultivation in Japanese Neo-Confucianism: The Life and Thought of Kaibara Ekken, 1630–1740.* Albany: State University of New York Press.

Unschuld, Paul U. 1986. *Medicine in China: A History of Pharmaceutics.* Berkeley: University of California Press.

Yamakami, Izumo. 1981. *Miko no rekishi: Nihon shukyo no botai.* Tokyo: Yuzankaku.

Yamazaki, Tasuku. 1953. *Edoki-zen Nihon iji hōsei no kenkyu.* Tokyo: Chugai Igakusha. LL.D. diss., Nihon University, 1950.

IV. JAPAN. B. CONTEMPORARY JAPAN

Due to Japanese society and its distinctive historical understanding of medicine and the role and responsibilities of the physician, it was not until the 1960s that the bioethical and sociolegal concerns about the practice of medicine began to be deliberately reflected, and only during the 1980s that the notions of autonomy and rights in medicine, and of bioethics in general, became gradually influential (Kimura, 1979, 1987a, 1987b).

In the long tradition of Japanese medical practice, the Confucian notion of *jin* (benevolence) has been one of the most important ethical elements; medicine itself is known as *jinjyutsu* (the art of *jin*). Physicians, as conduits of *jin,* were required to act with benevolence toward their patients and were responsible for the welfare of patients in a fiduciary (trust) relationship (Kimura, 1991a). It was obligatory to use medicine, a gift of benevolence, for the good of others even without payment. Physicians fulfilled their responsibility toward their patients and the patients' family members by acting in a paternalistic and authoritative way; the Japanese, nurtured in the Confucian ethos to respect law, order, authority, and social status, acquiesced without murmur to the superior knowledge of the physician.

Traditionally, the socially reinforced mentality of thinking of oneself as a member of a group rather than as an individual could be seen as one key element to understanding the sense of "related-ness" in the Japanese society (Doi; Mitchell; Johnson). This unique character can be interpreted in the framework of "related-autonomy" or the making of autonomous decisions in relationship striving for harmony (*wa*) with other people in the Japanese cultural bioethics. The sense of relatedness and codependence extend to all living beings and to one's bond with the environment.

In keeping these twin notions of related-autonomy and harmony (*wa*) in mind, this entry will discuss the contemporary Japanese approach to various issues and problems of bioethics, in light of the social, cultural, and historical milieu in three stages of chronological development.

Confucian Virtues in a Paternalistic Medical Tradition (1868–1937)

In 1868, feudal samurai in particular *han* (local provinces), such as Satsuma, Choshu, Tosa, and Hizen, initiated the restoration of political power to Emperor Meiji after the Tokugawa shogunate's reign of 265 years (1603–1867). The Confucian ethical teaching, dominant among the samurai during the Tokugawa shogunate, was integrated into Kyoiku Chokugo (the Educational Edict of the Emperor, 1890) as the basis for moral teaching in the elementary school curriculum; the classes were compulsory. (This edict was not abolished until 1948.) Confucian ethics, as embodied in this edict, attributes great mercy and benevolence to the emperor and affirms the importance of virtues such as loyalty to the emperor as the head of the "state-family," and filial piety and respect for parents. It also emphasizes the importance of brotherhood and sisterhood, obedience to law and maintenance of order, the necessity of education, and devotion to the state (exemplified for men in military service). Grassroots movements for liberty and civil rights in the political process (*jiyuu-minkin undo*) were increasingly popular but were suppressed by the emperor's proclamation of the Meiji Constitution in 1889, which consolidated political power in the hands of the emperor and established the Diet (parliament) in his name. Modern Japanese medical ethics cannot be isolated from this social and political milieu. The strong paternalistic nature of Japanese medical practice is the natural outcome of Confucian teaching, which calls for respect of the master and for his authority as a source of unquestionable wisdom and truth.

As Japan became more open to the West, the Dutch ceased to be the sole source of Western culture, and other nationalities replaced them. The process of modernizing Japan began in the second half of the nineteenth century and continued into the twentieth century, aided by *oyatoi gaikokujin* (foreign advisers) from Western countries, hired by the Japanese government to provide development advice in industry, education, government, finance, science, technology, and medicine. Japan, seeking models for modernization, was drawn to the German approach because of the success and progress of German science and technology, and the similarity of the German authoritarian political system under the Prussian Kaiser to its own under the emperor. Official acceptance of Western, particularly German, medicine guided the development of Japanese policy on medical administration and education and set the course for the future (Oshima).

German physicians left a legacy of authoritarianism in medical education and practice that had far-reaching effects on the majority of the Japanese medical community. This approach, combined with the Confucian self-righteousness in rendering benevolence to the patient, undermined the development of any notion of patients' rights. Research became the supreme interest at many university hospitals, and patients who presented interesting cases were treated as research material. All of these influences can be seen in the Isei (seventy-six guidelines for medical administration) drafted by Sensai Nagayo in 1874. Traditional Japanese medicine (*waho*) and Chinese medicine (*kanpo*) have been out of the mainstream of medical science in Japan since the adoption of Isei, although acupuncture and moxibustion (quick, light heat from an ignited powder of medicinal leaves at key points of the body, called *tsubo*) have remained as folk medicine with popular support among the public (Otsuka).

As capitalism became established in Japan, serious social and economic inequities exacerbating the health problems (e.g., widespread tuberculosis, malnutrition) of factory workers, miners, farmers, and fishery workers became evident, particularly in the Taisho era (1912–1926). Even though the socially privileged physicians' group was not eager to address these health issues through social reform, some young physicians and medical students working for the settlement movement, introduced into Japan from England at the turn of the century, provided medical care in the slum areas of big cities such as Tokyo, Osaka, and Kobe in the 1920s. In 1919 the Medical Cooperative Movement (Iryo Seikyo Undo), which sought to establish community medical centers offering equal access, found great support among many Japanese (Seikyo).

During this period, Japanese medical ethics, guided by the two powerful influences of Confucian teaching and German authoritarianism, was generally understood simply to govern a physician's personal attitude in providing medical service to patients within the traditional model of a paternalistic trust relationship. It is important to note that during this time the eminent Japanese medical historian Yu Fujikawa asserted that physicians were bound by special obligations and responsibilities and must develop a special ethical consciousness in their daily practice. His advice was not accepted by Japanese medical experts, who were obedient to the military regime during the following war years.

Medical Loyalty to State and Authority (1938–1968)

Increasing concern about the health of the Japanese population led to the establishment of Koseisho, the Ministry of Health and Welfare, in 1938. The National Health Act and additional laws protecting factory workers were promulgated that same year. Many young radical physicians dealing with serious health problems among the population, such as tuberculosis, raised questions of justice and equitable distribution of resources, but concerns associated with the war with China (which began in 1937) now dominated. In reality, one of the government's main purposes in establishing the Koseisho was to strengthen the health of the nation to wage war. Similarly, the National Eugenic Law of 1940, promulgated ostensibly for the health of the people, reflected the government's desire for increased family size and the elimination of genetically transmitted diseases and defects. To achieve the latter goal, it authorized the use of a "eugenic operation"—voluntary or involuntary sterilization of individuals with mental illness or retardation and those thought to be at risk of transmitting genetic diseases or physical deformities to offspring. With the approach of war, the traditionally authoritarian, yet basically well intentioned, practice of medicine came under the control of a militaristic state regime; this had dreadful repercussions for medicine and medical ethics in modern Japan.

Several horrible and unethical human experiments performed during World War II were uncovered after the war. The similarity of response to state authority exhibited by Japanese physicians and by Nazi physicians has been viewed with dismay. German defendants accused of committing crimes against humanity were put on trial at Nuremberg, and the medical atrocities and experiments there recounted led to the development of the Nuremberg Code in hope of preventing such practices in the future. But Japanese medical experts serving in Unit 731, officially called the Water Supply and Epidemiological Disease Prevention Corps, who carried out and supervised experiments on Manchurian Chinese captives using bacteriological infections, frostbite, and mustard and poison gases, were not prosecuted by the international military court (Powell; Williams and Wallace).

Official documents exchanged between the United States and U.S. General Headquarters in Japan, now declassified and available at the U.S. National Archives, show that the U.S. military decided not to bring this case to trial. The interrogation task force of the occupation forces in Japan granted immunity to members of Unit 731, including the corps chief, on the condition that all related medical records and specimens be handed over to the United States (Kimura, 1997). The matter was regarded as highly important to national security because the United States wanted to prevent transfer of the medical knowledge gained through these experiments to the Communist governments in China and the Soviet Union (U.S. National Archives, 1949). The

Soviets held their own military trial at Khabarovsk for members of Unit 731 they had captured. Based on documentation and the testimony of witnesses, the accused were found guilty (Ivanov and Bogach).

The Kyushu University Medical School vivisection case also serves as an example of unethical experimentation. Eight American bomber pilots were captured in Japan after an air raid on Tokyo in 1945; some of them were sentenced to death by the local unit of the Japanese Imperial Army, but instead were used as objects of medical experimentation. To avoid prosecution by the Yokohama District Military Tribunal, one key person involved in this experimentation committed suicide; full details may never be known (U.S. National Archives 1949). The case served as the basis for a popular novel by Shusaku Endo, titled *Umi to dokuyaku* (1960), in which he dramatically depicts the quandary of a medical scientist tempted by unethical but very interesting experimentation. Endo's novel forced consideration of the meaning and place of ethics and medicine in Japanese society—which, he argued, lacked a standard of absolute value (Kimura, 1997).

Justified by state authority, professional experts in Japan sometimes lose critical consciousness and judgment. The Japanese national character nurtured during the Tokugawa era, and by an authoritarian government since the Meiji restoration, demands absolute obedience to the state and to authority. As Endo points out in his novel, such pressure often creates serious problems when individuals must make independent, and individual, ethical decisions. As a member of a group—such as a family, corporation, or community—and as a citizen, the individual Japanese tends to follow what other people do. Harmony (*wa*), or getting along with others, is an important element of the Japanese ethos for maintaining good relationships. To insist on individual opinions is regarded as egoistic and arrogant. Suppressing oneself in order to cope with other people is a daily practice in every aspect of life for the Japanese. This has serious ethical implications, especially in terms of weakening critical consciousness necessary in professional experts. The majority of Japanese medical experts and the lay public are not interested in drawing serious lessons from the horrible wartime human experiments because they reason that such actions are performed only in "abnormal war settings by abnormal people."

After the defeat of Japan, one of the first pieces of legislation implemented was the Eugenic Protection Law of 1948. Unlike the National Eugenic Law that it abolished and the Japanese Criminal Code, which since 1907 had held abortion illegal, the 1948 law permitted abortion for medical, and later for social and economic, reasons. Under the Japanese Criminal Code, abortion for other reasons remained a prosecutable offense. Nevertheless, because of vigorous opposition from advocates for the disabled, the new law did not provide legal justification for the abortion of a genetically defective fetus. The endorsement of this abortion law by the General Headquarters of General Douglas MacArthur aroused adverse reactions from religious bodies in Japan and the United States (Kimura, 1987a, 1987b). MacArthur defended the policy, saying that it had arisen from and was implemented by the Japanese Diet.

The way survivors of the atomic bombs dropped at Hiroshima and Nagasaki were treated by the Atomic Bomb Casualty Commission (composed of U.S. medical and genetic experts) is one of the historical sources of the development of Japanese bioethics because of its significance in discussions about the relationship between human beings and science, technology, and research. Individuals suffering from the effects of radiation came seeking treatment, but instead became material for research on radiation and collection of genetic data that were stored at the U.S. Atomic Energy Commission (AEC). This situation raised the serious issue of the researcher's responsibility to obtain fully informed consent for research. At that time, no government regulation or review boards existed to deal with the situation. The AEC is in fact the forerunner of the U.S. Energy Department, which initiated the Human Genome Project in the early 1980s on the basis of the voluminous data from the survivors of Hiroshima and Nagasaki (Cook-Deegan).

In 1951 the Japan Medical Association (JMA) issued a statement on physicians' ethics. This action clearly ushered in a new epoch in medical practice in Japan and signaled a return to the prewar state of medical ethics. Article I explicitly reaffirmed the fundamental and central place in medical practice of the ancient principle of *jin,* the benevolence of Confucian teaching, and asserted that physicians, as the elite of society, must embody the spirit of *jin,* always thinking about the welfare of the patient and the benefit of the treatment. Further, in cooperation with other professionals, physicians should take the initiative in social reform and, as ethically oriented people, should exercise great self-discipline (JMA, 1951).

In the 1960s Japanese society felt the effects of the worldwide trend of questioning established authority. Revolts occurred in many universities as dissatisfied medical students stood up against the traditionally paternalistic and authoritarian medical faculty they felt was exploiting them. Special legislation eased the unrest, but this first and radical challenge of the medical establishment, a very politically powerful group, had permanent ramifications for Japanese society and moved it into a new era.

Communal Involvement in Medical Decision Making (1969–2000s)

Toward the end of the 1960s, numerous social issues competed for attention in Japan. Health-related issues that drew increasing notice included air and water pollution, food additives, iatrogenic diseases (diseases caused by physicians), and the revival of *kanpo* (traditional Chinese medicine). There was also an increased emphasis on health. The growing number of older people focused attention on the need for healthcare for the elderly. Japan has been one of the most successful countries in decreasing the birthrate, and life expectancy in 2001 was the longest in the world, nearly eighty-five years for women and just over seventy-eight years for men (Minstry of Health, Labour, and Welfare). In 1997 the Long-term Health Care Insurance Law for the Elderly was enacted to create national mutual support systems for the elderly, who were traditionally cared for mainly by the family in the community. Advances in medical technology and healthcare have raised additional issues for the Japanese medical profession and society in general. The period from the late 1960s to the early 2000s has seen increased involvement in discussions about medical treatment and a strong desire to establish guidelines to protect the patient.

ORGAN TRANSPLANTATION. Progress in organ transplant technology created a demand to regulate and endorse cornea transplantation. A special law to this effect was enacted in 1958; it was combined with a law governing kidney transplantation in 1979.

The most vigorous public debate on bioethical issues was generated by the first heart transplant in Japan (1968), in which a heart was taken from a drowning victim and transplanted to a patient with heart failure. The patient died after eighty-three days. A surgeon at Sapporo Medical College, Juro Wada, was accused of mishandling the surgery on both the donor and the recipient, and questions arose about the justification for the transplant and about the criteria used to determine death; but Wada was never formally prosecuted. The aftermath of this case, however, gave rise to strong criticism of high-tech medical applications on ethical grounds. Concerns focused on the use of brain-based criteria of death, organ transplantation from brain-dead bodies, and the need to develop ethical guidelines to control the behavior of individual physicians who might seek fame through ill-prepared and drastic use of medical technology supposedly for the benefit of the patient.

This incident spawned the Patients' Rights Declaration in 1970 (Owatari et al.). This short, spontaneous expression of feelings, stating that the Wada case was a violation of the human rights of the patient and an example of the corruption of medicine and ethics, occurred in the public meeting at which Wada was accused of violating the donor's right to life.

In 1997 the Law on Transplantion went into effect. This law, reflecting the legal and ethical uniqueness of the Japanese situation, makes harvesting organs difficult because of two rigid consent provisions. The first provision is the requirement for advanced consent in accepting brain death. The "brain death criteria for death" box must be checked on the donor card, expressing the intention of the organ donor when alive. The second provision is the requirement for the consent of the family for harvesting organs from a brain-dead body. Article 6, Section 1, allows organ donation "in the event that a deceased person had during his lifetime expressed in writing his intent to donate organs to be used for organ transplants." Section 3 of the same article also states that "when the donor during his lifetime had expressed in writing his consent to the diagnosis—made based upon the provisions—and his family, informed of the removal, did not object to the diagnosis," organ transplants can be legally permitted (Kimura, 1998).

This law is supposed to promote—by endorsement—organ transplantation. From enactment through early 2003, however, Japan has had an only a small number (twenty-three) of organ transplants. Furthermore, these two elements of ethical and legal rigidness have made the enactment of more relaxed applications—such as allowing organ transplants involving infants—almost impossible to perform.

CRITERIA FOR DEATH. Leading objections to brain-death criteria are the fears that organs will be removed prematurely and that transplants will be performed in unacceptable circumstances (Kimura, 1991b). In Japan, transplantation of vital organs from dead bodies is rare because of a concern about causing the death of the donor. To a limited degree, anencephalic infants (those born without a brain or without a major part of the brain) have been used as sources for donor organs because they will die anyway, and because it is believed that they do not possess the fundamental consciousness necessary to be a human being. Declaration of death in the cases reported has ostensibly been based on the total cessation of heartbeat. Nevertheless, the use of organs from anencephalics has not been officially reported since 1981, because of clinical concerns about the condition of the organs from such donors and public concerns about the appropriateness of such practices (Kimura, 1989a).

Resistance to hastening death and harvesting organs also comes from the traditional Japanese image of human beings as completely integrated mind–body units, rather than as being composed of distinct and separate units of mind, body, and spirit. This mind–body unit, according to the Japanese, continues after death, so that removing an organ from a cadaver is seen as disturbing this spiritual and corporeal unity, not merely altering the physical body. It also explains why autopsies are abhorred in Japan (Fujita). According to the Buddhist and Shinto ways of thinking, this unity extends beyond the individual to all living things. To the Japanese, death disturbs the rhythm of all living things and therefore should not be hastened. Also, Confucian teaching places strong emphasis on family relationships and filial piety. There is a strong prohibition on harming one's body, because it is derived from one's parents (Kimura, 1991b).

In addition, in accepting the reality of human mortality, some Buddhists regard the extension of life by accepting organs from another individual's body as unnatural and unethical, because the procurement of those organs depends on the death of another person. Such an expectation of the death of someone else for the purpose of egoistic extension of life is not acceptable. Also, the totality of life should be supported by the notion of *arayashiki* (*alaya-vijnana*) (the fundamental consciousness within each individual being). This Buddhist notion holds that consciousness is not located solely in the brain; therefore the cessation of any one part or one organ (including the brain) of the individual does not extinguish consciousness and consequently cannot be regarded as the death of the individual person (Tamaki; Fujii). The basis for the uneasiness in accepting brain criteria for death and organ transplantation thus comes from both Confucian and Buddhist thought, which incorporate some ideas from Japanese traditional folk religions and Shintoism.

EUTHANASIA. Media coverage has made euthanasia one of the most debated topics in Japanese bioethics. The Japanese Euthanasia Society was established in 1976 (and was later renamed the Japan Society for Dying with Dignity [JSDD]), and the first international conference on euthanasia was held in Tokyo that same year. The Ninth International Conference of the World Federation of Right to Die Societies was organized by the JSDD and held in Kyoto in 1992. No legally established procedure for euthanasia exists in Japan, but as in many other countries, the use of elevated doses of narcotics to relieve suffering and pain is acceptable even at the risk of hastening death. According to Buddhist thought, the prolongation of life and suffering is not absolutely necessary, and ending the life of a dying, suffering patient might be regarded as a merciful act (Murakami).

A 1962 precedent-setting decision by the Nagoya High Court, which accepted the idea of euthanasia in principle, involved the case of a son who prepared poisoned milk as a result of his terminally ill father's repeated requests to die; the glass of milk was found by the man's wife, who, not knowing it was poisoned, gave it to her husband. Although

the court found this case to involve unacceptable mercy killing, the court's ruling established six criteria for allowable mercy killing:

(1) the patient's condition must be terminal and incurable, with no hope of recovery, and death must be imminent (as determined by modern medical knowledge and technology);

(2) the patient's pain must be so severe that no one should be expected to endure it;

(3) the sole purpose of the act must be to relieve the patient's suffering;

(4) a sincere request and permission are required from competent patients;

(5) in general, the act should be performed only by physicians; and

(6) an ethically acceptable method must be used.

The Nagoya High Court ruled that, although the first four criteria had been met, the final two conditions had not. The son was sentenced to four years' imprisonment with three years' suspended sentence.

In the light of medical and technological advances, the conditions once considered fatal can now be treated effectively or even cured. Better methods of pain control have been developed, and new centers for palliative care have been developed.

The ruling of Yokohama District Court on March 28th, 1995 is significant for its clear statement of the principle of individual autonomy based on the patient's own intention to stop treatment. In this case, the physician prosecuted for murder claimed he had a clear request from the patient's son to alleviate his father's suffering. Later, the son denied, when questioned, any intention to end his father's life. The ruling does not endorse familial decision making based on the presumed wishes of the patient, however, if the patient has communicated openly enough with family members about his or her view of life, character, and values, the family will be able to make a conjectural decision to end his or her life in a natural way without aggressive over treatment (Kimura, 1998).

TREATMENT OF THE MENTALLY ILL. The Japanese Mental Health Act was passed in 1950 to prevent private home confinement of the mentally ill in violation of an identified right to be cared for in institutional situations. In the 1980s, however, disclosures of violations of rights of psychiatric patients led to serious questioning of the routine admittance and institutional treatment of the mentally ill. In 1987 an important amendment to this act passed after a nationwide campaign in its favor by the mass media and a strong recommendation for its passage by a special investigative mission of the International Commission of Jurists in Geneva, Switzerland. The amendment enacted more rigorous procedures for involuntary hospitalization of the mentally disabled and established rehabilitation and treatment centers to protect the rights of patients with mental disabilities. The commission's involvement underscores the importance and necessity of international cooperation on bioethical issues, especially those related to patients' rights.

EDUCATION OF THE PUBLIC IN BIOETHICS. Bioethical issues raised in the 1960s caught the attention of much of Japanese society, and in the 1970s concerned citizens formed bioethics study groups in Tokyo, Kyoto, and Nagoya. By the 1980s, members of these groups participated as bioethics volunteers in medical service organizations. The nationwide concern with health and medical services in Japan led to a new declaration of patients' rights, which was issued in 1984 by a group of patients, lawyers, physicians, and journalists. While this document carried no official authorization, it was more systematic than its 1970 precursor and showed the impact of discussions in other countries. The General Assembly of Japanese Medical Cooperatives, an official medical service organization of the Japanese Association of Life Cooperatives Union with 250 hospitals and clinics and a membership of 1.5 million individuals, endorsed its own version of a patients' bill of rights in May 1991—the first such action by a medical organization (Seikyo). The Patients' Rights Legislation Movement, largely initiated by medical malpractice lawyers and other members of the lay public, began in 1991 to urge passage of a statute on informed consent and respect for patient autonomy in medical decision making.

ETHICS COMMITTEES FOR ADVANCED MEDICAL RESEARCH. The first medical ethics committee in Japan was established at the Tokushima University School of Medicine in 1982 in order to review in vitro fertilization (IVF) technology and its application to infertile women. As of 2003, each of the eighty medical schools and major hospitals had its own medical ethics committee reviewing cases such as segmental liver transplantation, gene therapy, and embryonic stem cell research. Due to a lack of national legislation regarding these review committees for the advanced medical research, each has a different composition. With the exception of a few lawyers and ethicists, the majority of the committees are composed of the same medical faculty and are male.

In 1991 the Greater Tokyo Metropolitan Government established the first hospital ethics committee with membership of nonmedical practitioners, and the committee opened all its meetings to the public. This committee serves as a policymaking body for the fourteen hospitals operated by the Tokyo Metropolitan Government. One of the epoch-making outcomes of the committee was the adoption of the "Patients' Bill of Rights for the Hospitals of Tokyo Metropolitan Government" in 2001.

BIOETHICS ORGANIZATIONS. Since the mid-1980s, medical professionals and government organizations have been involved in the study of bioethical issues. In 1984, the Ministry of Health and Welfare set up the Special Advisory Board on Life and Ethics; it published an official report in 1985, after a series of research conferences, then ceased activity. The Japan Medical Association also set up the interdisciplinary Bioethics Council, consisting of medical experts and professionals from philosophy, anthropology, biochemistry, law, and industry. The council dealt with topics related to technological applications in clinical settings such as IVF (1986), sex selection of the fetus (1987), brain death and organ transplantation (1989), and explanation and informed consent (1990).

The Japanese Association for Bioethics, established in 1987, publishes a journal and a newsletter, and has more than 800 members who attend the annual national meeting and international meetings. The Japanese Association for Philosophical and Ethical Research in Medicine, the Japanese Society of Ethics, and the Japanese Society of Medical Law are also concerned with bioethical issues as they affect their respective disciplines.

In the early 2000s, the Bioethics Committee of the Science and Technology Council (part of the Ministry of Education, Culture, Sports, Science and Technology) has been active on bioethical issues relating to biomedical research, such as cloning. The Health and Welfare Council of the Ministry of Health, Labour and Welfare is also dealing with bioethical issues, mainly relating to clinical medicine. These two ministries worked with the Ministry of Economy, Trade and Industry to prepare a document titled "Ethics Guidelines for Human Genome/Gene Analysis Research," which was released in 2001. They jointly made an official announcement of the Guideline in 2001 for the first time as a result of cooperative work in bioethics public policy in Japan.

BIOETHICAL TRENDS IN COURT DECISIONS, CODE OF ETHICS, AND LEGISLATION. One of the most controversial legal issues relating to bioethics in the 1990s was the revelation that HIV-contaminated blood products were used for hemophiliac patients without heat processing, resulting in around 1,600 people being infected with HIV. After more than seven years of legal struggle, the Ministry of

Health and Welfare, pharmaceutical corporations, and the plaintiffs in the case agreed to a settlement involving a compensation fee of about 400,000 U.S. dollars per person.

In 1996 the Eugenic Protection Law was amended, and its name was changed to the Maternal Protection Law. In addition to deleting the word *eugenic* from the name, the new law eliminated all provisions related to eugenic operations, including the lists of genetic diseases that were the subject of eugenic operations, such as Hansen's disease (leprosy). The discriminatory Law for the Prevention of Leprosy, in effect since 1907, was abolished in 1996 following the initiation of legal action against the government of Japan. Later, in 2001, the Kumanoto District Court ruled against the Ministry for its responsibility and the government gave up the appeal. Diet members adapted an unanimous resolution on the issue of Hansen's disease expressing sincere remorse and apologized for committing human rights violations for over 90 years.

The bioethical principle of autonomy was strongly affirmed by a 1997 decision of the Tokyo High Court relating to a Jehovah's Witness who had been given a blood transfusion, a medical treatment forbidden by his religion. The decision was made in favor of the plaintiff, as he had not been told that he might be given a blood transfusion under certain circumstances. The notion of "informed consent" was thus taken seriously in legal terms in the context of religious beliefs and bioethical conflicts of decision making when life is at stake (Kimura, 2000).

In 2000, the Japan Medical Association adopted the "Code of Medical Ethics" in six provisions in simplified form. The emphasis on the public role of medical service and contribution to the society through medical works can be seen in provision five (JMA, 2000).

The social concerns facing the increasing number of elderly population and the need of mutual support systems by the local and state and government has led to the realization of "The Long Term Care Insurance Law " in 2000. This was the reflection of the shift in values from traditional ethos of family support to the mutual, societal support mainly to be managed by the community (Kimura, 2002; Ministry of Health, Labour and Welfare, 2003).

Toward Bioethics of Cultural Harmony: The Cloning Prohibition Law in Japan

The contemporary discussion of bioethics in Japan started as a movement among the lay public in the late 1970s. This fact remains symbolic and important in many respects, as evidenced by the increased degree of individual decision making about desired medical treatment, as well as in all areas of daily life.

Japan continues to struggle to recognize bioethics as integral to all spheres of life and to discuss public policy and the environment, as well as to deal with the tension between Western values and traditional Japanese cultural practices. Bioethics has been proposed and developed in Japan as a supra-interdisciplinary endeavor embracing all traditional academic disciplines in equal partnership, for the valuable exchange of ideas and criticism each field has to offer (Kimura, 1986)

There are specific cultural values and customs that are distinctive and non-Western in pattern, but there is heterogeneity, too, and in any case, ethical values change, particularly among the younger generations in Japan. It is true that different cultural and ethical values should be respected, such as key concepts of the dignity of each human person, the importance of the family unit, and community life. But justification of any act or behavior against human dignity and the rights of the person for the sake of cultural tradition is not acceptable.

The notion of harmony is reflected in Article 1 of the Law concerning the Regulation of Cloning Technologies and Other Similar Technologies Relating to Humans, which went into effect in June 2001. This article states that one purpose of the law is to "harmonize the society and peoples' lives with the development of science and technology."

In the international community of the twenty-first century, with the globalization of values focusing on a universally accepted notion of fundamental human rights, the reality of limited resources, and the increasing necessity of mutual cooperation, it is useful to emphasize the twin notion of "related-autonomy" and the Japanese principle of harmony (*wa*) in cultural bioethics.

RIHITO KIMURA (1995)
REVISED BY AUTHOR

BIBLIOGRAPHY

Asyoa, Masahiko. 1996. *Shinto no seishi kan. (The view of life and death in Shintoism)* Tokyo: Perikansha.

Committee for the Investigation of Issues in Organ Transplantation, Japanese Association of Indian and Buddhist Studies. 1990. "Report of the Committee." *Journal of Indian and Buddhist Studies* 39(1): 291–301.

Cook-Deegan, Robert. 1994. "The Gene Wars: Science, Politics, and the Human Genome." New York: W.W. Norton & Company.

Doi, Takeo. 1971. *Amae no kozo.* Tokyo: Kobundo. Translated by John Bester under the title *The Anatomy of Dependence.* Tokyo: Kodansha, 1973.

Endo, Shusaku. 1960. *Umi to dokuyaku.* Tokyo: Bungei Shunju Sha. Translated by Michael Gallagher under the title *The Sea and Poison.* Tokyo: Charles E. Tuttle, 1973.

Fujii, Masao. 1991. "Buddhism and Bioethics." In *Theological Developments in Bioethics, 1988–1990,* edited by B. Andrew Lustig. Dordrecht, Netherlands: Kluwer.

Fujikawa, Yu. 1941. *Nippon Igakushi.* Tokyo: Nissin Shoin.

Fujita, Shinichi. 1980. *Seito shi no mirai.* Tokyo: Asahi Shimbun-sha.

Gomer, Robert, Powell, John W., and Röling, Bert V. A. 1981. "Japan's Biological Weapons, 1930–1945." *Bulletin of the Atomic Scientists* 37(8): 43–53.

Harding, T. W. 1985. *Human Rights and Mental Patients in Japan: Report of a Mission.* Geneva, Switzerland: International Commission of Jurists.

Ivanov, N., and Bogach, V. 1989. *Unlawful Weapon: Who Speaks of Bacteriological Warfare.* Khabarovsk, Russia: Khabarovsk Publishing House. Translated into Japanese by Keisuke Suzuki and Kuniko Nakanishi under the title *Kyofu no Saikinsen.* Tokyo: Kobunsha, 1991.

Japan Ministry of Health and Welfare. Minister's Secretariat. Statistics and Information Department. 1993a. *Health and Welfare Statistics in Japan.* Tokyo: Health and Welfare Statistics Association. In English.

Japan Ministry of Health and Welfare. Minister's Secretariat. Statistics and Information Department. 1993b. *Heisei 4-nen yusei hogo tokei hokoku.* Tokyo: Kosei Tokei Kyokai.

Japan Social Insurance Agency. 1992. *Outline of Social Insurance in Japan.* Tokyo: Japan International Social Security Association.

Japan Medical Association (JMA). 1951. *Physicians' Ethics.* Tokyo: Author.

Japan Medical Association (JMA). 1990. *Setsumei to Doi.* Tokyo: Author.

Japan Medical Association (JMA). 1992. *Makki Iryo ni nozomu Ishi no arikata nitsuiteno Hokoku.* Tokyo: Author.

Japan Medical Association (JMA).2000. "I no Rinri Koryo" (Code of Medical Ethics). *Journal of Japan Medical Association* 124(2).

Japan Medical Association (JMA), ed. 1968. *Ishi rinri runshu.* Tokyo: Kanehara Shuppan.

Japan Medical Association (JMA), ed. 1974. *Raifu Saiensu no Shinpo,* no. 1.

Johnson, Frank A. 1993. *Dependency and Japanese Socialization: Psychoanalytic and Anthropological Investigation into "Amae."* New York: New York University Press.

Kajikawa, Kin-ichiro. 1989. "Japan: A New Field Emerges." *Hastings Center Report* 19 (spec. suppl., July/August): 29–30.

Kimura, Rihito. 1979. "Seimeisosajidai no Shogeki: Baioeshikkusu no chosen" (The impact of life-manipulation era: A challenge of bioethics). *Fukuin to Sekai* (The gospel and the world) 34(11): 26–32.

Kimura, Rihito. 1986. "Bioethik als Metainterdisziplinare Disziplin." *Medizin Mensch Geseeschaft* 11(4): S.247–253.

Kimura, Rihito. 1987a. "Bioethics as a Prescription for Civic Action: The Japanese Interpretation." *Journal of Medicine and Philosophy* 12(3): 267–277.

Kimura, Rihito. 1987b. *Inochi o kangaeru: Baioeshikkusu no susume* (Thinking of life: An introduction to bioethics). Tokyo: Nippon Hyoron Sha.

Kimura, Rihito. 1989a. "Anencephalic Organ Donation: A Japanese Case." *Journal of Medicine and Philosophy* 14(1): 97–102.

Kimura, Rihito. 1989b. "Ethics Committees for 'High-Tech' Innovations in Japan." *Journal of Medicine and Philosophy* 14(4): 457–464.

Kimura, Rihito. 1991a. "Fiduciary Relationships and the Medical Profession: A Japanese Point of View." In *Ethics, Trust, and the Professions: Philosophical and Cultural Aspects,* edited by Edmund D. Pellegrino, Robert M. Veatch, and John P. Langan. Washington, D.C.: Georgetown University Press.

Kimura, Rihito. 1991b. "Japan's Dilemma with the Definition of Death." *Kennedy Institute of Ethics Journal* 1(2): 123–131.

Kimura, Rihito. 1991c. "Jurisprudence in Genetics." In *Ethical Issues of Molecular Genetics in Psychiatry,* ed. Radim J. Srám, S. Bulyzhenkov, V. Bulyzhenkov, et al. Berlin: Springer-Verlag.

Kimura, Rihito. 1993. "Asian Perspectives: Experimentation on Human Subjects in Japan: Bioethical Perspectives in a Cultural Context." In *Ethics and Research on Human Subjects: International Guidelines,* edited by Zbigniew Bankowski and Robert J. Levine. Geneva, Switzerland: Council for International Organizations of Medical Sciences.

Kimura, Rihito. 1997. "Verbrechen gegen die Menschlichkeit: Die vergesseneGeschichte Japans." In *Ethik und Medizin 1947–997: Was leistet die kodifizierung von Ethik?,* eds. U. Troehler and S. Reiter-Theil. Wallstein Verlag.

Kimura, Rihito. 1998a. "Death, Dying, and Advance Directives in Japan: Sociocultural and Legal Points of View." In *Advance Directives and Surrogate Decision Making in Health Care-United States, Germany, and Japan,* eds. Hans-Martin Sass, Robert M. Veatch, and Rihito Kimura. Baltimore, MD: Johns Hopkins University Press.

Kimura, Rihito. 1998b. "Organ Transplantation and Brain Death in Japan—Cultural, Legal and Bioethical Background." *Annals of Transplantation* 3(3): 55–58.

Kimura, Rihito. 1999. "Genetic Diagnosis and Gene Therapy in the Cultural Context: Social and Bioethical Implications in Japan." In *Gene Therapy and Ethics,* ed. Anders Nordgren. Uppsala: Acta Universitatis Upsaliensis.

Kimura, Rihito. 2000. "Jibun no Inochi wa Jibunnde Kimeru" (make your own decision for your own life). Tokyo: Shuei Sha.

Kimura, Rihito. 2002. "Bioethical Public Policy and the Making of the 1997 Japanese Long-Term Care Insurance Law." In *Aging and Social Policy: A German-Japanese Comparison,* eds. H. Conrad and R. Lutzeler. Munich: Iudicium Verlag.

Minami, Hiroko. 1985. "East Meets West: Some Ethical Considerations." *International Journal of Nursing Studies* 22(4): 311–318.

Ministry of Health, Labour, and Welfare. 2003. *Annual Report on Health, Labour, and Welfare 2001–2002: Life of Active Working Generation Around the Economy.* Tokyo: Author.

Oshima, Tomoo. 1983. "The Japanese-German System of Medical Education in the Meiji and Taisho Eras (1868–1926)." In *The History of Medical Education: Proceedings of the 6th International Symposium on the Comparative History of Medicine— East and West,* edited by Teizo Ogawa. Tokyo: Saikon.

Otsuka, Yasuo. 1976. "Chinese Traditional Medicine in Japan." In *Asian Medical Systems: A Comparative Study,* edited by Charles M. Leslie. Berkeley: University of California Press.

Owatari, Hajime et al., eds. 1970. *Wada shinzo shoku o kokuhatsusuru: Igaku no shinpo to byosha no jinken.* Tokyo: Hoken Dojin Sha.

Powell, John W. 1980. "Japan's Germ Warfare: The U.S. Cover-up of a War Crime." *Bulletin of Concerned Asian Scholars* 12(4): 2–17.

Prime Minister's Ad Hoc Research Commission on Brain Death and Organ Transplantation. 1992. *Important Issues Relating to Brain Death and Organ Transplantation (Recommendations).* Tokyo: Ministry of Health and Welfare.

Seikyo Iyobukai. 1982. *Iryo Seikyo no Rekishi to Tokucho.* Tokyo: Iryo Seikyo.

Tamaki, Koshiro. 1993. *Seimei Towa Nanika.* Kyoto, Japan: Hozokan.

Tokyo Metropolitan Government. 2001. *Patients' Bill of Rights.* Tokyo: Hospitals Ethics Committee for the Hospitals of Tokyo Metropolitan Government.

U.S. National Archives. December 1947–June 1949. *Trial Case No. 394: Volume I, Record of Trial in the Case of United States vs. Kajuro Aihara, et 29.* Record Group 331. Record of General Headquarters, Supreme Commander of the Allied Powers. Box 1331, folder nos. 3 and 4. Suitland, MD: Author.

U.S. National Archives. 1949. *Interrogation of Certain Japanese by Russian Prosecutor, August 1, 1947, and Enclosure: Interrogation of Certain Japanese by Russian Prosecutor—The Problem, May 2, 1947.* Record Group 165. Records of the War Department, General and Special Staffs. Reference SWNCC 351/2/D. Suitland, MD: Author.

Williams, Peter, and Wallace, David. 1989. *Unit 731: Japan's Secret Biological Warfare in World War II.* New York: Free Press.

V. SOUTHEAST ASIAN COUNTRIES

Southeast Asia is part of the continent where the major faiths arose; it is still a melting pot of different religious traditions and cultural beliefs, including animism and magic. Despite the rapid social change Southeast Asia has been undergoing, these religious and cultural beliefs remain vital, conditioning people's perceptions, values, attitudes, and behaviors in health and all other areas. An understanding of these beliefs is imperative for the implementation of projects in medicine and public health, and for the maintenance and improvement of public welfare.

This article will first analyze the different types of traditional medicine in Southeast Asian countries, particularly Thailand, the Philippines, Malaysia, and Indonesia, their concepts of health and disease, methods of healing, their practitioners, and their ethics. Second, it will discuss some central biomedical issues in the practice of modern medicine, and the current efforts to teach the new medical ethics at medical schools in these countries. Finally, it will argue as a matter of great urgency the need to promote and strengthen bioethical education and research in Southeast Asia, in order to enable its medical community to cope with the new ethical and moral dilemmas, challenges to its traditional morality and religion.

Magic, Religion, and Naturalism

Medical systems in Southeast Asian countries may be classified into two types, traditional medicine and modern (scientific) medicine. Traditional medicine in turn can be very broadly grouped into three general types, depending on whether it is dominated by magic, religion, or naturalism. Beliefs concerning health, disease and its treatment, and preventive measures are in accord with the type of traditional medicine practiced. When magic is the focus, disease is believed to be caused by sorcery, and countersorcery and other spells are used as medical remedies. Similarly, when religion predominates, disease is attributed to supernatural forces, which must be appealed to or propitiated. When it is dominated by naturalism, disease is defined in terms of natural processes and the imbalance of elements or opposing forces in the body, and a judicious equilibrium is the basis of medical practice.

These traditional medical systems are often a blend of two or more types. Traditional Chinese medicine in Singapore, for example, is largely secular or naturalistic but includes magico-religious elements. Traditional Thai and Malay medicine is mainly magico-religious but is also permeated by elements of naturalistic medicine.

Healers, Shamans, and Mediums

Traditional medicine is integrated into a complex of beliefs and values comprising the worldview of Southeast Asian peoples. The magico-religious medicine of Southeast Asian countries is derived from magico-animistic beliefs that suffuse their cultures. In this cultural orientation, healers are shamans and mediums, and healing is effected through sorcery, exorcism, and spirit possession, assisted when necessary by herbal concoctions and massage.

Spirit possession is believed to be a channel by which deities or spirits of a high order (e.g., spirits of monks or saints) use their divine power to heal the sick. Healing includes a diagnosis of illness and the performance of corresponding magical rites. These magical activities are usually conducted within the religious framework of the healer. Thai Buddhist shamans, for example, do not practice on *wan phra,* a Buddhist Sabbath observed at the four phases of the moon, and they make use of recitations from the Pali Buddhist texts. The Malay Muslim shamans add verses from the Qur'an to their healing, while the Taoist shamans in Singapore recite Tao incantations in their practice.

Herbalists, Folk Medicine Doctors, and Monks

While the magico-religious medicine of Southeast Asia is tied to its culture, its naturalistic medicine is heir to the Indian ayurvedic medical system and traditional Chinese medicine. In these medical traditions disease is understood as a disturbance of inner equilibrium that can be corrected through the administration of herbal solutions. Thus this form of medicine is designated as naturalistic or herbal, and its practitioners are known as herbalists, ayurvedics, or folk medicine doctors. In Thailand many of these healers are Buddhist monks, who usually combine herbal treatment with religious rituals (e.g., the taking of religious vows and the sprinkling of lustral water) and meditation. Some of these monks have been credited with successful rehabilitation of drug addicts. The use of meditation differentiates traditional Thai medicine from the medicines of other Southeast Asian countries.

Medical Ethics in Traditional Medicine

The preoccupation of traditional medicine with magic, religion, and herbal concoctions is due to its holistic approach to health and healthcare. The practitioners work on their patients at both the physical level and the psychological/spiritual level. While herbal concoctions are mainly used to cure patients' physical illness, magico-religious rites have a therapeutic effect on their minds. The rites reassure patients of divine blessing and protection, and strengthen their self-confidence.

This traditional method of healing may be especially suitable today for Southeast Asians, who, living in societies with increased urbanization and industrialization, need physical, psychological, and spiritual care to enable them to cope with such change and the strains and stresses of modern life. Modern Western medicine with its advanced knowledge and technology has more effective means of healing, but it divides the patient into organ systems and treats only those parts of the person that are afflicted by a specific disease, rather than the whole person. Southeast Asians, who do not divide the person in such a way but need treatment with scientific medicine, will often seek traditional medicine as a supplement to scientific medicine. For example, a patient with a brain tumor might request magico-religious rites from a Buddhist shaman in order to ensure the success of an operation to be performed by a neurosurgeon. It was reported in the Thai press that the patient who uses this approach experiences such an operation with great calm and recovers more quickly.

Medical ethics in Southeast Asian traditional medicine is not codified but is inherent in the values and practices of its practitioners. Some of these healers are Buddhist monks whose ethic of conduct approximates the Buddhist ideal of showing compassion and loving kindness. For example, they do not charge fees and solicit no gifts for their healing. Other healers may demand fees for their service, but their code of ethics requires that they be under some self-imposed moral restraints, for example, that they not practice for monetary gain; that they serve their patients impartially, with only their benefit in mind; and that they not take cases that they cannot treat successfully. Having no common standard of practice to follow, the healers' success depends on their own virtues and healing powers. Their services are sought as long as they can instill belief and faith. They sink into anonymity when they are seen as charlatans or when doubt about their powers arises.

Modern Medicine and Healthcare Allocation

Modern medicine came to Southeast Asia during the colonial period, starting in the eighteenth century. Since then it has made tremendous progress. It has greatly benefited people in Southeast Asia, but beneath the surface of these benefits there is a multitude of attendant ethical problems.

The most important concerns the macroallocation of limited healthcare resources, specifically, grave inadequacies and inequalities in their distribution. Nearly 80 percent of the population of Southeast Asia lives in rural areas. Most of these people are poor and need more medical services than affluent people. Their health depends mostly on medical services provided by the government through hospitals and public health centers. Yet many of these services are inaccessible to them. In Thailand, for example, 62 percent of doctors and nurses are in Bangkok, where most of the country's hospitals are, while there are too few doctors and nurses in the provinces, where most of the people are. There are also too many hospitals in Bangkok and too few neighborhood clinics and public health centers in rural areas.

Southeast Asian countries, eager to bring the benefits of modern medicine to their people, have modeled patterns of healthcare and education of health personnel in their countries on those in more affluent and developed nations in the West, particularly Britain and the United States, without regard to social, economic, and cultural differences. As a result, limited healthcare resources are allocated to catastrophic or hospital-oriented medicine, despite the fact that most of the diseases afflicting the majority of people in these countries are preventable. Even though it has become increasingly clear that these patterns are irrelevant to the health needs of developing Southeast Asian countries, Western-trained health policymakers are very reluctant to deviate from these models, which are being questioned even in the developed nations where they originated.

Politically pressured to show more concern for the poor, governments in some Southeast Asian countries are now acting to correct some of the imbalance of resource allocation. The present Thai government, for example, though still following Western models, has increased funding for preventive health measures and public health services. More provincial hospitals and health clinics are being built, and paramedics and auxiliaries trained to staff them. Thai medical schools now require medical graduates to spend at least three years in the provinces and rural areas, and a plan is being devised to provide incentive subsidies to doctors and nurses working in poor rural areas. Many more corrective measures are needed to create a just and reasonable allocation of the country's overall healthcare resources such that the general standard of health and healthcare can be raised nationwide.

Shortages of health personnel in Southeast Asia have been aggravated by the fact that so many doctors and nurses are lured from their homelands, where they are in desperately short supply, to serve the less critical health needs of affluent nations. The Filipino Department of Health, for example, reported in 1990 that two hundred towns in the Philippines had no resident doctors and that seven out of ten persons died without even being seen by a physician. Only an estimated 32 percent of all qualified Filipino doctors and nurses practice their profession in their own country. This shortage of doctors and nurses, typical of developing Southeast Asian countries, makes it much more difficult for governments to provide adequate healthcare to many of their people.

Human Experimentation

Another important ethical issue in Southeast Asia concerns human experimentation. Since the adoption of modern medicine in the nineteenth century, medical schools in Southeast Asian countries have become more research oriented and are increasingly moving into the area of human experimentation. In violation of international agreements, Western researchers who have been restricted in the kind of human experiments they may do in their own countries are turning to Southeast Asia to conduct their research where there is less public awareness of the issue and less government regulation. These researchers are usually assisted by Southeast Asian colleagues, who engage in all kinds of human experimentation no longer permitted in the West, including forms of psychosurgery and genetic experiments. Drug testing and tests of new contraceptives have been carried out in Southeast Asian countries on a massive scale. Nearly all of these experiments use poor people as subjects, without their informed consent. Abuse of poor patients and the violation of their human rights in public hospitals often occur.

The governments and the medical communities in Thailand and the Philippines have taken some measures to prevent the exploitation of the poor by researchers. In 1985 the National Research Council of Thailand formulated guidelines for research involving human subjects; these guidelines were later revised and made more elaborate. In 1987 the Philippine Council for Health Research and Development published *National Guidelines for Biomedical Research Involving Human Subjects,* similar to those delineated by the World Medical Association at Helsinki in 1964 and revised at Tokyo in 1975. These guidelines on human experimentation laid special emphasis on voluntary informed consent of research subjects. Unfortunately, both in Thailand and in the Philippines there is as yet little compliance with these guidelines or accountability for their violation.

The creation of national ethics committees and institutional review committees in Thailand and the Philippines is another Southeast Asian response to the issue of human experimentation. These institutional committees are concerned primarily with the evaluation of the scientific value of research proposals; the national ethics committees are expected to deal with the ethical aspects of experiment proposals and their protocols. Both the proper role and the composition of national ethics committees are still being debated. At present such committees are far from being instruments for effective control of experimentation in Southeast Asian countries. The Thai committee, for example, does not scrupulously supervise procedures for gaining the needed informed consent. Nor does the committee intervene when it believes an experiment is being conducted without proper ethical consideration. A 1988 study in Thailand indicated that often the procedures followed in many hospitals made it unlikely that the patients were fully informed or gave genuinely voluntary consent. Though many questions are being raised about it, this national committee could become an effective means to prevent morally questionable experiments on human subjects from being performed.

Traditional Morality and New Ethical Issues

The traditional morality of Southeast Asia is permeated by the ethical traditions of Hinduism, Buddhism, Christianity, and Islam. The emergence of modern medicine has produced many new ethical issues that challenge traditional morality. For example, within this morality is the cardinal Buddhist principle of *adhimsa,* which directs that life not be taken and harm not be done. Modern medicine with its advanced technologies has produced ethical dilemmas concerning how to abide by these precepts. For example, does removal of a life-support system constitute violation of these precepts? Is allowing a seriously defective infant to die untreated a form of *harming* or *killing*? Is it morally acceptable for patients to take their own lives in cases of lingering terminal illness or chronic severe pain or disability? Is it morally acceptable that doctors or nurses act upon the expressed desire of patients and assist them in committing suicide when they are unable to act for themselves or to find the means to do so? Is removal of a kidney from a live donor a morally justified form of harming?

Traditional morality also dictates that we not deceive others. One of the five precepts of Buddhist morality prohibits falsehood. Does this include failing to tell a terminally ill patient the truth about his or her prognosis? Is administering placebos a morally justified exception to the moral rule against deception? Can the patient be deceived about a treatment if the doctor or nurse thinks it is in the patient's best interest? Must all the truth about a double-blind trial in human research be told in order to obtain the *informed consent* that the new medical ethics calls for? These are examples of new questions raised as a result of the encounter between modern medicine and traditional morality in Southeast Asia. Traditional morality is no more prepared to deal with these new moral issues than are the Southeast Asian scientists and physicians caught in the middle of them.

The development of modern medicine has raised questions about the adequacy of traditional morality. For example, the traditional Buddhist concept of death as the cessation of all vital functions cannot accommodate the recent development in modern medicine, in which some cells or organs may be sustained by artificial means after the cessation of all vital functions. Nor does it facilitate early retrieval of organs for transplantation. Southeast Asians must rethink and reinterpret the applications of their traditional morality to cope with the advanced knowledge and technologies of modern medicine. For example, as technologies for behavior control and modification are available through drugs, electrostimulation, electroshock treatments, psychological manipulation, psychosurgery, and genetic engineering, the traditional precept of "do no harm" to an existent being may be stretched to cover the question of whether we have the right to *create* a being of our own design.

Teaching and Other Bioethical Activities

Southeast Asian medical students usually learn about medical ethics in classes, and from time to time through lectures outside of regular classes. They are also encouraged to follow the example of morally respected elder doctors. In the past the teaching of medical ethics at medical schools in Southeast Asian countries was integrated into other courses and was primarily concerned with professional etiquette as developed in the West or culled from the teachings of Buddhism, Hinduism, or Islam.

The new medical ethics, or bioethics, was initiated in Southeast Asian countries as a response of scholars and medical professionals to the impact of modern medicine on the life and well-being of people in their countries. Through the combined efforts of Christian clergy and doctors, the Center for Biomedical Ethics Development was established in Indonesia in 1983, primarily to enhance the development of bioethics and Christian values in medicine. Its present activities include the formulation of hospital ethical codes for Indonesian doctors and nurses, and the promotion of bioethics education at hospitals and universities through lectures, seminars, and regular meetings.

Also in 1983, the Bioethics Study Group, consisting principally of Western-trained philosophers and doctors, was established at Mahidol University, a major education and research university in Thailand, to initiate the teaching of bioethics at the university and to bring the awareness of bioethical issues to the public and concerned authorities. By 1988 three full-credit, separate courses were being taught. Through these courses students are exposed to bioethical issues and the way these issues are being addressed and resolved in the United States and other Western countries. They are also encouraged to engage in ethical reflection on those issues as they arise in Thailand, and to find solutions that reflect Thai cultural values. The group has planned to initiate a graduate program in bioethics in 1993 and has created small teams at six other medical schools to stimulate and promote bioethical activities there.

The Southeast Asian Center of Bioethics was established in the Philippines in 1987 by a group of Catholic priests and doctors as a result of the visit of the International Federation of Catholic Universities in the same year. Since its inception the Center has focused its activities on the promotion of interest in and concern with bioethics through teaching, research, seminars, and monthly meetings to discuss bioethical issues confronted by the scientific and medical community in the Philippines. Thus the value of bioethics is appreciated in Thailand, Indonesia, and the Philippines, but it is less recognized in other countries.

All the work done in bioethics has been based on Western models of health and healthcare delivery systems, and on principles derived from the Western moral tradition and specific ethical issues that are relevant to the particularities of Western culture. It is urgent that Southeast Asian academics and medical professionals begin the task of defining and clarifying bioethical issues as they affect their own countries' health and healthcare systems, and that they find resolutions in keeping with the moral principles, values, priorities, and social needs of their countries.

PINIT RATANAKUL (1995)

BIBLIOGRAPHY

Bryant, John. 1969. *Health and the Developing World.* Ithaca, NY: Cornell University Press.

De Castro, Leonardo D. 1990. "The Philippines: A Public Awakening." *Hastings Center Report* 20(2)(March–April): 27–28.

Heinze, Ruth-Inge. 1988. *Trance and Healing in Southeast Asia Today.* Bangkok: White Lotus.

Kleinman, Arthur. 1980. *Patients and Healers in the Context of Culture: An Exploration of the Borderland Between Anthropology, Medicine and Psychiatry.* Berkeley: University of California Press.

Leslie, Charles, ed. 1976. *Asian Medical Systems: A Comparative Study.* Berkeley: University of California Press.

Mitchell, David, ed. 1982. *Indonesian Medical Traditions: Bringing Together the Old and the New.* Clayton, Victoria: Monash University.

Philippine Council for Health Research and Development. 1985. *National Guidelines for Biomedical Research Involving Human Subjects.* Manila: Author.

Ratanakul, Pinit. 1988. "Bioethics in Thailand: The Struggle for Buddhist Solutions." *Journal of Medicine and Philosophy* 13(3): 301–312.

Ratanakul, Pinit. 1990. "Thailand: Refining Cultural Values." *Hastings Center Report* 20(2): 25–27.

Tumbiah, S. J. 1973. "Form and Meaning of Magical Acts: A Point of View." In *Modes of Thought: Essays on Thinking in Western and Non-Western Societies,* pp. 199–229, ed. Robin Horton and Ruth Finnegan. London: Faber and Faber.

MEDICAL FUTILITY

• • •

For the first three decades after the introduction of life-sustaining medical technology in the 1970s and 1980s, a central question was: When can patients or their families refuse life-sustaining interventions—including interventions wanted by physicians? More recently, an opposite question has been asked and heavily debated: When can physicians unilaterally refuse patient or family requests for life-sustaining interventions on the basis that such interventions would be futile? This debate has shed light on many issues, including the difference between positive and negative rights; the difference between futility and rationing as a basis for denying care; the nature of professional responsibility; and the optimum way to discuss end-of-life choices with patients and their families. In the end, however, futility has remained an elusive concept, and most commentators have rejected unilateral decisions by physicians in favor of good communication and institutional policies for negotiating disputes.

Positive versus Negative Rights

Arguably, the most prominent debate in bioethics from the early 1960s to the early twenty-first century has been the one surrounding the right to refuse treatment. From Karen Quinlan to Nancy Cruzan, the United States has seen a series of court decisions, professional guidelines, and laws that establish the rights of patients or their surrogates to make end-of-life decisions. These cases, however, all involved patients or families who sought to limit life-sustaining treatment in the face of physicians or institutions who wanted to continue treatment. It is simply mistaken to argue that because patients have a right to refuse treatment they also have a right to demand it.

The rights delineated in treatment refusal cases were negative rights, the right to be left alone and to not be touched without consent; such rights can be traced to the Constitutional rights of privacy, liberty, and religious choice, or to the common-law right against battery. In contrast, a positive right, the right that something be done, implies both the patient's right to choose a specific intervention and a coexisting obligation of the physician to provide it (Brett and McCullough). Claims to negative rights are generally considered to be more powerful than claims to positive rights.

It is obvious that patients do not have rights to treatment that falls well out of the standard of care—for example, hip replacement surgery when there is nothing wrong with the patient's hip. But do U.S. citizens have a right to beneficial care? The answer to that question is being hotly debated in the political arena and does not appear to be near resolution. Those in favor of limiting futile care argue that a patient cannot demand a treatment that is futile when a general right to medical care that is clearly beneficial has not yet been established.

Defining Futility

While the word *futility* has a categorical ring, it is actually quite difficult to define with precision. Futility must always be discussed with a specific intervention and result in mind. Intervention A is futile if it is not successful in achieving goal B. In contrast, intervention A might be successful in achieving goal C. Without specifying interventions and goals, discussions about futility can be misleading or confusing. For example, asking a patient if she would like to be put on a mechanical ventilator identifies a specific intervention, but no goal. One goal might be to stay alive as long as possible, even if this means spending the last weeks of life in an intensive care unit, attached to the machine. Another goal might be to recover, be removed from the ventilator, and return home. Without discussing specific goals, the patient's acceptance or refusal of mechanical ventilation leaves too much to the imagination.

In their 1990 article, "Medical Futility," Larry S. Schneiderman and his colleagues distinguished between the effects of a given medical intervention and its benefits. They argued that "the goal of medical treatment is not merely to cause an effect on some portion of the patient's anatomy, physiology, or chemistry, but to benefit the patient as a whole" (Schneiderman, Jecker, and Jonsen, p. 950). They also stated that futility should be defined within the context of evolving standards of care and that the goal of medicine is to achieve a benefit above a certain minimum qualitative or quantitative threshold.

Quantitative futility implies that the chance of achieving a specific goal, while statistically possible, is very improbable and cannot be systematically produced. Critics point out that physician experience is insufficient to form a consistent and reliable basis for quantitative judgments about futility. Moreover, physicians themselves do not agree about what the threshold should be for quantitative futility (McCrary et al.). Published series of cases are few in number and do not take adequate account of patient variables such as severity of illness or other, co-existing medical problems.

Qualitative futility, according to Schneiderman and colleagues, involves an intervention that may have a good chance of having a specific effect, but the effect provides no benefit to the patient. The problem here is that *benefit* is a value-laden notion, and patients may not have the same values as physicians (Youngner, 1988). Schneiderman and colleagues' two examples of qualitative futility illustrate this point. Their first example is the state of permanent unconsciousness. A patient in this condition, they argued, has no right to be sustained in a vegetative state. Critics, however, point out that a minority of persons (including a minority of physicians) does see such life as meaningful, and that in a pluralistic democracy it would be wrong for individual physicians to impose their *majority* values on others.

Schneiderman and colleagues cited patients who require constant monitoring, ventilatory support, and intensive care nursing as their second example of qualitative futility. While acknowledging that sometimes such patients might have worthwhile goals, for example, living long enough to say good-bye to a relative, Schneiderman and colleagues argued that judgment about the validity of the goal should be left to the *compassion* of the physician. Many would see this as an outmoded and unacceptable form of paternalism.

Thus, while the notion of futility captures an important concern about the harmful overtreatment of patients at the end of their lives, it remains difficult to define with precision. As we will see later, rather than serving as a trump card that physicians can play to unilaterally overrule the wishes of patients and family, discussions about futility may be most useful in stimulating a process of communication and negotiation about setting realistic patient-centered goals.

Futility and Rationing

The notion of futility is often confounded with that of rationing and justified by the need to limit the cost of healthcare. Despite important parallels between the concepts of rationing and futility (both have implications for resource consumption and the cost of care), they have distinct moral and conceptual meanings (Jecker and Schneiderman). Futility represents a clinical judgment that a specific intervention will not be successful in achieving a specific goal for a specific patient. Rationing means that interventions that do provide benefit will be denied to at least some persons who could benefit from them. While it is true that withholding futile care could save money, a treatment is futile whether resources are scarce or abundant. Futility is a judgment based on empirical evidence and clinical experience. Rationing is based on theories of social justice—that is, who is more deserving of limited medical resources. Rationing is a public issue and, in a democracy, should be resolved through the political process. Futility, at least according to its defenders, is an objective medical determination. As such, they argue, it can be defined by physicians. Certainly, in a rational scheme of cost management, futile treatments should be eliminated before beneficial ones are rationed.

Professional Responsibility

Much of the impetus for acting on futility judgments has come from physicians and nurses who think they are violating important professional values—to help and do no harm—when they cave in to demands for futile interventions, such as cardiopulmonary resuscitation (CPR). Physicians are more than body mechanics who follow the orders of patients no matter what the consequences to those patients. CPR, for example, is a very aggressive, but notoriously ineffective, intervention in severely debilitated and dying patients. It involves multiple invasive procedures that often cause tremendous suffering (e.g., broken ribs) and a loss of dignity.

Avoiding Futility Confrontations

Too often, confrontations about futility are the result of poor communication and the conditions under which care is delivered in acute care settings. For example, health professionals sometimes fail to identify and set treatment goals. In their discussions with patients and families, health professionals focus on specific treatment interventions rather than on the goals that such interventions may or may not achieve. Questions such as, "Do you want us to start your heart again if it stops?" or "Do you want to be placed on a mechanical ventilator if you stop breathing?" are confusing, and even misleading, until potential goals of those particular interventions have been discussed and agreed upon.

Medical interventions are not ends in themselves; they are means of achieving desired goals. The job of the physician is first to help identify patients' goals and then to help them select among the treatments that can achieve those goals. For example, if a specific patient's goal is to return home with an independent lifestyle, aggressive interventions such as CPR and mechanical ventilation might well fail to meet that goal. On the other hand, if the patient's goal is extended life, even if its quality is significantly compromised, the aggressive intervention may not be futile at all. Sometimes the most difficult task of the physician is to help the patient and family come to terms with the reality that the

goal they seek—for example, recovery and return home—cannot be achieved. Until goals have been understood and agreed upon, conversation about a particular treatment intervention is unlikely to be productive.

Sometimes, patients or families make unreasonable demands for care because they simply do not understand the clinical realities. It is not good practice to ask people if they want to be resuscitated when they do not know that the chances of resuscitation are small (near zero in patients with multiple failing organs) and the harms great (e.g., broken ribs, collapsed lungs). In a 1988 article, Donald J. Murphy reported that only 10 percent of multiply impaired elderly patients in a particular nursing home had "do not resuscitate" orders. A new medical director began informing patients and their families about the seriousness of their medical conditions, the burdens of aggressive intervention, and the small likelihood of success. As a result, twenty-three of twenty-four patients chose not to be resuscitated in the event of cardiac arrest.

Confusion is another reason patients and families demand treatment that physicians think is futile. There is no evidence that physicians agree on what counts as futility. Therefore, a patient or family may well become confused after talking with different physicians, each of whom has a different notion about whether the situation is futile. Moreover, confusion is aggravated by fragmentation and discontinuities in patient care. In large medical centers, patients are often seen by several specialist consultants. Each is responsible for one organ system and may communicate information that does not accurately reflect the overall prognosis of the patient. Communication may be further confused in academic teaching hospitals by the fragmentation of care caused by monthly rotations of medical trainees and supervising physicians, and shift changes for nurses and other healthcare professionals. If patients are lucky enough to have primary care physicians in the community, those physicians are too often not available to coordinate and manage the care of their patients who are in the hospital. The most important strategy for resolving conflicts about care at the end of life is to help everyone involved in a patient's care operate with a common understanding of the realistic medical prognosis and to then focus on the goals of the patient and family that are achievable (Youngner, 1994).

Sometimes, demands for futile treatment grow out of mistrust. Although some people are suspicious by nature, people often have good reasons for mistrust. For example, patients and families may have heard previous predictions of doom that were not fulfilled. Others may have had dealings with physicians who were not straightforward. Socioeconomic and cultural factors may also influence perceptions and attitudes. African Americans, for example, have good historic reasons for mistrusting physicians and the institutions where they receive care. The legacy of the Tuskegee Syphilis Study, during the middle of the last century, remains a part of African-American consciousness. During this study, in which African-American men were enrolled, the researchers left the subjects untreated for syphilis so that the natural course of the disease could be studied. Even today, remnants of racial inequities remain in the U.S. healthcare system. For example, in many urban hospitals, few members of the medical staff and administration are minorities, whereas large numbers of the patients are. In addition, many people who are poor or members of minority groups have inadequate access to healthcare unless they are extremely ill. There is also evidence that minority and lower economic status are associated with preferences for more aggressive care (Garrett et al.). It is little wonder that some persons are suspicious when told by strange physicians in the middle of the night that further life-sustaining efforts would be futile.

Conclusions

There seems to be a growing consensus that futility has not been adequately defined or accepted by the medical community and the public. By and large, courts have rejected the notion that physicians should make unilateral judgments about what counts as a benefit to a patient or what chance is a chance worth taking. Paul R. Helft and his colleagues, in their 2000 article, "The Rise and Fall of the Futility Movement," concluded that a consensus has not been reached regarding the arguments for the supremacy of the rights of physicians or patients/families in judging futility. Instead, many clinicians and institutions have shifted the focus to developing a framework for discussing and resolving futility disputes. For example, some authors have emphasized a preemptive approach in which primary care physicians take responsibility for setting goals and discussing futile treatments before a crisis develops. In both Denver and Houston, community-wide policies have been developed that neither define futility nor give physicians unilateral power to act on their futility judgments (Murphy and Barbour; Halevy and Brody). Instead, these policies outline formal steps for conflict resolution in healthcare institutions.

STUART J. YOUNGNER

SEE ALSO: *Beneficence; Competence; Health Policy in the United States; Medicine, Art of; Medicine, Profession of; Nursing Ethics; Pain and Suffering; Professional-Patient Relationship; Responsibility; Technology*

BIBLIOGRAPHY

Brett, Alan S., and McCullough, Lawrence B. 1986. "When Patients Request Specific Interventions: Defining the Limits of the Physician's Obligation." *New England Journal of Medicine* 315(21): 1347–1351.

Garrett, J. M.; Harris, R. P.; Norburn, J. K.; et al. 1993. "Life-Sustaining Treatment during Terminal Illness: Who Wants It?" *Journal of General Internal Medicine* 8: 361–368.

Halevy, Amir, and Brody, Baruch A. 1996. "A Multi-institutional Collaborative Policy on Medical Futility." *Journal of the American Medical Association* 276(7): 571–574.

Helft, Paul R., Siegler, Mark, and Lantos, John. 2000. "The Rise and Fall of the Futility Movement." *New England Journal of Medicine* 343(4): 293–296.

Jecker, Nancy S., and Schneiderman, Lawrence S. 1992. "Futility and Rationing." *American Journal of Medicine* 92: 189–196.

McCrary, S. Van; Swanson, J. W.; Youngner, Stuart J.; et al. 1994. "Physician's Quantitative Assessments of Medical Futility." *Journal of Clinical Ethics* 5: 100–105.

Murphy, Donald J. 1988. "Do-Not-Resuscitate Orders: Time for Reappraisal in Long-Term-Care Institutions." *Journal of the American Medical Association* 260(14): 2098–2101.

Murphy, Donald J., and Barbour, E. 1994. "GUIDe (Guidelines for the Use of Intensive Care in Denver): A Community Effort to Define Futile and Inappropriate Care." *New Horizons* 2(3): 326–331.

Schneiderman, Lawrence S.; Jecker, Nancy S.; and Jonsen, Albert R. 1990. "Medical Futility: Its Meaning and Ethical Implications." *Annals of Internal Medicine* 112(12): 949–954.

Veatch, Robert M., and Spicer, Carol M. 1992. "Medically Futile Care: The Role of the Physician in Setting Limits." *American Journal of Law and Medicine* 18: 15–36.

Youngner, Stuart J. 1988. "Who Defines Futility?" *Journal of the American Medical Association* 260(14): 2094–2095.

Youngner, Stuart J. 1994. "Applying Futility: Saying No Is Not Enough." *Journal of the American Geriatrics Society* 42: 887–889.

MEDICAL GENETICS: PRACTICE OF MEDICAL GENETICS

SEE *Genetic Testing and Screening*

MEDICARE

• • •

At its inception in 1966, the Medicare program was understood as a way to assure elderly persons a stable place in the mainstream of American medicine. Over the first quarter-century of its operation, however, Medicare increasingly came to be viewed as an instrument to influence the character and costs of doctors, hospitals, and health insurance. In 1986 Medicare marked its twentieth birthday with considerable fanfare. In 1991, along with American medicine, Medicare faced severe financial pressures, and its silver anniversary was not celebrated; nor was its thirty-fifth anniversary much celebrated on June 30, 2001.

The Origins of Medicare

When the Great Depression made economic insecurity a pressing national concern, the social insurance reformers thought health insurance should be part of a comprehensive American scheme of social protection. From 1936 through the late 1940s, there were recurrent calls to incorporate universal health insurance within America's nascent welfare state. But, despite the broad public support for national health insurance, a conservative coalition in Congress defeated such measures (Marmor, 1973).

By 1952 the original architects of Social Security, well aware of this frustrating opposition, had formulated a plan of incremental expansion of government health insurance. The proponents of what became known as Medicare restricted the category of beneficiaries to retired persons, while retaining the conceptual link to social insurance. Medicare would provide retirees with limited hospitalization insurance—a partial plan for that part of the population whose financial fears of illness were as real as their difficulty in purchasing health insurance at an affordable cost. So began the long battle to turn a national health insurance proposal acceptable to the public into one passable by the Congress.

These origins had much to do with the initial design of the Medicare program—and with the expectations of how it would develop over time. The incrementalist strategy assumed that hospitalization coverage was the appropriate first step in benefits and that wider benefits would be enacted later under a common pattern of Social Security financing. Likewise, the strategy's proponents assumed that eligibility would be expanded gradually to include most, if not all, of the population, extending first, perhaps, to children and pregnant women. Medicare enthusiasts took for granted that the rhetoric of enactment should emphasize the expansion of access to medical care, not its regulation and reform. The clear aim was to reduce the risks of financial disaster for older people and their families, and the clear understanding was that Congress would demand a largely hands-off posture

toward the doctors and hospitals providing the care Medicare would finance. Some twenty-five years after the program's enactment, it is taken for granted that how—or how much—one pays for medical care affects the care given. In the buildup to the passage of the Medicare bill (in July 1965), however, no such presumption existed.

Once this incrementalist proposal was outlined, who and what shaped its fate? Medicare's principal antagonists, and their adversarial methods, illustrate a familiar American form of ideological politics. The most prominent opponents—national medical, business, and labor organizations—engaged in open, hostile communication and brought into their opposing camps many groups whose economic interests were not directly affected by the Medicare outcome. Both the contest and the contestants remained remarkably stable from 1952 to 1964—two well-defined camps with opposing views reigned, and few groups remained impartial or uncommitted.

The particular features of the political environment in 1965 help explain details of the original Medicare program that remain problematic decades later. The overwhelming Democratic victory of 1964 seemed to guarantee that hospitalization insurance for older Americans would pass in 1965. President Lyndon B. Johnson's commitment to Medicare was made plain in his presidential campaign, and the new Congress of 1965 acted to prevent further delays in the president's Great Society agenda. The result, however, was far more complex than expected. The certainty that a Medicare bill would be enacted transformed the struggle from a polemic over Medicare's wisdom to a complicated strategy game about exactly what the program would do. Out of that game came the benefits, financing, and administrative design of the operational Medicare program. Few participants had expected Medicare to pay physicians at all, let alone their "reasonable and customary" charges in a new "Part B" of the program. And, while reimbursing hospitals (under Part A) using the Blue Cross formula of reasonable costs was anticipated, the Department of Health, Education, and Welfare hardly imagined the inflationary impact this would have.

The Development of Medicare

Initially, Medicare's administrators accommodated the demands of medical providers for a largely hands-off stance by public regulators. Out of this period—described by Columbia University political scientist Lawrence Brown in 1985 as "consensual corporatism"—emerged rapid inflation in Medicare's expenditures and the fumbling efforts to find acceptable means to control its costs.

From 1972 to the beginning of the 1980s, Medicare's woes were masked by the national preoccupation with the mix of inflation and unemployment known as stagflation, with broader proposals to reform American medicine, and with the growing appeal of *pro-competitive* alternatives to public regulation of discrete programs like Medicare and Medicaid. This period was characterized by the growing dispersal of government regulation among federal and state agencies (what Brown called "inverted corporatism"). The frustrating experience with health planning, with experiments in hospital reimbursement, and with the rapid growth of costs prompted broader reform approaches. A striking illustration of both the problems and the frustration was the addition of a special disease program under Medicare: one for all Americans suffering from renal failure. Enacted with great fanfare in 1972, the End-Stage Renal Disease Program grew rapidly—in beneficiaries, in costs, and in complexity. And it soon became a symbol of disappointment with traditional ideas of government health insurance (Starr). Throughout the 1970s, health policy experts produced a bewildering array of reform proposals, but Medicare's reform remained a special world of policy specialists, congressional committees, and the responsible executive agency, Social Security's Bureau of Health Insurance, until the Health Care Finance Agency (HCFA; now called the Centers for Medicare and Medicaid Services, or CMS) took over in 1977.

A third period of Medicare's administrative history—which Brown labeled "technocratic corporatism"—flowered in the 1980s. With universal health insurance dislodged from the national agenda, the attention of policymakers and technical experts returned to Medicare itself. Medicare and Social Security had been protected under the mantle of social-insurance theories of entitlement, and by the elderly population's reputed political clout. That protected status was what the budget and tax politics of the 1980s were to challenge.

Three developments exemplify this period, which extended to the mid-1990s. First, there were continuing efforts to reduce the rate of expenditure growth in Medicare, efforts that initially shifted costs to the elderly population, and later burdened hospitals and physicians. Second, there was the surprisingly rapid enactment in 1983 of a new form of hospital reimbursement within Medicare: the widely noted diagnosis related group (DRG) method of prospective payment. Developed by technocrats in the academy and within HCFA, supported by policy experts within the Congress, and with some operational trials in New Jersey, DRGs dominated the hospital world of the 1980s and symbolized the faith in scientific, apolitical answers to Medicare's troubles. At this time, there was no specific provision for monitoring the quality of hospital care, though there was no question of the potential effects on patient care of changing hospital financial incentives so drastically (Smith).

The third development, a new federal institution named the Prospective Payment Commission, became the monitor of DRGs, and later in the decade it spawned a similar institution for Medicare's Part B medical insurance, the Physician Payment Review Commission. It was assumed that the associated peer review organizations would take care of balancing Medicare's cost and quality.

The irony of the Reagan era is that an administration committed ideologically to free markets produced the most obvious examples of administered prices—the payment of hospitals by the diagnosis related group method—in American medicine. At the same time, increases in the medical expenses paid directly by elderly persons prompted what came to be known as the *catastrophic debacle* of 1987–1989. The Reagan administration proposed, and the Congress more generously delivered, a complicated piece of legislation to cover the catastrophic expenses of the elderly. A firestorm of protest erupted over the financing of this benefit expansion (affecting largely the more affluent elderly), and in 1989, for the first time in Medicare's history, the Congress repealed a benefit that had been regarded as a gift to the program's beneficiaries.

Twenty-five years after enactment of the Medicare program, its budget woes were part of the national preoccupation with increasing public deficits. The catastrophic debacle had symbolized and worsened the charges of *generational inequity,* with *greedy geezers* caricatured as the enemies of America's children, future, and tradition of fairness. With deficits untamed, further cuts in Medicare's rate of expenditure growth remained on the policy agenda in 1992 and thereafter, even as the nation debated more comprehensive forms of medical-care reform.

Attempts at Reform

In fact, the period between 1992 and 2002 was full of surprises. Anyone who observed the fight over the Clinton health-reform proposal would hardly have expected Republican leaders in the Congress to later promote a system of vouchers for Medicare that resembled Clinton's model of universal vouchers. In debates over the Balanced Budget Amendments of 1997 and later, previous critics of managed competition for all Americans became advocates for using that model for Medicare. The puzzle is why this apparent reversal took place.

Understanding the reversal requires distinguishing Republican philosophical distaste for *big government* initiatives (like the Clinton proposal) from Republican pragmatism about how to control the budgets of existing federal programs (like Medicare). Vouchers for Medicare seemed, in the mid-1990s, an acceptable way to reduce federal expenditures and secure the balanced budget that fiscal policy conservatives had long sought (White). The presumption of the voucher advocates was that Medicare beneficiaries with a fixed sum (euphemistically described as *premium support*), would shop for the insurance plan they wanted, with competition among plans holding down inflation. Relying on that reasoning, advocates projected considerable savings from what Medicare had been predicted to spend in the decades ahead. And, with that, the game shifted to promoting expanded benefits, especially the coverage of prescription drugs that Medicare did not insure outside of the hospital environment. With cost control predicted, benefits expanded, competition at work, and choice to be enhanced, the conventional claim by the late 1990s was that Medicare would finally be ready for the twenty-first century.

The suggestion that Medicare required fundamental alteration is precisely what a substantial proportion of the elite political community believed at this time. What is striking upon reflection is how unsubstantiated were the premises from which the reform proposals proceeded. Medicare was supposedly not sustainable in its traditional form. Sure to "run out of money" over time, Medicare was regularly labeled as archaic and out of touch with medical realities. This was what the Bipartisan Commission on the Future of Medicare sought to communicate in 1999, though their proposal fell short of enough votes in the commission.

In fact, Medicare was hardly unsustainable. In 1997–1998, Medicare's outlays increased by only 1.5 per cent, and for most of its history its costs have increased no more than the private health insurance plans with which it has been compared. The claim that Medicare was archaic represented sheer perversity. The developments in American medical care during the 1990s had made managed care a source of jokes among ordinary Americans, not a model to be followed. The appeal to the supposed virtues of competition among managed-care plans was more interest-group rhetoric than a reflection of popular consultation or defensible policy analysis.

Just as with the birth of Medicare, the changing partisan composition of the Congress made a crucial difference in the nature of the claims about Medicare at the close of the century. The question for Medicare's future in the spring of 1999 was whether liberal Democrats could persuade President Clinton to reject the type of reform proposal his own rhetoric had helped to generate. And, by the fall, they succeeded.

Efforts to change Medicare reflect presumptions about the proper role of government in American life and the purposes of social insurance in paying for medical care. Medicare's fate will be linked to controversies about managed care and whether Medicare should embrace or reject its expansion. The agenda—and Medicare's place on it—is subject to transformation by both electoral and economic shifts, and no one can claim with certainty what the political and economic environment will be like a few years hence, let alone decades. What can be concluded, however, is that the politics of Medicare will continue to produce two types of policy disputes. First are the relatively narrow policy conflicts in which the ideological cleavages in the larger public are substantially irrelevant, and second are those relatively rare but important disputes where the deepest divides in the American political world are crucially relevant. This is what Medicare's origins and programmatic history reveal.

THEODORE MARMOR (1995)
REVISED BY AUTHOR

SEE ALSO: *Access to Healthcare; Aging and the Aged; Health Insurance; Justice; Medicaid*

BIBLIOGRAPHY

Ball, Robert M. 1988. "The Original Understanding on Social Security: Implications for Later Developments." In *Social Security: Beyond the Rhetoric of Crisis,* ed. Theodore R. Marmor and Jerry L. Mashaw. Princeton, NJ: Princeton University Press.

Brown, Lawrence D. 1985. "Technocratic Corporatism and Administrative Reform in Medicare." *Journal of Health Politics, Policy and Law* 10(3): 579–599.

Hirshfield, Daniel S. 1970. *The Lost Reform: The Campaign for Compulsory Health Insurance in the United States from 1932 to 1943.* Cambridge, Eng.: Cambridge University Press.

Jost, Timothy Stoltzfus. 2003. *Disentitlement?: The Threats Facing Our Public Health-Care Programs and a Rights-Based Response.* New York: Oxford University Press.

Marmor, Theodore R. 1973. *The Politics of Medicare,* rev. ed. Chicago: Aldine.

Marmor, Theodore R. 1988. "Coping with a Creeping Crisis: Medicare at Twenty." In *Social Security: Beyond the Rhetoric of Crisis,* ed. Theodore R. Marmor and Jerry L. Mashaw. Princeton, NJ: Princeton University Press.

National Academy of Social Insurance. 1999. *Medicare and the American Social Contract.* Washington, D.C.: Author.

Numbers, Ronald L. 1978. *Almost Persuaded: American Physicians and Compulsory Health Insurance, 1912–1920.* Baltimore: Johns Hopkins University Press.

Oberlander, Jonathan. 2003. *The Political Life of Medicare.* Chicago: University of Chicago Press.

Smith, David G. 1992. *Paying for Medicare: The Politics of Reform.* New York: Aldine de Gruyter.

Starr, Paul. 1982. *The Social Transformation of American Medicine.* New York: Basic Books.

Vladeck, Bruce C. 1999. "Plenty of Nothing: A Report from the Medicare Commission." *New England Journal of Medicine* 340(10): 1503–1506.

Whitbeck, Caroline. 1985. "Why the Attention to Paternalism in Medical Ethics?" *Journal of Health Politics, Policy and Law* 10(1): 181–187.

White, Joseph. 2001. *False Alarm: Why the Greatest Threat to Social Security and Medicare Is the Campaign to "Save" Them.* Baltimore: Johns Hopkins University Press.

MEDICINE, ANTHROPOLOGY OF

• • •

Medical anthropology is the cross-cultural study of health, illness, and medical systems. Medical anthropologists describe how the collective meanings, social institutions, and dynamics of political power in a particular society construct local forms of medical knowledge and therapeutic action that are differentially distributed across gender, age, ethnic, and class lines. From hundreds of studies a deeper understanding has been gained of variation in illness beliefs and behavior and of pluralism in healing practices (see, e.g., Good, 1977; Janzen; Kleinman, 1980; Leslie; Lock; Nichter). Yet there are also universals in the mediation of suffering and in the therapeutic process about which the comparative method provides a special insight (see Kleinman, 1988a, 1988b).

Medical anthropologists or anthropologists of medicine (the terms are interchangeable) have brought different paradigms to bear on the study of health and disease. Ecological, political-economic, and applied public-health or clinical perspectives are all to be found in the literature. Yet since the 1970s the most original anthropological contribution is what has come to be called a meaning-centered or social constructionist paradigm.

In this perspective, the central concern is with the way that illness categories and experiences reflect culture, and in turn contribute to social change. Thus, Gilbert Lewis (1975), working with a small-scale preliterate society near the Sepik River of Papua New Guinea, shows how that society's master symbols are reflected in the illness behavior of withdrawal and isolation of seriously sick members and in the "days of shining red" animated by healing rituals. The

smells, tastes, sights, sounds, and sensibility of everyday responses to shamans' songs among aboriginals in the Malaysian rain forest and Malays in rice-farming villages (Laderman, 1991; Roseman); of routine coping processes through which Haitian villagers make accusations about the sources of AIDS (Farmer); and of the social as well as personal experience of sadness among Yolmo Sherpas in Nepal (Desjarlais)—all are patterned by deep cultural codes and social structures. Much the same cultural dialectic between persons and collective institutions has been shown to pattern interactions in psychiatric emergency rooms in North America (Rhodes); in the training of medical students to see patients through the lens of biomedical reductionism at Harvard Medical School (Good, 1993); and in the practices of oncologists in Tokyo, Rome, Oaxaca, and Boston (Good et al.).

Global social change has proliferated, not limited, the numbers and types of traditional healers in both richer, industrialized societies and poorer, industrializing ones (McGuire). Industrialization on a worldscale has neither undermined traditional medical beliefs nor foreclosed on folk health practices; yet such global social change has made much less clear the division between *traditional* and *modern.* One finds in the so-called East Asian industrial dragons, for example, a greatly complex mesh of attitudes, values, and practices. There is no simple giving way of *tradition* to Western orientation; indeed, both tradition and Westernization are routinely reinvented. The Japanese may be moving to accept brain death as a marker of the end of human life, and thereby facilitate organ transplantation, which has been severely constrained by Buddhist ideas; but it is a movement strongly contested by large numbers of Japanese who maintain traditional values about death together with the most advanced technological orientation.

Patients and their families, when it comes to serious illness, are pragmatic; they cross back and forth between the professional and folk domains of healthcare. Scientific knowledge has not replaced cultural common sense but been integrated with it (Kleinman, 1980; Nichter). Biomedicine has been the leading edge of a worldwide culture of science, yet in Asian and African societies biomedical institutions and relationships have become indigenized in ways that reflect those societies' master values and particular forms of social life. As a result there are both certain similarities and even greater dissimilarities in the ways professional and lay members of those societies make therapeutic decisions, handle life and death events, respond to chronicity and disability, and negotiate the complexities of care (Laderman, 1983; Last and Chavunduka; Rhodes; Sargent; Young, 1977).

Because of their concern for value orientations and everyday decision making, anthropologists have written about the ethical sides of health and healthcare. For example, Peter Kunstadter (1980) and Morton Beiser (1977) wrote about the ethical quandaries that development projects, including medical ones, introduced into traditional communities, because the services they provide are temporary and therefore raise expectations that eventually will be frustrated. Mary Jo Good and colleagues (1993) and Margaret Lock and Christina Honda (1990) examined the moral exigencies of truth telling about cancer and determining death in biomedicine in Japan. Paul Unschuld (1979) analyzed the corpus of Confucian and traditional Chinese medical writings on ethical issues, and concluded that professional and cultural values of the literati class colluded to control the medical marketplace. Arthur Kleinman (1980) found that healers in Taiwan in the 1960s and 1970s—whether traditional Chinese medical practitioners, shamans, or physicians—were viewed ambiguously: as morally powerful to heal, yet potentially immoral sources of economic gain and even of evil power (sorcery). This finding is rather widespread cross-culturally.

Horacio Fabrega (1990), writing explicitly about an ethnomedical approach to medical ethics, saw biomedicine's ethical preoccupations growing from Greek medicine and the popular morality of ancient Greece. Following many anthropologists, he asserts that in small-scale, preliterate societies, healing and religion are inseparable; thus, for Fabrega medical mores are tied to ritual and theology in these societies. In larger-scale societies—both peasant and posttraditional—the specialized division of labor leads to practitioners who are popularly viewed both as healers and as financially benefiting from the healer's trade. Fabrega argues that all the great non-Western traditions of healers use ethical injunctions to control access to practice and to proscribe certain alternative healers as quacks. He asserts that *bioethics* is a unique version of medical ethics made possible by the development of biomedicine with its knowledge of biology and powerful biological applications.

Writing for a collection of social-science treatments of bioethics, Richard Lieban (1990), himself an anthropologist, focuses on anthropological interest in the ethical aspects of controversial folk practices—such as female circumcision, differential assistance to male children, and the lack of regulation of folk healers—as examples of what anthropologists can offer to bioethical issues in international health (see also Scheper-Hughes; Korbin; Gruenbaum; Kleinman, 1982). Allan Young (1990), in the same volume, demonstrates the value of ethnographic accounts of the hidden moral dimensions of psychiatric practice in a Veterans Administration unit for treating combat-related posttraumatic stress disorder among veterans who had served in the Vietnam War.

What characterizes anthropological approaches to ethical issues, in medicine as well as other fields, is an emphasis on questions that emerge out of the grounded experiences of sick persons, families, and healers in local contexts. Anthropologists have critiqued universal ethical propositions just as their professional perspective has led them to critique universalist models for economic development. In place of universalist propositions—philosophical or political-economic—anthropologists have focused upon the local interactions of everyday life and the moral issues in which they are clothed. In Isaiah Berlin's (1979) apt metaphor, they are more the fox than the hedgehog. The latter type of intellectual (e.g., the moral philosopher or the psychoanalyst) knows one big thing about the human experience, while the former (e.g., the historian or anthropologist) knows many small, particular things.

The remainder of this entry will adumbrate what anthropological studies tell us about health, illness, and care that is relevant to the practice of bioethics. Starting with a cross-cultural critique of leading bioethical orientations and commitments, the more powerful anthropological contributions will be reviewed, followed by a brief discussion of the possibilities and problems with a culturalist orientation. From the anthropological perspective, bioethics shares with biomedicine several determinative cultural orientations that constrain the standard approach to ethical issues in patient care. The anthropological approach, therefore, becomes particularly useful because of the comparative understanding it offers of often unexamined biases.

The *ethnocentrism, psychocentrism,* and *medicocentrism* central to biomedicine are prominent in the standard bioethical approach (see Lock and Gordon; Weisz). Most philosophically trained bioethicists draw on what Charles Taylor (1989) describes as the orthodox sources of the self in the Western philosophical tradition. The great works in that tradition, from those of the Greeks down to the present, assume an individuated self, set off from the collective—single, unchanging, and self-defining. Thereby, inter alia, the autonomy of the person is claimed to be a paramount value along with the ideas of justice and beneficence. From a cross-cultural perspective this intellectual commitment is problematic.

In the major non-Western societies—such as China, India, Japan, Indonesia, and most African societies—few people hold that the isolated individual is the locus of responsibility for therapeutic choice, or that therapy should work to maximize the individuation of the sick person. Rather, there is a paramount sociocentric consensus in which social obligation, family responsibility, and communal loyalty outweigh personal autonomy in the hierarchy of ethical principles. The self is viewed as sociocentrically enmeshed in inextricable social networks, ties that make interpersonal processes the source of vital decisions. More than 80 percent of the planet's population lives in cultures outside of North America and Western Europe or are members of minority ethnic groups outside of the Euro-American majority. That bioethics is able to avoid serious engagement with these alternative ethical traditions must represent one of the last tenacious holds of ethnocentric mentality. Indeed, there is evidence that bioethicists are commencing such decentering cultural engagements (Jennings; Loewy).

Similarly, from an ethnographic perspective, the use of abstract concepts of justice and beneficence as universal ethical principles in decision making is suspect because of the failure to take into account the local worlds in which patients and practitioners live—worlds that involve unjust distributions of power, entitlements, and resources. It is utopian, and therefore misleading, to apply the principles of justice and beneficence to practical clinical problems, unless we first take into account the brutal reality of the unjust worlds in which illness is systematically distributed along socioeconomic lines and in which access to and quality of care are cruelly constrained by the political economy. Beneficent social contracts may make good theory, but they deny empirical experience in local social worlds. Loewy's "beneficent community," which he claims is concerned with minimizing the suffering of its members, is a charming romance; no one lives in such a utopian state. Rather, real communities are sources of suffering at least as much as potential sources of assistance. They do not contain social contracts; but they are filled with different interests, status differences, class divisions, ethnic conflicts and factionalism. Little is gained by instantiating utopian virtues; indeed, much is lost, since illusion and exaggeration distort the practical realities of living.

The third "centrism"—medicocentrism—emerges from comparative studies as yet another bias of standard bioethical discourse. Like biomedicine, bioethics begins with professional definitions of pathology. The disease viewed as pathological physiology, and the professionally authorized array of treatment interventions, define the clinical situation (see Canguilhem). The experience of illness is made over, through the application of ethical abstractions such as those described above, into a contextless philosophical construct that is every bit as professionally centered and divorced from patients' suffering as is the biomedical construction of disease pathology.

The bioethicist, of course, is supposed to take into account the patient's perspective. But by and large the contextually rich illness narrative is reinterpreted (also thinned out) from the professional biomedical standpoint in order to focus exclusively on the value conflicts that it is held to instantiate. The folk categories of patients and indigenous healers are provided with only limited legitimacy. If they can be restated in the abstract terms of the standard bioethical orthodoxy, they are provided a place in the analysis. But if they cannot, then folk categories lose their authoritative imprint to define what is at stake for patients and families.

Take ideas, for example, of *suffering*—a powerful folk category worldwide. One is surprised to find so many professional ethical volumes in which this word does not appear as an entry in the index. Ethical systems that leave the problem of suffering (and related concepts of endurance and courage) to particular theological traditions cannot adequately engage the human core of illness and care. Here perhaps the standard version of bioethics shares yet another biomedical bias, the rejection of teleology. Biomedicine banishes the concepts of purpose and ultimate meaning to religion; yet most patients and practitioners struggle to make sense of illness with respect to great cultural codes that offer coherent interpretations of experience (cf. Frye).

Medicocentrism also leads bioethicists to construct cases that are centered in the professionally approved institutional structures of biomedicine—such as hospitals or nursing homes—despite the fact that most illness episodes, as social studies reveal, are experienced, interpreted, and responded to in the context of the family. The family—the mundane cultural setting of illness and care, where local social processes are so greatly influential—and the workplace frequently disappear in bioethical discourse, to be replaced by the biomedical staging of more extreme, even exotic value conflicts. Of course, the immense panoply of settings for healing is even less visible or audible in the bioethical construction of clinical reality.

This all too black-and-white portrait of bioethics is intended to draw out and highlight its deep difficulties and their cultural sources. In the practical flow of events, the working bioethicist struggles to overcome the constraints that limit his or her engagement with the obdurate particularity and inexpedient uncertainty of human subjects. And for that very reason he or she will find an ethnographic orientation to be liberating.

In contrast with the bioethicist, the ethnographer begins with the lived flow of interpersonal experience in a deeply particular local world. Not the Western tradition or North America, nor even New York State—which are too unspecified to provide a positioned *view from somewhere*—but, rather, the Puerto Rican community in the South Bronx, upper-middle-class Scarsdale, a working-class section of Queens, or a network of Russian immigrants in Brooklyn becomes the setting for grounding moral analysis in the concrete historicity, micropolitical economy, and ethnicity of a local world. Even within such a localized flow of experience, perspectives and preferences are further defined by gender, age, and other social categories of persons: for example, the cultural situation of poor women in rural Haiti who are responding to AIDS (Farmer and Kleinman). These indexes of social experience situate groups and their individual members along axes of power such that the forces of macrosocial pressures—economic depression, war, forced uprooting, ethnic conflict, state violence, the organizational control of substance abuse, the social structural sources of chronic illness and disability—are systematically attenuated for some, yet amplified for others. Some become successful or at least are protected; others are victims.

Each local world is characterized by what is at stake for its members. That structure of relevance—compared to a belief or a convention—gives to the meanings of illness and to treatment expectations the sense of something much closer to natural law. Families hold the world to be a certain way as an article of fundamental faith in local reality. In the infrapolitics of family, workplace, and community, which is empirically discoverable, the processes of strategic negotiation and interpersonal engagement over what is at stake can be properly regarded as processes through which a local moral order is constituted and expressed. Culture, then, is built up out of the everyday routines and rhythms of social life. It is the medium of experience, for example, in which one person's chronic pain affects an entire work unit, a family member's Alzheimer's disease is shared as an illness reality by the entire family, and cancer care is negotiated among parents, child, and professional care providers.

Hospitals, clinics, and disability programs also are grounded in the particularity of local worlds, as is the bioethicist. The ethnographic task for the practicing bioethicist, then, becomes the discovery of the meanings and relationships in distinctive local worlds, and their actual impact on particular patients, families, and practitioners. This is a kind of cultural analysis of moral conflicts and negotiations over plans and practices that make up the flow of everyday living. As part of this ethnographic work, the bioethicist needs to elicit the perspectives of the participants and place them in the contexts of family, workplace, and medical system. The bioethicist's involvement should be to facilitate communication and to help negotiate conflicting orientations. In this work, it is necessary to protect the participants from the dehumanizing imposition of hegemonic principles. This focus on the positioned, intersubjective perspectives of participants in a local context is a radically

different vision of how to proceed with the ethical analysis of a case than that which originates in a philosophical quest for an illusory *transpositional objectivity*, a synthesis valid for an entire context, which in the anthropological vision is the problem, not the solution (Sen).

More specifically, anthropological analysis draws attention to the institutional context of ethical decision making (see Bosk; Fox; Mizrahi). Social institutions—a particular type of hospital, a clinic for alternative care, or a religious facility—refigure ethical issues in terms of efficiency and other technical criteria that make up everyday social routines. Hence, the special characteristics of a Veterans Administration hospital, a university-based teaching hospital, a military hospital, a member of a for-profit hospital chain, or a highly cost-conscious HMO constrain the day-to-day social processes that create the local moral order. What is at stake for a resident in training in a teaching hospital—generating new knowledge, securing a place in the academic hierarchy, and so on—is noticeably different from what is at stake for a senior physician at a small community hospital. The difference signals a distinctive institutional context for deciding what level of treatment is *routine,* which kinds of issues will be highlighted as *ethical* problems, when families will be involved, and so on. Quite obviously, such institutional contexts will also be distinctive cross-culturally.

In Japan, even in a university teaching hospital, the practice has been not to disclose to patients that they are suffering from cancer but to allow key family members to decide if and when the *truth* will be told. In China, family members will stay in the hospital with the patient to do the nursing, prepare meals, and make all the major decisions, even for the family head when he is seriously ill.

In Zaire and Senegal, members of the kinship-based therapy management group, including perhaps the doctor and the nurse, will decide if the patient is to be part of a research protocol (Beiser). In a Seventh-Day Adventist mission hospital run by American staff in Borneo, the structure for identifying and resolving a moral dilemma draws on a religious ideology that suffuses the institutional context in a manner that greatly differentiates this hospital from nearby hospitals run by transplanted Javanese Muslims or local animists. The responses of North American and Chinese psychiatrists to depressed patients in the United States and China have been compared with respect to their decidedly different institutional contexts for determining what kinds of therapeutic behaviors represent good care and what kinds of moral messages will be given and received in the patient-doctor interaction (Kleinman, 1988b). Renée Fox and Judith Swazey (1984) have shown how physicians in a Chinese hospital draw on both Confucian views and

Communist ideology to authorize local patterns of ethical decision making that challenge North American orientations. And cultural historians disclose how bioethics in North America has emerged out of the social problems and responses of a particular era (Rothman).

Besides cultural critique and comparison, what practical contributions can anthropology make to bioethics? The cultural formulation of diagnostic and therapeutic issues clearly should be as significant to the consulting bioethicist as it frequently can be made to be for the consulting physician, especially when the patient and family come from cultural and ethnic backgrounds that differ from those of their professional caregivers, or when the setting is outside North America (Kleinman, 1982). That formulation involves systematic steps in placing the illness and treatment experience in the culturally grounded context of family, work, and medicalsocial welfare systems, through the application of a mini-ethnography—a description and interpretation of how those settings affect, and are affected by, the illness. Cultural formulation identifies lay and professional explanatory models, compares them for evidence of cultural bias or conflict, and sets out a process of negotiation to assure cultural sensitivity (see Helman, 1984; Kleinman, 1988a; Rogler). These are technical procedures that should be part of the repertoire of the bioethicist. Ethnographic knowledge of the core ethical orientations and social patterns of different communities will be especially significant in planning and implementing medical research in ethnic minority and non-Western settings (Christakis).

What are the limits of cultural analysis, cross-cultural comparison, and the sensibility to variation and differences that come under the term *cultural relativism*? While epistemological and even ontological relativism—willingness to entertain the idea that there is no single form of knowledge or being in local worlds—will seem defensible to many, ethical relativism of the radical variety—the idea that there are no ethical standards cross-culturally—will not. Are such practices as infanticide of female children in South Asia, ritual murder of elderly women accused of being illness-causing witches in East Africa, and rationing of care based on color status under apartheid acceptable because the dominant group says they are? Clearly, this would be an unacceptable conclusion. Behind it lurks the terrible transmogrification of medicine under the Nazis, when biomedical ideology and technology, dominated by Nazi values, prepared the way for the death camps (Kleinman, 1988b; Proctor).

The anthropological argument advanced in these pages is for elicitation and engagement with alternative ethical formulations, a constrained relativism; it is for affirmation of differences, not automatic authorization of any standard or practice as ethically acceptable because it is held by some people, somewhere (Shweder; Wong). The limit to ethical relativism is that the bioethicist must compare alternative ethical formulations with those ethical standards he or she holds for the evaluation of a particular problem in a particular context. The outcome of such an evaluation could be acceptance or rejection of the alternatives or of the bioethicist's own standards, or some form of negotiation and compromise.

The idea of radical cultural relativism is unacceptable to all but a small group of diehards. It is, moreover, a serious misinterpretation of what ethnography, cultural analysis, and cross-cultural comparison have contributed: the idea that before we apply an ethical category we hold to be universal, we had better understand the context of practice and ideas that constitute a local moral world. The job should be to situate a bioethical problem in that local ethos in order to understand what is at stake for the participants, what is contested, and thereby to offer a cultural formulation of conflicting ethical priorities. That having been done, there are at least three further steps. First, we need to systematically compare local and professional bioethical standards for that particular problem; second, we need to negotiate that part of the difference on which both parties deem it ethical to compromise; and third, where a cross-cultural ethical conflict cannot be so resolved, both parties should specify the nature of the problem for further adjudication (Kleinman, 1982). This ethnographic strategy does not commit the deep error of assuming that "all goods, all virtues, all ideals are compatible, and that what is desirable can alternately be united into a harmonious whole without loss" (Williams, p. xvi). Compromise and negotiation may not resolve ethical conflicts; and even where they do, some losses must occur. The quest is not for integration and unification, but for multicultural pluralism.

Where possible, it is the obligation of the bioethicist not only to respect the specific views of others and to affirm the validity of the process of alternative moral formulations, but also to develop deep knowledge about those viewpoints and to test those alternative categories and practices for potential ways to resolve ethical conflict. This ethnographic approach emphasizes the process of engagement and negotiation with the lived moral orientations of others; it attempts to minimize the application of those bioethical standards that derive from the Western philosophical tradition, to settings for which they lack coherence and validity. In all other areas of cross-cultural research and practice this is the established procedure. This approach also protects the responsibility of the professional bioethical consultant not to accept value decisions that contravene human rights and other pannational moral conventions. But it makes this universalist responsibility the final stage in a process of cultural translation that gives priority, initially at least, to alternative worlds of experience interpreted in their own terms. Perhaps the cardinal contribution of the medical anthropologist to bioethics is to deeply humanize the process of formulating an ethical problem by allowing variation and pluralism to emerge and receive their due, so that ethical standards are not imposed in an alien way; rather, these standards will then be realized as the outcome of reciprocal participatory engagement across different worlds of experience.

ARTHUR KLEINMAN (1995)
BIBLIOGRAPHY REVISED

SEE ALSO: *Alternative Therapies: Social History; Body: Cultural and Religious Perspectives; Death: Cultural Perspectives; Health and Disease: Anthropological Perspectives; Human Nature; Medical Ethics, History of; Medicine, Sociology of; Mental Illness: Cultural Perspectives; Women, Historical and Cross-Cultural Perspectives*

BIBLIOGRAPHY

Beiser, Morton. 1977. "Ethics in Cross-Cultural Perspective." In *Current Perspectives in Cultural Psychiatry,* pp. 125–139, ed. Edward F. Foulks, Ronald M. Wintrob, Joseph Westermeyer, and Armando J. Favazza. New York: Spectrum.

Berlin, Isaiah. 1979. "The Hedgehog and the Fox." In *Russian Thinkers.* Harmondsworth, Eng.: Penguin.

Bosk, Charles. 1979. *Forgive and Remember: Managing Medical Failure.* Chicago: University of Chicago Press.

Bowker, John. 1970. *Problems of Suffering in Religions of the World.* Cambridge, Eng.: Cambridge University Press.

Butt, Leslie. 2002. "The Suffering Stranger: Medical Anthropology and International Morality." *Medical Anthropology* 21(1): 1–24; discussion 25–33.

Canguilhem, George. 1989 (1966). *The Normal and the Pathological,* tr. Carolyn R. Fawcett. New York: Zone Press.

Christakis, Nicholas. 1988. "The Ethical Design of an AIDS Vaccine Trial in Africa." *Hastings Center Report* 18(3): 31–37.

Csordas, Thomas J., ed. 1994. *Embodiment and Experience: The Existential Ground of Culture and Self (Cambridge Studies in Medical Anthropology, 2).* New York: Cambridge University Press.

Desjarlais, Robert. 1993. *Body and Emotion: The Aesthetics of Illness and Healing in the Nepal Himalayas.* Philadelphia: University of Pennsylvania Press.

Fabrega, Horacio. 1990. "An Ethnomedical Perspective on Medical Ethics." *Journal of Medical Philosophy* 15(6): 592–625.

Fabrega, Horacio, Jr. 1997. *Evolution of Sickness and Healing.* Berkeley, CA: University of California Press.

Farmer, Paul. 1992. *AIDS and Accusation: Haiti and the Geography of Blame.* Berkeley: University of California Press.

Farmer, Paul, and Kleinman, Arthur. 1989. "AIDS and Human Suffering." *Daedalus* 118(2): 135–160.

Fox, Renée C. 1990. "The Evolution of American Bioethics: A Sociological Perspective." In *Social Science Perspectives on Medical Ethics,* pp. 201–227, ed. George Weisz. Boston: Kluwer.

Fox, Renée C., and Swazey, Judith P. 1984. "Medical Morality Is Not Bioethics—Medical Ethics in China and the United States." *Perspectives in Biology and Medicine* 27(3): 336–360.

Frye, Northrop. 1982. *The Great Code: The Bible and Literature.* Toronto: Academic Press.

Good, Byron J. 1977. "The Heart of What's the Matter: The Semantics of Illness in Iran." *Culture, Medicine and Psychiatry* 1: 25–58.

Good, Byron J. 1993. *Medicine, Rationality and Experience.* Cambridge, Eng.: Cambridge University Press.

Good, Mary Jo; Hunt, Linda; Munakata, T.; and Kobayashi, Y. 1993. "A Comparative Analysis of the Culture of Biomedicine: Disclosure and Consequence for Treatment and the Practice of Oncology in the United States, Japan and Mexico." In *Health and Health Care in Developing Countries: Sociological Perspectives,* ed. Peter Conrad and Eugene Gallagher. Philadelphia: Temple University Press.

Gruenbaum, Ellen. 1982. "The Movement Against Clitoridectomy and Infibulation in Sudan: Public Health Policy and the Woman's Movement." *Medical Anthropology Newsletter* 13: 4–12.

Hahn, Robert A. 1995. *Sickness and Healing: An Anthropological Perspective.* New Haven, CT: Yale University Press.

Helman, Cecil. 1984. *Culture, Health and Illness: An Introduction for Health Professionals.* London: Wright.

Helman, Cecil. 1990. *Culture, Health and Society: An Introduction for Health Professionals,* 2nd edition. Boston: Wright.

Heriot, M. J. 1996. "Fetal Rights Versus the Female Body: Contested Domains." *Medical Anthropology Quarterly* 10(2): 176–194.

Janzen, John. 1978. *The Quest for Therapy in Lower Zaire.* Berkeley: University of California Press.

Jennings, Bruce. 1990. "Ethics and Ethnography in Neonatal Intensive Care." In *Social Science Perspectives on Medical Ethics,* pp. 261–272, ed. George Weisz. Boston: Kluwer.

Kleinman, Arthur. 1980. *Patients and Healers in the Context of Culture: An Exploration of the Borderland Between Anthropology, Medicine, and Psychiatry.* Berkeley: University of California Press.

Kleinman, Arthur. 1982. "Problèmes culturels associés aux recherches cliniques dans les pays en voie de développement." In *Médecine et expérimentation,* ed. Maurice A. M. de Wachter. Cahiers de bioéthique, no. 4. Quebec: Presses de l'Université Laval.

Kleinman, Arthur. 1988a. *The Illness Narratives: Suffering, Healing, and the Human Condition.* New York: Basic Books.

Kleinman, Arthur. 1988b. *Rethinking Psychiatry: From Cultural Category to Personal Experience.* New York: Free Press.

Kleinman, Arthur. 1997. *Writing at the Margin: Discourse Between Anthropology and Medicine.* Berkeley, CA: University of California Press.

Korbin, Jill, ed. 1981. *Child Abuse and Neglect: Cross Cultural Perspectives.* Berkeley: University of California Press.

Kunstadter, Peter. 1980. "Medical Ethics in Cross-Cultural and Multicultural Perspectives." *Social Science and Medicine* 14B(4): 289–296.

Laderman, Carol. 1983. *Wives and Midwives: Childbirth and Nutrition in Rural Malaysia.* Berkeley: University of California Press.

Laderman, Carol. 1991. *Taming the Wind of Desire: Psychology, Medicine and Aesthetics in Malay Shamanistic Performance.* Berkeley: University of California Press.

Last, Murray, and Chavunduka, Gordon, eds. 1986. *The Professionalization of African Medicine.* Manchester, Eng.: Manchester University Press.

Leslie, Charles, ed. 1976. *Asian Medical Systems: A Comparative Study.* Berkeley: University of California Press.

Lewis, Gilbert. 1975. *Knowledge of Illness in a Sepik Society: A Study of the Gnau, New Guinea.* London: Athlone.

Lewis, Gilbert. 2000. *A Failure of Treatment (Oxford Studies in Social and Cultural Anthropology).* New York: Oxford University Press.

Lieban, Richard W. 1990. "Medical Anthropology and the Comparative Study of Medical Ethics." In *Social Science Perspectives on Medical Ethics,* pp. 221–239, ed. George Weisz. Boston: Kluwer.

Lock, Margaret. 1980. *East Asian Medicine in Urban Japan: Varieties of Medical Experience.* Berkeley: University of California Press.

Lock, Margaret, and Gordon, Deborah, eds. 1988. *Biomedicine Examined.* Boston: Kluwer.

Lock, Margaret, and Honda, Christina. 1990. "Reaching Consensus About Death: Heart Transplants and Cultural Identity in Japan." In *Social Science Perspectives on Medical Ethics,* pp. 99–120, ed. George Weisz. Boston: Kluwer.

Lock, Margaret; Young, Allan; and Cambrosio, Alberto, eds. 2000. *Living and Working With the New Medical Technologies: Intersections of Inquiry (Cambridge Studies in Medical Anthropology,* no. 9). New York: Cambridge University Press.

Loewy, Erich. 1991. *Suffering and the Beneficent Community: Beyond Libertarianism.* Albany: State University of New York Press.

Marshall, Patricia A., and Koenig, Barbara A. 2003. *Anthropology and Bioethics.* New York: Cambridge University Press.

Mattingly, Cheryl. 1998. *Healing Dramas and Clinical Plots: The Narrative Structure of Experience (Cambridge Studies in Medical Anthropology,* 7). New York: Cambridge University Press.

Mattingly, Cheryl, and Garro, Linda C., eds. 2000. *Narrative and the Cultural Construction of Illness and Healing.* Berkeley, CA: University of California Press.

McGuire, Meredith. 1988. *Ritual Healing in Suburban America.* New Brunswick, NJ: Rutgers University Press.

Mizrahi, Terry. 1986. *Getting Rid of Patients: Contradictions in the Socialization of Physicians.* New Brunswick, NJ: Rutgers University Press.

Morris, David B. 2000. *Illness and Culture in the Postmodern Age.* Berkeley, CA: University of California Press.

Nichter, Mark. 1989. *Anthropology and International Health: South Asian Case Studies.* Dordrecht, Netherlands: Kluwer.

Proctor, Robert. 1988. *Racial Hygiene: Medicine Under the Nazis.* Cambridge, MA: Harvard University Press.

Rhodes, Lorna. 1991. *Emptying Beds: The Work of an Emergency Psychiatric Ward.* Berkeley: University of California Press.

Rogler, Lloyd H. 1990. "The Meaning of Culturally Sensitive Research in Mental Health." *American Journal of Psychiatry* 146: 296–303.

Romanucci-Ross, Lola; Moerman, Daniel E.; Moerman, Daniel R.; et al., eds. 1997. *The Anthropology of Medicine: From Culture to Method,* 3rd edition. Westport, CT: Bergin & Garvey.

Roseman, Marina. 1991. *Healing Sounds from the Malaysian Rainforest: Temiar Music and Medicine.* Berkeley: University of California Press.

Rothman, David J. 1990. "Human Experimentation and the Origins of Bioethics in the United States." In *Social Science Perspectives on Medical Ethics,* pp. 185–200, ed. George Weisz. Boston: Kluwer.

Sargent, Carolyn. 1989. *Maternity, Medicine and Power.* Berkeley: University of California Press.

Scheper-Hughes, Nancy, ed. 1987. *Child Survival: Anthropological Perspectives on the Treatment and Maltreatment of Children.* Boston: D. Reidel/Kluwer.

Sen, Amartya. 1992. "Objectivity and Position: Observation, Categorization and the Assessment of Suffering." In *Health and Social Changes,* ed. Lincoln Chen, Arthur Kleinman, and Norma Wave. New York: Oxford University Press.

Shweder, Richard A. 1990. "Ethical Relativism: Is There a Defensible Version?" *Ethos* 18(2): 205–218.

Strathern, Andrew, and Stewart, Pamela J. 1999. *Curing and Healing: Medical Anthropology in Global Perspective.* Durham, NC: Carolina Academic Press.

Taylor, Charles. 1990. *Sources of the Self: The Making of the Modern Identity.* Cambridge, MA: Harvard University Press.

Unschuld, Paul. 1979. *Medical Ethics in Imperial China: A Study in Historical Anthropology.* Berkeley: University of California Press.

Weisz, George, ed. 1990. *Social Science Perspectives on Medical Ethics.* Boston: Kluwer.

Whyte, Susan Reynolds; Van Der Geest, Sjaak; and Hardon, Anita. 2002. *Cultural Perspectives on Medicine.* New York: Cambridge University Press.

Williams, Bernard. 1981. "Introduction." In *Concepts and Categories: Philosophical Essays,* by Isaiah Berlin. Harmondsworth, Eng.: Penguin.

Wong, Dennis B. 1984. *Moral Relativity.* Berkeley: University of California Press.

Young, Allan. 1977. "Order, Analogy, and Efficacy in Ethiopian Medical Divination." *Culture, Medicine and Psychiatry* 1(2): 183–199.

Young, Allan. 1990. "Moral Conflicts in a Psychiatric Hospital Treating Combat-Related Posttraumatic Stress Disorder (PTSD)." In *Social Science Perspectives on Medical Ethics,* pp. 65–82, ed. George Weisz. Boston: Kluwer.

Vaughan, M. 1994. "Healing and Curing: Issues in the Social History and Anthropology of Medicine in Africa." *Social History of Medicine* 7(2): 283–295.

MEDICINE, ART OF

• • •

In the art of medicine physicians themselves become the diagnostic and therapeutic instruments that apply the knowledge and skills of medicine. The art of medicine includes not only what is required for a physical diagnosis and for healing, but also the ability to apply the generalized knowledge of medicine and medical science to individual patients. This latter aspect includes knowing the particularity of the patient, knowing how to shape the doctor's knowledge of medicine to the particular patient, and developing the relationship between patient and doctor. Discrete skills serve these goals, among them understanding the behavior of patients and doctors, using the doctor-patient relationship for diagnostic and therapeutic ends, good judgment and decision making, and effective communication.

For bioethics, considering the art of medicine offers challenges because aspects of the art arise from the singular traits of sick persons and the special character of the doctor-patient relationship. These put in doubt the validity of some ideas about patients' independent self-representation and self-determination that have been important in the recent development of bioethics.

In this context art does not refer to the general meaning of aesthetics or the fine arts. Instead, it is derived from the Greek word *techné*, meaning craft or skill. This distinction is important because it is commonly said, in error, that the art of medicine cannot be taught. Crafts and skills are said to be learned from others. The ancient Greeks classified medicine as one of the original arts, along with weaving, carpentry, and geometry. On the other hand, mere skill is not all there is to this art, which must be served by a deeper practical understanding of its complex subject, as in Aristotle's *phronesis* (sound, considered judgment) or the Hippocratic phrase, "Life is short and the art is long." It was only with the rise of science in the seventeenth century that the term began to have its current meaning of the personal skills of physicians. In the twentieth century, the "art of medicine" has been sharply distinguished from the "science of medicine" and has come to have a somewhat pejorative connotation.

The Effects of Science on the Art of Medicine

The identification of the art of medicine with subjectivity and particularity is what has led to its recent loss of stature. It has been an article of faith of medical science in the twentieth century that objective scientific evidence would eventually replace the subjectivity of the transaction between an individual patient and physician. A further canon of medical science is that the knowledge and the science make the diagnosis and effect the treatment. The individuality of the physician is irrelevant; doctors are interchangeable. However, as Samuel Gorovitz and Alasdair MacIntyre have pointed out, generalizations of scientific medicine from systems that may not involve humans and by abstraction from observations of particular patients must be reparticularized to this patient, at this time, in this context, by this physician (Gorovitz and MacIntyre). In the care of sick persons, there are no sharp distinctions between medical science and the art of medicine, since both kinds of knowledge reside in the individual physician. It is his or her individuality that allows the physician to practice the art of medicine. An impersonal agency like a computer can deploy the science of medicine, but a particular doctor must adapt this knowledge to an individual patient. To do this appropriately requires both tacit and manifest knowledge within the doctor.

Patterning knowledge to the patient is generally known as medical judgment—acquiring and integrating both subjective and objective knowledge to make decisions in the best interests of the patient. Recent advances in studies of the theory and practice of medical decision-making do not fully encompass clinical judgment, because they have focused more on solving problems that arise from the uncertainties of medical information than on the consequences that follow from the relevance or meaning medical information may have for the particular patient.

The tendency of physicians and medicine to conflate the patient with the disease obscures the importance of the art of medicine. It is impossible, however, for physicians to confront or treat diseases. Because they can only treat the patient who has the disease, the art of medicine will always be essential.

How the Individuality of the Patient Makes a Difference

THE DISTINCTION BETWEEN DISEASE AND ILLNESS. *Disease* is the pathoanatomical or pathophysiological entity that manifests itself in symptoms that the patient experiences and the doctor discovers (Cassells, 1985a). Diseases are abstractions that have no concrete existence except as instantiated in particular patients. *Illness* is the patient's experience of the effects of the disease process; it includes not only the symptoms—alien sensations or perceptions of distorted function—but the interpretations and meanings of the symptoms. The illness also embraces the impact of altered function on behavior and social existence. It is the illness that the patient presents to the physician as reported symptoms and dysfunctions. While the physician may be primarily interested in the disease, the ethicist should be concerned with the illness because of its effects on the patient, his or her relationships, and the community that put in doubt the moral agency of the sick person.

THE EFFECTS OF THE INDIVIDUALITY OF THE PATIENT. Onset, course, treatment, and outcome of identical diseases vary from patient to patient because of individual variation from the molecular level to the whole person to the community. The contribution of the individual to differences in his or her illness is sometimes difficult to appreciate if one thinks only about the acute infectious diseases or trauma. Chronic diseases, which produce the greatest burden of illness in the U.S. population, provide better examples. For example, diabetes in adults is genetically determined, but its severity and manifestations are influenced by variation in diet and exercise pattern from person to person. In addition, the availability, type, and utilization of medical care play parts in the effects of diabetes. Because disease is a process that occurs over time, the responses of the patient to the disease manifestations become part of the illness itself, as they alter the patient's behavior and change the illness. For example, whether patients report symptoms, visit physicians, take prescribed medications, alter their lifestyle, accept illness as inevitable, or fight its every intrusion—each of these factors has an influence on the illness and expresses the individuality of the sick person. Each modification requires a change in the approach of the physician dictated, for the most part, not by medical science but rather arising from the doctor's art. The physician can affect the patient only through the doctor-patient relationship, which is central to the practice of medicine and its art, but differences among individuals—for example, their degrees of trust versus suspicion, openness versus shyness, or friendliness versus hostility—influence the kind of relationship formed.

The Different Perspectives of Patients and Physicians

The patient's perspective on his or her affliction is different from the physician's. In such crucial dimensions as time, space, and the meaning of specific medical objects (such as bodily organs, technological devices, and medications), patients' experience of their world diverges from that of the physician, whose scientific perspective on their disease includes objective measures of time and space and precise definitions of objects (Toombs). In the case of hypertension, for example, patients may feel threatened with a stroke by this moment's elevated blood pressure, even though the dangers of hypertension lie in its effects on the heart, kidneys, and blood vessels over long periods. To patients, the felt immediacies of other disease threats also seem more a result of their seriousness than of their actual temporal proximity.

A patient's focus on a particular symptom depends more on the patient's interpretation of the symptom than it does on the actual experienced events. For example, a patient who interprets his or her chest pain as signaling heart disease may not be aware of, pay attention to, or report associated shoulder or neck pain that would tell the doctor that the chest pain is secondary to an entrapped cervical nerve and not heart disease. Further, patients rarely understand the probabilistic nature of medical information—that the facts of a case are most often not simply true or false, but only true with degrees of confidence—and even when they do, it is difficult for them to understand the meaning of these probabilities for them. Objectivity, always difficult, is virtually impossible for the sick person because of the nature of illness. Important alterations in thought processes, such as the inability to see things from the perspective of others and a concreteness of thought usually characteristic of children, accompany only serious illness, but this is where the reflections generated by bioethics are most important (Cassell, 1985b).

More than just medical science determines the physician's perspective of the patient's illness. Besides diagnostic and treatment goals that draw heavily on medical science, physicians have other aims. Some, such as the desire to save or prolong life, relieve pain, avoid doing harm, and provide information, are patient-centered. Others, such as being trustworthy and truthful, relate to their relationships with patients. As physicians among other physicians they also want to maintain their knowledge, to be considered good doctors by their peers, and to uphold the standards of their profession. Many of these ends are professional in nature, are part of the socialization of doctors, and reach back to antiquity. They, too, distinguish the doctor's point of view from that of even informed patients.

Although doctors and patients may appear to speak the same language about the same subjects, their differing viewpoints ensure that a physician may remain within the medical-scientific worldview and not attend to the patient's concerns. The care of the terminally ill often exemplifies such dissonance. Here, one of the ends of medical practice—staving off death as long as possible—may be at odds with the patient's desire not to be in pain or suffer. A necessary aspect of the physician's art is to understand the patient's goals and adjust professional aims and medicine's tools to these ends. This is the meaning of sayings throughout medical history exemplified by that of Bela Schick, "First the patient, second the patient, third the patient, fourth the patient, fifth the patient, and then maybe comes the science." That this principle is often violated or ignored does not obviate its centrality for the art of medicine.

The Doctor-Patient Relationship

The special nature of the relationship between doctor and patient has been appreciated since antiquity (Laín Entralgo). As much a part of sickness and medicine as the diseases that make people ill, this relationship makes a sick person a patient and a medical person a doctor and a clinician. It is the vehicle through which physicians exercise their authority (not to be confused with authoritarianism), without which the practice of the art is impossible (Needleman). An examination of the way the relationship is formed and its potential for effectiveness suggests that this special bond is a basic part of the human condition with cultural and social dimensions (Cassell, 1991).

In emergencies, when doctor and patient have never previously met, the power of the relationship can become effective immediately. Within moments a doctor who is a stranger can ease pain, make panic subside, and improve breathing. (Physicians can also worsen symptoms and exacerbate panic by wrong actions.) The bond between doctor and patient is effective across cultural boundaries, even in the presence of antagonisms, and despite sometimes formidable social and environmental impediments.

Physicianhood is a role—a set of performances, duties, obligations, entitlements, and limitations connected to a function or status. The socialization of medical students includes learning about the doctor's role so that they emerge both as physicians and in the role of physicians. Given its sociocultural nature, it has its counterpart in the patient, who provides for the doctor's words and action access to the patient and the patient's body not available to ordinary relationships. Because the connection between doctor and patient is bilateral, the power of sickness to make patients susceptible to change at all levels of the human condition is matched ideally by the power of this benevolent relationship to induce physicians to extend themselves at all levels.

Physicians, because of the relationship, are enabled to see the authentic person through the mess of sickness, read the history of self-determined purposes in the life before illness, and understand the aesthetic whole that is the patient's life prior to the unwelcome intrusion of disease. In a modern extension of the art, they therefore have the opportunity and obligation to help the patient maintain autonomy, which, for the sickest, would be almost impossible outside the relationship. Clinical ethicists share in this opportunity when and if the patient extends this special bond to them (Zaner).

These aspects of the doctor-patient relationship are frequently obscured from view or even contravened in the high technology atmosphere of modern medical centers. The patient's trust is necessary for the most successful diagnosis and treatment, and therapeutic intimacy arising out of the relationship creates confidence. As part of their art, skilled practitioners actively nurture the relationship, not only encouraging its growth and promoting trust by the patient, but negotiating between empathic intimacy and objectivity. One skill in the art of clinicians lies in coming as close as ethically possible to intimacy while maintaining independence of action. A strong bond is essential in negotiating the difficulties and uncertainties of serious illness. It is equally important in supporting and teaching patients through the long trajectory of chronic illness.

The Behavior of Sick Persons and Doctors

THE BEHAVIOR OF SICK PERSONS. Even mild sickness alters behavior; profound sickness alters behavior profoundly. This is culturally acknowledged by what has come to be known as the sick role, the exemption from everyday duties and obligations granted to sick persons. Changes in functioning are not merely those associated with the disordered part—for example, the inability to move around because of back pain. Sickness induces changes in cognitive function and in relationships with self, body, and others. Patients who are sufficiently ill—for example, in life-threatening infectious diseases, congestive heart failure, for a few days after bypass surgery, or in long-term hospitalizations—although they are cognitively normal by conventional measures, have patterns of reasoning that Jean Piaget showed in children under six. For example, the sick frequently fail a classic test of reasoning about the conservation of volume. Two containers identical in size, shape, and the volume of water they contain are shown to the patient with the statement, "These two glasses have the same amount of water." The contents of one glass is then emptied into a tall thin cylinder and the patient is asked, "Which one of these has more water?" Sick persons will frequently indicate the tall thin cylinder. They may say, "I know that it shouldn't have more water, but it does" (Cassell, 1985b).

Sick persons usually are also unable to alter their perspective sufficiently to understand the viewpoint of another. A child's alphabet block shows this in its simplest form. Even if the block is rotated so that they have seen all of its sides, when looking at one face, they cannot report what is on the opposite face. One can routinely demonstrate many other similar changes in reasoning, of which the patient is almost always unaware. Because of the similarity of their reasoning (and other traits) to children, these characteristics have been considered regression. To avoid the error of treating the sick like children, it seems wiser to realize that this altered behavior is sickness expressing itself. Thus, in appropriate circumstances, patient self-determination will be enhanced by offering no more than two concretely worded alternatives at a time and avoiding choices couched in abstractions.

The sick are attached to their caregivers. How their attachment is expressed varies from love to anger or rebelliousness. The skillful physician is aware that these emotions are not directed at the doctor as a particular person (about whom the patient usually knows very little) but at the doctor in the role (Landis). As such, they are not to be taken personally but should be used in diagnosis or treatment. Changes in the patient's relationship to the body are also a common characteristic of illness. The patient may become angry with the body because of what it has done to the patient, as though the disease was something the body "did" to the patient. Relationship to the body influences the patient's other illness behavior and reactions to the events of the sickness and its treatment.

Illness brings about dependency on others and often induces feelings of loss of control, helplessness, inadequacy, and failure. As a result, it may awaken unconscious conflicts and cause the patient to act toward the physician as if he or she were the patient's parent. The artful physician, aware of the problems that may follow reawakening of early childhood experiences or feelings and behavior brought on by

illness, knows and acts in the knowledge that the sick person within the doctor-patient relationship may seem quite different in presentation and behavior from the same person when he or she is well.

THE BEHAVIOR OF DOCTORS. Physicians, too, may behave differently in the presence of the sick than they do outside the doctor-patient relationship. Physicians' interactions with their patients may evoke feelings of anger, sexual attraction, sadness, grief, failure, rejection, and omnipotence, among others (Maoz et al.). Many years ago a psychiatrist, Michael Balint, recognizing that physicians are not trained to deal with the feelings clinical events evoke in them, organized physician discussion groups (Balint). Although sometimes replicated, these so-called Balint groups have not been widely employed. Awareness of whether and how doctors' feelings and behavior interfere with their care of patients is important because physicians' experience of their patient's feelings is an essential source of information about the illness.

Physicians are powerful people who must employ their power judiciously if it is to do good and not harm (Brody). Yet, doctors are rarely trained in how to use their power or even to be aware that they have power, which may be abused perhaps more easily than it is used. An irreducible inequity of power between patient and doctor inheres in the clinical situation. Codes of medical ethics reaching back to antiquity and modern bioethics directly address this problem. It is widely recognized, however, that if physicians are not virtuous, all the precepts, principles, and regulations surrounding their conduct will be useless. Edmund Pellegrino and David Thomasma explain the virtues necessary to achieve the ends of the clinical encounter and the good of the patient, namely, to be made well again if possible, or to cope with sickness, pain, suffering, and impending death if necessary. These virtues include conscientious attention to technical knowledge and skill, compassion, beneficence, benevolence, honesty, fidelity to promises and to the patient's good, prudence, and wisdom (Pellegrino and Thomasma). Walsh McDermott believes that thoroughgoingness and self-discipline are also central virtues of the good clinician (McDermott). It requires a good person to be a good doctor—now, as in times past. As Paracelsus said, "The art of medicine is rooted in the heart. If your heart is false, you will also be a false physician; if your heart is just, you will also be a true physician."

It is difficult for a scientific (and cynical) era such as ours to accept the unavoidable necessity for virtue in doctors. As a consequence, the active training of doctors in the virtues of the good physician has largely been abandoned in the untested and probably wrong belief that medical virtue cannot be taught. During medical school and in postgraduate training, however, those who become doctors do learn, even if only through socialization, to restrain the employment of their skills in situations where more harm than good may follow, to be self-critical and admit error (at least to each other), to pursue the good of the patient, and to act benevolently (Bosk).

Medical Decision Making

Physicians are constantly making judgments, many of which are moral. The skill of exercising judgment, which has defied systematization, is the ability to apply the general to the particular; in medicine, this means to the particular patient, clinical situation, or context. To do this, physicians must obtain information of three distinct kinds—brute facts (also known in medicine as hard data); values; and aesthetics (patterns, relationships among the elements of a situation, and degrees of order or disorder). Often doctors are not aware of much of the information in the latter two categories that enters their judgments. Because of the necessity for such information, which is often neither obvious nor easily demonstrated, the art of medicine requires heightened skills of observation and synthesis. The art also requires that some systematic understanding be brought to judgment.

Alvan Feinstein was the first to closely examine the logic that underlies physicians' decisions; his work generated the field of clinical epidemiology (Feinstein, 1967, 1985). Feinstein's primary concern was the background evidence that the study of groups of people would provide for clinical decisions in patient care. Those who have followed him have elaborated his basic message and methods to assist physicians in judging the utility of a piece of evidence or information in the diagnosis or treatment of a particular patient (Wulff; Fletcher et al.; Sackett et al.). These writers have elaborated basic principles that determine the diagnostic meaning of a piece of clinical information, for example, a finding on physical examination, the result of a blood test, or a clinical measurement. The accuracy and validity of the test or measurement are important, as might be expected, but so is the likelihood that *any* similar patient would have the disease or state that is being tested for.

Put another way, to know how helpful a piece of information is diagnostically, one has to know the chance that any such patient truly has the disease. For example, even if a test for a rare disease is 99 percent accurate, when a large population of healthy people is tested and someone has a positive test, the chances are small that the person has the disease. The test will probably have been a false positive. Alternatively, in a population in a region where the disease is common, a positive test probably means the person has the disease. The test will have been a true positive. Because many conclusions of the clinical epidemiologists based on Bayesian mathematics are counterintuitive, their work has been extremely important in bringing objectivity and precision to decision making. (In the example given above, when the test is 99 percent accurate but the disease is rare, a patient who tests positive has only about a 10 percent chance of having the disease.) Terms such as specificity, sensitivity, and positive predictive value, which denote quantified measures of modern medical decision making, are now commonly heard in discussions about particular patients. Modern physicians must not only be conversant with these methods; they must also explain them to each patient so that the patient can participate effectively in the decision-making process.

Physicians rarely realize the degree to which each patient is different. Consequently, particularizing the generalizations of medical science to fit an individual patient requires great skill. The desires, needs, concerns, intentions, and purposes of patients are statements of values that must be elicited if they are to enter decision making. They are often faulted as hopelessly subjective and consequently not up to the standard of the hard data employed in the decision-making methods discussed above. A patient's desire for a certain outcome may be subjective, but the statement of that aspiration is objective and can be validated and given precision within degrees of confidence through discussion with the patient and attention to the pattern of the patient's previous actions and purposes. The artful physician is obligated to develop the mastery that gives these values decision-making weight—they are expressions of the patient's autonomy. Attempts to circumvent the need for such mastery by developing standardized methodologies, such as scales and questionnaires to assess individual values, have not proved clinically useful. It remains necessary, therefore, for the clinician to know the sick person to the greatest degree possible so that good clinical judgments can be made.

The clinical situation, like the disease and the illness, is always changing; therefore, decision making that integrates values and other clinical information constantly occurs in clinical medicine. Shifts occur not only because of the evolving process of the disease, but also because of the ongoing responses of both doctors and patients. In addition, the place care is given (home, doctor's office, hospital, etc.) and who else is involved (family, friends, medical students, etc.) influence the process of the illness. It is obvious why clinical judgments are not confined to the initial diagnosis or decisions about therapy.

The art of medicine requires that the physician be always mindful of changes in the circumstances, the illness, and the capacity of the patient. Although the formal principles of modern decision making may not always be applicable, newer ideas about the probabilistic nature of judgment and the need to integrate hard and soft data constantly inform the work of the artful physician.

Doctor-Patient Communication

The ability to employ the spoken language to obtain information from and about the sick person, gain the patient's cooperation, and provide information to the patient is a central element in the art of medicine. Doctor-patient communication is unlike many other verbal transactions, despite its use of ordinary language. The patient is in the conversation with the doctor for a specific purpose that is vital for the patient and diagnostically or therapeutically significant for the physician. The patient and the doctor have important joint purposes in the service of which the conversation is both necessary and crucial.

The patient wants the doctor to pay attention to his or her symptoms and concerns about the illness, and is worried lest these not be properly expressed or their importance not be appreciated. Doctors want to hear the clues to the diagnosis that only the patient's story can convey. Yet, some things that are important to the patient may not be of interest to the doctor and vice-versa. If the doctor attends solely to the evidence for disease, discarding everything else the patient says as irrelevant, then he or she may find the disease, but discard the sick person. A person's utterances convey not only the overt description of his or her actions and beliefs, but also the significance of the objects and events under discussion to the speaker. This other aspect of the speaker's message—the description of self of which the speaker is often unaware—lies in the specific choice of words, syntax, and paralanguage (Cassell, 1985c). The attentive, artful physician, listening to these specific aspects of the spoken language, has the opportunity to know more about the patient.

Conversation with the patient offers the doctor the opportunity to discover the patient's presuppositions and the beliefs according to which the patient assigns meanings. Similarly, doctors can inform their patients about the medical presuppositions and concepts that inform the doctors' actions. Such exchanges help avoid or correct the miscommunications that inevitably arise because of the differing perspectives of doctor and patient. Just as the patient's language informs the doctor about the patient, the doctor's utterances reveal himself or herself to the patient. The virtues of physicians are not abstractions, but are displayed in speech and actions. Trust is built by means of conversation as well as by action; compassion is communicated in words, in nonverbal communication, and in action. The constant flow of spoken (and unspoken) language provides a doctor the opportunity to build his or her knowledge of the patient and provides a patient evidence of the physician's skill and fidelity.

The doctor also has the specific responsibility of informing the patient about what is the matter, what it means, what actions might be taken, what options exist, and what choices the patient must make. The same is true, on occasion, of communication with the patient's family or significant others. Information, however, is also a therapeutic tool. Doctor-patient communication provides the physicians the opportunity to convey information that reduces the patients' uncertainties, enables the patient to act in his or her own best interests, and strengthens the relationship between the doctor and patient. On the other hand, poorly or inadequately communicated information can increase uncertainty, paralyze action, and destroy the relationship.

A specific aspect of doctor-patient communication is breaking bad news. When it is done poorly, it can destroy hope and leave a patient in shambles. As part of the art of medicine, doctors must learn to convey bad news so well that patients are enabled to make truly self-representative and self-determined choices (Buckman).

Patients, like everybody else, act and react because of what things mean to them. Meaning includes not merely denotative aspects of words, objects and events, but their connotative, or value-laden, content as well. With its cognitive and affective aspects, meaning has an impact on the physical and spiritual responses of the sick. By changing patients' meanings, physicians can alter, sometime profoundly, the patient's experience of illness (Cassell, 1985a). The effective use of spoken language, with its power of creating and altering the meaning of wellness and illness, is an important aspect of the art of medicine.

ERIC J. CASSELL (1995)

SEE ALSO: *Compassionate Love; Emotions; Healing; Health and Illness; Information Disclosure, Ethical Issues of; Medicine, Profession of; Narrative; Pain and Suffering; Professional-Patient Relationship; Social Medicine; Trust; Value and Valuation; Virtue and Character*

BIBLIOGRAPHY

Balint, Michael. 1957. *The Doctor, His Patient, and the Illness.* London: Pitman.

Bosk, Charles L. 1979. *Forgive and Remember: Managing Medical Failure.* Chicago: University of Chicago Press.

Brody, Howard. 1992. *The Healer's Power.* New Haven, CT: Yale University Press.

Buckman, Robert. 1988. *I Don't Know What to Say: How to Help and Support Someone Who Is Dying.* Toronto: Key Porter.

Cassell, Eric J. 1984. "How Is the Death of Barney Clark to be Understood?" In *After Barney Clark: Reflections on the Utah Heart Program,* ed. Margery W. Shaw. Austin: University of Texas Press.

Cassell, Eric J. 1985a. *Clinical Technique.* Vol. 2 of *Talking with Patients.* Cambridge, MA: MIT Press.

Cassell, Eric J. 1985b. *The Healer's Art.* Cambridge, MA: MIT Press.

Cassell, Eric J. 1985c. *The Theory of Doctor-Patient Communication.* Vol. 1 of *Talking with Patients.* Cambridge, MA: MIT Press.

Cassell, Eric J. 1991. *The Nature of Suffering: And the Goals of Medicine.* New York: Oxford University Press.

Feinstein, Alvan R. 1967. *Clinical Judgment.* Baltimore, MD: Williams and Wilkins.

Feinstein, Alvan R. 1985. *Clinical Epidemiology: The Architecture of Clinical Research.* Philadelphia: W. B. Saunders.

Fletcher, Robert H.; Fletcher, Suzanne W.; and Wahner, Edward H. 1988. *Clinical Epidemiology: The Essentials,* 2nd edition. Baltimore, MD: Williams and Wilkins.

Gorovitz, Samuel, and MacIntyre, Alasdair C. 1975. "Toward a Theory of Medical Fallibility." *Hastings Center Report* 5(6): 13–23.

Laín Entralgo, Pedro. 1969. *Doctor and Patient,* tr. Frances Partridge. New York: McGraw-Hill.

Landis, David A. 1993. "Physician, Distinguish Thyself: Conflict and Covenant in a Physician's Moral Development." In *Perspectives in Biology and Medicine* 36(4): 628–641.

Maoz, Benjamin; Rabinowitz, Stanley; Herz, Michael; and Katz, Halva Elkin. 1992. *Doctors and Their Feelings: A Pharmacology of Medical Caring.* Westport, CT: Praeger.

McDermott, Walsh. 1982. "Education and General Medical Care." *Annals of Internal Medicine* 96(4): 512–517.

Needleman, Jacob. 1985. *The Way of the Physician.* San Francisco: Harper & Row.

Pellegrino, Edmund D., and Thomasma, David C. 1988. *For the Patient's Good: The Restoration of Beneficence in Health Care.* New York: Oxford University Press.

Sackett, David L.; Haynes, R. Brian; and Tugwell, Peter. 1991. *Clinical Epidemiology: A Basic Science for Clinical Medicine,* 2nd edition. Boston: Little, Brown.

Toombs, S. Kay. 1992. *The Meaning of Illness: A Phenomenological Account of the Different Perspectives of Physician and Patient.* Boston: Kluwer.

Wulff, Henrik R. 1981. *Rational Diagnosis and Treatment: An Introduction to Clinical Decision-Making,* 2nd edition. Oxford: Blackwell Scientific.

Zaner, Richard M. 1993. *Troubled Voices: Stories of Ethics and Illness.* Cleveland: Pilgrim.

MEDICINE, PHILOSOPHY OF

• • •

Over the last two and a half millennia—since the beginnings of Greek philosophy and medicine—there have been rich conceptual reflections regarding medical findings, reasoning in medicine, the status of knowledge claims in medicine, and the special concepts that structure the science and art of medicine. The philosophy of medicine is a corpus of considerations and writings uniting these reflections by contributors as diverse as Plato, Aristotle, and Galen; René Descartes, Immanuel Kant, and Georg W. F. Hegel; and contemporary thinkers. Because these examinations of medicine are philosophical in different senses, the term *philosophy of medicine* is ambiguous, covering a heterogeneous field of intellectual concerns. For the purpose of this overview, they have been collected under four categories.

The first category, speculative philosophy of medicine, has existed from the beginning of medicine. Speculative medicine may be characterized as the attempt to discover the basic philosophical principles that lie behind the practice of medicine. Here philosophy attempts to discover theoretical frameworks or foundations that give shape or content to clinical data. In this sense, philosophy of medicine provides a priori points of departure for medical knowledge and practice. The second category, the logic of medicine, brings together attempts to clarify the character of scientific reasoning in medicine. It identifies the basic principles that make medicine a coherent science. This category of philosophy of medicine studies, for example, the way in which diagnoses are made and judged to be accurate in medical practice and research. A third area of the philosophy of medicine may be understood as a subspecialty of philosophy of science. This area is concerned with what is accepted as *knowledge* in medicine and the healthcare professions. Much of the recent exploration of the status of concepts of health and disease or the status of the unconscious and explanation in psychoanalysis falls into this third category. Finally, a fourth category describes the explorations of other philosophical issues that have special salience in healthcare, for example, the nature of persons and its implications for the morality of abortion. Philosophy of medicine in this fourth sense would include bioethics.

Just as there is ambiguity concerning the meaning of "philosophy" in "philosophy of medicine," so there is ambiguity about the compass of medicine. Medicine can be construed as a body of knowledge, skills, and social practices concerned with the health and pathology of humans. In its modern sense, medicine encompasses theory and practice, science and art. Traditionally medicine is the origin of all systematic concerns with healing, including nursing and the allied health sciences. The focus of the philosophy of medicine, as a consequence, can have a broad or narrow scope.

The Philosophy of Medicine as Speculative Medicine

The ancient Greek philosophers sought to understand the world on a rational rather than a supernatural basis. Early Greek medicine was influenced by philosophers who held that the primary goal of a scientist was to find one basic principle or set of principles that would explain the natural world known by the senses. These physicians developed theories as to how the body worked and how diseases might be understood and controlled. At first, there was little concern to justify these theories in experience or observation. One finds, then, a tension in early Greek medicine between those physicians who grounded medicine in rational speculation—the rationalists—and those who grounded medicine in experience—the empiricists.

This tension is evident in the Hippocratic corpus. In the corpus there is approval for theorizing that "lays its foundation in incident, and deduces its conclusions in accordance with phenomena" (Jones, p. 313). Nevertheless, the Hippocratic author rejects the systematic sweep of more speculative thought:

> Certain physicians and philosophers assert that nobody can know medicine who is ignorant what a man is; he who would treat patients properly must, they say, learn this. But the question they raise is one for philosophy; it is the province of those who, like Empedocles, have written on natural science, what man is from the beginning, how he came into being at the first, and from what elements he was originally constructed. (Jones, p. 53)

The author is rejecting what might be termed speculative or metaphysical medicine—namely, the attempt to construct a theory of medicine on the basis of self-evident, or basic, principles or concepts. The author also writes that medicine has no need of "an empty postulate," a concept that is not based in experience, because it has at hand the means for verifiable knowledge.

René Descartes (1596–1650) held that he could determine the fundamental laws of metaphysics, physics, and medicine (Descartes) by reason alone, without appeal to experience. On the basis of his work in speculative, metaphysical medicine, Descartes predicted that he would live an additional century or so, achieving a life span of one and a half centuries. He believed his own theories would issue in simple revisions of daily routine leading to such extensions of life expectancy (Descartes). Descartes's *Treatise of Man* (1662) attempts a mechanistic anatomy and physiology expressed in terms of matter and motion. Descartes explains how the human body works by comparing it to a machine. He found that this mechanistic approach could explain the physical functioning of the human body but not rational behavior. Still, Descartes's philosophical reflections concerning the body provided a framework for later explanations of human functioning that also relied on mechanical metaphors.

The success of Isaac Newton (1642–1727) in offering systematic explanations in physics inspired attempts to do this in medicine. The eighteenth-century Scottish physician John Brown (1735–1788), for example, suggested that the concept of excitability could serve medicine as the concept of gravity had served Newtonian physics: as the single concept upon which all explanations of health and disease could ultimately rest. Stimulation or excitation and response to it, he argued, resulted in an equilibrium or disequilibrium that defined *health* and *disease,* respectively. If an imbalance became too extreme, death would result. Brown's work attracted the attention of philosophers, including Hegel (1770–1831). This philosophy of medicine—as the gray area between scientific, empirical medicine and the philosophy of nature—led to the modern understanding of medicine that brings together empirical observation and theoretical construction (Tsouyopoulos).

Twentieth-century historians of medicine have appreciated this interplay between empirical and speculative medicine under the title "philosophy of medicine." William Szumowski in 1949 and Owsei Temkin in 1956 spoke of the importance of the philosophy of medicine. It is to Szumowski that much of the rebirth of the interest in this term, perhaps first coined by Elisha Bartlett in 1844, can be attributed.

Lester King (1978) has used the term to identify the theoretical reflections undertaken by both physicians and philosophers engaged in speculative as well as other conceptual explorations of medicine.

The Philosophy of Medicine as the Logic of Medicine

The relationship between medical reasoning and medical practice has been an area of perennial philosophical controversy and investigation. In ancient Greek and Roman medicine, the disputes between the rationalists and empiricists were, in part, disputes about how knowledge claims in medicine ought to be justified. By the Renaissance, medicine had failed to achieve the success in healing that is often attributed to it today. This failure to achieve therapeutic success led to attempts to make medicine more *scientific,* in the hope of duplicating the success of fields like astronomy and physics. Thomas Sydenham (1624–1689), whose *Observationes medicae* appeared in a third edition in 1676, proposed a disciplined methodology of observation and treatment. Sydenham brought to medicine the scientific method of Francis Bacon (1561–1626), which sought to ground reasoning in experience, observation, and data.

This method, however, raised questions about observer bias of which Syndenham was aware. The principal difficulty is that an investigator's findings may be influenced by his or her presuppositions. These concerns about observer bias were taken up in the eighteenth century by such theoreticians of medicine as François Boissier de Sauvages de la Croix (1706–1767) in his *Nosologia methodica sistens morborum classes juxta sydenhami mentem et botanicorum ordinem* (1768). Influenced by the writings of Thomas Sydenham and Carolus Linnaeus, Sauvages organized diseases into a structure of class, order, genus, and species. In his *Nosologia* there is an appreciation of medical observation as well as a concern for a logical rigor that sought to coherently relate observations to predicted outcomes. Sauvages's principal undertaking included a classification of diseases primarily based on their signs and symptoms rather than on their causes. He also sought to tie observed signs of illness to relationships that had been noted between past, present, and predicted future states of patients. The logical rigor of disciplined observation and the collection of facts is also evident in the work of William Cullen (1710–1790) and Thomas Percival (1740–1804).

The major revolutions in medical understanding born of advances in anatomy and physiology in the late eighteenth and nineteenth centuries, along with the recognition that many established treatments did not work, required a fundamental reassessment of medicine. Philosophical reflections concerning medical reasoning gave way to major treatises concerning the character of reasoning in medicine. Works such as Sir Gilbert Blane's *Elements of Medical Logick* (1819), Elisha Bartlett's *Philosophy of Medical Science* (1844), and F. R. Oesterlen's *Medizinische Logik* (1852) range from listing the elementary principles of life to concern with material fallacies in medicine, including excessive deference to authority, fashion, or speculative reasoning without sufficient empirical observation. Oesterlen's work, which advanced criteria for inductive reasoning in medicine based on the work of John Stuart Mill, included an analysis of the methods and means of medical investigation, the character of the inductive method in medicine, and the status of experiments, hypotheses, analogies, terminologies, definitions, and classifications. He viewed medical logic as the application of general logical principles to the field of medicine for the purpose of securing a coherent inductive and empirical science that would be free from a priori speculation. His work was followed by other studies, including Władysław Bieganski's *Logika medycyny* (1894) and Richard Koch's *Die ärztliche Diagnose* (1920).

Growing philosophical sophistication characterizes twentieth-century assessments of medical knowledge and medical reasoning. Types of medical knowledge may correspond to the different functions of medicine. Medicine can be understood in a threefold manner: biological medicine, clinical research, and clinical practice. Biological medicine is concerned mainly with scientific research in biology, whereas clinical research is focused on the development of the knowledge and technology used in clinical medicine. Finally, the area of clinical practice involves the realities of patients and disease. A philosophical concern of those writing on the logic of medicine has been to clarify the nature of each type of medical knowledge and the relationship of these different areas of medical knowledge and reasoning to one another (Wulff et al., 1986).

Since the middle of the twentieth century, a renewed interest in the logic of medical reasoning and the character of medical decision making has been expressed in the computer reconstruction of differential diagnosis. This literature has examined the logic and principles of medical reasoning—for example, the applicability of Bayes's Theorem to medical decision making (Lusted; Wulff, 1976); the logic of the taxonomy of disease and classification, including the application of set theory to the analysis of clinical judgments (Feinstein); and the role played by morbidity, mortality, and other costs in determining when and how diagnoses are framed. For example, because of the human and financial costs, one will be much more concerned about false positive diagnoses of AIDS than of athlete's foot. Recent works have given special attention to the process of making diagnoses, including the principles of differential diagnosis (Caplan, 1986; Engelhardt et al.; Wulff, 1976), as well as the elaboration of nosologies as instruments for gathering clinical information. Many of these reflections have stressed the hidden role of values and conceptual assumptions in the process and logic of medical diagnosis (Schaffner; Peset and Gracia; King, 1982).

The Philosophy of Medicine as the Philosophy of the Science of Medicine

Philosophy of medicine may also be understood as a self-conscious reflection on the status of special concepts, such as health and disease, deployed in medicine. Rudolf Virchow (1821–1902), for example, argued that designating a state of affairs as an *illness* has a stipulative character; that is, such concepts are defined by agreement and there are no clear natural types or divisions of nature corresponding to nosological categories. This sense of the philosophy of medicine places the accent on issues in the theory of knowledge and the examination of what should count as a medical theory or explanation. In this, it is distinguished from speculative philosophy of medicine and from the more narrow concerns with the rules of evidence and inference proper to medicine that are the focus of medical logic and medical decision theory.

Since the 1950s a considerable literature has developed that is directed to the status of concepts such as health, disease, illness, disability, and disorder. Whether such concerns constitute a subspecialty of the philosophy of science is disputed (Caplan, 1992; Wulff, 1992). There has also been interest in the character of medical explanation (Canguilhem). This literature has also explored the application of such terms to nonhuman animals. In addition, there has been attention to the extent to which these concepts are normative and the extent to which nonnormative, value-free concepts can be elaborated. Those who have argued in favor of weak or strong normative understandings of concepts such as health, disease, and illness have also addressed the character and kind of values that structure such concepts. Investigations have included the extent to which concepts of disease are instrumental to medical practice, or instead identify natural divisions in reality. In addition, there have been attempts to place medicine within the general compass of philosophical explorations of scientific theory (Kliemt). Finally, the significant changes about the relationship of theories, facts, and values in the understanding of the history and philosophy of science that occurred in the 1960s and 1970s were anticipated in Ludwik Fleck's 1935 study of changes in the meaning of syphilis and venereal disease from the fifteenth to the early twentieth century (Fleck).

The Philosophy of Medicine as the Collection of Philosophical Interests in Medicine

Even if one were to hold that medicine offers no conceptual or philosophical problems not already present in the subject matter of the philosophy of science or the philosophy of biology (Caplan, 1992), there would still be merit in exploring the ways in which philosophical study and analysis can be directed to the understanding of medicine, as well as to the healthcare sciences and arts in general. In this sense, the philosophy of medicine encompasses the ways in which the philosophy of science, the philosophy of biology, the philosophy of mind, moral philosophy, and so on are engaged in order better to understand medicine. Perhaps one would wish to characterize such explorations as philosophy about medicine rather than of medicine, in the sense that the tools, analyses, and insights of philosophy in general are brought to the particular subject matter of medicine. Calling this endeavor the philosophy of medicine underscores the heuristic advantage of treating the domain as a whole, as a single focus of attention. There is also the advantage of recognizing that general issues of justice, fairness, rights, and duties confront the special challenge of taking account of the development of humans from conception to death.

In medicine, special questions of intergenerational justice become salient, distinctions between human biological and human personal life are raised, the irremediable character of loss must be confronted, and comparisons must be made between claims for the alleviation of suffering versus the postponement of death. Though the definitions of futility, of ordinary versus extraordinary treatment, and of the beginning of life and the beginning of death may arise outside the compass of medicine, such definitions take on a special philosophical cast and character in the context of medicine. The recognition that there is this special concatenation of conceptual issues is appreciated in employing the term *philosophy of medicine*. This use of the term approximates the one employed by the European Society for the Philosophy of Medicine and Health Care (founded 1987), which encompasses bioethics within a constellation of philosophical concerns and undertakings. The philosophy of medicine as speculative medicine, as the logic of medicine, and as the philosophy of the science of medicine all spring from the acknowledgment that medicine constitutes one of the cardinal areas of intellectual and moral attention, central to human life, and is worthy of sustained conceptual analysis and philosophical regard.

H. TRISTRAM ENGELHARDT, JR.
KEVIN WM. WILDES (1995)
BIBLIOGRAPHY REVISED

SEE ALSO: *Medicine, Anthropology of; Medicine, Art of; Medicine, Profession of; Medicine, Sociology of; Professional-Patient Relationship: Historical Perspectives*

BIBLIOGRAPHY

Bartlett, Elisha. 1844. *An Essay on the Philosophy of Medical Science.* Philadelphia: Lea and Blanchard.

Bieganski, Władysław. 1894. *Logika Medycyny.* Warsaw: Kowalewski.

Blane, Gilbert. 1819. *Elements of Medical Logick.* London: T. and G. Underwood.

Canguilhem, Georges. 1978. *On the Normal and the Pathological,* tr. Carolyn R. Fawcett. Dordrecht, Netherlands: D. Reidel.

Caplan, Arthur L. 1986. "Exemplary Reasoning? A Comment on Theory Structure in Biomedicine." *Journal of Medicine and Philosophy* 11(1): 93–105.

Caplan, Arthur L. 1992. "Does the Philosophy of Medicine Exist?" *Theoretical Medicine* 13(1): 67–77.

Carrick, Paul. 2001. *Medical Ethics in the Ancient World.* Washington, D.C.: Georgetown University Press.

Carson, Ronald A., and Burns, Chester R., eds. 1997. *Philosophy of Medicine and Bioethics: A Twenty-Year Retrospective and Critical Appraisal (Philosophy and Medicine,* vol. 50). New York: Kluwer Academic Publishers.

Culver, Charles M., and Gert, Bernard. 1997. *Philosophy in Medicine.* New York: Oxford University Press.

Descartes, René. 1983 (1644). *Principles of Philosophy,* tr. Valentine R. Miller and Reese P. Miller. Dordrecht, Netherlands: D. Reidel.

Engelhardt, H. Tristram; Spicker, Stuart F.; and Towers, Bernard, eds. 1979. *Clinical Judgment: A Critical Appraisal.* Dordrecht, Netherlands: Kluwer.

Engelhardt Jr., H. Tristam, ed. 2000. *The Philosophy of Medicine: Framing the Field.* New York: Kluwer Academic Publishers.

Feinstein, Alvan R. 1967. *Clinical Judgment.* Baltimore: Williams and Wilkins.

Fleck, Ludwik. 1979 (1935). *Entstehung und Entwicklung einer wissenschaftlichen Tatsache: Einführing in die Lehre vom Denkstil und Denkkollektiv. Basel: Benno Schwabe.* tr. Fred Bradley and Thaddeus J. Trenn as *Genesis and Development of a Scientific Fact.* Chicago: University of Chicago Press.

Humphreys, Paul. 1989. *The Chances of Explanation: Causal Explanation in the Social, Medical, and Physical Sciences.* Princeton, NJ: Princeton University Press.

Jones, William H. S., tr. 1923. *Hippocrates.* New York: Putnam.

Khushf, George. 1997. "Why Bioethics Needs the Philosophy of Medicine: Some Implications of Reflection on Concepts of Health and Disease." *Theoretical Medicine* 18(1–2): 145–163.

King, Lester S. 1978. *The Philosophy of Medicine: The Early Eighteenth Century.* Cambridge, MA: Harvard University Press.

King, Lester S. 1982. *Medical Thinking: A Historical Preface.* Princeton, NJ: Princeton University Press.

Kliemt, Hartmut. 1986. *Grundzüge der Wissenschaftstheorie: Eine Einführung fur Mediziner und Pharmazeuten.* Stuttgart, Germany: Gustav Fischer.

Koch, Richard. 1920. *Die ärztliche Diagnose.* Wiesbaden, Germany: Bergmann.

Kopelman, Loretta M., and McCullough, Laurence. 1999. "Hume, Bioethics, and Philosophy of Medicine." *Journal of Medicine and Philosophy* 24(4): 315–321.

Lusted, Lee B. 1968. *Introduction to Medical Decision Making.* Springfield, IL: Charles C. Thomas.

Percival, Thomas. 1776. *Philosophical, Medical, and Experimental Essays.* London: Joseph Johnson.

Pellegrino, Edmund D. 2001. "The Internal Morality of Clinical Medicine: A Paradigm for the Ethics of the Helping and Healing Professions." *Journal of Medicine and Philosophy* 26(6): 559–579.

Pellegrino, Edmund D. 2001. "Philosophy of Medicine: Should it be Teleologically or Socially Construed?" *Kennedy Institute of Ethics Journal* 11(2): 169–180.

Pellegrino, Edmund D., and Thomasma, David C. 1997. *A Philosophical Basis of Medical Practice: Toward a Philosophy and Ethic of the Healing Professions.* New York: Oxford University Press.

Peset, José Luis, and Gracia, Diego, eds. 1992. *The Ethics of Diagnosis.* Dordrecht, Netherlands: Kluwer.

Schaffner, Kenneth F., ed. 1985. *Logic of Discovery and Diagnosis in Medicine.* Berkeley: University of California Press.

Szumowski, W. 1949. "La Philosophie de la médicine, son histoire, son essence, sa dénomination et sa définition." *Archives internationales de l'histoire des sciences* 9: 1097–1141.

Temkin, Owsei. 1956. "On the Interrelationship of the History and the Philosophy of Medicine." *Bulletin of the History of Medicine* 30(3): 241–251.

Tsouyopoulos, Nelly. 1982. *Andreas Roschlaub und die romantische Medizin: Die philosophischen Grundlagen der modernen Medizin.* Stuttgart, Germany: Gustav Fischer.

Wulff, Henrik. 1976. *Rational Diagnosis and Treatment.* Oxford: Blackwell Scientific Publications.

Wulff, Henrik. 1992. "Philosophy of Medicine—from a Medical Perspective." *Theoretical Medicine* 13(1): 79–85.

Wulff, Henrik R.; Pedersen, Stig Andur; and Rosenberg, Raben. 1986. *Philosophy of Medicine: An Introduction.* Oxford: Blackwell Scientific Publications.

van der Eijk, Philip. 2004. *Medicine and Philosophy in Greek and Roman Antiquity.* New York: Cambridge University Press.

MEDICINE, PROFESSION OF

• • •

Professionalism is what distinguishes the professions. It gives each the character by which it is known. In our time many occupational groups have striven for professional status in a quest for authority, prestige, and income. "Professionalism, professionalization, and the professions are increasingly central to any grasp of modern societies," Nathan Glazer claims, "yet persistently elude proper understanding" (p. 34). Many sociologists have written about the characteristics of professions, but most agree that all professions possess the five elements identified by Ernest Greenwood:

> systematic body of theory;
> authority to define problems and their treatment;
> community sanctions to admit and train its members;
> ethical codes that stress an ideal of service to others;
> a culture that includes the institutions necessary to carry out all of its functions.

Jeffrey Berlant, following German sociologist and economist Max Weber's (1881–1961) theory that professionalization is a form of monopolization, lists the steps in the process:

> creation of a commodity—in the case of medicine and law, services for a fee;
> separation of performance of the service from the satisfaction of the client, which means that a cure need not be guaranteed;
> creation of scarcity by reducing supply and increasing demand;
> monopolization of supply and control of privileges by legal means, such as licenses;
> restriction of group membership, such as admission to study or to hospital staff;
> elimination of internal competition;
> development of group solidarity and cooperation.

The attributes used to describe professions include responsibilities and privileges, both derived by social contract. It is important to remember that the terms of the social contract change with changing social and economic conditions, and hence may vary from one region or historical period to another. Thus professionalism cannot provide a permanent set of values or standards. Instead it offers a series of guidelines designed to help specific people in specific places resolve important conflicts that arise from the nature of their duties. Each society has evolved some of its own standards, based on its own structure, values, and technological capabilities. Some standards of professional behavior originating in modern industrial societies may be meaningless in other cultural settings (Hughes).

In medicine, historical changes can be illustrated with the example of specialization. Today, specialization is cited as a hallmark of professions. In nineteenth-century U.S. medicine, however, the doctor who specialized was often looked upon as a quack (Rosen, Stevens). Today the physician who claims to have knowledge and expertise in all of medicine would be looked upon with suspicion.

To pose the question "When did medicine become professional?" is like asking "When did medicine become modern?" There are elements of professionalism and of modernity in ancient Greek medicine, as there are in the medicine of the Middle Ages, the Renaissance, and the eighteenth century. The definitions of a profession that appeared in the literature in the early part of the twentieth century, which stressed urbanization and industrialization as prerequisites for the existence of a medical profession, are no longer held. Although it has been true that an industrializing society is a professionalizing society, so far as medicine is concerned there was professionalization long before industrialization (Goode).

Professionalism in medicine developed in a continuous historical process, beginning in antiquity with institutions like state physicians and fraternities of physicians such as the Asclepiads, continuing with the medieval medical guilds, medical schools, and licensing requirements. The modern period, especially after about 1700, is characterized by the emergence of such institutions as medical societies, medical literature, licensing laws, and codes of ethics. In the twentieth century the professional is the recognized expert with special qualifications, and the professional ideal has become a hallmark of modern society (Bledstein, Perkin).

The medical profession of the mid-nineteenth century was very different from the profession of a century later. Yet in both periods many of the characteristics of professionalism were readily evident. The modern model of professionalism—university-based, peer-controlled, and based on merit rather than birth—is derived from the criteria we now use to study professions. Earlier forms of professionalism may have had quite a different set of characteristics; for this reason, the historical dimension of professions becomes increasingly central to an understanding of the development of medicine. The professional character of medicine has always been derived, in good part, from the institutional participation of the physician. These social and legal institutions provide credibility for medicine as a profession (Hall).

Despite the centrality of the professions in the United States, scholars have only recently begun to trace their history (Brown; Calhoun; Haber; Hatch; Kett; Kimball). With a few exceptions, such as Daniel H. Calhoun, historians have not deemed it necessary to engage in comparative histories of the professions, leaving this to sociologists (Abbott; Berlant; Freidson, 1970; Larson; Mechanic, 1968; Rothstein). Although Eliot Freidson has claimed that the status of scholarship in the professions is in a "state of intellectual shambles" (Freidson, 1984, p. 5), the historian Thomas Haskell has noted that "there is really no longer any excuse for scholars working on the professions to be divided into two shops, one made up of people who try to explain what professions are, without ever grasping how they came into being; the other composed of people who try to understand how they came into existence, without being quite sure what they are" (Haskell). For medical historians, generally, as John Burnham has pointed out, it was not until after World War II that the subject of the professions moved to the center stage of history.

Andrew Abbott's review of the sociological literature of the professions is a concise summary of how modern societies have institutionalized expertise as professionalism. He describes the professionalizing process in terms of a series of jurisdictional disputes. These disputes over the professional boundaries of medicine in the nineteenth and twentieth centuries do explain much of medicine's history (Abbott). Samuel Bloom's history of the field of medical sociology traces its institutional formation.

During the last few decades of the twentieth century, when social historians began to depict medicine as oppressive and more interested in social control than in social melioration, medicine began to be subjected to much closer analysis of its professional attitudes, values, and styles. Medicine as a twentieth-century profession could not always get what it wanted, but until the mid-1960s and the passage of Medicare and Medicaid legislation, it had great success in resisting what it did not want. As the twentieth century drew to a close, this negative power had begun to diminish with increasing speed.

Medicine as a Profession in Antiquity

Much of what we have come to believe about ancient medicine we have inherited from the views of nineteenth-century scholars, who tended to create a picture of ancient medicine that reflected their own contemporary institutions (Nutton).

In early Greek antiquity, Homer portrayed doctors among the fighting heroes: "A doctor," he wrote, "is worth many men put together …" (Nutton, p. 15). Plato, in his *Laws,* described doctors and doctors's assistants, who were also called doctors: "These, whether they be free-born or slaves, acquire their art under the direction of their masters, by observation and practice and not by the study of nature— which is the way in which the free-born doctors have learned the art themselves and in which they instruct their own disciples" (Plato, p. 307–309). The Hippocratic physician was a craftsman, and despite the high status of some of the crafts, there were in ancient Greece as yet none of the restrictive practices of the guilds of later centuries (Edelstein; Temkin, 1953). Only in one of the Hippocratic works, the *Oath,* was there a clear description of a closed, family-like guild that restricted entry to outsiders. But this does not represent Hippocratic medicine as a whole (Edelstein). Since ancient times it has been true that there have been several classes of doctors, and patients have always received care depending upon their own station in life and that of their doctor. Recent new scholarship about the Hippocratic Oath reaffirms its historical importance but also stresses its complexity. It should not simply be ascribed to the followers of Pythagoras, as Temkin, in 2002, and Dale C. Smith have noted.

The Alexandrian Library was one of the earliest institutional influences on medicine. It was here, according to the second-century physician/scholar Galen, that the writings of Hippocrates and the Coan school in which he taught were first assembled (Nutton). The ancient Greek physician did not receive a scholarly or systematic training; such was left to those who became philosophers and rhetoricians. Galen claimed that the best physician is also a philosopher. This implied that medicine could be understood only in terms of natural philosophy—biology, chemistry, and physics. Such a lofty sentiment implied that medicine was for the benefit of the whole community rather than for the private gain of the physician. This was the ideal toward which medicine should strive, according to Galen. It is a professional ideal we still recognize (Horstmanshoff).

The Medieval Medical Profession

In the later Middle Ages, with the development of cities, the rise of commerce, and the creation of universities, doctors found an expanding market for their services. These developments, in turn, led to the development of medical faculties in the universities, the passage of laws that defined the minimum education required for the physician, and a more rigorous definition of medical competence. Thus the trappings of professionalism and professional organizations became more evident after 1050. Debates began about what were the appropriate standards for a license to practice medicine, and who was to define the criteria and to enforce them. In the thirteenth century, the battle over training and licensing was between the new universities and their faculties of medicine, and the trade companies or guilds. University-educated physicians formed a professional elite. Guilds became the formal licensing bodies in some of the Italian cities, but generalization is difficult (Park, 1992).

In Florence, the medical profession can be traced to the medieval guilds, such as the Guild of Doctors, Apothecaries, and Grocers, established in 1293. It was a protective association and asserted monopoly privileges. Medicine was considered one of the prestigious occupations, along with law, banking, commerce, and notary practice. What really elevated some of the practitioners of medicine, and hence the whole profession, was that they taught and wrote. These activities, not just medical practice itself, elevated medicine from a mechanical to a liberal occupation and from an art to a science (Park, 1985). Medicine's place in the universities assured it an important and enduring role in the intellectual life of modern society.

Since the medieval period, universities have been the key to the professionalization of medicine, although in some countries, such as Great Britain and the United States, there were periods when medical schools were quite separate from the university. In antiquity the institutions that we associate with professionalization of medicine did not yet exist, though there were certainly groups of healers who were united by rudimentary professional bonds. In the Middle Ages, medicine became a more distinct, high-status, and terminal occupation (Bullough).

In the Middle Ages, then, medicine as a healing activity became distinguishable from medicine as a branch of higher learning. In the twelfth century, King Roger II of Sicily and his grandson, Frederick II, instituted licensing examinations by the masters of the School of Salerno. The objectives were to ensure competence and honesty to protect both society's and the profession's interests. There was as yet, however, neither uniform licensing nor a uniform medical profession in medieval and early Renaissance Europe (Siraisi).

Guild controls and restrictions were justified in the fifteenth century, as they would be in the twentieth, by members who claimed they needed to maintain high standards of competence and proper professional behavior. With an increasing service sector of the economy and an increase of prestige once it became a university faculty, medicine gained in stature (Cipolla).

The Medical Professions in Early Modern Europe

In late-fifteenth- and early-sixteenth-century England, there was little order in the practice or regulation of medicine. In 1511 Henry VIII introduced some governmental control. Although the parliamentary legislation he secured created no organized group of physicians, it brought a measure of state control over medical practice and made way for the conferral of substantial powers on medical groups. It stipulated that no one could practice physic or surgery in London or seven miles around without a license from the Bishop of London or the Dean of Saint Paul's Cathedral, and it required an examination of all candidates for licensure before a panel of experts selected by those officials.

The three main corporations or guilds of medical practitioners in early modern England were the Physicians, the Surgeons, and the Apothecaries. While they did represent a fairly distinct division of labor, their separation, particularly in the countryside, was not as rigid as often portrayed; in the early-sixteenth century there was as yet little order and no real regulation of practitioners. Margaret Pelling has argued cogently for the importance of the guild tradition in the history of medicine's professionalization in sixteenth- and seventeenth-century Great Britain. Earlier historiography of medicine often depicted professionalization as a continuous process, ultimately ending in the triumphal terms of the profession as we know it today. The strength of the social history of medicine, as that history is understood in the early-twenty-first century is to reveal the many complexities of and byways to what was earlier assumed to be a much straighter path to modernity (Pelling, 1987, 1998; Pelling and Webster).

In 1518, the humanist-physician Thomas Linacre (1460–1524) and five other physicians with university educations prevailed upon Henry VIII to grant them a charter for a Royal College of Physicians. Their resultant monopoly, however, extended only to London and its environs. The United Company of Barber Surgeons (made up of apprentice-trained barber-surgeons who carried out simple operations such as bleeding) received its charter in 1540, and the Guild of Apothecaries was granted a separation from the Company of Grocers (a rival guild) in 1617. Not until 1745 did George II grant the surgeons separate status from the barbers (Cook).

This tripartite division of British medicine is well known, but it should not be viewed as a simple or a unified system. In the rural areas, the surgeon-apothecary came to act as a general practitioner, and by 1809 was so acknowledged by name (Loudon). The physicians, who were at the top of the social scale of the medical practitioners, considered themselves gentlemen, had taken a classical university degree, received honoraria rather than fees, and made diagnoses, prescribed appropriate remedies, and made prognostic declarations for their patients. It was up to the apothecaries to give the remedies at the direction of the physicians. To the surgeons were left the tasks of bleeding, pulling teeth, setting fractures, and performing the few operations, such as amputations, that were carried out in this pre-anesthesia and pre-antiseptic age. For most of the population the medical tasks were often combined, as noted, or they were carried out by other healers such as midwives or a variety of traditional practitioners, some of whom were outright quacks (Christianson, Parry and Parry).

By the end of the seventeenth century, the apothecaries were intruding into the domain of the physicians so often that the College of Physicians brought suit against an apothecary by the name of James Rose, charging him with the practice of medicine for which he was not licensed. In 1703, hearing the case on appeal, the House of Lords ruled that the apothecaries could charge for medical advice as well as for the drugs supplied to the patient. This landmark case legalized the function of the apothecaries as ordinary practitioners of medicine in London. They were already enjoying these rights by custom in the countryside. Adam Smith, in his *The Wealth of Nations* (1776), recognized the apothecaries as the physicians of the poor (Hamilton; Holloway, 1966a, 1966b).

In France, a medical profession also existed prior to the period of industrialization. The profession that appeared abruptly at the time of the revolution in France at the end of the eighteenth century replaced one that had existed in somewhat different form (Gelfand, 1981, 1984; Ramsey). It was especially the professional character of the surgeons that changed abruptly in the 1790s. Earlier in the century, the surgeons already had a legal status, received their initial training as apprentices, and had a versatile medical practice including medicine and pharmacy as well as surgery, but still had a relatively equal social relationship with their patients. Thus the French surgeons—the ordinary practitioners, as Toby Gelfand described them—were more socially inclusive than would be the case in the twentieth century. With the breakdown of elitist distinctions, the post-revolutionary profession in which surgery and medicine were now united was generally even less elitist and exclusive than the earlier French physicians had been. However, in the course of the nineteenth century, elitism appeared in French medicine as it did in the professions in other countries. The new elitism was increasingly based on merit rather than on status, on accomplishment rather than on birth. Much of the history of medical professionalism is included in the history of medical education, but until recently we had had little comparative work. In 1995, Bonner filled this gap for Western Europe and North America for the two centuries after 1750.

The Medical Professions in Early U.S. History

American professionalism originated in the traditions and practices of seventeenth- and eighteenth-century England. Although any occupation might be termed *a profession,* the recognized learned or liberal professions continued to be law, medicine, and divinity. These required a collegiate education; exposure to the classics and the liberal arts curriculum provided the breadth of mind and personal character necessary for a gentleman. As a gentleman, the physician had a professional duty to play a role in all community affairs.

The North American colonies did not offer an attractive field for professional physicians until well into the eighteenth century. Unlike England, the North American colonies provided few examples of organizational development in medicine. The colonial environment required that practitioners assume all functions of the healing art and eliminated a form of rivalry that had brought about organization in England, where some medical groups had united to prevent the encroachments of others. Frontier conditions usually isolated physicians and discouraged organizational growth. The shortage of the ideal gentleman-physician in the colonies broke the traditional distinctions and divisions of medical labor. Thus, prior to the early 1700s, in the first century of colonial history, there were few doctors, no medical institutions, and little focus on medicine as a profession. Some healers were mainly working as midwives; others were ministers, whose professional identity was with religion, not medicine (Benes and Benes, Watson).

After 1700, as some historians have noted, there was a deterioration of the public's health as measured by a variety of vital statistics. This produced some increased demand for higher levels of medical skills. Besides the needs presented by the changing diseases and diminishing life expectancy, there were also great strains in the occupational structure. Fathers had typically passed to their sons their pulpits and their land. When population increased and there were neither enough pulpits nor sufficient land, the sons began to seek alternatives. Since many ministers also practiced medicine, it was natural that some of their sons turned to medicine as a career (Hall).

After 1750, some of the professional aspects of medicine became more visible, especially in the northern colonies. Young physicians with English and Scottish educations and degrees now began to want the institutional trappings for their profession. With the aid of Benjamin Franklin, the Pennsylvania Hospital was founded in Philadelphia in 1751. Modeled on the British voluntary hospitals, it was intended mainly to care for the sick poor and to provide medical teaching for young men who wished to become doctors. In the 1760s, the first medical schools appeared in Philadelphia and New York. The first colonial medical society was founded in New Jersey in 1766, and an early licensing law was passed in New York City in 1760. By the turn of the nineteenth century, a rudimentary medical profession existed, though it was responsive to local forces and conditions and had no national unity as yet. In many areas midwives continued to supply medical services to families and still routinely assisted at most births (Ulrich).

Although some medical leaders, such as John Morgan of Philadelphia, hoped to establish the British distinctions of physician, surgeon, and apothecary on the American side of the Atlantic, neither the social climate nor the political realities allowed it. As Richard H. Shryock has noted, it was not that the British distinctions were simply rejected in the more egalitarian ethos of the colonies. In fact, very few physicians had emigrated and there was no way to educate sufficient numbers in the colonies. The surgeon-apothecary or general physician simply assumed the title of doctor in the colonial setting. Like the merchants in North America, physicians, in the absence of a nobility, became part of the upper class (Shryock, 1960).

Licensing (and thus a rudimentary form of professional control) began to appear in the late eighteenth century, however these laws were not yet a means to restrict the practice of medicine as distinctly as they later would be. Licensing in the early nineteenth century merely gave those who were deemed legal physicians the right to sue for their fees. It did not as yet give the doctors any control over the medical marketplace. As a form of public recognition, licenses were uncontroversial; but as an attempt to be restrictive, they quickly became a source of sharply divided opinions. Some physicians, such as John Bard (1716–1799) and his son Samuel (1742–1821) in New York, favored restricting the practice of medicine. Others, such as Benjamin Rush (1745–1813) in Philadelphia, believed in "every man his own physician." Rush claimed medicine was sufficiently simple that anyone could learn to practice it.

Medical Practice in the Mid-Nineteenth-Century United States

During the mid-1800s in the United States, medicine was by no means a unitary profession. Its increasing professionalization was accomplished and stimulated by a similar process in science generally (Daniels). In both fields, compensation slowly increased. A wide variety of healers gave their allegiance to one or another medical philosophy, such as the Homeopaths and Eclectics, or followed the therapeutic doctrines of quite rigid systems, such as the Thomsonians or the water-cure doctors. Even among the so-called regular physicians, there was a wide diversity of education, medical belief, and medical practice (Kett, Rothstein).

In the three decades prior to the Civil War, the Jacksonian period, popular democracy had profound effects on the professions. Most states and localities repealed licensing laws for medicine, and what determination of professional competence there had been was transferred from the profession to the people. Contrary to the course of regulation in England, where the Apothecaries Act of 1815 and the Medical Registration Act of 1858 brought some order and governmental control to medicine, the North American states were abandoning regulatory efforts (Holloway, 1966a, 1966b; Shryock, 1967).

Between 1830 and 1850, the number of medical schools in the United States nearly doubled, from twenty-two to forty-two. The rising number of *regular* graduates produced by these largely profit-seeking, faculty-owned institutions competed with established practitioners, while the new schools lowered requirements to compete for students.

The physicians who established the American Medical Association (AMA) in 1847 had as their avowed goal the improvement of medical education (Davis). In drafting unrealistic requirements for admission to medical schools, however, they became vulnerable to charges that they sought merely to preserve the apprenticeship system and destroy most medical schools. By 1860, however, graduates of the many new medical schools founded in the nineteenth century outnumbered the so-called *irregular* doctors by a ratio of ten to one (Kett). Since the regular physicians as yet had no real claim to controlling medical activities, their professional strategy in these middle decades may be seen in the attempts to raise the standards of medical education by raising entrance and graduation requirements. Such strategy, while only partially successful before the ideology of science was added to the banner of reform at the end of the century, was aimed at reducing or at least controlling the number of doctors being produced.

The AMA, facing apathy among many regular physicians and hostility from sectarian groups, could do little to reduce physician supply or improve the quality of medical practice (Rothstein). Nor could the association move effectively to enforce its own version of professional ethics. It adopted substantially the principles of Thomas Percival's *Medical Ethics* (1803), which deals with topics such as the duties of physicians and surgeons and their "moral rules of conduct." Robert Baker and his colleagues have told the story of the origins, evolution, and fate of the 1847 AMA code, and have included the code itself and supporting documents in their useful book.

At the time of the Centennial celebrations in 1876, John Shaw Billings characterized three classes of physicians among the predominant or regular members of the medical profession. There were a few among them, he noted, who loved "science for its own sake, whose chief pleasure is in original investigations, and to whom the practice of their profession is mainly, or only, of interest as furnishing material for observation and comparisons. Such men are to be found for the most part only in large cities where libraries, hospitals, and laboratories are available for their needs...." A much larger group of physicians, Billings claimed, was mainly interested in "money, or rather the social position, pleasures, and power, which money only can bestow." These doctors are well-educated because "it pays," according to Billings. But the great majority of physicians, Billings concluded, were not well-educated, having memorized only enough of the medical textbooks as was needed to gain a diploma (Billings, p. 479).

It was difficult enough for male physicians to achieve professional status in the United States during the nineteenth century, but for women it was even harder. Elizabeth Blackwell (1821–1910), the first woman to receive a medical degree from a regular American school, in 1849, thereafter wrote frequently on the important role women could play in bringing to medicine greater professional status (Blackwell). The admission of women to medical schools varied from region to region, but with only occasional exceptions it was less than 10 percent of the total. Not until the late-twentieth century did the proportion increase markedly, reaching 30 to 40 percent by 1990.

Like their male counterparts, women physicians also founded their own medical institutions, including hospitals, medical schools, and societies (Morantz-Sanchez). After 1876 there was token representation of women in the AMA; full membership was not granted until the early-twentieth century. The American Medical Women's Association was founded in 1915, but by then most of the women's medical colleges had closed or merged with predominantly male schools. In 1910, at the time of Abraham Flexner's report on U.S. and Canadian schools of medicine, only three of the seventeen women's medical schools still existed, and only half of all the 155 North American schools admitted women for the study of medicine. While virtually all accepted women by the middle of the twentieth century, as late as 1959, twenty-eight schools still explicitly said they preferred men (Walsh, 1992; Bonner, 1992; More).

Blacks who wished to study medicine had an even harder time. Todd Savitt has described ten black medical schools existing in 1900 (Savitt). A decade later only three survived. The AMA refused to accept black physicians for membership until the 1940s, so the National Medical Association, founded in 1895, served to promote the professional concerns of black physicians (Cobb, Morais).

Professionalization of Medicine in the Early Twentieth Century

Robert Wiebe and other historians have seen the increasing professionalization of medicine around the turn of the twentieth century as a key element in the emergence of a growing and more influential middle class in American society (Wiebe). The expanding middle class both increased the demand for professional services and also provided recruits for the professional ranks (Johnson). It also provided students for the growing universities and readily embraced science as the key to future progress of medicine. Science came to be the cornerstone of the reforms in medical education (Ludmerer, Rosenkrantz).

The reforms in medical education that occurred in the early years of the twentieth century were funded and spurred on by philanthropic foundations such as those established by industrialist and philanthropist Andrew Carnegie (1835–1919) and the Rockefeller family, but also came from within the profession itself. In 1900 only 8,000 of the country's 120,000 physicians belonged to the AMA. With reorganization based on a federation of the state and local medical societies, membership grew to over 70,000 by 1910, about 60 percent of all physicians.

The *new medicine* of the 1890s included a physiology heavily influenced by chemistry and physics. This new physiology in turn stimulated departures in experimental pharmacology as well as scientific hygiene. More medical schools, following the lead of a few such as Harvard and the University of Pennsylvania, became integral parts of universities—not merely in name, but in financing, administration, and educational philosophy as well. Schools of medicine began to assume what they called a university point of view, according to which research was an opportunity and a *natural* activity for all instructors (Weed).

In contrast to the medical professionalism of the early nineteenth century, which Thomas Bender has called a *civic* professionalism, the professionalism associated with the new medicine was based firmly on disciplinary loyalties. The values of late-nineteenth- and early-twentieth-century medicine were drawn increasingly from science and, by the middle of the twentieth century, from the medical specialties and their societies and journals rather than from localities or universities.

Science and research provided the main rationale for a firmer link between medicine and the university. For the would-be reformers of early-twentieth-century medical education, such as Henry Pritchett of the Carnegie Foundation, William H. Welch of Johns Hopkins, and Abraham Flexner, the future of medicine depended upon such a relationship. Flexner's 1910 survey, sponsored by the Carnegie Foundation and assisted by the AMA's Council on Medical Education, included visits to all 155 North American schools of medicine and osteopathy. The resulting report, a classic of the muckraking tradition of the Progressive period, is a landmark in the history of medical education. Now best viewed as a catalyst for continuing change rather than as a source for new or revolutionary ideas, the Flexner Report was a clear statement of the importance of science for medicine (Hudson). For Flexner, the data derived from the patient in the clinic or at the bedside was as scientific as that discovered in the laboratory.

The sciences basic to medicine—chemistry, physics, and biology—provided the foundation students needed to study and to understand the preclinical sciences such as anatomy, physiology, microbiology, pharmacology, and biochemistry. And from the advancing knowledge about health and disease derived from these preclinical sciences, the practice of medicine was to be placed on a firm scientific basis. Science—and therefore science-based medicine—was best taught and learned in the university setting.

In the decades after 1910, the Rockefeller philanthropies and other foundations provided millions of dollars to build up academic medicine in many universities. Teaching and research became full-time professional duties for an increasing number of faculty.

Flexner's report documented the inadequacies of many schools and accelerated the closing or merging of some of them. The number of schools fell from a high of 166 in 1904 to a low of 76 in 1929; it began only slowly to rise again in the following decades, reaching 127 in the early 1980s.

By the 1930s, with several newly discovered specific remedies available for diseases such as diabetes, pernicious anemia, and after 1937, for pneumonia, medicine was once again viewed by the public as a true profession, a special calling. But despite continuing discoveries of new therapies and spectacular new technologies for viewing the body and how it works, by the mid-1980s observers of the American medical scene were saying that "the profession is increasingly being seen as more nearly a commercial enterprise with vested economic interests than a calling of professionals whose foremost concern is the well-being of the patient" (Iglehart, p. 324). This profound shift in the public perception of medicine was accompanied by the increasing number of liability suits and the corporatization of medical care (Starr). The coming of the corporation doubtless has been both a positive as well as negative organizational force. A business view has become dominant in hospitals and medical schools, as well as in the private practice of medicine.

Medicine has never been a homogeneous profession. It is perhaps even more disparate at the beginning of the twenty-first century than it has ever been. Until the 1960s, most doctors in the United States ran their practices like independent small businesses. In the corporate world of the late-twentieth century, by contrast, bureaucracy came to define medical practice better than autonomy. Legal challenges to the status of the profession have also questioned whether medicine and the law have acted to restrain trade, as in the 1975 U.S. Supreme Court decision *Goldfarb v. Virginia State Bar* (Rodwin, Sheehan). In that case a young lawyer brought suit against his own profession because he found that no lawyer would perform a title search for a house he was negotiating to buy for anything less than one percent of the purchase price. This commonly fixed price, he argued, violated the Sherman Antitrust Act. The case became a landmark for application of the antitrust laws to all the professions.

Medical professionalism in the context of American culture has always been faced with two apparently conflicting ideals that have shaped its history. Professions, by their very nature exclusionary, have been forced to grow and to prosper in a society that has prized egalitarianism. Equal opportunity has been a basis for American society since colonial days, yet increasingly the medical profession has drawn its recruits from the more privileged strata of U.S. society.

Also, still characteristic of late-twentieth-century medical practice, the patient is often not in a position to judge the quality, the necessity, or the extent of the services provided by the physician. This has remained true despite much more consumer (patient) involvement in medical decision making since the 1960s. As is true for the notion of egalitarianism in society, this continuing separation of esoteric medical knowledge from that which is commonly held provides potential ethical dilemmas for doctors.

A continuing paradox has prevailed in medicine of the late-twentieth century. The more effective medical services have become, the greater has been the demand for them. At the same time they have become increasingly expensive and so more difficult to obtain by many, and nearly inaccessible to those with no insurance coverage. Thus two conflicting concepts of medical care that have always existed in American medicine continue: medicine as a public service and as a private enterprise (Brieger).

Organized medicine in current usage usually refers to the dominant professional societies that have worked in both the professional and the political realms to help doctors achieve or preserve desired ends such as social status, economic rewards, or professional authority. Since one of the hallmarks of a profession is its organizations, the term organized medicine is redundant, albeit commonly used. We have come to assume considerable political power on the part of organizations such as the AMA, the Association of American Medical Colleges, the American College of Physicians, and the American College of Surgeons. While their positive power may have waned somewhat in recent decades as consumer interests have become much stronger, medical organizations until the 1960s were very effective in preventing measures they did not believe were in their best interest from becoming public policy or law (Burrow, 1963, 1977).

GERT H. BRIEGER (1995)
REVISED BY AUTHOR

SEE ALSO: *Medical Codes and Oaths; Medicine, Anthropology of; Medicine, Philosophy of; Medicine, Sociology of; Nursing as a Profession; Professional-Patient Relationship*

BIBLIOGRAPHY

Abbott, Andrew D. 1988. *The System of Professions: An Essay on the Division of Expert Labor.* Chicago: University of Chicago Press.

Baker, Robert B.; Caplan, Arthur L.; Emmanuel, Linda; and Latham, Stephen R., eds. 1999. *The American Medical Ethics Revolution, How the AMA's Code of Ethics Has Transformed Physicians' Relationships to Patients, Professionals, and Society.* Baltimore: Johns Hopkins University Press.

Bender, Thomas. 1979. "The Cultures of Intellectual Life: The City and the Professions." In *New Directions in American Intellectual History,* ed. John Higham and Paul K. Conkin. Baltimore: Johns Hopkins University Press.

Benes, Peter, and Benes, Jane Montague, eds. 1992. *Medicine and Healing.* Boston: Boston University Press.

Berlant, Jeffrey L. 1975. *Profession and Monopoly: A Study of Medicine in the United States and Great Britain.* Berkeley: University of California Press.

Billings, John Shaw. 1876. "A Century of American Medicine, 1776–1876, Literature and Institutions." *American Journal of Medical Sciences* 71: 439–480.

Blackwell, Elizabeth. 1895. *Pioneer Work in Opening the Medical Profession to Women: Autobiographical Sketches.* London: Longmans, Green.

Bledstein, Burton J. 1976. *The Culture of Professionalism: The Middle Class and the Development of Higher Education in America.* New York: W. W. Norton.

Bloom, Samuel W. 2002. *The Word as Scalpel, A History of Medical Sociology.* New York: Oxford University Press.

Bonner, Thomas N. 1992. *To the Ends of the Earth: Women's Search for Education in Medicine.* Cambridge, MA: Harvard University Press.

Bonner, Thomas N. 1995. *Becoming a Physician: Medical Education in Great Britain, France, and the United States, 1750–1945.* New York: Oxford University Press.

Bonner, Thomas N. 2002. *Iconoclast, Abraham Flexner and a Life in Learning.* Baltimore: Johns Hopkins University Press.

Brieger, Gert H. 1970. "The Medical Profession: Problems of Our Image." *New Physician* 19(10): 845–847.

Brown, JoAnne. 1992. *The Definition of a Profession: The Authority of Metaphor in the History of Intelligence Testing, 1890–1930.* Princeton, NJ: Princeton University Press.

Bullough, Vern L. 1966. *The Development of Medicine as Profession; or, The Contribution of the Medieval University to Modern Medicine.* New York: Hafner.

Burnham, John C. 1998. *How the Idea of Profession Changed the Writing of Medical History,* London: Wellcome Institute for the History of Medicine.

Burrow, James G. 1963. *AMA: Voice of American Medicine.* Baltimore: Johns Hopkins University Press.

Burrow, James G. 1977. *Organized Medicine in the Progressive Era: The Move Toward Monopoly.* Baltimore: Johns Hopkins University Press.

Calhoun, Daniel H. 1965. *Professional Lives in America: Structure and Aspiration, 1750–1850.* Cambridge, MA: Harvard University Press.

Christianson, Eric H. 1987. "Medicine in New England." In *Medicine in the New World: New Spain, New France, and New England,* ed. Ronald L. Numbers. Knoxville: University of Tennessee Press.

Cipolla, Carlo M. 1973. "The Professions: The Long View." *Journal of European Economic History* 2(1): 37–52.

Cobb, W. Montague. 1981. "The Black American in Medicine." *Journal of the National Medical Association* 73(Supplement): 1185–1244.

Cook, Harold John. 1986. *Decline of the Old Medical Regime in Stuart London.* Ithaca, NY: Cornell University Press.

Daniels, George H. 1967. "The Process of Professionalization in American Science: The Emergent Period, 1820–1860." *Isis* 58(2): 151–166.

Davis, Nathan Smith. 1855. *History of the American Medical Association from Its Organization up to January, 1855,* ed. Samuel Worcester Butler. Philadelphia: Lippincott, Grambo.

Edelstein, Ludwig. 1943. "The Hippocratic Oath: Text, Translation and Interpretation." *Bulletin of the History of Medicine,* suppl. (1): 1–64.

Flexner, Abraham. 1910. *Medical Education in the United States and Canada: A Report to the Carnegie Foundation for the Advancement of Teaching.* Birmingham, AL: Classics of Medicine Library.

Freidson, Eliot. 1970. *Profession of Medicine: A Study of the Sociology of Applied Knowledge.* New York: Dodd, Mead.

Freidson, Eliot. 1984. "Are Professions Necessary?" In *The Authority of Experts: Studies in History and Theory,* ed. Thomas L. Haskell. Bloomington: Indiana University Press.

Freidson, Eliot. 1986. *Professional Powers: A Study of the Institutionalization of Formal Knowledge.* Chicago: University of Chicago Press.

Gelfand, Toby. 1981. "The Decline of the Ordinary Practitioner and the Rise of a Modern Medical Profession." In *Doctors, Patients, and Society: Power and Authority in Medical Care,* ed. Martin S. Staum and Donald E. Larsen. Waterloo, Canada: Wilfrid Laurier University Press.

Gelfand, Toby. 1984. "A *Monarchical Profession* in the Old Regime: Surgeons, Ordinary Practitioners, and Medical Professionalization in Eighteenth-Century France." In *Professions and the French State, 1700–1900,* ed. Gerald L. Geison. Philadelphia: University of Pennsylvania Press.

Gevitz, Norman, ed. 1988. *The Other Healers: Unorthodox Medicine in America.* Baltimore: Johns Hopkins University Press.

Glazer, Nathan. 1978. "The Attack on the Professions." *Commentary* 66(5): 34–41.

Goldfarb v. Virginia State Bar, 421 U.S. 773 (1975).

Goode, William J. 1969. "The Theoretical Limits of Professionalization." In *The Semi-Professions and Their Organization: Teachers, Nurses, Social Workers,* ed. Amitai Etzioni. New York: Free Press.

Greenwood, Ernest. 1957. "Attributes of a Profession." *Social Work* 3(2): 45–55.

Haber, Samuel. 1991. *The Quest for Authority and Honor in the American Professions, 1750–1900.* Chicago: University of Chicago Press.

Hall, Peter Dobkin. 1984. "The Social Foundations of Professional Credibility: Linking the Medical Profession to Higher Education in Connecticut and Massachusetts, 1700–1830." In *The Authority of Experts: Studies in History and Theory,* ed. Thomas L. Haskell. Bloomington: Indiana University Press.

Hamilton, Bernice. 1951. "The Medical Professions in the Eighteenth Century." *Economic History Review* 4(2): 141–169.

Haskell, Thomas L., ed. 1984. *The Authority of Experts: Studies in History and Theory.* Bloomington: Indiana University Press.

Hatch, Nathan O., ed. 1988. *The Professions in American History.* Notre Dame, IN: University of Notre Dame Press.

Holloway, S. W. F. 1966a. "The Apothecaries Act, 1815: A Reinterpretation. Part I: The Origins of the Act." *Medical History* 10(2): 107–129.

Holloway, S. W. F. 1966b. "The Apothecaries Act, 1815: A Reinterpretation. Part II: The Consequences of the Act." *Medical History* 10(3): 221–236.

Horstmanshoff, N. F. J. 1990. "The Ancient Physician: Craftsman or Scientist?" *Journal of the History of Medicine and Allied Sciences* 45(2): 176–197.

Hudson, Robert P. 1992. "Abraham Flexner in Historical Perspective." In *Beyond Flexner: Medical Education in the Twentieth Century,* ed. Barbara Barzansky and Norman Gevitz. New York: Greenwood Press.

Hughes, Everett C. 1965. "Professions." In *The Professions in America,* ed. Kenneth S. Lynn. Boston: Houghton Mifflin.

Iglehart, John K. 1986. "Federal Support of Health Manpower Education." *New England Journal of Medicine* 314(5): 324–328.

Johnson, Terence J. 1972. *Professions and Power.* London: Macmillan.

Kett, Joseph F. 1968. *The Formation of the American Medical Profession: The Role of Institutions, 1780–1860.* New Haven, CT: Yale University Press.

Kimball, Bruce A. 1992. *The True Professional Ideal in America: A History.* Oxford: Basil Blackwell.

Larson, Magali Sarfatti. 1977. *The Rise of Professionalism: A Sociological Analysis.* Berkeley: University of California Press.

Loudon, Irvine. 1986. *Medical Care and the General Practitioner, 1750–1850.* Oxford: Clarendon Press.

Ludmerer, Kenneth M. 1985. *Learning to Heal: The Development of American Medical Education.* New York: Basic Books.

Mechanic, David. 1968. *Medical Sociology: A Selective View.* New York: Free Press.

Mechanic, David. 1976. *The Growth of Bureaucratic Medicine: An Inquiry into the Dynamics of Patient Behavior and the Organization of Medical Care.* New York: Wiley.

Morais, Herbert M. 1976. *The History of the Afro-American in Medicine.* Cornwells Heights, PA: Association for the Study of Afro-American Life and History.

Morantz-Sanchez, Regina M. 1985. *Sympathy and Science: Women Physicians in American Medicine.* New York: Oxford University Press.

More, Ellen S. 1999. *Restoring the Balance: Women Physicians and the Profession of Medicine, 1850–1995.* Cambridge, MA: Harvard University Press.

Nutton, Vivian. 1992. "Healers in the Medical Market Place: Towards a Social History of Graeco-Roman Medicine." In *Medicine in Society: Historical Essays,* ed. Andrew Wear. Cambridge, Eng.: Cambridge University Press.

Park, Katharine. 1985. *Doctors and Medicine in Early Renaissance Florence.* Princeton, NJ: Princeton University Press.

Park, Katharine. 1992. "Medicine and Society in Medieval Europe, 500–1500." In *Medicine in Society: Historical Essays,* ed. Andrew Wear. Cambridge, Eng.: Cambridge University Press.

Parry, Noel, and Parry, José. 1976. *The Rise of the Medical Profession, A Study of Collective Social Mobility.* London: Croom Helm.

Pelling, Margaret. 1987. "Medical Practice in Early Modern England: Trade or Profession?" In *The Professions in Early Modern England,* ed. Wilfrid R. Prest. London: Croom Helm.

Pelling, Margaret. 1998. *The Common Lot: Sickness, Medical Occupations and the Urban Poor in Early Modern England.* London: Longman.

Pelling, Margaret, and Webster, Charles. 1979. "Medical Practitioners." In *Health, Medicine, and Mortality in the Sixteenth Century,* ed. Charles Webster. Cambridge, Eng.: University Press.

Percival, Thomas. 1803. *Medical Ethics; or, A Code of Institutes, and Precepts, Adapted to the Professional Conduct of Physicians and Surgeons.* Manchester, Eng.: S. Russell.

Perkin, Harold J. 1989. *The Rise of Professional Society: England since 1880.* London: Routledge.

Pernick, Martin S. 1985. *A Calculus of Suffering: Pain, Professionalism, and Anesthesia in Nineteenth-Century America.* New York: Columbia University Press.

Peterson, M. Jeanne. 1978. *The Medical Profession in Mid-Victorian London.* Berkeley: University of California Press.

Plato. 1926. *Laws,* tr. Robert Gregg Bury. New York: G. P. Putnam's Sons.

Ramsey, Matthew. 1988. *Professional and Popular Medicine in France, 1770–1830: The Social World of Medical Practice.* Cambridge, Eng.: Cambridge University Press.

Rodwin, Marc A. 1993. *Medicine, Money, and Morals: Physicians' Conflicts of Interest.* New York: Oxford University Press.

Rosen, George. 1944. *The Specialization of Medicine with Particular Reference to Ophthalmology.* New York: Froben Press.

Rosenkrantz, Barbara Gutmann. 1985. "The Search for Professional Order in 19th-Century American Medicine." In *Sickness and Health in America: Readings in the History of Medicine and Public Health,* 2nd edition rev., ed. Judith Walzer Leavitt and Ronald L. Numbers. Madison: University of Wisconsin Press.

Rothstein, William G. 1972. *American Physicians in the Nineteenth Century: From Sects to Science.* Baltimore: Johns Hopkins University Press.

Savitt, Todd. 1992. "Abraham Flexner and the Black Medical Schools." In *Beyond Flexner: Medical Education in the Twentieth Century,* ed. Barbara Barzansky and Norman Gevitz. New York: Greenwood Press.

Sheehan, Mark T. 1975. "What the Goldfarb Decision Means to the Medical Profession." *Journal of Legal Medicine* 3(10): 21–25.

Shryock, Richard Harrison. 1960. *Medicine and Society in America: 1660–1860.* New York: New York University Press.

Shryock, Richard Harrison. 1967. *Medical Licensing in America, 1650–1965.* Baltimore: Johns Hopkins University Press.

Siraisi, Nancy G. 1990. *Medieval and Early Renaissance Medicine: An Introduction to Knowledge and Practice.* Chicago: University of Chicago Press.

Smith, Dale C. 1996. "The Hippocratic Oath and Modern Medicine." *Journal of the History of Medicine and Allied Sciences* 51: 484–500.

Starr, Paul. 1982. *The Social Transformation of American Medicine.* New York: Basic Books.

Stevens, Rosemary. 1971 (reprint 1998). *American Medicine and the Public Interest.* Berkeley: University of California Press.

Temkin, Owsei. 1953. "Greek Medicine as Science and Craft." *Isis* 44: 213–225.

Temkin, Owsei. 2002. "What Does the Hippocratic Oath Say?" In *On Second Thought and Other Essays,* ed. Owsei Temkin. Baltimore: Johns Hopkins University Press.

Ulrich, Laurel T. 1990. *A Midwife's Tale: The Life of Martha Ballard, Based on Her Diary, 1785–1812.* New York: Knopf.

Walsh, Mary Roth. 1977. *Doctors Wanted, No Women Need Apply: Sexual Barriers in the Medical Profession, 1855–1975.* New Haven, CT: Yale University Press.

Walsh, Mary Roth. 1992. "Women in Medicine Since Flexner." In *Beyond Flexner: Medical Education in the Twentieth Century,* ed. Barbara Barzansky and Norman Gevitz. New York: Greenwood Press.

Warner, John Harley. 1986. *The Therapeutic Perspective: Medical Practice, Knowledge, and Identity in America, 1820–1885.* Cambridge, MA: Harvard University Press.

Watson, Patricia. 1991. *The Angelical Conjunction: The Preacher-Physician of Colonial New England.* Knoxville: University of Tennessee Press.

Weed, Lewis H. 1931. "Experimentation in Medical Education." *Southern Medical Journal* 24(12): 1116–1121.

Wiebe, Robert H. 1967. *The Search for Order: 1877–1920.* New York: Hill and Wang.

MEDICINE, SOCIOLOGY OF

• • •

The sociology of medicine is characterized by a wide variety of concerns, approaches, and perspectives (Mechanic, 1978; Freeman and Levine; Fox; Waitzkin, 1991). The concerns of medical sociologists cover such diverse areas as the distribution and etiology of disease and impairments; disease concepts and their social construction; cultural and social responses to health and illness and the use of services; health and illness behavior and its determinants; sociocultural aspects of medical care and the social organization of helping services; the organization of the health occupations and the processes of providing care; social factors affecting trends in death and illness; the sociology of the health occupations; the social organization of the hospital; and comparative health organization. In collaboration with other disciplines, the field includes the study of social change and healthcare; changing technology and its role in care; medical education; public-health organization; stress, disease, and coping; social and community psychiatry; the social context of legal and ethical dilemmas; and medical politics.

Many medical sociologists attempt to illuminate how individuals define and respond to situations as they cope with the expectations and demands of their physical and social environment, how some types of response lead to stress and illness, and how services are used to reestablish social and personal equilibrium. Helping institutions can be examined similarly in terms of how the behavior of health personnel and organizations responds to problems of resources, time, and other situational constraints. All people, whether patients or health personnel, seek to establish mastery over their life and work environments, to reduce uncertainty, and to obtain gratification and esteem for their efforts.

One important aspect of medical sociology concerns how certain problems become manifest in a population, how they are defined, and how patients with these problems enter particular channels of care. The field also deals with the nature of therapeutic encounters between patients and practitioners, modes of communication and influence, types of discourse, and how all these are influenced by the cultural context, social characteristics of patient and therapist, changing knowledge and technology, organizational and payment arrangements, and resource constraints.

From a sociological perspective, medicine can be regarded as a sustaining or integrative institution in society (Parsons). Not only does it provide assistance to persons afflicted with disease and other life problems; it also serves as an important means for alleviating social distress and for excusing failures in social functioning or failures to meet social expectations (Mechanic, 1978; Kleinman, 1986). Medicine also has important social control functions that facilitate the removal of individuals from social settings to relieve tensions—whether in the family, in work settings, or in the community at large. It may also facilitate financial compensation or social benefits, for example, access to services or products, such as drugs, that are restricted to those who are not deemed ill.

The role of the physician, then, has not only technical dimensions but also social and moral ones. While the technical expertise of practitioners refers to a limited range of situations, their clientele and the scope of problems they deal

with are very broad. Many of the judgments a physician makes are not medical judgments but decisions based on social considerations and values. Even those aspects of the medical role that appear to be purely technical, such as the labeling of disease, the specific management of the patient, and the choice of medications or other treatments, have profound consequences for performance of social roles and obligations as well as for future life opportunities. Patients' problems often result in part from conflicts with other persons and social groups, and the physician can sometimes help resolve difficulties by taking either the patient's or an adversary's perspective. Such conflicts are particularly evident in such areas as military, industrial, and prison medicine, where the physician is not the patient's personal agent, but they occur to some extent in many private patient-care contexts as well.

Patient flow from a community population to various helping agencies is usually thought to result almost exclusively from the occurrence of illness in that population, in contrast with other factors. Indeed, other factors distorting the selection process, such as differential propensities to seek care, are seen as *disturbances* that require correction through patient education or such economic disincentives as deductibles and coinsurance. Although illness is usually the major determinant of help-seeking, it fails to explain by itself much of the evident variation between those who seek and those who do not seek assistance (Mechanic, 1978).

It is common, for example, for medical scientists to assert that discovering a cure for an illness such as the common cold, one of the most frequent reasons for consulting a physician, would profoundly alleviate physical limitations, industrial absenteeism, and the loss of productive labor. But to the extent that the common cold is often an excuse rather than the reason for work absenteeism or seeking medical care, a *cure* might have much less social effect than commonly believed. If people who seek care for the common cold do so because they are unhappy or hate their employment, then the visit to the doctor may be little more than a justification for more complex motivations and behavior. There are various social and cultural inhibitions against persons openly acknowledging personal life problems, and often such problems are shielded by presentations of seemingly trivial illness. This process is now commonly referred to as somatization (Kleinman, 1986).

Medicine involves a distinctive set of meanings that limit the interpretations of patients' concerns (Waitzkin, 1991). Such meanings may obscure social problems and dilemmas and their causes, narrowing the range of possible remedies. This *medicalization* subsumes important social and ethical issues within clinical judgments that escape careful scrutiny. The differential diagnostic approach, which structures how doctors are educated and how they address problems, affects the ability of doctors and patients to explore comprehensively the sources of distress and disease as well as their implications for well-being (Waitzkin, 1983, 1991; Kleinman, 1986).

Social Distribution of Health, Illness, and Medical Care

Although the concept of health is difficult to define, numerous studies demonstrate that longevity, absence of impairment, and less illness and disability are associated with favorable socioeconomic conditions (Mechanic, 1989b). Many of the health problems of the poor stem from unfavorable environmental conditions, poor nutrition, and lifestyles harmful to health. Because persons of lower socioeconomic circumstances are less likely to receive high-quality services—whether because of limited income, less readiness to seek necessary care, or inaccessibility of facilities—they are more likely to suffer from disabilities, higher mortality, and secondary conditions (Bunker et al., 1989).

Secondary conditions, such as decubitus ulcers, cardiopulmonary problems, and psychological depression, are often causally related to an initial illness and occur because the primary condition is poorly managed (Institute of Medicine). Since 1965 social programs in the United States have given some attention to the equity in the provision of medical services, and the historic inverse relationship between socioeconomic status and use of physician services has been reversed. But socioeconomic differences continue to persist for many specialized services and for preventive care. Although mental disorders are very prevalent in the lowest socioeconomic groups (Robins and Regier), psychological and social services are particularly inadequate for the poor.

The poor suffer from other problems in the medical care sector. They are least likely to share assumptions and meanings with health practitioners, and thus most likely to suffer from misunderstandings and confusions resulting from such incompatibilities. They are likely to feel more embarrassed, anxious, and intimidated in dealing with medical personnel, and are less likely to receive care congruent with their values or life perspectives. They are frequently used as subjects for teaching and research, particularly in experiments that bring no particular benefits to the patient (Barber et al.); and they are more likely to have difficulty granting informed consent, particularly where explanations are quick and perfunctory (Gray). The poor not only have more illness and problems and less access to medical care relative to need but also are treated with less consideration and respect than affluent patients.

Above and beyond socioeconomic status differences, race and ethnic differences account for variations in health. Although much of the excess in mortality and morbidity among blacks and Hispanics is attributable to socioeconomic disadvantage, other factors associated with race and ethnicity are pertinent, including differences in culture and health-relevant behavior, discrimination, and biological differences.

Still other aspects of social stratification, including age and gender, are important determinants of health status. Age and gender affect exposure to risk and disease occurrence through both biological and social pathways linked to these characteristics. The prevalence of chronic disease and disability increases with age but is influenced as well by the individual's social participation and social networks, sense of personal efficacy, and subjective well-being, which vary over the life cycle.

Large differences in health indicators and health behavior are also found between men and women. The fact that women live longer than men is in part biological, but it is also substantially affected by different styles of behavior and response among men and women. Most of the higher mortality in men can be attributed to behaviors such as substance abuse, poor nutrition, risk-taking, and violence. Many other social factors, such as marital status and household structure, are associated with patterns of health and disease (Mechanic, 1978).

Organization of Medical Care

If medicine has social and ethical as well as technical dimensions, how do we develop organizational settings that can apply the necessary technical expertise in ways that respond to the patients and their unique individual and social needs? Even the very best hospitals and medical organizations often treat patients without empathy or respect, and show limited interest in managing their medical problems in light of their family, work, and community circumstances (Duff and Hollingshead; Kleinman, 1988). The personnel who carry out these institutions' medical functions behave as they do, not because they are inhumane, but because the pressures and constraints of work, the priorities they have been taught, and the reward structures of which they are a part direct their attention to other goals and needs. Successful modification of service institutions requires significant revisions in the organizational arrangements and incentives that affect the work of personnel and the tasks they perform. In a materialistic culture where persons may respond to money and prestige incentives more readily than to more lofty motivations, the design of economic and prestige incentives and an awareness of how they affect decisions become important elements in shaping behavior.

Some attention has been devoted to how the economic structure of medicine affects the work of physicians and other personnel. Fee-for-service incentives often result in high levels of professional commitment, a willingness to work hard, and responsiveness to those who pay the fees. They also often encourage excessive use of medical, surgical, and pharmaceutical modalities to earn more income. Data from a variety of nations suggest that when attempts are made to manipulate the system by increasing payments associated with certain procedures, these incentives shape what physicians do (Glaser). The difficulty with any such piecework system is that it tends to discourage procedures that are important but for which only modest or no remuneration is provided. Since payment systems typically reward technical procedures, the most neglected aspects are those concerned with social care, listening to the client, patient education, and grappling with ethical issues. Physicians are best rewarded financially when they provide the largest number of discrete technical services.

One antidote to the perversities of piecework medicine is to pay by salary or capitation (a uniform payment for each person the physician cares for), but these approaches also have disadvantages. Under such systems physicians are more likely to limit their work efforts, appear less committed to their work, and seem less flexible and responsive to the individual needs and circumstances of their patients (Mechanic, 1989a). Thus, the same incentive conditions that make it possible for physicians to allocate their time within their own concepts of the value of varying types of caring and curing—conditions that may dampen a tendency to overutilize expensive and perhaps dangerous therapies—may also encourage withholding necessary services or result in an unwillingness to respond to important concerns of patients.

Doctors paid by capitation seem to adjust their efforts in relation to the payments they receive, a form of perceived distributive justice. This concept is shaped by knowledge of the circumstances of other doctors with comparable training in different work settings. Many of the difficulties in capitation payment result because patient load is heavy and payment is small for each patient. The heavy patient load and the doctor's limited work hours encourage a pattern of care that many patients find unresponsive. But time and patient demand are not the only factors involved in the way physicians deal with social and ethical problems in their practice. Physicians may have more or less tolerance for a wide scope of work; may be more or less willing, and feel more or less competent, to deal with family problems, alcoholism, sexual adjustment, or child-care problems. To the extent that physicians are properly trained to deal with the broader problems of medical care, and thus feel more competent in their clinical management, they may be more willing to deal openly with social and ethical challenges. Many physicians probably avoid dealing with psychosocial issues because they feel an effective therapy is lacking; however, they often readily accept the responsibilities to treat physical illnesses for which they also lack effective treatment. It may be that a sense of confidence and clinical experience are more important than the objective efficacy of the care.

In the creation of new medical settings, the problem is how to maximize the advantages of both fee-for-service and capitation medicine while compensating for their more undesirable aspects. People are ingenious in undermining and thwarting incentive systems that are not sensitive to their work problems, that increase their uncertainties, or that appear inequitable. To design an organizational system adequately requires intimate appreciation of how individuals actually manage their work, rather than utopian but unrealistic conceptions of how people should function.

Sociology of the Health Occupations

The attention in this article to doctors, in contrast with nurses, technicians, pharmacists, or social workers, is no accident. Although physicians constitute less than one-tenth of personnel in the health sector, they define and dominate the nature of decision making and the division of labor in medicine (Freidson; Starr; Mechanic, 1991). Physician dominance is in part a process in which doctors gain political legitimacy that protects them against economic competition from other health workers and helps preserve their professional autonomy. Increasingly, the physicians' dominance is being challenged by a variety of forces in the society: by administrators wishing to achieve economies of production through shifting traditional medical tasks to less trained personnel; by government wishing to control the growing costs of medical care; and by such professional groups as nurses who wish to improve their own political power, income, and status. Thus, the health sector is characterized by increasing political acrimony and collective politics (Stevens).

Ethical Dilemmas and the Sociology of Healthcare

The advances of medical knowledge and technology confront modern society with awesome social and ethical dilemmas. Among these questions is whether an ever-increasing proportion of our gross national product ought to be spent on expensive modalities that provide marginal gains in health and longevity. Are such investments not better made in preventive approaches and environmental amelioration or in other social goals?

Bioethics has been more an activity with a normative focus than a field of inquiry that seeks to investigate the implications of varying courses of action (Wikler; Fox). During the two decades in which bioethics has grown as a discipline, relatively few bioethicists have utilized sociological materials and methods, and relatively few sociologists have studied bioethics (Weisz). Ethical reflection in healthcare could be very much enhanced by a sociological perspective that examines the empirical setting and implications of a given ethical choice. Whether to accept organs from live donors or allow subjects to participate in experiments posing possible danger to themselves must depend at least to some extent on the actual psychological and social consequences of such participation. The fact that such volunteers often experience great satisfaction from their participation is no small part of such policy considerations (Fellner and Schwartz; Gray). Similarly, the willingness to expend great resources in heroic efforts to extend life, irrespective of function, must be weighed against the consequences of extended lives for such patients and their loved ones. Sociological perspectives and methodology can contribute to the ultimate ethical decisions by clarifying some of the human factors relevant to resolving the conflicts between competing social and ethical values.

DAVID MECHANIC (1995)
BIBLIOGRAPHY REVISED

SEE ALSO: *Health and Disease: Sociological Perspectives; Organ Transplants, Sociocultural Aspects of; Professional-Patient Relationship; Race and Racism*

BIBLIOGRAPHY

Armstrong, David. 1997. *Outline of Sociology as Applied to Medicine,* 4th edition. New York: Oxford University Press.

Barber, Bernard; Lally, John J.; Makarushka, Julia L.; and Sullivan, Daniel. 1973. *Research on Human Subjects: Problems of Social Control in Medical Experimentation.* New York: Russell Sage Foundation.

Bird, Chloe; Conrad, Peter; and Fremont, Allen, eds. 2000. *Handbook of Medical Sociology,* 5th edition. Englewood Cliffs, NJ: Prentice Hall.

Bloom, Samuel William. 2002. *The Word as Scalpel: A History of Medical Sociology by Samuel William Bloom.* New York: Oxford University Press.

Bunker, John P.; Gomby, Deanna S.; and Kehrer, Barbara H., eds. 1989. *Pathways to Health: The Role of Social Factors.* Menlo Park, CA: Henry J. Kaiser Family Foundation.

Cockerham, William C. 2000. *Medical Sociology,* 8th edition. Englewood Cliffs, NJ: Prentice Hall College Division.

Cockerham, William C., ed. 2001. *The Blackwell Companion to Medical Sociology (Blackwell Companions to Sociology).* Williston, VT: Blackwell.

Das, Veena. 1999. "Public Good, Ethics, and Everyday life: Beyond the Boundaries of Bioethics." *Dadelus* 128(4): 99–133.

Duff, Raymond S., and Hollingshead, August de Belmont. 1968. *Sickness and Society.* New York: Harper & Row.

Fellner, Carl H., and Schwartz, Shalom H. 1971. "Altruism in Disrepute." *New England Journal of Medicine* 284(11): 582–585.

Fox, Renée C. 1989. *The Sociology of Medicine: A Participant Observer's View.* Englewood Cliffs, NJ: Prentice-Hall.

Fox, Renée C. 1998. *Sociology of Medicine: A Participant Observers View.* Englewood Cliffs, NJ: Prentice Hall.

Freeman, Howard E., and Levine, Sol, eds. 1989. *Handbook of Medical Sociology.* 4th edition. Englewood Cliffs, NJ: Prentice-Hall.

Freidson, Eliot. 1970. *Professional Dominance: The Social Structure of Medical Care.* New York: Atherton.

Glaser, William A. 1970. *Paying the Doctor: Systems of Remuneration and Their Effects.* Baltimore: Johns Hopkins University Press.

Gray, Bradford H. 1975. *Human Subjects in Medical Experimentation: A Sociological Study of the Conduct and Regulation of Clinical Research.* New York: Wiley.

Institute of Medicine. Committee on a National Agenda for the Prevention of Disabilities. 1991. *Disability in America: Toward a National Agenda for Prevention.* Washington, D.C.: National Academy Press.

Kleinman, Arthur. 1986. *Social Origins of Distress and Disease: Depression, Neurasthenia, and Pain in Modern China.* New Haven, CT: Yale University Press.

Kleinman, Arthur. 1988. *The Illness Narratives: Suffering, Healing and the Human Condition.* New York: Basic Books.

Mechanic, David. 1978. *Medical Sociology,* 2nd edition. New York: Free Press.

Mechanic, David. 1989a. *Painful Choices: Research and Essays on Health Care.* New Brunswick, NJ: Transaction Publishers.

Mechanic, David. 1989b. "Socioeconomic Status and Health: An Examination of Underlying Processes." In *Pathways to Health,* pp. 9–26, ed. John P. Bunker, Deanna S. Gomby, and Barbara H. Kehrer. Menlo Park, CA: Henry J. Kaiser Family Foundation.

Mechanic, David. 1991. "Sources of Countervailing Power in Medicine." *Journal of Health Politics, Policy and Law* 16(3): 485–498.

Parsons, Talcott. 1951. *The Social System.* New York: Free Press.

Pippin, R. B. 1996. "Medical Practice and Social Authority." *Journal of Medicine and Philosophy* 21(4): 417–437.

Robins, Lee N., and Regier, David A., eds. 1991. *Psychiatric Disorders in America: The Epidemiologic Catchment Area Study.* New York: Free Press.

Starr, Paul. 1982. *The Social Transformation of American Medicine.* New York: Basic Books.

Stevens, Rosemary. 1989. *In Sickness and in Wealth: American Hospitals in the Twentieth Century.* New York: Basic Books.

Waitzkin, Howard. 1983. *The Second Sickness: Contradictions of Capitalist Health Care.* New York: Free Press.

Waitzkin, Howard. 1991. *The Politics of Medical Encounters: How Patients and Doctors Deal with Social Problems.* New Haven, CT: Yale University Press.

Wcitz, Rose. 2000. *The Sociology of Health, Illness, and Health Care: A Critical Approach.* Belmont, CA: Wadsworth Publishing Co.

Weiss, Gregory L., and Lonnquist, Lynne E. 2002. *The Sociology of Health, Healing, and Illness,* 4th edition. Englewood Cliffs, NJ: Prentice Hall.

Weisz, George, ed. 1990. *Social Science Perspectives on Medical Ethics.* Philadelphia: University of Pennsylvania Press.

Wikler, Daniel. 1991. "What Has Bioethics to Offer Health Policy?" *Milbank Quarterly* 69(2): 233–251.

MENTAL HEALTH, MEANING OF MENTAL HEALTH

• • •

Notions of *health* and *mental health* neither arose nor developed in a cultural and conceptual vacuum; their ancestral and contemporary kindred and relationships are multiple and far-reaching. Traces of their past live on in present quandaries and controversies. The interpretation and analysis that follow are historical and sociocultural, as well as philosophical and clinical.

Historical and Philosophical Background

NEAR EASTERN AND CLASSICAL CONCEPTS. Our story begins with the high civilizations of the ancient Near East. Initially, disturbances in customary and acceptable human functioning were experienced and interpreted in magico-religious and moral modes. Ancient Near Eastern personhood blended into a cosmos permeated by the divine and comprising countless interactions among fluid and loosely bounded beings and forces. Demarcations such as those between religion and medicine, psychic and somatic, material and immaterial, or spiritistic, natural, and supernatural would have been incomprehensible to early Egyptians and Mesopotamians. Even surgical and pharmaceutical interventions were accompanied by prayer, rituals, and magical formulas and paraphernalia.

Much the same can be said for the people of Mycenaean and Homeric Greece, whose worldviews and concepts of human beings were inseparable and thoroughly magical, animistic, and religio-moral. Cognition, affect, and motivation were experienced as divinely or demonically implanted, or else literally *inspired* from the ambient air. The earliest Homeric internalizations of motivation were localized to a semiautonomous region of the midriff or diaphragm called *phthumos.* As in Near Eastern antiquity, all sickness or disease, including madness, was magical (caused by spells or curses), demonic, or religious and moral (caused by divine possession, or divine punishment for ritualistic infractions, taboo-breaking, and sins of all sorts).

Health or *wellness* referred equally to states of the cosmos, society, or person. For example, the Egyptian goddess Maat personified a diffuse constellation of truth, balance, and right ordering or right acting, understood as antithetical to the primal chaos of the universe. Likewise, preclassical Greek ideas of health or wholeness were religio-moral, the corrections of imbalances. These metaphors and concepts of equilibrium, refined and codified by the classical Greeks, have remained central to modern Western medical and psychiatric norms or ideals of healthy functioning.

Classical Greece is commonly deemed the birthplace of both the psychological individual and secular medicine. Actually, however, medicine's vocational identity, cosmology, and philosophical anthropology were still imbued with religious aspects. The Greeks invoked deities such as Asklepios/Apollo; and nature itself (Physis), and humanity as part of it, remained divinized. Maladies, healing, and health were at once medical and sacred. The more medical facet of Hippocratic doctors' *health* and *disease* concepts concerned the bodily humors and their ratios to one another (balance versus excess or deficiency). Madness was explicated humorally as well, in a sort of proto-"physiological psychology" and psychopathology (Jackson); and the brain was considered the organ of mental activity.

By contrast, Plato and his philosophical successors disseminated a psyche-body dualism that influenced Western medicine for centuries. Plato characterized as "divine" physicians who were also philosophers, who thus knew soul as well as body. Nevertheless, he apparently thought such practitioners so rare that he roundly criticized doctors' practices of "dietetics"—which included what we would call counseling, lifestyle management, and prevention. In line with his dualism, Plato argued that philosophers were the rightful "physicians of the soul," thereby inaugurating a lengthy tradition of philosophical therapy. Such philosophers progressively adopted medical models and metaphors for the psyche in states of wellness and disease (*pathē*). In the first and second centuries C.E., Epictetus termed the philosopher's lecture room a "hospital"; he likened the pain necessary in spiritual and moral healing to that in medical measures such as the lancing of an abscess (see Edelstein). Centuries later, Sigmund Freud characterized analysis with surgical metaphors, and Henri Ellenberger thought psychoanalysis itself a latter-day version of philosophical healing.

The Hellenistic and Roman Stoics and Epicureans were other famous proponents of psychotherapeutic philosophy. Like all philosophical physicians, they were infatuated with metaphors of balance. The soul's health was equated with states such as *ataraxia* or *apatheia* (equilibrium, tranquility, serenity). The Stoic idealization of reason, and concomitant depreciation of passion, probably influenced subsequent rationalistic criteria for mind in health and illness. In any event, Plato and company, with their dualism and healing ambitions, paved the way for current concepts of mental health and psychotherapy. Nonetheless, their images of such health were spiritual/ethical, and their healing was dialectical and pedagogical—and, hence, a far cry from our ostensibly metaphysically and morally neutral mental health and psychotherapy; though Freud himself emphasized the educational and ethical aspects of analysis far more than any presumable medical ones (Wallace, 1986).

Aristotle, Plato's greatest pupil, avoided a frankly dualistic mind-body position and touted the philosopher's role as ethical teacher. The doctrine of the *golden mean* and prudential and moral virtues, or *character ethics,* held the place in Aristotle's philosophy that had been occupied by psychical or spiritual health in Plato's. This "golden mean," yet another manifestation of balance, was the cardinal feature of the virtues—for example, courage as the midpoint between temerity and timidity. In light of the individualistic thrust of ancient philosophical therapies such as Stoicism and Epicureanism, and of many present-day psychotherapies and notions of mental health, it is noteworthy that Aristotle considered his Ethics and Politics integral to each other. Citizenship, reflecting the individual's self-acknowledged embeddedness in a community, was central to Aristotle's idea of proper human functioning. Whereas we might accuse Aristotle of collapsing mental health into social ethics, he might have charged us with the reverse.

MEDIEVAL AND RENAISSANCE CONCEPTS. In the Christian West, institutionalized medicine was in priestly hands. The closest thing to medical schools were monastic, and most medieval infirmaries were operated by the Church. Medical theory and therapy followed the Hellenistic Galen's final codification of humoralism and anatomy. Madness was explained and treated somatically, as well as with the prayers and healing rites offered for any severe medical condition.

Somatic perspectives on madness meshed nicely with the Church's Platonic dualism, since the immortal and immaterial soul, unlike the body and brain, was not corruptible by disease. Meanwhile, the Church continued to use medical metaphors for many spiritual and moral problems. It is hard to know whether some of these approximated our nonpsychotic and less severe categories of mental illness—such as *dysthymia* or the *personality disorders*; aspects of the latter clearly falling under the traditionally moral purview. Medieval clerics themselves meditated over gray zones, such as whether acedia, a common monk's affliction, was sin (slothfulness) or disease (a mild form of melancholia) (Jackson). There was nothing corresponding to contemporary concepts of mental health. Norms and ideals were spiritual and moral, biblically and theologically derived.

Thomas Aquinas added loss of free will to irrational thinking and behavior as another cardinal sign of madness. This has influenced juridical processes up to the present, posing problems to psychiatrists espousing determinism (i.e., that all human mentation and behavior are causally necessitated). It has also borne on contemporary conceptions of mental health, some presupposing a capacity for nonnecessitated choosing (e.g., humanistic and existentialist) and others (e.g., classical psychoanalytic and neuromolecular) usually not. The ramifications for morality and ethics are obvious (Wallace, 1986).

As the great universities arose between the twelfth and the fourteenth centuries, they incorporated monastic medicine. Nonpriestly physicians returned to the scene, but medical theory and the treatment of madness remained much the same. There was no real secularization in Europe until the Renaissance, with its novel and heightened forms of individualism among certain educationally and financially favored segments of Europe's populations and its protopsychological concept *imaginatio,* a catchall for feeling, imagination, and fantasy (the very items ignored by hitherto hyperrationalistic norms of personhood).

This same period, however, witnessed the Inquisition, and its mass persecution of heretics and alleged witches. Medical men such as Johannes Weyer, with special interests in madness, argued that accused and "confessed" witches were actually insane, one of the few conditions that legally exonerated them. Still, Weyer's diagnoses were not purely medical, for he thought the witches' delusions had been implanted by Satan. Many modern historians of psychiatry have lauded Weyer for his insight and courage (e.g., Zilboorg). Some psychiatrists and psychoanalysts, including Freud, followed Weyer's example and facilely diagnosed whole institutions and cultures as psychopathological. Several decades of careful scholarship suggest that most "witches" were not in fact psychotic (e.g., Spanos). Furthermore, concepts of normality and pathology are complex, and they vary greatly from one culture or historical period to another. Moreover, transferring concepts of mental health and illness from the individual domain to the arenas of groups, cultures, and even families is questionable at best (Ackerknecht, 1971; Wallace, 1983).

SEVENTEENTH- AND EIGHTEENTH-CENTURY CONCEPTS. The seventeenth century was characterized by the continuing expansion of individualism and by a rationalism that paid less attention to aspects of personality, such as *imaginatio,* explored by the Renaissance. Irrationality became the key criterion for madness, giving the social philosopher Michel Foucault (1965) the ostensible grounds for his thesis that seventeenth-century asylums were filled with persons who had violated their era's canons of reason and socially acceptable behavior. Foucault alerted us to possible linkages between sociocultural and political-economic special interests, and psychiatric institutions, concepts, and practices—including formulations of mental health and illness.

The epoch from 1600 to 1750, then, was a watershed in many ways. Its scientific paradigms, ultrarationalism, and sociocultural-economic developments paved the way for the West's ensuing secularism and capitalism. The coming age would require and give rise to different forms of humanity, with novel notions and modes of well-being, dysfunction, and distress. Not coincidentally, it would also spawn a new medical specialty: psychiatry.

Contemporary Concepts and Issues

The mid-eighteenth century constitutes the headwaters of the stream that culminates in the modern or postmodern mental-health complex. The rise of economic capitalism, with its emphasis on free-market competition and individual acquisitiveness, went hand in hand with the progressive breakdown of traditional social-political structures and cultural institutions, along with the Christian worldview that had hitherto sustained them. New modes of personhood appeared, modes that were exquisitely self-aware and self-oriented, shunning binding institutional and interpersonal commitments, and shrewdly combining hedonism with "social adjustment."

The Enlightenment witnessed novel varieties of what we would designate as *functional* (versus *organic*) psychiatric disorders: the *vapors, nerves,* and so forth, resembling *conversion, dissociative, anxiety, dysthymic, personality-disordered,* and *neurotic* categories (American Psychiatric Association, 1987). Initially comprehended and treated somatically with *magnetism,* or hypnosis, they were gradually conceptualized psychologically. Feminist historians (e.g., Decker) interpret these experiential and behavioral configurations as disguised forms of women's rebellion against male-dominated society.

Meanwhile, in early and mid-eighteenth-century Great Britain, a new breed of physicians began devoting their practices to madness. The most brilliant of these "mad-doctors," Alexander Crichton, influenced Philippe Pinel, generally called psychiatry's father. Previously an internist, Pinel flourished in post-Revolutionary and early nineteenth-century France. Until then, madness had not been institutionally medicalized. Asylums typically fell under lay management, with doctors no more than general medical consultants. Pinel's orientation was psychological as well as medical, and he came to favor abbreviated systems of diagnostic classification. However, his successors in the powerful French clinical school, presuming the inevitable degeneration of many conditions, became progressively and pessimistically *organic.* Notions approximating mental health were far from their minds.

Contemporary German psychiatry was pursuing a semimystical and Romantic psychological path (Ellenberger). Abstruse and difficult to summarize, it conceptualized nature and humankind as manifestations of a World Spirit or Soul. Although often obscure and moralistic, it contributed some genuine psychological insights, including many on unconscious mentation and motivation. In England and the United States, despite some admixture of somatic theory and practice, early nineteenth-century psychiatry—or *alienism,* as it was called (thus underscoring its subjects' social estrangement)—was predominantly psychologically and sociotherapeutically oriented. The Anglo-American *moral treatment* movement envisioned the then relatively small country asylum as a healing family, with the medical superintendent its *father.* For much of the nineteenth century, the word *moral* still denoted an amalgam of what was later divided into *mental* or *psychological,* and *moral* or *ethical.*

As the twentieth century approached, the number and size of asylums grew geometrically; treatment became custodial, and Anglo-American and European psychiatry grew increasingly neuropathologically inclined. Its interest in diagnostic classification and the results of autopsies contributed to what Foucault (1973) called the "objectification" of the patient. The rise of organic and custodial psychiatry reflected many social and demographic changes in the United States: rapidly increasing population; greater social and geographic mobility; replacement of small and culturally homogeneous communities by urban centers swelled by immigration; the continuing disempowerment of institutional religion; movement toward monopolistic capitalism, an orientation toward productivity and consumerism; individualism and waning local charity; and generally changing social mores. Together, such factors made moral therapy unworkable and led to further transformations in popular conceptions of personhood in wellness and illness. Communities and even families transferred responsibilities for their psychiatrically disturbed members to the large central facilities.

It is likely that such facilities came to house many who were merely elderly, socially deviant but not criminal, and economically unproductive. Certain contemporaneous *diagnoses*—such as *volitional old maid, vagabond,* and *eccentric character*—would be laughable if they had not also been socially coercive. State hospitals usually fell under the autonomy of those social agencies that dealt with the socially and economically marginal and dependent (see Grob, 1973, 1983). Drawing on such historical sources, as well as on present-day events, a school of social scientists and political philosophers underlines the status quo-supporting and professionally self-serving features of psychiatry and its related disciplines, including their diagnostic schemata and notions of health and illness (e.g., Foucault, 1965, 1973; Ingleby; Horwitz). These include gender, socioeconomic class, and ethnic biases (e.g., Chesler; Russell).

The organic orientation of the second half of the nineteenth century promoted a seemingly paradoxical soul-body or mind-body dualism among Anglo-American psychiatrists. In their view, psychiatric disturbance or disease was wholly a function of body and brain; the soul or mind, being immaterial and immortal, was not susceptible to disease. Such a schema, which obviously protected their theological tenets, virtually ruled out ideas of mental health and illness, and practices such as secular psychotherapy. Nevertheless, psychotherapeutic perspectives began forming in the late nineteenth century. They emerged among outpatient neurologists who were encountering increasing percentages of functionally disordered patients, and among psychologically minded psychiatrists, who were treating ambulatory patients with milder problems. The distress and dysfunction these professionals were treating became less commonly experienced and interpreted in religious and moral terms. Such problems were therefore less amenable to healing through confession, penance, and recommitment to the Catholic ideology, institutions, and community, or to their Protestant counterparts, often including more counseling ("the cure of souls").

Twentieth Century

To serve these new varieties of troubled persons, innovative therapies arose in the latter nineteenth century and the first decade of the twentieth. These *mind-cure* or *healthy-mindedness* approaches, as William James (1902) named them, comprised purely secular healings; heterodox religious approaches such as Seventh-Day Adventism and Christian Science; Americanized variations of Eastern religions and philosophies; and various integrations of religious, medical, and psychiatric proposals. In Europe, psychoanalysis emerged, the prototype of twentieth-century secular therapies and the ultimate progenitor of most current psychological theories and treatments. Psychoanalysis and its offshoot dynamic schools would contribute significantly to the clinical and popular dissemination of concepts of mental health and mental illness.

By 1910, events were gathering momentum. The important Mental Hygiene Movement, a joint lay-psychiatric venture, had been formed in Boston in 1909 (by former mental patient Clifford Beers and Harvard psychiatrist E. E. Southard). Though it had been started to improve the plight of the severely mentally ill (formerly the *mad*), its concerns shifted swiftly toward mild-to-moderate psychiatric problems and to community mental hygiene, which led eventually to the burgeoning community mental-health movement of the 1950s, 1960s, and 1970s. This movement, like the dynamic therapies, fueled public preoccupation with mental health (Grob, 1983).

During these same decades, psychiatrists in the United States had begun moving toward acute-treatment psychiatric facilities and wards in general hospitals, the *psychopathic* units that treated less chronically severe patients—those with acute crises, neurotic symptoms, and personality problems of all sorts. Outpatient work continued to grow as well. Clinical psychology and social work started evolving as professions. General medicine's public-health and preventive wings, joined by lay *wellness* proponents, enlarged their territory, too. These developments have led many critics, such as Ivan Illich (1976), to speak of medical and psychiatric *imperialism,* the *medicalization* of society, and so forth. Indeed, as early as 1856, physicians such as Oliver Wendell Holmes contended that doctors and deterministic medicine should replace priests and religion as society's moral arbiters. The eminent medical historian Owsei Temkin (1977) charges that health has become a "summum bonum," whose values encroach on morality and ethics (e.g., the virtual criminalization of smokers). Don Browning (1987) points out the various ethical, social-valuational, and cosmological dimensions of the major psychotherapeutic approaches.

Many have commented on the normative-prescriptive aspects of the mental-health and mental-illness concepts of the multifarious psychiatric and clinical psychological vantages.

Definitions of *health* as broad as the World Health Organization's (1991) "state of complete physical, mental, and social well-being," certain epidemiologic projects (Srole et al.), and categorizations of *mental disorder* as extensive as those of the American Psychiatric Association (1987, 1994), seem to ground the accusations of Illich and others. Aspects of hitherto *normal* aging are deemed *disease* and treated as such, and similar attitudes toward features of other developmental periods could be cited. Indeed, pathology has narrowed the domain of human physiology to the point that doctors and the public alike view death itself as all but a potentially preventable disease.

In any event, though most philosophers of general medicine (e.g., Pellegrino and Thomasma; Kass) declare promoting *health* to be the physician's primary objective, few medical authors conceptualize and elaborate it very explicitly. More often it is a negative notion—the *absence* of significant disease or illness. Although conceptions of mental health in psychiatric and related practitioners' textbooks and treatises are frequently negative as well, the writers of such books are more likely to attempt *positive* conceptions than are their general medical counterparts. Daniel Offer and Melvin Sabshin (1966, 1984, 1991) list dozens of notions or definitions of mental health by theorists and therapists of many persuasions. These range from simplistic extremes such as "social adjustment" or "self-actualization," to more complex and reflective notions. Some assess mental health, like mental illness, by dimensions and degrees; others proffer categorical constructs of both. There are naturalistic-universal, psychological, sociocultural-contextual, and biopsychosocial ones. In short, the ways of classifying conceptions and criteria of mental health are potentially exhausting. Through surveying an immense range of pertinent sources, Marie Jahoda (1959, 1977) identified the six indexes of mental health that appear most frequently: (1) the individual's attitudes toward himself or herself; (2) the person's "style and degree of growth, development, or self-actualization"; (3) a central synthesizing psychological function, or "integration"; (4) "autonomy," or "independence from social influences" (the single most cited index); (5) adequacy of reality perception; and (6) mastery of the environment.

However useful they may be, these criteria can hardly claim to be purely natural or scientifically derived; they are clearly a function of time- and place-bound cultural contexts, as well as of presupposition-laden psychological orientations. It is not so much a question of whether they imply values, for no theories and concepts escape their authors' values altogether. Rather, the questions concern the kinds of values, and their relationships to one another and to those in other endeavors and institutions.

Of Jahoda's indexes, most are self-oriented, depicting the natural and social environment as something virtually inimical to personal well-being. The "healthy" are independent of its influences, mastering it to their self-actualizing ends—which, ironically, may be quite serviceable to those of the prevailing political economy. Of course, there are also formulations of "mental health" at the opposite, or socially conformist, pole; their professional exponents probably have frequently fallen into the service of dominant socioeconomic agendas. In any case, Jahoda's analysis suggests that there are other sorts of dangers associated with ideas of mental health. Such common extremes in positive conceptions of mental health make one wonder whether they should be attempted at all. The American Psychiatric Association (1987) avoids defining mental health.

Many of the profoundest students of human experience and behavior, such as Freud, have not issued definitive pronouncements on mental health. Freud's theories and observations contain many items relevant to assessing dimensions and degrees of psychic well-being and its reverse (Wallace, 1986; Vergote; Wallwork). Nevertheless, apart from hearsay attributions to him of the spare desideratum *Lieben und Arbeiten* (loving and working), Freud bequeathed us no extensive positive constructions of mental health. In fact, he stressed the continuum from neurosis to "normality." Nor did he harbor utopian ambitions for psychoanalytic therapy, firmly denying that it promised happiness or contentment. It was quite enough if treatment alleviated the analysand's more troublesome, historically determined psychic and interpersonal conflicts, misapprehensions of self and others, and modes of gratifying and inhibiting hitherto repressed or symptomatically expressed desires and strivings. Such imperfect but significant transformations enhance the patient's grasp of his or her particular life's realistic problems and possibilities. Freud had no notions akin to Abraham Maslow's and Carl Rogers's of the easy and automatic harmonization between "self-actualization" and the requirements for a humane and civilized society. His concept of adaptation, hardly collapsible into Darwin's, implied neither mastery of nor submission to the sociocultural and political-economic surround, but rather a prudent and moral interweaving of "autoplastic" (self-transformative) and "alloplastic" (environmentally altering) activities (see Hartmann; Wallace, 1986; Vergote; Wallwork).

Although Freud was capable of psychoanalytically masked moral and metaphysical judgments, such as those about religion, he was usually quite sensitive to the interface between moral/ethical perspectives and theoretical/clinical ones. Psychoanalytic insights and findings might inform the ethical enterprise, but Freud did not think moral values themselves could be deduced from analytic premises. Regarding moral values in the psychoanalytic endeavor itself, he emphasized honest self-awareness and its potentially beneficent personal and interpersonal effects (Wallace, 1986; Rieff). Freud intended the clinician's analytic neutrality, with its customary suspension of explicit moral evaluation, purely as a means to enhance the patient's disclosure and self-discovery; it was confined to the consulting room and not suggested as a recipe for living.

Conclusion

Given the historical and cross-cultural variations in modes of conceptualizing personhood and ascribing abnormality, as well as the vicissitudes of sociocultural and natural environments, it makes little sense to seek timeless and placeless notions of health, illness, or even disease, psychiatric or otherwise. The extraordinarily complicated overlap and mutual determination among formulations and applications of mental health, and a host of external institutions, ensure that the former will reflect and affect myriad sociocultural dimensions and processes. Insofar as ethical and metaphysical purviews are separable from scientific and medical/psychiatric theories and findings, one cannot facilely deduce moral values and ethical systems from the latter.

A biopsychosocially oriented functionalism proffers the least metaphysical and reductionistic, and the most comprehensive and open, model of the human organism in its ongoing cultural and natural milieu. This conceives of self-conscious and symbolizing personhood as the complexly integrated function of a plethora of subsidiary structures and functions, interacting both among themselves and with aspects of the physical and sociocultural ambience. It avoids either a dualistic or a mechanistic stance on humankind; it affirms the necessity of psychosocial, as well as biomedical and neurobiological, approaches to persons in health and illness (Wallace, 1990). Moreover, it permits medicine, psychiatry, and the mental-health disciplines a public philosophy open to dialogue with vantages from ethics, theology, jurisprudence, politics, and elsewhere (Wallace, 1992). In other words, a *Homo sapiens* does not comprise separate ontological compartments of spirit, morals, mind, and body. Rather, he or she is appreciated as a self-consciously reflective whole, with a history in a community, whose various experiences and activities require separate, but overlapping and interrelating, spiritual, moral, medical/psychiatric, and social perspectives. However one understands mental health and mental illness, they point toward forms of distress,

disability, and well-being that are real and pervasively human concerns.

EDWIN R. WALLACE IV (1995)

BIBLIOGRAPHY

Ackerknecht, Erwin. 1968. *A Short History of Psychiatry,* 2nd edition, rev., tr. Sula Wolff. New York: Hafner.

Ackerknecht, Erwin. 1971. *Medicine and Ethnology: Selected Essays.* Baltimore: Johns Hopkins University Press.

American Psychiatric Association. 1987. *Diagnostic and Statistical Manual of Mental Disorders: DSM-III-R,* 3rd edition, rev. Washington, D.C.: Author.

American Psychiatric Association. 1994. *Diagnostic and Statistical Manual of Mental Disorders,* 4th ed. Washington, D.C.: Author.

Berrios, German E. 1987. "Dementia During the Seventeenth and Eighteenth Centuries: A Conceptual History." *Psychological Medicine* 17(4): 829–837.

Browning, Don S. 1987. *Religious Thought and the Modern Psychologies: A Critical Conversation in the Theology of Culture.* Philadelphia: Fortress.

Chesler, Phyllis. 1973. *Women and Madness.* New York: Avon.

Decker, Hannah S. 1991. *Freud, Dora, and Vienna 1900.* New York: Basic Books.

Edelstein, Ludwig. 1967. *Ancient Medicine: Selected Poems of Ludwig Edelstein,* ed. Owsei Temkin and Clarice L. S. Temkin. Baltimore: Johns Hopkins University Press.

Ellenberger, Henri F. 1970. *The Discovery of the Unconscious: The History and Evolution of Dynamic Psychiatry.* New York: Basic Books.

Foucault, Michel. 1965. *Madness and Civilization: A History of Insanity in the Age of Reason,* tr. Ronald Howard. New York: Vintage.

Foucault, Michel. 1973. *The Birth of the Clinic: An Archaeology of Medical Perception,* tr. Alan M. Sheridan Smith. New York: Pantheon.

Grob, Gerald N. 1973. *Mental Institutions in America: Social Policy to 1875.* New York: Free Press.

Grob, Gerald N. 1983. *Mental Illness and American Society, 1875–1940.* Princeton, NJ: Princeton University Press.

Hartmann, Heinz. 1960. *Psychoanalysis and Moral Values.* New York: International Universities Press.

Horwitz, Allan V. 1982. *The Social Control of Mental Illness.* New York: Academic Press.

Illich, Ivan. 1976. *Medical Nemesis: The Expropriation of Health.* New York: Pantheon.

Ingleby, David, ed. 1980. *Critical Psychiatry: The Politics of Mental Health.* New York: Random House.

Jackson, Stanley W. 1986. *Melancholia and Depression: From Hippocratic Times to Modern Times.* New Haven, CT: Yale University Press.

Jahoda, Marie. 1959. *Current Concepts of Positive Mental Health.* New York: Basic Books.

Jahoda, Marie. 1977. *Freud and the Dilemmas of Psychology.* New York: Basic Books.

James, William. 1902. *The Varieties of Religious Experience: A Study in Human Nature.* New York: Longmans Green.

Kass, Leon R. 1988. *Toward a More Natural Science: Biology and Human Affairs.* New York: Free Press.

Offer, Daniel, and Melvin Sabshin. 1966. *Normality: Theoretical and Clinical Concepts of Mental Health.* New York: Basic Books.

Offer, Daniel, and Melvin Sabshin, eds. 1984. *Normality and the Life Cycle.* New York: Basic Books.

Offer, Daniel, and Melvin Sabshin, eds. 1992. *The Diversity of Normal Behaviors: Further Contributions to Normatology.* New York: Basic Books.

Pellegrino, Edmund D., and David C. Thomasma. 1981. *A Philosophical Basis of Medical Practice: Toward a Philosophy and Ethic of the Healing Professions.* New York: Oxford University Press.

Rieff, Philip. 1959. *Freud: The Mind of the Moralist.* New York: Viking.

Russell, Denise. 1994. "Psychiatric Diagnosis and the Interests of Women." In *Philosophical Perspectives on Psychiatric Diagnostic Classification,* eds. John Z. Sadler, Osborne P. Wiggins, and Michael A. Schwartz. Baltimore: Johns Hopkins University Press.

Spanos, Nicholas P. 1985. "Witchcraft and Social History: An Essay Review." *Journal of the History of the Behavioral Sciences* 21(1): 60–66.

Srole, Leo; Thomas S. Langer; Stanley T. Michael; Marvin K. Opler; and Thomas A. C. Rennie. 1962. *Mental Health in the Metropolis: The Midtown Manhattan Study.* New York: McGraw-Hill.

Temkin, Owsei. 1977. *The Double Face of Janus and Other Essays in the History of Medicine.* Baltimore: Johns Hopkins University Press.

Vergote, Antoine. 1988. *Guilt and Desire: Religious Attitudes and Their Pathological Derivatives,* tr. Michael H. Wood. New Haven, CT: Yale University Press.

Wallace, Edwin R., IV. 1983. *Freud and Anthropology: A History and Reappraisal.* New York: International Universities Press.

Wallace, Edwin R., IV. 1986. "Freud as Ethicist." In vol. 1 of *Freud Studies: Appraisals and Reappraisals: Contributions to Freud Studies,* ed. Paul Stepansky. Hillsdale, NJ: Analytic Press.

Wallace, Edwin R., IV. 1990. "Mind, Body and the Future of Psychiatry." *Journal of Medicine and Philosophy* 15(1): 41–73.

Wallace, Edwin R., IV. 1992. "Psychiatry: The Healing Amphibian." In *Does Psychiatry Need a Public Philosophy?,* ed. Don S. Browning and Ian S. Evision. Chicago: Nelson/ Hall.

Wallace, Edwin R., IV. 1994. "Psychiatry and Its Nosology: A Historico-Philosophical Overview." In *Philosophical Perspectives on Psychiatric Diagnostic Classification,* eds. John Z. Sadler, Osborne P. Wiggins, and Michael A. Schwartz. Baltimore: Johns Hopkins University Press.

Wallwork, Ernest. 1991. *Psychoanalysis and Ethics.* New Haven, CT: Yale University Press.

World Health Organization. 1991. *Mental Disorders: Glossary and Guide to the Classification in Accordance with the 10th Revision of the International Classification of Diseases.* Geneva: Author.

Zilboorg, Gregory. 1935. *The Medical Man and the Witch during the Renaissance.* Baltimore: Johns Hopkins University Press.

POSTSCRIPT

Western definitions and concepts of mental health have continued to multiply into the twenty-first century—usually permutations and combinations of desiderata already treated. However, there is a strengthening minority position taking sociocultural (including political-economic) and even spiritual parameters into account—both in definitions of mental health and in theories of causation of mental disorders (Kleinman and Good). This cadre is led by transcultural psychiatrists and psychological/psychiatric anthropologists (GAP). Western psychiatry is being cogently examined as one ethnopsychiatry among others (Kleinman). DSM-III and DSM-IV Axis I disorders such as Major Depression differ in core, and not merely peripheral, signs and symptoms—begging the question of whether psychiatry is dealing with different nosological entities (Kleinman and Good).

On the positive side, the psychiatrist and philosopher K. W. M. Fulford has proposed a notion of mental illness as "failure of action," rather than as the DSM-IV's "disturbed functioning." The latter implies component pathophysiological lesions about which the evidence is still very equivocal (Wallace, Radden, and Sadler; Ross and Pam; Bentall; Lewontin, Rose, and Kamin). "Failed action" refers to a variety of distressing or disabling experiences and behaviors that the person is unable to control (i.e., consciously will and enact otherwise). A definition of mental health is of course implied in this, and could be worked out conceptually. Fulford's notion does not rule out the potential explanatory and therapeutic applicability of both neurobiological/pharmacological and psychosocial/psychotherapeutic approaches.

A far more complex and controversial theorist of disease/illness and, by implication, of what he now prefers to call "normality" rather than "health" is Boorse (Boorse, 1977). Attacked by most bioethicists and medical philosophers (Humber and Almeder), Boorse has staunchly argued for human species-specific biostatistical, ostensibly objective and value-neutral, criteria for disease (Boorse, 1975). Initially limiting his argument to general medical *disease,* he later moved to biostatistically-based criteria for *illness* and for the mental disorders as well (Boorse, 1975, 1997). In a 1997 book chapter, he skillfully defended himself against a plethora of critics.

Since it is impossible to address his annexation of mental disorders (and, by implication, mental health) without appreciating Boorse's general medical concept of disease/illness, one must begin with the latter. His biostatistical criteria for disease/illness are extremely spare and Darwinian: the preservation of the individual (as opposed to the group or population) and his/her reproductive fitness. *Disease* is component pathophysiological dysfunction or subfunction *within* the organism. It is key to realize that Boorse is concerned with *medical scientific* (i.e., the pathologist's) or *theoretical* criteria for disease. He is not occupied with *practical* clinical diagnosis (which often deals with syndromes) or the *clinical* investigative and therapeutic manner of the physician. However, it is important to note that he appreciates the necessity for "disease-plus" concepts of humanitarian and ethical clinical behavior.

Moreover, in concerning himself with disease as *intra-organismic* component pathophysiological dysfunction or subfunction, he does not argue that the nexus of etiology is delimited to the subcomponent or even the organism itself. He includes physical environmental trauma and psychosocial causation (in the general medical, as well as psychiatric, realms). *Illness* is the systemic molar or total organismic (which may include the mind) subfunction or dysfunction accompanying the *disease.* Hence, *illness* represents the same sort of Darwinian impairment already addressed with reference to *disease.* By Boorse's criteria, it is possible to: (a) have a *disease* without an *illness* (e.g., molar dysfunction)—though eventually, of course, many or most diseases will also become illnesses; and (b) an illness (e.g., influenza) without a disease (e.g., delimited internal pathology).

One must also recognize that Boorse's biostatistical, Homo-sapiens-typical criteria are related to gender, age, and (to some extent) ethnic or racial reference-groups. This prevents a post-menopausal woman (who has lost reproductive fitness), a middle-aged man with some degree of "male pattern baldness," or a pygmy with group-wide growth-hormone subfunction from being deemed *diseased* or *ill.* Nevertheless, things become more complicated for Boorse with African or African-American individuals heterozygous for sickle-cell disease. On the one hand, this state is survival-promoting in malarial environments, but not at higher altitudes at which other "races" are not so vulnerable. Boorse attempts to sidestep this with his construct of "standard environment." This is problematic not only for general medical disease/illness, but especially for mental and behavioral functioning, since climatic, historical, and sociocultural relativity render the idea of a Homo-sapiens-specific standard physical and sociocultural environment suspect.

Finally, this author finds Boorse's insistence that component or circumscribed internal pathophysiology alone defines disease as bizarrely narrow; it excludes systemic dysfunction or subfunction, as well as the molecular level to which many pathological disease-formulations are now turning.

Turning especially to psychiatry, Boorse likewise stresses internal component pathology. To his credit, he considers psychological concepts a necessary subset of biological ones—to grasp human species-specific, symbolically-mediated mentation, communication, and behavior. This author has argued similarly in both monistic-dual-aspect and functionalist models of the mind-body relation (Wallace, 1988, 1990, 1997). In other words, Boorse contends that not only cerebral or extra-cerebral component pathophysiology (and here he chides biological psychiatry for its predominantly molecular approach) may be pathognomonic for mental disorders, but so might *component psychological functions* such as unconscious intrapsychic conflict among the psychoanalytically-conceived mental agencies and subsidiary functions. However, his delimitation of disease/illness criteria to individual self-preservation and reproductive fitness are problematic for notions of mental disorder and normality. For example, in non-Western cultures with intact, supportive kinship and community networks, psychiatrically-untreated schizophrenia does not pose the same personal survival or even reproductive fitness risks that occur in the urbanized West, with its relative dearth of community and kinship networks. And most DSM-IV Axis II sufferers (from perhaps Western culture-bound syndromes) often experience no increased physical survival or reproductive-fitness risks. In short, Boorse's two Darwinian criteria are insufficiently robust for a concept of mental disorder/illness, much less for *normality* or *mental health.*

Pending further research, some varieties of the major mental disorders may turn out to be diseases in the Boorsian circumscribed pathophysiological (or even molecular) sense. However, this author suspects that most (Axis II) mental disorders (which keep multiplying over time in new editions of the DSM) will remain best understood in the psychosocial categories of human biological discourse.

In conclusion, there is nothing in Boorse's argument as applied to psychiatry that would countenance psychiatry's recent (patently, if partly, economically-motivated) turn to a radical neurobiological/pharmacological reductionism. Such an approach entails the concomitant jettisoning of psychosocial/psychotherapeutic approaches that demand a more laborious intimacy with the patient-as-person-in-an-ambience rather than as simply the epiphenomenon of a twisted molecule or component brain limbic pathophysiology. Again, Boorse asserts that disease- and illness-plus concepts and approaches are necessary to anyone who would be an ethical and competent clinician.

Space does not permit treatment of the recent evolutionary psychiatry of Randolph Nesse and George Williams, and others. They are obsessively committed to imagining historically remote conditions in which disorders is incapacitating as schizophrenia were once adaptive (i.e., atavism).

EDWIN R. WALLACE IV

BIBLIOGRAPHY

Bentall, Richard P., ed. 1992. *Reconstructing Schizophrenia.* London: Routledge.

Boorse, C. 1975. "On the Distinction between Disease and Illness." *Philosophy and Public Affairs* 5: 49–68.

Boorse, C. 1997. "A Rebuttal on Health." In *What Is Disease?*, eds. J. M. Humber and R. F. Almede. Totowa, NJ: Humana Press.

Eisenberg, L. 1977. "Disease and Illness: Distinctions between Professional and Popular Ideas of Sickness." *Culture, Medicine, and Psychiatry* 1: 9–23.

Engel, G. 1977. "The Need for a New Medical Model: A Challenge for Biomedicine." *Science* 196: 129–136.

Fulford, K. W. M. 1989. *Moral Theory and Medical Practice.* New York: Cambridge University Press.

Group for the Advancement of Psychiatry (GAP), Committee on Culture. 2002. *Cultural Assessment in Clinical Psychiatry.* Washington, D.C.: American Psychiatric Publishing, Inc.

Humber, James M. and Almeder, Robert F., eds. 1997. *What Is Disease?* Totowa, NJ: Humana Press.

Kleinman, Arthur. 1988. *Rethinking Psychiatry: From Cultural Category to Personal Experience.* Glencoe, IL: Free Press.

Kleinman, Arthur, and Good, Byron, eds. 1985. *Culture and Depression: Studies in the Anthropology and Cross Cultural Psychiatry of Affective Disorder.* Berkeley: University of California Press.

Lewontin, R. C.; Rose, Stephen; and Kamin, Leon J. 1984. *Not in Our Genes: Biology, Ideology, and Human Nature.* New York: Pantheon Books.

Nesse, Randolph M. and Williams, George C. 1994. *Why We Get Sick: The New Science of Darwinian Medicine.* New York: Times Books.

Osgood, Charles E.; May, William H.; and Miron, Murray S. 1975. *Cross-Cultural Universals of Affective Meaning.* Urbana: University of Illinois Press.

Ross, Colin A., and Pam, Alvin. 1995. *Pseudoscience in Biological Psychiatry.* New York: John Wiley and Sons.

Stigler, James W.; Schweder, Richard A.; and Herdt, Gilbert. 1990. *Cultural Psychology: Essays on Comparative Human Development.* New York: Cambridge University Press.

Wallace, Edwin R. 1988. "Mind–Body: Monistic Dual-Aspect Interactionism." *Journal of Nervous and Mental Disease* 176: 4–22.

Wallace, Edwin R. 1990. "Mind–Body and the Future of Psychiatry." *Journal of Medicine and Philosophy* 15: 41–73.

Wallace, Edwin R. 1994. "Psychiatry and Its Nosology: An Historico-Philosophical Overview." In *Philosophical Issues in Psychiatric Diagnostic Classification,* eds. J. Sadler, M. Schwartz, and O. Wiggins. Baltimore: Johns Hopkins University Press.

Wallace, Edwin R. 1997. "Psychiatry's Sickness and Its Biological Cure." *Psychiatry: Interpersonal and Biological Processes* 60: 89–99.

Wallace, E. R.; Radden, J.; and Sadler, J. 1997. "The Philosophy of Psychiatry: Who Needs It?" *Journal of Nervous and Mental Disease* 185: 67–73.

SEE ALSO: *Children: Mental Health Issues; Coercion; Confidentiality; Disability; Electroconvulsive Therapy; Informed Consent: Issues of Consent in Mental Healthcare; Institutionalization and Deinstitutionalization; Life, Quality of; Mental Health, Meaning of Mental Health; Mental Health Therapies; Mental Illness; Mentally Disabled and Mentally Ill Persons; Patients' Rights: Mental Patients' Rights; Psychiatry, Abuses of;* and other *Mental Health Services* subentries

MENTAL HEALTH SERVICES

• • •

I. Settings and Programs
II. Ethical Issues

I. SETTINGS AND PROGRAMS

Since the mid-1950s, fundamental transformations have taken place in the size, location, diversity, funding, and attitudes toward mental health services in the United States, changing the organized response to the identification and treatment of mental health problems. These changes have altered the central policy and ethical questions that arise in the mental health system as a whole. When involuntary commitments to custodial mental hospitals dominated the system, the central issues involved inappropriate social control. In the diversified system based upon community care and treatment that has evolved, the most pressing issues include how to fund and deliver services to the most seriously ill persons, allocate services to meet a potentially huge demand, and improve service delivery outside the traditional system of mental healthcare.

Evolution of Mental Health Services

Until the mid-1960s, two separate systems dominated mental health services: public mental institutions that treated a large population of inpatients and a smaller private sector that provided most outpatient psychotherapy. Large, impersonal, custodial facilities dominated the inpatient sector and housed poor, isolated, severely mentally ill persons (often elderly) for long periods of time (Grob, 1973). Most residents lacked family ties or were committed as a last resort by their families. The flaws of these institutions are well known: huge size, overcrowding, geographic isolation, involuntary confinement, depersonalization, coercion, and custodial emphasis (Goffman). Nevertheless, they provided the most seriously ill persons an integrated range of services—housing, food, symptom management, respite from stressful community conditions, medical treatment, and a locus for social interaction—in one centralized location. Alongside the core of state mental hospitals, a smaller outpatient sector dominated by private psychiatrists practicing analytic psychotherapy treated clients who could afford those services (Hale).

The mental health system at the beginning of the twenty-first century is much different. A revolution in mental health services began in 1955, when the average number of residents in state and county mental hospitals started to decline from a peak of 550,000, to 370,000 in 1969 and about 60,000 by 1998 (CMHS, 2001). Taking into account a growing general population, the number of residents in state and county mental hospitals fell from 339 per 100,000 persons in 1955 to 91.5 in 1975, and to only 21 in 1998 (CMHS, 2001). Typical patients in state hospitals have also changed: from the elderly to the young; from long-term to short-term patients; and from persons with deteriorating and untreatable diseases of the brain to ones suffering from concurrent substance abuse disorders.

As state mental hospitals became institutions of last resort for the most intractable patients, alternative forms of inpatient care grew substantially. Less than 10 percent of admissions to twenty-four-hour care facilities occurred in state and county mental hospitals in 2000, a four-fold decline since 1969 (CMHS, 2001). Most inpatient psychiatric services now take place in general hospitals, private psychiatric hospitals, specialized chemical dependency units, nursing homes, and residential treatment centers for children (Kiesler and Simpkins). These facilities generally do not treat the same types of persons who had been found in public mental institutions: Their residents are more likely to have

affective and substance abuse disorders and less likely to have schizophrenia.

The overall growth in mental health service provision has also been dramatic. Between 1955 and 1997, the total number of patient episodes in mental health organizations rose more than 600 percent—from 1.7 million to 10.7 million (CMHS, 2001). By 1994, all expenditures for mental health and substance abuse services exceeded $68 billion (Mechanic). In constant dollars (with 1969 as baseline), spending by mental health organizations increased from $3.3 billion in 1969 to $5 billion in 1994.

Most of the growth in mental health services stemmed from the expansion of outpatient treatment. From only 23 percent of total mental health episodes in 1955, outpatient episodes grew to 76 percent of episodes in 1998. Nevertheless, inpatient episodes consume over 80 percent of expenditures for mental health (Kiesler and Simpkins). The number of mental health professionals also expanded commensurately during this period. For example, in 1975 about 20,000 licensed psychologists practiced in the United States; this figure grew to 46,000 in 1986 and to at least 73,000 by 1997 (CMHS, 1998). The growth of mental health professionals who are psychiatric social workers, school psychologists, marriage and family therapists, and counselors was even greater. For example, between 1972 and 1994 the number of full-time psychiatric social workers nearly quintupled and there were nearly twenty times the number of professionals in the category of *other mental health workers* (CMHS, 2001).

The analogue to the growing number of mental health professionals is the greater number of persons who seek help from them. By 1983, about 23 million people—15 percent of the adult population of the United States—sought some type of treatment for mental health or addiction problems over the course of a year (Regier, Narrow, Rae, et al.). Population surveys also indicate a growing readiness of the public to use mental health services. One large national survey showed that while less than 1 percent of respondents sought help from psychologists, counselors, and social workers for mental health problems in 1957, 18 percent of respondents reported seeking professional services in 1996 (Swindle, Heller, Pescosolido, et al.).

Another striking trend has been the expansion of psychotropic medications. In the decade between 1985 and 1994 alone, the proportion of psychiatric outpatient visits in which psychiatrists prescribed an antidepressant increased from 23 percent to 49 percent, and the number of prescriptions for psychotropic medications soared from about 33 million to about 46 million (Pincus, Tanielien, Marcus, et al.). Three of the seven most-prescribed drugs of any kind are now antidepressants (Horwitz). These drugs are not imposed on unwilling patients, but are highly sought-after and valued therapeutic aids promoted to the general public through ubiquitous advertising campaigns (Kramer).

Reasons for Changes in Mental Health Services in the United States

A number of technological, ideological, legal, and economic reasons led to the steep decline in the use of traditional mental institutions and the growth of mental health services. The introduction of psychotropic drugs in the mid-1950s provided an efficient and effective technology that could be used easily in community settings. The ideology of mental health professionals after World War II emphasized a broad concept of mental illness, noninstitutional care, and treatment for a wide array of emotional and social problems (Grob, 1991). Judicial and legislative mandates regarding mental health services also began to change in the late 1960s toward specific and restrictive standards for commitment and the expansion of civil rights during and after commitment proceedings (Appelbaum).

The locus of authority for mental health services also shifted after World War II. Until that time, states and localities were responsible for providing services. The creation of the National Institute for Mental Health in 1949 and the passage of the Community Mental Health Centers Act of 1963 created partnerships between the federal government and localities that bypassed hospital-dominated state mental health systems (Grob, 1991). The hundreds of community mental health centers that emerged in the 1960s and 1970s, however, did not serve the same population as the state hospitals, but instead provided psychotherapy to people suffering from emotional, behavioral, marital, and family problems. These centers made mental health services more accessible, brought more services to lower socioeconomic and minority populations, and enhanced the acceptability of mental health treatment. They did not, however, replace the services state hospitals once provided to chronically ill persons, and generally neglected the most seriously mentally ill (Rochefort).

Out of the array of technological, ideological, judicial, and political reasons for changes in mental health service provision, shifts in patterns of reimbursement were especially important. Although not developed to serve the mentally ill, Medicaid (a program jointly administered and funded by federal and state governments to bring medical services to the poor and disabled) and Medicare (a federal program funding medical care for the elderly and persons who have received disability payments for two or more years) grew into large sources of funding for mental health services. The eligibility of facilities to receive Medicaid and Medicare

funds contributed to the changing patterns of inpatient services outlined above. Elderly persons with mental illnesses were transferred from state mental institutions ineligible for Medicare dollars to nursing homes that could receive these funds. Likewise, treatment episodes in general hospitals increased because federal programs reimburse inpatient psychiatric episodes in these settings but not in public mental institutions.

Changing patterns of private reimbursement have also altered the nature of mental health services. Private insurance coverage for both inpatient and outpatient services greatly expanded between the 1950s and 2000, although not at a level comparable to that for physical illnesses. Expanded eligibility of nonphysicians, including psychologists, nurses, and social workers, for third-party reimbursement has increased the pool of mental health professionals who provide outpatient treatment. A multitude of practitioners with different disciplinary allegiances, therapeutic ideologies, and treatment techniques have come to serve clients with acute disorders (Frank and Frank). Despite the great expansion of mental health services, however, no comprehensive system in communities has emerged to replace the services that persons with the most serious and long-term illnesses received in state hospitals.

Another recent change in service delivery is the rise of managed mental healthcare (Mechanic). Managed care refers to a variety of organizational forms that impose routinized strategies to monitor, regulate, and review the treatment that professionals provide patients in order to provide cost-effective care. Managed care is becoming the dominant form of treatment for mental health problems, and about three-quarters of persons with private health insurance now are in some kind of managed care plan (Kiesler). The principles of managed care dictate more rule-following, standardization, and regulated treatments that often conflict with individualized treatment plans (Luhrmann). Because persons with mental illness often require extensive and varied services, the requirements for their successful treatment often conflict with the restrictions and rigidities of managed care organizations.

International Mental Health Services

The major trends in the United States mirror changes in the provision of mental health services in most developed nations. Although the pace of deinstitutionalization differs across countries, the use of public inpatient facilities has sharply declined throughout most of the West (World Health Organization, 2001; Goldberg and Thornicroft). Persons who do enter inpatient facilities usually have short lengths of stay that typically average about one month or less. For example, the number of people occupying hospital beds in the United Kingdom fell even faster than in the United States, from a peak of 152,000 in 1954 to 39,500 in 1993. Italy has implemented the most ambitious plan of deinstitutionalization, which aims to completely eliminate all admissions to public mental hospitals (Donnelly).

The decline of public inpatient institutions has been accompanied by a decentralization of psychiatric services in most European and other developed societies (World Health Organization, 2001). Most of the smaller number of hospitalizations now occur in general hospitals and in facilities operated by non-profit or private agencies rather than by the national government. As in the United States, there has been a strong movement toward treatment in small facilities located in residential neighborhoods. Indeed, the ideology of community treatment—emphasizing keeping persons out of institutions, treating them in neighborhoods near their homes, and strengthening informal social support systems—is perhaps even stronger in Europe than in the United States. Client-centered movements of consumers of psychiatric services are also active in many countries. These movements have had a good deal of success in opposing mental hospitalization, coercive forms of psychiatric treatment, social stigma, and the power of psychiatric professionals, and in developing self-help groups of users.

There are exceptions to the general trend of declining use of inpatient hospitalization and increasing amounts of community treatment. For example, rates of occupied psychiatric beds in Japan increased between the 1960s and 1990s, and Japan has the highest number of inpatients of any country in the world (Shinfuku, Sugawara, Yanaka, et al.). Because public funds support inpatient treatment in private hospitals, these institutions have a financial incentive to admit many patients and keep them for long periods. In addition, most poor countries have rudimentary systems of outpatient treatment and the small amount of psychiatric care they provide typically occurs in large, antiquated inpatient facilities (World Health Organization, 1996).

Despite the success of most developed countries in reducing inpatient psychiatric populations, a number of common problems remain. Some of these problems are systemic. As in the United States, there is limited coordination between agencies that provide treatment, housing, social services, and social control. Insufficient amounts of adequate community housing also typify mental health systems. In addition, the most seriously disturbed and chronic patients continue to need inpatient care, severely straining the resources of most systems. Other problems stem from a poor fit between traditional modes of service delivery and particular types of clients (Goldberg and Thornicroft). The provision of mental health services to persons who are poor, homeless, immigrants, and substance abusers will be especially problematic in coming years. Most European nations have large immigrant populations who resist voluntary mental health treatment and are often subject to coercive forms of social control. Mental health systems rarely have enough personnel from minority backgrounds who could better relate to these patients. As in the United States, psychiatric patients who have co-morbid substance abuse problems are particularly difficult to treat within most mental health systems. As well, few mental health programs have established successful outreach programs to the homeless mentally ill. While the ideology of community treatment now dominates mental health service provision in nearly all developed countries, the implementation of this ideology lags behind.

Ethical Issues

The ethical issues that arose in a mental health system dominated by state hospitals were related to involuntary commitments, inappropriate hospitalizations, neglectful or abusive treatments and the validity of the label of *mental illness* itself (Szasz). In the huge but uncoordinated mental health system of the 2000s, the most pressing issue is to create coordinated service delivery systems for seriously disturbed persons. The dominance of medical models devised for specific acute conditions hampers efforts to create comprehensive services. Medicare and Medicaid, which were developed to finance treatment for acute physical conditions, usually do not cover long-term, comprehensive services that promote community living (although many states do use Medicaid options to finance a number of community-based services). Managed care organizations rarely have the expertise to provide appropriate treatment to persons with serious mental illnesses and lack the capacity to provide comprehensive mental health services (Mechanic). Drug therapies that form the core of medically-oriented treatment are effective in alleviating the symptoms of, although not curing, mental illness. These treatments are beneficial, but cannot address the needs for housing, monetary assistance, vocational training, and social interaction of seriously mentally ill persons who live in the community. The extent to which drug therapies cause harmful side effects is controversial (Healy; Valenstein). The dominant organizational forms and treatments in mental healthcare create great difficulties in developing comprehensive care programs for persons with serious mental illnesses.

COMMUNITY TREATMENT. A broad consensus has developed among consumers, families, and mental health professionals that community—rather than institutional—treatment is most consistent with the values of individual autonomy and choice that underlie contemporary policies toward disabled populations. In addition, evidence is accumulating that most persons with serious mental illnesses benefit more—and at no greater cost—from comprehensive community treatment programs than from hospital care (Mechanic and Rochefort). Although there is little evidence that comprehensive community treatment is cheaper than hospital care, such programs need not cost more than inpatient treatment (Weisbrod, Test, and Stein).

With the exception of a minority of violent, dangerous, and self-destructive persons, outpatient programs can allow seriously mentally ill persons to remain in the community with the help of an intensive range of mental health, psychosocial, and vocational services. One effective model uses assertive community treatment teams of mental health professionals who provide services in clients' natural living environments on a seven-day-a-week, twenty-four-hour-a-day basis (Stein and Test). The staffs of these programs do not wait for patients to seek help, but aggressively offer treatment when they think it is needed. The aggressive enforcement of medication compliance and occasional hospitalizations has created concern that these programs can be overly paternalistic and coercive (Diamond and Wikler). Such interventions, however, might be necessary to keep the most difficult, disruptive, and noncompliant persons in community settings over the long term. The Fountain House program, which emphasizes job rehabilitation and the creation of a family-like atmosphere, is another effective, but less intensive, model for community treatment (Beard).

Despite the advantages of community-based treatment for the most seriously ill, skewed funding and administrative structures have precluded its widespread establishment. States continue to fund state mental hospitals disproportionately: 60 percent of state funding goes to hospitals that serve only 7 percent of the seriously mentally ill (Sharfstein, Stoldine, and Goldman, 1993). Opposition from public employee unions and local communities that are economically dependent on state hospitals often prevents shifting funds from inpatient treatment to intensive community treatment programs. Likewise, federal and private reimbursement programs fund relatively expensive treatment in inpatient facilities outside of public mental institutions, but will not usually cover treatment in clients' homes or in noncoercive residential facilities in the community.

Fragmented administrative authority for mental health services also prevents the development of integrated service systems. Service delivery for the seriously mentally ill typically involves an unplanned and uncoordinated mix of visits to emergency rooms, short-term stays in inpatient units, inadequate outpatient treatment, and a variety of entitlement programs that may not meet the special needs of the

mentally ill (Bloche and Cournos). Different agencies with different missions provide housing, financial assistance, vocational training, medical treatment, and mental healthcare to the mentally ill (Mechanic and Rochefort). Mechanisms such as comprehensive case management and mental health authorities that assume organizational, financial, and clinical responsibility over a range of residential and psychosocial services can help coordinate the various agencies that provide these services (Morrissey, Callaway, Bartko, et al.). Solutions for serious mental illness must go beyond the development of effective drug treatments or psychotherapies to encompass a variety of systemic and organizational factors.

The philosophy of community treatment has also led to new and complicated issues regarding family responsibility for caregiving. Many family caregivers—typically mothers—are aging, ill, and lacking in resources to provide adequate care (Lefley). Yet the scarcity of community treatment programs means that families often must provide housing, monetary and emotional support, symptom management, and personal care to seriously ill adult children. Although mental health professionals are now less likely than in the past to view families as pathogenic, they still too readily blame or neglect family members instead of appreciating the value of family resources. Likewise, confidentiality requirements that allow widespread information flow between mental health professionals but preclude the sharing of information with family caregivers need reconsideration (Petrila and Sadoff).

The manifest failures of deinstitutionalization—especially the highly visible problems of the homeless mentally ill—have given rise to public demand to reinstitute civil commitment for the most obtrusive among the seriously mentally ill. In fact, federal entitlement programs have allowed most formerly institutionalized patients to avoid homelessness (Goldman, Adams, and Taube). The more visible homeless mentally ill are likely to be young persons in urban areas with concurrent substance abuse disorders who have never experienced lengthy hospitalizations and who are resistant to traditional mental health service delivery (Lamb). While young, chronic, and sometimes homeless mentally ill persons present a particularly challenging task for mental health service delivery, flexible and nontraditional programs of service delivery that emphasize the provision of adequate housing can best meet the special needs of this population (Bachrach).

INAPPROPRIATE SERVICE PROVISION. While the most seriously ill persons are often unable to obtain needed services, the mental health system overemphasizes inpatient services for persons who could more efficiently and economically be treated in outpatient settings. Particularly troubling is the fact that reimbursement patterns and financial pressures to fill inpatient beds drive service delivery. Paradoxically, while many states have reduced hospital services for the most seriously mentally ill to save costs without providing needed treatment in the community, less seriously ill persons—especially those with affective and substance abuse disorders—are often unnecessarily treated through inpatient episodes in both general and private hospitals. Few data exist about the accessibility, quality, and effectiveness of mental health services in these settings, although good evidence from randomized studies shows that most patients who receive care in hospitals could receive more effective and less costly care as outpatients (Kiesler and Sibulkin). Youths under eighteen are particularly likely to be committed to residential facilities; contrary to trends in other age groups, inpatient treatment for youths rapidly increased from the 1980s to 2000 (CMHS, 2001). There is no evidence, however, that such treatment is necessary, effective, or appropriate, although it is very expensive (Kiesler and Simpkins).

A more effective and efficient mental health service system would place less emphasis on expensive inpatient interventions and more emphasis on comprehensive, long-term community services for the chronically ill. The disabilities associated with serious mental illnesses require long-term care that is responsive to the episodic and recurrent nature of these disorders. For the acutely disturbed, such a system would de-emphasize extended psychotherapy while supporting short-term, directed interventions of proven effectiveness (Kiesler).

Another obstacle to creating a more effective and efficient system lies in the largely hidden nature of much mental health service delivery. Despite the large and growing number of mental health professionals, general physicians are the leading providers of mental health services, accounting for about half of all mental health and addictive treatment services (Regier, et al.). Conversely, about 20 to 30 percent of medical visits are for mental, rather than physical, health problems. However, primary physicians often do not appropriately recognize and treat mental disabilities. Professional training of physicians should place more emphasis on the appropriate diagnosis and response to mental disorders in primary practice. Nonphysicians, such as nurse practitioners, could also play a greater role in the treatment of psychological problems in medical settings. Nursing homes—where growing numbers of the psychiatrically-disturbed elderly reside without receiving adequate mental healthcare—are another location where psychiatric need and mental health service provision are mismatched.

An additional problem of mental health services lies in the expansive definition of mental illness. Once equated

with psychotic disorders, the definition of mental illness now includes a wide scope of emotional, behavioral, and psychophysiological disorders (American Psychiatric Association). These definitions encompass many ordinary problems of living as well as serious mental illnesses (Kirk and Kutchins; Horwitz). Those who hold an expansive view of mental health often call for mental health service provision to a wide spectrum of persons who suffer from mental disorders but who do not seek treatment. Advocates of this view cite statistics from community surveys showing that about 16 percent of the U.S. population has a current mental health or addictive disorder, about 30 percent have such disorders over a one year period, and up to 50 percent suffer a disorder over the course of their lifetimes (Regier, et al.,; Kessler, Beglund, Zhao, et al.). These surveys also indicate that only about 13 percent of disordered persons seek help from a mental health or addiction specialist, and only about 30 percent seek any help at all for their problem. In this view, there is a tremendous unmet need for mental health services in the community.

The emphasis on unmet need for mental health services has generated calls for parity in coverage of the treatment of mental and physical health problems. Most third party payers impose higher co-payments for mental health treatment, limit the number of mental health visits and total amount of payment for mental health treatments, and refuse to pay for the treatment of many mental health conditions. Advocates for parity argue that such restrictions unfairly discriminate against persons with mental health problems. Efforts to bring parity had some success when the U.S. Congress passed the Domenici-Wellstone Amendment in 1996. That legislation, with many restrictions and limitations, requires parity of limits on the treatment of mental health and other medical conditions (Mechanic). The Amendment, however, has not brought about major improvements in the funding of mental healthcare.

Advocates of parity between mental health and other conditions do not generally define the specific conditions to which parity should apply. A different view is that, instead of seeking parity in treatment for all mental health conditions, the highest priority for care should be the much smaller group of persons who have severe disorders that lead to serious functional impairments. Surveys that ask respondents if they or someone in their household has a serious mental illness that interferes with their daily life find prevalence rates of between 2 to 3 percent of the population (Kessler, et al.). Because these lower estimates still involve between four and six million people, and because services are finite, there is a clear need for some allocation criteria for mental health services (Boyle and Callahan). Targeting services toward individuals who neither perceive a need for mental healthcare nor suffer from serious functional limitations could be wasteful and ineffective and could direct attention away from the many unmet service needs of the people who are in the most desperate circumstances. Mental health reforms can reasonably include high co-payments for persons with less severe disabilities who desire psychotherapy, as well as higher standards of accountability for psychotherapeutic techniques eligible for reimbursement. These principles could help reorient service delivery toward community treatment of the most seriously ill without generating the huge costs of meeting the total demand for mental health services (Frank, Goldman, and McGuire).

SUCCESSES OF MENTAL HEALTH SERVICES. The many failures of the current U.S. mental health system should not detract from its successes. The expanded federal role in funding mental health services through Medicaid and Medicare has the potential to create a more adequate community-based system that is sensitive to the needs of the seriously mentally ill (Koyanagi and Goldman). States with the will to do so have the ability to devise more effective mental health systems, especially through the creative use of Medicaid waivers. The growth of public mental health treatment has led to declining social class differences in the receipt of services. Changing cultural definitions and understandings of mental disorders have lessened, although not eliminated, the stigma of mental illness and have increased public willingness to seek mental healthcare. Although flawed in many ways, there is more accessibility to mental health services than ever before.

Conclusion

U.S. mental health services at the beginning of the twenty-first century consist of unplanned and uncoordinated services driven by patterns of reimbursement originally developed to treat problems of physical health. Deinstitutionalization diminished the role of state hospitals without replacing the services once found in these settings. The most seriously ill obtain the least adequate treatment, while reimbursement patterns that emphasize acute care in hospital settings create inappropriate and unnecessary inpatient episodes for persons who could be treated equally well through less expensive outpatient therapy. As costs for all types of healthcare have escalated to reach 14 percent of the gross national product, and as managed care organizations have proliferated, some sort of controls over mental health service provision are inevitable. Reforms that would lead to a more equitable and effective system would place less reliance on expensive inpatient care and long-term psychotherapy and more on comprehensive and continuous community care for the most seriously ill, and short-term and directed care

for the acutely ill. The knowledge exists about what changes are needed in mental health service provision, although fiscal inefficiencies, administrative fragmentation, and professional resistance might prevent reform. It will be difficult to create a mental health system that responds as adequately to the most seriously disordered as to the less seriously disturbed—but such a system will be more humane.

ALLAN V. HORWITZ (1995)
REVISED BY AUTHOR

SEE ALSO: *Children: Mental Health Issues; Coercion; Confidentiality; Disability; Electroconvulsive Therapy; Informed Consent: Issues of Consent in Mental Healthcare; Institutionalization and Deinstitutionalization; Life, Quality of; Mental Health, Meaning of Mental Health; Mental Health Therapies; Mental Illness; Mentally Disabled and Mentally Ill Persons; Patients' Rights: Mental Patients' Rights; Psychiatry, Abuses of; and other Mental Health Services subentries*

BIBLIOGRAPHY

American Psychiatric Association. 1992. *Diagnostic and Statistical Manual of Mental Disorders: DSM IV.* Washington, D.C.: Author.

Appelbaum, Paul S. 1994. *Almost a Revolution: Mental Health Law and the Limits of Change.* New York: Oxford University Press.

Bachrach, Leona L. 1992. "What We Know About Homelessness Among Mentally Ill Persons: An Analytical Review and Commentary." *Hospital and Community Psychiatry* 43(5): 453–464.

Beard, John H. 1982. "The Rehabilitation Services of Fountain House." In *Alternatives to Mental Hospital Treatment,* ed. Leonard I. Stein and Mary Ann Test. New York: Plenum Press.

Bloche, M. Gregg, and Cournos, Francine. 1990. "Mental Health Policy for the 1990s: Tinkering in the Interstices." *Journal of Health Politics, Policy and Law* 15(2): 387–411.

Boyle, Philip J., and Callahan, Daniel. 1993. "Minds and Hearts: Priorities in Mental Health Services." *Hastings Center Report* 23(5): S3–S23.

Center for Mental Health Services (CMHS). 1998. *Mental Health, United States, 1998.* Washington, D.C.: U. S. Government Printing Office.

Center for Mental Health Services (CMHS). 2001. *Mental Health, United States, 2000.* Washington, D.C.: U. S. Government Printing Office.

Diamond, Ronald J., and Wikler, Daniel I. 1985. "Ethical Problems in the Community Treatment of the Chronically Mentally Ill." In *The Training in Community Living Model: A Decade of Experience,* ed. Leonard I. Stein and Mary Ann Test. San Francisco: Jossey-Bass.

Donnelly, Michael. 1992. *The Politics of Mental Health in Italy.* London: Tavistock.

Frank, Jerome D., and Frank, Julia B. 1991. *Persuasion and Healing: A Comparative Study of Psychotherapy,* 3rd edition. Baltimore: Johns Hopkins University Press.

Frank, Richard G.; Goldman, Howard H.; and McGuire, Thomas G. 1992. "A Model Mental Health Benefit in Private Insurance." *Health Affairs* 11(3): 98–117.

Goffman, Erving. 1961. *Asylums: Essays on the Social Situation of Mental Patients and Other Inmates.* New York: Doubleday.

Goldberg, David, and Thornicroft, Graham, eds. 1998. *Mental Health in our Future Cities.* East Sussex, Eng.: Psychology Press.

Goldman, Howard H.; Adams, Neal H.; and Taube, Carl A. 1983. "Deinstitutionalization: The Data Demythologized." *Hospital and Community Psychiatry* 34(2): 129–134.

Grob, Gerald N. 1973. *Mental Illness and American Society, 1875–1940.* Princeton, NJ: Princeton University Press.

Grob, Gerald N. 1991. *From Asylum to Community: Mental Health Policy in Modern America.* Princeton, NJ: Princeton University Press.

Hale, Nathan G., Jr. 1995. *The Rise and Crisis of Psychoanalysis in the United States: Freud and the Americans, 1917–1985.* New York: Oxford University Press.

Healy, David. 1997. *The Anti-Depressant Era.* Cambridge, MA: Harvard University Press.

Horwitz, Allan V. 2002. *Creating Mental Illness.* Chicago: University of Chicago Press.

Kessler, Ronald C.; Beglund, P. A.; Zhao, Shanyang; et al. 1996. "The 12-Month Prevalence and Correlates of Serious Mental Illness (SMI)." In *Mental Health, United States, 1996,* ed. R. Manderscheid and M.A. Sonnenschein. Washington, D.C.: U.S. Government Printing Office.

Kessler, Ronald C.; McGonagle, Katherine A.; Zhao, Shanyang; et al. 1994. "Lifetime and 12-Month Prevalence of DSM-III-R Psychiatric Disorders in the United States: Results From the National Comorbidity Survey." *Archives of General Psychiatry* 51: 8–19.

Kiesler, Charles A. 2000. "The Next Wave of Change for Psychology and Mental Health Services in the Health Care Revolution." *American Psychologist* 55: 481–87.

Kiesler, Charles A., and Sibulkin, Amy E. 1987. *Mental Hospitalization: Myths and Facts About a National Crisis.* Newbury Park, CA: Sage.

Kiesler, Charles A., and Simpkins, Celeste G. 1993. *The Unnoticed Majority in Psychiatric Inpatient Care.* New York: Plenum.

Kirk, Stuart A., and Kutchins, Herb. 1992. *The Selling of DSM: The Rhetoric of Science in Psychiatry.* New York: Aldine de Gruyter.

Koyanagi, Chris, and Goldman, Howard H. 1991. "The Quiet Success of the National Plan for the Chronically Mentally Ill." *Hospital and Community Psychiatry* 42(9): 899–905.

Kramer, Peter D. 1992. *Listening to Prozac: A Psychiatrist Explores Antidepressant Drugs and the Remaking of the Self.* New York: Viking.

Lamb, H. Richard. 1993. "Lessons Learned from Deinstitutionalisation in the U.S." *British Journal of Psychiatry* 162(May): 587–592.

Lefley, Harriet P. 1987. "Aging Parents as Caregivers of Mentally Ill Adult Children: An Emerging Social Problem." *Hospital and Community Psychiatry* 38(10): 106–107.

Luhrmann, T.M. 2000. *Of Two Minds: The Growing Disorder in American Psychiatry.* New York: Alfred A. Knopf.

Mechanic, David. 1999. *Mental Health and Social Policy: The Emergence of Managed Care.* Needham Heights, MA: Allan & Bacon.

Mechanic, David, and Rochefort, David A. 1992. "A Policy of Inclusion for the Mentally Ill." *Health Affairs* 11(1): 128–150.

Morrissey, Joseph P.; Callaway, Michael; Bartko, W. Todd; et al. 1993. "Local Mental Health Authorities and Service System Change: Evidence from the Robert Wood Johnson Foundation Program on Chronic Mental Illness." *Milbank Quarterly* 72: 49–80.

Petrila, John P., and Sadoff, Robert L. 1992. "Confidentiality and the Family as Caregiver." *Hospital and Community Psychiatry* 43(2): 136–139.

Pincus, Harold A.; Tanielian, Terri L.; Marcus, Steven C.; et al. 1998. "Prescribing Trends in Psychotropic Medications: Primary Care, Psychiatry, and Other Medical Specialties." *Journal of the American Medical Association* 279: 526–531.

Regier, Darrel A.; Narrow, William E.; Rae, Donald S.; et al. 1993. "The De Facto U.S. Mental and Addictive Disorders Service System." *Archives of General Psychiatry* 50(2): 85–94.

Rochefort, David A. 1984. "Origins of the 'Third Psychiatric Revolution': The Community Mental Health Centers Act of 1963." *Journal of Health Politics, Policy, and Law* 9(1): 1–30.

Sharfstein, Steven S.; Stoldine, Anne M.; and Goldman, Howard H. 1993. "Psychiatric Care and Health Insurance Reform." *American Journal of Psychiatry* 150(1): 7–18.

Shinfuku, Naotake; Sugawara, Susumu; Yanaka, Teruo; and Kimura, Mariko. 1998. "Mental Health in the City of Kobe, Japan." In *Mental Health in Our Future Cities,* ed. David Goldberg and Graham Thronicroft. East Sussex, Eng.: Psychology Press.

Stein, Leonard I., and Test, Mary Ann. 1980. "Alternative Mental Hospital Treatment: 1. Conceptual Model, Treatment Program, and Clinical Evaluation." *Archives of General Psychiatry* 37(4): 392–397.

Swindle, Ralph; Heller, Kenneth; Pescosolido, Bernice; and Kikuzawa, Saeko. 2000. "Responses to Nervous Breakdowns in America over a 40-Year Period." *American Psychologist* 55: 740–49.

Szasz, Thomas S. 1974. *The Myth of Mental Illness: Foundations of a Theory of Personal Conduct,* rev. edition. New York: Harper & Row.

Valenstein, Eliot S. 1998. *Blaming the Brain: The TRUTH About Drugs and Mental Health.* New York: The Free Press.

Weisbrod, Burt; Test, Mary Ann; and Stein, Leonard I. 1980. "Alternative to Mental Hospital Treatment: II. Economic

Benefit Cost Analysis." *Archives of General Psychiatry* 37(4): 400–405.

World Health Organization. 1996. *Global Action for the Improvement of Mental Health Care: Policies and Strategies.* Geneva: Author.

World Health Organization. 2001. *Mental Health in Europe: Country Aspects from the WHO European Network on Mental Health.* Copenhagen: Author.

II. ETHICAL ISSUES

At the beginning of the twenty-first century, American society is engaged in a continuing critical reexamination of fundamental issues in health matters. As healthcare reforms progress through the social and political process, the opportunity exists to remedy past failures in the management of health resources, to renew fundamental values and commitments to individual and public health, and to shape new priorities for a system of healthcare that is both fiscally sound and ethically justified. The most pressing challenge is to allocate health resources to those in need of them without unfairly compromising other cherished social goods such as education and defense, or other ideals such as economic prosperity and self-determination. This challenge is made even more complex by the relentless growth in technological and scientific achievements, and an ever-widening public concern about their responsible use and distribution in society.

Of increasing concern to many in American society is the system of goods and services to provide care to the mentally ill. The mental health system of the 2000s is a complex web of intersecting and often competing factors that reflect changing ideas regarding mental illness and the resources that are needed to deal with it. The mental health field is characterized by a stunning diversity of problems that reflect the complex shifts in society over the past several decades. Whether these problems are considered in terms of diagnosis, level of dysfunction or disorder, duration of symptoms or disease, or social attitudes regarding concepts of deviancy and dangerousness, mental illness is a problem of enormous complexity and heterogeneous characteristics. The ethical issues are no less complex, and raise some of the deepest philosophical questions regarding mind and body, the nature of suffering, the range of human potentialities, and the conflicts between individual and societal needs.

Although ethical considerations are implicit in nearly every aspect of mental healthcare, the emphasis in this article is on ethical aspects of the mental health service system. The most dominant issue is the problem of justice and the derivative question of how to strike a fair and equitable balance between the requirement that society protect its citizens from harm and its simultaneous duty to protect and promote the moral, legal, and civil rights of each individual. Answers to this particular question continue to be reflected in various mental health directives and policies that define the field of mental health services. In various ways, these directives and policies document the extent to which the problems of mental illness are valued or disvalued by society, the eligibility criteria of those persons who may receive society's goods and those who will not, and the perceived importance of mental health to the vitality and character of the nation.

This article addresses the issues of equity, parity, and fragmentation in relation to considerations of justice, and supports the argument that mental health concerns should be given higher priority in the healthcare system of the future.

The Mental Health Service System

Mental illness affects people throughout the entire life cycle, including all age groups and socioeconomic strata (Regier, Narrow, Rae, et al.; U.S. Surgeon General). According to one estimate, approximately one-third of Americans will experience some form of a mental disorder at some point in their lives; of the 28 to 30 percent of all adults who experience mental disorders in a year, 2.6 percent have chronic, severely disabling conditions such as schizophrenia (Kessler, Berglund, Zhao, et al.). Psychiatric patients are more likely than the general population to have substance abuse disorders as well. Furthermore, although 28.1 percent of the population received diagnosis of mental or addictive disorders in one year, only about 15 percent received any mental health services in that time frame (Regier, et al.; U.S. Surgeon General). In 1990, the annual direct cost of mental and substance-abuse services in the United States was estimated to be $99 billion. Indirect costs, such as lost days of work, has added another $79 billion (Rice and Miller; U.S. Surgeon General).

Many mental and substance abuse disorders are severe and chronic, and thus often produce emotional and financial burdens for patients and families that last a lifetime. Although 28 to 30 percent of all adults experience mental disorders in a year, only one third of this population receives mental healthcare (U.S. Surgeon General). Similarly, despite the fact that 7.5 million children in the United States under the age of eighteen suffer from an emotional problem severe enough to require treatment, as many as 70 to 80 percent do not receive the services they need (U.S. Office of Technology Assessment). Finally, Americans over sixty-five years of age are at high risk of developing mental disorders because of reputed stressors associated with aging, including concomitant physical illness, increasing isolation, and diminished social supports. Studies demonstrate, however, that just over half of older adults with mental disorders are provided services through the mental health sector (U.S. Surgeon General). The rest, often referred by physicians—whose poor abilities to recognize the psychological symptoms of older adult patients have been documented—obtain services from the general health sector. Consequently, many older adults with mental health problems may not receive the services they need from qualified mental health professionals (Gatz and Smyer).

The current system of mental healthcare in the United States is enormously complex and has the following characteristics that differentiate it from the more general system (Phelen, Link, Stueve, et al.; U.S. Surgeon General):

1. Mental health services are dependent upon public funding and are frequently subject to a high degree of government regulation.

2. Mental health services are provided by an increasingly diverse set of professionals, including psychiatrists, social workers, psychiatric nurses, and mental health counselors. Increasingly, these services are offered in a variety of settings, including state and mental hospitals; general, private, and government hospitals with psychiatric units; community mental health centers; nursing homes; and specialized alcohol, drug, and addiction disorder treatment units.

3. These diverse settings may alter the transaction between a patient and therapist, and create threats to the often private and intimate character of the therapeutic relationship.

4. The chronically mentally ill and other severely disordered persons constitute a highly dependent population that presents extraordinary challenges for administrators and providers attempting to maintain a responsive, accountable, and humane program.

5. Disputes regarding the diagnosis and etiology of mental health disorders and the efficacy of their treatments persist and make it difficult to evaluate the utility of treatment programs.

6. The boundaries of mental health services are difficult to define, and create diverse sets of expectations and conflicts regarding *medical* and *social* models of disease.

7. Mental health services are generally perceived as having a poor public image and as valuable for only a small group in society who have aberrant emotional or behavioral conditions.

These characteristics provide a clear portrait of the complex issues faced by mental health practitioners and policymakers. They may explain some of the reasons why mental healthcare has a low position on the American agenda.

Vulnerability

Illness of any kind, but especially mental illness, exacerbates the need to depend on others for help and to trust that this dependence will not be exploited or manipulated. Many severely mentally ill persons remain dependent on the healthcare and mental health services systems to provide necessities of life. The human tragedies generated by severe mental disorders are considerable; often not only the health and well-being of individuals but also that of their families and communities are destroyed. Persons with chronic mental illness such as schizophrenia, bipolar illness, and psychoses that impair or distort decision-making abilities may be particularly vulnerable to possibly unjustified paternalistic interventions in their lives. Although the stigma attached to the use of mental health services may be diminishing, it still endures in some forms, thus increasing the vulnerability of the mentally ill to negative social judgments. These vulnerabilities create moral obligations on the part of society and its institutions to provide the resources to meet basic human needs and promote policies that include strategies to avoid discrimination, stigmatization, and the exploitation of dependence. These obligations are grounded in moral beliefs regarding society's duty to help those who are weak or vulnerable, and on the moral principles of care and trust that form the basis of the therapeutic relationship between patient and provider (Carter).

Historical Features of Mental Health Services

Although mental healthcare represents a significant part of the overall healthcare system, it has been separated from the mainstream of healthcare by historical, institutional, and conceptual barriers. Historically, mental healthcare was linked to social welfare policies; mentally ill persons incapable of living in society were separated from it not so much because they were sick as because they were viewed as disruptive to society. They were cared for in local or state asylums. These institutions, and the cycles of reform they mirror, have been the subject of well-documented historical works (Deutsch; Foucault; Grob, 1991). Of relevance in this article are the underlying moral and social reasons that justified the various services provided within these institutions. For instance, in the early 1800s social reformers and physicians began to lobby against a shared responsibility by the state and local governments for providing services to the mentally ill. As a result, many mentally ill persons become wards of the state (Boyle and Callahan). In the institutions of the mid-nineteenth century, *treatment* consisted of providing a calm, humane, and disciplined environment. The ethical justification for these services was that the state could meet its responsibilities to the individual, family, and community by providing medical treatment for acute problems and humane, custodial care for those with chronic problems. Furthermore, the health of the general public could be served by protecting society from the threat of disease or dependency (Grob, 1992).

In the early twentieth century, the United States began to embrace the view that the individual is responsible for meeting the basic needs of life. Society, in the form of federal or state government institutions, would intervene only when an illness placed excessive burdens on the afflicted individual or family, when the disease posed a danger or threat to the community, or when the individual lacked the necessary resources to deal with it. Vulnerable people, such as those with tuberculosis, mental illness, or mental retardation, could obtain needed services such as those provided in the mental institutions of the day. There was no broad right of access to healthcare services; rather, the dominant social policy focused on the value of serving only those with special needs. Mental health policy in the 1940s was based on the assumption that society had an obligation to provide a severely and chronically ill person with both care and treatment in public mental hospitals. Gradually, in response to economic and cultural shifts, these mental hospitals became increasingly custodial and bureaucratic (Grob, 1992).

In the years following World War II, radical transformations shook American culture, and new ideas regarding individual and societal rights emerged. The social activism and political unrest of the 1960s provided the backdrop for a number of shifts in thinking about the nation as a whole. States began to reconsider their policies regarding the mentally ill, and people who had been cared for in mental hospitals were moved to newly created community alternatives. In the 1960s, the movement to deinstitutionalize the mentally ill was partly based on the idea that the chronically mentally ill could receive support in the community without infringement of their civil rights. The other assumption that fueled policies of deinstitutionalization was derived from intellectual and scientific disputes within the practice of psychiatry. Disagreements about the definition of mental illness, diverse explanations of its causes, and skepticism about treatment efficacy generated controversy and ambiguity. These disagreements in turn affected the nature of the services available to those with mental disorders.

Monumental revolutions in ideas regarding individual, civil, women's, and fetal rights provoked fundamental questions about the role of the state in a free democracy, and the power of technology to alter constructs such as life and death. As these social and intellectual events converged, new attitudes regarding the nature of medical care, research on human subjects, and the value components of therapeutic relationships began to be reflected in legal decisions, social policy, and ethical discourse. In the field of mental health, ethical concepts of autonomy, informed consent, and paternalism began to appear in the literature. Psychiatrists, social workers, psychologists, and other mental health providers began to critically examine their relationships with patients, colleagues, society, and the state. They were confronted with new puzzles, such as how to respect the recently enhanced rights to autonomy and individual freedoms, and yet protect society from the potentially harmful actions of a mentally ill person. Ethical values were often in conflict with other values, thereby dividing professional loyalties and obligations (Reiser, Bursztajn, Appelbaum, et al.).

In response to shifts in public values and attitudes, the federal government began to endorse social welfare programs aimed at prevention; new programs attempted to ameliorate the social problems that were said to foster mental illness. Mental health policy increasingly began to rely on federal government programs to administer, manage, fund, and reimburse for these services. The passage of the Omnibus Reconciliation Act of 1981 effectively eliminated previous policies that had emphasized community care outside the mental hospital (Kiesler). Federally-sponsored programs such as Medicare and Medicaid initiated cost-based reimbursement strategies that fueled the evolving rhetoric of the *right to healthcare,* and fed the expectation that such a right would be funded. Congressional passage of the Tax Equity and Fiscal Responsibility Act of 1982 and the Medicare Prospective Payment System (PPS) in 1982 altered this expectation by restricting future payments for inpatient hospital services.

These events, and many others detailed elsewhere, foreshadowed the current public debate regarding the existence and scope of this *right to healthcare* and its numerous philosophical, conceptual, economic, political, and social ramifications.

All of these transformations in ideology influenced policy directions and contributed to the evolution of a diffuse, heterogeneous system of services that provided a diverse set of services to assist the adjustment of the mentally ill to life outside the mental hospital. For instance, in the 1960s the view that mental illness did not require psychodynamic intervention, and that those experiencing *problems in living* could find the support they needed in the community, led to the policy of deinstitutionalization. This policy of transferring patients from public mental hospitals to community-based mental health centers, coupled with the emergence of psychotropic agents to control their symptoms, profoundly altered the mental health system.

Although many writers have analyzed the mixed impact on mental health services brought about by this policy (Mechanic and Rochefort), others underscore its abject failures in helping the seriously ill or reducing the number of inpatient services (Geller; Lamb and Bachrach). Other writers have argued that the community mental health policies not only overlooked the social and human needs of the severely ill, but also bifurcated therapeutic or treatment services from care and support services. The former were identified more with, and included in, the medical healthcare system, whereas the latter were affiliated with the welfare or social system. This bifurcation inadvertently distorted priorities, with more focus applied to providing therapeutic services in outpatient settings for a broadly defined population (Grob, 1992). Still others have argued that with the closure of state mental hospitals and related services, many chronically and severely ill individuals found themselves with nowhere to go for needed services and help (Lamb and Bachrach). Transformations in mental health laws to protect the mentally ill and promote their rights began to dominate intellectual discourse. New laws demonstrated the evolutions in understanding of the concepts of confinement, commitment, access to services, and the scope of individual autonomy in treatment decisions (La Fond). In the last decades of the twentieth century, mental health law became an able instrument of advocacy and protection of the civil, legal, and ethical rights of the mentally ill (Perlin; La Fond).

Access

Changes in the way mental health services are defined, distributed, delivered, and financed have produced a number of ethical concerns related to justice and other ethical principles. One of these is the problem of access to services. In the United States, healthcare is ordinarily covered by private or public insurance. Insurance reimbursement policies were originally constructed to shield both patient and provider against the worry about costs once an illness actually occurred. Reimbursements were quite generous and uncontested, with third parties acting as silent partners in the negotiation between physician and patient for needed services. The result of this is now obvious: a highly inflationary system with rapidly accelerating healthcare expenditures (Fuchs), which has in turn led to the growing managed care system.

Obviously, the 16 percent of the U.S. population currently estimated to be without public or private health insurance will also be without financial insurance against psychiatric or addictive disorders (Bureau of the Census). Yet even where insurance is provided, mental health insurance benefits are not on par with those in the general medical

sector (U.S. Surgeon General). Moreover, Medicare and Medicaid place restrictions on the amount and setting of services for psychiatric and addictive disorders, thus further restricting the access and availability of needed resources for the mentally ill. While opportunities for mental health services increasingly exist under Medicare, only 5 percent of Medicare funding at present goes for mental health (U.S. Surgeon General). Finally, office-based care by psychiatrists, and often by other mental health providers, is generally covered by insurance firms but is rarely equivalent to other office-based physician care (Frank, Goldman, and McGuire, 1992).

Thus, although policies have been aimed at treating mental illness on an outpatient basis, all the incentives in insurance programs send the signal that inpatient treatment is what will be reimbursed. Of all mental health expenditures, an estimated 70 percent are designated for inpatient care. Many health insurance policies will reimburse fully for hospitalized care, but only partially cover outpatient care, and pay even less for prevention services. Nursing homes have not been integrated into any mental health system, although the Nursing Home Reform Act of 1987 mandates "active treatment." The predictable mental health needs of an aging population have not been factored into health policies, thus widening the gap between perceived need and access to service for a substantial segment of the population (Gatz and Smyer).

Moreover, simply being labeled as receiving treatment for a mental disorder can affect an individual's access to the general healthcare system. This occurs through the practice of medical underwriting, a process that denies individuals health insurance because of a *medical disorder* for which they received care in the past (Boyle and Callahan). These forms of discrimination not only impair the individual's access to services that are otherwise standard, but also further the antiquated idea of the dualism between mind and body.

These restrictions on the access and availability of services through insurance and financing mechanisms create inequities in many parts of the system. First, many Americans, especially the poor and underinsured, cannot afford the cost of needed mental healthcare. Second, many uninsured people at risk for major mental and/or addictive disorders will be denied appropriate prevention services and be inadequately protected against the possibility of catastrophic financial harm. Third, failure to provide meaningful access to services within the mental health system results in inappropriate and excessive use of the general resources of healthcare, creating further inequities for individual consumers and providers, and increasing the economic burden on the general medical economy as a whole. These inequalities of access to needed care are unacceptable to a decent and humane society (U.S. President's Commission; U.S. Surgeon General). Some of them may be explained by historical accounts of the various ideological, political, and societal events that helped produce them, but they are not justified from an ethical point of view. Any society concerned with the well-being of its citizens cannot promote the importance of healthcare in achieving well-being while allowing people to suffer because of arbitrary barriers to healthcare.

Parity

A related ethical issue has to do with whether funding of treatment for mental health conditions should be equal to that of the general health sector. Many commentators have noted a lack of parity both between the two healthcare systems and within the mental health system itself. The latter can be expressed as both the disparity of treatment between kinds of mental illness, and the disparity of treatment between different degrees of mental illness severity.

Despite several major legislative efforts in the 1990s and early 2000s, there is little evidence that any significant change in mental health parity has occurred. Aside from failing to be passed by Congress, these bills failed to greatly affect parity for many reasons, including: covering only a subset of the population; covering only selected illnesses, often based on an archaic and fictional division of the mental and the biological; only covering certain severities of illness, often based on diagnosis of a specific illness or by level of debilitation; exemptions for small businesses, or for large cost increases; unequal limits on annual costs, lifetime costs, outpatient visits, days of inpatient care, per visit co-payments, or annual deductibles; and a variety of nearly nonquantifiable disparities in the quality of care provided (Rochefort, 1996; National Advisory Mental Health Council, 1998,2000; Geller; U.S. Surgeon General's Report).

One such piece of federal legislation passed into law in 1996 was the Mental Health Parity Act (MHPA) (Domenici/ Wellstone), which required all group health plans already covering mental healthcare to have equal cost restrictions on yearly and lifetime benefits as traditional medical and surgical services. The MHPA had little effect on parity due to provisions within the act that allowed for exemptions for small businesses and for businesses that experienced an increase in cost because of the act. Moreover, 87 percent of employers' plans that complied with the MHPA had one or more methods of restricting mental health benefits more than traditional medical or surgical services. Congress allowed the MHPA to expire in 2001 and failed to pass the proposed 2001 Mental Health Equitable Treatment Act (S. 543), which attempted to address most of the problems with the 1996 MHPA (Gitterman, et al.; Barry and Frank; Geller; General Accounting Office).

The greater focus on mental health parity by the federal government spread to the state legislatures with similarly ineffective results. As of 2001, thirty-one states had adopted mental health parity requirements for employee health insurance, with all but five doing so after the passage of the 1996 MHPA. However, the 1974 Employee Retirement Income Security Act prevents states from regulating self-insured plans, thus limiting the affected population to those in group health plans (Gitterman, et al.; General Accounting Office; National Advisory Mental Health Council, 1998, 2000).

Two possible successes for parity have occurred, though their future is unclear. First, President Clinton announced at the First White House Conference on Mental Health in 1999 that health plans for all federal employees must cover mental health at full parity (though the durability of this order was unclear with the change in administration in 2000). Second, the Americans with Disabilities Act (1990) provides some hope for protection for people with severe mental disabilities to receive basic mental health services and protection from discrimination, but the constitutionality, and thus the future, of the ADA is questioned by some (Geller).

In general, parity legislation has thus far had only a small effect on parity itself. Parity legislation appears to encourage the presence of managed care, which results in lower or stable costs for mental healthcare. In general, these lower costs seem to come from a combination of increased efficiency and lower quality and accessibility (National Advisory Mental Health Council, 1998, 2000; General Accounting Office; U.S. Surgeon General).

For decades, U.S. health policy has been centered on the short-term, acute-care general hospital, despite the fact that this does not match the population's health needs; this continued focus points to the problems of parity of mental health services between different groups within the population. Preventive services have until recently been largely neglected, as have the needs of chronically ill elderly, children, and youth. While healthcare in the acute-care hospital in the United States is arguably the best in the world, in mental health, care *outside* a hospital is demonstrated to be better and less expensive than care in the hospital (Kiesler). This raises the caveat that simply mimicking the flawed policies of the general health system may not necessarily prove to be the best strategy for mental health policymakers of the future, even though it may lead to greater parity between the two systems (Kiesler; U.S. Surgeon General). Arbitrary limits on outpatient services, inpatient hospitalizations, community-based health services, and higher co-payments for mental health services reflect the way mental health is disvalued in society, and its inferior status compared with physical health. Whenever a society establishes a priority system for the kinds of goods and services it makes available to its members, questions of fairness are evoked. If a society assigns insufficient or inadequate resources to a segment of the population at risk for or suffering from mental and addictive disorders without appropriate justifications, it violates ethical commitments to social beneficence, liberty, compassion, and justice.

Fragmentation

One of the most difficult ethical problems confronting the current mental health service system is the striking lack of coordination and collaboration among other human service agencies. The current mental health system is remarkable for a pronounced variation in the use of institutional and community-based services, admission rates, lengths of stay and services, and multiple funding sources and patterns.

Fragmentation in services is a consequence of developments in the larger healthcare system, as well as of the lack of integration in legal, social, economic, and scientific aspects of health policy. These problems stem from a cluster of ambiguities that prevail in the field of mental health: the diversity of beliefs regarding the concept of mental disease or disorder (Wakefield; U.S. Surgeon General); deeply-rooted cultural beliefs regarding behavior that seems inexplicable, bizarre, or threatening; and disagreement about which social policies to adopt in regard to persons whose autonomy is impaired by mental disorder, especially when this impairment may lead to the possibility of harm to self or others. Serious conceptual and normative questions regarding the definition of mental illness have led to practical disagreements about when and how to intervene. As of the mid-1990s, models of mental illness ranged from the purely medical model and its psychotherapeutic or psychoanalytical interventions, to a model that emphasizes the unity of biological, psychological, social, and personal factors in health and illness. Different mental health therapists subscribe to a variety of different theories on the nature of mental health. Specialists disagree, for example, about the boundary between mental illness and other forms of deviancy, and about the relative contributions of individual, family, environmental, and social variables in producing mental disorders (Rochefort, 1989). It has also been noted that a significant portion of the fragmentation and lack of coordination within the mental health system may be due to idiosyncratic factors related to politics, prejudice, and professional or civic self interest (Rochefort, 1989).

The lack of precise criteria to define and classify mental illness apparently has the following result: Both the person with catatonic schizophrenia, incapable of functioning in social life, and the person with an obsessive-compulsive neurosis, whose behavior is simply bothersome, are labeled as mentally ill. Both may be in need of some treatment to reduce distressing symptoms, but these services may be quite distinct from one another, and they raise significantly different concerns regarding what should count as a *mental health service* and what should not.

Thus, despite great expansion of mental health services, the system is remarkably fragmented. Without a centralized organization or locus of responsibility, quality of and accountability for services remain fragmented (U.S. Surgeon General). On the systemic level, the problem of fragmentation seems to have produced the following: under-treatment of the seriously and chronically ill; undervaluing of prevention services, rehabilitation, and long-term care; diminished access to available services for those with or at risk of mental and addictive disorders; restrictive barriers to insurance entitlement; and a generally lower position on the national healthcare agenda, despite data that demonstrate the efficacy of treatment for many forms of mental disorder.

These ambiguities exert a profound influence on normative and value questions, and can have a direct effect on the kind of mental health policy that is developed and the priorities it has in the overall healthcare agenda (Rochefort, 1989; Mowbray, Grazier, and Holter). Ultimately society's norms and values determine what kinds of services and resources will be made available, to whom they will be targeted, where they will be provided, and how they will be financed. Disparities of access and status provoke dilemmas of choice regarding principles of justice, on the one hand, and principles of cost-effectiveness on the other. They also expose the genuine difficulty of deciding which values should govern the policymaking process, when not all values can be equally promoted. For example, if society decides to purchase mental health services because of underlying commitments to humanitarian goals, then policy should probably be directed toward those individuals who have the most serious conditions and greatest needs. However, if society purchases mental health services because of commitments to principles of social or economic utility, then policy efforts would need to be driven by cost-benefit analyses and outcomes. In this instance, priority might be given to those individuals with depression, anxiety disorders, and alcohol addiction, because of the likelihood they would recover sufficiently to return to productive society (Klerman, Olfson, Leon, et al.). The principle of favoring the least well-off would have to be balanced against other considerations of justice that might be based on utilitarian assessments of what might provide the greatest benefits to the greatest number of people.

These priority decisions ultimately reflect political and social value judgments about how much society is willing to invest in caring for its mentally ill citizens. Although disagreements persist on a number of conceptual, scientific, and professional issues, there does seem to be consensus on one essential point: Mental health must have a higher status in the healthcare system. Furthermore, setting priorities regarding the relative value of mental health services will require a decision process based on principles of fairness, non-abandonment of those in need, public accountability, and objectivity (Boyle and Callahan; U.S. Surgeon General).

Ethical Values in Contemporary Mental Health Policy

Since the publication of the influential Flexner Report in 1910, the U.S. healthcare system has been based on a medical model firmly anchored to the concepts of scientific, physical medicine and notions of medical treatment and cure. Ideas of prevention, health, and public health were relegated to the "back porch" (Smith). American society has structured its health policies, programs, professions, and institutions on this model for many decades, as though there were little relationship between mental and physical health. However, there is a growing body of empirical knowledge that documents the role of mental state in the maintenance and deterioration of good physical health, and in the treatment and recovery from physical illness (Praeger and Scallet).

Contemporary mental health policy, whether developed in terms of prevention, accessibility to needed services, rehabilitation, or maintenance of persons most greatly in need, is in a process of change. These changes reflect shifting concepts of mental illness, new etiological formulations of mental disease, treatment interventions, epidemiological trends, past program successes and failures, and the broader social, political, and economic currents (Rochefort, 1989; Rochefort, 1996). Ultimately, policies represent society's effort to deal with one of the most difficult and persistent human problems: how to balance the classic conflict between the power of the state to act for the good of society, and the responsibility of society to ensure the full expression of individual rights and freedoms. Questions concerning who has the legitimate power to control the lives of the mentally ill continue to provoke philosophical debate. In contemplating the public and scholarly discourse in the mental health field over the past several decades, several difficult questions regarding past policies must be confronted before new ones are generated. For instance, what ethical values, if any, were promoted by policies of deinstitutionalization? Has the goal of returning the mentally ill and disabled to the community for care enhanced the rights of individuals, or has it produced in them, or their communities, some greater harm? How will mental health policy of the future balance the competing claims of liberty, equality, and social beneficence?

Such questions represent difficult value choices, made more complex by a climate of increasing public distrust (Jellinek) and scarcity of fiscal resources (Morreim). Past assumptions of political liberalism and economic expansion are no longer valid. Instead, policies of allocation are becoming more explicitly value-directed, not simply regarding cost-containment or efficiency but on principles of equity, justice, and compassion (Jennings). Allocation policies, insofar as they are regarded as socially legitimate and politically acceptable, may then be understood to be a mechanism by which society seeks to define and to express its sense of self, its values, and its integrity (Childress). In a time of great transition and transformation of the healthcare system at large, American society is at a crossroad in its attempt to understand the health of the human mind and of all the forces that seek to promote and sustain it (Praeger and Scallet). It is a time of constructive chaos, in which the very mission and telos of healthcare are being redefined. Along with this redefinition, the opportunity exists to raise the status of the mental health services field from the "poor stepchild of the health care delivery system" (Boyle and Callahan, p. 53) to a level that conjoins mental and physical well-being and integrates biomedical and behavioral knowledge regarding health parameters. To accomplish this, it will be necessary to pay close attention to issues of equity in the access, availability, and efficacy of all health-related services, and to avoid arbitrary demarcations between mental and physical well-being (U.S. Surgeon General; Mowbray, et al.).

At the beginning of the twenty-first century, there is clear and urgent need for serious ethical reflection on which values and priorities should govern the mental health policies of the future. What is needed is an integrated, comprehensive, and equitable strategy that builds on knowledge and research in mental and physical health, and links these to appropriate and beneficial services for those in need of them. Problems of individual and social justice penetrate all areas of society, but are especially powerful in relation to the needs of the mentally ill, and to the communities in which they live. Undoubtedly, care and treatment of the mentally ill pose a range of ethical concerns that will continue to challenge society well into this century.

MICHELE A. CARTER (1995)
REVISED BY AUTHOR

SEE ALSO: *Children: Mental Health Issues; Coercion; Confidentiality; Disability; Electroconvulsive Therapy; Informed Consent: Issues of Consent in Mental Healthcare; Institutionalization and Deinstitutionalization; Life, Quality of; Mental Health, Meaning of Mental Health; Mental Health Therapies; Mental Illness; Mental Institutions, Commitment to; Mentally Disabled and Mentally Ill Persons; Patients' Rights: Mental Patients' Rights; Psychiatry, Abuses of; Psychoanalysis and Dynamic Therapies; Psychopharmacology;* and other *Mental Health Services* subentries

BIBLIOGRAPHY

Barry, Colleen L., and Frank, Richard G. 2002. "Economics and the Surgeon General's Report on Mental Health." *Psychiatric Services* 53: 409–411.

Boyle, Philip J., and Callahan, Daniel. 1993. "Minds and Hearts: Priorities in Mental Health Services." *Hastings Center Report* 23(5): S1–S23.

Carter, Michele A. 1993. "Ethical Framework for Care of the Chronically Ill." *Holistic Nursing Practice* 8(1): 67–77.

Childress, James F. 1979. "Priorities in the Allocation of Health Care Resources." *Soundings: An Interdisciplinary Journal* 62(3): 256–274.

Deutsch, Albert. 1937. *The Mentally Ill in America: A History of Their Care and Treatment from Colonial Times.* Garden City, NY: Doubleday, Doran.

Foucault, Michel. 1973. *Madness and Civilization: A History of Insanity in the Age of Reason,* tr. Richard Howard. New York: Vintage.

Frank, Richard G.; Goldman, Howard H.; and McGuire, Thomas G. 1992. "A Model Mental Health Benefit in Private Health Insurance." *Health Affairs* 11(3): 99–117.

Fuchs, Victor R. 1984. "The Rationing of Medical Care." *New England Journal of Medicine* 311(24): 1572–1573.

Gatz, Margaret, and Smyer, Michael A. 1992. "The Mental Health System and Older Adults in the 1990s." *American Psychologist* 47(6): 741–751.

Geller, Jeffrey L. 2000. "The Last Half-Century of Psychiatric Services as Reflected in *Psychiatric Services.*" *Psychiatric Services* 51: 41–67.

Gitterman, Daniel P., et al. 2001. "Does the Sunset of Mental Health Parity Really Matter?" *Administration and Policy in Mental Health* 28(5): 353–369.

Grob, Gerald N. 1983. *Mental Illness and American Society, 1875–1940.* Princeton, NJ: Princeton University Press.

Grob, Gerald N. 1991. *From Asylum to Community: Mental Health Policy in Modern America.* Princeton, NJ: Princeton University Press.

Jellinek, Michael. 1976. "Erosion of Patient Trust in Large Medical Centers." *Hastings Center Report* 6(3): 16–19.

Jennings, Bruce. 1993. "Health Policy in a New Key: Setting Democratic Priorities." *Journal of Social Issues* 49(2): 169–184.

Kiesler, Charles A. 1992. "U.S. Mental Health Policy Doomed to Fail." *American Psychologist* 47(9): 1077–1082.

Kessler, R. C.; Berglund, P. A.; Zhao, S.; et al. 1996. "The 12-Month Prevalence and Correlates of Serious Mental Illness." In *Mental Health, United States, 1996,* ed. R. W. Manderscheid and M. A. Sonnenschein. Washington, D.C.: U. S. Government Printing Office.

Klerman, Gerald L.; Olfson, Mark; Leon, Andrew; and Weissman, Myrna. 1992. "Measuring the Need for Mental Health Care." *Health Affairs* 11(3): 23–33.

La Fond, John Q. 1994. "Law and the Delivery of Involuntary Mental Health Services." *American Journal of Orthopsychiatry* 64(2): 209–222.

Lamb, H. Richard, and Bachrach, Leona L. 2001. "Some Perspectives on Deinstitutionalization." *Psychiatric Services* 52: 1039–1045.

Mechanic, David, and Rochefort, David A. 1992. "A Policy of Inclusion for the Mentally Ill." *Health Affairs* 11(1): 128–150.

Morreim, E. H. 1989. "Fiscal Scarcity and the Inevitability of Bedside Budget Balancing." *Archives of Internal Medicine* 149(5): 1012–1015.

Mowbray, Carol T.; Grazier, Kyle L.; and Holter, Mark. 2002. "Managed Behavioral Health Care in the Public Sector: Will It Become the Third Shame of the States?" *Psychiatric Services* 53(2): 157–170.

National Advisory Mental Health Council. 1998. *Parity in Financing Mental Health Services: Managed Care Effects on Cost, Access and Quality: An Interim Report to Congress by the National Advisory Mental Health Council.* Bethesda, MD: Department of Health and Human Services, National Institutes of Health, National Institute of Mental Health.

National Advisory Mental Health Council. 2000. *Insurance Parity for Mental Health: Cost, Access, and Quality: Final Report to Congress* (NIH Publication No. 00–4787). Washington, D.C.: Department of Health and Human Services, National Institute of Health, National Institute of Mental Health.

Perlin, Michael L. 1994. "Law and the Delivery of Mental Health Services in the Community." *American Journal of Orthopsychiatry* 64(2): 194–208.

Phelan, J.; Link, B.; Stueve, A.; and Pescosolido, B. l997. "Public Conceptions of Mental Illness in 1950 in 1996: Has Sophistication Increased? Has Stigma Declined?" Paper presented at the meeting of the American Sociological Association, Toronto, Ontario.

Praeger, Denis J., and Scallet, Leslie J. 1992. "Promoting and Sustaining the Health of the Mind." *Health Affairs* 11(3): 118–124.

Regier, Darrel A.; Narrow, William E.; Rae, Donald S.; et al. 1993. "The De Facto U.S. Mental and Addictive Disorders Service System: Epidemiologic Catchment Area Prospective 1-Year Prevalence Rates of Disorders and Services." *Archives of General Psychiatry* 50(2): 85–94.

Reiser, Stanley Joel; Bursztajn, Harold J.; Appelbaum, Paul S.; and Gutheil, Thomas G. 1987. *Divided Staffs, Divided Selves: A Case Approach to Mental Health Ethics.* New York: Cambridge University Press.

Rice, D. P., and Miller, L. S. 1996. "The Economic Burden of Schizophrenia: Conceptual and Methodological Issues, and Cost Estimates." In *Schizophrenia/Handbook of Mental Health Economics and Health Policy,* vol. 1, ed. Massimo Moscarelli, Agnes Rupp, and Norman Sartoris. Chichester, New York: Wiley.

Rochefort, David A. 1996. "Mental Health Reform and Inclusion of the Mentally Ill: Dilemmas of U.S. Policy-Making." *International Journal of Law and Psychiatry* 19(3–4): 223–237.

Rochefort, David A., ed. 1989. *Handbook on Mental Health Policy in the United States.* New York: Greenwood Press.

Smith, David R. 1994. "Porches, Politics, and Public Health." *American Journal of Public Health* 84(5): 725–726.

U.S. Office of Technology Assessment. 1986. "Children's Mental Health: Problems and Services—A Background Paper." Washington, D.C.: U. S. Government Printing Office.

U.S. President's Commission for the Study of Ethical Problems in Medicine and Biomedical and Behavioral Research. 1983. *Securing Access to Health Care: A Report on the Ethical Implications of Differences in the Availability of Health Services.* Washington, D.C.: U. S. Government Printing Office.

U.S. Surgeon General. 1999. "Mental Health: A Report of the Surgeon General." Rockville, MD: U.S. Department of Health and Human Services, Substance Abuse and Mental Health Services Administration, Center for Mental Health Services, National Institutes of Health, National Institute of Mental Health.

Wakefield, Jerome C. 1992. "The Concept of Mental Disorder: On the Boundary Between Biological Facts and Social Values." *American Psychologist* 47(3): 373–388.

INTERNET RESOURCES

Bureau of the Census. 1996. "Health Insurance Coverage: 1996. Table A. Health Insurance Coverage Status and Type of Coverage." Available from <http://www.census.org>.

Centers for Medicare and Medicaid Services. 1996. "Health Insurance Portability and Accountability Act. Pub. L. No. 104–191, 110 Stat1936." Available from <http://cms.hhs.gov>.

General Accounting Office. 2000. "Document GAO/T–HEHS–00–113: Mental Health Parity Act: Employers; Mental Health Benefits Remain Limited Despite New Federal Standards." Available from <http://www.gao.gov>.

MENTAL HEALTH THERAPIES

• • •

The endless variety of mental health therapies can be sorted out and compared only if it is recognized that they differ both in the ends for which they strive and in the means they employ to reach these ends. Some therapies are directed toward straightforward and concrete goals such as symptom relief. Relaxation training to address performance anxiety is one example. Other therapies are directed toward more complex and abstract goals, such as an increased capacity for intimacy. Psychoanalytic therapy to improve the quality of one's romantic relationships is one example. Psychotherapeutic techniques can be compared and contrasted only if this difference in their goals is appreciated. The goals of therapy are at least partially implicit in the method of therapy employed by the therapist. Because no one therapist is skilled in all types of psychotherapy, choosing a therapist usually means choosing a therapy—a fact that patients choosing a therapist often do not understand.

The Goals of Therapy

This question of who should choose the goals of therapy is a form of the classic dilemma concerning paternalism in medicine, which involves balancing concern for patient welfare with respect for patient autonomy. Sidney Bloch (1982, 1989) has discussed this dilemma as it applies to psychotherapy. Beneficence dictates that therapists do whatever they think is best for their patients. Respect for autonomy means allowing patients the freedom to decide for themselves what is best. Because compromised mental health so often means compromised autonomy, balancing these values in psychotherapy can be particularly difficult. Therapists frequently believe that they should promote the capacity for autonomy in their patients even if the patients want only to feel better. In his 1989 article, Bloch described how he grappled with whether to address only his patient's distressing writer's block, as she preferred, or to explore the forces behind her general loss of autonomy. Her ability to choose rationally between short-term and long-term goals for therapy, such as relief from distress and greater capacity for choice, might itself have been compromised.

Clearly, psychotherapy must be conducted with some idea of mental health as a goal and a value. Thomas Szasz, a practicing psychiatrist who does not believe that mental disorders are diseases or that mental illness compromises personal autonomy, has long accused psychotherapists of inculcating social and ethical values under the guise of scientific medical treatment. If therapists are not restoring their patients' lost capacity for choice, then they can only be brainwashing them to make choices as the therapists would. Because psychotherapy aims for the value-laden goal of mental health, it blurs the boundary between science and ethics more than other medical therapy. It has features that are associated with science, such as theories of causation, experiments, and experts. But psychotherapy also must always contain elements from ethics, because if it is not in part an "ideology of healthy conduct" (Karasu, p.91), it has no direction or goal. Doing psychotherapy is in part providing medical treatment and in part providing ethical education.

Because it is not possible to be perfectly value-neutral, vigilance and restraint concerning the imposition of values upon one's patient are among the foremost duties of the psychotherapist. Dynamically trained therapists are schooled concerning the dangers of *countertransference*, the distortion of the therapeutic process by the therapist's personal preferences and history. There are also dangers beyond the personal level. Each system of therapy operates with a value-laden notion of mental health, toward which it strives. Those therapies directed toward the relief of symptoms, such as depression and anxiety, strive toward distress-free function in a given environment. Normally this presents no particular ethical challenge. But in certain environments, relief of distress may be problematic. For example, Robert Jay Lifton, in his 1985 book, *Home from the War,* discussed the situation of American soldiers in Vietnam who were opposed to the war. The therapist treating patients in such situations faces the ethical question of whether the distress or the situation is pathological and needs changing.

Those therapies that operate with more elaborate models of mental health involving mature ego defenses, character development, or adaptive coping encounter different conflicts. Psychoanalytic thought long conceptualized homosexuality as a distorted or degenerate form of intimacy necessarily associated with character pathology. This evaluation of homosexuality has changed in recent years. But the challenge of distinguishing normal and pathological modes of human relationship will remain for psychodynamic psychotherapy because it defines mental health in terms of character. There are now those arguing that sadomasochistic or pedophilic relationships are not necessarily pathological.

In general, mental health treatment promotes adaptation to one's current social environment. It therefore tends to reinforce the prevailing norms of society. This is true both for *supportive* psychotherapy, which shores up a patient's usual ways of maintaining self-esteem, and for *uncovering* psychotherapy, which challenges these defenses in order to promote more mature modes of managing conflict and disappointment. The Austrian neurologist Sigmund Freud (1856–1939) proposed the capacity "to love and to work" as the mark of mental health. No better succinct summary of functions that indicate mental health has been made since. Nevertheless, the values of capitalist and bourgeois Victorian culture lie implicit in this prescription. Is adaptation to a repressive society indicative of mental health? Feminists have criticized models of love available to women. Marxists have criticized alienated labor as a legitimate lifetime pursuit.

Freud, and nearly all psychotherapists since, treated primarily upper- and middle-class Caucasians. The goals of therapy and the therapeutic means used have been derived within this class context. Public funding for psychotherapy has been and continues to be scant. Psychotherapy is considered by society to be less of a necessity than medical care. Community mental-health centers did do some psychotherapy in the 1960s and 1970s but are now directed toward medication and case management of the chronically mentally ill. It is virtually impossible in most states to obtain psychotherapy without insurance or discretionary income.

Whether psychotherapy can reach beyond its historical boundaries of class and race is not yet clear. It has traditionally addressed an educated, articulate, and motivated group of patients from the same social class and culture as the therapist. Because most psychotherapy is done with individual patients, it addresses individuals as the primary cause of their own problems. This is a valid approach to the denial practiced by middle-class patients concerning their life difficulties but may not be fair to lower-class patients facing poverty and prejudice. Proponents of *radical therapy* have tried to respond to this challenge by pathologizing the victimizing situation instead of the victimized individual. They thus construe the therapist as an agent for social as well as individual change. This approach avoids the problem of the therapist normalizing patients to the status quo. But it maximizes the problem of value imposition by the therapist, who now encourages the patient to reject society's view of the honorable life in favor of one advocated by the therapist. A middle ground has recently been explored through attempts to adapt psychotherapy to indigent patients through the addition of adjunctive social services (Wells et al.).

Mental health therapies not only respond to culture but also shape the culture within which they operate. As the values of mental health therapy have diffused into Western society, they have become a target for criticism. Since Philip Rieff spoke of "the triumph of the therapeutic" in 1966, numerous philosophers and sociologists have joined in criticizing "therapeutic values" that promote the welfare of the individual over that of the community. In 1978 Christopher Lasch accused the psychotherapies of promoting a form of narcissism in Western culture through the promotion of selfish motives and ignoring the broader social interest. In his 1971 book, *Against the Self-Images of the Age,* Alasdair MacIntyre specifically criticized the imposition upon society of such goals as personal satisfaction and interpersonal effectiveness. He contended that ethical evaluation of these goals had been bypassed in deference to the general idea of therapy. Whether the goal of self-gratification has gained preeminence as a result of therapy, or whether therapy has grown as part of a larger trend within society to look toward the individual as the vehicle for fulfillment, is beyond the scope of this entry.

Modes of Therapy

Though there are over 200 psychotherapies and supporting philosophies presently in use by mental health professionals, most of these have not been scientifically tested for effectiveness. Only a few of these therapies can be considered specifically in this entry. Emphasis will be given to recently developed and proven therapies. Although Hans J. Eysenck's claim, from his 1953 book, *Uses and Abuses of Psychology*, that psychotherapy in general offers no better chance for recovery from psychological distress than does spontaneous remission has been repeatedly disproved, it is not clear what aspects of psychotherapeutic technique account for its effectiveness. Responding to the question of whether one form of psychotherapy was better than another, Lester Luborsky and colleagues could only quote the nineteenth-century English writer Lewis Carroll and ask, "Is it true that 'everyone has won and all must have prizes'?" There has been much research since the late 1970s demonstrating therapeutic effects specific to the type of psychotherapy used, but the evidence favoring effects not specific to a particular psychotherapeutic method still predominates.

A number of reasons have been proposed to explain these findings (Beutler and Crago). First, there is strong evidence that a good therapist–patient match is a more powerful predictor of therapy outcome than is treatment method. Second, the measures used to assess efficacy for experimental treatment groups may be insensitive to important differences in outcome between individual patients. Furthermore, the goals sought by different therapies may be so different as to not be adequately captured by a common measure of outcome. Third, differences in the level of psychotherapist experience may have more impact than differences in psychotherapy approach. An attempt has been made to produce therapy manuals for clinical trials that minimize these factors. But these manuals have also come under criticism as retarding the therapist's ability to respond to the individual needs and style of the patient. In summary, it has been difficult to show the advantage of one psychotherapeutic method over another because personal elements of the patient–therapist interaction, not easily tested by current methods, appear to be critical to therapeutic success.

PSYCHODYNAMIC THERAPY. A number of therapies derive their understanding of the patient and the modes of therapeutic action from Freudian psychoanalysis. Almost from the moment that Freud formulated the foundations of psychoanalysis, they were subject to revision by his followers

such as Carl Jung, Alfred Adler, and Karen Horney. Elaborations of psychoanalytic theory in the direction of ego psychology by Anna Freud and Erik Erikson, and in the direction of object-relations theory by Melanie Klein and Donald Winnicott, have been especially influential in contemporary psychodynamic psychotherapy. Nevertheless, there are important similarities among these different approaches. They all consider unconscious forces to be important in psychopathology and insight into these forces to be therapeutic. Contemporary psychodynamic therapies derived from these theories continue to use the therapeutic relationship to reveal unconscious determinants of behavior. However, various features of the treatment are modified, such as its frequency and duration (e.g., through brief dynamic therapy); its metapsychology (e.g., through self-psychology); or its understanding of basic conflicts (e.g., through existential psychotherapy).

In brief dynamic therapy, treatment is more focused, short-term, and directive than in classical psychoanalysis. Whereas the latter may involve four to five sessions per week over a period of years in psychoanalysis, brief dynamic therapy may be completed in as few as ten to twenty weekly sessions. The therapist tries to elucidate a *core-conflictual theme* that is then explored. Typical difficulties in one particular area of life, such as assertiveness on the job, are the focus of treatment. Like psychoanalysis, brief dynamic therapy considers the re-creation of important conflicted relationships in the relationship with the therapist— transference—to be an essential therapeutic tool. Lester Luborsky, David Malan, Habib Davanloo, Hans Strupp, Peter Sifneos, and John Mann have articulated different types of brief dynamic therapy. Its effectiveness has been demonstrated in the treatment of stress and bereavement, late-life depression, and adjustment, affective, and personality disorders (Goldfried, Greenberg, and Marmar).

Brief dynamic therapy is not simply a compressed form of psychoanalysis; it holds unique benefits and risks. Exploration of the patient's psyche is focused but intense. Patients must be well motivated, have a circumscribed problem, and be able to tolerate an unsettling and persistent confrontation of their customary psychological defenses. Therefore, appropriate selection of patients is crucial to the success of this mode of therapy.

Self-psychology, another descendant from psychoanalysis, was developed by Heinz Kohut (1913–1981) as an elaboration of the psychoanalytic concepts of narcissism and the self. Kohut conceived psychopathology in terms of deficits in the self rather than conflicts among unconscious drives. Kohut defined "self" as an independent center of initiative. Self-psychology sees the most fundamental psychological need to be the organization of the individual's psyche into a cohesive configuration, the self. The self must then establish sustaining relationships between itself and its surroundings.

The therapist, through empathic understanding, establishes herself as one of these sustaining relationships for the patient. Once the therapist has been established as a *self-object*, the stage is set for *transmuting internalization*, whereby the self of the patient is gradually able to perform those functions previously provided by the therapist. This occurs through gradual frustration of the patient's need for a perfectly empathic other. The result is the restoration of the self as a center of initiative, compatible with one's ideals and talents and capable of providing a sense of purpose to one's life.

Rather than presenting ethical challenges entirely different from other dynamic therapies, self-psychology highlights the power and peril present in all the transference-based therapies. In order to be effective, the therapist must become a *self-object* for the patient, that is, a source of self-esteem. Thus, the process of developing a cohesive and autonomous self in this therapy will involve periods of intense dependence and vulnerability for the patient.

Existential psychotherapy is heir to the humanist and client-centered approaches that flourished in the 1960s. Existential therapy is a psychodynamic therapy because it is primarily concerned with the interaction of psychological forces within the individual but, compared with psychoanalysis and its near cousins discussed above, "it is based on a radically different view of the specific forces, motives, and fears that interact in the individual" (Yalom, p. 8). Existential dynamics are not developmental in the way that Freudian psychodynamics are. Rather than focusing on how the past is recapitulated in the present, existential therapy focuses upon fundamental intentions or choices that are part of the "future-becoming-present." Irvin D. Yalom has detailed four "ultimate concerns" with which existential therapy deals: death, freedom, isolation, and meaninglessness.

Because existential psychotherapy rests its theory of psychopathology on universal human concerns, it sees a fundamental continuity between the normal and the pathological. Psychological symptoms are seen as a natural part of confronting the dilemmas and paradoxes of human life. This can mean that the patient seeking to *just feel better* or to pass from the pathological to the normal can be at odds with the existential therapist, who considers dread an inescapable part of life. For similar reasons, it has also been difficult to do good empirical research on existential psychotherapy. This form of therapy focuses upon the personal creation of meaning, thus presenting a view of the psyche not especially amenable to causal analysis. Existential and humanistic psychotherapies have generally had more theoretical than practical appeal. They offer a rich image of the psyche, devoid of reductionistic formulas, but have not found wide pragmatic application in reducing the distress of individual patients.

COGNITIVE-BEHAVIORAL THERAPY. Since the 1970s, a "cognitive revolution" has largely overtaken behaviorism in psychology. In psychotherapy, this revolution emerged in the form of cognitive–behavioral therapy. While behaviorism treated the mind as a black box upon which the powers of environmental reinforcement act, cognitivism holds that interpretations by the individual determine what constitutes positive or negative reinforcement in a given situation. Controlled clinical trials have demonstrated the efficacy of cognitive therapy for depression, chronic pain, anxiety, and a variety of other disorders. In cases of mild to moderate severity, its efficacy is similar to that of antidepressant medication, and it may provide a lower rate of relapse in such conditions as panic disorder (Beck, Emery, and Greenberg).

Cognitive–behavioral therapy essentially consists of training in problem solving. Cognitive therapy is based on the assumption that distress originates from ineffective responses to difficult life circumstances. Mediating between life events and emotions, and driving these responses, are spontaneous interpretations or *automatic thoughts* that are subject to a variety of common distortions. Therapy targets these cognitive distortions, such as overgeneralization and arbitrary inference, by helping the patient make a scientific "turn to the evidence" for these thoughts. Cognitive–behavioral therapy usually includes "homework" for the patient both of a cognitive (e.g., recording automatic thoughts) and a behavioral (e.g., completing small mastery-enhancing tasks) nature. The natural focus of cognitive therapy is upon the present situation and interpretations, though it is possible to plumb ever deeper into the personal assumptions and habits that lie behind current automatic thoughts. Because of this focus on the here and now, cognitive–behavioral therapy tends to be much more simple and straightforward than the psychodynamic therapies described above. Cognitive-behavioral therapy is focused on the amelioration of the current episode of depression or anxiety, whereas psychodynamic therapies also strive to address those factors that make a patient predisposed to episodes of depression and anxiety.

Cognitive therapy portrays mental health in terms of an absence of distorting cognitions. This lends a value-free, scientific air to this psychotherapy that may, however, not be entirely accurate. A body of research exists that suggests depressed persons' perceptions and judgments (especially of interpersonal situations) are quite accurate and realistic, whereas nondepressed persons show systematic optimistic biases and distortions (Taylor and Brown). If cognitive therapists are not bringing their patients back into the light of interpersonal truth, then the therapy can take on the flavor of "brainwashing for better social functioning." As discussed above, there is a tendency among all forms of psychotherapy to adapt patients to their current social milieu.

NONTRADITIONAL THERAPIES. A vast array of practices are marketed to improve well-being. Many are scientifically unproven, and some violate ethical precepts held dear by the more traditional psychotherapies. Massage therapy, Rolfing, bioenergetics, and a host of other techniques use physical methods, including the touching of the patient by the therapist, to relieve psychological as well as physical problems. These therapies function as psychotherapies insofar as they associate the release of muscle tension with the release of emotional tension. One of Freud's disciples, Wilhelm Reich (1897–1957), pioneered the idea of character armor as muscle tension and the incorporation of massage into psychotherapy.

Other therapies use techniques derived from Eastern religions to increase well-being. Meditation and guided imagery, for example, have become standard techniques at stress-management clinics. In the medical setting, they are stripped of their metaphysical elements and presented as secular relaxation training. This training varies in sophistication from deep-breathing exercises to Buddhist mindfulness meditation. The rationales offered for these therapies similarly vary from physiological calming to appreciation of the fundamental emptiness and interdependence of all events. There is mounting evidence of the effectiveness of this kind of treatment for stress-related physical disorders such as headaches or back pain. Certain sectors of society, however, remain suspicious of the religious roots of these treatments. These nontraditional therapies challenge people's sense of the proper boundary between psychotherapy and sexual gratification, on the one hand, and between psychotherapy and religious practices, on the other.

Ethical Issues in the Psychotherapies

Developing a method by which to choose the appropriate psychotherapy is a problem that has only recently received serious attention. Traditionally, the therapy received was determined by the therapist one selected. The appropriateness of the therapy was judged by the intuition of therapist and patient. The attempt to derive a *differential therapeutics* in psychotherapy, comparable with that found in other areas of medicine, is in its infancy. All patients with similar levels of depression do not need the same type or duration of therapy. In psychotherapy, unlike in physical medicine, diagnosis alone is inadequate to select appropriate psychotherapy. For example, more than a diagnosis of major depressive episode must be known about the patient, such as the person's individual history and personality. Researchers are working to specify the "intermediate-level psychological determinants of problems that mediate between diagnostic grouping and type of intervention" (Goldfried, Greenberg, and Marmar, p. 685).

The importance of factors other than technique to psychotherapy outcome has led some to stress the centrality of the therapeutic alliance in the treatment process. Section 1 of the psychiatric annotations to the first edition of the American Psychiatric Association's (APA) *Principles of Medical Ethics* (1973) states, "The doctor–patient relationship is such a vital factor in effective treatment of the patient that the preservation of optimal conditions for development of a sound working relationship should take precedence over all considerations" (p. 1060). Within this relationship, the greatest challenge for the therapist is the appropriate use of power. The *transference relationship* detailed above gives the therapist tremendous influence over the patient's life, which must be balanced by a viable *therapeutic partnership* (Karasu).

Informed consent for psychotherapy has been proposed as one way to address these concerns. In medical practice, informed consent usually means a discussion between patient and doctor about the risks and benefits of an invasive treatment prior to its initiation. The application of informed consent, even in this regard, has lagged in the area of psychotherapy. Informed consent is often thought unnecessary or implicit for something as low-tech as psychotherapy. But Peter S. Jensen and colleagues argued in 1989 that "informed consent is more than just an ethical or legal obligation: inherent in the process of informed consent is the potential for the enhancement of clinical work" (p. 379). That is, informed consent offers an opportunity to establish the treatment alliance on solid ground. Frank discussion of both the limitations and the benefits of therapy diminishes the illusion of therapist omniscience and patient helplessness so commonly present at the initiation of therapy.

Boundaries of Therapy

Psychotherapy has been criticized as *the purchase of friendship*. Because both friendships and therapeutic relationships are ideally honest, intimate, and supportive, the question of their difference is a natural one. The crucial difference is mutuality or reciprocity: friends serve each other's needs. A therapist is paid to serve the patient's needs. The therapist uses professional expertise to fashion a relationship with his patient that addresses and corrects the patient's psychopathology. The patient is not obligated to entertain, fascinate, or gratify the therapist; responsibilities are limited to regular attendance and payment for sessions. The theory is that a patient concerned with his therapist's well-being cannot give adequate priority to his own recovery.

In practice, this boundary between therapist and friend is more fuzzy. Therapists must find their patients worthy of interest and concern if therapy is to succeed. It is difficult for therapists to develop deep concern for their patients and yet to not need their approval or companionship. Most therapies proscribe social contact between therapist and patient in order to better define the therapist's role and task. Some therapies, such as those that offer *re-parenting,* specifically promote social therapist–patient contacts outside of sessions. Though some find this expansion of the power of the therapeutic relationship helpful, most would consider the lack of clear boundaries dangerous.

The most egregious violation of boundaries in psychotherapy is sexual contact between therapist and patient. Approximately 5 percent of psychiatrists and psychologists admit having sexual contact with their patients (Lakin). Given the intensely intimate atmosphere of therapy, such temptations are understandable. Nevertheless, sexual contact with a psychotherapy patient is considered the worst possible exploitation of the transference relationship. This is because therapists who become involved sexually with a patient are exploiting the trust established for therapeutic purposes for their own sexual gratification. The APA prohibits all sexual contact with current and former patients.

While there is general agreement that sexual gratification of the therapist is always a sign of exploitation and to be avoided, how this avoidance is accomplished is subject to considerable variation. Psychoanalysts allow free expression of all sexual fantasies concerning the therapist but prohibit all touching. Massage therapists and others who do body work rely upon the emotional release prompted by touch but avoid all sexual conversation.

Confidentiality has traditionally been one of the most important ways in which the boundaries of therapy are respected. Frank and open discussion of the patient's deepest hopes and fears is essential to psychodynamic therapy and would be inhibited by the possibility of public disclosure by the therapist. The stigma associated with psychotherapeutic treatment means that disclosure to employers, colleagues, or neighbors can produce actual damage to the patient's social well-being.

Since the 1976 *Tarasoff v. Regents of the University of California* case, which mandated that psychotherapists warn identifiable potential victims of violence, patients' rights to therapist confidentiality have been limited when "disclosure is necessary to avert danger to others." Justice Matthew A. Tobriner's comment in this case, "The protective privilege ends where public peril begins," means that therapists weighing disclosure must consider the public good as well as the good of their patients. Psychotherapy cannot exist in a legal and moral vacuum within society. The *Tarasoff* decision has at times, however, been used to expand the therapist's social responsibility for potentially dangerous patients. This responsibility can include not only warning potential victims of patient violence, on the basis of uncertain evidence, but also testifying against one's patients in court and providing preventive detention in psychiatric units for those considered potentially violent.

Mental Health in the Medical Model

Dynamic psychiatry, which emphasized the role of psychological processes and reactions, dominated mental healthcare for three-fourths of the twentieth century. This psychiatry had blurred the line between normal and pathological psychological processes, claiming that unconscious forces operated in both. Dynamic psychiatry focused on case formulation, a highly individualized, semibiographical account of the important events, relationships, and unconscious forces in a patient's life. Though these formulations could be formulaic or reductive (e.g., jokes about "head shrinking"), their intention was to bring out the unique situation of the individual.

In 1980 the 3rd edition of the APA's *Diagnostic and Statistical Manual of Mental Disorders* (*DSM-III*) appeared, signaling the beginning of a new hegemony for diagnostic psychiatry. Diagnostic psychiatry, in contrast with dynamic psychiatry, sought to find the ways that patients were fundamentally similar to each other. It emulated the central role that diagnosis played in the rest of medicine. While the state of psychiatric science precluded a classification of diseases based on etiology (causes) and tissue pathology, psychiatric diagnosticians were able to provide categories of symptoms called mental disorders that were linked with prognosis, family history, and treatment implications. These categories allowed researchers to reliably document the prevalence of specific disorders, to determine the efficacy of treatments in groups of similar patients, and to explore patterns of inheritance for these disorders.

The overall effect of these changes was to bring psychiatry in much closer alignment with the prevailing medical model. Public mental health shifted away from community-focused efforts to improve overall mental health and toward preventing and treating specific disorders in individuals. Psychiatric research became tightly linked with specific disorders and much more concerned with the biological causes of these disorders. Aided by improvements in psychopharmacology, the emphasis in treatment also shifted from psychosocial to biological treatments. There are ethical implications of the focus on psychiatric diagnosis as well as ethical concerns about the use of psychopharmacology, and these issues are discussed next.

DSM-III, and its descendants, *DSM-III-R* (1987) and *DSM-IV* (1994), are designed to be symptom-based classifications that do not attempt to determine the causes of the disorders described. Some vestiges of causation remain (e.g., in the adjustment disorders, post-traumatic stress disorder, and the bereavement exclusion for major depression), but they are few. Clinicians used to distinguish between reactive (i.e., externally caused) and endogenous (i.e., internally caused) depressions, but this has fallen out of favor because of a lack of biological treatment implications. Psychiatric diagnosis simply looks at the symptoms displayed by the individual to determine if psychopathology is present. By suspending consideration of causation, psychiatric diagnosis removes the patient from her life. The diagnostic system has no way of encoding whether the symptoms constitute a *reasonable* or *unreasonable* response to the stresses of daily life (Horwitz). Clinicians must still make these determinations (e.g., is the top priority for treatment this woman's depression or her abusive husband?). But the diagnostic system offers little assistance in these essential and difficult determinations. Some have argued that deciding whether the person or the situation is *crazy* is the central ethical dilemma of psychiatric practice. It is claimed that this issue was behind the abuse of psychiatry for political purposes that occurred in the Soviet Union (Fulford, Smirnov, and Snow).

Diagnostic psychiatry has been widely criticized, generally by proponents of dynamic psychiatry, for minimizing the role of psychological processes in mental disorders. But a more serious flaw may be its omission of social factors in these disorders. A purely symptom-based diagnostic system necessarily omits consideration of the social context within which the symptoms arise. This decontextualization of mental disorders makes them appear to be problems of individuals rather than problems of society. Research and treatment becomes focused within individuals and their brains rather than where and how the individuals live. Psychiatric diagnosticians may counter that it is difficult to change the social context through clinical interventions. This is certainly true, but it is not an adequate excuse for a psychiatry that places all responsibility for misery that is manifested as mental disorders within the individual. Some psychiatrists have begun to argue against the claim that psychiatric diagnosis is neutral, objective, and disinterested. They have urged a move to a postmodern focus that emphasizes social and cultural contexts, recognizes the values implicit in definitions of mental health, and works to minimize medical control of coercive interventions (Bracken and Thomas).

Managed Mental Healthcare

Mental health services have never been distributed according to any systematic assessment of population need. Cultural and financial barriers have meant that upper-class patients have greater access to mental health services even though the distress of patients in lower classes may be more severe and disabling. Psychiatrists have historically gravitated toward patients interested in their services, so mental healthcare is among the most geographically and socioeconomically maldistributed of all medical specialties.

Some aspects of this mental health service maldistribution have been changing. Beginning in the 1970s, there was tremendous growth in the number of nonmedical psychotherapists and in clients seeking their services. Following the introduction of Prozac in 1987, there has been great expansion in the prescription of antidepressant medications, especially in primary-care medical settings (Olfson et al.). In the last years of the twentieth century, mental healthcare thus became generally more available to middle-class Americans. During this same period, overall medical costs for society were rising rapidly. In the 1990s, managed care arose as a method to contain these costs. Though mental healthcare comprised only a small percentage of these costs, insurers saw mental healthcare as discretionary and subject to no natural limits. Managed care therefore imposed strict limits on mental healthcare, especially on the number of psychotherapy visits and the number of inpatient psychiatric days. The overall result of these trends is that more people have access to more limited mental healthcare.

Managed care has reduced the average number of psychotherapy visits per patient and increased the proportion of patients who receive medication rather than psychotherapy. This has increased the number of patients who can receive mental health services, but it has left many practitioners feeling that they can no longer deliver adequate services to anyone whose care is covered by medical insurance. Rather than accept the limits imposed by managed care, many of the most skilled psychiatrists and psychologists have simply opted out of the medical insurance system. This is because therapists have traditionally understood that their duties involved providing good care to individual patients. Therapists are primarily concerned with the patient in their office, not with all the potential patients in the community. What responsibility society and individual therapists have for the mental health of the general community has been neither decided nor seriously debated.

Body, Mind, and Spirit in Psychiatry

Managed care has sharpened the tension between a dynamic psychiatry of the mind and a diagnostic psychiatry of the brain, but it did not create this tension. Its roots lie deep in the difference between the humanities and the natural sciences. Simply put, the former emphasizes a personal, first-person, and subjective perspective on the human situation. The latter emphasizes an impersonal, third-person, and objective perspective on the human situation. The battle for supremacy or synthesis of these perspectives is currently being waged within psychiatry. Anthropologist Tanya Luhrmann summarized this battle in her 2000 book, *Of Two Minds: The Growing Disorder in American Psychiatry,* which takes up a conflict over the nature of competent and compassionate practice in psychiatry. The battle achieved prominence in a lawsuit over the psychodynamic versus psychopharmacologic treatment of severe depression in a physician (Klerman; Stone). Many clinical issues are included in this battle. Perhaps the most central is the relative priority accorded to self-understanding versus symptom relief. Psychodynamic psychiatrists are trained that sometimes symptom relief must wait to allow self-understanding to occur. Psychopharmacologists believe that it is most important to provide relief to the suffering patient and that self-understanding can come later.

This is also a battle about the relation between disease and self in psychiatry, about the nature of empathy and compassion for those with psychiatric disorders, and even about the nature of humanity. Families of patients with serious mental illnesses, such as schizophrenia, are strong advocates of the disease model in psychiatry through organizations such as the National Alliance for the Mentally Ill. They have been successful at raising money for research and clinical care for mental illnesses seen as brain diseases. They see the disease model as the best way to fight the stigma of mental illness that has held back progress in clinical care. This model also takes the focus off the family environment as a cause for mental illness.

Some patients with mental illness, however, take strong exception to the disease model. As one patient with schizophrenia was quoted, "Can you imagine how insulting it would be if you turned to me and said, 'I'm sorry you have a diseased brain.'? When it gets right down to it, the medical model is an insult to me. To say I have a diseased brain does not validate me. I have a complicated thought system, with different behaviors" (Luhrmann, p. 267). This patient does not accept the sharp distinction between his disease and himself. Schizophrenia is too much of who he is. If psychiatry cannot offer him a cure of his disease, why should he accept that he is damaged rather than just different?

Indeed, it has always been difficult to separate disease and self in psychiatry. So many psychiatric symptoms seem like willful misbehavior or self-inflicted suffering, that observers are inclined to make a moral judgment rather than a medical diagnosis. Severe mental illnesses distort a person's intentions as well as the person's behavior, so it is difficult to see the person as distinct from the disease. Diagnostic psychiatry minimizes the role of intentions in misbehavior, explaining that the disease rather than the person is speaking. Psychodynamic psychiatry leaves this misbehavior partially in the realm of intentions by attributing it to unconscious forces. Thus diagnostic psychiatry sees the pain of mental illness as arising outside the self, whereas psychodynamic psychiatry sees it as arising from within the self.

These differences are important because they shape people's attitudes toward some of the most severe forms of human suffering. How people approach the pain of others strongly determines the nature of the human community. That is why mental health therapies have ethical implications beyond the medical setting.

MARK D. SULLIVAN (1995)
REVISED BY AUTHOR

SEE ALSO: *Autonomy; Behavior Control; Behaviorism; Behavior Modification Therapies; Children: Mental Health Issues; Coercion; Confidentiality; Divided Loyalties in Mental Healthcare; Freedom and Free Will; Informed Consent; Institutionalization and Deinstitutionalization; Mental Health, Meaning of Mental Health; Mental Health Services; Mentally Disabled and Mentally Ill Persons; Patients' Rights: Mental Patients' Rights; Psychoanalysis and Dynamic Therapies; Psychopharmacology; Sexual Ethics and Professional Standards*

BIBLIOGRAPHY

American Psychiatric Association (APA). 1973. "The Principles of Medical Ethics with Annotations Especially Applicable to Psychiatry." *American Journal of Psychiatry* 130: 1056–1064.

American Psychiatric Association (APA). 1994. *The Diagnostic and Statistical Manual of Mental Disorders: DSM-IV,* 4th edition. Washington, D.C.: Author.

Beck, Aaron T.; Emery, Gary; and Greenberg, Ruth L. 1985. *Anxiety Disorders and Phobias: A Cognitive Perspective.* New York: Basic.

Beutler, Larry E., and Crago, Marjorie. 1987. "Strategies and Techniques of Prescriptive Psychotherapeutic Intervention."

Psychiatry Update: American Psychiatric Association Annual Review 6: 378–397.

Bloch, Sidney. 1982. *What Is Psychotherapy?* Oxford: Oxford University Press.

Bloch, Sidney. 1989. "The Student with a Writing Block: The Ethics of Psychotherapy." *Journal of Medical Ethics* 15(3): 153–158.

Bracken, Patrick, and Thomas, Philip. 2001. "Postpsychiatry: A New Direction for Mental Health." *British Medical Journal* 322(7288): 724–727.

Elkin, Irene; Shea, M. Tracie; Watkins, John T.; et al. 1989. "National Institute of Mental Health Treatment of Depression Collaborative Research Program: General Effectiveness of Treatments." *Archives of General Psychiatry* 46(11): 971–982.

Eysenck, Hans J. 1953. *Uses and Abuses of Psychology.* London: Penguin.

Fulford, K. W.; Smirnov, A. Y.; and Snow, E. 1993. "Concepts of Disease and the Abuse of Psychiatry in the USSR." *British Journal of Psychiatry* 162(6): 801–810.

Gabbard, G.O. 2002. "Post-Termination Sexual Boundary Violations." *Psychiatr Clin North Am* 25(3): 593–603.

Goldfried, Marvin R.; Greenberg, Leslie S.; and Marmar, Charles. 1990. "Individual Psychotherapy: Process and Outcome." *Annual Review of Psychology* 41: 659–688.

Horwitz, Allan V. 2002. *Creating Mental Illness.* Chicago: University of Chicago Press.

Jensen, Peter S.; Josephson, Allan M.; and Frey, Joseph. 1989. "Informed Consent as a Framework for Treatment: Ethical and Therapeutic Considerations." *American Journal of Psychotherapy* 43(3): 378–386.

Karasu, Toksoz. 1981. "Ethical Aspects of Psychotherapy." In *Psychiatric Ethics,* ed. Sidney Bloch and Paul Chodoff. Oxford: Oxford University Press.

Klerman, Gerald L. 1990. "The Psychiatric Patient's Right to Effective Treatment: Implications of *Osheroff v. Chestnut Lodge.*" *American Journal of Psychiatry* 147(4): 409–418.

Kohut, Heinz. 1971. *The Analysis of the Self: A Systematic Approach to the Psychoanalytic Treatment of Narcissistic Personality Disorders.* New York: International Universities Press.

Lakin, Martin. 1988. *Ethical Issues in the Psychotherapies.* Oxford: Oxford University Press.

Lasch, Christopher. 1978. *The Culture of Narcissism: American Life in an Age of Diminishing Expectations.* New York: Norton.

Lifton, Robert Jay. 1985. *Home from the War: Vietnam Veterans, neither Victims nor Executioners.* New York: Basic.

Luborsky, Lester; Singer, Barbara; and Luborsky, Louise. 1975. "Comparative Studies of Psychotherapies: Is It True That 'Everyone Has Won and All Must Have Prizes'?" *Archives of General Psychiatry* 32(8): 995–1008.

Luhrmann, Tanya. 2000. *Of Two Minds: The Growing Disorder in American Psychiatry.* New York: Knopf.

MacIntyre, Alasdair C. 1971. *Against the Self-Images of the Age: Essays on Ideology and Philosophy.* New York: Schocken.

Olfson, Mark; Marcus, Steven C.; Druss, Benjamin; et al. 2002. "National Trends in the Outpatient Treatment of Depression." *Journal of the American Medical Association* 287(2): 203–209.

Rapp, Morton S. 1984. "Ethics in Behaviour Therapy: Historical Aspects and Current Status." *Canadian Journal of Psychiatry* 29(7): 547–550.

Rieff, Philip. 1966. *The Triumph of the Therapeutic: Uses of Faith after Freud.* Chicago: University of Chicago Press.

Stone, Alan A. 1990. "Law, Science, and Psychiatric Malpractice: A Response to Klerman's Indictment of Psychoanalytic Psychiatry." *American Journal of Psychiatry* 147(4): 419–427.

Szasz, Thomas. 1989. "Psychiatric Justice." *British Journal of Psychiatry* 154(6): 864–869.

Tarasoff v. Regents of the University of California. 17 Cal. 3d 425, 551 P.2d 334, 131 Cal. Rptr. 14 (1976).

Taylor, Shelley E., and Brown, Jonathan D. 1988. "Illusion and Well-Being: A Social Psychological Perspective on Mental Health." *Psychological Bulletin* 103(2): 193–210.

Wells, Kenneth B.; Miranda, Jeanne; Bauer, Mark S.; et al. 2002. "Overcoming Barriers to Reducing the Burden of Affective Disorders." *Biological Psychiatry* 52(6): 655–675.

Yalom, Irvin D. 1980. *Existential Psychotherapy.* New York: Basic.

MENTAL ILLNESS

• • •

I. Definition, Use and Meaning

II. Cultural Perspectives

III. Issues in Diagnosis

I. DEFINITION, USE AND MEANING

The concept of mental illness, including its lay counterparts such as madness and insanity, has been subject to widely different interpretations since classical times and between different cultures (Robinson). Models of mental disorder, as they are now called, continue to be hotly contested between different stakeholder groups in mental health right up to the present day (Fulford et al., 2003). Running through these differences and disputes, as outlined later in this entry, is a tension between what may be called moral and scientific models. Mental illness, understood in terms of this tension, is poised between the everyday moral world of free agency, subjectivity and reasons, and a scientific world of determinism, objectivity and causal laws.

How the tension between moral and medical models of mental illness is resolved in a period of unprecedented advances in the neurosciences—in behavioral genetics, in functional brain imaging, and in psychopharmacology—is critical to a range of ethical issues in psychiatry: the insanity defense (Robinson), ethical aspects of diagnosis (Dickenson and Fulford, ch. 4), the nature of autonomy in psychiatry and psychotherapy (Hinshelwood, 1995, 1997), the boundary between medical psychiatric treatment and social control (Bloch and Reddaway; Fulford, Smirnoff and Snow), the growing role of users (or consumers) in the design and delivery of services (Department of Health), and not least, the fight against prejudice and discrimination, that brand of internal racism (Fulford and Radden) to which all those concerned with mental health, whether as users or as providers of services, remain subject.

This entry explores the meaning of the concept of mental illness, not directly, by way of a critique of the very large number of competing definitions available in the literature, but indirectly, by way of the use made of the concept in practice. This approach —examining the use of concepts as a guide to their meanings—is exemplified by the work of the English philosopher J. L. Austin (1911–1960) and others working mainly in Oxford in the middle years of the twentieth century (Warnock, 1923–1995). The approach, called linguistic analysis or ordinary language philosophy, although relatively neglected by subsequent generations of philosophers (Williams, 1929–2003), and certainly very far from being a philosophical panacea (Fann), provides a conduit or bridge between philosophical theory and medical practice (Fulford 1989, 1990, 2001). In psychiatry, linguistic analysis offers a number of helpful insights into: (1) the nature of the problem presented by the concept of mental illness; (2) the methods available for tackling the problem; and (3) the outcomes that can be expected in tackling problems of this kind.

The Problem: Many Definitions

Difficulties in the use of the concept of mental illness have traditionally been assumed to reflect difficulties of definition. This assumption, of a genetic link between difficulties of use and difficulties of definition, was not unreasonable given the successes of psychiatry in the second half of the twentieth century in improving the reliability of its diagnostic categories by clarifying the definitions of many of its key diagnostic terms: The US-UK Diagnostic Project (Cooper et al.), for example, and the International Pilot Study of Schizophrenia (World Health Organization, 1973), showed that difficulties in the use of the concept of schizophrenia were indeed due to difficulties of definition (discrepant rates

of diagnosis turned out to reflect discrepant definitions). There are, furthermore, as this entry shall explore, many examples of continuing difficulties both in the use of the concept of mental illness and in its definition. These examples, however, understood linguistic analytically, point, not to the traditional assumption of a genetic link between use and definition, but rather to the need for a reformulation of the problem as one of difficulty in the use of the concept of mental illness *rather than* a difficulty of definition.

CASE EXAMPLE: SIMON. Simon, a forty-year-old African-American lawyer, was threatened with a malpractice action, which he believed to be racially motivated, by a group of colleagues. Although he had never been a particularly religious man, he responded to this situation by setting up a makeshift altar in his front room and praying all night. In the morning he found that wax had run down from a candle on to his bible, marking out certain words and phrases. This is how he described his experience: "I got up and I saw the seal (wax mark) that was in my father's bible and I called (my friend) and I said, you know, something remarkable is going on over here. I think the beauty of it was the specificity by which the sun burned through. It was … in my mind, a clever play on words." Simon continued to have similar experiences for eighteen months. His *seals* meant nothing to anyone else. But for Simon they were direct communications from God, showing that he was "…the living son of David…and captain of the guard of Israel."

TWO CLASSIFICATIONS, TWO DEFINITIONS, TWO DIAGNOSES. Simon's story, which is based on a real person's experiences, comes from a study of the differences between delusion and spiritual experience carried out by a British psychologist Mike Jackson, at the time working as a doctoral student with Gordon Claridge at Magdalen College, Oxford (Jackson, 1997; Jackson and Fulford). The study included blind ratings using one of the first carefully standardized instruments for assessing a person's mental state, the Present State Examination (PSE). Developed by John Wing, John Cooper and Norman Sartorius at the Institute of Psychiatry in London, the PSE includes a glossary of carefully crafted definitions that, together with a standardized interview schedule, allow the identification of over one hundred symptoms and signs of mental disorder with high degrees of reliability (Wing, Cooper, and Sartorius). PSE ratings of Simon's story identified his experience as a delusional perception, a form of primary delusion. The PSE defines this as a delusion which is "based upon sensory experiences (delusional perceptions) in which a patient suddenly becomes convinced that a particular set of events has a special meaning" (Wing, Cooper and Sartorius, p. 172–173).

What then does this delusional perception mean diagnostically? There are currently two major classifications of psychiatric disorders, chapter V of the tenth edition of the *International Classification of Diseases* (ICD-10), produced by the World Health Organization under the direction of Norman Sartorius (World Health Organization (WHO), 1992), and the fourth edition of the *Diagnostic and Statistical Manual* (DSM-IV),, produced by a taskforce of the American Psychiatric Association (APA) chaired by Allen Frances (APA, 1994).

The ICD-10 and the DSM-IV classifications are in many respects similar. In particular both are descriptive in orientation. That is to say, both seek to define mental disorders as far as possible descriptively, by reference to the presence of specific symptoms, like delusional perception, of known reliability. Yet ICD-10 and DSM-IV suggest radically different diagnoses in Simon's case. In ICD-10 delusional perception (as defined in the PSE) is one of a number of symptoms that, if present, are sufficient for a diagnosis of schizophrenia (or of some other psychotic illness—affective, organic, or other—depending on associated features). According to ICD-10, then, Simon had schizophrenia (or some related psychotic disorder). DSM-IV, by contrast, requires for a diagnosis of schizophrenia, not only one or more of the relevant symptoms (summed up in its Criterion A), but also deterioration in social and/or occupational functioning (Criterion B of "social/occupational dysfunction," p. 285). And inquiry about Simon's social and/or occupational functioning, reveals that, far from deteriorating, as required by Criterion B, it actually *improved!* He was empowered and guided by his experiences, idiosyncratic as they were; he won his court case; and his career consequently went from strength to strength. By the lights of ICD-10, then, Simon had a psychotic illness (albeit one with, in this instance, a benign course); but by the lights of DSM-IV, he had a positive (albeit idiosyncratic) spiritual experience.

MANY DEFINITIONS OF MENTAL ILLNESS. On first inspection, it is somewhat disconcerting, at least from psychiatry's point of view, to find that its two major classifications, although closely similar in their scientific orientations, should yield radically different ways of understanding Simon's story. This is the more surprising given that those responsible for the two classifications worked hard to make them compatible. Simon's case, furthermore, is not marginal in these classifications: Karl Jaspers, the founder of modern descriptive psychopathology, placed delusion among the central symptoms of mental disorder (Jaspers, 1913a); and the case for a medical model of mental disorder is regarded by many as being strongest for the psychoses. It was for this reason that Thomas Szasz, notorious for the slogan *mental illness is a myth* (Szasz, 1960), called schizophrenia, in the title of a later paper, the "sacred symbol of psychiatry" (Szasz, 1976).

Disconcerting, though, as this incompatibility between ICD and DSM may be, viewed in its historical context it is but a manifestation of the long-running tension between medical and moral understandings of madness. As noted at the start of this entry, this tension runs across many cultures and back at least as far as classical Greece (Robinson). In the early-twentieth century, the tension surfaced in Jaspers's insistence on the need for both causal (medical) and meaningful (moral) accounts of psychopathology (Jaspers, 1913b). Psychiatry, for much of the twentieth century, ran mainly with the causal side of Jaspers's psychopathology. But the tension continued to be evident in the conflicting scientific and hermeneutic interpretations of psychoanalysis (Ricoeur), in the rediscovery of meanings by psychology, and of causes by phenomenology, in the second half of the twentieth century (Fulford et al., 2003), and, perhaps most transparently of all, in the so-called debate about mental illness in the 1960s and 1970s (Siegler and Osmond; Caplan et al). In this debate the medical (causal-disease) model of mental disorder was directly opposed by a variety of non-medical models— for example, psychological (Eysenck), social role theory (Scheff), labeling theory (Rosenhan), political (Foucault), existential (Laing) and moral (Szasz 1960, 1987). Each of these alternatives to the medical model sought to shift our understanding of mental disorder away from the causal-disease framework of medicine towards frameworks in which, to varying degrees and in different ways, agency and subjectivity are retained. Szasz's model is among the most overtly moral in the sense that he takes mental disorders to be problems of living, defined by psychosocial, ethical, and legal norms, to which we should respond, not passively, by seeking treatment, but actively, by taking responsibility for them.

It has been rightly pointed out, in respect of this debate, that the term medical model in fact covers a number of rather different models (Macklin); and that psychiatry, in particular among medical disciplines, aspires to a balanced biopsychosocial approach in which different models represent no more than perspectives on (McHugh and Slaveney) or levels of (Tyrer and Steinberg) the subject. Modern psychiatric textbooks all emphasize the importance of considering social and psychological aspects of mental disorder alongside the biological. Anecdotal reports, nonetheless, from people who actually use services (Campbell), taken together with both surveys (Rogers, Pilgrim and Lacey), and empirical social science research (Colombo et al.), all suggest that, in practice, mental health professionals, whatever their theoretical commitment to a broad biopsychosocial model, tend in practice still to be guided by very different implicit models in their approach to their work.

MANY DEFINITIONS OF BODILY ILLNESS. The range and diversity of competing models of mental illness has been subject to different interpretations, none particularly flattering to psychiatry (Phillips). At best, psychiatry is taken to be scientifically primitive (Boorse, 1976), our use of models being assumed to be a temporary expedient reflecting the "limited information" about mental illness currently available (Tyrer and Steinberg, p. 2). Linguistic analysis, by contrast, offers a positive rather than negative interpretation, an interpretation in which the different models represent different aspects of the meaning of mental illness with complementary, rather than competing, roles in clinical work and research. This positive interpretation will be discussed further in the section on Outcomes. But a first linguistic analytic step towards it is to see that, so far as definition is concerned, one is *no more able to define bodily illness than mental illness.*

From the perspective of those wedded to a genetic link between transparency of definition and ease of use, this may seem to be a somewhat surprising claim. For the concept of bodily illness, after all, if not wholly unproblematic in use, is at least considerably less so than that of mental illness: In contrast with even the central cases of mental illness, such as schizophrenia, there is no dispute about whether heart attacks or appendicitis, for example, as central cases of bodily illness, are diseases.

That bodily illness, nonetheless, is no easier to define than mental illness, is shown by three considerations:

1. There is an on-going debate about the meaning of bodily illness, less high profile, certainly, than the debate about the meaning of mental illness, but, if anything, growing in volume and intensity rather than moving towards resolution. As recently as 2002, Richard Smith, the editor of a leading medical journal in the United Kingdom, the British Medical Journal, reignited the debate about the meaning of bodily illness by asking where we should draw the boundary of disease (Smith).

2. The derivations of some of the most contested positions on the meaning of mental illness stand in direct line of descent from equivalent positions on the meaning of bodily illness. Thus current attempts to define mental illness employing criteria derived from evolutionary biology (e.g., Neander, Wakefield) are derivative, through the work of the American philosopher Christopher Boorse (1975, 1976, 1997), on an earlier debate, which started in respiratory medicine, about the definition of bodily illness (e.g., Scadding).

3. Much of the debate about mental illness, although indeed ostensibly a debate about the meaning of mental illness, actually turns on differences of view about the meaning of *bodily* illness. The critical difference between Thomas Szasz (1960), for example, and his British opponent, the psychiatrist R. E. Kendell, the difference that led to their respective moral and medical interpretations of mental illness, was a difference in their understandings of the meaning not of mental illness but of bodily illness: Szasz took genuine illnesses as instantiated by a series of examples of bodily illness to be defined by anatomical and physical norms, which, being absent in putative mental illnesses, made mental illness a myth; Kendell took genuine illnesses as instantiated by (many of the same) examples of bodily illness to be defined by evolutionary norms of reduced life/reproductive expectations, which, being satisfied by (many) putative mental illnesses made mental illness no different in principle from bodily illness (see Fulford, 1989, ch. 1). Similar differences about the meaning of bodily disorder continue to drive current debates about the meaning of mental disorder (Fulford, 2000).

These three points about the concept of bodily illness have been spelled out at some length because they are the lynch pin of the linguistic analytic reformulation of the problem of mental illness. It is a matter of observation that the concept of mental illness is more problematic in *use* than that of bodily illness. But since bodily illness turns out to be no more transparent to *definition* than mental illness, the difficulties associated with the use of mental illness are unlikely to be derived (directly at least) from difficulties of definition. This is the sense in which, as indicated at the start of this section, the problem of mental illness is one of use *rather than* definition. The problem itself, indeed, reformulated linguistic analytically, turns out to be as much a problem of bodily illness as of mental illness. Before spelling out this reformulation of the problem more precisely, though, a brief look at two definitional blind alleys, the causal blind alley, and the dualism blind alley, is necessary.

THE CAUSAL BLIND ALLEY. One of the most widespread misperceptions in so-called biological psychiatry is that our current difficulties in defining mental illness will be resolved by future scientific advances. The origin of this misperception is the success of physical medicine in developing diagnostic tests to detect the *causes* of bodily illness, the employment of these tests diagnostically, and their incorporation into classifications of disease. A disease, so defined, is a change in the structure/function of the body that has a tendency to cause illness. But causation *as such* does not define pathology (health no less than illness is *caused*). The chain of causation does indeed, on this model, flow from disease (the change in bodily structure/function) to illness (the changes in the patient's experience and/or behavior). But the flow of *meaning* runs the other way, from illness to disease. It is the status of an experience and/or behavior *as* pathology which determines the status of the underlying bodily causes of that experience and/or behavior *as* pathology, not vice versa.

If, therefore, as in the case of many bodily illnesses, an experience and/or behavior is unequivocally pathological, the underlying causes of that experience and/or behavior will be unequivocally pathological as well. Conversely, though, if, as in the case of many mental illnesses, an experience and/or behavior is only *equivocally* pathological, then the underlying causes of that experience and/or behavior will be only *equivocally* pathological as well. Causation, then, or more precisely knowledge of causation, is, for the purposes of conceptual clarification, a blind alley. (See Fulford, 1989, chapter 4, for a more detailed treatment, including the place of "stipulative definition," in Urmson's sense of the term.).

THE DUALISM BLIND ALLEY. A second widespread misperception is that our difficulties with mental illness are derived in some (generally undefined) way from the (supposed) ills of Cartesian dualism, the separation of mind and brain as distinct substances. This misperception is evident in the positions of those both for and against the concept of mental illness (see, e.g., respectively, Roth and Kroll; Szasz, 1998). It can be taken as two rather different claims. As a claim that *solving* the mind body problem will solve the problem of mental illness, it substitutes for our local difficulties with mental illness, some of the deepest and most intransigent problems of general metaphysics—not much of a bargain, conceptually speaking! As a claim, alternatively, that there is no *real* difference between mind and body, and hence no real difference between mental illness and bodily illness, it simply begs the (operative) practical question, namely, just why mental illness (conventionally denoted) is so problematic in use compared with bodily illness. Either way, then, dualism, or more precisely the denial of dualism, is, like causation, a conceptual blind alley.

The distinction between bodily *illness* and mental illness it is worth adding, is, anyway, readily drawn at the relevant level, i.e. of experience and/or behavior (Fulford, 1989, chapters 5, 7 and 8). Thus, bodily illness is concerned (mainly) with movements (e.g. paralysis), perceptions (e.g. blindness) and bodily sensations (e.g. nausea, dizziness, and pain), while mental illness is concerned (mainly) with the higher mental functions, such as emotion, desire, volition,

belief and motivation. The distinction between mental illness and bodily illness, drawn in this (ordinary language) way, is entirely neutral, equally to the provenance of different causal theories (biological, social, psychological, etc), and to the many different philosophical propositions on the mind-body problem. It is also, as will be shown below (section on Outcomes), the basis for a positive way of understanding the more problematic *use* of mental illness compared with bodily illness, derived from philosophical value theory.

A LINGUISTIC-ANALYTIC REFORMULATION OF THE PROBLEM OF MENTAL ILLNESS. The problem of mental illness, then, to return to the starting point of this section, really is a problem in use rather than a problem of definition. There *is* a problem of definition, certainly, but it is a problem of definition of the generic concept of *illness* (including related concepts of pathology, such as disease, dysfunction and disorder) whether bodily or mental.

This reformulation of the problem can be further clarified in terms of the linguistic-analytic distinction between lower-level and higher-level concepts. Thus the traditional assumption, that difficulties in the use of the concept of mental illness have their origin in difficulties of definition, was based, as noted above, on twentieth-century successes, as in the US-UK Diagnostic Project, in solving difficulties in the use of psychopathological concepts by clarifying their definitions. The psychopathological concepts in question, however, were all, linguistic-analytically speaking, lower-level concepts—the lower-level delusion of guilt, for example, proved easier to define than the higher-level concepts of delusion and psychosis. From the perspective of the traditional assumption, this was an (unexplained) failure of the definitional program. From the perspective of linguistic analysis, by contrast, it is a reflection of a property common to all concepts, namely, that higher-level concepts in general, although used with often effortless facility, are peculiarly difficult to define.

A standard non-medical example is the concept of time. Most of the time, the concept is used (as in this sentence) seamlessly. Yet, if pressed, one would not be able to define it. Saint Augustine (354–430), the early Christian philosopher and Archbishop of Hippo, in his *Confessions,* said, "So what is (a) time? If no one asks me, I know; if they ask and I try to explain, I do not know" (Bk. II, ch. 14, No. 17). We *can* define lower-level concepts, of course: a watch face is, simply, the display side of a watch; a watch is, almost equally simply, an instrument for measuring time; but time is … here, as with the concept of illness, we get stuck.

We can extend the parallel with the concept of time. For with time, as with the concept of illness, there are contexts in which the concept *does* run into difficulties in use. In the case of illness, difficulties in use arise in psychological medicine. In the case of time, difficulties in use arise in theoretical physics, for example. In theoretical physics, the difficulties in use arise because the concept of time has to be used in contexts and at scales very different from those in which it developed. Some might argue for a broadly parallel explanation in the case of illness: the French philosopher and historian, Michel Foucault (1926–1984), for example, argued that the concept of mental illness arose by extension from that of bodily illness as a response to the work ethic of the industrial revolution (Foucault); and, as will be discussed in the Conclusions, there is indeed a sense in which the concept of illness is increasingly under pressure through scientific advances in medicine, much as that of time has been in physics. But Foucault's explanation, and others like it, all fail to explain the long history of difficulties about the concept of mental illness, stretching back, as indicated at the start of this entry, at least 2,500 years.

The question, then, that should be asked regarding the concept of illness, is not why it is difficult to define: this is an interesting question, philosophically, that we can indeed ask of higher-level concepts in general. But the question that should be asked is just why the concept of illness is relatively difficult to use in psychological medicine compared with bodily medicine. Reformulated in this way, furthermore, in linguistic-analytic terms, the problem is no longer a problem merely of mental illness at all. The challenge, for analysis, is, indeed, to explain why mental illness is relatively *problematic* in use. But there is an equal and opposite challenge to explain why bodily illness, although no less easy to define, is relatively *un*-problematic in use. So how should we go about this?

The Method: Philosophical Field Work

The method of linguistic analysis, noted above, of focusing on the use of concepts as a guide to their meanings, directly exploits the fact that, with higher-level concepts, people are better at using than defining them. Austin, whose now classic paper, "A Plea for Excuses," illustrates the linguistic-analytic approach, called this philosophical "field work" (Austin, p. 25). As already noted, linguistic analysis is neither unproblematic nor a panacea. There is, furthermore, no *a priori* reason why someone may not still come up with a definition, a neat formula or code, which encapsulates the full meaning of illness, higher-level concept as it is, and explains, even-handedly, its relatively problematic use in psychiatry and its relatively unproblematic use in bodily medicine. There is no *a priori* reason, similarly, why someone may not come up with a simple formulaic definition of

some other related higher-level concept, such as health (Nordenfelt) or disorder (Wakefield). Nonetheless, linguistic analysis, as a method, can be used to good effect both negatively, to critique proposed definitions of mental illness and related concepts, and positively, to raise awareness of aspects of the meanings of these concepts which would otherwise tend to remain hidden.

NEGATIVE USE OF LINGUISTIC ANALYSIS: AS A CRITIQUE OF DEFINITIONS. Linguistic analysis, then, involves attending to language use. Normally we attend to the message. Linguistic analysis involves taking a step back, as it were, and attending to the language—to the actual words and phrases—in which the message is delivered.

As applied to proposed definitions, this stepping back and attending to language use can be helpful in its own right. Jerome Wakefield, for example, has argued in a series of impressively detailed articles (e.g., Wakefield, 1999, 2000), that dysfunction, as a component of his proposed definition of disorder (the other component is harm), can be defined value-free by reference to evolutionary norms. In this Wakefield stands in direct line of descent not only from Boorse, Kendell, Scadding and others in the debate about disorder (noted above), but also from a long line of philosophers working on the concept of function in biology (e.g., Neander; Thornton). Wakefield's enthusiasm and his rhetorical style make him a particularly effective current advocate of this approach. If one steps back, though, from his message and considers the words in which his proposed definition of dysfunction is actually expressed, it is possible to see that many of these are, in part, ambiguous as to factual and evaluative meaning. The terms in which Wakefield's definition of dysfunction are expressed, that is to say, can be used (as is required to support his claim to a value-free definition) descriptively; but they can also be used evaluatively. His definition includes the word "failure," for example (Fulford, 1999, p. 412). From a linguistic analytic perspective, then, there has to be a suspicion that while the rhetorical effectiveness of Wakefield's claim to a value-free *definition* of dysfunction is carried by presenting us with the value-free side of the meanings of these terms, the actual *work* (the linguistic work) of the concept of dysfunction as it is actually used (even by Wakefield) nonetheless depends (in part but essentially) on the evaluative side of their meanings (Fulford, 2000).

Others have succeeded in producing unambiguously value-free definitions of relevant terms. Boorse, for example, whose work was also noted above, defined disease stipulatively as a "... deviation from the natural (= statistically typical) functional organization of the species ... " (1975, p. 59), adding, to cover endemic diseases, that disease should be "… mainly due to environmental causes" (1975, p. 59). Boorse's definition of disease, then, unlike Wakefield's definition of dysfunction, is indeed unambiguously value-free. But its persuasiveness, even as a stipulative definition, is undermined by the fact that Boorse himself continues to *use* the term disease with clear evaluative connotations. Thus his value-free criterion of statistical deviation becomes, only four lines later, the value-laden "*deficiencies* in functional efficiency" (1975, p. 59 [emphasis added]) and the value-free "environmental causes" becomes, again only a few lines later, the value-laden "*hostile* environment" (1975, p. 59 [emphasis added]). Boorse has rightly pointed out that this is very far from being a knockdown argument against his definition of disease (Boorse, 1997). But from a linguistic-analytic perspective it is at least suggestive that the *meaning* of disease, and hence the *use* that people (including Boorse himself) make of the term, does include an essential element of evaluation.

The slips that Boorse, and others (Fulford, 2000), make from value-free definition to value-laden use, can be understood in terms of the idea that words are, as Austin put it, "our tools" (p. 24). Based on this then, we can say that Boorse defines say, a hammer, stipulatively in terms only of its handle (equivalent to the fact part of the meaning of disease/dysfunction). But as soon as he has to use a hammer for real, the head (equivalent to the value part) becomes essential. Without the handle, to extend the analogy, the hammer cannot do the job we require of it; but the use that we actually make of a hammer for *real,* shows that the head (the value part) is essential as well.

Further examples of use providing a critique of definition are to be found in psychopathology. As already noted, the reliability of psychiatric diagnosis has been much improved by careful definition at least of lower-level psychopathological terms. The *validity* of psychiatric diagnosis, on the other hand, far from being improved, has in some cases actually been prejudiced by attempts to extend the approach of simple formulaic definition from lower-level to higher-level concepts. Delusion, for example, a term, as noted above, of central importance in descriptive psychopathology, is regularly defined in textbooks by criteria that transparently fail to encompass the full uses of the term in practice (Fulford, 1989, ch. 10).

The concept of psychosis, a step higher up the hierarchy than delusion, provides an even more dramatic example. In ICD-9 (World Health Organization, 1978), mental disorders were divided up (consistently with traditional descriptive psychopathology) primarily into psychotic and non-psychotic varieties. In ICD-10 and DSM-III (American Psychiatric Association, 1980), this primary division was abandoned on the grounds essentially that the concept of psychosis is resistant to operational definition, both classifications adopting instead a larger number of primary divisions (10 for ICD-10; 15 plus Personality Disorders and V codes for DSM-III). Closer inspection, however, shows that these new primary divisions contain, implicitly or explicitly, the traditional subdivisions into psychotic and non-psychotic categories (Fulford, 2003a). In other words ICD-10 and DSM-III are, so far as the psychotic/non-psychotic division is concerned, just ICD-9 and traditional descriptive psychopathology, turned upside down! The implication, linguistic analytically, is that the psychotic/non-psychotic distinction, difficult as the concept of psychosis is to define, continues, like the head of the hammer in the example above, to be essential to the set of conceptual tools that we need in speaking of psychopathology.

POSITIVE USE OF LINGUISTIC ANALYSIS: TO RAISE AWARENESS. The above examples should all be understood, on the linguistic analytic model, as showing, not that this or that proposed definition is wrong, but that it is incomplete. The continued use of a concept with a meaning that is denied or excluded in a proposed definition, shows that the meaning in question is, again like the head of a hammer in our example above, essential to the work that that concept does for us, linguistically speaking. Linguistic analysis, then, as a former Professor of Psychiatry at the Institute of Psychiatry in London, Sir Denis Hill, put it, is in this respect like psychoanalysis, a consciousness-raising exercise (personal communication). Examining the actual use of concepts for real thus helps to raise awareness of aspects of their meanings which, otherwise, would be neglected or ignored.

It is important to be clear that very little is claimed for this positive use of linguistic analysis. In the first place, examining the use of concepts, is, as Austin put it, in the title to an informal talk on the subject, no more than "… one way of possibly doing one part of philosophy" (Warnock, p. 6): or, again, ordinary language, although always the first word, "… is *not* the last word" (Austin, p. 27). Then second, linguistic analysis is no Royal Road to a grand unified theory. Like empirical scientific work, linguistic analysis is piecemeal, tackling doable projects, and satisfied with small increments in understanding. As Austin, again, pointed out, this means that the work of linguistic analysis, like the work of a scientific research program, can be broken down across a team or community of researchers, in contrast to the lone scholar model traditional in philosophy (Warnock, ch. 1). And all this in turn means, finally, that linguistic analysis can be connected with other methods, philosophical and empirical, with, as will be explored in the next section, outcomes that are well-grounded and directly relevant to policy, practice, training, and research in mental health.

Outcomes: From Meaning to Usefulness

Recent linguistic-analytically oriented work on the concept of mental illness has been focused on raising awareness of the role particularly of evaluation (of judgments of good and bad) alongside description in our psychopathological concepts. The American psychiatrist, John Sadler, for example, has carried out a detailed study of the epistemic values shaping the construction of the diagnostic categories of personality disorder in DSM-IV (Sadler, 1996). Such epistemic values include coherence, comprehensiveness, simplicity, instrumental efficiency, and relevance. Sadler explored the roles of such values in shaping DSM-IV, however, not by general speculation, but by careful analysis of the language of a foundational paper on the classification of these disorders by the man who, as noted above, was later to become chair of the DSM-IV taskforce, Allen Frances published in 1982. Frances, like the DSM taskforce itself (APA, 1994, p. xv), was concerned (rightly) with the evidence base of the classification of personality disorders. Work in the philosophy of science, though, suggests that proposals for classifying these disorders would be likely to be driven, also, by epistemic and other kinds of evaluation (Luntley). Sadler's analysis showed that this was in fact so, and it defined precisely the kind and impact of some of the values actually involved.

THEORY: A MORE COMPLETE VIEW. The significance of Sadler's work, consistently with the consciousness-raising outcomes of linguistic analysis, is not to undermine the scientific basis of psychiatric classification. It is rather to show how the *science* of diagnostic classification (to the extent that this is confined to the evidence-base of our classifications) is combined with (generally unrecognized but nonetheless logically operative) *evaluations*. The importance of this more complete view of what another Oxford philosopher Gilbert Ryle (1900 – 1976) would have called the logical geography of our classifications, is evident in the case history of Simon at the start of this article. DSM, despite its claims to being a descriptively-based classification, is shot through with evaluations (Fulford, 1994). The DSM (like ICD) *is* descriptive, of course; but it is also evaluative. And Criterion B, the criterion of social/occupational dysfunction at the heart of the DSM classification, which, as discussed above, turned out to be crucial to the differential diagnosis in Simon's story, is a case in point. An

exclusively factual account of dysfunction requires that Criterion B be understood, like the symptoms in Criterion A, as a matter exclusively of evidence. But when it comes to social and occupational functioning, it is hard to avoid the conclusion that what counts as good or bad functioning is, in part, a matter also of value judgments. In Simon's case, then, the operative diagnostic criterion, as to the differential diagnosis between delusion and spiritual experience, was not a descriptive but an *evaluative* criterion.

This of course raises the question of why evaluation is so much more prominent in psychiatric classification and diagnosis compared with their counterparts in bodily medicine. The answer one gives to this question depends on which model of disorder one accepts. Szasz, at one extreme, argued, as noted above, that psychiatry is value-laden in this way because mental disorders are really moral not medical problems. Kendell, Boorse (1976), and others have argued that psychiatry is value-laden because it is at a primitive stage of its development as a science. Linguistic analysis suggests a third kind of answer, namely that it is because psychiatry is concerned with areas of human experience and behavior, such as emotion, desire, volition, belief, and sexuality, in which human values *differ widely and legitimately*.

Thus, values, according to this linguistic-analytic answer, stand alongside facts in the definition of diagnostic concepts in *all* areas of medicine, bodily as well as mental. But the conditions with which bodily medicine is typically concerned, like heart attacks for example, tend to be painful and life threatening, and, hence, *bad* conditions by anyone's standards. There is no Criterion B for a heart attack, therefore, not because there is no evaluative element in the diagnostic concepts used in cardiology, but because what counts as bad functioning in hearts is widely agreed upon, hence is not problematic diagnostically, and hence can (generally) be safely ignored in practice. Where, however, cardiology, and disciplines like it, are, in this sense, evaluatively *simple*, psychiatry is evaluatively *complex*. Psychiatry *needs* a Criterion B in cases like Simon's, therefore, or some equivalent evaluative criterion, because what counts as bad functioning in areas such as emotion, desire, volition, belief, and sexuality, is *not* widely agreed upon, hence *is* problematic diagnostically, and hence *cannot* be safely ignored in practice.

This linguistic-analytic interpretation of the more value-laden nature of mental illness, which we owe to yet another Oxford philosopher, R. M. Hare, provides at least one reason why, in terms of the linguistic-analytical reformulation of the problem of mental illness developed in the first part of this article, the use of illness is relatively problematic in psychiatry while being relatively unproblematic in physical medicine. It is now clear that this is not because bodily illness is easier to define than mental illness, still less because psychiatry is less scientific than bodily medicine, but because psychiatric diagnostic concepts are evaluatively more complex than diagnostic concepts employed in (most) areas of bodily medicine.

PHILOSOPHY INTO PRACTICE. The recognition that the concept of mental illness is, in the sense just outlined, evaluatively complex, has been the basis for a number of recent developments taking philosophical theory into the heartland of mental health practice.

In the United Kingdom, for example, new training programs, aimed at giving mental health practitioners the skills for effective decision making where legitimately different values are in play (Fulford, Williamson, and Woodbridge), have been developed within the National Service Framework, a policy document defining the U.K. government's core strategies on mental health (Department of Health). These training initiatives draw in particular on the principles and skills-base of Values-Based Practice (Fulford, 2003b), and on research combining linguistic analysis with empirical social science methods to explore the different models of disorder implicit in multi-disciplinary teams (Colombo et al.). They are also closely linked with recovery-oriented and other innovative user-centered approaches to the development and delivery of services (Allott et al.). On a wider international canvas, these initiatives connect with practically-oriented research employing a growing number of other philosophical methods, including the German philosopher and mathematician Gottlob Frege's (1848–1925) logic of relations (Van Staden and Kruger), the use of discursive methods to reveal the meaning and intentionality implicit in the speech and behavior of Alzheimer's disease sufferers (Sabat), and a whole series of studies in phenomenological psychopathology (e.g., Musalek, Stanghellini).

Linguistic analysis, then, in itself and combined with other methods, empirical and philosophical, can help to clarify the place and roles of the evaluative elements of meaning in the concept of mental illness, adding fine-grained, and hence potentially practically useful, detail to our understanding of the concept.

There is of course a good deal more to the meaning of mental illness (and of our concepts of disorder generally) than just this element of evaluation. Many of the most difficult problems in the use of the concept turn, indeed, not on whether someone is in a *bad* condition (as in Simon's case), but on whether they are in a bad condition of a kind that is properly thought of as an *illness* (the problems associated with the insanity defense, noted at the start of the entry, for example). The DSM, in an important caveat,

rightly emphasizes that psychopathology is not defined by negative value judgments alone (DSM-IV refers specifically to social value judgments, APA, p. xxi–xxii). Values, then, as the DSM's caveat makes clear, although indeed necessary (along with facts) to the definitions of psychopathological concepts, are very far from being sufficient.

This brings the argument back to the wider debate about models into which, as noted above, the long-running historical tension between scientific and moral understandings of mental illness has resolved in recent decades. Coming back to this debate, though, within the now more complete view of the conceptual structure of medicine revealed by linguistic analysis, opens up to psychiatry an extensive resource of powerful philosophical methods for exploring the full richness and subtlety of its diagnostic concepts: besides analytic philosophy (e.g., Bolton and Hill), such methods include discursive analyses of the inter-personal creation of meaning (Gillett; Harré), hermeneutics (e.g., Widdershoven and Widdershoven-Heerding), existentialism (e.g., Morris), the phenomenologies of both Martin Heidegger (1889–1976) (e.g., Bracken) and Maurice Merleau-Ponty (1907–1961) (e.g., Matthews), and classical philosophy (Megone). Contrary to the causal blind alley, furthermore, noted above, research in these new areas of philosophical psychopathology (Graham and Stephens), as those most directly concerned have been among the first to recognize (Andreasen), is set to become more, not less, important with future advances in the neurosciences.

The practical impact of such research, it is important to add, understood within a (linguistic-analytically) more complete view of the conceptual structure of medicine, will not be to secure the dominance of any one model, medical, moral or otherwise; still less will it be to create a super model, an unstable oil-and-water amalgam of incompatible elements of meaning. The impact of such research will be, rather, to clarify, piecemeal but progressively, the elements of the different models and thus to endorse their roles as complementary ways of understanding what is, after all, at the center of mental healthcare, the distinct perspectives of individual people with particular experiences of mental distress and disorder. If mental illness is a complex and multifaceted concept, this is because, encompassing as it does such areas of human experience and behavior as emotion, desire, volition, belief and sexuality, it reflects the complex and multifaceted aspects of human nature itself. Psychiatry, above all among medical disciplines, is concerned, not just with bodies or with parts of bodies, nor even just with minds or with parts of minds, but with what the Oxford philosopher Kathleen Wilkes, in the title of her seminal 1998 book on the relationship between philosophy and psychopathology, reminded us are *real people*.

Conclusions: Psychiatry First

This article has explored the problems raised by the concept of mental illness through the lens of linguistic analysis as exemplified particularly by mid-twentieth-century philosophers of the Oxford school, such as J. L. Austin. Although not currently fashionable in philosophy in general, in relation to the concept of mental illness this approach has a number of clear implications, summarized here under problem, method and outcomes.

As to the problem of the concept of mental illness, linguistic analysis shows that this should be reformulated in terms of use rather than definition. The challenge is not, directly, to *define* the concept of mental illness, since the (relatively) unproblematic concept of bodily illness turns out to be no less difficult to define. The challenge, rather, is to explain, even handedly, why mental illness should be relatively *problematic in use* while bodily illness is relatively *unproblematic in use*, despite both concepts being equally difficult to define. The method suggested by linguistic analysis, correspondingly, is to focus on use rather than definition, to step back from the message (proposed definitions) and become more attentive to the language (the actual words and phrases) in which the message is expressed. This approach delivers no simple formulaic definition. Combined with other methods, though, philosophical and empirical, it has a number of outcomes relevant to policy, practice, training, and research in mental health. These outcomes, as illustrated in this entry, amount to one answer to why mental illness is relatively problematic in use compared with bodily illness, namely, because mental illness, in contrast to bodily illness, is concerned, characteristically, with areas of human experience and behavior, such as emotion, desire, volition, belief, and sexuality, in which human values differ widely and legitimately.

K. W. M. FULFORD

SEE ALSO: *Medicine, Anthropology of; Mental Health, Meaning of Mental Health; Mental Health Services; Mental Institutions, Commitment to; Mentally Disabled and Mentally Ill Persons; Psychiatry, Abuses of; Psychopharmacology; Psychosurgery, Medical and Historical Aspects of;* and other *Mental Illness* subentries

BIBLIOGRAPHY

Allott, Piers; Loganathan, L; and Fulford, K. W. M. 2003. "Discovering Hope for Recovery from a British Perspective." *International Innovations in Community Mental Health,* Special issue of *Canadian Journal of Community Mental Health* 21(2).

American Psychiatric Association. 1980. *Diagnostic and Statistical Manual of Mental Disorders,* 3rd edition. Washington, D.C.: American Psychiatric Association.

American Psychiatric Association. 1994. *Diagnostic and Statistical Manual of Mental Disorders,* 4th edition. Washington, D.C.: Author.

Andreasen, Nancy C. 2001. *Brave New Brain: Conquering Mental Illness in the Era of the Genome.* Oxford: Oxford University Press.

Austin, J. L. 1956–1957 (reprint 1968). "A Plea for Excuses." In *The Philosophy of Action,* ed. A. R. White. Oxford: Oxford University Press.

Bloch, S., and Reddaway, P. 1977. *Russia's Political Hospitals: The Abuse of Psychiatry in the Soviet Union.* Southampton: The Camelot Press.

Boorse, Christopher. 1975. "On the Distinction Between Disease and Illness." *Philosophy and Public Affairs* 5: 49–68.

Boorse, Christopher. 1976. "What a Theory of Mental Health Should Be." *Journal of Theory Social Behaviour* 6: 61–84.

Boorse, Christopher. 1997. "A Rebuttal on Health." In *What is Disease?,* ed. J. M. Humber, and R. F. Almeder. Totowa, NJ: Humana Press.

Bolton, Derek, and Hill, J. 1996. *Mind, Meaning and Mental Disorder: The Nature of Causal Explanation in Psychology and Psychiatry.* Oxford: Oxford University Press.

Bracken, Patrick. Forthcoming. *Meaning and Trauma in the Post-Modern Age: Heidegger and a New Direction for Psychiatry.* London: Whurr Publishers.

Campbell, Peter. 1996. "What We Want From Crisis Services." In *Speaking Our Minds: An Anthology,* ed. J. Read, and J. Reynolds. Basingstoke, Eng.: The Macmillan Press Ltd for The Open University.

Caplan, Arthur L.; Engelhardt, T.; and McCartney, J. J., eds. 1981. *Concepts of Health and Disease: Interdisciplinary Perspectives.* Reading, MA: Addison-Wesley Publishing Co.

Colombo, Anthony; Bendelow, G.; Fulford, K. W. M.; and Williams, S. 2003. "Evaluating the Influence of Implicit Models of Mental Disorder on Processes of Shared Decision Making within Community-Based Multi-Disciplinary Teams." *Social Science & Medicine* 56: 1557–1570.

Cooper, John E.; Kendell, R. E.; Gurland, B. J.; et al. 1972. *Psychiatric Diagnosis in New York and London,* Maudsley Monograph No. 20. London: Oxford University Press.

Department of Health. 1999. *National Service Framework for Mental Health—Modern Standards and Service Models.* London: Author.

Dickenson, Donna, and Fulford, K.W.M. 2000. *In Two Minds: A Casebook of Psychiatric Ethics.* Oxford: Oxford University Press.

Eysenck, Hans J. 1960. "Classification and the Problem of Diagnosis." In *Handbook of Abnormal Psychology,* ed. H. J. Eysenck. London: Pitman Medical Publishing Company Ltd.

Fann, K. T., ed. 1969. *Symposium on J. L. Austin.* London: Routledge and Kegan Paul.

Foucault, Michel. 1973. *Madness and Civilization: A History of Insanity in the Age of Reason.* New York: Randon House.

Frances, Allen. 1982. "Categorical and Dimensional Systems of Personality Diagnosis: A Comparison." *Comprehensive Psychiatry* 23: 516–527.

Fulford, K. W. M. 1989. *Moral Theory and Medical Practice.* Cambridge, Eng.: Cambridge University Press.

Fulford, K. W. M. 1990. "Philosophy and Medicine: The Oxford Connection." *British Journal of Psychiatry* 157: 111–115.

Fulford, K. W. M. 1994. "Closet Logics: Hidden Conceptual Elements in the DSM and ICD Classifications of Mental Disorders." In *Philosophical Perspectives on Psychiatric Diagnostic Classification,* ed. J. Z. Sadler; O. P. Wiggins; and M. A. Schwartz. Baltimore: Johns Hopkins University Press.

Fulford, K. W. M. 1999. "Nine Variations and a Coda on the Theme of an Evolutionary Definition of Dysfunction." *Journal of Abnormal Psychology* 108(3): 412–420.

Fulford, K. W. M. 2000. "Teleology without Tears: Naturalism, Neo-Naturalism and Evaluationism in the Analysis of Function Statements in Biology (and a Bet on the Twenty-First Century)." *Philosophy, Psychiatry, & Psychology* 7(1): 77–94.

Fulford, K. W. M. 2001. "Philosophy into Practice: The Case for Ordinary Language Philosophy." In *Health, Science and Ordinary Language,* ed. L. Nordenfelt. Amsterdam: Rodopi.

Fulford, K. W. M. 2002. "Values in Psychiatric Diagnosis: Executive Summary of a Report to the Chair of the ICD-12/DSM-VI Coordination Task Force (Dateline 2010)." *Psychopathology* 35: 132–138.

Fulford, K. W. M. 2003a. "Insight and Delusion: from Jaspers to Kraepelin and Back Again Via Austin." In *Insight and Psychosis,* 2nd edition, ed. X. F. Amador, and A. S. David. New York and Oxford: Oxford University Press.

Fulford, K. W. M. 2003b. "Ten Principles of Values-Based Medicine." In *Companion to the Philosophy of Psychiatry,* ed. J. Radden. New York: Oxford University Press.

Fulford K. W. M.; Morris, K. M.; Sadler, J. Z.; and Stanghellini, G. 2003. "Past Improbable, Future Possible: An Introduction to Nature and Narrative." In *Nature and Narrative: An Introduction to the New Philosophy of Psychiatry,* ed. K. W. M. Fulford; K. M. Morris; J. Z. Sadler; and G. Stanghellini. Oxford: Oxford University Press.

Fulford, K. W. M., and Radden, J. 2002. "From the Guest Editors." *Bioethics* 16(5) iii–xiii.

Fulford, K.W.M.; Smirnoff, A.Y.U.; and Snow, E. 1993. "Concepts of Disease and the Abuse of Psychiatry in the USSR." *British Journal of Psychiatry* 162: 801–810.

Fulford, K. W. M.; Thornton, T.; and Graham, G. 2003. *The Concise Oxford Textbook of Philosophy and Psychiatry.* Oxford: Oxford University Press.

Fulford, K. W. M.; Williamson, T.; and Woodbridge, K. 2002. "Values-Added Practice." *Mental Health Today* (October): 25–27.

Gillett, Grant. 1997. "A Discursive Account of Multiple Personality Disorder." *Philosophy, Psychiatry, & Psychology* 4(3): 213–222.

Graham, George, and Stephens, G. Lynn. 1994. *Philosophical Psychopathology.* Cambridge, MA: The MIT Press.

Hare, R. M. 1952. *The Language of Morals.* Oxford: Oxford University Press.

Harré, Rom. 1997. "Pathological Autobiographies." *Philosophy, Psychiatry, & Psychology* 4(2) 99–110.

Hinshelwood, R. D. 1995. "The Social Relocation of Personal Identity as Shown by Psychoanalytic Observations of Splitting, Projection and Introjection." *Philosophy, Psychiatry, & Psychology* 2(3): 185–204.

Hinshelwood, R. D. 1997. "Primitive Mental Processes: Psychoanalysis and the Ethics of Integration." *Philosophy, Psychiatry, & Psychology* 4(2) 121–144.

Jackson, Michael C. 1997. "Benign Schizotypy? The Case of Spiritual Experience." In *Schizotypy. Relations to Illness and Health,* ed. G. S. Claridge. Oxford: Oxford University Press.

Jackson, Michael C., and Fulford, K. W. M. 1997. "Spiritual Experience and Psychopathology." *Philosophy, Psychiatry, & Psychology* 4: 41–66. Commentaries by Littlewood, R., Lu, F.G. et al, Sims, A. and Storr, A., and response by authors, pp. 67–90.

Jaspers, Karl. 1913a (reprint 1963). "Allgemeine Psychopathologie," tr. J. Hoenig, and M. W. Hamilton. *General Psychopathology.* Manchester, Eng.: Manchester University Press.

Jaspers, Karl. 1913b (reprint 1974). "Causal and Meaningful Connexions Between Life History and Psychosis." In *Themes and Variations in European Psychiatry,* ed. S. R. Hirsch, and M. Shepherd. Bristol, Eng.: John Wright and Sons Ltd.

Kendell, Robert E. 1975. "The Concept of Disease and Its Implications for Psychiatry." *British Journal of Psychiatry* 127: 305–315.

Laing, Ronald D. 1960. *The Divided Self.* London: Tavistock.

Luntley, Michael. 1996. "Commentary on *Epistemic Value Commitments.*" *Philosophy, Psychiatry, & Psychology* 3(3): 227–230.

Macklin, Ruth. 1973. "The Medical Model in Psychoanalysis and Psychotherapy." *Comprehensive Psychiatry* 14: 49–69.

Matthews, Eric. 1995. "Moralist or Therapist? Foucault and the Critique of Psychiatry." *Philosophy, Psychiatry, & Psychology* 2: 19–30.

McHugh, Paul R., and Slaveney, P. R. 1983. *The Perspectives of Psychiatry.* Baltimore: The Johns Hopkins University Press.

Megone, Christopher. 1998. "Aristotle's Function Argument and the Concept of Mental Illness." *Philosophy, Psychiatry, & Psychology* 5(3): 187–202.

Morris, Katherine J. 2003. "The Phenomenology of Body Dysmorphic Disorder;: A Sartrean Analysis." In *Nature and Narrative: An Introduction to the New Philosophy of Psychiatry,* ed. K. W. M. Fulford; K. J. Morris; J. Z. Sadler; and G. Stanghellini. Oxford: Oxford University Press.

Musalek, Michel. 2003. "Meanings and Causes of Delusions." In *Nature and Narrative: An Introduction to the New Philosophy of Psychiatry,* ed. K. W. M. Fulford; K. J. Morris; J. Z. Sadler; and G. Stanghellini. Oxford: Oxford University Press.

Neander, Karen. 1991. "Function as Selected Effects: The Conceptual Analysts Defense." *Philosophy of Science* 58: 168–184.

Nordenfelt, Lennart. 1987. *On the Nature of Health: An Action-Theoretic Approach.* Dordrecht, The Netherlands: D. Reidel Publishing Company.

Phillips, James. 2000. "Conceptual Models for Psychiatry." *Current Opinion in Psychiatry* 13: 683–688.

Ricoeur, Paul. 1970. *Freud and Philosophy,* tr. D. Savage. London: Yale University Press.

Robinson, Daniel. 1996. *Wild Beasts and Idle Humours.* Cambridge, MA: Harvard University Press.

Rogers, Anne; Pilgrim, D.; and Lacey, R. 1993. *Experiencing Psychiatry: Users' Views of Services.* London: The Macmillan Press.

Rosenhan, D. 1973. "On Being Sane in Insane Places." *Science* 179: 250–258.

Roth, Martin, and Kroll, J. 1986. *The Reality of Mental Illness.* Cambridge, Eng.: Cambridge University Press.

Ryle, Gilbert. 1980. *The Concept of Mind.* London: Penguin Books Ltd.

Sabat, Steven R. 2001. *The Experience of Alzheimer's Disease: Life Through a Tangled Veil.* Oxford: Blackwell Publishers.

Sadler, John Z. 1996. "Epistemic Value Commitments in the Debate over Categorical vs. Dimensional Personality Diagnosis." *Philosophy, Psychiatry, & Psychology* 3(3): 203–222.

Sadler, John Z., ed. 2002. *Descriptions & Prescriptions: Values, Mental Disorders, and the DSMs.* Baltimore: The Johns Hopkins University Press.

Scadding, J. G. 1967. "Diagnosis: the Clinician and the Computer." *The Lancet* 3: 877–882.

Scheff, Thomas. 1974. "The Labeling Theory of Mental Illness." *American Sociological Review* 39: 444–452.

Siegler, M., and Osmond, H. 1974. *Models of Madness: Models of Medicine.* New York: Macmillan.

Smith, Richard. 2002. "In Search of *Non-Disease.*" *British Medical Journal* 324: 883–891.

Stanghellini, Giovanni. 2000. "At Issue: Vulnerability to Schizophrenia and Lack of Common Sense." *Schizophrenia Bulletin* 26(4): 775–787.

Szasz, Thomas S. 1960. "The Myth of Mental Illness." *American Psychologist* 15: 113–118.

Szasz, Thomas S. 1976. *Schizophrenia: The Sacred Symbol of Psychiatry.* New York: Basic Books.

Szasz, Thomas S. 1987. *Insanity: The Idea and Its Consequences.* New York: John Wiley & Sons.

Szasz, Thomas S. 1998. "Commentary on 'Aristotle's Function Argument and the Concept of Mental Illness.'" *Philosophy, Psychiatry, & Psychology* 5(3): 203–208.

Thornton, Tim. 2000. "Mental Illness and Reductionism: Can Functions Be Naturalized?" *Philosophy, Psychiatry, & Psychology* 7(1): 67–76.

Tyrer, Peter, and Steinberg, D. 1993. *Models for Mental Disorder: Conceptual Models in Psychiatry,* 2nd edition. Chichester, Eng.: John Wiley and Sons.

Urmson, J. O. 1950. "On Grading." *Mind* 59: 145–169.

Van Staden, Werdie, and Kruger, C. 2003. "Linguistic Markers of Recovery: Semantic and Syntactic Changes in the Use of First Person Pronouns in the Course of Psychotherapy." In *Nature and Narrative: An Introduction to the New Philosophy of Psychiatry,* ed. K. W. M. Fulford; K. J. Morris; J. Z. Sadler; and G. Stanghellini. Oxford: Oxford University Press.

Wakefield, Jerome C. 2000. "Aristotle as Sociobiologist: The 'Function of a Human Being' Argument, Black Box Essentialism, and the Concept of Mental Disorder." *Philosophy, Psychiatry, & Psychology.* 7(1): 17–44.

Warnock, Geoffrey J. 1989. *J. L. Austin.* London: Routledge.

Widdershoven, Guy, and Widdershoven-Heerding, I. 2003. "Understanding Dementia: A Hermeneutic Perspective." In *Nature and Narrative: An Introduction to the New Philosophy of Psychiatry,* ed. K. W. M. Fulford; K. J. Morris; J. Z. Sadler; and G. Stanghellini. Oxford: Oxford University Press.

Wilkes, Kathleen V. 1988. *Real People: Personal Identity Without Thought Experiments.* Oxford: Clarendon Press.

Williams, Bernard. 1985. *Ethics and the Limits of Philosophy.* London: Fontana.

Wing, John K.; Cooper, J. E.; and Sartorius, N. 1974. *Measurement and Classification of Psychiatric Symptoms.* Cambridge, Eng.: Cambridge University Press.

World Health Organization. 1973. *The International Pilot Study of Schizophrenia,* vol. 1. Geneva: Author.

World Health Organization. 1978. *Mental Disorders: Glossary and Guide to Their Classification in Accordance with the Ninth Revision of the International Classification of Diseases.* Geneva: Author.

World Health Organization. 1992. *The ICD-10 Classification of Mental and Behavioural Disorders: Clinical Descriptions and Diagnostic Guidelines.* Geneva: Author.

II. CULTURAL PERSPECTIVES

In the late 1970s and early 1980s anthropological researchers began to focus on the cross-cultural study of health and illness, both mental and physical, and systems of healthcare. In looking at Western views of mental illness, one finds the imprint of culture on the diseases distinguished and characterized, the symptoms associated with those diseases, and the etiological theories.

Anthropology and Medicine

The critical and reflexive view that leads to the the dissolution of traditional Western categories derives from anthropology's cross-cultural nature and tradition of long-term research on indigenous languages. That research demonstrates the created nature of those categories and highlights the culturally constructed nature of Western realities, whether popular, medical, or scientific (Carlson; Fausto-Sterling, 1992; Gaines, 1992a, 1992b; Geertz, 1973, 1983; Gould; Kleinman and Good).

Biological and social and cultural anthropologists study health, illness, and medical systems around the world. Biological anthropologists tend to use U.S. biomedical conceptualizations and research strategies in cross-cultural contexts. Although some medical anthropologists utilize biomedical definitions of illness in *ethnomedical* and *ethnopsychiatric* studies of specific cultural or ethnic forms of medicine and psychiatry, usually in non-Western cultures, many have abandoned that practice (Gaines, 1998c).

Those researchers have joined social scientists from all fields who utilize interpretive perspectives. In medical anthropology such scientists initially focused on folk medical traditions. However, since the late 1970s many have reflected on and analyzed the cultures of professional medical systems in the West and elsewhere (Kleinman, 1980; Leslie; Lock) and the sciences on which those systems draw (Gaines, 1979, Gaines, 1998c; Hahn and Gaines; Townsend; Young, 1995). Increasingly, anthropologically trained researchers come from the psychiatric profession (Kleinman, 1977, 1988; Littlewood and Lipsedge).

Interpretive social sciences have replaced Enlightenment science's ideas of cause and effect and use of universal laws to explain human behavior. Explanation has been supplanted by understanding and interpretation derived from idealist forms of social science theory and philosophy. Both popular and scientific realities now are seen as creations or constructions that are locally fabricated. In medical anthropology *cultural constructivism* is a major interpretive perspective that focuses on medical systems (Gaines, 1991, 1998c).

The interpretive constructivist perspectives allow one to see both professional and folk psychiatries equally as ethnopsychiatries, that is, cultural psychiatries. Constructivism suggests that psychiatry is a problematic but locally meaningful experience-near, ongoing historical construction that is constituted by various forms of embodied and disembodied discourse (Gaines, 1991, 1992a).

Constructivist perspectives have affinities to the history and philosophy of science (Foucault; Gilman, 1988; Gould; Hacking, 1983) and to gender studies (Fausto-Sterling, 1992, 2000; Gaines, 1992b). They have made it possible to penetrate the veneer of medical and other sciences to reveal their cultural assumptions and biases concerning madness,

nature (human and otherwise), human development, human differences and biologies (gender, "race"), emotion, and identity (Duster; Fausto-Sterling, 1992, 2000; Gaines, 1987, 1992a, 1992b; Gaines and Farmer; Gilman; Kleinman and Good). Medical anthropology has added to these debates with ethnographic studies of healers, researchers, and patients in their cultural contexts (Gaines, 1979, 1992a; Hahn and Gaines; Kleinman, 1980, 1988; Lock; Marsella and White; Townsend; Young, 1995). Although each professional psychiatric tradition embodies culturally specific beliefs and values, they all represent their objects of concern (diseases) as real and universal. Depending on the culture or the cultural variations within a society, those realities are usually in the domain of nature but may have a more spiritual orientation (Gaines, 1998b).

Ethnopsychiatries represent distinct systems rather than versions of a unitary psychiatry. A review of mental illness in the cross-cultural record suggests that in other cultures illnesses often cannot be classified in accordance with Western nosologies such as the Diagnostic and Statistical Manuals (DSMs) of the American Psychiatric Association (APA). Novel disorders in traditional societies are not versions of homegrown disorders. Conversely, many disorders that are assumed to be natural entities in the West cannot be found in other cultures or lack key or even defining symptoms. This suggests that diagnostic criteria are altered to fit unruly entities into Western molds (Gaines, 1991; Gaines and Farmer; Kleinman, 1977, 1988; Kleinman and Good).

The Problem of Western Professional Psychiatry

A cultural focus on professional ethnopsychiatries, particularly that of the United States, shows that they differ in significant ways. This also shows a lack of a universally valid "gold standard" by which all forms of mental illness can be evaluated.

Although ethnopsychiatries can be expected to differ substantially, an advocate of biological causal realism would not expect that to be true of professional (ethno) psychiatries. The distinctiveness of ethnopsychiatries suggests their cultural construction; they are not the same psychiatry focused on *natural* illnesses as it is practiced in different countries.

Cross-Cultural Knowledge of Mental Illness

Research in ethnomedicine and ethnopsychiatry, in the philosophy of science and history, the history of medicine, and gender studies has converged to raise epistemological and ethical concerns for modern psychiatries in multicultural nation-states. Those concerns derive from the fact that popular and professional psychiatries have been revealed local cultural constructions. Hence, the key question of psychiatric systems—What is normal and what is abnormal?—may be posed in an ethical context: What are the ethical problems generated by one psychiatric theory or nosology applying its notions of normality and abnormality to members of distinct cultures in modern plural societies? A cultural assessment of U.S. professional ethnopsychiatry shows a diversity of opinions and the elusive nature of definitions and diagnoses of mental disorders, suggesting its inadequacy as a standard.

Are Mental Illnesses Natural and Universal? Deconstructing U.S. Ethnopsychiatry

The view that psychiatric illness is universal eschews culture as a formative influence and assumes that disorders have similar natures that are expressed everywhere. That is, each disorder is known by its symptoms, which by definition must be distinct, at least collectively, from those of other disorders. In this view, in studying mental illness cross-culturally, one studies the same things in different cultural settings.

To make that argument one must posit that psychiatric disorders are biologically based (biochemical or genetic) and thus are beyond culture. One also must assume that there is a single human psychology that can be manifested in aberrant forms. If this view is correct, the same disorders should be identified and treated in all professional and popular psychiatries. It is assumed that a professional psychiatry *discovers* those entities and then names and classifies them (e.g., American Psychiatric Association, 1987, 1994); it does not invent them.

Labeled phenomena exist apart from their labels, it is thought. However, psychiatry mistakes its labels for realities rather than models (Geertz, 1973) or representations of reality (Hacking, 1983) that are used for particular purposes. This view expresses an implicit empiricist theory of language, holding that disease labels correspond to independently existing entities in the natural world. However, the empiricist theory is a cultural theory about, not a factual description of, the relationship of language to the world (Hacking, 1983).

When differences in disease entities or in systems of classification (nosologies) across cultures are found, psychiatrists assume that those differences indicate that universal diseases are overlooked, mislabeled, or differently labeled by less sophisticated others. When professional psychiatries disagree, they assert that one is more *advanced* than the others (Kleinman, 1988; Kleinman and Good).

Both views are evolutionist in form and have little scientific merit. It now is known that cultures change historically, not through evolution, because of contact with and borrowing from other cultures as well as innovation. Cultures are distinct because of their unique histories, that are constituted as local culture and passed on through socialization. Cultures do not differ because they represent developmental stages of a single human *culture.*

It is inappropriate to assume that the understandings of U.S. professional ethnopsychiatry are more advanced than those of other countries. For one thing, U.S. psychiatry has borrowed many of its fundamental ideas from other cultures and used them for its own purposes. Also, U.S. psychiatry has changed its views of mental illness radically over time.

The changes have not been in a specific direction, building on past knowledge. Rather, they represent a shift in paradigms. U.S. psychiatry has had dominant etiological paradigms that have been social, hereditarianist biological, psychoanalytic, psychosocial (interpersonal), and biological. The sciences seen as key to psychiatric formulations also have changed over the years. They have included psychology, eugenics, biology, physiology, genetics, and neurology (Dowbiggin; Gaines, 1992b; Hacking, 1995; Kleinman, 1988; Littlewood and Lipsedge; Lurhmann; Young, 1995).

ANOREXIA NERVOSA, CHRONIC FATIGUE SYNDROME, AND MULTIPLE PERSONALITY DISORDER. *Anorexia nervosa.* The potentially fatal disorder anorexia nervosa is found widely among middle- and upper-income Euro-American women. However, it is seen only rarely outside that narrow sociocultural context even in the United States.

In cross-cultural work key features of the disorder, such as fear of obesity and a distorted body image in the very thin, are not found (Mezzich et al.). Researchers have suggested dropping those symptoms, but in that case how could one find the same disorder with different symptoms when the disorder is defined by its symptoms?

Chronic fatigue syndrome. Chronic fatigue syndrome (CFS) is a disorder for which the search for a biological cause failed, yet it is referred to as if a somatic cause had been isolated as chronic Epstein-Barr virus infection or immune dysfunction syndrome. This disorder, which is fairly common in the United States but confined to specific ethnic and social class levels, is found in few other cultures. Currently, a century-old U.S. term, *neurasthenia,* is being resurrected and applied to CFS, moving it into the province of psychiatry from general medicine, although a somatic cause still is being sought (Kleinman, 1988).

Multiple personality disorder. Multiple personality disorder is another condition that is found commonly in the

United States. It is invoked in criminal trials as a legal defense and in popular culture. However, it is absent from the classifications and practice of other professional psychiatries (See Hancking, 1995).

PERSONALITY DISORDERS. Several new disorders appeared in an appendix in DSM-III-R (American Psychiatric Association, 1987), including dependent personality disorder and sadistic personality disorder. Those terms appear to be gendered: The former is said to be found among women who "allow" physical abuse over time, and the latter among the men who abuse them. There was considerable political opposition to the tentative formulation of those disorders, which blame female victims of abuse while giving their abusers a legal defense. In English psychiatry the adoption of a premenstrual syndrome made it possible to explain women's injuries: they did it to themselves.

The gender component of those personality disorders recalls the history of U.S. psychiatry, in which traditional notions of women's nature were upheld by psychiatric findings, as were racist notions about minorities (Fausto-Sterling, 1992; Thomas and Sillen). A more explicitly racist psychiatry was that of South Africa, in which a lower psychological and psychiatric evolutionary status was attributed to *nonwhites* (Gaines, 1992a).

Depression and Schizophrenia

Two disorders are considered in biological psychiatry to be models of biogenetic mental diseases: depression and schizophrenia. However, the cross-cultural literature and the most advanced epidemiological studies have challenged that assertion (Gaines, 1992a; Kleinman and Good; Kleinman, 1988; World Health Organization). The formulations of those disorders in the West have been shown to conceal powerful cultural and moral assumptions about emotion, autonomy, sex, and gender as well as human difference (ethnic and so-called racial) (Gaines, 1992a, 1992b; Kleinman and Good).

To examine the epistomology of the formulations of depression and schizophrenia, one first must consider certain key underlying psychological dimensions. Those culturally defined dimensions are constructions of self, will, emotion, and cognition (Gaines, 1992b).

SELF. There are differences in cultural conceptions of self and person with respect to mental illness, its diagnosis, and its treatment. Conceptions of the self vary widely and may include spiritual elements. For example, it is common for people to have spirit siblings in Bali (Marsella and White), but this would be seen as pathological in the United States.

Formulations of the self in India, the Mediterranean countries, and Japan would be seen as incomplete, dependent, and/or unindividuated by U.S. psychiatric standards despite the fact that those familistic, interactionally altering *indexical* selves that maintain interactional harmony and family reputation exist in cultural environments that foster, support, and reward their *sociocentrism* (Marsella and White). Conversely, the *egocentric, referential* Northern European Protestant self (Gaines, 1992b; Marsella and White) with its asocial nature would be seen as antisocial, naïve, and alienated in other contexts. It is the locally conceived self in which psychological disorders occur. Logically, different selves must have different disorders and therefore require different healing strategies. To complicate matters further, many cultures do not exhibit a purely psychological self. Instead, they exhibit social selves (the self is a social psychological, not a psychological, phenomenon), and this is found even in Europe (Gaines, 1992b, 1998b; Marsella and White).

EMOTION AND COGNITION. The distinction between cognition and affect (thinking and feeling) in the West, which is central to the differentiation of psychiatric disease entities, does not exist universally in human nature or biology. The cross-cultural record indicates that these are cultural constructions (Kleinman and Good). Those findings challenge the validity of the construction of depression and schizophrenia as universal diseases grounded in biology, for the psychological domains in which disturbance is said to occur (cognition and affect) are not innate; they are Western cultural constructions.

DEPRESSION. Assessment methods for depression are often ethnocentric even when the approach is said to be entirely *descriptive,* as in DSM-III (1980), DSM-III-R (1987), and DSM-IV (1994). An example is dysphoric affect (an unpleasant, sad feeling), that is a central element of the Western depressive experience.

Dysphoric affect, although disvalued in some Western traditions, is highly valued in others, such as the Mediterranean world with its Latin Catholic, Orthodox, and Islamic traditions (Gaines, 1992a; Kleinman and Good), where suffering is seen as ennobling and indicative of divine interest in the sufferer (Gaines and Farmer). It serves as the basis for interaction in which the self is presented through the *rhetoric of complaint* as beset with problems and as a fellow sufferer (Gaines and Farmer).

In the Buddhist tradition recognition of the worthlessness of the world and the self and the futility of human activity is part of enlightened understanding (Kleinman and Good). Such thoughts therefore have positive personal value rather than being pathognomic: They are *eudysphoric* (Gaines, 1987).

The complexity of the dysphoric experience can be understood by reference to the interrelation of the cultural context and history, cultural psychology, symbols, and family, status, and gender roles and power relations that collectively contribute to its construction (Kleinman and Good; Gaines and Farmer). Only then is it possible to assess the need for assistance. The intricate patterning of social and cultural forces is complex and requires detailed contextual analysis (Good, 1994).

The patterning of symptoms can vary widely across cultures so that key features of Western-defined disorders such as depression are absent from the experience of members of other cultures even when they are diagnosed as depressed with U.S. psychiatric instruments. For example, there is no psychomotor retardation among *depressives* in France or Morocco, only short periods of dysphoric experience among the Hopi, and feelings of insight and satisfaction in Sri Lanka and India (Gaines and Farmer; Kleinman and Good).

No consistent definitive statement about the prevalence, the incidence, or even the forms of depressive manifestation across cultures can be made, although a variety of assessment techniques have been employed for that purpose (Kleinman and Good). One problem is that false positives appear in the West just as they do in epidemiological studies done in Mediterranean and other countries where there are social and personal values of suffering and social support for its expression.

In attempting to focus on a single disease entity known as depression one is confronted with a semantic problem. The term *depression* is used inconsistently in psychiatric literature. At various times and often in the same study it is used to refer to a mood, a disorder, and/or a symptom of a disorder. Some researchers stress a cognitive explanation of depression, and there are cognitive therapies that may equal or surpass biological/pharmacological interventions in speed and efficacy.

SCHIZOPHRENIA. Research on schizophrenia is hampered by a lack of consistent clarity of definition, particularly in regard to the boundaries of the disorder. Epidemiological, familial, twin, and adoption studies have been interpreted to suggest that a genetic factors is involved in schizophrenia. Although some work has shown a genetic or familial link in a few cases, no genetic link or common abnormality has been demonstrated or implicated in the vast majority of cases. Results involving genetic interpretations often are overstated, and important social/cultural information or explanations

are ignored (Duster). Claims implicating various genes as causative of schizophrenia have been withdrawn.

Many findings of central nervous system (CNS) dysfunction appear in the literature, but none is specific or shared by all people who have the diagnosis of schizophrenia. Also, no symptom of schizophrenia is unique to that disorder; all the symptoms associated with or diagnostic of it appear in other disorders described by U.S. psychiatry

The World Health Organization's (WHO) study of schizophrenia (1979) found that schizophrenic patients with similar symptoms on initial evaluation whose disorders met strict diagnostic criteria showed marked variability in the two-year to five-year course and outcome within and across research centers. Patients in developing countries had a much more favorable course and outcome than did those in developed countries.

The disorder is chronic in the West, but this is not the case in the Third World, where the majority people with schizophrenia return to normal functioning (World Health Organization). It has been argued that schizophrenia is a culture-bound, Western *ethnic psychosis,* one specific to a single culture or ethnic group (Devereux). Cultural expectations may play a central role in chronicity; cultures that expect chronicity produce it, and those which expect recovery foster it. WHO data on the prevalence and incidence of schizophrenia in different cultures have been interpreted as establishing *broad* similarities across cultures (World Health Organization), suggesting similar processes, but similarities appear only when contextual evidence is excluded (Kleinman, 1988).

The assertion of the biological nature of psychiatric disorders in certain psychiatries appears to be a result of a patterned misinterpretation of cultural or social phenomena as biological. Those misinterpretations appear to be expressions of a professional *thought model,* a patterned way of thinking (Devereux). This model is a reflection of a folk form of biological essentialism borrowed from German psychiatry as well as a result of narrow biological training (Devereux; Kleinman, 1988).

Challenges to that theory include a resurgent psychoanalytic theory, feminist analytic theories, new psychologies, and cultural psychiatric studies. The biological model has dominated the field in the United States (Luhrman), but some movement away from it can be seen in the inclusion of a "Glossary of Culture-Bound Syndromes and Idioms of Distress" (Mezzich et al.) in DSM-IV (1994). However, cultural thinking has not been centrally present in the text of any edition of the DSM since 1980, when the classifications were intentionally fashioned to promote biological definitions of illness.

The Biological Perspective: Science or Folk Theory?

Researchers believe that the biological emphasis is a result of a long process of scientific advances. Studies of the development of psychiatries in anthropology, philosophy, and the history of medicine and psychiatry suggest otherwise. The biological view in psychiatry has its origins not in science but in the traditional folk culture of Germany and is at least a thousand years old (Gaines, 1992b). That view is an expression of a cultural theory that is a form of biological essentialism. That essentialism holds that the essence of self and other in terms of identity (ethnicity and kinship) and moral worth is determined by biology. *Blut* ("blood") is thought to be inherited and determines a person's identity, character, and moral worth.

The modern versions of this theory are the constructions of *genetic* and other somatic differences that are alleged to exist among people with specific disorders. In this view people who have mental illnesses are *different* kinds of people (Gaines, 1992a).

Some psychiatries, especially U.S., Scandinavian, and Russian, tended to follow in the footsteps of the nineteenth-century dean of German psychiatry, Wilhelm Griesinger, and his follower Emile Kraepelin, the founder of comparative psychiatry. Griesinger and Kraepelin after him in the early twentieth century asserted a biological basis for mental disorders. Kraepelin maintained Griesinger's dictum that "mental diseases are brain diseases," a notion borrowed from German (idealist) philosophy and French racial biology of the late 1700s (Gilman).

In first third of the twentieth century Carl Schneider, in the German materialist (and the Nazi racialist) tradition, advanced the notion of the "first rank symptoms" of schizophrenia. Those symptoms were pathognomic, or definitively diagnostic, of the disorder. Although many were influenced by that formulation in the United States and elsewhere, there was no analysis of the veracity of Schneider's theory until the 1980s when it was discerned that these symptoms were not unique to schizophrenia.

That biological model is dominant in contemporary U.S. psychiatry, although it competed with psychoanalytic and psychosocial perspectives before winning out in 1980 with the publication of DSM-III (Luhrman). Although the biological interpretation of mental illness is said to be based on empirical scientific evidence, its source in a foreign popular culture is apparent.

Social categories from the wider, lay culture—*races*—are construed in science as distinct biological groups, just as they were in German psychiatry and in South Africa. However, U.S. and German notions of race appear in different contexts and are applied to different experiences and thus are not the same folk biological theories. In the United States both the biological psychiatric perspective and the social categories are borrowed and reworked historical cultural constructions, rather than modern advances in psychiatric science.

CULTURE AND THE CLASSIFICATION OF MADNESS. Professional psychiatric classifications of diseases (nosologies), along with the diseases that are classified, change over time. Those changes are seen in psychiatric traditions as improvements and progress that may be viewed in evolutionary terms; that is, Western classifications are different from others because they are more *evolved*.

Changes in classification often represent shifts in assumptions about mental disorders that are products of ideological conflicts, competing explanations for which no data or ambiguous data exist. Rather than pointing in any direction, those changes simply show shifts in dominant theoretical models or political ideologies. They also may represent the imposition of foreign formulations and institutions (Gaines, 1992a).

Terms are deleted or reintroduced, but such actions do not indicate advances. Neurosis appeared in the disease classifications of U.S. psychiatry from 1952 to 1980 but was deleted from the 1980 and later classifications. These classifications are biological in orientation and thus exclude clearly psychogenic illness terms such as neurosis despite ample clinical evidence of their existence. French and other psychiatries continue to use the term and diagnose the illness. There are also "reconstructions" (old terms used for new disorders) in professional psychiatry, such as neurasthenia applied to chronic fatigue syndrome in the United States.

Interpretive analyses of U.S. psychiatric classifications reveal the underlying culture-, gender-, and age-specific viewpoint (Germanic Protestant, male, adult) from which U.S. nosologies are created. Behavioral or ideational differences perceived in others who vary in age, culture, or gender from the ideal are interpreted as a lack of (self-) control expressed as pathology such as depressive illness or psychotic conditions and personality disorders. That deficit is perceived as being caused by differences in group (age, "racial," gender) biology (Gaines, 1992b) i.e., local biology, culturally constituted biologies (Gaines, 1998c). This suggests that classifications are largely a cultural psychological discursive formations, not a classification of naturally appearing diseases (Gaines, 1992b).

Biological essentialism may be seen to act as a psychological defense because it allows one to claim that the afflicted are biogenetically different from *normals*. That is, members of the psychiatric profession, it is presumed, are normal and thus could not have the same biological defects as does a mental patient (Devereux).

PHARMACOLOGY AND "ETHNIC BIOLOGY." Biological essentialism can be seen in research in U.S. psychiatry that focuses on the study of ethnicity and psychopharmacology (called *ethnic psychobiology,* an oxymoron). Regarded as cutting-edge research, those studies recognize *ethnic differences* in biochemistry. Findings suggest that different doses of particular agents are appropriate for members of different ethnic groups with the same psychiatric disorder. This research takes as its units of research members of *ethnic or racial* groups. Biomedicine assumes that these terms are synonymous and refer to genetically distinct groups. The allegedly distinct biological ("racial") groups that appear commonly in such research are *Hispanics* (a language group), *Asians* (a geographical designation), *blacks* (a color), *Native Americans* (a geographical designation), and *whites* or *Caucasians* (a color or geographical designation, respectively). Those groups are in reality social categories that were created by a particular culture in the last two centuries and adopted by health research. The *racial* designations and the biological theory underlying them are neither universal nor biological.

Research that assumes that members in each category are biologically defined assumes that the members of each category are identical, or nearly so, in genetic composition; what is true of one person belonging to a *race* is generalizable to all members of the putative group. This perspective has several flaws.

The notion of race varies from culture to culture and is absent from most cultures in the present time; it was absent from all cultures in the past. Other modern sciences have different notions of the number and membership of human races. Japanese science considers the Japanese, Koreans, Chinese, and Indians to be members of different *races,* and the Germanic theory separates Germans from all other *white* groups on genetic bases. One may ask with reference to U.S. research, Why is one *racial* theory accepted whereas others are rejected?

This research ignores the substantial variations in doses seen and clinically "proved" to be effective within so-called races, including Europeans, in the practice of different national psychiatries. For example, much larger doses of antipsychotics are needed for *white* U.S. patients than for French, English, and German patients. If those patients all belonged to the same race, that variation would not occur in doses that are predicated on *racial* affiliation.

Biology is assumed to be the basis of physical and genetic distinctiveness and to be stable over time. However,

physical anthropology and evolutionary biology have demonstrated that human biology has a common source (Africa) and is extremely plastic. That plasticity is responsible for the great morphological diversification of humankind that has occurred in the last 100,000 years (Gould).

These findings contradict the ideas of biological distinctiveness and constancy over time that the notion of race requires. In contrast, pharmacological work framed in racial/biological terms reflects the biological essentialism noted above. It serves to maintain the cultural construction of race and biological explanations of social and cultural differences. *Racial* biology is thus a form of what has been called local biology (Gaines, 1992a, 1998c).

Professional Ethnopsychiatry around the World

CHINESE PSYCHIATRY. Chinese psychiatry originally was borrowed from the West but also drew from classical Chinese medicine (Kleinman, 1988; Leslie). This suggests that psychiatry can be borrowed and adopted by a culture.

Because it represents China's understandings of Western notions of mental disorders, a number of Chinese disorders are unknown elsewhere. *Qi-gong* reaction is an acute episode that follows overly intense involvement in the *Qi-gong* exercises and breathing practices that are used to promote health and long life. Neither the condition nor the related health practice is known to U.S. psychiatry.

Shenjing shuairuo ("neurasthenia") is the most common psychiatric diagnosis in Chinese psychiatry (Kleinman, 1988; Mezzich et al.) and in areas within the sphere of Chinese influence. The label was borrowed from the United States, where the term was developed over a century ago but fell into disuse, as did the conception of disease it labeled (Kleinman, 1988).

Koro is an acute episodic event characterized by intense concern and anxiety about the withdrawal of the external genitalia into the body; it is related to the Chinese cultural belief that the genitals of the dead recede into the body. *Koro* is found in China and Southeast Asia, where there have been large epidemics. Western psychiatrists, ignorant about Chinese folk beliefs, might see *koro* as a psychosis or panic disorder.

In Chinese psychiatry psychological explanations are not regarded as sensible explanations of suffering (Kleinman, 1980, 1988; Kleinman and Good; Leslie). Patients present somatic (bodily) symptoms such as *koro* almost exclusively. Optimal intervention is somatic as well, often involving herbal medicines to enhance or unblock the passage of vital energies throughout the body. The physiological conception of mental phenomena is related to notions in India, where in the traditional Ayurvedic psychiatric theory mental phenomena are held to be expressions of bodily states, not psychological dynamics in the Western sense. Indian professional psychiatry is entirely somatopsychic (Leslie; Leslie and Young).

JAPANESE PSYCHIATRY. In Japanese psychiatry two important disorders are widely known in practice and in society: *shinkeishitsu* and *taijin kyofusho*. Both are considered social phobias in the West.

Taijin kyofusho presents as extreme concern over actions or personal hygiene that could be disturbing or disrespectful to others. *Shinkeishitu* is characterized by shyness, tension in social relations, feelings of inferiority, and fear of failure in maintaining appropriate interactions. It is treated successfully by Morita psychotherapy, a blend of Buddhism, German psychiatry, and understandings of Japanese life that is administered on an outpatient basis or in hospitals dedicated to the treatment of *shinkeishitu*. Inpatient treatments for this and most other disorders serious enough to warrant hospitalization are much longer than they are in the United States. This is expected by patients, who see the hospital as a second home and the psychiatrist as a teacher (Lock; Gaines, 1992a). There are a number of psychotherapies in Japan for which there are equivalents of neither the disorders nor the therapies in the West (Reynolds).

Several new disorders in Japanese psychiatry have been recognized by the medical anthropologist Margaret Lock (1980), including housewife syndrome and school refusal syndrome. Both relate to pressures for achievement and success and the relationship of the individual to the group in Japanese society and culture. In the Chinese and Japanese cases the importance of harmony, right role performance, and the social nature of the person is clear.

GERMAN PSYCHIATRY. In Germany research has demonstrated a striking parallel between lay beliefs about mental illness and those of mental health professionals (Townsend). In that country lay and professional segments believe that there are two basic types of mental illness: *Gemütskrankheit* (emotional sickness), which is transient and caused by outside events, and *Geisteskrankheit* (mental sickness), which is said to be inherited, chronic, and not amenable to treatment.

Since the twentieth century German psychiatry has attempted to formulate biological notions of serious mental illness and has influenced many other psychiatric systems, especially that of the United States. Psychiatry makes a sharp distinction between the ill and the well that strongly affects diagnosis and treatment. Mental patients are *different* kinds of people; they are biologically defective. Many family studies focusing on the inheritance of mental disorders have been done in Germany and Scandinavia (Duster; Townsend).

This biological notion was developed in the nineteenth century and was central to the mental hygiene movement of the Third Reich. Because those people were biologically defective, they could not be helped and were a burden to the *normal,* and their lives thus were *not worth living.* That ideology led to the killing of tens of thousands of mentally ill and retarded patients in a process that was the forerunner of the Holocaust.

That ideology also asserted that certain groups of people—so-called races (e.g., Jews, Slavs, Arabs, Gypsies, Celts, Latins, Africans, and people from the East)—although not insane, were nonetheless defective and represented a potential threat. In the German ideology defective and dangerous meant non-German.

SOVIET PSYCHIATRY. Before the dissolution of the Soviet Union Russian psychiatric practice was strongly influenced by German psychiatry and its biological approach. Also influenced by Pavlov, Soviet psychiatry banned psychological and psychoanalytic approaches. Marxist ideology attributed madness and other problems to the evils of nonsocialist economic systems. Because individuals manifested mental disturbances long after the revolution, the causes had to be personal and internal, not social or economic. Hence, dissent was seen as pathology.

Soviet psychiatry described a unique form of schizophrenia—creeping schizophrenia—whose symptoms were usually nonconformity and dislike of expected work duties. Diagnosis could lead to hospitalization and the administration of powerful drugs. The opening of the Soviet Union to the West included a new acceptance of psychoanalytic theory (Mitchell and Black).

FRENCH PSYCHIATRY. French psychiatry identifies and treats several disorders that are not known in the United States or elsewhere. The practice of psychiatry, like the society around it, is hierarchical and authoritarian (Gaines, 1992a). It developed a nonphysical notion of mental disorders in the late 1790s and therefore did not adopt German biological theorizing entirely despite the neurologist Jean-Martin Charcot's organic approach and the rise of hereditarianism. The latter helped the French psychiatric profession gain prominence and authority over the treatment of mental illness (Dowbiggin). French psychiatry historically has been much more intimately connected with the state than have other psychiatric establishments in the West (Dowbiggin; Foucault).

A number of conditions exist in France that have no equivalents in other countries, including *spasmophilie* (literally "prone to spasms" but referring to a variety of vague, nonspecific complaints that include tiredness, loss of appetite, and various somatic complaints) and *triste* (or *fatigué*) *tout le temps* (chronic sadness or tiredness as a result of a great loss or disappointment). In those formulations French ethnopsychiatry expresses its culture's notions of the burden and exquisite sadness of life (Gaines and Farmer; Marsella and White; Gaines, 1991). French psychotherapies aim not at change in but at recognition and acceptance of a historicized self.

French psychiatry has unique historical concerns, such as passion and obsession expressed as monomania (fixed ideas). It was in France that the notion of the toxic nature of the asylum developed.

Culture and Context: Beyond Biological Thinking

Sociologists have long considered social contexts in Western industrial societies as affecting people's psychological status. Classic studies suggested that there is a relationship between social class position, urban dwelling, and an increased incidence of certain forms of mental illness. Although the lower classes have a higher frequency of some illnesses, it was found that the upper classes have a higher frequency of others.

Researchers with anthropological expertise implicated high levels of social disorganization as contributing to increases in the incidence of mental illness. People subject to extreme pressures, such as discrimination and other forms of oppression, that limited their life chances would have less stable environments and therefore would be more vulnerable to psychological afflictions. It also is known that U.S. psychiatry commonly misdiagnoses members of minority groups, attributing serious mental illness to individuals largely on the basis of ethnic group and gender group membership rather than on the basis of symptoms. Thus, the same symptoms in members of different ethnic groups or genders produce different diagnoses and prognoses (Gaines, 1992a, 1992b; Kleinman, 1988; Littlewood and Lipsedge).

Related to social disorganization are the consequences of personal and group traumas such as accidents and criminal victimization (assault, rape, abuse) as well as war, state-sponsored violence and terror, racism, genocide and ethnocide, forced migration, epidemics, poverty, and starvation. Native Americans and African Americans have been the subjects of pogroms, genocide, and terrorism as well as abuse, discrimination, and neglect. It is difficult to deny that those experiences have had a considerable psychological impact.

Stress, a notion derived from World War II and modeled on combat experiences, is relevant in the United States for dispossessed ethnic groups and for veterans, as can be seen in the recent formulation of posttraumatic stress disorder (PTSD) (Young, 1995), which combines trauma and stress with ideas of the unconscious mind that are not found in most other cultures.

The notion of universal biological mental diseases limits the understanding of the known variety of detrimental as well as beneficial sociocultural conditions. It leads observers to see defective persons instead of social inequalities and to seek biological vulnerabilities instead of hopelessness born of despair or the horrors of war. It ignores conditions that are responses to noxious circumstances. As an example, there has been a move to redefine PTSD as a biological defect rather than a reaction to war in veterans and to persecution and torture among Latin American immigrants to the United States.

Biological reductionism cannot explain the appearance of mental disorders across cultures. Although all people are human, they do not have the same ways of living, feeling, thinking, and behaving. To argue that pathology is purely biological is to contradict the fact that normal behavior, although supported by biology, is not determined by it.

Standards of normality vary from culture to culture; what is sane in one culture is insane in another. There is no evidence of a biological basis for the heterogeneity of conceptions of normality and abnormality. The advances offered by biological psychiatry are considerably less than advertised: *Modern* views of the genetics and biology of madness recapitulate theories of eugenics and hereditarianism from the nineteenth century (Carlson; Dowbiggin; Foucault; Gaines, 1992b; Gould) and earlier.

Professional Psychiatries: Ethical Implications

Historical and cross-cultural studies of professional psychiatries suggest that each one is a cultural construction, not a system of dispassionate discernment of natural psychopathologies; there are psychiatries, not one psychiatry. The application of a single theory or practice in a culturally diverse world leads to an ethical question: Are there negative consequences of the application of one culture's psychological medicine as a standard of normality in the evaluation and treatment of cultural others, including immigrants (Gaines, 1998a)?

Bioethics in the United States has grown out of concerns involving personal autonomy (a cultural value), experimentation (including that in the Third Reich), technological change, and informed consent but also out of a cultural context that gives meaning to those concerns. Bioethicists sometimes excludes social, political, and cultural issues such as "race" and gender, asserting that those things lie outside its domain or that cultural others are "really" the same (Midgley). Such assertions ignore more than a century of cross-cultural research demonstrating the contrary. In much the same way biological psychiatry excludes cross-cultural and historical research that contradicts the current version of psychiatric reality. Thus, it is able to operate in a closed domain that ignores complex historical and cultural realities.

A universalistic bioethics that is beyond culture is illogical. What is ethical in one context is unethical in another. Telling a patient the diagnosis in Japan is unethical, not telling in the United States is (now) unethical; leaving a patient uninformed about a disorder or the rationale for treatment is normal and ethical in Japanese and Italian psychiatry but not in U.S. psychiatry.

Biological distinctions that are reified as *natural,* such as the concept of race in the United States, have negative consequences. Those distinctions produce unequal treatment, disproportionate institutionalization, and higher morbidity and mortality. Adherents of those social views do not address social justice.

Nearly a thousand years ago in Islamic medical ethics physicians were enjoined to be social activists and advocate better living conditions for their community members. That ideology potentially opens the door to change and adaptation as well as social justice. The need to integrate the importance of cultural and social differences into theory and practice while maintaining appropriate levels of care in the face of increasing cultural diversity is the moral dilemma of modern Western and Eastern professional psychiatries in a multicultural, postmodern world.

ATWOOD D. GAINES (1995)
REVISED BY AUTHOR

SEE ALSO: *Medicine, Anthropology of; Mental Institutions, Commitment to; Homosexuality; Mental Health, Meaning of Mental Health; Mental Health Services; Mentally Disabled and Mentally Ill Persons; Psychiatry, Abuses of; Psychopharmacology; Psychosurgery, Medical and Historical Aspects of; Race and Racism; Sexism; Women, Historical*

BIBLIOGRAPHY

American Psychiatric Association. 1987. *Diagnostic and Statistical Manual, Third Edition, Revised (DSM III-R).* Washington, D.C.: American Psychiatric Association.

American Psychiatric Association. 1994. *Diagnostic and Statistical Manual, Fourth Edition, Revised (DSM-IV).* Washington, D.C.: American Psychiatric Association.

Carlson, Elof Axel. 2001. *The Unfit: A History of a Bad Idea.* Cold Spring Harbor, NY: Cold Spring Harbor Laboratory Press.

Devereux, George. 1980. *Basic Problems of Ethnopsychiatry,* tr. Basia Miller Gulati and George Devereux. Chicago: University of Chicago Press.

Dowbiggin, Ian. 1991. *Inheriting Madness: Professionalization and Psychiatric Knowledge in Nineteenth-Century France.* Berkeley: University of California Press.

Duster, Troy. 1990. *Backdoor to Eugenics.* London: Routledge.

Fausto-Sterling, Anne. 1992. *Myths of Gender: Biological Theories about Women and Men.* New York: Basic Books.

Fausto-Sterling, Anne. 2000. *Sexing the Body: Gender Politics and the Construction of Sexuality.* New York: Basic Books.

Foucault, Michel. 1973. *Madness and Civilization: A History of Insanity In the Age of Reason.* New York: Vintage.

Gaines, Atwood D. 1979. "Definitions and Diagnoses." *Culture, Medicine and Psychiatry* 3(4): 381–418.

Gaines, Atwood D. 1987. "Cultures, Biologies and Dysphorias." *Transcultural Psychiatric Research Review* 24(1): 31–57.

Gaines, Atwood D. 1991. "Cultural Constructivism." In *Anthropologies of Medicine,* ed. Beatrix Pfleiderer and Gilles Bibeau. Wiesbaden, Germany: Vieweg und Sohn Verlag.

Gaines, Atwood D. 1998a. "Mental Illness and Immigration." In *Handbook of Immigrant Health,* ed. Sana Loue. New York: Plenum.

Gaines, Atwood D. 1998b. "Religion and Culture in Psychiatry: Christian and Secular Psychiatric Theory and Practice in the United States." In *Handbook of Religion and Mental Health,* ed. Harold G. Koenig. New York: Academic Press.

Gaines, Atwood D. 1998c. "From Margin to Center: From Medical Anthropology to Cultural Studies of Science." *American Anthropologist* 100(1): 191–194.

Gaines, Atwood D., ed. 1992a. *Ethnopsychiatry: The Cultural Construction of Professional and Folk Psychiatries.* Albany: State University of New York Press.

Gaines, Atwood D., ed. 1992b. "From DSM-I to III-R: Voices of Self, Mastery and the Other: A Cultural Constructivist Reading of U. S. Psychiatric Classification." *Social Science and Medicine* 33(1): 3–24.

Gaines, Atwood D., and Farmer, Paul E. 1986. "Visible Saints: Social Cynosures and Dysphoria in the Mediterranean Tradition." *Culture, Medicine and Psychiatry* 10(3): 295–330.

Geertz, Clifford. 1973. *The Interpretation of Cultures.* New York: Basic Books.

Geertz, Clifford. 1983. *Local Knowledge: Further Essays in Interpretive Anthropology.* New York: Basic Books.

Gilman, Sander. 1988. *Illness and Representation.* Ithaca, NY: Cornell University Press.

Good, Byron J. 1994. *Medicine, Rationality and Experience: An Anthropological Perspective.* Cambridge, Eng., and New York: Cambridge University Press.

Gould, Stephen Jay. 1996. *The Mismeasure of Man,* 15th anniversary edition. New York: W.W. Norton.

Hacking, Ian. 1983. *Representing and Intervening.* Cambridge, Eng., and New York: Cambridge University Press.

Hacking, Ian. 1995. *Rewriting the Soul: Multiple Personality and the Sciences of Memory.* Princeton, NJ: Princeton University Press.

Hahn, Robert A., and Gaines, Atwood D., eds. 1985. *Physicians of Western Medicine: Anthropological Approaches to Theory and Practice.* Dordrecht, Netherlands: D. Reidel.

Kleinman, Arthur. 1977. "Rethinking the Social and Cultural Context of Psychopathology and Psychiatric Care." In *Renewal in Psychiatry,* ed. Theo Manschreck and Arthur Kleinman. Washington, D.C.: Hemisphere.

Kleinman, Arthur. 1980. *Patients and Healers in the Context of Culture.* Berkeley: University of California Press.

Kleinman, Arthur. 1988. *Rethinking Psychiatry.* New York: Free Press.

Kleinman, Arthur. 1995. *Writing at the Margins: Discourse between Anthropology and Medicine.* Berkeley: University of California Press.

Kleinman, Arthur, and Good, Byron, eds. 1985. *Culture and Depression.* Berkeley: University of California Press.

Leslie, Charles. 1977. *Asian Medical Systems.* Berkeley: University of California Press.

Leslie, Charles, and Young, Allan, eds. 1992. "Paths to Asian Medical Knowledge." Berkeley: University of California Press.

Littlewood, Roland, and Lipsedge, M. 1982. *Aliens and Alienists: Ethnic Minorities and Psychiatry.* Harmondsworth, Eng.: Penguin Books.

Lock, Margaret. 1980. *East Asian Medicine in Urban Japan.* Berkeley: University of California Press.

Luhrmann, Tanya. 2000. *Of Two Minds.* New York: Knopf.

Marsella, Anthony, and White, Geoffrey, eds. 1982. *Cultural Conceptions of Mental Health and Therapy.* Dordrecht, Netherlands: D. Reidel.

Mezzich, Juan; Hughes, Charles; Good, Bryon; et al. 1994. "Outline for Cultural Formulation and Glossary of Culture Bound Syndromes." In *Diagnostic and Statistical Manual,* 4th edition. Washington, D.C. American Psychiatric Association.

Midgely, Mary. 1991. *Can't We Make Moral Judgements?* New York: St. Martin's Press.

Mitchell, Stephen, and Black, Margaret, eds. 1995. *Freud and Beyond: A History of Modern Psychoanalytic Thought.* New York: Basic Books.

Reynolds, David K. 1980. *The Quiet Therapies: Japanese Pathways to Personal Growth.* Honolulu: University Press of Hawaii.

Thomas, Alexander, and Sillen, Samuel. 1976 (1972). *Racism and Psychiatry.* Secaucus, NJ: Citadel.

Townsend, J. Marshall. 1978. *Cultural Conceptions and Mental Illness.* Chicago: University of Chicago Press.

World Health Organization. 1979. *Schizophrenia: An International Follow-up Study.* Chichester, Eng.: Wiley.

Young, Allan. 1981. "The Creation of Medical Knowledge: Some Problems of Interpretation." *Social Science and Medicine* 15B(3): 379–386.

Young, Allan. 1995. *The Harmony of Illusions: Inventing Post-Traumatic Stress Disorder.* Princeton, NJ: Princeton University Press.

III. ISSUES IN DIAGNOSIS

Diagnosis of mental or physical illness is the clinician's determination of a clinical state or disease. However, as used in ordinary discourse, *diagnosis* is both a noun, signifying or denoting a particular clinical state, as well as a verb, describing an activity or process of determining diseases and clinical states. Clinicians ask "What is the patient's diagnosis?" as well as "What is your approach to diagnosis?" Considerations of the denotative aspects of diagnosis implicate the general classification and nomenclature of disorders or diseases (nosology), while the notion of diagnosis as a clinical process implicates various normative considerations of diagnostic practice—that is, considerations of fair, valid, and elegant diagnostic procedure. Ethical issues concerning the diagnosis of mental illness concern all of these permutations.

Mental Illness and the Self-Illness Distinction

The ethical issues involved in the diagnosis of mental illness can be considered as closely related to, perhaps even derivatives of, the enigmatic character of mental illness itself. At the core of this enigmatic character is the relation between mental illness and the self. In Western societies, sufferers of *physical* illnesses, diseases, or injuries can almost always distinguish their sense of self (the sense of who they are, the ownership and experiential domain of their unique mental life) from their affliction. For instance, a patient may have cancer, heart disease, a brain tumor, a cold, or a broken leg, but these conditions are over and apart from who the patient is, her holistic identity as a person. Ordinary discourse about physical illnesses often betrays this ego-alien character, where common linguistic metaphors portray disease as a malign force from outside the self: "She was struck down by cancer." "He had a heart attack."

Through their character as afflictions of psychological experience, this phenomenal distinction between self and illness is blurred in the case of mental disorders. Consider a few examples. The experience of depression saturates a patient's perception of herself, where the depth of her sadness and self-doubt overwhelms her sense of competence and worth. A man's schizophrenia wildly transforms his views of and relations with others and the world. Even amidst recovery from a drug dependency, the addict longs for the pleasure and tranquillity of intoxication. As these examples of mental illness illustrate, the afflicted may be unable to distinguish features of the self from features of illness (e.g., "I am depressed," not "I have depression"). Further, the mentally ill person may even value, or seek to preserve, some features of the illness, as in the case of the addict noted above, or, as another example, the person with bipolar disorder (manic-depressive illness) seeking the euphoria, confidence, and vigor of mania.

This weakening or loss of the self/illness distinction sets the stage for other ambiguities, and with them, a host of actual and potential ethical problems concerning the diagnosis of mental disorders. The intermingling of the personal self and the manifestations of mental illness confound Western cultural assumptions about the sick role. Parsons's notion of the sick role involved a forgiving of the sick individual's usual responsibilities; in Western societies the physically-ill person is thought incapable of the full range of her usual responsibilities, so subsequently, such incapacities are excused. Because of the difficulties in distinguishing aspects of the self from the manifestations of mental illness, this forgiving attitude toward the sick is often absent in the case of mental illness. Moreover, the often incomprehensible, annoying, or bizarre behavior of the severely mentally ill may generate fear in observers. These and other factors conspire to generate the most prominent manifestation of the sick-role confound: stigma, the vilification of "the mad."

Social stigma adds the additional burden of shame, humiliation, and exclusion to the ordinary suffering of mental illness, a burden by and large not shared by individuals with physical illnesses. Stigma subsequently ups the ethical ante in diagnosis, as a mere diagnosis of mental illness often has stigma-driven adverse social consequences, consequences relatively independent of the features of the illness itself. For instance, stigma may manifest itself through insurance or employment discrimination, harsh attitudes toward the homeless mentally ill, unfounded generalizations about the mentally ill individual's capacities, or the avoidance of treatment for mental illness.

Stigmatization of what is today called *mental illness* has been present throughout the recorded history of madness (Porter). At the beginning of the twenty-first century, stigmatizing attitudes toward the mentally ill often are justified by the view that the manifestations of mental disorders are willful and responsible, and the mentally ill fully choose their misery, if indeed they are miserable at all. The most prolific spokesperson for this kind of view is Thomas Szasz, a psychiatrist who since the early 1960s has argued that mental illness is a metaphorical concept that functions to regulate deviant behavior outside the usual

sociocultural channels, such as the law, education, and religion (Szasz). For Szasz and like-minded authors, because psychiatric authority regulates deviance outside these usual channels in free societies, psychiatric practice undermines civil liberties on the one hand, and the responsible conduct of citizens, on the other. Psychiatric diagnosis, then, is an instrument of this subverted political authority.

Because of the aforementioned ambiguities concerning responsibility and the self/illness distinction, it is easy to recognize the general moral implications of either accepting or rejecting the Szaszian critique. If one accepts the Szasz position uncritically, one risks building a callous, uncaring society toward what could be catastrophic, with miserable illnesses affecting large numbers of people. If one does not take Szasz seriously, one risks stripping the *mentally ill* of their morality and their autonomy, as well as their unique value as individuals through reducing them to mere expressions of psychopathology or disease states. On the face of it, both these extremes seem unacceptable, so more recent work on the ethics of psychiatric diagnosis has focused on rethinking this problem or seeking a middle ground between conceiving the mentally ill as fully autonomous, responsible actors versus conceiving them as helpless, dependent incompetents.

Scientific Classification and Prudent Practice

Perhaps most influential in the scientific classification of mental illness has been the efforts of the American Psychiatric Association's committees on diagnosis to qualify and stipulate their diagnostic categories in ways that, in the ideal, serve to both constrain mental disorder diagnosis and validate it. This was not always the case. In the early twentieth century, official diagnostic classifications of mental disorders were primarily aimed for hospital registries and the accounting of patient flow. Only with the publication of the first edition of the American Psychiatric Association's *Diagnostic and Statistical Manual of Mental Disorders* (DSM) in 1952 was diagnostic classification intended as a tool of science and good clinical treatment. By the third edition (DSM-III) in 1980, and continuing to the present fourth edition (DSM-IV, 1994), the DSM's intentions have broadened even further (Wallace). Since DSM-III, the manuals have resolved to meet a number of objectives or goals:

1. To provide a useful aid to clinical diagnostic practice;
2. To provide a scientifically sound classification of psychopathology for mental health research;
3. To provide an enumerated coding system for record-keeping and billing purposes;

4. To provide a comprehensible nomenclature for education efforts; and, of particular interest for this discussion;

5. To provide an extensive introduction to the manual that specifies prudent diagnostic practice and use of the manual.

The capability of this or any other diagnostic manual to accomplish such an ambitious range of objectives has been a ongoing source of debate. Subsequently, ethics-oriented criticisms of the DSM editions often betray disagreement over the particular balance struck between the various objectives (Sadler). For instance, some critics have noted that enumerated, rigorously-defined and scientifically-tested diagnostic labels oversimplify the complex condition of mental illness and impede the ill from engaging in discussions about themselves and speaking on their own behalf (e.g., Kovel). On the other hand, other critics note that the DSMs are excessively tied to clinical diagnostic traditions and are not scientifically rigorous enough (summarized in Sadler, Hulgus, and Agich). The ethical implication here is that scientifically-compromised diagnostic categories undermine the moral justifications for interventions like involuntary hospitalization or involuntary treatment, or indeed, treatment at all. As a third example, commentators have noted tensions between the values of clinical utility and clinician acceptability in the DSMs versus the efforts to have DSM categories fully reflect rigorous scientific values like validity and reliability (Sadler, Hulgus, and Agich).

Diagnosis and Mental Health Pluralism

As might be expected under the conditions of the blurred self/illness distinction, mental illness has been subject to an extraordinary range of competing and contrasting formulations or understandings. Until the recent ascent of alternative medicine, physical medicine has enjoyed relatively little competition from rival clinical practices based upon non-biomedical explanatory models. This, however, has not been the case for mental illness, as the woes of the psyche have a long history of ministrations from diverse healing and/or helping traditions. What psychiatrists call *mental illness* may be conceived by nonmedical practitioners as spiritual crises, or as secular problems in living, or the result of supernatural forces, or irregularities in various moral, dietary, lifestyle, or other habits. Analogously, ministration to such psychic woes is offered by not just physicians, but pastors or spiritual advisors, hundreds of varieties of lay and professional counselors and psychotherapists, folk healers, alternative clinicians, family, neighbors, and friends. Any effort, then, to provide a common nomenclature for mental distresses is bound to generate disagreement, and the existence of such diverse resources is bound to generate controversy over the relative value of each.

In this sense, then, any mental illness diagnosis (in the broadest sense) under any system of clinical thought, medical or otherwise, can be construed as having an ideological character. Hence, for instance, biomedical psychiatry's predilection for prescribing pharmaceuticals for DSM-diagnosed mental disorders is criticized as the capitalist commodification of everyday life, while interpersonal narrative-based psychotherapies may be praised as more communitarian in their political alliances. Diagnostic practices, if they lend themselves to one or the other ideology, then, are similarly implicated. The DSM approach to this problem has been to develop inclusive and diverse committees in the construction of the DSMs, and invite *outsider* input so that the DSM categories reflect some measure of such pluralistic practices, and hence are open to a range of therapeutic options (Frances, First, and Pincus). The World Health Association's *International Classification of Diseases— ICD-10 Classification of Mental and Behavioural Disorders* (ICD) has sought to provide a common language for mental health practices all over the world, and in developing its classification solicits input from all of its member countries (WHO). As such, its ambitions as a diagnostic manual are necessarily more modest, focusing on providing an enumerated coding for record-keeping and billing, preferring fewer numbers of categories, and adhering more closely to practice conventions than the more innovative, and American-regional, DSM manuals. Nonetheless, the DSM manuals and the ICD manuals have a close relationship, as the DSM is obligated by international treaty to provide compatible diagnostic categories for the ICD manual, and in recent decades the development of each manual has been closely coordinated with the other.

Even within the biomedical paradigm, however, mental health practice (psychiatry, clinical psychology, psychiatric social work, and related fields) has been characterized by a diversity of theoretical formulations, empirical-scientific approaches, and conventions of practice. The approach of the American Psychiatric Association's DSM effort, along with the ICD classification of mental disorders, has been to work toward a diagnostic classification which minimizes, even perhaps eliminates, theoretical assumptions about the causes of mental illness. Moreover, with the DSM-IV effort, the process has included assembling comprehensive scientific literature reviews, a *consensus scholar* approach in interpreting aggregated studies, and extensive and detailed documentation of the developmental procedures and findings used in constructing the manual. With the addition of extensive field trials (empirical studies) of proposed or revised diagnostic categories, the DSM process aims to continuously improve the scientific validity and reliability of its diagnostic classification. Nevertheless, many non-psychiatric mental health practitioners lament having their own practicable alternatives and may view the DSM/ICD efforts as a *de facto* hegemonic effort by psychiatrists to dominate the mental health field (Beutler and Malik).

Inspired by the problem of adequately circumscribing psychiatric diagnosis (e.g., assuring that people diagnosed are truly ill, and those not so diagnosed are truly well), significant efforts have been made since DSM-III to provide a rigorous definition of mental disorder. This effort is part of the aforementioned goal to recommend good diagnostic practices in the DSM introductory material. Such definitions of mental disorder, and the concepts underlying them, were developed in the introductions to DSM-III and later editions. Since then, such attempts at defining mental illness have been subject to heated debate, as discussed by K. W. M. Fulford in his article "Mental Illness: I. Conceptions of Mental Illness" in this volume.

Preserving the Dignity of the Self

While short of providing explicit moral and aesthetic rules for the proper conduct of psychiatric diagnosis, the introductions to the DSM manuals do prescribe, and proscribe, clinician conduct in significant ways, though these guidelines for use of the DSMs are thought by some to be inconsistently read and heeded. For instance, recent editions of the manuals have included explicit categories and codes indicating diagnostic uncertainty; have used a *multiaxial* diagnostic system that provides for diagnosis of not just mental illness, but other factors like complicating physical illnesses, environmental stressors, and the global adaptive function of the individual; and have provided a *cautionary statement* recommending against the use of DSM categories in forensic or other nonclinical settings. At question is the efficacy of these efforts to facilitate a thoughtful and responsible diagnostic practice; critics claim that despite these efforts, the DSM is still used in a "cookbook" fashion and the individual under diagnostic evaluation is still likely to be labeled narrowly and conceived simplistically (discussed by various contributors in Sadler).

Amidst these clinician-generated efforts to provide fair and scientifically valid diagnoses, the diagnosed and the families of the mentally ill have increasingly organized to protect themselves against what they view often as stigma-generating diagnostic pigeonholing and the diminution of their sense of self (Luhrmann). This movement is most concretely manifested in the terms the mentally ill increasingly use to refer to themselves: no longer *patients,* but now often *clients, consumers, users,* and even *psychiatric survivors* of mental health services. At present the mentally ill have little to no input into how their conditions are classified in systems like the DSM and ICD or how diagnostic criteria are phrased, nor do they have much of a forum for their views about prudent diagnostic practices (Sadler). How much influence this advocacy on behalf of the mentally ill will have on mainstream mental health diagnosis and practice remains to be seen.

The issue of the autonomy of the mentally ill and the ethics of diagnosis have collided in recent controversies over the handling of consent in clinical research settings. The issues were crystallized at the end of the 1990s by a debate in the United States over the National Bioethics Advisory Commission's (NBAC) report addressing the issue of protecting human subjects, as well as protecting research participation, with subjects with impaired decision-making capacity (Roberts and Roberts). Driven by concerns over the allegedly vulnerable but needy mental illness population, the NBAC recommended a series of protections that, from the research community's perspective, would make the clinical research enterprise a burden on researchers and subject-participants: these recommendations would make consent procedures and participation arduous, and create the risk of denying this population access to research participation, subsequently reducing the social benefits of the research. A significant component to this debate was the degree to which any diagnosis of mental disorder qualifies the potential subject as having an *impaired decision-making capacity.*

Cross-Cultural Validity

In the context of economic globalization and increasing cultural interchange, recent thought about the validity of mental disorder diagnosis has addressed the question of the validity of mental disorder diagnosis across cultures. Does the DSM-IV diagnosis of Schizophrenia apply equally to a white Anglo-Saxon Protestant from Normal, Illinois as to a Bantu African tribesman? What about Obsessive-Compulsive Personality Disorder or Anorexia Nervosa?

The issue of cross-cultural validity of mental disorder diagnosis has three general ethical ramifications. The first ramification concerns cultural assumptions of normality. The second concerns the practical matter of accurate detection of psychopathology in multicultural settings. The third ramification concerns which values should prevail in judgments concerning health or psychopathology.

As Dona Davis has noted, the sexual performance norms assumed by, for instance, DSM-IV sexual disorders do not apply to cultures where *sexual performance* as a cultural construct does not exist. For instance, how can someone have *anorgasmia* or *premature ejaculation* where there is no expectation of female orgasm? (Davis). The normative assumptions (taken-for granted beliefs about what is normal, adaptive, or acceptable) underlying diagnostic systems like the DSM or ICD classifications can pose dilemmas for clinicians working in diverse settings, where, for instance, couples of mixed ethnic origin may have clashes over acceptable and unacceptable behaviors. Normative assumptions underlying mental disorder diagnoses push the clinician into taking culturally-relative moral stands related to cultural assumptions, and more subtly, may mask the very cultural assumptions and beliefs that effective treatment must make explicit.

As a second example, mental disorders (like anorexia nervosa) that are closely conceived within cultural normative assumptions and expectations may not occur or may manifest themselves differently in other cultures. Diagnostic conceptions or criteria that are skewed toward the assumptions and values of Western industrialized cultures may have false-negative and false-positive diagnostic implications in practice. If Third World clinicians are not looking for anorexia nervosa, if indeed it occurs, they will likely miss an authentic disorder (false negative diagnosis). If Western clinicians are looking for anorexia nervosa in Third World populations where it is not endemic, they may nevertheless find cases who are not truly ill (false-positive diagnosis). Culturally invalid mental disorder diagnosis is then an ethical problem because of harms posed by the systematic potential for false-negative and false-positive diagnosis.

A third ethical ramification of cross-cultural validity concerns how mental phenomena are valued. Michael Jackson and K.W.M. Fulford present a case of a man who meets standard examination criteria for psychosis with the exception that his experiences are adaptive, and have enhanced his functioning and life satisfaction. M. Fakhr El-Islam notes that psychosis can be interpreted in fundamentalist Islamic cultures as a prophet's response to spiritual or religious stagnation, and the psychotic symptoms can confer positively valued mystical insights. How mental *symptoms* are valued have important implications on whether such phenomena are truly pathological.

Conclusion

Because of the ambiguity between mental illness and the self, mental illness poses a complex range of ethical challenges, whether one is a scientist engaged in the study of these conditions, a person afflicted with mental illness, or a clinician helping an ill individual. Ethical concerns arise

from numerous directions, from the mere act of making a diagnosis, to considering the social impact of diagnosis, to the applicability of diagnosis across cultures.

JOHN Z. SADLER

SEE ALSO: *Beneficence; Coercion; Homosexuality; Mental Health, Meaning of Mental Health; Mental Health Services; Psychiatry, Abuses of; Psychopharmacology; Psychosurgery, Medical and Historical Aspects of; Race and Racism; Sexism; Women, Historical and Cross-Cultural Perspectives;* and other *Mental Illness* subentries

BIBLIOGRAPHY

American Psychiatric Association. 1952. *Diagnostic and Statistical Manual of Mental Disorders.* Washington, D.C.: Author.

American Psychiatric Association. 1980. *Diagnostic and Statistical Manual of Mental Disorders, Third Edition (DSM-III).* Washington, D.C.: Author.

American Psychiatric Association. 1994. *Diagnostic and Statistical Manual of Mental Disorders, Fourth Edition (DSM-IV).* Washington, D.C.: Author.

Beutler, Larry E., and Malik, Mary L., eds. 2002. *Rethinking the DSM: A Psychological Perspective.* Washington, D.C.: American Psychological Association.

Davis, Dona L. 1998. "The Sexual and Gender Identity Disorders." *Transcultural Psychiatry* 35(3): 401–412.

El-Islam, M. Fakhr. 2000. "Mental Illness in Kuwait and Qatar." In *Al-Junun: Mental Illness in the Islamic World,* ed. Ihsan Al-Issa. New York: International Universities Press.

Frances, Allen J.; First, Michael B.; and Pincus, Harold A. 1995. *DSM-IV Guidebook: The Essential Companion to the Diagnostic and Statistical Manual of Mental Disorders, Fourth Edition.* Washington, D.C.: American Psychiatric Press.

Jackson, Michael, and Fulford, K.W.M. 1997. "Spiritual Experience and Psychopathology." *Philosophy, Psychiatry, & Psychology* 4 (1): 41–66.

Kovel, Joel. 1982. "Book Review: *Diagnostic and Statistical Manual of Mental Disorders, Edition III.*" *The Einstein Quarterly Journal of Biology and Medicine* 1(2): 103–104.

Luhrmann, Tanya M. 2001. *Of Two Minds: An Anthropologist Looks at American Psychiatry.* New York: Vintage.

Parsons, Talcott. 1958. "Definitions of Health and Illness in the Light of American Values and Social Structure." In *Patients, Physicians, & Illness,* ed. E. G. Jaco. Glencoe, IL: The Free Press.

Porter, Roy. 2002. *Madness: A Brief History.* Oxford: Oxford University Press.

Roberts, Laura W., and Roberts, B. 1999. "Psychiatric Research Ethics: An Overview of Evolving Guidelines and Current Ethical Dilemmas in the Study of Mental Illness." *Biological Psychiatry* 46(8): 1025–1038.

Sadler, John Z., ed. 2002. *Descriptions and Prescriptions: Values, Mental Disorders, and the DSMs.* Baltimore: Johns Hopkins University Press.

Sadler, J. Z.; Hulgus, Y. F.; and Agich, G. J. 2001. "Hindsight, Foresight, and Having It Both Ways. A Rejoinder to R. L. Spitzer." *The Journal of Nervous and Mental Disease* 189(8): 493–497.

Szasz, T. S. 1961. *The Myth of Mental Illness: Foundations of a Theory of Personal Conduct.* New York: Hoeber-Harper.

Wallace, Edwin R. 1994. "Psychiatry and Its Nosology: An Historico-Philosophical Overview." In *Philosophical Perspectives on Psychiatric Diagnostic Classification,* ed. John.Z. Sadler, Osborne P. Wiggins, and Michael A. Schwartz. Baltimore: John Hopkins University Press.

World Health Organization. 1992. *The ICD-10 Classification of Mental and Behavioural Disorders.* Geneva: Author.

MENTAL INSTITUTIONS, COMMITMENT TO

• • •

Throughout the world there are legal mechanisms by which mentally ill persons can be sent to psychiatric hospitals even when they do not wish to go (Appelbaum). In the United States this sometimes is done through the criminal justice system: A person may be judged incompetent to stand trial for a crime because of mental illness or may be tried for a crime and found not guilty by reason of insanity and then committed to an institution for mentally ill criminal offenders. The more common type of commitment is civil, and usually no criminal offense is involved: A person is judged to require hospitalization because of his or her mental condition but does not consent to it, but if certain legal criteria are fulfilled, that person may be hospitalized against his or her will. Commitment is a legal process and often is discussed mainly in terms of its case and statutory legal history (Wexler). This entry discusses important ethical issues that underlie the process of civil commitment.

Commitment raises serious ethical concerns. It involves depriving persons of their freedom for days, weeks, or longer, usually by incarcerating them in a locked psychiatric facility. Commitment is one of the ethically most serious actions in which psychiatrists engage. However, neither the process of commitment nor its ethical justification (or the related issue of forced treatment) is mentioned in the American Psychiatric Association's extensive handbook on psychiatric ethics (American Psychiatric Association, 2001b).

In most states this violation of a person's civil liberties can be carried out initially on an *emergency* basis on the strength of one physician's signature on the appropriate form. Most people agree that it is preferable that a psychiatrist be the initial committing physician, but there are too few psychiatrists in many rural areas for this usually to be mandated by law.

After the emergency commitment form is signed, the person who is to be committed is taken to the nearest locked psychiatric facility authorized to receive committed persons. Medical personnel there usually have the authority to question the appropriateness of the commitment and even to refuse to detain the person. In most states, under modern law, a probable-cause judicial hearing is held within two to three working days in an appropriate local court to determine the justifiability of continued detainment.

The vast majority of admissions to psychiatric hospitals, however, are voluntary and do not involve the commitment process. A small minority of voluntary admissions, however, result from persons being told that they will be committed if they do not enter the hospital "voluntarily." There seems to be nothing inherently unethical about giving a person who otherwise would be committed the opportunity to avoid the commitment process in that way, assuming that the planned commitment is ethically justified. It seems clear, however, that these persons have not entered the hospital entirely voluntarily. In addition, it would be prima facie unethical for a physician to use this process deceptively by manipulating a person into entering a hospital by threatening a commitment that in fact would not be carried out.

Legal Criteria for Commitment

Both within and outside psychiatry there is dispute about the commitment criteria that should be written into state statutes. Statutory language varies from state to state (Arthur et al.). All U.S. state statutes stipulate that to be committed a person must be mentally ill, although this concept is defined variously. The existing continuum of positions is based on the width or narrowness of the additional statutory commitment criteria. (For an excellent discussion of one state's commitment laws see Behnke, Winick, and Perez.)

The broadest additional criteria are advocated by those who think that physicians should be able to commit anyone whom they sincerely believe would profit from commitment. At one time many states had statutes with this breadth. Arizona law, for example, as recently as 1981 allowed persons to be detained if they were "mentally ill and in need of supervision, care or treatment" (Wexler, p. 74). Criteria with this breadth seem unsupportable to most commentators. For example, many persons with a moderate degree of depression are mentally ill in that they satisfy the criteria in the *Diagnostic and Statistical Manual, Fourth Edition* (DSM- IV) (American Psychiatric Association, 1994) for having a psychiatric disorder, and treatment almost certainly would make them feel better. No one, however, thinks that in most cases they should be forced into a psychiatric hospital if they do not wish to go. Thus, more than *mental illness* is necessary to justify commitment.

A narrower position is taken by many psychiatrists (see Chodoff for a classic description of this position and Buchanan and Brock for clear arguments supporting it). In addition to requiring that a person be mentally ill, supporters of this position advocate a criterion stipulating that that person be *gravely disabled* or manifest a *serious disruption of functioning* as a result of the mental illness. Being physically dangerous to oneself (suicidal) or to others (homicidal or physically threatening) represents one type of serious disruption of functioning but not the only one. The behavioral and social disorganization shown by many manic persons, for example, although often not immediately physically threatening to themselves or to others, may in the long run cause those persons serious social and financial harm. Under a *serious disruption* criterion many of those individuals could be committed.

A narrower position still is that advocated by many civil libertarians and some psychiatrists (American Bar Association). A diagnosis of mental illness is required, and there must be a high probability that because of the mental illness a person is a serious physical threat to himself or herself or to others. A minority in this group would restrict the criterion further and require that there be good evidence of recent behavior toward oneself or others that was in fact physically harmful, but most believe that evidence of strong threats of physical harm is sufficient. Most also believe that dangerousness toward oneself can be evidenced not only by threats of suicide but also by extreme self-neglect so that, for example, starvation or untreated serious disease can constitute an immediate threat. However, without the threat of imminent dangerousness of some kind, commitment would not be allowed.

The position at the far end of the continuum is taken by those who believe that psychiatric commitment is never ethically justified and thus that there should be no commitment criteria. Thomas Szasz, a psychiatrist, has been the foremost spokesperson for this position. Szasz believes that the concept of mental illness is mythical and argues that those who manifest what others regard as the symptoms of mental illness should be judged only by the standards of criminal law: If they have broken a law, they may be arrested or otherwise constrained; if they have not, their freedom

should be preserved. Szasz believes that commitment is based on a false theory that "medicalizes" deviant behavior into illness and that psychiatrists who commit persons become unwitting arms of the criminal justice system.

For several reasons Szasz's position has not been persuasive to many people inside or outside psychiatry, including most civil libertarians. First, most scholars feel that some psychological conditions satisfy the criteria of a definition of *illness* (Gert, Culver, and Clouser, Margolis) and that Szasz's position has serious theoretical problems (Moore, Culver, and Gert) that he has not addressed. Second and more important, most believe that paternalistic interventions of the type that commitment usually represents are at least sometimes ethically justified.

The principal and enduring tension is between those who hold the two middle positions described above. Some states have commitment statutes closer to one, and some have statutes closer to the other. Those who advocate a broader criterion believe that dangerousness to oneself and others is only one of many manifestations of severe mental illness and that it is cruel and theoretically unjustifiable to ignore the needs of disordered or disabled persons, often homeless and wandering the streets, who clearly would benefit from treatment (Treffert, Peele, and Chodoff; American Psychiatric Association, 2001a). References are made to people "dying with their rights on" and to Janis Joplin's song line "Freedom's just another word for nothin' left to lose."

Those who advocate the narrower grounds fear that relaxing the criterion in the direction of *disruption of functioning* leaves the door open too wide to psychiatric paternalism and represents a threat to civil liberties. Images of forced psychiatric internment of political dissidents in the Soviet Union (Bloch and Reddaway) are invoked as a frightening example of giving psychiatrists the power to confine individuals who are not physically dangerous but only *disrupted* in their functioning. One of the necessary and willing prices of having a free society, they argue, is that people are free to make self-defeating choices and sometimes irrationally reject opportunities for help.

A cohort of persons are committable under a broader but not under a narrower set of criteria. An example is a person with a history of bipolar disorder who becomes increasingly hypomanic and is squandering his carefully accumulated savings in what are almost certainly hopeless financial schemes. He refuses all treatment. Everyone who knows him believes that his spending spree is due to his hypomania, that it would not be unethical to curtail his actions, and that if his behavior were curtailed, he almost certainly would be grateful later. However, although his current behavior is harmful to his long-term interests, he is not *dangerous to himself or others* as that criterion is explicated in many states.

Many persons, like this man, whose behavior meets broader but not narrower commitment criteria suffer from cyclical disorders: Their aberrant behavior occurs only episodically. Some authors have suggested that such persons might be offered during nonsymptomatic times the opportunity to create a contract stating that if their future behavior deviates from their usual behavior in certain specified ways, they will accept the use of appropriate interventions (confiscation of funds or forced hospitalization, *voluntary commitment*) that otherwise might not be legally permissible (Howell et al., Culver and Gert).

An important empirical issue discussed by Peele and Chodoff is the extent to which statutory criteria for commitment influence the behavior of psychiatrists. Are there patients who are not committed in states with narrow criteria who would be committed in states with broader criteria? Peele and Chodoff, after surveying the scanty evidence that exists on this point, conclude, "It appears that judges and juries base decisions about commitment on what they think is best for the person, regardless of formal criteria" (Peele and Chodoff, p. 436). This would be a useful issue to explore further.

Conceptual Issues Underlying Commitment

ETHICAL JUSTIFICATION. In discussing the ethical justification of commitment a distinction must be made between whether a commitment is intended primarily to help the person who is committed or to help others whom that person may be putting at risk (Gert, Culver, and Clouser; Buchanan and Brock). This distinction sometimes is not clear-cut because it is usually to the advantage of mentally ill persons to be prevented from harming others. The harm they might cause often would be serious and thus would constitute a crime. Committing the crime frequently would be a clear result of the mental illness—for example, obeying a voice commanding that someone be killed—and it is highly likely that the mentally ill offender would be apprehended, incarcerated, and then punished or at least hospitalized for a long time. Nonetheless, there is a distinction between paternalistic and nonpaternalistic commitments, and there is no doubt that the protection of others is the predominant reason for some commitments.

Paternalistic commitment. To the extent that commitment is intended to help the person who is committed, it essentially always qualifies as a paternalistic action. That is, the commitment is intended to benefit the committed person, it violates at least one moral rule (deprivation of freedom) and usually several, it is done without the consent of the person, and the person is at least minimally competent to give consent (Gert, Culver, and Clouser). Whether paternalistic commitment is ethically justified therefore depends on whether a particular commitment meets whatever theoretical criteria for justified paternalism are thought to be adequate.

Various sets of criteria, partly overlapping, have been proposed by Beauchamp and Childress, Buchanan and Brock, Childress, and Gert, Culver, and Clouser. Those criteria depend on theoretical concepts such as the degree of irrationality and voluntariness of the person's behavior and the balancing of physician beneficence and patient autonomy. None of those authors seems to believe that as a species of paternalism, there is anything qualitatively unique about committing mentally ill individuals. Thus, particular acts of commitment are measured directly against the theoretical criteria of the particular justification procedure that is proposed.

However, in the judgment of many authors (Culver and Gert; Buchanan and Brock), the presence of mental illness does play an indirect role in the justification of paternalistic commitment by sometimes affecting concepts that those authors believe are centrally important in the justification process. Thus, some suicidal desires may be regarded as not truly expressing an individual's autonomous wishes (Beauchamp and Childress), or some conditions of mental illness may be thought to affect a person's competence to make decisions (Buchanan and Brock).

Nonpaternalistic commitment. When commitment is not paternalistic, it must be ethically justified on other grounds. To commit persons in an attempt to prevent them from harming others represents a kind of preventive detention that ordinarily is not legally permitted in the United States. In the presence of some kinds of mental illness, however, it is argued by some that nonpaternalistic commitment may be ethically justified.

For example, two men are brought separately to the emergency room by the police. In each instance the police have been called because the man has just threatened to kill his wife. Each man admits to the emergency room psychiatrist that this is true. The first man has a history of paranoid psychotic episodes and in recent days has heard voices instructing him to kill his wife. The second man has no symptoms or history of major mental illness, but he and his wife have a history of chronic marital discord. In both cases the psychiatrist feels that there is a reasonably high probability that the man will harm his wife if he returns home.

On the basis of the fact that in some kinds of mental illnesses persons are not held responsible for their actions, it may be argued that it is ethically justified to commit the first man but not the second. The second man, for example, presumably has the volitional ability to will or to refrain from willing to harm his wife, whereas the first may not have the volitional ability to will not to harm her (Culver and Gert). Dangerous mentally ill persons sometimes are not considered capable of guiding their behavior in accordance with promulgated social rules (Brock).

PREDICTING POSSIBLE FUTURE HARM. Civil commitment always involves a doctor's appraising a person's physical and mental status and deciding whether commitment is warranted. Sometimes individuals may be committed because they are in such a disabled condition that even more serious future harm seems all but inevitable. A woman may, for example, be hallucinating continuously, be unresponsive to the questions or actions of others, and be significantly malnourished because of a lack of interest in food. Much more often, however, serious future harm is only a possibility: For example, a person has threatened suicide or is hearing voices urging her to harm someone, and the physician must try to predict how likely it is that the harm actually will occur.

The process of predicting possible future harm in the commitment setting has the following components (Grisso): The criterion is what is being predicted (for example, the person's suicide), the cues are discrete pieces of available information about a particular case at a particular point in time (for example, the person's age, sex, state of intoxication, and history of impulsivity), and the judgment is the physician's conclusion after assessing the case (for example, to commit or not to commit). These are three separate elements. Empirical research has focused separately on the correlations among them. The judgment-criterion correlation shows how well physicians do in predicting that particular persons will kill themselves. The cues-criterion correlation shows the extent to which suicides can be predicted from whatever facts about cases can be isolated and measured independently of physicians' judgments. The cues-judgment correlation shows which data about cases lead physicians to make one judgment or another.

A critically important issue with respect to prediction is the extent to which commitment does prevent future serious harm. There are few data addressing this issue. If it were known, for example, that 90 percent of the persons committed would have harmed themselves or others seriously if they had not been committed, most people probably would feel that commitment was ethically justified. Committing one hundred persons would avoid ninety instances of serious harm, although at the *cost* of committing ten persons who

would not have caused harm if they had not been committed. By contrast, if only one in a hundred persons would have harmed themselves or others, few would feel commitment was justified because ninety-nine persons would have suffered the evils of detainment to prevent one bad future outcome.

This kind of utilitarian calculus seems central to most writers who discuss the ethical justifiability of commitment. Commitment essentially always inflicts significant harm, but only sometimes does it prevent significant harm. Almost everyone acknowledges that even among those at relatively high risk of causing harm—for example, suicidal persons brought to an emergency room—only a minority would, if left alone, subsequently harm themselves. An emergency room physician thus faces a difficult task. To commit every person would be to commit too many, but which persons should be committed? Certain characteristics of persons (cues) are known to increase the likelihood of future harmful acts—for example, a history of impulsive or suicidal behavior, being inebriated, having access to lethal weapons, being male—but a physician must make a binary, yes-no decision about commitment, not a probability estimate.

Research (Monahan) suggests that physicians are poor predictors of whether harmful behavior will occur (judgment-criterion correlations). There is reason to believe that basing predictions on discrete, measurable pieces of information about a case (cues-criterion correlations) will yield greater accuracy (Monahan). There is, however, probably an upper limit to predictive accuracy; one reason for this is that whether a person commits a harmful act in the hours or days after a physician's assessment may depend at least as much on later fortuitous situational factors such as whether a friend returns a telephone call as on factors that can be measured during the assessment.

A very important statistical feature of prediction plays a key role in understanding the commitment process and making ethical judgements about it. In predicting relatively rare events such as the occurrence of a future suicide through the use of predictive signs of less than extremely high predictive accuracy (for example, a physician's judgment or whether a person has access to a lethal weapon), one inevitably will make a high proportion of false-positive predictions; that is, one frequently will predict future harm when in fact none will occur. This actuarial problem, which is an example of the application of Bayes' theorem, was described by Meehl and Rosen and later applied to the issue of commitment by Livermore, Malmquist, and Meehl.

Suppose that 10 percent of suicidal persons who are brought to an emergency room but are unwilling to be hospitalized would kill or harm themselves seriously if they were not committed. Suppose further that, using the available cues, physicians' predictions of who will and will not commit suicide have a sensitivity of 70 percent (*sensitivity* refers to the percentage of persons who will commit suicide whom physicians accurately predict will commit suicide) and a specificity of 70 percent (*specificity* refers to the percentage of patients who will not commit suicide whom physicians accurately predict will not commit suicide). It follows that physicians will commit and thus *save* seven of the ten persons destined for suicide but also will commit twenty-seven persons of every ninety persons (30% of ninety) who would not have killed themselves. These latter persons constitute false positives.

The ratio between the number of true positives (seven) and false positives (twenty-seven) shows that nearly four persons will be committed needlessly in order to save one. (These are hypothetical figures. Many would argue that subsequent suicide is rarer than 10 percent in the general psychiatric suicidal population and that 70 percent is too high an estimate of sensitivity (and of specificity); thus, the actual proportion of false positives would be much higher.) The physician would be correct a higher percentage of the time (90%) if he or she simply predicted that no one would commit suicide, but then none of the ten suicidal persons would be saved.

Is it ethically justified to commit four unwilling persons needlessly to save one life? Suppose empirical data existed (they do not) that enabled the construction of actuarial tables that would correlate the nature and number of signs and symptoms shown by mentally ill persons in emergency rooms with their subsequent likelihood of harming themselves or others if they were not committed (cue-criterion correlations). Each person thus could be assigned to a cohort: Some would have a one in five chance of harming themselves or others, some a one in ten chance, some one in twenty, some one in forty, and so forth.

Where should the line be drawn? What is the appropriate trade-off between saving one life and needlessly depriving many persons of their freedom? Reasonable people might disagree about where the line should be drawn, but this is a matter that could be opened to public debate. Psychiatrists probably have no special expertise in deciding where the threshold for commitment should be placed.

When confronted with the inevitable large numbers of false-positive commitments, some people recall the injunction often cited in connection with the U.S. criminal justice system—"Better that ten guilty persons go free than one innocent person suffer"—and conclude that civil commitment is ethically unjustified (Sartorius). Others, however, although concerned about the false-positive problem, believe that there are sufficient differences between the underlying conceptual justifications of the criminal justice system and the civil commitment system that some number of false positives can be tolerated in the civil system (Brock).

Conclusion

Although debates about involuntary hospitalization sometimes are framed in legal rather than ethical terms, it is important to be clear about the underlying ethical issues. Civil commitment involves incarcerating an unwilling person who has committed no crime for days, weeks, or longer. This type of prima facie unethical action requires clear justification in terms of a general moral theory. Current theoretical discussions of commitment emphasize concepts such as the degree of irrationality and the extent of voluntariness of a person's behavior. In applying theoretical concepts to the process of commitment it is critical to describe the components of the process clearly and take into account certain statistical features that are inherent in making predictions about a person's future behavior.

CHARLES M. CULVER (1995)
REVISED BY AUTHOR

SEE ALSO: *Autonomy; Behavior Control; Coercion; Competence; Human Rights; Institutionalization and Deinstitutionalization; Mental Illness; Mentally Disabled and Mentally Ill Persons; Patients' Rights: Mental Patients' Rights*

BIBLIOGRAPHY

American Bar Association. 1977. "Legal Issues in State Mental Health Care: Proposals for Change." *Mental Disability Law Reporter* 2(1): 57–159.

American Psychiatric Association. 1994. *Diagnostic and Statistical Manual of Mental Disorders, Fourth Edition* Washington, D.C.: Author.

American Psychiatric Association. 2001a. *Ethics Primer.* Washington, D.C.: Author.

American Psychiatric Association. 2001b. *Principles of Medical Ethics with Annotations Especially Applicable to Psychiatry.* Washington, D.C.: Author.

Appelbaum, Paul. 1997. "Almost a Revolution: An International Perspective on Involuntary Commitment." *Journal of the Academy of Psychiatry and Law* 25: 135–148.

Arthur, Lindsay G.; Haimovitz, Stephan; Lockwood, Robert W.; Dooley, Jeanne A.; and Parry, John W., eds. 1988. *Involuntary Civil Commitment: A Manual for Lawyers and Judges.* Washington, D.C.: American Bar Association.

Beauchamp, Tom L., and Childress, James F. 2001. *Principles of Biomedical Ethics,* 5th edition. New York: Oxford University Press.

Behnke, Stephen H.; Winick, Bruce J.; and Perez, Alina M. 2000. *The Essentials of Florida Mental Health Law.* New York: Norton.

Bloch, Sidney, and Reddaway, Paul. 1977. *Psychiatric Terror.* New York: Basic Books.

Brock, Dan W. 1980. "Involuntary Civil Commitment: The Moral Issues." In *Mental Illness: Law and Public Policy,* ed. Baruch A. Brody and H. Tristram Engelhardt, Jr. Boston: D. Reidel.

Buchanan, Allen E., and Brock, Dan W. 1989. *Deciding for Others: The Ethics of Surrogate Decision Making.* New York: Cambridge University Press.

Childress, James F. 1982. *Who Should Decide? Paternalism in Health Care.* New York: Oxford University Press.

Chodoff, Paul. 1976. "The Case for Involuntary Hospitalization of the Mentally Ill." *American Journal of Psychiatry* 133(5): 496–501.

Culver, Charles M. 1991. "Health Care Ethics and Mental Health Law." In *Law and Mental Health: Major Developments and Research Needs,* ed. Saleem A. Shah and Bruce D. Sales. Rockville, MD: U.S. Department of Health and Human Services.

Culver, Charles M., and Gert, Bernard. 1982. *Philosophy in Medicine: Conceptual and Ethical Issues in Medicine and Psychiatry.* New York: Oxford University Press.

Gert, Bernard; Culver, Charles M.; and Clouser, K. Danner. 1997. *Bioethics: A Return to Fundamentals.* New York: Oxford University Press.

Grisso, Thomas. 1991. "Clinical Assessments for Legal Decision Making: Research Recommendations." In *Law and Mental Health: Major Developments and Research Needs,* ed. Saleem A. Shah and Bruce D. Sales. Rockville, MD: U.S. Department of Health and Human Services.

Howell, Timothy; Diamond, Ronald J.; and Wikler, Daniel. 1982. "Is There a Case for Voluntary Commitment?" In *Contemporary Issues in Bioethics,* 2nd edition, ed. Tom L. Beauchamp and LeRoy Walters. Belmont, CA: Wadsworth.

Livermore, Joseph M.; Malmquist, Carl P.; and Meehl, Paul E. 1968. "On the Justifications for Civil Commitment." *University of Pennsylvania Law Review* 117(1): 75–96.

Margolis, Joseph. 1976. "The Concept of Disease." *Journal of Medicine and Philosophy* 1(3): 238–255.

Meehl, Paul E., and Rosen, Albert. 1955. "Antecedent Probability and the Efficiency of Psychometric Signs, Patterns, and Cutting Scores." *Psychological Bulletin* 52(3): 194–216.

Monahan, John. 1984. "The Prediction of Violent Behavior: Toward a Second Generation of Theory and Policy." *American Journal of Psychiatry* 141(1): 10–15.

Moore, Michael S. 1975. "Some Myths about 'Mental Illness.'" *Archives of General Psychiatry* 32(12): 1483–1497.

Peele, Roger, and Chodoff, Paul. 1999. "The Ethics of Involuntary Treatment and Deinstitutionalization." In *Psychiatric*

Ethics, ed. Sidney Bloch, Paul Chodoff, and Stephen A. Green. New York: Oxford University Press.

Sartorius, Rolf E. 1980. "Paternalistic Grounds for Involuntary Civil Commitment: A Utilitarian Perspective." In *Mental Illness: Law and Public Policy,* ed. Baruch A. Brody and H. Tristram Engelhardt, Jr. Boston: D. Reidel.

Szasz, Thomas S. 1970. *Ideology and Insanity: Essays on the Psychiatric Dehumanization of Man.* Garden City, NY: Anchor.

Treffert, Darold A. 1985. "The Obviously Ill Patient in Need of Treatment: A Fourth Standard for Civil Commitment." *Hospital and Community Psychiatry* 36(3): 259–264.

Wexler, David B. 1981. *Mental Health Law: Major Issues.* New York: Plenum.

MENTALLY DISABLED AND MENTALLY ILL PERSONS

• • •

I. Healthcare Issues

II. Research Issues

I. HEALTHCARE ISSUES

Primary healthcare providers for patients with mental illnesses bear the same ethical obligations as providers who serve patients with physical illnesses, yet they face special challenges in upholding those obligations. When mental illness causes a patient to be violent or suicidal, clinicians may confront situations in which their duties to the patient conflict with other ethical duties. At times, the decision about which duty to obey involves careful moral consideration. Additionally, because mentally ill persons are particularly vulnerable to abuse, the clinician has a special obligation to protect such patients against abuses.

For example, in the case of a patient who has attempted suicide, the duty to respect the patient's autonomy may conflict with the duty to protect the patient from harm. The patient may wish to go home, yet the clinician—who may be a physician in a hospital emergency room, a psychiatrist, or the patient's therapist—may decide to hospitalize the patient. At this point, the patient's fundamental right to refuse care has been denied. The moral justification may seem clear: The patient is not thinking rationally, so he or she should not be permitted to function autonomously. The patient deserves an explanation about why he or she is being hospitalized and has a right to information about the legal routes for challenging the decision.

It's true that in some cases, suicide may be a carefully reasoned choice. Far more often, though, planning or attempting to harm oneself results from a clinical depression or other psychiatric disorder. Discerning whether a patient's suicide reflects a rational decision is typically not possible in an emergency room setting. It would be ethical to hospitalize a patient to prevent suicide until a more thorough assessment could take place, including discussions with family members and or with healthcare providers who have known the patient over a long period of time.

Even when the clinician's overriding moral duties are clear, actual situations are complicated. There is often disagreement among patients, clinicians, families, and the courts about whether a patient's rights may be denied. This article explores common moral dilemmas in the medical and psychiatric care of individuals who are experiencing a major mental illness, such as schizophrenia or clinical depression, and those who suffer from the serious deficits in memory and intellectual functioning seen in dementia or mental retardation. Health professionals caring for such patients are likely to face one or more of the following questions and ethical concerns:

1. Does the person with mental illness have the capacity to decide about suggested treatments (informed consent for treatment)?

2. When is it ethical to hospitalize mentally ill persons against their will (commitment)?

3. Is it ethical to treat mentally ill persons against their will with psychiatric medications (coerced treatment)?

4. Is it ethical to use coercive methods to encourage a mentally ill person to comply with prescribed treatments (coerced compliance)?

5. When is it ethical to withhold information from a person because that person has a history of serious mental illness (truth-telling)?

6. When is it ethical to breach the confidentiality of a mentally ill patient (confidentiality)?

7. Under what circumstances is it ethical to withhold scarce health resources from a person because that person is seriously mentally ill (allocation of scarce resources)?

Informed Consent for Treatment

No patient should be treated by a doctor without first being informed about the nature of the treatment and then consenting to have the treatment. When a person with a history of serious mental illness is being treated for a medical condition, his or her doctors may consult a psychiatrist about the patient's capacity to make medical decisions.

Assessing the capacity to make medical decisions need not involve a comprehensive evaluation of intellectual functioning. A straightforward discussion regarding a patient's understanding of a specific medical decision is usually sufficient. The psychiatrist asks questions about the nature of the illness and possible treatments and determines from the responses if the patient understands the problem, the treatment choices, and the likely consequences of a given decision. A formal judgment of medical competence can only be made in court (Appelbaum and Grisso). However, the psychiatrist's informal evaluation can guide treatment in most clinical situations.

A person whose mental abilities are partly impaired may be competent to make certain decisions about medical care. This situation can arise with an elderly person who suffers from mild dementia or a younger person affected by mild mental retardation (Kaplan, Strang, and Ahmed). For this reason, decision-making capacity must be assessed on a case-by-case basis.

Also, a person who is incompetent at one time may be competent at another. Delirium and depression, conditions seen frequently among patients hospitalized for medical reasons, are examples of conditions that temporarily disrupt clear thinking. A person who is delirious or depressed may be found incompetent to refuse treatment, yet when the delirium clears or the depression lifts, that person is considered competent.

Consider the case of a thirty-five-year-old man with kidney failure (Shuchman and Wilkes). Doctors told him that he required dialysis to take over the function of his kidneys. The man refused dialysis, saying he would rather die. A psychiatrist determined that the man suffered from a severe depression that was interfering with his ability to think rationally, and the man was deemed lacking in the capacity to make medical decisions. Over time, and with treatment, including antidepressant medication, the depression resolved. Eventually, the man's doctors judged him capable of making treatment decisions. However, the man's uplifted spirits did not alter his desire to stop dialysis. The lifesaving technology was discontinued and he died within a few days. Though the outcome may be death, respect for patient autonomy requires that competent patients be allowed to refuse therapies (Angell; Hebert and Weingarten).

Commitment

Though involuntary confinement of mental patients decreased markedly over the last three decades of the twentieth century, it is still an essential tool used to protect patients who are potentially dangerous due to a mental illness. Since hospitalizing a patient against his or her will necessarily denies the patient's autonomy, it is essential that the act be morally justified. Yet, what qualifies as such justification is controversial.

During the 1960s, a person *in need of treatment due to mental disorder* met the criteria for involuntary admission to a psychiatric hospital in most states and provinces; in the 2000s, the criteria are significantly narrower. Individuals may be involuntarily hospitalized if they are deemed a danger to themselves (for example, if they are about to attempt suicide), a danger to others, or are unable to care for themselves due to mental illness. Typically, the assessment leading to involuntary hospitalization is done by a mental health professional, though such requirements vary in different states and provinces. Once confined, the person may be hospitalized for up to a few days. If commitment extends beyond a specified brief period, a court hearing generally must be held to determine whether further involuntary confinement is appropriate. The courts have also encouraged treatment of psychiatric patients in less restrictive settings than inpatient hospital wards when possible. Other treatment options include "day hospital" programs that allow patients to return home at night, and case management programs that ensure daily checks on outpatients.

In practical terms, the decision to hospitalize someone involuntarily is often a difficult one. Consider a woman who is depressed and has attempted suicide. She might be safest in a hospital, since there is a risk of her making a second suicide attempt while she remains depressed. But safety alone cannot be a reason for hospitalization, as very few of those who attempt suicide will go on to successfully complete suicides in the future. This woman might be safe outside a hospital if she is engaged in frequent outpatient counseling. Commonly, psychiatrists making a decision about committing a patient consider factors known to raise the risk that the person will be harmed or will harm themselves. For example, an individual who has made a serious suicide attempt in the past is at higher risk.

During the late 1980s, psychiatrists and patients' families began objecting to the narrowed commitment criteria, arguing that the rights of people with mental illness were being protected at the expense of their mental health (Appelbaum). These objections resulted in the grounds for commitment being broadened in some areas. The *outpatient commitment* system, in which outpatients are given court-ordered treatment or returned to the hospital in certain situations, is an example of the broadening of commitment laws to include individuals who are not clearly dangerous to themselves or others (Geller). This system, also referred to as *supervised discharge* or *community treatment orders* has been introduced in Australia, Canada, the United Kingdom, and

Europe as well as the United States. Though not problem-free, it appears to be an effective means of offering mental patients increased care with greater freedom than inpatient commitment provides (Swanson, Swartz, and Borum, et al. and Swartz, Swanson, and Wagner et al.).

Coerced Treatment

Ethics demands that a competent mental patient's refusal of treatment must be respected. Even a patient confined to a mental institution cannot be treated against his or her will, unless the patient poses an imminent threat of harm to others. This concept received extensive legal backing from court rulings during the 1980s. Courts in Massachusetts, New York, and California ruled that unless a patient was found incapable of making treatment decisions, he or she could not be treated involuntarily with antipsychotic medications. The rulings were motivated by reports that psychiatric medications were overused at mental hospitals and staff were often indifferent to patients' risks of drug side effects.

In many states and provinces, psychiatric medications have since evolved into a special legal category of treatment. Forcibly giving a patient psychiatric medication is only permissible if the patient is behaving in a violent manner or is actively threatening to do so. As a result, clinicians treating mental patients typically cannot medicate a refusing patient without involving the courts. By contrast, physicians do not need to consult a judge in order to commit mental patients to involuntary hospitalization. The result is that mentally ill and psychotic patients may be hospitalized against their will but cannot be medicated against their will (Appelbaum). In these situations, psychiatrists often seek permission from the courts to medicate the patient, arguing that the patient has benefited from medication before or is judged highly likely to benefit from medication.

The courts often grant the permission and treatment proceeds in a practice sometimes known as *medication over objection*. Studies suggest that once a court ruling in favor of treatment is issued, patients often accept oral antipsychotic medications under duress, thereby avoiding forced injections of medication (Greenberg, Moore-Duncan and Herron).

The more stringent criteria for involuntary medication became a focus of controversy on similar grounds as the controversy over narrower commitment criteria. Psychiatrists described mental patients who refuse medication as 'rotting with their rights on,' conveying the image of a person who is not thinking rationally and whose condition is steadily worsening, yet who cannot be treated appropriately or faces delays in treatment because of judicial restraints (Appelbaum and Gutheil).

The mid- to late 1990s saw the start of a movement towards the use of psychiatric *advance directives*. These are treatment guides prepared by chronically mentally ill patients who are capable of making decisions about their psychiatric treatment when they are functioning well but experience repeated episodes of impaired decision-making during relapses. Most states accept advance psychiatric directives in some form but a survey suggests that psychiatric *advance directives* are easily ignored in crisis situations (Backlar, McFarland, Bentson, Swanson and Mahler).

Another area of care in which doctors may seek legal opinions regarding involuntary medication involves severely mentally ill female patients who decline birth-control treatments. Some authors suggest that there are situations in which it would be ethical to act to prevent pregnancy in patients who are incompetent to make medical decisions (McCullough, Coverdale, Bayer, et al.). The courts have held that when a mentally incompetent woman is pregnant, decisions about her obstetric care should involve a determination about what the woman would want if she were competent (Curran). In practice, when a severely mentally ill woman becomes a mother, child-welfare agencies are asked to evaluate the woman's ability to care for her child. In extreme cases, this evaluation may lead to court proceedings that can result in the woman's losing custody of her child.

Coerced Compliance

The idea that a patient's decisions must be voluntary is central to the concepts of patient autonomy and informed consent. Exceptions to the idea of voluntariness, such as commitment and involuntary medication, have been viewed as last resorts for patients considered incapable of making rational decisions. Occasionally, however, coercive methods are used to encourage mentally ill individuals to comply with treatments, even when these individuals' decision-making capacities are not in question. Substance-abusing pregnant women comprise one group that is increasingly coerced into treatment, either via incarceration or via compulsory addiction treatment programs (Abel and Kruger). This use of coerced compliance has been supported by state courts as a means of protecting the woman's future child. Yet the practice is controversial because the potential protection it affords the fetus requires overriding a competent adult's treatment decisions (Chavkin and Paltrow).

The coercive methods used with chronic mental patients are more subtle. An example is a man with a chronic mental illness who received disability payments from the government because of his mental condition. The man's government check was sent to the mental-health clinic where he was treated. To receive his check, the man was required to show up for his therapy session. The therapist believed this was a useful technique for encouraging adherence to treatment in a patient with disorganized thinking.

Mental-health practitioners justify such paternalistic strategies as a means of preventing deterioration in a patient's condition but such clinical justifications may not stand up to moral scrutiny. Yet these kinds of practices would be ethical if they were discussed openly with the patient and the patient consented.

Truth-Telling

A physician or therapist who shields a patient from the truth about his or her illness may unwittingly cause mistrust of care providers and of the medical system in a patient who needs to depend on that system (Sheldon). Yet clinicians caring for seriously mentally ill individuals sometimes do withhold information.

In one example, a physician withheld a diagnosis of cancer from a patient with a history of depression and suicide attempts (Lo). The physician feared that disclosing to the patient that she had a terminal illness could precipitate a suicide attempt. His intention was to protect the patient from harm, but the patient probably should have been informed about her diagnosis.

Though patients in general are likely to be told their diagnoses, studies of patients in psychiatric hospitals from the 1980s found that important information was frequently withheld from such patients. For example, psychiatric patients were prescribed medicines without being informed about potentially serious risks of the medicines (Lidz, Meisel, Zerubavel, et al.; Beck). More recent studies suggest that patients continue to be underinformed about their medications (Schachter and Kleinman). For informed decision making, a patient needs to understand the benefits and risks of prescribed medications and why the doctor believes that the benefits outweigh the risks.

Patients, even those with mental illnesses and disabilities, expect and deserve to be told the truth. This does not mean that the truth should be disclosed insensitively. Health professionals should consider how to convey difficult information in a manner most appropriate to a particular patient, but the information should be provided. Psychiatric patients, like all medical patients, need to feel they can trust their healthcare providers.

Confidentiality

All doctor-patient relationships demand confidentiality. In the special setting of psychotherapy the need to protect a patient's privacy can be paramount. The special importance of confidentiality in psychotherapy was underscored by a 1996 Supreme Court ruling that protects a patient's statements to a psychotherapist from compelled disclosure (*Jaffee v. Redmond*).

But a patient's need for privacy must be balanced against the rights and needs of others. Suppose a man in treatment for alcohol abuse reveals that he has been aggressive toward his child while intoxicated. State laws mandate the reporting of incidents of child abuse, yet a physician or counselor who reported this man would breach the patient's confidentiality. Here, the clinician must consider whether the man's actions towards his child constitute an offense that must be reported in order to protect this child or others in the future. The decision is made all the more difficult because the man's treatment could help to keep his child safe from harm yet the man may leave treatment if he feels the clinician has betrayed him to state authorities.

Situations other than child abuse pose similar dilemmas. Rules about a physician's duty to warn and protect a person who is threatened by a patient now apply in most states and provinces. Such rules do not dictate a therapist's decision, however. Since the majority of threats made by patients do not represent serious danger to others, clinical judgment is required to decide whether a threat, that a patient utters during the course of a psychotherapy session or merits a breach in confidentiality (Weinstock).

Allocation of Scarce Resources

It would be unjust to withhold healthcare resources from a mental patient strictly due to her mental illness. Yet an exception is sometimes made in the case of extremely scarce resources, such as organ transplants. A patient who is chronically mentally ill and also has severe liver or kidney disease might benefit from a transplant. But persons who receive transplants require drug-induced immunosuppression for the rest of their lives to prevent graft rejection, and it can be difficult for mental patients to comply with such extensive follow-up care (Bunzel and Laederach). Reasoning that transplanted organs should go to patients who will reap the most benefit from them, transplant programs may withhold organs from individuals who are seriously mentally ill (Wolcott). In a survey of heart-transplant programs, most programs considered certain psychiatric conditions to be an absolute contraindication to transplant: A person who has schizophrenia with active psychotic symptoms, or a person with a history of multiple suicide attempts will be automatically denied a transplant (Olbrisch and Levenson).

Such automatic denials are not clearly ethical. In the event that a transplant candidate has a serious mental illness,

it is important that the potential for treating the mental illness be considered before the patient is refused a transplant (Council on Ethical and Judicial Affairs). The patient's desire to commit suicide, for example, may be caused by a treatable depression. For transplant programs, the question of how to respond to evidence of a patient's psychological instability is difficult. Case-by-case evaluations of individual patients may yield greater fairness in these sorts of situations than systematically applying formal guidelines. Some patients with mental illness may benefit from early intervention and psychosocial support, while other patients may be unable to adhere to post-transplantation treatment regimens even with help.

Conclusion

In a number of key areas, a mentally ill person may lose certain rights with regard to medical and psychiatric treatment due to the effects of mental illness. As a result, healthcare providers who care for such patients can face difficult ethical dilemmas. The decision to hospitalize a mentally ill person involuntarily is often easily justified on moral grounds. However, decisions to breach a patient's confidentiality, or to withhold scarce resources such as organ transplants, are generally not as clear. Finally, it is probably rare that a physician or therapist who withholds the truth from the patient, or coerces the patient into complying with a recommended treatment, will be acting in an ethical manner.

MIRIAM SHUCHMAN (1995)
REVISED BY AUTHOR

SEE ALSO: *Autonomy; Coercion; Confidentiality; Electroconvusive Therapy; Freedom and Free Will; Healthcare Resources, Allocation of: Microallocation; Information Disclosure, Ethical Issues of; Informed Consent: Issues of Consent in Mental Healthcare; Medicaid; Medicare; Mental Health Therapies; Mental Institutions, Commitment to; Patients' Rights: Mental Patients' Rights; Psychopharmacology; Psychosurgery, Ethical Aspects of,* and other *Mentally Disabled and Mentally Ill Persons* subentries

BIBLIOGRAPHY

Abel Ernest L, and Kruger, Michael. 2002. "Physician Attitudes Concerning Legal Coercion of Pregnant Alcohol and Drug Abusers." *American Journal of Obstetrics and Gynecology* 186: 768–772.

Angell, Marcia. 1984. "Respecting the Autonomy of Competent Patients." *New England Journal of Medicine* 310(17): 1115–1116.

Appelbaum, Paul S. 1987. "Crazy in the Streets." *Commentary* 83(5): 34–39.

Appelbaum, Paul S., and Grisso, Thomas. 1988. "Assessing Patients' Capacities to Consent to Treatment." *New England Journal of Medicine* 319(25): 1635–1638.

Appelbaum, Paul S., and Gutheil, Thomas G. 1979. "'Rotting with Their Rights On': Constitutional Theory and Clinical Reality in Drug Refusal by Psychiatric Patients." *Bulletin of the American Academy of Psychiatry and Law* 7(3): 306–315.

Appelbaum Paul S. 1994. *Almost a Revolution: Mental Health Law and the Limits of Change.* New York: Oxford University Press.

Backlar, Patricia; McFarland, Bentson H.; Swanson, Jeffrey W.; and Mahler Jo. 2001. "Consumer, Provider, and Informal Caregiver Opinions on Psychiatric Advance Directives." *Administration and Policy in Mental Health* 28(6): 427–441.

Beck, James C. 1988. "Determining Competency to Assent to Neuroleptic Drug Treatment." *Hospital and Community Psychiatry* 39(10): 1106–1108.

Bunzel, B., and Laederach, H. K. 2000. "Solid Organ Transplantation: Are There Predictors for Post-Transplant Noncompliance? A Literature Overview." *Transplant* 70(5): 711–716.

Chavkin, Wendy, and Paltrow, Lynn M. 2003. "Physician Attitudes Concerning Legal Coercion of Pregnant Alcohol and Drug Users." *American Journal of Obstetrics and Gynecology* 188(1): 298.

Council on Ethical and Judicial Affairs of the American Medical Association. 1995. "Ethical Considerations in the Allocation of Organs and Other Scarce Medical Resources Among Patients." *Archives of Internal Medicine* 155: 29–40.

Curran, William J. 1990. "Court-Ordered Cesarean Sections Receive Judicial Defeat." *New England Journal of Medicine* 323(7): 489–492.

Greenberg, W.; Moore-Duncan, L.; and Herron, R. 1996. "Patients' Attitudes Toward Having Been Forcibly Medicated." *Bulletin of the American Academy of Psychiatry & the Law* 24(4): 513–524.

Hebert, P., and Weingarten, M. 1991. "The Ethics of Forced Feeding in Anorexia Nervosa." *Canadian Medical Association Journal* 144: 141–144.

Kaplan, Kenneth H.; Strang, J. Peter; and Ahmed, Iqbal. 1988. "Dementia, Mental Retardation, and Competency to Make Decisions." *General Hospital Psychiatry* 10(6): 385–388.

Lidz, Charles W.; Meisel, Alan; Zerubavel, Eviatar; et al. 1984. *Informed Consent: A Study of Decision-Making in Psychiatry.* New York: Guilford.

Lo, Bernard. 2000. *Resolving Ethical Dilemmas: A Guide for Clinicians,* 2nd edition. Philadelphia: Lippincott Williams & Wilkins.

McCullough, Larry B.; Coverdale, John; Bayer, Timothy; and Chervenak, Frank A. 1992. "Ethically Justified Guidelines for Family Planning Interventions to Prevent Pregnancy in Female Patients with Chronic Mental Illness." *American Journal of Obstetrics and Gynecology* 167(1): 19–25.

Olbrisch, Mary Ellen, and Levenson, James L. 1991. "Psychosocial Evaluation of Heart Transplant Candidates: An International Survey of Process, Criteria and Outcomes." *Journal of Heart and Lung Transplantation* 10(6): 948–955.

Roth, Loren H. 1989. "Four Studies of Mental Health Commitment." *American Journal of Psychiatry* 146(2): 135–137.

Schachter, D., and Kleinman, I. 1998. "Psychiatrists' Documentation of Informed Consent." *Canadian Journal of Psychiatry* 43(10): 1012–1017.

Sheldon, Mark. 1982. "Truth Telling in Medicine." *Journal of the American Medical Association* 247(5): 651–654.

Shuchman, Miriam, and Wilkes, Michael S. 1988. "Who Is to Decide?" *New York Times Magazine* August 21: 44–46.

Swanson, Jeffrey W.; Swartz, Marvin S.; Borum, Randy; et al. 2000. "Involuntary Out-patient Commitment and Reduction of Violent Behaviour in Persons with Severe Mental Illness." *British Journal of Psychiatry* 176: 324–331.

Swartz, Marvin S.; Swanson, Jeffrey W.; Wagner, H. Ryan; et al. 1999. "Can Involuntary Outpatient Commitment Reduce Hospital Recidivism?: Findings From a Randomized Trial with Severely Mentally Ill Individuals." *American Journal of Psychiatry* 156: 1968–1975.

Weinstock, Robert. 1988. "Confidentiality and the New Duty to Protect: The Therapist's Dilemma." *Hospital and Community Psychiatry* 39(6): 607–609.

Wolcott, Deane L. 1990. "Organ Transplant Psychiatry: Psychiatry's Role in the Second Gift of Life." *Psychosomatics* 31(1): 91–97.

II. RESEARCH ISSUES

Protecting the interests of mentally ill and disabled people entails a delicate balance between two aims: a rigorous program of research into their medical problems and attention to the difficulties involved in using those people as subjects of research in ethically appropriate ways. Although the hope of understanding mental illnesses and disabilities depends on the results of medical research, persons who have those conditions are especially vulnerable to exploitation and abuse.

Research Guidelines

There are two major problems in conducting research on mentally ill and disabled persons. The first is competence, or decision-making capacity: Because of the nature of their problems some mentally ill and disabled subjects may not be able to make informed decisions about whether to participate in a research protocol. Issues surrounding informed consent are made even more problematic by the fact that mentally ill or disabled subjects may be living in institutions for patients with special mental disorders, and institutionalization can exert pressures that compromise a person's ability to make a free choice about participating in research. The second problem involves risk and the design of research studies. Under what circumstances, if any, can a mentally ill or disabled person be exposed to the risk of harm in a research study?

Some mentally ill or disabled persons may be incapable of giving valid informed consent to participate in a research study. However, prohibiting those potential subjects from participating would rule out much medical research that could benefit the subjects and others with similar disorders, in the long run harming the populations the studies are intended to protect. For that reason, since the last two decades of the twentieth century there has been a consensus that research on mentally ill and disabled persons can be justified in some cases, subject to certain conditions (National Bioethics Advisory Commission [NBAC]; Royal College of Psychiatrists [RCP]; Royal College of Physicians of London [RCPL], 1990; U.S. National Commission for the Protection of Human Subjects of Biomedical and Behavioral Research, 1978, 1979; Wing; World Medical Association; National Institutes of Health; Medical Research Council of Canada [MRCC]).

Perhaps the most important of those conditions is the stipulation that research on incompetent mentally ill or disabled persons should be allowed only if that research cannot be done on competent persons (National Bioethics Advisory Commission; Wing; U.S. National Commission for the Protection of Human Subjects, 1979). The guidelines for biomedical research proposed by the World Health Organization (WHO) and the Council for International Organizations of Medical Sciences (CIOMS) make that requirement explicit, arguing that because of the risks and burdens involved, medical research should not be done on individuals who are unable to choose to participate if it can equally well be done on competent adult volunteers (World Health Organization).

A second condition concerns the amount of risk to research subjects that may be allowed. Many professional and regulatory bodies state that research on incompetent subjects such as children and the mentally ill or disabled ordinarily is approvable only when the research involves a minimal risk or a minor increment over minimal risk to the subject ("Federal Policy for the Protection of Human Subjects"; Royal College of Physicians of London, 1996). According to this reasoning, some research on mentally ill or disabled persons may be ethically justifiable, subject to specific additional conditions, even if it is nontherapeutic (Wing; National Institutes of Health).

Of course, there is considerable room for controversy in defining minimal risk. U.S. federal policy compares minimal risk to the risks of the everyday life of a potential subject or those of a routine physical or psychological examination ("Federal Policy for the Protection of Human Subjects").

The Royal College of Physicians of London (1996) defines minimal risk as covering two types of situations: those that might involve negligible psychological distress, including other trivial reactions such as a mild headache or a feeling of lethargy, and those that involve very remote risks of serious injury or death, comparable with the risk of flying in a scheduled passenger aircraft.

It is widely agreed that research proposals involving mentally ill or disabled persons should be approved by an ethics committee charged with reviewing research proposals, such as an institutional review board. Research should not proceed if a competent subject objects. When a subject is unable to give properly informed consent, consent should be sought from an appropriate surrogate decision maker, such as a relative (World Medical Association).

Competence and Informed Consent

A fundamental ethical requirement for most medical research is the informed consent of the subject. For consent to be valid the subject must be capable of understanding the relevant implications of his or her decision to participate: the purpose, nature, and duration of the research; its possible risks and benefits; and so on. Because of the nature of some mental disorders, it is often unclear whether a mentally ill or handicapped person is capable of giving proper informed consent. Although many mental illnesses and disabilities do not affect those capabilities, it is the duty of a medical researcher to ensure that a potential subject of research is capable of making an informed decision whether to participate.

The ability to make that decision often is termed competence or decision-making capacity. A competent person should be capable of making a decision for which he or she legitimately can be considered accountable (Elliott). Competence ordinarily is defined in relation to a particular activity; a person can be competent to make some types of decisions but not others. For that reason assessments of competence ordinarily should focus on the task at hand, in this case understanding the implications of participating in a particular research protocol.

Most proposed standards for assessing competence focus on the process of reasoning involved in making a decision rather than on the outcome of the decision (U.S. President's Commission for the Study of Ethical Problems in Medicine and Biomedical and Behavioral Research, 1982; Buchanan and Brock; National Bioethics Advisory Commission). Because each person has different needs and values, often there is no single decision that can be judged correct for everyone. However, focusing primarily on a person's reasoning processes also can be problematic. A competent person sometimes may use faulty reasoning or make irrational decisions yet still be considered accountable for his or her choices (Elliott).

Probably the most influential tests of competence have dealt with consent to treatment rather than to research. A U.S. President's Commission report (1982) relates competence to three aspects of a person's mental abilities: (1) the possession of a set of values and goals, (2) the ability to communicate and understand information, and (3) the ability to reason and deliberate about one's choices.

However, competence criteria that focus primarily on rationality and reasonable deliberation may not be very helpful when the person making the choice has an affective disorder. For example, patients with depressive delusions may consent to hazardous research because they think they deserve to be punished (Elliott; Kopelman).

Furthermore, a mentally ill or disabled person may be able to satisfy a criterion partially but not fully or may be able to satisfy only some criteria. In cases like these it is a matter for debate how high the standards for competence should be set. For this reason some writers and professional bodies, including the U.S. President's Commission (1982), have endorsed a sliding-scale approach to assessing competence (National Bioethics Advisory Commission).

With this approach standards of competence are set higher for interventions with a risk-benefit ratio that is relatively worse and lower for interventions with a risk-benefit ratio that is relatively better. For example, to participate in a research protocol whose risks are great and whose benefits are small a subject might have to show not only that he or she understands the facts and issues but also that he or she *appreciates* the nature of the situation. This may be a very high standard of understanding: an affective as well as a cognitive recognition of the nature of the research, an awareness of how others view the decision, and an understanding that he or she has a mental disorder that is appropriate for study. In contrast, if the risk-benefit ratio is much better, the standard for competence might be set very low, for example, merely showing evidence of a choice to participate.

Even when a subject is clearly incompetent to give informed consent, many writers believe that research should not be done without the subject's assent; that is, researchers should ensure that the subject, to the degree that he or she is mentally capable, agrees to or expresses a positive interest in participating in the research. Research is much more difficult to justify when it is done in spite of a subject's verbal or behavioral objections (Wing). However, it is arguable that research without a patient's assent is justifiable if the patient is clearly incompetent and the research is therapeutic, involves minimal risk, has been consented to by an appropriate surrogate, and is clearly in the best interests of the patient.

Issues of competence and informed consent can be especially problematic in certain mentally ill patients whose competence may change over time. In the case of therapeutic research, for example, on antipsychotic medication, a research protocol may restore to competence a patient who previously was incompetent. In these situations the possible value of restoring the patient to competence should be part of the decision whether to enroll the patient in a research protocol. In cases in which a patient's competence fluctuates over time researchers should try to obtain consent at a time when the patient is best able to give it.

Further provisions may be needed to protect the interests of mentally ill and disabled patients who are incompetent or whose competence is questionable. The Belmont Report recommended that researchers seek the permission of third parties who are most likely to understand a subject's situation and act in that person's best interest (U.S. National Commission for the Protection of Human Subjects, 1979; National Bioethics Advisory Commission). Two standards have been employed widely in making decisions for incompetent patients: the best interests standard, in which third parties make decisions that are based on the interests of patients through the use of socially shared values, and in the case of previously competent patients the substituted judgment standard, by which third parties make decisions that are based on values and preferences the patient may have expressed in the past. The Belmont Report made the additional recommendation that those third parties be allowed to observe the research as it proceeds, with the option of withdrawing the subject from the research at any time (U.S. National Commission for the Protection of Human Subjects, 1979; National Bioethics Advisory Commission).

Institutionalized patients are often especially attractive as research subjects because their medication, diet, and compliance with a study can be monitored and controlled easily. Nevertheless, many writers have argued that institutionalized populations deserve special protection, pointing out the examples of the Willowbrook State School in New York, where mentally retarded children were injected with the hepatitis virus in 1956, and the Jewish Chronic Disease Hospital in Brooklyn, where nineteen chronically ill patients were injected with cancer cells in 1962 (U.S. National Commission for the Protection of Human Subjects, 1978; Kopelman). Some observers have argued that the fact of institutionalization invalidates informed consent and that research on mentally ill or handicapped persons in institutions should be ruled out entirely.

There are several grounds for the argument that institutionalization invalidates informed consent. One that has been rejected widely is that any person who has a mental illness or disability severe enough to warrant institutionalization is mentally incompetent to give informed consent. However, many people have illnesses or disabilities that impair them in ways that require institutional treatment but do not impair their ability to make competent judgments about participating in research. A second argument is that institutionalization itself deprives people of the ability to make their own decisions, for example, by placing them in a situation of constant subordination to authority (Annas et al.). A third argument is that institutions severely limit the choices available to their patients, thus placing constraints on their freedom of choice. Research on institutionalized patients also can be difficult for impartial external observers or regulatory bodies to monitor effectively. For these reasons many agencies and professional bodies require that researchers take special measures to guard against the manipulation of institutionalized subjects.

Risk and Study Design

At the turn of the twenty-first century a number of studies of mental illness attracted considerable criticism because their designs exposed subjects to an unacceptably high ratio of risk to benefit. The most controversial of those studies were placebo-controlled trials, symptom-provocation studies, and relapse studies.

PLACEBO-CONTROLLED TRIALS. The ethical controversy over certain placebo-controlled trials begins from the principle of clinical equipoise, according to which, before a randomized clinical trial can be started there must be genuine disagreement in the community of expert practitioners about which treatment is preferable (Freedman, 1987). If there is disagreement about whether a new psychiatric drug is superior to placebo, clinical equipoise would permit a trial to settle the question. However, would it be ethical to begin a trial comparing a new drug to placebo if there already was an effective standard treatment for the illness in question? According to the requirement for clinical equipoise, the answer is no.

Clinical equipoise is rooted in standards of sound clinical practice. The treatments offered to patients in a clinical trial must be in equipoise with the prevailing standard of care for the subject population in question so that the clinical care of those patients will not suffer as a result of enrollment in the trial. The Declaration of Helsinki states, "The benefits, risks, burdens and effectiveness of a new method should be tested against those of the best current prophylactic, diagnostic, and therapeutic methods" (World Medical Association).

In light of the proven efficacy of many psychiatric agents, it might be expected that placebo-controlled trials in psychiatry would be rare. However, new psychiatric agents are tested routinely against placebo even when failure to treat the illness in question adequately could cause serious harm to the subjects enrolled in the trial, such as patients with schizophrenia or major depression. Indeed, representatives of regulatory agencies such as the U.S. Food and Drug Administration and the Canadian Health Protection Branch have encouraged the use of placebo-controlled trials, especially in psychiatry, arguing that those trials are the only way to determine whether a new drug is effective (Addington). Defenders of placebo-controlled trials also argue that subjects are protected by the requirement for informed consent and that even if a subject's mental illness worsens during a trial, the symptoms of such illnesses are temporary, reversible, and not sufficiently harmful to warrant a prohibition against placebos.

It is difficult to see how major depression and psychosis can be considered insufficiently harmful to subjects, especially when both conditions are associated with a higher risk of suicide. It is also doubtful that informed consent will protect research subjects from enrolling in potentially harmful studies. Many investigators do not conduct an adequate discussion with patients about the risks and disadvantages of taking part in a study, and even when investigators disclose those risks, many patients do not understand them fully (Appelbaum et al.).

The requirement for clinical equipoise does not mean that all or even most placebo controls are unethical. As Benjamin Freedman (1990) has noted, placebo controls are justified in testing treatments for conditions:

1. that have no standard therapy,
2. whose standard therapy has been shown to be no better than placebo,
3. whose standard therapy is placebo,
4. whose standard therapy has been called into question by new evidence warranting doubt about its net therapeutic advantage, and
5. whose validated optimal treatment is not made freely available to patients.

Charles Weijer points out two additional situations in which placebo controls are permissible. If a particular population has failed to respond to first-line treatments for a condition and no proven second-line treatment exists, that population may be enrolled in a placebo-controlled trial. Also, if a new treatment simply is added onto a standard treatment, that treatment may be tested against placebo as long as all the subjects in the trial get the standard treatment either with the add-on or with placebo.

SYMPTOM-PROVOCATION STUDIES. Another controversial psychiatric study is the symptom-provocation study or challenge study. The purpose of those studies is to learn more about the pathophysiology of mental illnesses by provoking their symptoms in mentally ill subjects. For example, in a number of different studies published in the 1990s researchers gave schizophrenic subjects a variety of psychoactive drugs to exacerbate the symptoms of psychosis. Symptom-provocation studies have generated far more outrage in the popular press and among patient advocacy groups than in the bioethics and medical literature, in which they have been defended for their scientific merit (Whitaker; Miller and Rosenstein). However, in those studies, unlike most clinical trials, mentally ill subjects often are exposed to risks without any expectation of therapeutic benefit. Also, unlike many Phase I clinical trials, symptom-provocation studies are performed not on healthy volunteers but on ill patients. Indeed, the very purpose of those studies is to induce harmful symptoms in patients who already have mental disorders.

RELAPSE STUDIES. A third source of controversy in psychiatry involves relapse studies or washout studies. In relapse studies mentally ill subjects are taken off their regular medications to determine whether they will relapse into their illnesses, how long it will take them to relapse, or whether their health can be maintained without medication. In a widely reported study at the University of California at Los Angeles that began in the 1980s, researchers required that subjects with schizophrenia who had recovered from their symptoms be taken off their medication. After the study was concluded, a subject committed suicide (Katz; National Bioethics Advisory Commission).

Defenders of relapse studies have argued that many mentally ill patients, particularly those with schizophrenia, are maintained on medications that can cause serious and irreversible side effects and that "drug holidays" are often an accepted part of standard therapy. Critics point out that it is in the interests of most patients to be maintained on the therapeutic regimen that has worked for them, that such patients are not informed of the risks of relapse studies, and that a relapse may increase the risk of future relapses (Katz; Shamoo and Keay).

CARL ELLIOTT (1995)
REVISED BY CARL ELLIOTT
SUSAN PARRY

SEE ALSO: *Autonomy; Children: Healthcare and Research Issues; Confidentiality; Holocaust; Informed Consent: Consent Issues in Human Research; Mental Health Services: Settings and Programs; Mental Illness; Patients' Rights: Mental Patients' Rights; Psychiatry, Abuses of; Psychopharmacology; Research, Human: Historical Aspects; Research, Unethical; Research Ethics Committees; Research Policy;* and other *Mentally Disabled and Mentally Ill Persons* subentries

BIBLIOGRAPHY

Addington, Donald. 1995. "The Use of Placebos in Clinical Trials for Acute Schizophrenia." *Canadian Journal of Psychiatry* 40: 171–176.

Annas, George J.; Glantz, Leonard H.; and Katz, Barbara F. 1977. *Informed Consent to Human Experimentation: The Subject's Dilemma.* Cambridge, MA: Ballinger.

Appelbaum, Paul S.; Roth, Loren H.; Lidz, Charles W.; et al. 1987. "False Hopes and Best Data: Consent to Research and the Therapeutic Misconception." *Hastings Center Report* 17(2): 20–24.

Buchanan, Allen E., and Brock, Dan W. 1989. *Deciding for Others: The Ethics of Surrogate Decision-Making.* Cambridge, Eng., and New York: Cambridge University Press.

Elliott, Carl. 1997. "Caring about Risks: Are Depressed Patients Competent to Consent to Research?" *Archives of General Psychiatry* 54: 113–116.

"Federal Policy for the Protection of Human Subjects: Notices and Rules." 1991. *Federal Register,* part 2, 56(117): 28002–28032 (56 FR 28002).

Freedman, Benjamin. 1987. "Equipoise and the Ethics of Clinical Research." *New England Journal of Medicine* 317(3): 141–145.

Freedman, Benjamin. 1990. "Placebo-Controlled Trials and the Logic of Clinical Purpose." *IRB: Ethics & Human Research* 12(6): 1–6.

Katz, Jay. 1993. "Human Experimentation and Human Rights." *St. Louis Law Journal* 38: 7–54.

Kopelman, Loretta. 1997. "Moral Problems in Psychiatry." In *Medical Ethics,* 2nd edition, ed. Robert Veatch. Boston: Jones and Bartlett.

Medical Research Council of Canada, Natural Sciences and Engineering Research Council of Canada, and Social Sciences and Humanities Research Council of Canada. 1998. *Tri-Council Policy Statement: Ethical Conduct for Research Involving Humans.* Ottawa: Author.

Miller, Franklin G., and Rosenstein, Donald L. 1997. "Psychiatric Symptom-Provoking Studies: An Ethical Appraisal." *Biological Psychiatry* 42: 403–409.

National Bioethics Advisory Commission. 1998. *Research Involving Persons with Mental Disorders That May Affect Decisionmaking Capacity,* vol. 1. Rockville, MD: Author.

National Institutes of Health, Office for Protection from Research Risks. 1993. *Protecting Human Research Subjects: Institutional*

Review Board Guidebook, 2nd edition, rev. Washington, D.C.: Author.

Royal College of Physicians of London. 1990. *Research Involving Patients.* London: Author.

Royal College of Physicians of London. 1996. *Guidelines on the Practice of Ethics Committees in Medical Research Involving Human Subjects,* 3rd edition. London: Author.

Royal College of Psychiatrists. 2000. *Guidelines for Researchers and for Research Ethics Committees on Psychiatric Research Involving Human Participants.* London: Author.

Shamoo, Adil E., and Keay, Timothy J. 1996. "Ethical Concerns about Relapse Studies." *Cambridge Quarterly of Healthcare Ethics* 5(3): 373–386.

U.S. National Commission for the Protection of Human Subjects of Biomedical and Behavioral Research. 1978. *Research Involving Those Institutionalized as Mentally Infirm: Report and Recommendations.* Publication (OS) 78–0006 and Appendix (OS) 78–0007. Washington, D.C.: Author.

U.S. National Commission for the Protection of Human Subjects of Biomedical and Behavioral Research. 1979. *The Belmont Report: Ethical Principles and Guidelines for the Protection of Human Subjects of Research.* Washington, D.C.: Author. Reprinted in National Institutes of Health, 1993, pp. A6–13.

U.S. President's Commission for the Study of Ethical Problems in Medicine and Biomedical and Behavioral Research. 1982. *Making Health Care Decisions: A Report on the Ethical and Legal Implications of Informed Consent in the Patient-Practitioner Relationship.* Washington, D.C.: Author.

Weijer, Charles. 1999. "Placebo-Controlled Trials in Schizophrenia: Are They Ethical? Are They Necessary?" *Schizophrenia Research* 35(3): 211–218.

Whitaker, Robert. 2002. *Mad in America: Bad Science, Bad Medicine, and the Enduring Mistreatment of the Mentally Ill.* Cambridge, MA: Perseus.

Wing, John. 1999. "Ethics and Psychiatric Research." In *Psychiatric Ethics,* 3rd edition, ed. Sidney Bloch, Paul Chodoff, and Stephen A. Green. Oxford: Oxford University Press.

World Health Organization/Council for International Organizations of Medical Sciences. 2002. *International Ethical Guidelines for Biomedical Research Involving Human Subjects.* Geneva: Council for International Organizations of Medical Sciences.

World Medical Association. 2000 (1964). *Declaration of Helsinki: Ethical Principles for Medical Research Involving Human Subjects.* Edinburgh, Scotland: Author.

MERGERS AND ACQUISITIONS

• • •

Between 1980 and 2002 there were an unprecedented number of healthcare mergers and acquisitions in the United States, affecting hospitals and hospital systems, nursing facilities, clinics, physician group practices, pharmaceutical manufacturers, and managed-care and other health insurance providers. Predictably, this headlong rush toward consolidation and concentration has triggered increased scrutiny of such transactions by those state and federal agencies responsible for antitrust and tax regulation. It has also spurred increased reflection on the ethical issues at stake in these merger and acquisition decisions. Such issues include concerns about fidelity to organizational mission; effects of organizational restructuring upon community access to services and other benefits; impact upon the welfare, working environment, and overall culture of affected employees; and the prevention and resolution of conflicts of interest among involved parties.

The number and frequency of hospital mergers and acquisitions increased dramatically during the 1980s and early 1990s. The trend peaked in the period 1994–1997, according to data from Irving Levin Associates, with 163 deals completed in 1996 and a record 197 deals in 1997. During that period the number of hospitals belonging to health networks or systems also increased significantly, from 56.2 percent in 1994 to 70.9 percent in 1998. By the beginning of the new century, the frequency of deals had declined somewhat, to 86 in 2000 and 83 in 2001, yet these numbers remain much higher than pre-1990 levels. Among the factors apparently driving this high rate of merger and acquisition activity are reduced Medicare reimbursement rates, significantly increased managed-care pressures to provide more services at lower prices, and a declining market for inpatient hospital services.

Benefits and Burdens of Consolidation

Hospital mergers and acquisitions can provide substantial benefits for institutions, their employees, and the communities they serve. They can bring needed capital into a healthcare organization, providing economic vigor and repositioning in a difficult marketplace; offering opportunities for new or expanded service lines; and even ensuring survival and the capacity to provide services to those in need. They can strengthen an organization's bargaining power and provide economies of scale and increased efficiency, all of which could lead to decreased costs to consumers. And they can bring standardization to, and better assessment of, the quality of care delivered.

A 2002 study by Bazzoli and colleagues examined the self-reported reasons for merger cited by involved hospitals during the periods 1983–1988 and 1989–1996. For both groups, the top three reasons for merger were identical: to strengthen the institution's financial position, to achieve operating economies, and to consolidate services. Expansion of market share was another reason cited by a majority of respondents. Yet there were also certain changes in emphasis between the two study periods. Those citing expansion of visibility and service availability across the hospital's service area as a significant reason for merger increased from 33.3 percent in 1983–1988 to 53.2 percent in 1989–1996, while those citing expansion of provided service areas as a reason for merger decreased from 63.9 percent to 44.3 percent. In addition, respondents in the more recent period indicated an increasing emphasis upon nursing-staff downsizing as an intended cost-saving outcome of merger activity.

While the potential benefits of hospital consolidations via merger and acquisition can be manifold, these transactions can also create concerns about potential burdens for various stakeholders. One such concern has to do with the consequences of giving up local hospital control. When a community-based hospital merges with or is acquired by an organization or system headquartered elsewhere, especially out of state, what will the loss of local control mean in terms of the new organization's responses to the local community's specific needs? And what will be the postconsolidation status and level of service at the community-based hospital? Many consolidations, especially those involving a for-profit organization, include plans to increase profitability and market position by phasing out unprofitable service lines in favor of more profitable specializations. This can create hardships for communities—access to much-needed yet unprofitable services becomes more difficult, or the burden of providing these services is shifted to others. Another potential service limitation emerges when a merging or acquiring organization takes a strong religious or other principled position against providing certain services. Such consolidations raise understandable public concerns about whether reasonable access to those services will remain available within the community after consolidation.

Further, an increase in the price of services can be another potential community burden resulting from hospital merger or acquisition transactions. While consolidation-related efficiencies may allow for price reductions, or at least a hold on price increases, the newly consolidated and concentrated hospital organization will also have stronger market positioning and greater market power, and that power may be expressed through price increases. A 2000 study by Young and colleagues examined the relationship between market concentration and pricing patterns for three types of nonprofit hospitals: independent hospitals under local control, members of local hospital systems, and members of nonlocal hospital systems. The study showed that, in more concentrated markets, all three types of nonprofit hospitals exercised market power in the form of higher prices—and that hospitals that are a part of nonlocal systems were more aggressive in exercising this market power than either of the other hospital types.

Yet another community concern regarding hospital consolidations is their effect on the provision of charity care. According to American Hospital Association data, overall U.S. hospital expenses for uncompensated care (bad debt and charity care) were $18.5 billion in 1997, up from $6 billion in 1980 (Hall). Yet access to needed care remains difficult for many of the more than 42 million uninsured Americans who cannot afford that care. Thus, communities are often concerned about the effect of consolidation upon a local hospital's willingness to continue providing charity care, especially when a nonprofit community hospital is merging with or acquired by a for-profit hospital or system. There is evidence that for-profit hospitals are less likely to be accessible to the medically indigent and uninsured than nonprofit hospitals are, and that they tend to carry a smaller indigent-care load (Darr). One study of California nonprofit hospitals that were consolidated into for-profit organizations found that charity care declined in almost all cases analyzed. Moreover, in none of the deals did the sale proceeds, usually set aside in a foundation to provide charity care and other community benefits, sufficiently replace the community benefits provided by the former nonprofit hospitals (Mateo and Rossi).

One final area of community concern has to do with how consolidation might affect particular groups of internal stakeholders, namely hospital staff, trustees, and executives. Merger and acquisition activity can, and often does, involve downsizing and the loss of employment for some staff members. It can also lead to negatively perceived changes in working conditions, mission loyalty, and overall organizational culture. On the other hand, hospital executives and trustees, who are responsible for negotiating any possible consolidation, may be subject to various positive inducements, financial and otherwise, for their support of a transaction. Such a possibility appears all the more threatening to a community in which the actual details of a proposed consolidation have not been made public during the planning process.

Moral Obligations of Hospital Leaders

Community concerns have led to some significant changes in legal oversight of hospital consolidations at both state and federal levels, including transactions among nonprofit hospitals and between nonprofit and for-profit hospitals

(Peregrine). Yet it is clear that legal regulation cannot and will not ensure the fulfillment of healthcare leaders' moral obligations to the community as hospital consolidations are contemplated, planned, and executed. Nonprofit hospital trustees and executives, who are accountable for more than 80 percent of U.S. hospital beds, have particular fiduciary responsibilities to the communities served by their institutions, and there are specific moral obligations that should govern their participation in merger and acquisition activities.

MISSION PROTECTION. First, trustees and executives are responsible for upholding and protecting the mission and values of the institution they are already serving. According to the American Hospital Association Board of Trustees, a hospital's mission includes both caring for the sick and injured and improving community health, and any decisions regarding consolidation should thus emphasize the community's future health needs and the best overall organizational arrangements for meeting those needs. Trustees and executives, therefore, bear the moral obligation of participating in any proposed merger or acquisition as representatives of the community and its interests (Wilkins and Jacobson). They must ask how any proposed transaction would affect access to and delivery of health care in the community, seek independent assistance in assessing the impact of the transaction on the community, and work to avoid any unnecessary harmful effects upon quality of life in the community.

A critical aspect of a hospital's mission that should be protected, of course, is the provision of uncompensated care. Trustees and executives must consider the community's future health needs by ensuring that access to charity care will not be diminished or eroded by a merger or acquisition transaction, particularly when a nonprofit hospital is contemplating consolidation with a for-profit hospital or system. Further, as Leonard Weber points out, if a generally beneficial consolidation will also entail certain new community burdens, such as less-convenient location of services, then those segments of the community already experiencing greater social ills (such as poverty and environmental degradation) have a greater claim to be spared new social burdens than do better-off segments of the community.

In some instances a hospital's mission and values will involve specific principle-based exclusions from certain practices, as in the case of most Catholic hospitals' refusals to provide various reproductive services. When such an institution seeks a merger with or acquisition of another community hospital whose mission and values do not entail these service exclusions, then the obligation to consider the community's overall future health needs becomes somewhat more complex. Certainly the conscientious refusals of hospital leaders and sponsors to engage in certain practices should

be respected. Yet the general obligation of hospitals to ensure adequate community access to those services normally and legally available in other communities places a potential limit upon the moral right of hospitals to restrict permissible practices (Weber). This becomes an especially strong concern where the postconsolidation institution would be the community's sole provider. In such circumstances, the costs of consolidation may simply be too high.

AVOIDING CONFLICT OF INTEREST. Second, trustees and executives have a moral obligation to disclose any potential conflict of interest and to avoid any private benefit in a proposed consolidation. They should not receive money during a consolidation process—nor should they accept any other incentive offered as a means of securing support for the transaction, such as promises of a job or board membership after consolidation. Any such offers should be disclosed to all involved parties, and negotiation practices should be utilized that will fully separate decisions about the transaction from decisions about positions in the post-transaction institution (Weber). Trustees and executives must be able to assure the community, which they serve as fiduciaries, that personal gain incentives have been removed from the negotiating table, and that the community's best interests are represented there.

PUBLIC DISCLOSURE AND HEARINGS. Third, hospital leadership should make the consolidation process fully public. Trustees should ensure that all objectives and processes of the transaction are made available to the general public and the state attorney general, and they should require public hearings and suitable waiting periods so as to hear and respond to community concerns about the transaction. Community-based consumer organizations should also be consulted in order to assess implications of the proposed consolidation that may not be immediately apparent to trustees and executives (Wilkins and Jacobson).

FAIR MARKET VALUE. Fourth, nonprofit trustees and executives are responsible for ensuring fair market value for their institution in the transaction, particularly when a nonprofit hospital is being acquired by a for-profit hospital or system. This requires, among other things, ensuring independent valuation by a third-party firm with experience in the healthcare field. In addition, the methodology used in determining fair market value should be made a part of public disclosure of the negotiations. A significant portion of a nonprofit hospital's value that must be included in any assessment of fair market value is the community benefit it provides: the hospital's value to community members (as owners of it), the value it provides in uncompensated care, and the value it holds from past publicly funded investment are all part of its value.

Trustees and executives, as fiduciaries of the community, must ensure that community-benefit value is not lost in consolidation transactions and that community benefit in the form of charity care and other community health initiatives is guaranteed into the future. In the sale of a nonprofit hospital to a for-profit, this usually involves using that portion of the sale price designated as the community-benefit value to establish a nonprofit charitable foundation or trust whose assets will be used to fund charity care and community health ventures. Nonprofit executives and trustees should require that the terms of the foundation—particularly regarding who will control its assets and the specific purposes for which they may be expended—be detailed and clear before consolidation can be completed, and that the foundation will provide regular public reports on its efforts to promote community health (Wilkins and Jacobson).

STAFF AND EMPLOYEE INTERESTS. Fifth, in addition to their community-oriented fiduciary responsibilities, hospital trustees and executives also have responsibilities to their institutional and medical staffs. When any consolidation is considered, staff and employees must be fully informed and educated about its perceived need and its intended goals and processes—and their responses and concerns must be heard. Just as a community assessment is necessary to determine the community interests that are at stake in any proposed transaction, an organizational assessment is necessary to recognize specific organizational cultures and how they may or may not fit with the cultures of other merging or acquiring facilities. The employees and staff in each facility should be oriented to the culture, history, and mission of the other facility or system.

Further, employees of institutions facing consolidation may have concerns not only about postconsolidation culture and working conditions, but also about the prospect of staff downsizing and loss of employment. Quite often these concerns are well founded. If the organization's ability to continue serving the needs of the community will necessarily require staff downsizing, then the trustees and executives have an obligation to ensure, among other things, that: (1) all employees to be laid off will be given advance notice that includes detailed explanation of the necessity of and criteria for their selection; (2) employees to be laid off will have opportunity to appeal their selection if they have reason to believe the criteria were inappropriately applied; and (3) laid-off employees will be provided with significant outplacement services and interim benefits (Weber).

Exit Provisions

Perhaps predictably, the large number of hospital mergers and acquisitions have produced not only many successes, but also quite a few organizational and financial failures. As Michael Peregrine has noted, this reality may suggest a final obligation of nonprofit hospital trustees negotiating a consolidation—namely to incorporate termination provisions (known as *exit* or *unwind* provisions) within the transaction terms. These terms might specify what particular events would indicate a failure of the consolidation's objectives and thus trigger an unwinding, any required mediation or arbitration related to the implementation of the unwinding, the time period during which the trigger would remain effective, and the actual mechanisms for implementing the unwinding if the consolidation fails to achieve its objectives.

Hospitals are, as Kurt Darr notes, "social organizations with an economic dimension, rather than economic organizations with a social dimension." The recent history of U.S. healthcare offers many examples of how the economic dimension of hospitals may be enhanced through mergers and acquisitions. Yet a recognition of the primary social dimension of hospitals illuminates a variety of community-oriented moral responsibilities and obligations that must not be ignored in such transactions, even for the sake of economic enhancement.

JAMES B. TUBBS, JR.

SEE ALSO: *Access to Healthcare; Healthcare Systems; Profit and Commercialism*

BIBLIOGRAPHY

Bazzoli, Gloria J.; LoSasso, Anthony; Arnould, Richard; et al. 2002. "Hospital Reorganization and Restructuring Achieved through Merger." *Health Care Management Review* 27(1): 7–20.

Boyle, Philip J.; DuBose, Edwin R.; Ellingson, Stephen J.; et al. 2001. *Organizational Ethics in Health Care: Principles, Cases, and Practical Solutions.* San Francisco: Jossey-Bass.

Darr, Kurt. 1997. "The Social Responsibility of Hospitals." *Hospital Topics* 75(1): 4–7.

Hall, Robert T. 2000. *An Introduction to Healthcare Organizational Ethics.* New York: Oxford University Press.

Hofmann, Paul B. 1996. "Hospital Mergers and Acquisitions: A New Catalyst for Examining Organizational Ethics." *Bioethics Forum* 12(2): 45–48.

Hofmann, Paul B. 2000. "Incentive in Mergers and Acquisitions." *Healthcare Executive* 15(5): 61–62.

Kassirer, Jerome P. 1996. "Mergers and Acquisitions—Who Benefits? Who Loses?" *New England Journal of Medicine* 334(11): 722–723.

Peregrine, Michael W. 2001. "Legal Issues in Mergers and Acquisitions." *Health Progress* 82(3): 57–61.

Rubin, Susan, and Zoloth-Dorfman, Laurie. 1996 "Health Care Consolidation Raises Ethical Questions." *Modern Healthcare* 26(32): 76.

Weber, Leonard J. 2001. *Business Ethics in Healthcare: Beyond Compliance.* Bloomington: Indiana University Press.

Werhane, Patricia H. 1990. "The Ethics of Health Care as a Business." *Business and Professional Ethics Journal* 9(3/4): 7–20.

Wilkins, Aaron S., and Jacobson, Peter D. 1998. "Fiduciary Responsibilities in Nonprofit Health Care Conversions." *Health Care Management Review* 23(1): 77–90.

Wolff, Marie. 1993. "'No Margin, No Mission': Challenge to Institutional Ethics." *Business and Professional Ethics Journal* 12(2): 39–50.

Young, Gary J.; Desaum Kemal R.; and Hellinger, Fred J. 2000. "Community Control and Pricing Patterns of Nonprofit Hospitals: An Antitrust Analysis." *Journal of Health Politics, Policy and Law* 25(6): 1051–1082.

INTERNET RESOURCES

American Hospital Association Board of Trustees. 1997. "Community Accountability with Changes in the Ownership or Control of Hospital or Health Systems." Available from <http://www.hospitalconnect.com/aha/advocacy-grassroots/advocacy/position/ownership.html>.

Irving Levin Associates. 2002. Press releases regarding Health Care Mergers and Acquisitions. Available from <http://www.levinassociates.com/pressroom/>.

Lahiri, Indra, and Sedicum, Austin. 2000. "Mergers and Acquisitions as a Diversity Issue for Health Care—WDG." Workforce Development Group. Available from <http://www.workforcedevelopmentgroup.com/>.

Matteo, Julio, and Rossi, Jaime. 1999. "White Knights or Trojan Horses? A Policy and Legal Framework for Evaluating Hospital Consolidations in California." Consumers Union. Available from <http://www.consumersunion.org/health/>.

METAPHOR AND ANALOGY

• • •

Many of our practices and much of our discourse in healthcare hinge on metaphor and analogy, whose significance is sometimes overlooked because they are considered merely decorative or escape notice altogether. Despite their relative neglect, they significantly shape our interpretations of what is happening as well as what should happen. This entry will examine metaphor before considering analogy, particularly analogical reasoning, noting their overlap where appropriate.

Metaphors in Bioethics

NATURE AND FUNCTION OF METAPHORS. Perhaps because medicine and healthcare involve fundamental matters of life and death for practically everyone, and in often mysterious ways, they are often described in metaphors. For instance, physicians may be viewed as playing God, or acting as parents, and nurses seen as advocates for patients, while medicine itself may be interpreted as warfare against disease. Metaphors involve imagining something as something else, for example, viewing human beings as wolves or life as a journey. "The essence of metaphor," according to George Lakoff and Mark Johnson, "is understanding and experiencing one thing through another" (p. 5). More precisely, metaphors are figurative expressions that interpret one thing in terms of something else (Soskice).

In contemporary philosophical literature on metaphor, critics have challenged some traditional conceptions, contending that metaphors are more than merely ornamental or affective ways to state what could be stated in a more literal or comparative way, and that they can be and often are cognitively significant (see, e.g., Black, 1962, 1979; Ricoeur; Soskice). According to the traditional substitution view, a metaphorical expression is merely a substitute for some equivalent literal expression. For example, the metaphorical expression "John is a fox" substitutes for the literal expression "John is sly and cunning." One common version of the substitution view, what philosopher Max Black (1962) calls a comparison view (elements of which can be found in Aristotle), construes metaphor as the presentation of an underlying analogy or similarity. Hence, metaphor is "a condensed or elliptical simile" (Black, 1962), or it is a "comparison statement with parts left out" (Miller). "John is a fox," for example, indicates that "John is like a fox in that he is sly and cunning." According to such views, metaphors are dispensable ways to express what could be expressed differently, but they often appeal to the emotions more effectively than their equivalent literal expressions or comparisons would do.

By contrast, many recent theories of metaphor stress its cognitive significance. In an early and very influential essay, Black (1962) defended an interaction view of metaphor, in which two juxtaposed thoughts interact to produce new meanings, through the metaphor's "system of associated commonplaces" or "associated implications." The metaphor—for instance, "wolf" in "man is a wolf"—serves as a "filter" for a set of associated implications that are transferred from the secondary subject (*wolf*) to the principal subject (*man*) in the sentence. In a full interaction or interanimation view of metaphor, the transfer of meaning occurs both ways, not merely from the secondary subject to the principal subject (Soskice).

Metaphors highlight and hide features of the principal subject, such as the physician who is viewed as a parent or as a friend, by their systematically related implications (Black, 1962; Lakoff and Johnson). When argument is conceived as warfare, for example, the metaphor highlights the conflict involved in argument, while it hides the cooperation and collaboration, involving shared rules, that are also indispensable to argument. Our metaphors thus shape how we think, what we experience, and what we do by what they highlight and obscure.

Metaphors are often associated with models. For instance, we have both metaphors and models of the doctor-patient relationship. The physician may be viewed through the metaphor of father and the patient through the metaphor of child, and their relationship may be interpreted through the model of paternalism. Models, for our purposes, state the network of associated commonplaces and implications in more systematic and comprehensive ways—according to Black, "every metaphor is the tip of a submerged model" (1979, p. 31).

Metaphors and models may be good or bad, living or dead. Both metaphors and models can be assessed by how well they illuminate what is going on and what should go on. We can distinguish descriptive and normative uses of metaphors and models, without admitting a sharp separation between fact and value. For instance, the metaphor of physician as father (or parent), and the model of paternalism (or parentalism), may accurately describe some relationships in medicine, or they may suggest ideal relationships in the light of some important principles and values.

MEDICINE AS WAR. The metaphor of warfare illuminates much of our conception of what is, and should be, done in healthcare. This metaphor emerges in the day-to-day language of medicine: The physician as the captain leads the battle against disease; orders a battery of tests; develops a plan of attack; calls on the armamentarium or arsenal of medicine; directs allied health personnel; treats aggressively; and expects compliance. Good patients are those who fight vigorously and refuse to give up. Victory is sought; defeat is feared. Sometimes there is even hope for a "magic bullet" or a "silver bullet." Only professionals who stand on the firing line or in the trenches can really appreciate the moral problems of medicine. And they frequently have "war stories" to relate. Medical organization, particularly in the

hospital, resembles military hierarchy; and medical training, particularly with its long, sleepless shifts in residencies, approximates military training more than any other professional education in our society (Childress).

As medicine wages war against germs that invade the body and threaten its defenses, so the society itself may also declare war on cancer or on AIDS under the leadership of its chief medical officer, who in the United States is the surgeon general. Articles and books even herald the "Medical-Industrial Complex: Our National Defense." As Susan Sontag notes, "Where once it was the physician who waged *bellum contra morbum*, the war against disease, now it's the whole society" (p. 72).

The military metaphor first became prominent in the 1880s, when bacteria were identified as agents of disease that threaten the body and its defenses. The metaphor both illuminates and distorts healthcare. Its positive implications are widely recognized—for instance, in supporting a patient's courageous and hopeful struggle against illness and in galvanizing societal support to fight against disease. But the metaphor is also problematic. Sontag, who was diagnosed with cancer in the late 1970s, reports that her suffering was intensified by the dominance of the metaphor of warfare against cancer. Cancer cells do not just multiply; they are *invasive*. They *colonize*. The body's *defenses* are rarely strong enough. But since the body is under attack (*invasion*) by *alien* invaders, counterattack is justified. Treatments are also often described in military language:

> Radiotherapy uses the metaphors of aerial warfare; patients are "bombarded" with toxic rays. And chemotherapy is chemical warfare, using poisons. Treatment aims to "kill" cancer cells (without, it is hoped, killing the patient). Unpleasant side effects of treatment are advertised, indeed overadvertised. ("The agony of chemotherapy" is a standard phrase.) It is impossible to avoid damaging or destroying healthy cells (indeed, some methods used to treat cancer can cause cancer), but it is thought that nearly any damage to the body is justified if it saves the patient's life. Often, of course, it doesn't work. (As in: "We had to destroy Ben Suc in order to save it.") There is everything but the body count. (Sontag, p. 65)

Such "military metaphors," Sontag suggests, "contribute to the stigmatizing of certain illnesses and, by extension, of those who are ill" (p. 99). Other ill individuals have found the military metaphor unsatisfactory for other reasons. For instance, as a teenager, Lawrence Pray originally tried to conquer his diabetes, but his struggles and battles were futile and even counterproductive. Then over time he came to view his diabetes not as an *enemy* to be *conquered,* but as a *teacher.* Only then did he find a personally satisfactory way of living (Pray and Evans).

Still others with illness, by contrast, have found the military metaphor to be empowering and enabling. In her wide-ranging study of pathographies, that is, autobiographical descriptions of personal experiences of illness, treatment, and dying, Anne Hunsaker Hawkins identifies several "metaphorical paradigms" that offer themes of "an archetypal, mythic nature." In addition to illness as a battle, she notes illness as a game or sport (a subset of the military metaphor), illness as a journey into a distant country, illness as rebirth or regeneration— and, on a somewhat different level, healthy-mindedness as an alternative to contemporary medicine. While pathographies are individualized statements, they provide "an immensely rich reservoir of the metaphors and models that surround illness in contemporary culture" (p. 25). These various metaphorical paradigms structure individuals' interpretations of their experiences of illness. Patterns emerge in individuals' selection of metaphors. They vary in part according to the illness involved—for example, the military metaphor is more common in descriptions of experiences with cancer and AIDS, while the rebirth metaphor is more common in descriptions of a critical life-threatening event, such as a heart attack. Furthermore, the military metaphor is more prevalent than the journey metaphor because it better fits the experience of modern medicine—for instance, it is easier to construe the physician as a *general* in a war than as a *guide* on a journey. Nevertheless, these various metaphors are often mixed and complementary. They can be evaluated, Hawkins suggests, according to their capacity to enable and empower ill persons, for instance, by restoring a sense of personal dignity and worth. And, while expressing larger sociocultural patterns, the individual's choice of a particular metaphor is a creative act of assigning meaning to his or her illness.

The metaphor of warfare has been further challenged in modern medicine because of its apparent support for overtreatment, particularly of terminally ill patients, because death is the ultimate enemy, just as trauma, disease, or illness is the immediate enemy. Physicians and families under the spell of this metaphor frequently find it difficult to let patients die. *Heroic* actions, with the best available weapons, befit the military effort that must always be undertaken against the ultimate enemy. Death signals defeat and forgoing treatment signals surrender. Some clinicians even feel more comfortable withholding (i.e., not starting) a treatment for cancer, for instance, than they do withdrawing (i.e., stopping) the same treatment, in part because withdrawing treatment implies retreat.

According to its critics, the invocation of the military metaphor often fails to recognize moral constraints on waging war. "Modern medicine," William May writes, "has tended to interpret itself not only through the prism of war but through the medium of its modern practice, that is, unlimited, unconditional war," in contrast to the just-war tradition (1983, p. 66). In the spirit of modern total war, "hospitals and the physician-fighter wage unconditional battle against death" (1983, p. 66). One result is that many patients seek assisted suicide or active euthanasia in order to escape from this warfare's terrorist bombardment. Traditional moral limits in the conduct of war include the principle of discrimination, which authorizes direct attacks on combatants but not on noncombatants. In medical care, the opposing combatant is the disease or death, not the patient. However, the patient is regularly the battleground and sometimes even becomes the enemy. Furthermore, in accord with the just-war tradition's requirement of reasonable prospect of success and proportionality, the treatment should offer the patient a reasonable chance of success; his or her suffering must be balanced against the probable benefits of prolongation of life.

Other problematic or ambiguous implications of the war metaphor appear in the allocation of resources for and within healthcare. First, under the military metaphor, society's healthcare budget tends to be converted into a defense budget to prepare for and conduct war against disease, trauma, and death. As a consequence, the society may put more resources into healthcare in relation to other goods than it could justify, especially under a different metaphor, such as nursing or business (see below). Indeed, the society may overutilize healthcare, especially because technological care may contribute less to the national defense of health itself—through the reduction of morbidity and premature mortality—than other factors, such as the reduction of poverty.

Second, within the healthcare budget, the military metaphor tends to assign priority to critical care over preventive and chronic care. It tends to concentrate on critical interventions to cure disease, perhaps in part because it tends to view health as the absence of disease rather than a positive state. It tends to neglect care when cure is impossible. A third point is closely connected: In setting priorities for research and treatment, the military metaphor tends to assign priority to terminal diseases, such as cancer and AIDS, over chronic diseases. Fourth, medicine as war concentrates on technological interventions, such as intensive-care units, while downplaying less technological modes of care.

In short, the military metaphor has some negative or ambiguous implications for a moral approach to healthcare decisions: It tends to assign priority to healthcare (especially medical care) over other goods, and, within healthcare, to critical interventions over chronic care, killer diseases over disabling ones, technological interventions over care, and heroic treatment of dying patients rather than allowing them to die in peace.

Some of the negative or ambiguous implications of the war metaphor for healthcare can be avoided if, as noted earlier, the metaphor is interpreted in accord with the limits set by the just-war tradition. However, the war metaphor may require supplementation as well as limitation. It is not the only prominent metaphor for healthcare; since the early 1980s its dominance has been threatened by the language of economics and business, as reflected in the language of a healthcare industry. Providers deliver care to consumers, seek or are forced to seek productivity in light of cost-effectiveness or cost-benefit analyses, and may be concerned with "resource management, managed-care systems, and market strategies" (Stein, p. 172). This metaphor also highlights and hides various features of contemporary healthcare. Many critics of this metaphor worry that the language of efficiency will replace the language of care and compassion for the sick and equity in distribution of healthcare. Nevertheless, this metaphor has become more and more pervasive and persuasive as the structure of medicine and healthcare has changed, and as concerns about costs have become more central in societal discussions. Patients often fear undertreatment as hospitals and professionals seek to reduce costs, in contrast to their earlier fears of overtreatment under the war metaphor.

Both military and economics metaphors illuminate contemporary healthcare. But they may not be adequate, even together, to guide and direct healthcare. Whether any particular metaphor is adequate or not will depend in part on the principles and values it highlights and hides. Others have proposed nursing, a subset of healthcare, as a supplementary metaphor for the whole of healthcare, because of its attention to caring more than curing and to hands-on rather than technological care. Even though this metaphor of nursing is also inadequate by itself, it could direct the society to alternative priorities in the allocation of resources for and within healthcare, particularly for chronic care.

THE WAR AGAINST AIDS. Even as the military metaphor has been partially displaced by business and economics metaphors in the changing structure of healthcare, it has gained favor as a way to describe and direct society's response to the major epidemic of the acquired immunodeficiency syndrome (AIDS). Societies often resort to the metaphor of war when a serious threat to a large number of human lives requires the mobilization of vast societal resources, especially when that threat comes from biological organisms, such as viruses, that invade the human body. And AIDS activists have appealed to the military metaphor in an effort to galvanize society and to marshal its resources for an effective counterattack against the human immunodeficiency virus (HIV) that causes AIDS. However, critics charge that the war on AIDS has diverted important resources away from other important wars, such as the war against cancer.

Other controversies have emerged. From the beginning of the war against AIDS, identification of the enemy has been a major goal. Once the virus was identified as the primary enemy, it also became possible to identify human beings who carry or harbor the virus. This technology then led to efforts to identify HIV-infected individuals, even through mandatory screening and testing, as potential enemies of the society. In social discourse and practice, the carrier tends to become an enemy as much as the virus he or she carries, especially since society views many actions that expose individuals to the risk of HIV infection as blameworthy. Thus, the metaphor of war often coexists with metaphors of AIDS as punishment and as otherness (Ross, 1989a, 1989b; Sontag). In this specific case of war against AIDS, just as in the general war against disease, the military metaphor would be less dangerous if society adhered to the constraints of the just-war tradition, rather than being tempted by a crusade.

RELATIONSHIPS BETWEEN HEALTHCARE PROFESSIONALS AND RECIPIENTS OF CARE. Relationships between physicians and other healthcare professionals, on one hand, and patients, on the other, have been described and directed by a wide variety of metaphors and models (Childress and Siegler). For example, William May (1983) has identified images of the physician as fighter, technician, parent, covenanter, and teacher; Robert Veatch has identified several major competing models of physician-patient relationships: engineering, priestly (which includes the paternalistic model), collegial, and contractual models. Other metaphors such as friend and captain of the ship have also been used (King et al.).

Some critics contend that such models are *whimsical gestalts,* that many other arbitrary models could be invented—for example, bus driver or back-seat driver—and that moral points can and should be made more directly (Clouser). Such criticisms overlook how metaphors and models function in the interpretation and evaluation of interactions between physicians and patients. They miss the role of imagination, which can be defined as "reasoning in metaphors" (Eerdman). For example, opponents of paternalistic medical relationships usually do not eschew all use of metaphor; instead they offer alternative metaphors, such as partnership or contracts. And these various metaphors may be more or less adequate to describe what occurs and to direct what should occur in health care.

Metaphors and models highlight and hide features of the roles of physicians and other healthcare professionals by their various associated implications. For example, viewing the physician as a parent—or specifically as a father, based on the nineteenth-century model of the family—highlights some features of medical relationships, such as care and control, while hiding others, such as the payment of fees. In their use to describe, interpret, and explain relationships, such metaphors are subject to criticism if they distort more than they illuminate. And when they are offered to guide relationships and actions, they are subject to criticism if they highlight only one moral consideration, such as the physician's duty to benefit the patient or to respect patient autonomy, while hiding or obscuring other relevant moral considerations. It is also appropriate to consider the feasibility of various ideal relationships in light of significant personal, professional, and institutional constraints.

Several metaphors may be necessary to interpret healthcare as it is currently structured and to guide and direct actions, practices, and policies in healthcare. Some metaphors may fit some relationships better than others; for example, relations in clinical research, family practice, and surgery may be illuminated respectively by the metaphors of partner, teacher-student, and technician-consumer. Furthermore, not all of these metaphors conflict with each other; some may even be mutually supportive as well as compatible, for example, contractor and technician.

NURSING AS ADVOCACY. Major changes in the conception of nursing correlate with alterations in its primary metaphors. Whether situated within the military effort against disease or viewed as physicians' handmaidens and servants, nurses have traditionally been expected to cultivate passive virtues, such as loyalty and obedience. Their moral responsibility was primarily directed toward physicians and institutions, such as hospitals, and only secondarily toward patients. This interpretation of responsibility was shaped in part by nursing's military origins in the nineteenth century, as well as by societal conceptions of gender (Winslow; Bernal). Then in the 1970s, nursing was reconceived through the metaphor of advocacy. Nurses became advocates for *clients* and *consumers* (the term *patient* was often rejected as too passive). This legal metaphor, drawn from the advocate as one who pleads another's cause, especially before a tribunal of justice, highlights active virtues such as courage, persistence, and perseverance, and views the nurse as primarily responsible to the patient or client. This metaphor is explicit or implicit in formal nursing codes, and it is also featured in a large number of nurses' stories of advocacy and conflict in healthcare (Winslow; Bernal).

Critics note that the metaphor of advocacy reduces the range of services traditionally offered by nurses; it is thus insufficiently comprehensive (Bernal). In addition to distorting the human experience of illness, it distorts nursing by focusing almost exclusively on patients' or clients' rights, construed mainly in terms of autonomy, and it neglects positive social relationships in healthcare (Bernal). It highlights conflict among healthcare professionals because it implies that some of them do not adequately protect the rights of patients. Thus, the metaphor frequently supports a call for increased nursing autonomy as a way to protect patient autonomy. Because of its adversarial nature, many question whether the metaphor of advocacy can adequately guide relationships among healthcare professionals in the long run, even if it is useful in the short run. The metaphor may also assume that the nurse's responsibility to the patient/client is always clear-cut and overriding, even though nurses may face serious conflicts of responsibility involving patients, other individuals, associates, and institutions (Winslow). At the very least, sympathetic commentators call for further clarification of the metaphor of advocacy (Winslow); while critics seek alternative metaphors and models, such as covenant (Bernal), partnership, teamwork, or collegiality, that appear to offer more inclusive, cooperative ideals.

PLAYING GOD AND OTHER METAPHORS OF LIMITS. "Playing God" has been a common metaphor for both describing and directing the activities of scientists, physicians, and other healthcare professionals. They have been criticized for usurping God's power—for instance, the power over life and death—by letting patients die or by using new reproductive technologies.

There are theological warrants for playing God in the Jewish and Christian traditions, which affirm the creation of human beings in God's image and likeness. Thus, Paul Ramsey calls on those who allocate healthcare to play God in a fitting way: We should emulate God's indiscriminate care by distributing scarce lifesaving medical technologies randomly or by a lottery rather than on the basis of judgments of social worth.

Despite a few such positive uses of the metaphor of "playing God," the metaphor is generally used to identify two aspects of divine activity that should not be imitated by humans: God's unlimited power to decide and unlimited power to act. On one hand, users of this metaphor demand scientific and medical accountability over unilateral decision making. On the other hand, critics call for respect for substantive limits—for example, not creating new forms of life (U.S. President's Commission, 1982).

Edmund Erde contends that statements such as "doctors should not play god" are so unclear that they cannot function as commands and do not articulate a principle; thus, they cannot be followed because agents do not know how to conform their actions to them. Nor do they explain why certain actions should not be undertaken. Such phrases are, Erde argues, "metaphoric in that they tuck powerful feelings and images into descriptive language that cannot be understood literally" (p. 606). Any activity, such as mercy killing, that is "labeled `playing god' carries the implication that it is clearly wrong" (p. 607). These phrases are used for situations in which agents face choices, but one option is considered immoral and is rejected as arrogantly and presumptuously playing God. The background of intelligibility of this metaphor, according to Erde, is found in the Western idea of the great chain of being, which identifies appropriate responsibilities at each level and opposes the usurpation of power and the failure to respect limits.

Other important and widespread metaphors of limits include the "thin edge of the wedge" and the "slippery slope," both of which warn against undertaking certain actions because other unacceptable actions will inevitably follow. Examples regularly appear in debates about euthanasia. Even though such metaphors are often misused, they are appropriate in some contexts. In each use of these metaphors, important moral questions require attention—the evaluation of the first action and subsequent actions—and important conceptual and empirical questions must be addressed in order to determine whether the putatively bad consequences will inevitably follow what might be innocuous first steps. (Similar questions emerge for some analogies, such as the Nazi analogy, which is also widely invoked to oppose such practices as mercy killing.)

METAPHORS FOR BIOETHICS AND BIOETHICISTS. The role and function of the bioethicist have often been construed in metaphorical terms. The common language of *applied ethics* invokes the metaphor of engineering as an application of basic science that does not contribute to basic science. The expertise of applied ethicists resides in their ability to apply general theories and principles to specific arenas of human activity. The metaphor of application has been widely challenged on the grounds that it is too narrow and distorts much that is important in bioethics. The term *applied* suggests that ethicists are problem solvers rather than problem setters, that they solve puzzles rather than provide

perspectives, that they answer rather than raise questions, and that they begin from theory rather than from lived experience. It implies a limited technical or mechanical model of ethics.

The term *applied* distorts the numerous theoretical controversies in bioethics, and neglects the way bioethics may help to resolve or recast some theoretical controversies. At the very least, the metaphor of application may need to be supplemented by various other metaphors for the task of practical ethics and the role of the practical ethicist: "Theoretician, diagnostician, educator, coach, conceptual policeman, and skeptic are also supplemental or alternative roles to that of the technician" (Caplan, p. 30).

Some other metaphors are drawn from ancient religious roles, such as prophet or scribe. Yet another metaphor is *conversation,* which is prominent in approaches to bioethics that emphasize interpretation, hermeneutics, and narrative. And the *stranger* has been proposed as the best metaphor for the ethicist in professional education because his or her outside perspective can challenge ordinary assumptions (Churchill).

Suggestions emerge at various times to retire all metaphors, not merely some metaphors in some realm of discourse—for instance, Sontag proposes retiring all metaphors for illness. However, it is not possible to strip our discourse in science, medicine, and healthcare, or in biomedical ethics, of all metaphors. Instead, we must use metaphors with care and must carefully assess their adequacy in descriptive and normative functions.

Analogies in Bioethics

ANALOGIES AND ANALOGICAL REASONING. Often metaphors and analogies are presented in ways that indicate their substantial overlap. Indeed, for the comparison view of metaphor, there is little difference between them, because metaphors are compressed analogies. Some recent theories of metaphor have stressed, by contrast, that metaphors create similarities rather than merely expressing previously established and recognized similarities or analogies. According to Black, comparison views of metaphor fail because they reduce the ground for shifts of meaning (from the secondary subject to the primary subject) to similarity or analogy (1962). Nevertheless, there is a strong consensus that metaphorical statements presuppose some resemblance, even when they also create resemblance (Ricoeur). Black later conceded that metaphors "mediate an analogy or structural correspondence." Metaphor is, roughly speaking, "an instrument for drawing implications grounded in perceived analogies of structure between two subjects belonging to different domains" (1979, p. 32). And yet metaphor does not merely compare two things that are similar, but rather enables us to see similarities in what would be regarded as dissimilar.

Metaphors and analogies are thus closely related, with metaphors both expressing and creating similarities. In general, good metaphors function cognitively to generate new meaning and insight, by providing new perspectives; while good analogies extend our knowledge by moving from the familiar to the unfamiliar, from the established to the novel. In stretching language and concepts for new situations, analogy does not involve the imaginative strain often evident in the use of metaphors (Soskice). Nevertheless, the differences in function between metaphors and analogies should not be exaggerated.

The term analogy derives from the Greek *analogia,* which referred to mathematical proportion. "An analogy in its original root meaning," Dorothy Emmet observes, "is a proportion, and primarily a mathematical ratio, e.g., 2: 4: : 4: X. In such a ratio, given knowledge of three terms, and the nature of the proportionate relation, the value of the fourth term can be determined. Thus analogy is the repetition of the same fundamental pattern in two different contexts" (p. 6).

Analogical reasoning proceeds inductively, moving from the known to the unknown. It appears prominently in problem solving and thus is featured in research in cognitive science and artificial intelligence (Helman; Keane). For instance, computer problem-solving programs must search for analogous problems that have been successfully solved to generate solutions to new problems whether in highly structured domains such as law or in less structured domains.

Analogical reasoning has an important place in moral discourse, not only because of its importance in problem solving, but also because of the widely recognized moral requirement to treat similar cases in a similar way. Often stated as a principle of universalizability or of formal justice or formal equality, dating back at least to Aristotle, the requirement to treat similar cases in a similar way also appears in the common law's doctrine of precedent. The basic idea is that one does not make an acceptable moral or a legal judgment—perhaps not even a moral or legal judgment at all—if one judges that X is wrong, but that a similar X is right, without adducing any relevant moral or legal difference between them. In general, analogical reasoning illuminates features of morally or legally problematic cases by appealing to relevantly similar cases that reflect a moral or legal consensus (precedent). Of course, much of the moral (or legal) debate hinges on determining which similarities and differences are both relevant and significant.

Since the early 1980s ethicists have directed new attention to the role of analogical reasoning in case-oriented or casuistical judgments in bioethics and elsewhere. In *The Abuse of Casuistry,* Albert Jonsen and Stephen Toulmin identify "the first feature of the casuistic method" in its classical formulations as "the ordering of cases under a principle by paradigm and analogy" (p. 252). For instance, the rule prohibiting killing is set out in *paradigm cases* that illustrate its most manifest breaches according to its most obvious meaning. Moving from simple and clear cases to complex and uncertain ones, casuists examine various alternative circumstances and motives to determine whether those other cases violate the rule against killing. They seek analogies that permit the comparison of "problematic new cases and circumstances with earlier exemplary ones," that is, the similar cases that constitute presumptions (Jonsen and Toulmin, p. 316).

Despite the claims of some modern casuists, it is not clear that analogical reasoning distinguishes casuistical from principlist approaches. For instance, in analyzing the novel microallocation problems of modern medicine, Paul Ramsey appealed to the analogous "lifeboat" cases—when some passengers have to be thrown overboard in order to prevent the lifeboat from sinking—as a way to interpret the requirements of the principle of equality of opportunity in distributing scarce lifesaving medical technologies such as kidney dialysis. Because principles and rules are indeterminate, and because they sometimes conflict, analogical reasoning can be expected in case judgments—mere application cannot be sufficient.

Analogies are often divided into two main types: analogies of attribution and analogies of proportion (Cahill). The analogy of attribution involves a comparison of two terms or analogates, both of which have a common property, the analogon, that appears primarily in one and secondarily in the other. As Thomas Aquinas noted, *healthy* is used primarily for a person in a state of health (a *healthy* person) and secondarily for those medicines and practices that help to maintain or restore health (e.g., a *healthy* diet) or specimens that provide evidence of the body's health (e.g., *healthy* blood). By contrast, in the analogy of proportion, the analogates lack a direct relationship, but each of them involves a relationship that can be compared to a relationship in the other (Cahill). This second type is most common in analogical reasoning in biomedical ethics, as is evident in debates about maternal-fetal relations and abortion, where analogies of attribution also appear, particularly with reference to the fetus.

Analogical reasoning in debates about maternal-fetal relations. Debates about maternal-fetal relations, including pregnant women's decisions to abort and to decline cesarean sections, illustrate the pervasiveness and importance of analogical reasoning. Traditionally, abortion has been construed as directly killing the fetus, an innocent human being, in violation of the duty of nonmaleficence. Hence, in traditional Roman Catholic moral theology, direct abortions are tantamount to homicide. Sometimes the analogy of the *unjust aggressor* appears in situations where the pregnancy threatens the pregnant woman's life or health; but it has not been accepted in official Catholic thought the way the similar analogy of the *pursuer* has been accepted in some Jewish thought to justify abortions when there is such a threat.

Some feminists and others have attempted to recast the debate about abortion to focus on the basis and extent of the pregnant woman's obligation to provide bodily life support to the fetus. Often accepting, at least for purposes of argument, the premise that the fetus is a human being from the moment of conception (or at some time during the pregnancy), they argue that this premise does not entail that the pregnant woman always has a duty to sustain the fetus's life regardless of the circumstances of pregnancy, the risks and inconveniences to the pregnant woman, and so forth. Their arguments often proceed through analogies to other hypothetical or real practices or cases, on the assumption that a judgment about those practices or cases will entail a similar judgment about abortion.

The fantastic abortion analogies introduced by Judith Jarvis Thomson (1971) have been particularly influential and controversial. In one of her artificial cases, an individual with a rare blood type is kidnapped by the Society of Music Lovers and attached to a famous violinist who needs to purify his system because of his renal failure. Part of the debate concerns whether relevant analogies can be found in such fantastic, artificial cases, in contrast to actual real-life cases. For example, against Thomson, John Noonan opposes abortion in part by appeal to a U.S. tort-law case, in which the court held liable the hosts who had invited a guest for dinner but then put him out of their house into the cold night even though he had become sick and fainted and requested permission to stay (Noonan).

Some feminists and others contend that other analogous real-life legal and moral cases support the pregnant woman's free decision to continue or to discontinue her pregnancy. For many the relevant analogous cases concern living organ and tissue donation. Such donations are conceived as voluntary, altruistic acts that should not be forced by others even to save the potential recipient's life. They are *gifts of life*. Requiring a pregnant woman to continue the pregnancy until birth imposes on her a heavier burden than others are expected to bear in analogous circumstances, such as a parent who could save a child's life by donating a kidney. Thus, the provision of bodily life support, whether through donating an organ or allowing the fetus to use the uterus, has been conceived as a gift of life that should not be legally enforced (Mattingly; Jung).

According to Lisa Sowle Cahill, much analogical reasoning about pregnancy overlooks what is unique about maternal-fetal relations and thus obscures the morally relevant features of pregnancy or makes some relevant features more significant than they are. Many analogies problematically narrow our moral perspective on abortion by portraying the inception of pregnancy as accidental and the fetus as strange, alien, and even hostile. Furthermore, they often rely on the connotative meanings of their terms, particularly as embedded in a story, such as Thomson's case of kidnapping the unwilling blood donor. Examples also appear in the rhetoric of abortion opponents who, for instance, speak of the fetus as a *child*, and thereby distort the unique dependence of the fetus on the pregnant woman (Cahill). Finally, Cahill contends, justifications of abortion based on analogy often rest on liberal convictions that special responsibilities derive only from free choice.

For all these reasons, Cahill holds that analogical reasoning needs supplementation through direct examination of the unique features of maternal-fetal relations, particularly total fetal dependence, and of the ways these unique features qualify maternal, professional, and societal obligations. She argues that, as a category or class of moral relations, pregnancy "is unique among human relations at least because in it one individual is totally and exclusively dependent on a particular other within a relation which represents in its physical and social aspects what is *prima facie* to be valued positively" (p. 283). Hence, she argues, most analogies hide what is distinctive and unique about pregnancy, even though they identify some morally relevant features of maternal-fetal relations.

With the emergence of other maternal-fetal conflicts, particularly regarding cesarean sections to benefit the fetus, similar debates have emerged about the appropriateness of the analogy with living organ and tissue donation. For instance, in the case of A.C. (1990), the majority of the court held that, just as courts do not compel people to *donate* organs or tissue to benefit others, so they should not compel cesarean sections against the will of pregnant women to benefit potentially viable fetuses. The dissenting opinion rejected the analogy with organ and tissue donation, insisting that the pregnant woman "has undertaken to bear another human being, and has carried an unborn child to viability," that the "unborn child's" dependence upon the mother is unique and singular, and that the "viable unborn child is literally captive within the mother's body" (A.C., *In re,*).

Even though analogies with organ and tissue donation are now widely invoked to oppose state control of pregnant women's decisions regarding both abortion and cesarean sections, there are important differences between these two contexts. In the abortion debate, pregnancy is viewed as the provision of bodily life support and is itself analogous to the donated organ. In the debate about cesarean sections, the surgical procedure is analogous to organ donation—the potentially viable fetus is removed for its own benefit rather than to benefit some other party as in organ or tissue donation. In the abortion debate, the pregnancy is viewed as invasive; in the debate about cesarean sections, the surgical procedure is invasive. The central issue is whether state coercion in these cases to benefit the fetus is morally and legally acceptable. The debate hinges in part on the appropriateness of the living organ and tissue donation as an analogy. Even the critics of the analogy engage in analogical reasoning, but they deny that the similarities are more morally or legally relevant and significant than the dissimilarities. Defenders of governmental coercion could also hold that the moral or legal precedent is mistaken and that organs and tissues should sometimes be conscripted or expropriated from living persons.

Similar disputes appear in other areas of contemporary bioethics—for instance, in debates about whether mandatory testing or screening for antibodies to the human immunodeficiency virus, which causes AIDS, can be justified by analogy to accepted practices of mandatory testing or screening; and in debates about whether transplantation experiments using human fetal tissue, following deliberate abortions, are analogous to the complicitous use of materials or data from the morally heinous Nazi experiments. In these cases, as in many others, the debates focus to a great extent on the relevance and significance of the proposed analogies.

Conclusions

Debates in biomedical ethics are often debates about which metaphors and analogies illuminate more than they distort. Far from being merely decorative or affective, metaphors and analogies are central to both discourse and practice. They must be evaluated specifically according to how well they function to describe and/or direct actions and relationships. Even though in recent bioethics metaphors and analogies have sometimes been offered as ways to circumvent or transcend principles and rules, particularly through attention to cases, narratives, and aesthetic dimensions of experience, they are not necessarily incompatible with principles and rules. Analogical reasoning is important within frameworks of principles and rules, as well as in casuistry, and metaphors and models often succeed or fail depending on how well they express the full range of relevant moral considerations.

JAMES F. CHILDRESS (1995)

SEE ALSO: *Abortion; Cancer, Ethical Issues Related to Diagnosis and Treatment; Children: History of Childhood; Embryo and Fetus; Epidemics; Ethics; Holocaust; Literature and Medicine; Moral Status; Narrative; Responsibility; Value and Valuation; Women, Historical and Cross-Cultural Perspectives*

BIBLIOGRAPHY

A.C., *In re.* 1990. 57B A.2d 1235 (D.C. App.).

Bernal, Ellen W. 1992. "The Nurse as Patient Advocate." *Hastings Center Report* 22(4): 18–23.

Black, Max. 1962. "Metaphor." In *Models and Metaphors: Studies in Language and Philosophy,* pp. 25–47. Ithaca, NY: Cornell University Press.

Black, Max. 1979. "More About Metaphor." In *Metaphor and Thought,* pp. 19–43, ed. Andrew Ortony. Cambridge, Eng.: Cambridge University Press.

Cahill, Lisa Sowle. 1982. "Abortion and Argument by Analogy." *Horizons* 9(2): 271–287.

Caplan, Arthur L. 1980. "Ethical Engineers Need Not Apply: The State of Applied Ethics Today." *Science, Technology, and Human Values* 6(33): 24–32.

Childress, James F. 1982. *Who Should Decide? Paternalism in Health Care.* New York: Oxford University Press.

Childress, James F., and Siegler, Mark. 1984. "Metaphors and Models of Doctor-Patient Relationships: Their Implications for Autonomy." *Theoretical Medicine* 5(1): 17–30.

Churchill, Larry R. 1978. "The Ethicist in Professional Education." *Hastings Center Report* 8(6): 13–15.

Clouser, K. Danner. 1983. "Veatch, May, and Models: A Critical Review and a New View." In *The Clinical Encounter: The Moral Fabric of the Patient-Physician Encounter,* pp. 89–103, ed. Earl E. Shelp. Dordrecht, Netherlands: D. Reidel.

Eerdman, David V. 1969. "Coleridge as Editorial Writer." In *Power and Consciousness,* pp. 187–201, ed. Conor Cruise O'Brien and William Dean Vanech. New York: New York University Press.

Emmet, Dorothy Mary. 1945. *The Nature of Metaphysical Thinking.* New York: St. Martin's Press.

Erde, Edmund L. 1989. "Studies in the Explanation of Issues in Biomedical Ethics: II. On 'On Playing God,' etc." *Journal of Medicine and Philosophy* 14(6): 593–615.

Hawkins, Anne Hunsaker. 1993. *Reconstructing Illness: Studies in Pathography*. West Lafayette, IN: Purdue University Press.

Helman, David H., ed. 1988. *Analogical Reasoning: Perspectives of Artificial Intelligence, Cognitive Science, and Philosophy*. Dordrecht, Netherlands: Kluwer Academic Publishers.

Jonsen, Albert R., and Toulmin, Stephen. 1988. *The Abuse of Casuistry: A History of Moral Reasoning*. Berkeley: University of California Press.

Jung, Patricia Beattie. 1988. "Abortion and Organ Donation: Christian Reflections on Bodily Life Support." *Journal of Religious Ethics* 16(2): 273–305.

Keane, Mark T. 1988. *Analogical Problem Solving*. Chichester, England: Ellis Norwood.

King, Nancy M. P.; Churchill, Larry R.; and Cross, Alan W. 1988. *The Physician as Captain of the Ship: A Critical Reappraisal*. Dordrecht, Netherlands: D. Reidel.

Lakoff, George, and Johnson, Mark. 1980. *Metaphors We Live By*. Chicago: University of Chicago Press.

Mattingly, Susan S. 1984. "Viewing Abortion from the Perspective of Transplantation: The Ethics of the Gift of Life." *Soundings* 67(4): 399–410.

May, William F. 1975. "Code, Covenant, Contract, or Philanthropy." *Hastings Center Report* 5(6): 29–38.

May, William F. 1983. *The Physician's Covenant: Images of the Healer in Medical Ethics*. Philadelphia: Westminster Press.

Miller, George. 1979. "Images and Models, Similes and Metaphors." In *Metaphor and Thought*, pp. 202–250, ed. Andrew Ortony. Cambridge, Eng.: Cambridge University Press.

Noonan, John T. 1974. "How to Argue About Abortion." New York: Ad Hoc Committee in Defense of Life.

Pray, Lawrence, and Evans, Richard, III. 1983. *Journey of a Diabetic*. New York: Simon and Schuster.

Ramsey, Paul. 1970. *The Patient as Person: Explorations in Medical Ethics*. New Haven, CT: Yale University Press.

Ricoeur, Paul. 1977. *The Rule of Metaphor: Multi-Disciplinary Studies of the Creation of Meaning in Language,* tr. Robert Czerny. Toronto: University of Toronto Press.

Ross, Judith. 1989a. "Ethics and the Language of AIDS." In *The Meaning of AIDS: Implications for Medical Science, Clinical Practice and Public Health Policy,* pp. 30–41, ed. Eric T. Juengst and Barbara A. Koenig. New York: Praeger.

Ross, Judith. 1989b. "The Militarization of Disease: Do We Really Want a War on AIDS?" *Soundings* 72(1): 39–50.

Sontag, Susan. 1990. *Illness as Metaphor; and, AIDS and Its Metaphors*. New York: Doubleday Anchor Books.

Soskice, Janet Martin. 1985. *Metaphor and Religious Language*. Oxford: Clarendon Press.

Stein, Howard F. 1990. *American Medicine as Culture*. Boulder, CO: Westview Press.

Thomson, Judith Jarvis. 1971. "A Defense of Abortion." *Philosophy and Public Affairs* 1(1): 47–66.

U.S. President's Commission for the Study of Ethical Problems in Medicine and Biomedical and Behavioral Research. 1983. *Splicing Life*. Washington, D.C.: U.S. Government Printing Office.

Veatch, Robert M. 1972. "Models for Ethics in Medicine in a Revolutionary Age." *Hastings Center Report* 2(3): 5–7.

Winslow, Gerald R. 1984. "From Loyalty to Advocacy: A New Metaphor for Nursing." *Hastings Center Report* 14(3): 32–40.

MILITARY PERSONNEL AS RESEARCH SUBJECTS

• • •

A key ethical issue in the use of military personnel as research subjects is whether individuals in the armed services are free to accept or decline participation in research. Voluntary participation has been recognized as an essential requirement for ethical human experimentation; it is the cornerstone of the Nuremberg Code, issued in 1947 as part of the prosecution of Nazi physicians. Some bioethicists have expressed concerns that military discipline, with its emphasis on following orders and the chain of command, may constrain an individual's ability to make uncoerced decisions about participation in research. It is not clear, for example, how participation in a research study differs significantly from other hazardous duties expected of military personnel.

Negotiating the balance between respect for individual autonomy and the needs of the military is more problematic when nations are at war. During World War II, the medical needs of the military were invoked to justify the experimental use of vaccines and drugs in military populations, as well as nontherapeutic research on conscientious objectors, orphans, prisoners, and the mentally ill. Nearly 60,000 American military personnel were recruited through "lies and half-truths" into secret tests of mustard agents (sulfur and nitrogen mustard) and Lewisite (an arsenic compound) (Pechura and Rall). In the Persian Gulf War of 1991, the military's decision to seek a waiver of its own regulations about informed consent for the administration of investigational drugs and vaccines to American servicemen and servicewomen prompted controversy between critics who condemned this deviation from the Nuremberg Code and supporters who argued that the principle of preventing unnecessary harm to military personnel made the decision necessary (Howe and Martin; Annas and Grodin). These issues, which have received little sustained analysis, require greater attention from bioethicists.

Historical Use of Military Subjects

Historically, the armed forces have provided both unique opportunities and special needs for the study of human health and disease. "He who would become a surgeon," observed the Greek physician Hippocrates, "should join the army and follow it" (Hume, p. 78). Early efforts in disease prevention and treatment reflected the practical concerns of maintaining military personnel in good condition. One of the earliest clinical trials involving human subjects was conducted by the Scottish naval surgeon James Lind (1716–1794), who administered six different treatments to twelve sailors suffering from scurvy, and observed the beneficial effect of oranges and lemons in recovery from the disease (Carpenter).

Traumatic injuries from guns and other weapons have provided distinctive opportunities for military physicians to study human anatomy and physiology. In the 1820s, American army surgeon William Beaumont investigated the process of human digestion in a live subject after his repeated efforts failed to close the gunshot wound to French–Canadian trapper Alexis St. Martin's stomach. Beaumont developed an employment contract with his research subject, who agreed to allow physiological experiments in exchange for room, board, and wages. Beaumont also persuaded the trapper to enlist in the U.S. Army, giving the physician more complete control of his subject and rendering St. Martin's "faithless absconding" subject to military law (Numbers).

The rise of experimental science and the germ theory of disease in the late nineteenth century increased experimentation involving human beings. The Medical Department of the U.S. Army expanded its efforts to control infectious diseases, the major cause of mortality in the military before World War II. All U.S. Army commanders were directed to cooperate with the Medical Department to secure volunteers for experimental inoculations or other medical investigations approved by the War Department (Dow). Both the British and the American armed forces conducted experiments with newly developed vaccines for typhoid fever and other diseases (Tigertt). The introduction of aviation and its rapid development after World War I accelerated military research with human subjects (Pitts).

Introduction of Participant Consent

The shift from therapeutic experiments to nontherapeutic research in the early twentieth century fostered more formal arrangements with research subjects. In 1900 Major Walter Reed and members of the U.S. Army's Yellow Fever Board adopted the first written agreements between research subjects and experimenters. The Spanish immigrants who participated signed contracts that described compensation for subjects (civilians received $100 in gold and an additional $100 if they contracted the disease) and identified some of the risks of participation (Lederer). American physicians working in the Philippines followed Reed's example; prisoners in Manila's Bilibid Prison signed agreements written in their own dialect for medical research studies (Chernin; Lederer). During World War I, some physicians continued the policy of having written agreements with American soldiers who participated in infectious disease research (Sellards).

The success of the yellow fever research gained public approval for human experimentation. Public reaction to the research-related deaths of Army nurse Clara Maas and two Cuban volunteers, however, led the surgeon general to suspend the Army's work on a yellow fever vaccine in 1902. Most published reports of military medical research emphasized the voluntary nature of participation. References to cash payments and better duty assignments raised questions about the pressures to volunteer. In principle, American military personnel, although required to undergo standard medical procedures to enhance their military fitness, retained the right to refuse participation in medical experiments (Johnson).

The advent of World War II spurred massive changes in the organization and funding of medical research. The Committee on Medical Research, part of the Office of Scientific Research and Development, sponsored clinical research projects on an unprecedented scale. Pressures to find solutions for military medical problems encouraged investigators to conduct numerous trials with human subjects. As historian David J. Rothman has observed, the arguments that were used to justify sending men into combat were also invoked to sanction the use of conscientious objectors and civilians—prisoners, orphans, the retarded, and the mentally ill—in nontherapeutic research for military needs.

The wartime research ethos continued into the Cold War era. Both military and civilian researchers increasingly used human beings in experiments with little regard for the principles of consent and voluntary participation elaborated in the Nuremberg Code, or in the regulations governing research adopted by the secretary of defense in 1953 but classified as top secret until 1975 (Annas, Glantz, and Katz). During the Cold War, some 250,000 men and women were exposed to radiation as part of state-sponsored nuclear testing in Nevada and the South Pacific. In the early 1950s the American military conducted indoctrination and panic studies on troops at atom bomb tests (Moreno). Between 1955 and 1967, the U.S. Army and the Air Force supported more than eighteen research projects on the effects of hallucinogenic drugs on human performance in the United States and Canada (Annas and Grodin). Many of the nearly seven thousand servicemen who participated in drug tests at the Army Chemical Center at Edgewood Arsenal, Maryland, apparently received little information about the risks they incurred as a result of their participation in lysergic acid diethylamide (LSD) studies. Army investigators similarly failed to inform the more than one thousand participants about risks they incurred in tests of various nerve gases (Downey).

Amid the public condemnation of the LSD studies and the exposure of large numbers of servicemen to harmful radiation in the race to develop an atomic arsenal, the U.S. Army, Navy, and Air Force revised policies for research involving military personnel. In 1972 the American military banned all tests of nerve gases involving human subjects, and in 1974 issued new regulations for research on military personnel. In 1983, U.S. Department of Defense Directive 3216.2, "Protection of Human Subjects in DoD-Supported Research," established a uniform policy for research involving human subjects throughout the Department of Defense. In addition to adhering to the regulations for the protection of human subjects of the Department of Health and Human Services, the guidelines charged the military chain of command to ensure that the fundamental rights, welfare, and dignity of human subjects be protected to the maximum extent possible (Winter). Research involving American military personnel received greater scrutiny in the 1980s (Howe, Kark, and Wright; Maningas). Some military research subjects have received compensation for injuries they sustained in tests conducted without their knowledge.

New Complications in Military Research

Biological and chemical weapons pose some special problems for military personnel. Nations have approached the search for effective protections against these weapons in different ways. Whereas the American military discontinued the testing of toxic chemicals on human beings, the British Ministry of Defense continued to test antidotes for nerve gases on volunteer soldiers. Critics of the experimental exposure of soldier volunteers to nerve gases have cited safety concerns, as well as doubts that soldiers were "capable of giving full and informed consent to participate in complex toxicological experiments" (Mason, p. 30). Other North Atlantic Treaty Organization (NATO) countries have conducted similar testing of protective gear and drugs against nerve gas and a wide variety of other chemical weapons.

The threat of chemical and biological weapons in the Persian Gulf War in 1991 led the U.S. Food and Drug Administration (FDA) to grant the Department of Defense's request for a waiver of federal informed-consent regulations for administering investigational drugs and vaccines to troops stationed in Kuwait. Although the threat of chemical weapons did not materialize, the successful waiver of informed consent raised distinctive issues for military physicians. In the absence of informed consent, should a military physician follow orders and administer an investigational drug? Another related question for the military physician is whether his or her primary responsibility is the welfare of an individual patient or the success of a military mission (Howe; Annas).

Issues posed by research on military personnel are complex. As bioethicist George Annas has argued, these issues require critical attention in peacetime, since they are "not susceptible to rational analysis in wartime" (Annas, p. 773).

SUSAN E. LEDERER (1995)
REVISED BY AUTHOR

SEE ALSO: *Research, Human: Historical Aspects; Research Policy: Vulnerable Groups; Research, Unethical; Warfare: Chemical and Biological Weapons; Whistleblowing in Healthcare*

BIBLIOGRAPHY

Annas, George J. 1992. "Changing the Consent Rules for Desert Storm." *New England Journal of Medicine* 326(11): 770–773.

Annas, George J.; Glantz, Leonard H.; and Katz, Barbara F. 1977. *Informed Consent to Human Experimentation: The Subject's Dilemma.* Cambridge, MA: Ballinger.

Annas, George J., and Grodin, Michael A. 1991. "Commentary" (to "Treating the Troops," by Howe and Martin). *Hastings Center Report* 21(2): 24–27.

Annas, George J., and Grodin, Michael A., eds. 1992. *The Nazi Doctors and the Nuremberg Code: Human Rights in Human Experimentation.* Oxford: Oxford University Press.

Bean, William B. 1977. "Walter Reed and the Ordeal of Human Experiments." *Bulletin of the History of Medicine* 51(1): 75–92.

Carpenter, Kenneth J. 1986. *The History of Scurvy and Vitamin C.* Cambridge, MA: Cambridge University Press.

Chernin, Eli. 1989. "Richard Pearson Strong and the Iatrogenic Plague Disaster in Bilibid Prison, Manila, 1906." *Review of Infectious Diseases* 11(6): 996–1004.

Dow, William S. 1925. "The Possibility of Medical Research in the Military Service Because of Its Complete Control over Personnel." *Military Surgeon* 56(2): 129–144.

Downey, Thomas J. 1975. "Report on Human Experimentation Conducted or Funded by the U.S. Army." *Congressional Record* 121: 27934–27938.

Howe, Edmund G. 1986. "Ethical Issues Regarding Mixed Agency of Military Physicians." *Social Science and Medicine* 23(8): 803–815.

Howe, Edmund G., Kark, John A., and Wright, Daniel G. 1983. "Studying Sickle Cell Trait in Healthy Army Recruits: Should the Research Be Done?" *Clinical Research* 31(2): 119–125.

Howe, Edmund G., and Martin, Edward D. 1991. "Treating the Troops." *Hastings Center Report* 21(2): 21–24.

Hume, Edgar E. 1943. *Victories of Army Medicine: Scientific Accomplishments of the Medical Department of the United States Army.* Philadelphia: J.B. Lippincott.

Johnson, W. H. 1953. "Civil Rights of Military Personnel Regarding Medical Care and Experimental Procedures." *Science* 117: 212–215.

Lederer, Susan E. 1995. *Subjected to Science: Human Experimentation in America Before the Second World War.* Baltimore: Johns Hopkins University Press.

Levine, Carol. 1989. "Military Medical Research: 1. Are There Ethical Exceptions?" *IRB* 11(4): 5–7.

Levine, Robert J. 1991. "Commentary" (to "Treating the Troops," by Howe and Martin). *Hastings Center Report* 21(2): 27–28.

Maningas, Peter A. 1989. "Combat Casualty Care Research and Informed Consent." *Military Medicine* 154(2): 71–73.

Mason, Ian. 1987. "Porton Defends Nerve–Gas Tests on Humans." *New Scientist,* July 16: 30.

Moreno, Jonathan D. 2000. *Undue Risk: Secret State Experiments on Humans.* New York: W.H. Freeman.

Numbers, Ronald L. 1979. "William Beaumont and the Ethics of Human Experimentation." *Journal of the History of Biology* 12(1): 113–135.

Pechura, Constance, and Rall, David P., eds. 1993. *Veterans At Risk: The Health Effects of Mustard Gas and Lewisite.* Washington, D.C.: National Academy Press.

Pitts, John A. 1985. *The Human Factor: Biomedicine in the Manned Space Program to 1980.* Washington, D.C.: NASA.

Rothman, David J. 1991. *Strangers at the Bedside: A History of How Law and Bioethics Transformed Medical Decision-Making.* New York: Basic Books.

Sellards, Andrew W. 1919. "Insusceptibility of Man to Inoculation with Blood from Measles Patients." *Johns Hopkins Hospital Bulletin* 30: 257–268.

Tigertt, William D. 1959. "The Initial Effort to Immunize American Soldier Volunteers with Typhoid Vaccine." *Military Medicine* 124: 342–349.

Winter, Phillip E. 1984. "Human Subject Research Review in the Department of Defense." *IRB* 6(3): 9–10.

MINORITIES AS RESEARCH SUBJECTS

• • •

In 1984 Margaret Heckler, secretary of the U.S. Department of Health and Human Services (HHS), established the Task Force on Black and Minority Health to investigate the health status and health needs of minority groups in the nation. A year later, that panel presented its report, noting the lack of data about many aspects of minority health and the need for greater inclusion of minorities (defined as blacks, Hispanics, Asian/Pacific Islanders, and Native Americans) in medical research projects (U.S. Department of Health and Human Services, 1985). In response, the National Institutes of Health (NIH), the largest financial supporter of medical research in the United States, began to urge that grant applicants include African-Americans and other minorities as research subjects in their projects. Applicants not incorporating minorities in proposed studies were expected to provide "a clear rationale for their exclusion" (U.S. Department of Health and Human Services, 1988, p. 3). The NIH Revitalization Act of 1993 turned those suggestions into requirements that minorities (categorized as American Indian or Alaskan Native, Asian or Pacific Islander, Black-Not of Hispanic Origin, and Hispanic) must be included in all NIH-supported biomedical and behavioral clinical research projects involving human subjects, except where clear and compelling rationale and justification existed for their exclusion from such studies (U.S. Department of Health and Human Services, 2000, 2002).

The HHS task force's rationale for promoting data-gathering and research studies on minorities was both practical and humanitarian: to "understand … the reasons underlying the longstanding disparity of health status in the United States" between minorities and the majority population, in order "to prevent or reduce much of the illness and death experienced by minorities in disproportion to their representation in the American population." Those reasons, according to the report, included "physiological, cultural and societal factors" (U.S. Department of Health and Human Services, 1985, vol. 1, p. 37). Therefore, Americans needed to conduct research and gather information about the health, health environment, and healthcare practices of all citizens in order to improve everyone's health.

The African-American Experience

Historically, U.S. medical researchers included—even preferred to use—minorities (for example, immigrants from Ireland, Germany, eastern Europe, and Africa) in their research studies; not until recently, however, did they select members of these groups for the humanitarian reasons delineated in the HHS task force report. In general, researchers used minorities as experimental subjects because they were easily exploited; they studied minority health when minority health threatened the majority population (for example, in times of epidemics). The African-American health experience provides a good historical example of these research practices. While examples of the use of other racial and ethnic minorities for human experimentation in the United States may be cited individually or during certain time periods, white employment of blacks for such purposes was a consistent practice that, sadly, encompasses the entire sweep of U.S. history.

Almost from the time of white settlement of the American continent, whites noted differences between themselves and blacks in health matters such as disease immunities and susceptibilities, and reactions to medications. Self-interest was an important factor in whites' use of blacks as objects of research and study in antebellum times. The following examples illustrate that self-interest. Blacks were unwilling immigrants to the New World—they were enslaved—and were, for their white owners, an economic investment. White physicians thus needed to know as much as possible about caring for their black patients when illness struck. Furthermore, blacks, especially house servants or laborers in small businesses or farms, often worked in close physical proximity to whites. It was important for whites to recognize and study the medical differences between themselves and blacks in order to understand the risk of contracting diseases brought into their homes or workplaces by ailing slaves (Savitt, 1978). Antebellum southern physicians like Josiah Clark Nott of Mobile and Samuel Cartwright of New Orleans spent parts of their careers noting and writing about black medical distinctiveness (Breeden). They and slaveholders did mostly observational and statistical studies, occasionally engaged in physical human experiments on African-Americans, and published their ideas in agricultural and medical journals (Savitt, 1982).

After Emancipation in 1865, concern about the spread of diseases prevalent among blacks to the entire population continued to motivate whites to study black illness. They noted a steep rise in such lethal diseases as tuberculosis among the newly freed population, and predicted the decline and disappearance of blacks from the United States by the turn of the twentieth century. Morbidity and mortality studies conducted by insurance companies confirmed these dire predictions and made it difficult for blacks to obtain life insurance (Haller, 1970b; Torchia, 1977). Further, African-Americans became the object of numerous medical studies and articles (Haller, 1970a; Torchia, 1977). Physicians in the late nineteenth century reported on the state of black health in their regions or in the South as a whole. Some prominent African-Americans, W. E. B. Du Bois in particular, engaged in research on the health status of blacks and published their findings to refute the misleading conclusions whites had drawn. In particular, Du Bois pointed out the inaccuracies and unscientific approach of those researchers who purportedly found blacks' brains smaller and less developed than whites' brains; reminded readers that whites also suffered greatly from consumption (tuberculosis), alcoholism, and syphilis; and pointed out that other factors besides race, especially living conditions and economic status, influenced people's health or susceptibility to disease.

Beginning in the 1890s, a significant population shift of African-Americans from the rural South to northern cities (termed the Great Migration) increased white awareness of black health problems and encouraged physicians all over the country to study diseases that affected both groups, such as tuberculosis and syphilis (Torchia, 1975, 1977; Jones). Diseases that primarily afflicted blacks, however, such as sickle-cell anemia, discovered in 1910, were not widely studied or publicized even in the black medical and lay communities. That disinterest in sickle-cell anemia did not change until the 1950s, when it was recognized as a molecular genetic disease, the first of its kind (Savitt, 1981; Scott; Wailoo). The civil rights movement of the 1950s and 1960s further raised the consciousness of white Americans about the exclusion of blacks from many aspects of American life, including healthcare and medicine. The HHS task force report of 1985 made explicit the need to include blacks in the mainstream of U.S. biomedical research.

Use of Other Minority Groups

African-Americans have a unique history as research subjects in the United States. They were not the only voiceless minority in American history, however, and not the only group used as research subjects. In the South most of the experimental subjects were black; in the North they were usually poor, recent ethnic immigrants, like the Irish, Germans, and eastern Europeans. Many of their graves were robbed by medical students or professional body snatchers known as *resurrectionists,* and their bodies were dissected. The segregated blacks and the poor white minorities who used the public hospitals and clinics run by U.S. medical schools became the objects of experiments and of surgical or medical demonstrations by teachers on behalf of their students (Bynum; Humphrey; Lederer; Bowman). As historian of medical research Stanley J. Reiser stated about the nineteenth and especially the early twentieth centuries: "[S]ome physicians viewed hospital patients as an experimental population from whom knowledge could be gained, and on whom students could also learn" (p. 11). This was the cost to the poor of obtaining free or low-cost medical care.

Investigators felt little need to ask these voiceless people for consent to perform experiments (Lederer). Until the 1947 Nuremberg Code—the result of blatant misuse of a minority population (Jews in Nazi Germany) for unregulated medical experimentation—there was no uniform requirement for gaining consent from research subjects in medical experiments. Even after 1947, minority groups were exploited in the United States. In one often-cited example, researchers in San Antonio, Texas, studied a group of Mexican-American women visiting a clinic to obtain birth-control assistance. Wishing to discover whether the reported side effects of birth-control pills were physiological or psychological, the researchers gave one group of women a placebo and instructed them to use a vaginal cream in addition. The patients in the study did not know they might receive a placebo or that using the vaginal cream alone put them at substantially greater risk for becoming pregnant. Seven women involved in the study became pregnant (Veatch).

The Tuskegee Syphilis Experiment

The most notorious example in American history of experimentation on members of a minority group without their consent was the Tuskegee Syphilis Experiment. Between 1932 and 1972 the U.S. Public Health Service (PHS) conducted an investigation into the natural history of untreated syphilis on four hundred unsuspecting black men from Macon County, Alabama. Building their research on an 1890s study of untreated syphilis among white males in Oslo, Norway, PHS officials wished to determine if racial differences existed in the natural course of the disease. The African-American men selected for the Tuskegee experiment thought that they were part of a select group receiving special medical care. In fact, they were receiving no care at all for their syphilis.

Physicians and officials from the Alabama State Board of Health, the Macon County Health Department, and the Tuskegee Institute, as well as local physicians, cooperated with the PHS in establishing the project, shunting the unwitting subjects to government physicians for their medical care, or providing the PHS with medical facilities for physical examinations and autopsies. The experiment continued even after the Nuremberg Code went into effect in 1947, after penicillin became available for the treatment of syphilis in the 1950s, and after the PHS had instituted strict guidelines on the use of human subjects in experiments funded by the NIH and other of its agencies in 1966 (Brandt; Jones; U.S. Department of Health, Education, and Welfare; Reverby). Those guidelines were reemphasized when the Tuskegee story became public in 1972, bringing home to the medical research community the importance of obtaining informed consent from research subjects, and of avoiding bias and using caution and sensitivity when considering the need for racial and ethnic medical studies.

Current Humanitarian Approach to Research Using Minority Participants

Since the 1985 HSS task force report, numerous articles have appeared discussing results of research that included minority population groups. The dilemma researchers face in reporting and interpreting their results has now become separating innate biological factors from cultural ones as determinants of the phenomena under study (e.g., disease incidence, drug efficacy, behavioral differences). There is general agreement among researchers that race is a social construct which becomes less and less meaningful in multicultural/multiethnic societies where interbreeding over decades or centuries has occurred. Definitions of white and black, for example, differ within and among countries and often are also tied to social and economic status. Diseases and behaviors express themselves for reasons that can relate to such non-biological factors as stress, diet, and living conditions. Minorities, having once served as the misused objects of research and human experimentation because it was convenient and in the self-interest of the majority population, have again been singled out to serve as research subjects for U.S. medicine—though for different and more humanitarian reasons. Interpreting and understanding the results of medical research that includes minority groups and sub-groups has now become the challenge (Benowitz; King; Osborne and Feit; Schwartz; Witzig; Wood).

TODD L. SAVITT (1995)
REVISED BY AUTHOR

SEE ALSO: *Holocaust; Information Disclosure, Ethical Issues in; Race and Racism; Research, Human: Historical Aspects;*

Research Policy: Vulnerable Groups; Research, Unethical; Warfare: Chemical and Biological Weapons; Whistleblowing in Healthcare

BIBLIOGRAPHY

Benowitz, Neal L. 2002. "Smoking Cessation Trials Targeted to Racial and Economic Minority Groups." *Journal of the American Medical Association* 288(4): 497–499.

Bowman, Phillip J. 1991. "Race, Class, and Ethics in Research: Belmont Principles to Functional Relevance." In *Black Psychology,* 3rd edition, ed. Reginald L. Jones. Berkeley, CA: Cobb and Henry.

Brandt, Allan M. 1978. "Racism and Research: The Case of the Tuskegee Syphilis Study." *Hastings Center Report* 8(6): 21–29.

Breeden, James O. 1976. "States-Rights Medicine in the Old South." *Bulletin of the New York Academy of Medicine* 52(3): 348–372.

Bynum, William. 1988. "Reflections on the History of Human Experimentation." In *The Use of Human Beings in Research: With Special Reference to Clinical Trials,* ed. Stuart F. Spicker, Ilai Alon, Andre de Vries, and H. Tristram Engelhardt, Jr. Dordrecht, Netherlands: Kluwer.

Du Bois, W. E. B. 1906. *The Health and Physique of the Negro American: Report of a Social Study Made under the Direction of Atlanta University.* Atlanta, GA: Atlanta University Press.

Haller, John S., Jr. 1970a. "The Physician Versus the Negro: Medical and Anthropological Concepts of Race in the Late Nineteenth Century." *Bulletin of the History of Medicine* 44(2): 154–167.

Haller, John S., Jr. 1970b. "Race, Mortality, and Life Insurance: Negro Vital Statistics in the Late Nineteenth Century." *Journal of the History of Medicine and Allied Sciences* 25(3): 247–261.

Humphrey, David C. 1973. "Dissection and Discrimination: The Social Origins of Cadavers in America, 1760–1915." *Bulletin of the New York Academy of Medicine* 49(9): 819–827.

Jones, James H. 1981. *Bad Blood: The Tuskegee Syphilis Experiment.* New York: Free Press.

King, Talmadge E., Jr. 2002. "Racial Disparities in Clinical Trials." *New England Journal of Medicine* 346(18): 1400–1402.

Lederer, Susan E. 1995. *Subjected to Science: Human Experimentation in America before the Second World War.* Baltimore: Johns Hopkins University Press.

Osborne, Newton G., and Marvin D Feit. 1992. "The Use of Race in Medical Research." *Journal of the American Medical Association* 267(2): 275–279.

Reiser, Stanley J. 1978. "Human Experimentation and the Convergence of Medical Research and Patient Care." *Annals of the American Academy of Political and Social Sciences* 437: 8–18.

Reverby, Susan M., ed. 2000. *Tuskegee's Truths: Rethinking the Tuskegee Syphilis Study.* Chapel Hill: University of North Carolina Press.

Savitt, Todd L. 1978. *Medicine and Slavery: The Diseases and Health Care of Blacks in Antebellum Virginia.* Urbana: University of Illinois Press.

Savitt, Todd L. 1981. "The Invisible Malady: Sickle Cell Anemia in America, 1910–1970." *Journal of the National Medical Association* 73(8): 739–746.

Savitt, Todd L. 1982. "The Use of Blacks for Medical Experimentation and Demonstration in the Old South." *Journal of Southern History* 48(3): 331–348.

Schwartz, Robert S. 2001. "Racial Profiling in Medical Research." *New England Journal of Medicine* 344(18): 1392–1393.

Scott, Robert B. 1970. "Sickle Cell Anemia—High Prevalence and Low Priority." *New England Journal of Medicine* 282(3): 164–165.

Torchia, Marion M. 1975. "The Tuberculosis Movement and the Race Question, 1890–1950." *Bulletin of the History of Medicine* 49(2): 152–168.

Torchia, Marion M. 1977. "Tuberculosis Among American Negroes: Medical Research on a Racial Disease, 1830–1950." *Journal of the History of Medicine and Allied Sciences* 32(3): 252–279.

U. S. Department of Health and Human Services. 1988. "Inclusion of Minorities in Study Populations." *NIH Guide for Grants and Contracts* 17: 2–3.

U. S. Department of Health and Human Services. 2002. "NIH Instructions to Reviewers for Evaluating Research Involving Human Subjects in Grant and Cooperative Agreement Applications, April 5, 2002." Document NIH/OER/OEP V7.

U. S. Department of Health and Human Services, Task Force on Black and Minority Health. 1985. *Report of the Secretary's Task Force on Black and Minority Health,* 7 vols. Washington, D.C.: U. S. Government Printing Office.

U. S. Department of Health, Education and Welfare. Public Health Service. Tuskegee Syphilis Study Ad Hoc Advisory Panel. 1973. *Final Report of the Tuskegee Syphilis Study Ad Hoc Advisory Panel.* Washington, D.C.: U. S. Government Printing Office.

Veatch, Robert M. 1971 (reprint, with "Editor's Note," in *Ethical Issues in Modern Medicine,* ed. John Arras and Robert Hunt. Palo Alto, CA: Mayfield, 1983). "'Experimental' Pregnancy." *Hastings Center Report* 1: 2–3.

Wailoo, Keith. 2001. *Dying in the City of the Blues: Sickle Cell Anemia and the Politics of Race and Health.* Chapel Hill: University of North Carolina Press.

Witzig, Ritchie. 1996. "The Medicalization of Race: Scientific Legitimization of a Flawed Social Construct." *Annals of Internal Medicine* 125(8): 675–679.

Wood, Alastair J. J. 2001. "Racial Differences in the Response to Drugs—Pointers to Genetic Differences." *New England Journal of Medicine* 344(18): 1393–1396.

INTERNET RESOURCE

U.S. Department of Health and Human Services. 2000. "NIH Guidelines on the Inclusion of Women and Minorities as

Subjects in Clinical Research." Available from <http://grants.nih.gov/grants/funding/women–min/guidelines–update.htm>.

MISTAKES, MEDICAL

• • •

With its report, *To Err is Human: Building a Safer Health System,* The Institute of Medicine (IOM) Committee on the Quality of Health Care in America performed a commendable public service. The report dramatized the extent of a hitherto under-appreciated public problem, harm to patients because of medical error. The report estimates that between 44,000 and 98,000 deaths occur each year due to adverse medical events, that one-half of these *adverse events* are preventable, that the total cost of these medical misadventures is between 17 and 29 billion dollars, and that the events rank eighth in causes of deaths in the United States.

The report does more than locate a problem largely unrecognized by the public. It points to faulty systems, rather than individual's performance flaws, as the source of the majority of adverse events. The report also sets forward policy recommendations to meliorate the problem. The IOM recommended a triad familiar to those who study safety and post-hoc accounts of accidents: 1) training to improve the performance of personnel, 2) developing new technologies to improve the performance of fallible human operators, and 3) implementing new procedures to improve the over-all functioning of the healthcare delivery system. These changes will bring to medicine the philosophies and work routines of *total quality improvement.*. The IOM report sets for itself the laudable operational goal of halving medical errors over five years. Success depends in large part on the providers of medical care accepting the IOM's diagnosis and implementing its treatment plan. There will be resistance on both fronts. No change will occur without a re-thinking of how healthcare providers define their obligation to provide quality care.

Error as a Systems Problem

The IOM report defines error in a way most involved in patient care would find unfamiliar: "the failure of a planned action to be completed as intended (i.e. error of execution) or the use of the wrong plan to achieve an aim (i e., error of planning)" (p. 28). This definition seems to ignore uncertainty inherent in medical practice. "An adverse event is an injury caused by the medical management rather than

underlying condition of the patient. An adverse event attributable to error is a *preventable adverse event*" (IOM, p.28). The IOM's definitions presuppose that what should be done is clear, that outcomes are unproblematically attributable to treatment alone, and that what constitutes an *error* is not subject to debate. Notably, Troyen Brennan, one of the researchers involved in the Harvard Medical Practice Study (HMPS) questioned whether error or preventable adverse events are easily distinguishable from more innocent treatment failures (Brennan).

While the IOM report uncritically accepts the HMPS and subsequent replications and extensions of it and uses the HMPS to shape the basis of the IOM's recommendations, researchers have raised multiple questions about the HMPS findings and their interpretation. The HMPS bases its estimates of adverse events and preventable adverse events on retrospective chart reviews. Death was among the criteria used to select charts for reviews. This raises the strong suspicion that both *outcome* and *hindsight* bias influenced reviewers's judgments of the appropriateness of care. Researchers looked at physicians's responses to patient vignettes describing identical diagnoses and treatments but varying with respect to positive and negative outcomes. In these studies, doctors are more likely to find medical error in cases with negative outcomes. Even when raters are asked to pay no attention to outcomes, they still judge the treatment with poor outcomes more negatively than when identical treatment has a positive outcome. The HMPS does not establish a direct link between specific errors and outcomes nor does it address the possibility of attribution error or spurious causality. Finally, McDonald, Weiner, and Hui, have suggested that counting deaths attributable to error, as in the IOM report, is too gross a measure. Many of those who died from the identified errors had terminal diagnoses and complex multi-system problems. A more precise measure of the burden of error may be *days of life lost* (McDonald, Weiner, and Hui). None of these criticisms suggest that medical error does not constitute a serious problem or that there is not substantial room for improving medical care systems. However, reservations about the methods and assumptions of the HMPS and the IOM report suggest that reducing medical error is more complex and may leave more room for debate than the IOM report acknowledges.

One goal of the IOM report is to shift attention away from individual professionals's performance and to focus on system performance. The report embraces *normal accident theory,* a blend of organizational and management theory, cognitive psychology, and human factors engineering to understand and explain the occurrence of preventable adverse events (Perrow). The theory holds that modern technological systems are *error prone* (Paget) and that we should think of certain mishaps as *normal accidents.* Errors and mistakes, with all their baleful consequences seldom result solely from individual failings—what Charles Perrow a leading proponent of this approach, calls *ubiquitous operator error.* Rather, errors and mistakes are embedded in the organization of complex technological work like medicine. The two structural features most important to the production of normal accidents (in medicine, preventable adverse events) are interactive complexity and tight coupling. That is, each component of the system is intrinsically complicated and each component's performance affects the functioning of other system parts. Small deviations from expected performance ramify through the system in unpredictable ways through unanticipated feedback loops creating large consequences. For a complex technological undertaking such as medicine, this is an unpleasant fact.

The IOM report focuses on a rejoinder to normal accident theory, *highly reliable organizational theory,* to remedy the problem. This approach acknowledges that errors can never be eliminated and concentrates on what organizational features allow workers to operate risky and complex technological systems, such as nuclear-powered aircraft carriers, with a minimum of untoward incidents. The theory relies on work structures that have redundancy and overlap; teams that encourage constant communication among and between the ranks; constant surveillance and monitoring for even the smallest deviation from expectations; flexible authority systems that permit even low-ranking workers to question those with the highest authority; a rich oral culture that constantly uses stories to remind workers of behavior that can create trouble; a reporting system that takes note of *near-misses* and is constantly self-correcting and non-punitive when trouble arises; and technology designed to be user-friendly and cue workers to avoid the most common errors (Roberts; Rochlin, Laporte, and Roberts; Weick; Weick and Roberts).

Error in Professional Culture

Through its pleas to end inaction regarding adverse events and its call to break the pattern of *naming, blaming and shaming* engaged in by professionals, the IOM report acknowledges the need to change the shopfloor culture of medicine. Curiously, the IOM report neglects workplace studies of physician attitudes, beliefs, and behavior. As a result, the report ignores leverage points for and barriers to change in physician culture. Worksite studies of physicians concentrate on how doctors negotiate and understand the meaning of such terms as adverse event, preventable adverse event, and *negligent error.* Their meanings are not fixed but are fluid and flexible, highly dependent on context.

One of the earliest discussions of medical mistakes, by Everett C. Hughes, suggests a rough calculus for the frequency of mistakes, based on the skill and experience of the worker and the complexity of the task. Because academic hospitals involve front-line workers (students, residents, and fellows) who may have little experience and because many of the clinical problems encountered often deviate far from the routine, one might expect to find a fair number of mistakes and errors in such institutions. However, says Hughes, hospital work is organized to control and limit the occurrence of mistakes. The organization of physician work in teaching environments also reduces the recognition of error and makes responsibility and accountability difficult to pinpoint. Hughes describes a set of *risk-sharing* and *guilt-shifting* devices that obscure exactly where in a chain of events the error or mistake occurred. These work practices include supervision, cross-coverage, consultation, and case conferences. These practices make it harder to see and correct individual mistakes, or for that matter, system errors. Errors are a feature of the workplace, and an elaborate division of social and moral labor prevents mistakes and errors from coming plainly into view.

Eliot Freidson describes the social processes used in a group of physicians to bury mistakes and to sustain a *structured silence* about mistakes. Freidson's results are striking given that the group that he observed was designed self-consciously to maintain the highest imaginable professional standards. In a setting designed to maximize surveillance by colleagues of each other's behavior, Freidson found that peer monitoring and surveillance were unsystematic at best. Referral relations structured colleagues's knowledge of one another's performance. Knowledge gathered in this way was haphazard; the two main sources for information were patient gossip and colleague complaints. Regular procedures or mechanisms for evaluating colleague performance and sharing the results of such evaluations did not exist. Once an individual physician's knowledge and dissatisfaction with the poor performance with another group member had crossed some threshold for action, few options for action were open. Freidson labeled the most immediately available informal action employed by group members *the talking to.* Colleagues confront the offender, who either clears the air with a non-defensive response or increases distrust with defensive one. If the results of a talking to were unsatisfactory, a physician could engage in a private boycott by refusing to refer additional patients to the offending colleague. The possibility of formally making a complaint and having a physician removed from the group existed but was so administratively cumbersome as not to be a realistic option. In Freidson's work we see that that notions of error, mistake, and competence are conceived within the work group at the level of the individual and that there is a general reluctance to deal with these issues through formal organizational measures.

Charles L. Bosk's *Forgive and Remember: Managing Medical Failure* examines how surgical residents learn to separate blameless errors from blameworthy mistakes in the course of their training. Errors appear blameless, largely, if they are seen as part of the normal learning process. Attending faculty anticipate that inexperienced residents will make some technical or judgmental mistakes. These errors are considered a normal consequence of providing opportunities to the unpracticed. Errors are blameworthy when, in the eyes of senior surgeons, it is difficult to sustain a claim that a resident acted in good faith. Bosk identified two types of blameworthy errors: (1) normative errors, which breach universal rules concerning physician behavior and (2) quasi-normative errors, which mark a resident's failure to conform to an attending surgeon's cherished, but often idiosyncratic, way of doing things. A source of great confusion for residents is the fact that attending surgeons treat breaches of personal preferences as seriously as breaches of universal rules. Technical and judgmental errors, so long as they are not repeated, especially on a single rotation, are forgiven. Not so with normative and quasi-normative error; residents who commit these breaches are often dismissed from training programs. This public punishment, just as Émile Durkheim (1933) long ago suggested, works: (1) as a general deterrence for the not yet corrupted; (2) as reinforcement to the norms of the group; and (3) as a device to increase solidarity among those that share a commitment to the community.

Each of the studies reviewed above has a different focus and emphasis. However, when they, and other similar research that concentrates on the dynamics of the work group, are assessed together, a number of themes to which the recommendations of the IOM Report do not give sufficient weight emerge. These themes include the following:

1. The inherent uncertainty of medical action—diagnosis and treatment are assessed in prospect, probabilistically. After action is taken results are known and uncertainty evaporates. The relation between a treatment and outcome once so cloudy now appears over-determined.

2. The essentially contestable nature of error itself—everyone knows errors are untoward events whose occurrence needs to be minimized. What medical workers do not agree on is what happened and why. In each instance, we can agree that errors, in general, are to be avoided, while disagreeing, in each instance, that this action was an error.

3. The medical profession tolerates *normal error*. Workers in the same occupation share the same

difficulties and have an artful appreciation of all the factors that can create negative outcomes in the face of what otherwise looks like flawless technical performance. What medical workers have in common is an understanding of the ever present possibility for the unexpected negative outcome and a set of beliefs about work that allow such outcomes to be neutralized.

These themes underscore how, on the one hand, the IOM Report is an attempt to encourage the medical profession to take more responsibility for its obligation to the larger society and, on the other, just how difficult that task is.

Perhaps these difficulties are seen most clearly in the recommendations to increase reporting of near misses. For such reporting to be effective, however, the participants in the current system have to possess the ability to recognize the events that they need to report. Workplace studies of error demonstrate, however, that workers's ability and/or willingness to do this should not be taken for granted. Inherent uncertainty, the essentially contested nature of error, and the normal tolerance for the risks of the workplace, when combined with the intense production pressure of hospital practice all create barriers to seeing near misses. What is not seen cannot be reported. What is not reported cannot be learned from. Successful implementation of the IOM recommendation requires that the context of the workplace be taken into account.

Ethics and Medical Error

Two issues dominate the ethical concerns associated with mistakes in medicine: disclosure and accountability. However, as the preceding discussion reveals, a third matter deserves moral scrutiny: definitions of terms. We need to know what counts as error before we can conclude who has a duty to reveal what information, who has the right to receive information, and how professional and legal systems should respond to misadventure.

Classic thinking about mistakes has focused on process and outcome. People may proceed erroneously (begin the wrong operation, administer the wrong medication, fail to do something prescribed or indicated) and, through care or good luck prevent or escape harm. On the other hand, things may expectedly work out poorly for the patient (e.g., they may die, as in the previous discussion) even though, upon close examination, no one omitted appropriate actions, committed inappropriate acts, or otherwise behaved *wrongly*. In many cases of adverse outcome, one simply finds a great deal of uncertainty about what happened and why. Medicine's lack of complete understanding of disease and physiology leaves a much unexplained or even inexplicable.

At the very least, despite human desire to eliminate doubt and fix blame, the world of human medicine leaves a great deal up in the air when one wishes to say a doctor, nurse, pharmacist, or other healthcare worker erred or that a system failed. Finding egregious behavior is easy; the problems arise when an observer does not like what has happened but cannot readily point a finger at the cause.

Starting in the last quarter of the twentieth century, attitudes and practices towards disclosure of clear-cut medical error changed from guild-like self-protectionism to more forthright, perhaps preemptive truth-telling. That is, both medical ethicists and risk managers now counsel practitioners to tell patients or their legally authorized representatives (parents, guardians, among others) when an obvious error occurs. Few now suggest hiding an overdose, administration of a mismatched blood product, or some clearly preventable difficulty in the operative field. Philosophers and lawyers take a pragmatic approach here. Not only do people want to know when something has gone wrong, not only do some argue wronged individuals have a right to know, the consequences of failed cover-ups include overwhelming anger and much larger jury awards. As Sissela Bok pointed out in *Lying: Moral Choice in Public and Private Life,* in a socially complex world, including that of modern medicine, lying just does not succeed.

Note, however, that the generally accepted admonition to tell the truth often fails to provide practical help. Did the surgical assistant pull *too hard* on the retractor, resulting in a lacerated artery and a much-prolonged operation for microvascular repair? Was this negligence or something about the patient's fragile tissues? If the patient's recovery is unimpeded, does it matter? Do patients and surrogates want to know every detail of what happened? Might *full disclosure* inappropriately undermine trust? While there might be objective agreement that the degree of disclosure should somehow follow the desires or psychological needs of patients, loved ones, and legal surrogates, it is not at all clear how one determines, in advance, how much an individual or family member wants to know in a given situation.

Regarding accountability, many problems remain. If the assistant in the hypothetical operation was a surgical intern scrubbing in on this kind of operation for the first time, how does that fact influence an assessment of whether she made a culpable mistake or made an excusable error? The legal system usually acknowledges that trainees do not bear the same level of responsibility as their supervisors—much of the time lawsuits drop involved students and residents from being named defendants in malpractice actions. However, there are no reliable systems for determining how professionals or society should factor (in)experience into judgments about moral responsibility for things going awry.

Bosk, in his book on surgical training, *Forgive and Remember: Managing Medical Failure,* distinguishes between technical and normative error. This distinction assists in understanding that surgeons use social and behavioral standards to assess residents's ethics, but it is not clear how the law or patients can or ought to use such an approach.

How best to respond to ethically suspect or clearly wrong behavior must also be considered. Answers here might also take into account context as well as the specific acts or omissions. How might sleep deprivation play a role in evaluating someone's mistake? Would it or should it matter if the individual's lack of sleep were a result of staying on duty in the middle of a snow storm that precluded replacement staff from reaching the hospital? Should reactions to first offenses be limited, especially for those in training? Focused (re)education may suffice for the cognitive components of error. However, whether reviews of professional standards and obligations can effectively ethically rehabilitate those who seem morally indifferent or disinclined to take their duties as professionals seriously is not really known. Finally, relatively little attention has been paid to the affective consequences of mistakes on those who make them. As Joel Frader notes in "Mistakes in Medicine: Personal and Moral Responses," routine reactions to error should include counseling and support for those involved, especially regarding the guilt and fear common following errors that have produced or nearly resulted in serious harm.

The sometimes-conflicting contemporary Western tendencies to blame/find fault, to seek revenge or at least receive compensation for tragedy, and to excuse the young/naïve/inexperienced also clash with the move toward seeing medical error as a matter of system faults. If complicated processes inevitably include both faulty O-rings and distracted practitioners, those who feel wronged cannot easily point fingers and extract their pound of flesh. Moreover, systems-thinking may itself have negative unintended consequences. First, further diffusion of responsibility, beyond teams and identifiable persons, may decrease incentives to ferret out even recurring, systematic causes of error. If someone who must stop the buck cannot be identified, perhaps everyone will stop caring about reducing the incidence and seriousness of medical error. Second, turning away from notions of individual moral responsibility may allow (even more) moral bad actors to proceed through professional educational and monitoring systems and inflict their damage on patients, family members, colleagues, subordinates, and institutions.

Possible Solutions

The above considerations do not make for obvious or easy answers to the problems of medical mistakes. Regardless of the faults of the HMPS and the IOM report, it seems clear that much medical practice, at least that occurring in the modern hospital, does involve complex technological systems with multiple occasions and places for things to go wrong. Better attention to the components of *through-put* may indeed identify opportunities to implement technical fixes and safety checks. For example, computer order-entry of medications certainly can eliminate difficulties associated with illegible handwriting. Given the right software, such systems can markedly reduce errors associated with errors in dosing, misspelling of drug names, and so on. Barcodes on medication packets and patient identification bands may lower the incidence of administering drugs to the wrong patient. Routines of repeating oral orders back to the doctor—similar to what happens between pilot and co-pilots—may clarify confusion-prone exchanges and prevent some mishaps. Such interventions will likely bring on their own problems. Almost certainly, typing orders into a computer increases the amount of time physicians have to spend at that task. The additional time and potential for (inappropriate) inferences of lack of respect involved in oral repetition may create inefficiencies and raised tensions on the wards and in the operating room.

There is a clear need to continue and strengthen efforts to inculcate a sense of individual moral responsibility into healthcare professionals. Indeed, the idea that providers owe specific duties to patients (or clients) that transcend selfish goals constitutes the essence of what it means to become or remain a professional. While the U.S. healthcare education system has more or less, depending on local culture and resources, institutionalized ethics teaching at the student level, further medical training in residencies and fellowships often lack organized approaches and/or appropriately trained or experienced ethics educators, not to mention adequate role models. Of course, ethics education assumes trainees can and do learn ethical behavior at that relatively late stage of personal development. Perhaps healthcare education and training need better systems for identifying and screening-out individuals predictably inclined to behave in undesirable ways. (Such an effort would, in turn, assume valid and reliable methods to *weed out* disfavored characteristics.)

Current systems for professional *regulation* are notoriously ineffective in recognizing and intervening when doctors misbehave, even when they do so repeatedly. In hospitals organized medical staff systems for detecting and intervening in the face of misconduct and impairment face legal fear (of libel and restraint of trade lawsuits) and patterned social inhibition (*old boy* networks and other manifestations of group solidarity, as in *there but for the grace of God go I* concern). State regulatory bodies have unclear standards, inadequate resources, and some similar solidarity-based reluctance to act. Professional associations often lack mechanisms for investigating, judging, and acting on claims of misconduct or malfeasance. Without the devotion of considerable resources and a real dedication to making mechanisms for professional social controls actually work, healthcare providers should continue to expect malpractice lawyers to thrive.

Conclusions

At the end of the twentieth century, mistakes in medicine began to receive attention appropriate to their contribution to morbidity and mortality in the healthcare system. Public policy began to concentrate on recurring, systematic underlying causes of medical error and borrow concepts from cognitive science, social psychology, and organizational behavior to address the pervasive problem of medical mistakes. Whether this approach to improving patient safety will reduce the incidence or seriousness of medical error remains to be seen, especially as industrial thinking has not paid close attention to the actual and powerful culture of medicine. Also unclear is the effect that an impersonal line of attack on the problem will have on professional morality. Too great an emphasis on technical fixes may erode the sense of personal ethical obligation to patients that society wants its healthcare professionals to hold dear.

JOEL E. FRADER
CHARLES L. BOSK

SEE ALSO: *Competence; Harm; Malpractice, Medical; Medicine, Profession of; Responsibility*

BIBLIOGRAPHY

Bok, Sissela. 1979. *Lying: Moral Choice in Public and Private Life.* New York: Vintage Books.

Bosk, Charles. 1979. *Forgive and Remember: Managing Medical Failure.* Chicago: University of Chicago Press.

Brennan, Troyen. 2000. "The Institute of Medicine Report—Could it do Harm?" *New England Journal of Medicine* 342(15): 1123–1125.

Brennan, Troyen; Leape, Lucien; Nam, N. M.; et al. 1991. "Incidence of Adverse and Negligence in Hospitalized Patients: Results of the Harvard Medical Practice Study I." *New England Journal of Medicine* 324: 370–376.

Caplan, R. A.; Posner, K. I.; and Cheney, F.W. 1991. "Effects of Outcomes on Physician Judgments of Appropriateness of Care." *Journal of American Medical Association* 265: 1957–1969.

Cook, Richard, and Woods, David. 1994. "Operating at the Sharp End: The Complexity of Human Error." In *Human*

Error in Medicine, ed. Marilyn Bogner. Hillsdale, NJ: Lawrence Erlbaum.

Davis, Fred. 1960. "Uncertainty in Medical Diagnosis: Clinical and Functional." *American Journal of Sociology* 66: 259–267.

Durkheim, Émile. 1933. *The Division of Labor in Society,* tr. George Simpson. Glencoe, IL: The Free Press.

Fox, Rénee C. 1957. "Training for Uncertainty." In *The Student Physician: Introductory Studies in the Sociology of Medical Education,* ed. Robert K. Merton, George Reader, and Patricia L. Kendall. Cambridge, MA.: Harvard University Press.

Frader, Joel. 2000. "Mistakes in Medicine: Personal and Moral Responses." In *Margin of Error: The Ethics of Mistakes in the Practice of Medicine,* ed. Susan B. Rubin and Laurie Zoloth. Hagerstown, MD: University Publishing Group.

Gawande, Atul. 2002. *Complications: A Surgeon's Notes on an Imperfect Science.* New York: Metropolitan Books.

Hughes, Everett C. 1951. "Mistakes at Work." *Canadian Journal of Economics and Political Science* 17: 320–327.

Kohn, Linda T.; Corrigan, Janet M.; and Donaldson, Molla S., eds. 2000. *To Err Is Human: Building a Safer Health System.* Washington, D.C.: National Academy Press.

Leape, Lucien; Brennan, Troyen, Laird, N. M.; et al. 1991. "The Nature of Adverse Events in Hospitalized Patients: Results of the Harvard Medical Practice Study II." *New England Journal of Medicine* 324: 370–376.

McDonald, C.J.; Weiner, M.; and Hui, S.L. 2000. "Deaths Due to Errors Are Exaggerated in Institute of Medicine Report." *Journal of the American Medical Association* 284: 93–95.

Paget, Marianne. 1988. *The Unity of Mistakes: A Phenomenologiacal Account.* Philadelphia: Temple University Press.

Parsons, Talcott. 1951. "Social Structure and Dynamic Process: The Case of Modern Medical Practice." In *The Social System.* New York: The Free Press.

Perrow, Charles. 1984. *Normal Accidents: Living with Hight Risk Technologies* New York: Basic Books.

Reason, James. 1990. *Human Error.* New York: Cambridge University Press.

Roberts, Karlene. 1990. "Some Characteristics of One Type of High Reliability Organization." *Organizational Science* 1: 160–176.

Rochlin, Gene; La Porte, Todd; and Roberts, Karlene. 1987. "The Self-Designing High Reliability Organization: Aircraft Carrier Flight Operations at Sea." *Naval War College Review* (Autumn): 76–90.

Thomas, E. J.; Studder, D. M.; Burstin, H. R.; et al. 2000. "Incidence and Types of Adverse Events and Negligent Care in Utah and Colorado." *Medical Care* 28: 261–271.

Weick, Karl. 1987. "Organizational Culture as a Source of High Reliability." *California Management Review* 29: 112–127.

Weick, Karl, and Roberts, Karlene. 1993. "Collective Mind in Organizations: Heedful Interrelating on Flight Decks." *ADM Inistrative Science Quarterly* 38: 357–381.

MORAL STATUS

· · ·

Moral status is a concept that deals with who or what is so valuable that it should be treated with special regard. Many cases are simple. A pebble on the beach is thrown into the water without a second thought. It is one of trillions of such rocks that for billions of years have rushed in and out with the tide. Beach pebbles possess no moral standing in themselves, although certain pebbles and sand may be treated with special regard for other reasons.

But the people bathing on that same beach are totally different. To wantonly toss one of them into that same water would constitute an immoral, reprehensible act. That is because normal adults possess interests and rights that morally obligate people to highly regard their well-being. But what about the toddler experiencing her first beach day, a dog joyfully retrieving a ball, the coral reef just offshore, the seaweed within sight? Does each entity have moral status? By what criteria does society decide? And once that is settled, is moral status absolute, or do circumstances and conflicting interests make a difference?

Moral status is not a new concept, but it does constitute a new entry in the third edition of this encyclopedia. Its inclusion likely relates to the fierce battle in Western, particularly American, society over the moral status of the human embryo. This issue is perhaps the most contentious bioethical debate in the early years of this new century. It follows and is related to the abortion debate, decades old but still controversial. The moral status of fetal and now embryonic human life commands attention because it juxtaposes questions of sex, identity, faith, humanity, and healing.

In this entry, theories dealing with single standards or issues—personhood, sentience, and environment—will be delineated and then compared with a multistandard approach for resolving questions of moral status. Then, leading moral theories are applied to the societal dilemma of care for patients with Alzheimer disease.

The Moral Status of a Human Embryo

President George W. Bush, believing that protectable human life begins at conception, asked Congress in his 2003 state of the union address to "pass a law against all human cloning." This president reflects the views of many Americans. The Roman Catholic Church and a host of conservative Protestants almost uniformly hold pre-embryonic human life as sacred—and hence of the highest moral status.

William E. May, a Jesuit moralist, acknowledges a significant difference between the capacities of a human embryo and a normal adult. Human individuals of intelligence and self-consciousness are "moral beings" because they have the capacity to comprehend, love, and choose. Although they are moral beings, because they are "minded" entities, their moral status is no greater than any other human being's, because all humans, including embryos, are "beings of moral worth." All share "something rooted in their being human beings," beginning at conception. This "something" is the soul, "the principle immanent in human beings, a constituent and defining element of their entitative makeup, that makes them to be what they and who they are: beings of moral worth capable of becoming minded entities or moral beings; it is a principle of immateriality or of transcendence from the limitations of materially individuated existence" (p. 425).

Protestant Scott Klusendorf, reflecting a similar view, contrasts a human "nature" or essence with the capacity for certain "functions" or abilities. A fetus may lack functional ability, but it "is nonetheless a person because he or she has a human nature from the moment of existence."

The origin of the idea that human nature is a manifestation of an eternal essence is ancient. Its roots go back at least to Plato, and extend up through the early church fathers to Aquinas and on to the philosophers Descartes and Kant.

Religious conservatives are not the only ones who are against a medical technology that violates the human embryo. For example, secular moralist Hans Jonas is particularly concerned about a genetics technology that could produce autonomous organisms. "If it is a categorical imperative for mankind to exist, then any suicidal gambling with that existence is categorically forbidden." Out of profound respect for the human product of a long trial of evolution, Jonas protests against humans playing as "creators at the roots of our being, at the primal seat of its mystery."

Despite the fervent pleas for recognition of the preembryo's full moral status, the majority of embryologists and bioethicists favor therapeutic use. The primary bioethical rationale is twofold: the supposed minimal moral status of preembryos, and possible use of them for treating up to an estimated 128 million Americans (American Association for the Advancement of Science) with a wide variety of ills.

Both opponents and advocates of therapeutic use agree that after conception nature doesn't delimit a threshold for moral status. Opponents argue for conception, but conception itself is more process than event. In the life sciences what earlier seemed an event is now known otherwise because of advanced instrumentation that can record microscopic change over milliseconds. In light of modern embryology, Ronald Green, in his *The Human Embryo Research Debate,* argues that bioethics should recognize that certain moral presuppositions underlie the choice of an ethically significant point on the "curve of biological change." In opposing transcendental and evolutionary determinists, he contends that the very idea that personal values lead one to choose morally particular points in an ongoing biological process, "converts us from passive identifiers of biologically fixed truths to active choosers of markers on life's spectrum" (p. 26).

Common belief holds that the zygote comes into existence when the sperm and ovum unite. But just when that union occurs is now unclear. The ovum chemically signals uterine sperm, not yet in the fallopian tubes. If that invitation doesn't initiate the union, there are other options: (1) when the successful sperm penetrates the ovum wall (zona pellucida) into the egg's cytoplasm, immediately emitting electrochemical charges that seal the zona; (2) when after the eight-cell stage the paternal chromosomes become active; or (3) when syngamy (literally, "spouses joining together") occurs, the pairing of twenty-three male and female chromosomes, eighteen to twenty-four hours after zona penetration. Thus, Green states, the "moment" of fertilization is a series of processes that take twenty-four to forty-eight hours. Moreover, for the next ten days the embryo may divide, resulting in twins, triplets, or larger multiple sets of offspring (pp. 27–29).

The moral status assigned to a preembryo depends on one's presuppositions. However, most conservatives and liberals alike tend to be asymmetrical in how they view a human's moral status at life's beginning and ending. That is because human life *attains* moral status due to its *nature,* but *loses* moral status due to *function* deficit.

On the one hand, at life's beginning, human genetic nature is prized, although function is minimal. For example, a universal ban exists on use of embryos for research after their fourteenth day, when the embryonic disk is pinhead size, and has only a fifty-fifty chance of live birth eight and one half months hence. No organs exist, and neurological cell differentiation is forty days off. Viability is five months ahead and dawning self-consciousness a year away.

Yet, on the other hand, at life's end, function—or its loss—is paramount, although human nature continues to be quite evident. When an adult is pronounced dead by neurological criteria, the heart hardly ceases to beat as it is transplanted from one body into another. Death has been pronounced, though millions of neurons may still be firing, just not coordinating any vital bodily functions. Spinal cord reflexes may be sufficiently coordinated to cause spontaneous limb movement, even as vital organs are procured for transplantation.

The above opposing, contemporary notions of the moral status of human tissue—be it pre-brain or post-brain—are a concrete illustration of how diverse ethical assumptions yield different moral conclusions. Society's assigning of moral status may be quizzical to some ideal observer, for it is a complicated process which not only involves logic, but also varying cultures, traditions, and religious beliefs—in a word, civilization, in all its variety.

Leading Single-Standard Moral Theories

Contemporary bioethicists divide into two camps on moral status: those who advocate a single standard and those who are eclectic. Three leading single-standard theories concern personhood, sentience, and environment.

PERSONHOOD. The personhood standard sounds simple, but it can have such diverse and conflicting meanings that some philosophers, particularly Ruth Macklin, question the value of its use. Nevertheless, moral agents are so conscious and appreciative of their own personhood that this criterion inevitably emerges as a primary consideration. Three primary views of personhood exist: genetic, mental, and developmental.

Genetic personhood, sometimes called minimalist or low personhood, includes all human beings, regardless of age or developmental stage. Although this position is more commonly called sanctity of life, it is included here because it has an important, biologically inclusive view of personhood. The Roman Catholic Church's statement on doctrine, "Respect for Human Life in Its Origins and on the Dignity of Procreation," (Vatican) speaks of the human embryo as "the unborn child" who "must be cared for, to the extent possible, in the same way as any other human being."

John T. Noonan argues that from conception until whole brain death, human beings possess necessary and sufficient qualities for full moral status. The criterion for personhood is simple and straightforward: If your parents are human, "you are human." Although the theory is clear, the implementation of its logical implications is limited. For example, if preembryos are of highest moral status, a national assault on the natural tragedy of early spontaneous embryonic abortions (over 60% of fertilized eggs) would be appropriate—or at least a vocal bemoaning of this wanton waste of human life.

Mental personhood is the category most commonly associated with personalist theory. Mental personalists hold that an autonomous individual's brain function warrants the highest moral status. The origin of this view was the Enlightenment philosopher Immanuel Kant (1724–1804). He believed that only a moral agent possesses the autonomy and freedom to attain full moral status, so he excluded women, children, and animals because they were considered to be deficient in mental capacity.

Several modern bioethicists have argued extensively for the significance of cerebral functioning. This capacity is variously perceived to include individuals who are: self-conscious and capable of self-direction (Engelhardt), able to enter meaningful relationships (McCormick), capable of minimal independent existence (Shelp), or in possession of a minimal IQ of 20 to 40 (Fletcher). Michael Tooley, author of *Abortion and Infanticide,* argues that his notion of personhood is common sense and that most people would agree

that anything that has, and has exercised, all of the following capacities is a person, and that anything that has never had any of them is not a person: the capacity for self-consciousness; the capacity to think; the capacity for rational thought; the capacity to arrive at decisions by deliberation; the capacity to envisage a future for oneself; the capacity to remember a past involving oneself; the capacity for being a subject of nonmomentary interests; the capacity to use language. (1983, p. 349)

Tooley not only views prenatal human life as of limited moral status, he is a self-described "radical" in advocating limited infanticide. Peter Singer, in his 1979 book, *Practical Ethics,* basically agrees with Tooley.

H. Tristram Engelhardt Jr., author of the 1996 book, *The Foundation of Bioethics,* joins with other mentalists in viewing cerebral function as of highest importance morally. But he disagrees with Tooley and Singer on infanticide. According to Engelhardt, although newborns do not possess an intrinsic right to life, high moral status is "imputed" to them because of their vital social and cultural role. Critics, such as David H. Smith (2001), argue that this concession is inconsistent.

Singer's notion of significant moral status does not include human newborns, but it does include several mammals: chimps, monkeys, and probably cetaceans. A similar conclusion on mammals is held by Mary Anne Warren and Tom Regan, who each offer different rationales.

Developmental personhood, a variation of the mentalist type, contends that the closer an entity approaches undisputed personhood, such as a normal human adult possesses, the higher the moral status. This intuitive, commonsense approach is held by thinkers as diverse as biologist Clifford Grobstein, Catholic theologian Lisa Sowle Cahill, Protestant ethicist James W. Walters, (1997), and philosophers Warren and Judith Jarvis Thomson, the latter suggesting that a "newly fertilized ovum, a newly implanted clump of cells, is no more a person than an acorn is an oak tree" (p. 199).

In his 1997 book, *What Is a Person?*, Walters advocates the notion of "proximate personhood" as a developmental scheme positing three markers to aid in more concretely identifying the aspects of moral value that indicate escalating moral status. First, potentiality for undisputed personhood is important because the embryo is unlike any other tissue. After implantation in a young woman, if development is normal, an embryo will likely grow to adulthood. Given the advances in cloning technology, the notion of potentiality may not be as significant as it was, but because the gestating fetus, featured in large full-color coffee-table books, is such a powerful symbol of life, a developing fetus connotes more about life than it may intrinsically possess.

The second marker is development toward undisputed personhood. Strictly speaking, a nine-month fetus, or even a newborn, is no more a moral agent than is an early fetus or embryo. Most people, however, intuitively view the moral status of a preembryo as different from that of an advanced fetus. The more closely a fetus/newborn approximates a normal, mature individual, the greater its moral status. It is not that the newborn possesses great intrinsic moral status, but that its moral status is bestowed because of parents' and society's need to value something so personally symbolic.

A third marker is emotional bonding of the parents to the fetus or newborn. The greater the bond, the more moral worth is ascribed to the fetus/newborn. In his 1992 book, *Freedom and Fulfillment,* Joel Feinberg views infanticide as immoral for utilitarian reasons, arguing that the common good and social utility are the moral basis for the loving treatment of newborns. This third marker of proximate personhood, "bonding of," is a social criterion, whereas "potentiality for" is intellectual and "development toward" is physical.

The mental and developmental personhood views are powerful in underscoring the salience of the human brain, without which moral discussion would be impossible. Yet people intuitively sense that there is more to moral status than abstract mental capacity. For example, brilliant sociopaths ostensibly have the highest (personal) moral status, and are treated accordingly, whereas wolves are sometimes killed by hunters. Yet wolves, sentient and highly intelligent animals,

mate for life, love their offspring and that of others, work cooperatively with other wolves, never kill for sport, and often share food. The eighteenth-century Scottish philosopher David Hume claims in his *Treatise of Human Nature* that he does not know of a convincing argument for the view that thinking is superior to nest building, because each is a "wonderful and unintelligible instinct in our souls" (p. 179). Thus, as important as development toward and achievement of personhood is, common sense suggests there is more to moral status.

SENTIENCE. Contrary to personhood's focus on the intellect, a number of thinkers contend that thinking is overrated. The English philosopher Jeremy Bentham (1748–1832), in his book titled *An Introduction to the Principles of Morals and Legislation,* claims that the pains and pleasures of animals matter: "The question is not, Can they reason; nor, Can they talk? but, Can they suffer?" (p. 283). Henry Sidgwick agrees, observing in *The Methods of Ethics* (1874) that given the utilitarian goal of maximizing pleasure, it would be "arbitrary and unreasonable" to exclude "any pleasure of any sentient being" (p. 414).

Moral consideration of nonhuman animals was revolutionary 200 years ago, and it still is. Concerned about challenges to human status, physician-ethicist Willard Gaylin asserts in his 1990 book *Adam and Eve and Pinocchio*:

> The order of change between the chimpanzee and the human being is of such a magnitude as to represent a break, a discontinuity. We are not the next step, or even a giant leap forward. We are a parallel and independent entity; a thing unto ourselves; in a class of our own; sui generis.... The distance between man and ape is greater than the distance between ape and ameba. (p. 12)

The moral status of animals has varied throughout human history. In the Ten Commandments, God commanded a Sabbath rest for people and cattle alike. Yet the father of modern Western philosophy, René Descartes (1596–1650), starkly contrasts immortally ensouled humans—even madmen—with even the brightest animals, which are merely divinely created "machines" driven by organ-derived passions. The anguished crying and screams of animals are but the grinding of a machine's gears and levers.

Nevertheless, if sentience, the capacity to sense pleasure and pain, is the sole criterion for judging moral status, where in the evolutionary scale is the line between sentience and nonsentience? Rats and mice are intelligent, sentient creatures, but humans hardly respect them. Yet the nineteenth-century English naturalist Charles Darwin, who studied earthworms, considered them sentient, even capable of some form of reason. Earthworms, after a drenching rain, slither onto hard surfaces, suggesting a basic sentience. Worms have identifiable sense organs and nervous systems, unlike unicellular animals such as amoebas. Nevertheless, there is dispute among knowledgeable microbiologists even about whether single-celled organisms can be sentient, with the American zoologist Herbert Spencer Jennings (1868–1947) claiming that if amoebas were large animals and a part of everyday human experience, their behavior would suggest feelings of pain and pleasure, hunger and desire.

If a moral line cannot be drawn between humans and all other animals, and if even amoebas may possibly be primitively sentient, are we to consider all 750,000 species of animal life sentient? In *Practical Ethics,* Singer draws a line between shrimp and oysters, the latter possessing a very simple nervous system. He further argues that different species have different interests. For example, only persons are sentient, self-aware beings who can conceptualize their own futures. The great apes, and possibly cetaceans, pigs, dogs, and cats, are persons; but mice, birds, and other small-brained animals are probably not. Thus for Singer, possession of sentience is necessary for full moral status, but it is not sufficient. Highest moral status is reserved for normal adult humans.

Following the lead of Bentham and Sidgwick, Singer advances a thoroughgoing utilitarian argument for determining moral status. Singer's utility is nuanced, however, taking into account a penetrating criticism of classical utilitarianism, namely that people value ends beyond enjoying pleasure and avoiding pain. Singer's preference utilitarianism holds that an individual's good is determined by that person's preferences or values. Further, in calculating the universal good, the preferred interests of all sentient beings are weighed equally: "The principle of equal consideration of interests acts like a pair of scales, weighing interests impartially. True scales favor the side where the interest is stronger or where several interests combine to outweigh a smaller number of similar interests; but they take no account of whose interests they are weighing" (1979, p. 19).

The idea of preferences or interests presupposes at least rudimentary mental life. And if organisms care if their interests are met, they may register this in behaviors suggesting pain or pleasure. Nonsentient organisms, by Singer's definition, cannot have interests and hence have no sense of pain or pleasure. Nevertheless, the boundary between sentience and nonsentience is indistinct, at best.

The notion of interests is controversial. In his 1980 book, *Interests and Rights,* Raymond Gillespie Frey argues that only humans can have interests, because interests presuppose beliefs, and beliefs require complex language use, a singularly human capacity. Steven Sapontzis decries such moral elevation of abstract rationality in his 1987 book, *Morals, Reason, and Animals.* He shows that most people are only sometimes rational, and they live by emotion, hope, rhetoric, eccentricity, and intuition as well. Reason has no unique moral quarter, because there is no generally recognized method of rationality that commands categorical obligation.

Sapontzis argues for animal-human equality, but he especially uses *reasons* to advance his claim that reason is overrated. Thus with Sapontzis, as with most other sentience-focused thinkers, humans, at least implicitly, receive preeminent moral status. It is no mere coincidence that human beings usually end up possessing the highest moral status via the rules of moral sentience they have devised.

ENVIRONMENT. "Environmental ethics stretches classical ethics to the breaking point," declares Holmes Rolston III, a leading environmental philosopher (p. 33). The radical significance of environmental ethics is that it alone raises the issue of whether there are nonsentient entities that can be objects of duty.

This issue was poignantly raised in 1973 by Richard Sylvan's thought experiment: Imagine you are the last human on Earth and you are about to die, and the idea occurs to you of gleefully destroying the last remaining redwood tree. The ethics of this "last person" dilemma raises important issues: for example, the nature and breadth of ethics and the moral status of organisms as individuals, as progeny of ecosystems, and even as possible moral equals.

Classical ethical theory, with its focus on the individual, is typified by Kant's autonomous person as the only morally considerable end in itself. But the post-Kantian John Rawls, author of *A Theory of Justice* (1971), desires to include children and other nonrational humans in his moral universe, so he defines persons as those who have the "capacity" for rationality, even if it is undeveloped.

Like sentience-focused ethicists, other thinkers are moving beyond what Robert Elliot calls "unjustifiable human chauvinism." Of course, humans are only a small part of nature, and now the moral status of other aspects of nature—trees, rivers, mountains, rare plant species—is on the ethics horizon. Environmental ethics challenges society to risk exploring uncharted terrain, to go beyond anthropocentric culture. Advocates contend that it is more serious than rights for rocks, citing how revolutionary the early steps leading to rights for women, children, and ethnic minorities were. With the increasing rate of environmental deterioration, these new thinkers suggest that environmental ethics is as important as medical or business ethics. Rolston contends that the planet's deterioration is as great a threat as nuclear war—and more probable.

Max Oelschlaeger, editor of *Postmodern Environmental Ethics* (1995), perceives a "linguistic turn" in contemporary ethical reflection. No longer is language seen as mirroring the real world; language is inseparable from humans' personal spaciotemporal culture. Language is not representative of an independent reality but rather plays an "ontogenetic" role in defining the human, "meaningful world." Humans are more "biologically underdetermined" and more culturally driven than previously thought. The ecocrisis originates in and is sustained by the older conception of language. Calling for a postmodern consciousness of language, Oelschlaeger suggests that "modern ethical theory is linguistically naïve" (pp. 2–9). He decries the separation of theory and practice, advocating a new cultural language of, above all else, environmental sustainability.

Individual organisms and complex ecosystems. On both deontological (duty-oriented) and utilitarian grounds, extending moral status to sentient beings makes sense. But on what basis is life itself the threshold of moral status? If speciesism (the moral elevation of a species simply because of its nature) exists, by a similar logic the charge of "sentientism" applies to animal rightists who would arbitrarily prohibit extension of moral consideration to all of life.

Animals can and should experience a good life, but biocentrists believe the standard for moral status is too high. They point to how interests can be served and harms avoided by letting all organisms fulfill their unique ends—loosely specifiable biological goals whose fulfillment results in a type of flourishing. Plants have no subjective life, only an objective one. "Nothing matters to a tree, but much is vital to it," says Rolston, who is an advocate for a "vital ethic" (p. 34). Deep, or thoroughgoing, ecologists explain that to act contrary to the purposes of a plant means that one impedes the plant's biologically given goals.

Whereas anthropomorphism holds that all moral status somehow relates to human well-being, biocentrism sees all life as possessing moral status. Paul Taylor and Gary E. Varner argue for biological individualism—that each organism of life possesses intrinsic value. That each organism possesses independent value follows from the premise that each organism's flourishing makes the world a better place.

Further, Taylor is a species egalitarian in that he sees all criteria that devalues any life-form as an equally arbitrary, immoral imposition. Varner agrees that all living things have intrinsic moral value, but contends that not all live entities are morally equal. He believes that it is softheaded to think

that pulling a carrot is as wrong as killing a horse. A plant has only biological needs, whereas a horse also has sentient interests in life, and a human can possess complex interests that are not found in lower forms of life.

Unlike Taylor and Varner, most environmental philosophers tend to be holistic rather than individualistic. That is, they express more moral concern for ecosystems and species than for individual living things. Rolston rejects the confines of classical ethics, in part because of its fixation on individual entities: "In an evolutionary ecosystem, it is not mere individuality that counts; the species is also significant because it is a dynamic life-form maintained over time. The individual represents (re-presents) a species in each new generation. It is a token of a type, and the type is more important than the token" (p. 35).

Can moral status be assigned to ecosystems? If so, then logically the moral standing of a species would likely trump almost, if not all, claims of individual animals or plants when there is a serious conflict. Most environmentalists are primarily concerned with preserving evolutionary processes, and this involves predation that could sometimes be stopped by human intervention. Natural ecosystems appear to exist beyond the moral categories that have served anthropocentric interests in the past. Only environmental ethics challenges society to sort out maxims between conventional anthropomorphic morality and urgent planetary needs.

Multi-Standard Theory

In the postmodern era, confidence in single theories of right and wrong has diminished. Because academics keenly sense the historical conditionedness of every human construct, it is no happenstance that leading moral philosophers are eclectic in moral theory.

As indicated above, however, there are very thoughtful single-standard thinkers. In his 1989 book, *In Defense of the Land Ethic,* J. Baird Callicott, for instance, consciously rejects ethical eclecticism because in hard cases it inevitably leads to "moral incommensurability." This occurs because competing moral claims employ differing terms that thwart decisive comparison and resolution.

Nevertheless, a powerful case is made for a more modest, multi-standard theory. In Rawls's influential *A Theory of Justice,* the basis for choosing ethical theory is "reflective equilibrium." Rawls develops this concept in the context of arguing for an "original position" of personal anonymity hypothesized behind a "veil of ignorance," from which one chooses ideal norms of justice. The conditions of that initial situation are generally shared and "preferably weak." Those conditions are Socratically conceived, working "from both ends," going back and forth, altering conditions of the original position, making and withdrawing judgments.

One postulates reasonable conditions and assumes principles that finally match one's "considered judgments duly pruned and adjusted." This conceptual give and take is Rawls' reflective equilibrium: "It is an equilibrium because at last our principles and judgments coincide; and it is reflective since we know to what principles our judgments conform and the premises of their derivation." Rawls's notion of justice does not come from self-evident premises or principles; "instead, its justification is a matter of the mutual support of many considerations, of everything fitting together into one coherent view" (pp. 20–21).

Following Rawls' lead, Tom L. Beauchamp and James F. Childress, in *Principles of Biomedical Ethics* (2001), develop their own coherence theory. They too begin with "considered judgments," basic societal warrants, such as religious tolerance, that are accepted at first without "argumentative support." An ethical issue, considered in light of one's paradigmatic considered judgments, prompts a careful, nuanced assessment and then a more general account of the issue's moral warrants. All elements considered, one weighs and trims, cuts and adds, attempting maximal coherence. The resulting action guides are never absolute, however, and if their inadequacy is too great the process of finding appropriate norms begins anew. Regardless, ethical coherence is dynamic, as continually "we revise, generalize, specify, and balance moral beliefs" (pp. 397–400).

Warren, in her carefully reasoned 1997 book, *Moral Status: Obligations to Persons and Other Living Things,* advocates a "Multi-Criterial" theory, a commonsense, pragmatic approach to determining moral status, appealing to her readers' moral intuitions. It is such common/good sense intuitions, she notes, that give rise to ethical reflection and judgment in the first place. Warren argues that the burden of demonstrating the inadequacy of a society's given morality—its faulty reasoning or inadequate empirical data—rests on those who would challenge it.

Commonsense morality gains empirical support from the faltering of many single-standard advocates when confronting hard cases. Single-standard theorists are indispensable in focusing attention on society's specific moral inadequacies. These theorists often blink, however, when their theories are pushed to the limits; they often fail to take their rationales to their logical conclusions. For example, Roman Catholic thinkers do not call for a huge medical initiative against early naturally aborted human embryos. Engelhardt modifies his high-standard personhood by "imputing" moral status to human newborns. And Taylor argues for the equality of all life-forms, but if mosquitoes were spreading malaria, would he morally disallow eradication efforts?

The case that Warren makes for a "sliding scale" of moral status appeals to the basic moral intuitions of many people. The evolutionary scale extends from amoebas to normal human adults, with the more neurologically complex beings accorded greater moral status.

Despite its appeal, the multi-standard approach also has its downside. It can easily provide an ethical justification for the moral status quo. For example, despite Warren's argument for heightened sensitivity to the relative moral status of all organisms, she provides justification for several practices that many humane persons find morally objectionable: meat eating (and thus implicitly, factory farming), sport hunting, and sometimes caging animals. Acceptance of each of these practices is carefully nuanced, but their practice, according to Warren, can be a moral option.

Another related problem with a multi-standard, common morality is that by its very nature it fails to foster morally prophetic voices. Perhaps society's view of moral status is best served by a chorus of voices articulating various conceptions of moral status, thus stimulating careful thought about an array of viewpoints. In this way, democratic societies foster humane progress in ethical sensitivity. The relevance of competing bioethical theories is tested by many real-life dilemmas, not least of which is the modern scourge of Alzheimer disease.

Individuals with Alzheimer Disease

Concomitant with the advantages of longer lifespans is today's challenge of Alzheimer disease. Of course, the moral status of the newly diagnosed Alzheimer patient is very high, but what of the individual with severe Alzheimer disease? The case of Alzheimer disease is a fitting condition for comparison of the four leading theories' indications of moral status.

PERSONHOOD. The genetic variety of this theory would appear to be simple: As long as there is organic life, there is high moral status. However, the Vatican, holding the genetic view on perinatal life, favors a natural death in senescent cases. Mental (and developmental) personhood theory puts a premium on the moral standing of the fully competent person, suggesting that the registered wishes of an autonomous person for his or her care as an Alzheimer patient should morally hold.

An important unresolved issue, however, is whether the will of the fully competent person should trump the desires of the partially demented patient when a discrepancy exists regarding future care. In her response to Ronald Dworkin's autonomy argument for the fully competent person, Rebecca Dresser argues that the partially competent patient's current desires should be heeded, because the patient's present condition was not clearly foreseen, and, given that the patient will never return to full competence, these wishes should override earlier directives.

SENTIENCE. Sentience theory aims to maximize pleasure and minimize pain in all sentient creatures. As an Alzheimer patient's senses wane, moral status similarly decreases. To avoid speciesism, this view is egalitarian in that whatever treatment is good for nonhuman animals is appropriate for Alzheimer patients of similar sentience. Singer argues for equal consideration of interests, but not all interests are equal. Self-conscious beings receive "prior consideration," as they have a heightened capacity for suffering—or for happiness. In a different vein, Singer, who argues strongly for voluntary active euthanasia, says that it should be banned if the consequences of nonvoluntary euthanasia in demented patients would lead to "insecurity and fear" among possible future dementia patients (1979, p. 139). In practice, mainline personhood theory would assign a lower moral status to a moderately advanced Alzheimer patient than would sentience theory. This is because in Alzheimer disease, incompetence in reasoning precedes incapacity for sensual experience.

ENVIRONMENT. Given environmental theory's priority on the biosphere and ecosystems, the moral status of individual Alzheimer patients, it would seem, is hardly on the ecological radar screen. Nevertheless, environmental theory has considerable, albeit indirect, relevance: This iconoclastic theory dethrones the rational man (and it was *man* in the Enlightenment) as the exclusive measure of moral status.

Rawls continues the anthropomorphic scheme in *A Theory of Justice,* making an aside to demented individuals: "Those more or less permanently deprived of moral personality may present a difficulty. I cannot examine this problem here, but I assume that the account of equality would not be materially affected" (p. 510). Rawls's and previous philosophers' social contract models have fostered equality and other human goods, but this model's purview is narrow. According to Mary Midgley, in her 1995 article titled "Duties Concerning Islands," the social contract is a valid aspect of common morality, but it now dominates ethics, whereas ordinary people see moral claims more broadly. Midgley proclaims that humans have real moral duties to an array of entities beyond "sane, adult humans": for instance, the dead, the insane, embryos of all animals, artifacts, rivers,

countries, landscapes, and the biosphere. By casting the moral net far beyond adult humans, Midgley shatters the wall dividing rational persons from the rest of life, thus supporting at least the relative moral status of all Alzheimer patients.

MULTI-STANDARD. Stephen Post exemplifies an ethical eclecticism in his extensive writing on Alzheimer disease. Like environmental ethical theorists, Post decisively rejects the identification of moral status with rationality. In his *The Moral Challenge of Alzheimer Disease,* he criticizes modern society's "hypercognitive" values of rationality and memory. Post appears to be against mainline personhood ethics, calling Alzheimer patients "persons" and citing them as Earth's neediest people who deserve "preferential moral significance." Post may be more personalist than he knows, however, because in the Dworkin–Dresser debate he sides with Dworkin's contention that the fully competent person's wishes trump the later, counterexpressions of a demented mind. And, further, Post equates being a valuable human being with one's capacity to "will, feel, and relate." Overall, however, Post is closest to the sentience camp because after the Alzheimer patient advances beyond a sentient state, he sees invasive, life-prolonging treatment as an "assault" on a patient oblivious to its purpose. As long as the Alzheimer patient can sense any pleasure in life, loved ones should embrace this live, sentient individual in light of what was once so much more. No vitalist, Post concludes the second edition of his book as follows: "Death is not the enemy; the only real enemy is the burden of technologically protracted morbidity under conditions of severe dysfunction" (p. 142).

Why a particular entity is treated with special regard, thus receiving a certain moral status, is dependent on what ethical standard one holds—personhood, sentience, environment, or ethical eclecticism. And why a person embraces one standard rather than another is finally a metaethical issue (literally, an issue beyond ethics; an issue involving one's religious or philosophical worldview). In liberal societies the existence of various foundational religious and philosophical positions ensures continued lively discussion of moral status, made possible by a consensus that other persons have significant moral status, thus allowing for such social debate.

JAMES W. WALTERS

BIBLIOGRAPHY

Beauchamp, Tom L., and Childress, James F. 2001. *Principles of Biomedical Ethics,* 5th edition. New York: Oxford University Press.

Bentham, Jeremy. 1823 (reprint 1970). *An Introduction to the Principles of Morals and Legislation,* ed. J. H. Burns and H. L. A. Hart. London: University of London Press.

Cahill, Lisa Sowle. 1992. "Defining Personhood: A Dialogue." *Conscience* 13(1): 19–28.

Callicott, J. Baird. 1989. *In Defense of the Land Ethic: Essays in Environmental Philosophy.* Albany: State University of New York Press.

Darwin, Charles. 1881. *The Formation of Vegetable Mould, Through the Action of Worms.* London: John Murray. Cited in James Rachels, *Created from Animals: The Moral Implications of Darwinism* (New York: Oxford University Press, 1991).

Descartes, René. 1976. "Animals Are Machines." In *Animal Rights and Human Obligations,* ed. Tom Regan and Peter Singer. Englewood Cliffs, NJ: Prentice-Hall.

Dresser, Rebecca. 1986. "Life, Death, and Incompetent Patients: Conceptual Infirmities and Hidden Values in the Law." *Arizona Law Review* 28: 376–379.

Dworkin, Ronald. 1986. "Autonomy and the Demented Self." *Milbank Quarterly* 64(suppl. 2): 4–16.

Elliot, Robert. 1995. "Introduction." In *Environmental Ethics,* ed. Robert Elliot. New York: Oxford University Press.

Engelhardt, H. Tristram, Jr. 1996. *The Foundations of Bioethics,* 2nd edition. New York: Oxford University Press.

Feinberg, Joel. 1992. *Freedom and Fulfillment: Philosophical Essays.* Princeton, NJ: Princeton University Press.

Fletcher, Joseph. 1979. *Humanhood: Essays in Biomedical Ethics.* New York: Prometheus.

Frey, Raymond Gillespie. 1980. *Interests and Rights: The Case against Animals.* Oxford: Clarendon Press.

Gaylin, Willard. 1990. *Adam and Eve and Pinocchio: On Being and Becoming Human.* New York: Viking.

Green, Ronald M. 2001. *The Human Embryo Research Debate: Bioethics in the Vortex of Controversy.* New York: Oxford University Press.

Grobstein, Clifford. 1988. *Science and the Unborn: Choosing Human Futures.* New York: Basic.

Hume, David. 1739–1740 (reprint 1960). *A Treatise of Human Nature,* ed. L. A. Selby-Bigge. Oxford: Clarendon Press.

Jennings, Herbert Spencer. 1906. *Behavior of the Lower Organisms.* New York: Columbia University Press. Cited in Charles Birch and John B. Cobb Jr., *The Liberation of Life* (Denton, TX: Environmental Ethics Books, 1990).

Jonas, Hans. 1985. "Technology, Ethics, and Biogenetic Art: Observations on the New Role of Man as Creator." *Communio* 12(1): 92–107.

Klusendorf, Scott. 2001. "Death with a Happy Face: Peter Singer's Bold Defense of Infanticide." *Christian Research Journal* 23(3): 22–25, 42–46.

Macklin, Ruth. 1983. "Personhood in the Bioethics Literature." *Milbank Memorial Fund Quarterly: Health and Society* 61(1): 35–57.

May, William E. 1976. "What Makes a Human Being to Be a Being of Moral Worth?" *Thomist* 40(3): 416–443.

McCormick, Richard A. 1991. "Who or What Is the Preembryo?" *Kennedy Institute of Ethics Journal* 1(1): 1–15.

Midgley, Mary. 1995. "Duties Concerning Islands." In *Environmental Ethics,* ed. Robert Elliot. New York: Oxford University Press.

Noonan, John T. 1983. "An Almost Absolute Value in History." In *Moral Problems in Medicine,* 2nd edition, ed. Samuel Gorovitz, Ruth Macklin, Andrew L. Jameton, et al. Englewood Cliffs, NJ: Prentice-Hall.

Oelschlaeger, Max, ed. 1995. *Postmodern Environmental Ethics.* Albany: State University of New York Press.

Post, Stephen G. *The Moral Challenge of Alzheimer Disease: Ethical Issues from Diagnosis to Dying,* 2nd edition. Baltimore: Johns Hopkins University Press.

Rawls, John. 1971. *A Theory of Justice.* Cambridge, MA: Harvard University Press.

Regan, Tom. 2001. *Defending Animal Rights.* Urbana: University of Illinois Press.

Robertson, John A. 1991. "What We May Do with Preembryos: A Response to Richard A. McCormick." *Kennedy Institute of Ethics Journal* 1(4): 293–302.

Rolston, Holmes, III. 2002. "Values in and Duties to the Natural World." In *Environmental Ethics: What Really Matters, What Really Works,* ed. David Schmidtz and Elizabeth Willott. New York: Oxford University Press.

Sapontzis, Steven. 1987. *Morals, Reason, and Animals.* Philadelphia: Temple University Press.

Shelp, Earl E. 1986. *Born to Die? Deciding the Fate of Critically Ill Newborns.* New York: Free Press.

Sidgwick, Henry. 1874 (reprint 1966). *The Methods of Ethics.* New York: Dover.

Singer, Peter. 1975. *Animal Liberation: A New Ethics for Our Treatment of Animals.* New York: Avon.

Singer, Peter. 1979. *Practical Ethics.* New York: Cambridge University Press.

Smith, David H. 2001. "Who Counts?" *Journal of Religious Ethics* 12(2): 240–255.

Steinbock, Bonnie. 1992. *Life before Birth: The Moral and Legal Status of Embryos and Fetuses.* New York: Oxford University Press.

Stone, Christopher D. 1987. *Earth and Other Ethics: The Case for Moral Pluralism.* New York: Harper and Row.

Taylor, Paul. 1986. *Respect for Nature: A Theory of Environmental Ethics.* Princeton, NJ: Princeton University Press.

Thomson, Judith Jarvis. 1978. "A Defense of Abortion." In *Contemporary Issues in Bioethics,* ed. Tom L. Beauchamp and LeRoy Walters. Encino, CA: Dickenson.

Tooley, Michael. 1972. "Abortion and Infanticide." *Philosophy and Public Affairs* 2(1): 37–65.

Tooley, Michael. 1983. *Abortion and Infanticide.* Oxford: Clarendon Press.

Varner, Gary E. 1998. *In Nature's Interests? Interests, Animal Rights, and Environmental Ethics.* New York: Oxford University Press.

Vatican. 1987. "Respect for Human Life in Its Origins and on the Dignity of Procreation." *Origins* 16(March): 697–711.

Walters, James W. 1997. *What Is a Person? An Ethical Exploration.* Urbana: University of Illinois Press.

Warren, Mary Anne. 1997. *Moral Status: Obligations to Persons and Other Living Things.* Oxford: Oxford University Press.

MORMONISM (CHURCH OF JESUS CHRIST OF LATTER-DAY SAINTS), BIOETHICS IN

• • •

The religious movement that has become known worldwide as *Mormonism* began in an obscure region in New York State in the 1820s. The founder, Joseph Smith, Jr., declared to both followers and opponents that he had, beginning at age 14, received a series of visions and revelations from God, Jesus Christ, and angelic messengers. Smith maintained that through these divine ministrations, he had received authorization to "restore" the gospel of Jesus Christ in its purity and fullness to the world (*Pearl of Great Price* (PGP)). A principal form of tangible evidence for Smith's divine call was the production of a new scriptural record, called *The Book of Mormon,* which related an account of God's promises to the peoples of the western hemisphere. Smith, as well as close associates, stated that he had translated the text from inscribed golden plates through divine inspiration, and the Book of Mormon was published in 1830 (*Book of Mormon* (BM)). The terms Mormon and Mormonism derive from the title of this book, although the terms were most frequently invoked as epithets by opponents of the new religion.

Ecclesiastical Overview

In April 1830, Smith organized the *Church of Christ* in Fayette, New York. An aggressively evangelistic religion from the beginning, the new church gained adherents and inspired animosity as it gradually followed the westward migration of the American frontier, moving its central locus to Ohio, Missouri, and Illinois during the next fifteen years. Smith continued to receive revelations, which were first compiled in 1835 into another new record of scripture,

entitled *The Doctrine and Covenants.* In 1837, Smith was instructed to call the organization "The Church of Jesus Christ of Latter-Day Saints" (LDS), the title by which the religion is formally known today. This title contains four defining themes:

(1) *Church*—The organization was deemed to be the repository of divine truth and ritual practices necessary for the salvation of human beings.

(2) *Jesus Christ*—The church was to understand itself as authorized and governed by the resurrected Jesus Christ, and not to take its identity from a book (the Mormon church) or a person. A theocratic hierarchy was established within which Joseph Smith (and his successors) were acknowledged as "prophets" or spokesmen through whom Christ would reveal his will for the church and for the world. Their ecclesiastical office and responsibility was portrayed as similar to that of Moses for the people of Israel (DC).

(3) *Latter-Day*—Church teachings were to emphasize a millenarian eschatology; the world was considered to be in its "final days" prior to the return or "second coming" of Jesus Christ.

(4) *Saints*—All members of the religion were to be known officially as "saints," as was deemed the practice of early Christianity.

The population concentration of communities of saints in what were at the time sparsely settled regions of the frontier often led to conflicts with previously-existing institutions, including churches, business, and political systems. Smith was frequently imprisoned, typically on charges of sedition or for posing threats to public morality. On one such occasion, in June 1844, Smith and his brother were murdered in a jail in Carthage, Illinois. After a period of controversy over Smith's successor, the senior member of the remaining ecclesiastical leadership, Brigham Young, assumed the role of presiding officer of the church and eventually was acknowledged as the "prophet" (Arrington and Bitton).

Beginning in 1846, Brigham Young led the LDS migration to a geographically isolated, and hence, religious oasis, founding Salt Lake City and other communities in the Great Basin and Rocky Mountains. Indeed, within the next three decades, fueled in large measure by emigrants from the British Isles, Young was responsible for organizing over 350 settlements in what are now seven states.

It also fell to Young to make a public announcement of the religious practice that would make the religion a pariah for the next seventy-five years, "plural marriage" or polygamy. Joseph Smith had initiated this practice among leading church elders in the 1840s. Smith prayed over the question of why the biblical patriarchs Abraham, Isaac, and Jacob, as well as the kings David and Solomon, had been allowed to have plural wives and concubines. The divine answer, he claimed, was a revelation regarding the "new and everlasting covenant of marriage," which included the eternal bond of the marital and family relationship, and permitted the "sealing" of faithful males to additional wives in special circumstances (DC). Plural marriage continued to receive formal endorsement by Smith's successors until 1890, when a *Manifesto* issued by prophet Wilford Woodruff officially renounced the practice (DC). In the intervening period, the U.S. government passed several laws that permitted the confiscation of ecclesiastical property and fines and imprisonment for practitioners. Despite well over a century of emphasis on monogamous marriage and the nuclear family, the polygamy legacy continues to be part of the public identity of the LDS religion. Indeed, splinter groups continue the theology and practice of polygamy in remote areas of southern Utah, and northern Arizona and northern Mexico.

In the post-polygamy era, ecclesiastical leaders made a concerted effort to move the church into the mainstream of American religious culture and social life (Bush, 1993). It sought to portray itself as exemplifying the work ethic of the larger culture, while ensuring a welfare program for those unable to work. Leaders advocated the family unit, structured around heterosexual marriage, as not only divinely required but a social necessity. The historical hostility to political and legislative paternalism was gradually transformed into a committed patriotism, with the U.S. Constitution portrayed as a divinely inspired document to be defended.

The acculturation of the LDS church to American civic mores was accompanied by the continuation of evangelism virtually worldwide. Since the middle of the twentieth century, church membership has grown eleven-fold to just over 11 million adherents, the majority of whom reside outside the United States. The twenty-first century internationalization of what was a very small and exclusive movement in the nineteenth century is the most significant ecclesiastical challenge at this time.

Scriptures, Authority, and Agency

As indicated previously, a distinctive feature of the LDS religious tradition from its inception is its explicit acceptance of continuing divine revelation, including an "open canon" of scripture. There are four recognized books of scripture, collectively known as *the standard works,* in that they provide "the standard" against which truth and error can be discerned. The source of Joseph Smith's original questioning about religious truth was the *Holy Bible;* in

ecclesiastical practice and discourse, the King James Version is used as authoritative. The Bible does not have preeminence in the faith, however; that distinction is claimed by the *Book of Mormon,* which was described by Smith as "the keystone of [LDS] religion" (p. 194). An *article of faith* (comparable to a creedal statement) written by Smith in response to a query about the basic beliefs of the religion asserts: "We believe the Bible to be the word of God as far as it is translated correctly. We also believe the Book of Mormon to be the word of God" (PGP, p. 60).

The two books in principle are held to be theologically complementary, and both are considered authentic renditions of ancient history. *The Bible* is portrayed as the story of the word of God and the covenants of God's people in the Semitic, Hebraic, Jewish, and Hellenistic world. The *Book of Mormon* is considered to be the story of God's word and the covenants of his people among the original inhabitants of the continents of the Americas (c.a. 2000 B.C.E.–400 C.E.). At the core of both texts, the tradition believes, is a testament of Jesus Christ as Savior of the world. Indeed, responding to long-held perceptions that Mormons were not Christians, the *Book of Mormon* was given a subtitle in the 1980s, *Another Witness of Jesus Christ.*

A third authoritative text is *The Doctrine and Covenants,* which is comprised of some of the revelations and writings of Joseph Smith from 1823 to 1844, as well as some additional proclamations, declarations, and revelations promulgated by Smith's successors and accepted by the ecclesiastical body as canonical. The most recent addition to this book occurred in 1978. A fourth book, known as the *The Pearl of Great Price,* was not officially accepted as scriptural until 1880. It contains writings on the Genesis creation narrative attributed to the biblical figures Abraham and Moses, as well as a short history authored by Joseph Smith about his religious experiences.

These four texts constitute the ecclesiastical standards for assessing both sacred and secular knowledge. They are not, however, self-interpreting or always directly applicable to situations that individuals may confront in everyday experience. A second distinctive feature of the LDS religious tradition is that it relies on a lay clergy, which is hierarchically organized under the direction of two bodies of ecclesiastical leadership known as *The First Presidency* and *The Quorum of the Twelve Apostles.* These groups, typically comprised of fifteen males, were originated by Joseph Smith and are the principal resource not only of ecclesiastical governance, but also for scriptural interpretation (DC). In a tradition that does not have any formally trained priests or theologians, the scriptural interpretations rendered by the *general authorities* as these groups are called, are indispensable authoritative guides. Moreover, the LDS canon makes it clear that when general authorities speak as moved by divine influence, their words are the "ecclesiastical equivalent" of canonized scripture. The tradition is emphatic in claiming that God's words and works are "endless," and cannot be fully contained in one book, or even four books, but also include the words (and actions) of these ecclesiastical leaders (DC, PGP).

Divine influence is not confined to such leaders, however. Each baptized member receives a blessing that enables that person to receive the companionship of the divine spirit for his or her own personal, familial, religious, and even vocational, roles in life. Indeed, LDS scripture teaches that each person born into the world is given the capacity for "moral agency." Moral agency grants to capable persons the freedom of making decisions about moral right and wrong, virtue and vice, and good and evil. There are safeguards, however, that prevent a collapse of moral agency into subjectivism. First, while individuals are free to choose their actions, they cannot freely choose the consequences of their choice, and will be held accountable (by conscience, peers, God, etc.) for their actions. Second, the tradition teaches that human beings are more apt to choose the good and virtuous through relying on divine influence, whether that is manifested in the form of individual discernment or revelation, or from teachings of ecclesiastical leaders, or from the canonical scriptures. The concept of moral agency overlaps in important respects the bioethical principle of respect for autonomy; these similarities and differences will be highlighted in the section below on bioethical questions.

The Christian Status of Mormonism

Joseph Smith, Jr. insisted that he was an instrument in God's hands in restoring the good news or gospel that Jesus Christ had preached, as recorded in the *New Testament* and then practiced in the primitive Christian church. Smith's message of restoration was, however, often perceived by others as a demonic perversion of Christian faith. As Smith wrote of the response to his first vision, a minister "treated my communication … with great contempt, saying it was all of the devil, that there were no such things as visions or revelations in these days; that all such things had ceased with the apostles.…" (PGP, p. 50). The question of the Christian status of Mormonism has remained an enduring issue and source of controversy since the latter's inception.

Smith also maintained that the fundamental principle of the LDS religion concerned the redemption of humanity through the suffering, death, and resurrection of Jesus Christ, a theological claim that would seem to be in harmony with traditional Christian doctrine. However, Smith's call to restore and proclaim this gospel to the world in its last days presupposes that contemporaneous Christian religions

had departed in some way from Jesus's invitation to salvation. As LDS theology developed, primarily in the formative years from 1830 to 1844, substantive differences with traditional Christian thought emerged over such matters as:

> The nature of the Trinity;
> The concept of the Fall and original sin;
> The redemptive efficacy of Christ's sacrifice;
> The necessity and timing of baptism;
> The relationship of grace, faith, and works;
> The presence of spiritual gifts (such as prophecy and healing);
> The authority of extra-biblical sacred writing;
> The source of ecclesiastical authority;
> The meaning of divine revelation.

In the judgment of most Christian writers and denominations, LDS answers to these issues of orthodoxy, or right belief, have been cumulatively sufficient to place the tradition outside the boundaries of the Christian communion. This judgment has been reinforced by attitudes about particular LDS practices and rituals. Most prominently, these included the revulsion (informed by mores of the Victorian age) against polygamy, the LDS practice of which confirmed judgments of doctrinal deviation. Moreover, LDS evangelical zeal, with its presumption of privileged access to divine truth, seemed to run contrary to the emerging ethos of ecumenism and respect for religious pluralism. LDS evangelistic exclusivity has been reinforced by ritualistic exclusivity: The most sacred of LDS rituals, including the covenant of marriage, are performed in *temples,* special houses of worship that are not accessible to the public.

To be sure, in an age of increasing acceptance of religious pluralism, the Mormon version of the Christian message no longer seems to elicit a pariah designation among most mainstream Christian denominations in the United States. The Christian status question is currently most compelling among evangelical Protestant churches, particularly in areas of the world where there is evangelistic *competition* for converts.

Indeed, the evolving internationalization of the LDS Church has stimulated interest about commonalities and differences with the classical world religions, including Buddhism, Hinduism, Islam, and Judaism, as well as many indigenous faiths. Historically and conceptually, the LDS tradition situates itself within the Abrahamic family of religions including Islam and Judaism, as well as Christianity. However, LDS scripture indicates that God has provided religious truth to all peoples (BM); figures such as the Buddha, Confucius, Lao Tse, Mohammed, and Moses, as well as sacred writings such as the Qur'an or the Upanishads are considered prophetic figures and revelations of divine wisdom for their specific cultures and eras.

Worldview and Bioethics

LDS teachings on bioethics are embedded within a comprehensive worldview of divine design, human destiny, and ultimate meaning. Within LDS discourse, the worldview is most commonly referred to as "the plan of salvation." It includes the eternal nature of the self, the pre-mortal existence of persons, mortality as an educational and probationary realm, and genealogical research and liturgical rituals to offer salvation to individuals who have died.

PRE-MORTAL LIFE. A distinctive teaching of LDS theology is that all persons are spirit children of God, in whose presence they lived as individual selves in a life prior to mortality. During this pre-mortal existence, human spirits received instruction about their eternal nature and destiny, and the necessity of experiencing mortality. In this realm, all spirit selves subsequently born on earth made a defining use of their moral agency, choosing to accept God's plan for salvation articulated by and embodied in Jesus Christ.

This narrative of human origins informs certain LDS perspectives on bioethics questions at the beginning of life. The plan of salvation requires that all spirit children of God experience mortal life. This narrative is connected, in direct and indirect ways, to judgments on such issues as procreation and contraception, reproductive technology and abortion, and use of pre-conceptual and pre-natal genetic testing (Campbell, 1993).

MORTALITY. In the narrative of salvation, mortal life has very specific purposes. Mortality first of all provides each of God's spirit children with a physical body. In contrast to theological dualism or Cartesian mechanism, LDS scripture asserts that the human "soul" is constituted by spirit *and* body (DC).

Second, mortality is the proving ground for the responsible use of moral agency. Mortal life is unavoidably made of encounters that require persons to use their agency. These choices, to one degree or another, manifest the extent of their fidelity to their pre-mortal promise to follow the plan of God. The commandments articulated by God's Son and by God's prophets illuminate the ultimate purpose of these choices.

These mortal purposes and choices set out further LDS perspectives on bioethics issues. The theology of embodiment underlies positions on procreation, transplantation, and a health code known as *the Word of Wisdom* (DC). This teaching emphasizes a healthy diet through consumption of such things as herbs, fruits, and grains, as well as the discriminating use of meat, which is to be *used sparingly,* only in times of excess hunger and cold. The prohibitions of the Word of Wisdom are more culturally familiar, and more ecclesiastically enforced; they include specific prohibitions on the use of tobacco, consumption of wine or strong drink (alcohol), and *hot drinks* (which tradition has interpreted to refer to coffee and tea) (Bush, 1993).

Although there is, as described below, general ecclesiastical guidance on numerous bioethics issues, in almost all circumstances, this guidance directs adherents to rely ultimately on their personal moral agency. The two circumstances in which ecclesiastical teaching restricts or proscribes agency concern the intentional taking of life in abortion and euthanasia.

RESEARCH AND RITUALS FOR THE DEAD. The plan of salvation is universal in scope—God seeks to redeem all his spirit children—but is respectful of moral agency. All persons, regardless of their cultural or temporal epoch, must receive a fair opportunity to be educated about the plan, and the restoration to God's presence through the redemption offered by Jesus Christ. Persons cannot be held responsible for complying with theological commandments and moral standards about which they have no knowledge. With this knowledge, persons are positioned to enact their agency most fully. This understanding provides a theological warrant for a principle of informed consent.

LDS teaching acknowledges that its evangelical programs notwithstanding, in point of fact relatively few persons have received this opportunity during their mortal sojourn. What of those billions of persons who have lived and died without awareness of the gospel of Jesus Christ and its restoration? A defining mission of the LDS Church is to encourage its members to participate in genealogical research and trace ancestral lines. Such research intends, in part, to identify deceased persons who have not been informed of the story of salvation. This education, LDS scripture maintains, occurs through evangelization in the post-mortal world of disembodied spirits (DC). Meanwhile, living persons assume the role of proxies for the deceased and perform essential liturgical rituals of salvation, such as the covenants of baptism and marriage. Moral agency for the living is coupled with presumed consent for the dead to manifest the universal and eternal reach of the divine plan.

Specific Questions in Bioethics

Formal LDS engagement with contemporary medical ethics can be traced to a June 1974 ecclesiastical document entitled

Attitudes of The Church of Jesus Christ of Latter-Day Saints toward Certain Medical Problems. This statement was developed in the aftermath of the court decision in *Roe v. Wade* (abortion rights) and promulgated in 1977 in the wake of *In the Matter of Quinlan* (right to die). A good portion of the document was eventually incorporated into the general policy manual of the church, *The Church Handbook of Instructions* (CHI), and soon became an authoritative basis for local ecclesiastical leaders (Bush, 1979). These attitudes have undergone generally minor modifications in the intervening years in response to pastoral concerns and developments in biomedical technology and its professional regulation. What follows is a short overview of current guidelines on nine questions of bioethics shaped by issues at life's beginning and ending.

LIFE BEGINNINGS. *Abortion.* The LDS Church "opposes elective abortion for personal or social convenience" (CHI, 157). *Exceptions* to this prohibition may occur in circumstances where (1) medical prognosis confirms that continuation of the pregnancy places the life or good health of the mother in serious danger; or (2) the pregnancy is a result of rape or incest; or (3) a medical finding that "the fetus has severe defects that will not allow the baby to survive beyond birth" (CHI, p. 157).

Artificial Insemination, In Vitro Fertilization (IVF), and Surrogacy. The responsibility for resorting to artificial insemination by husband (AIH) or artificial insemination by donor (AID) should be determined by the married couple. The major ecclesiastical concern has to do with third-party gametes and about a supportive family structure for the child. Thus, both AID and IVF using donor gametes are "strongly discouraged," as such may complicate family harmony, but in both circumstances, ecclesiastical concerns acknowledge that the ultimate responsibility for such a decision is left to the married couple. Sperm donation and surrogacy are likewise strongly discouraged, but no decision-making latitude is explicitly recognized. The strongest ecclesiastical concern is directed to AID for single women, which "is not approved," and may incur ecclesiastical discipline (Hinckley).

Contraception. Of any LDS ecclesiastical teaching on medical ethics, the position and rationale regarding contraception has undergone the most extensive revision in the past quarter century. The moral agency of the couple is affirmed: "The decision as to how many children to have and when to have them is extremely intimate and private and should be left between the couple and the Lord" (CHI, p. 158).

Sterilization. Current ecclesiastical policy affirms: "The Church strongly discourages surgical sterilization as an elective form of birth control" (CHI, p. 160). Surgical sterilization is a consideration only in circumstances of (1) medical conditions that seriously jeopardize life or health, or for (2) persons who are mentally incompetent and not responsible for their actions owing to experiencing a birth defect or serious trauma.

LIFE ENDINGS. *Cremation.* Currently, cremation is "not encouraged" as a matter of ecclesiastical policy, but the final decision about disposition is entrusted to the agency of the family.

Dissection and autopsy. The contemporary ecclesiastical attitude is framed in terms of *permission*—autopsies may be performed—provided the following procedural guidelines are fulfilled: (1) compliance with applicable law, and (2) consent of the deceased's loved ones or family.

Euthanasia. Even as civil and professional society has become more tolerant of euthanasia and physician-assistance in suicide, the ecclesiastical attitude has become more rigid (Campbell, 1994). The 1970s term *mercy killing* has been discarded in current teaching and replaced by a definition of euthanasia: "Euthanasia is defined as deliberately putting to death a person who is suffering from an incurable condition or disease" (CHI, p. 156). This definition also encompasses "so-called assisted suicide." Resort to euthanasia is considered to "violate the commandments of God," although ecclesiastical instruction does not specify which commandments are contravened.

Transplantation. The donation of bodily organs for post-mortem transplant or research is a matter for individual conscience and agency.

Treatment termination. There is no obligation to "extend mortal life by means that are unreasonable" (CHI, p. 156). The determination of *unreasonable,* and implicitly, *reasonable* means is a matter for family determination, who may engage in prayer and fasting to receive divine guidance, as well as consult with professional caregivers, about end-of-life decisions. While there is no explicit ecclesiastical direction on the subject of advance directives, both the silence on the subject and the LDS cultural attitude that preparation alleviates fear suggest they may be appropriate mechanisms for members faced with end-of-life choices.

Ecclesiastical instructions on the above issues are very cryptic and do not provide explicit theological rationales for the conclusions addressed (e.g., the general prohibition of abortion makes no reference to the moral status of the fetus). However, as described above, these teachings are embedded within the broader LDS worldview of the plan of salvation, and this suggests some principles that the bioethics conclusions seem to presume, or without which the ecclesiastical teaching is incoherent. These principles include respect for moral agency, embodiment, family integrity, protection of the vulnerable, the sanctity of human life, and stewardship (Campbell, 1992, 1994). Some important issues in bioethics that are noteworthy for their omission in both ecclesiastical guidance and LDS writing in general include research on human subjects (as well as stem cell research), genetic screening and therapy, access to health care, and determination of death.

COURTNEY S. CAMPBELL

SEE ALSO: *Authority in Religious Traditions; Christianity, Bioethics in; Family and Family Medicine; Natural Law; Women, Historical and Cross-Cultural Perspectives*

BIBLIOGRAPHY

Abbott, Deborah, ed. 2002. *The Latter-Day Saints Tradition: Religious Beliefs and Healthcare Decisions.* Chicago: The Park Ridge Center.

Arrington, Leonard, and Bitton, Davis. 1979. *The Mormon Experience: A History of the Latter-Day Saints.* New York: Knopf.

The Book of Mormon: Another Witness of Jesus Christ. Salt Lake City, UT: The Church of Jesus Christ of Latter-Day Saints.

Bush, Lester E., Jr. 1993. *Health and Medicine Among the Latter-Day Saints: Science, Sense, and Scripture.* New York: Crossroad Publishing.

Bush, Lester E., Jr., ed. 1979. "Mormon Medical Ethical Guidelines." *Dialogue* 12(3): 97–106.

Campbell, Courtney S. 1993. "Embodiment and Ethics: A Latter-Day Saint Perspective." In *Theological Development in Bioethics: 1990–1992,* ed. B. Andrew Lustig. Dordrecht, The Netherlands: Kluwer Academic Publishers.

Campbell, Courtney S. 1995. "Ecclesiology and Ethics: An LDS Response." In *Theological Development in Bioethics: 1992–1994,* ed. B. Andrew Lustig. Dordrecht, The Netherlands: Kluwer Academic Publishers.

Church Handbook of Instructions (CHI). 1998. Salt Lake City, UT: The Church of Jesus Christ of Latter-Day Saints.

The Doctrine and Covenants (DC). 1981. Salt Lake City, UT: The Church of Jesus Christ of Latter-Day Saints.

Hinckley, Gordon B. 1987. "Reverence and Morality." *Ensign* 17(5): 46–47.

The Pearl of Great Price (PGP). 1981. Salt Lake City, UT: The Church of Jesus Christ of Latter-Day Saints.

Quinlan, In the Matter of, 70 N.J. 10 (1976).

Roe v. Wade, 410 U.S. 113 (1973).

Smith, Joseph Fielding. 1977. *Teachings of the Prophet Joseph Smith.* Salt Lake City, UT: Deseret Book.